ECOLOGY OF SOIL-BORNE PLANT PATHOGENS

Prelude to Biological Control

Rhizoplane of mustard (*Brassica nigra*) root from garden soil; electron micrograph, $\times$ 32,000. Part of outer epidermal wall of nonpiliferous cell, showing microfibrillar network with clearly defined pits and bacteria in situ. The thin coating of mucilage and cutin has been removed during ultrasonic treatment. Bacteria may be attached in or near pits. (See F. M. Scott, pages 145, 152.)

ECOLOGY OF
SOIL-BORNE PLANT PATHOGENS

Prelude to Biological Control

◄

An International Symposium on
Factors Determining the Behavior of Plant Pathogens in Soil
Held at the University of California, Berkeley, April 7-13, 1963
Edited by
KENNETH F. BAKER *and* WILLIAM C. SNYDER
R. R. Baker/J. D. Menzies
F. E. Clark/L. I. Miller
A. W. Dimock/Z. A. Patrick
W. A. Kreutzer/Mary Rubo

◄

UNIVERSITY OF CALIFORNIA PRESS
Berkeley, Los Angeles: 1965

Sponsored by
The Agricultural Board
National Academy of Sciences—
National Research Council
Washington, D.C.

Financial support provided by
National Science Foundation,
National Institutes of Health,
United States Department of Agriculture

►

Foreword

KENNETH F. BAKER AND WILLIAM C. SNYDER—*Department of Plant Pathology, University of California, Berkeley*

►

When plants emerged from warm primeval seas and invaded the land in the Devonian Period, about 300 million years ago, they were undoubtedly accompanied by fungi and bacteria which had been parasitizing them for millions of years. As roots evolved, they were invaded in turn. Certainly, fossil roots of the Carboniferous show extensive invasion by fungi (Fig. 1). Thus, parasitic fungi and bacteria have been part of the environment of roots for at least as long as the soil itself. It is, therefore, to be expected that the interactions between the parasite, root, and soil, and between parasitic and saprophytic microorganisms, have become extremely complex. Those organisms which did not adjust to this competitive state, by one means or another, did not survive. A state of fluctuating biological balance thus developed for each native habitat, and was self-adjusting for the relatively slow evolutionary and climatic changes.

When man began cultivating crops 8,000-9,000 years ago, the stage was set for frequent, rapid, and drastic ecological changes. With intensification of agriculture, losses from root diseases have increased as the buffering effect of biological controls diminished. When biological control is temporarily or permanently inhibited, severe outbreaks of root disease occur. A well-known example is the epidemic root disease that follows pathogen reintroduction into soil so treated by heat or chemicals as to destroy most of the microflora. It needs to be kept in mind, however, that root disease, like pathogenesis in general, is the exception rather than the rule. Indeed, biological control of root pathogens must be generally and effectively operative for there to be as little root disease as there is.

The study of soil microorganisms has developed rapidly in the last decade, in part due to man's need to understand this reservoir of disease organisms that attack both him and his crops. Although it is generally recognized that interactions of microorganisms constitute an important limiting factor to survival of disease organisms in soil, widespread utilization of such biological control awaits greater understanding of the processes involved. As clearly indicated in this symposium, effectiveness and dependability of biological control of root pathogens is enhanced when it is integrated with other control procedures, such as cultural manipulations, soil disinfestation, crop sequence, or

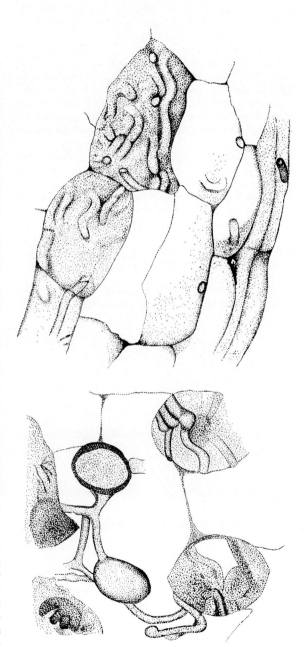

Fig. 1. Mycelia and vesicles of a fossil fungus in the cortex of rootlets of *Amyelon radicans* from English Coal Measures, Carboniferous Period of the Paleozoic, perhaps 230,000,000 years ago. (T. G. B. Osborn, Ann. Bot. 23: 603-661. 1909).

fertilizer practices. In this it resembles other plant-disease controls, for there are few successful single-shot methods in phytopathology.

Some of man's applications of biological control have proved successful or even spectacular, especially where chemical control has not been economically feasible and suitable resistant varieties have not been available. *Phymatotrichum* root rot of cotton may be successfully combated in the southwestern United States by disking into the soil an immature crop of peas in the spring, prior to planting cotton. *Ophiobolus* root rot ("take-all") of wheat may be controlled by rotating a nonhost, such as oats, with the wheat. *Streptomyces* scab of potato is effectively kept in check in California, where the crop is grown on the same land year after year, by growing a crop of soybeans in the fall after the potato harvest, and turning it under while still green. In another area in California, serious losses from *Fusarium* root of bean are avoided by growing a barley crop in rotation with the beans. *Sclerotium* stem rot of peanuts is prevented in the southern United States by keeping the top few inches of soil free from undecomposed organic litter. A serious *Fomes* rot of rubber tree crowns and roots is kept under control cheaply and rather spectacularly in Malaya by growing a variety of legume as a ground cover between the rows of trees. The legume is attacked by the pathogen, which dissipates its energy without attacking the rubber tree. In the mushroom industry numerous competitive "weed molds" are effectively controlled by improving aeration during composting and by carefully manipulated temperatures during "pasteurization" and spawning. The mushroom industry thus provides an outstanding example of effective biological manipulation of soil microflora for the benefit of a crop.

Soil microorganisms present one of the most complex, difficult, and rewarding present areas of exploration. Contact with this frontier has been established by the disciplines of plant pathology, microbiology, soil science, plant physiology, plant anatomy, biochemistry, bacteriology, nematology, mycology, virology, and zoology. Penetration in depth has, however, awaited the overcoming of this compartmentalization of the scattered, diffuse, isolated, and uncorrelated knowledge in these fields. It is increasingly clear that mastery of the soil microflora will come only when we understand the obscure complex of nonparasitic organisms, even though the pathogens have seemed the logical point of attack.

This was the first international symposium on the biological control of soil organisms. Since the field is new, emphasis was placed on background information drawn from many fields, as reflected in the title of these proceedings. To some this may be a disappointment, but most scientists will agree that this is a proper starting place. "It is no small part of the function of science to define the limits of knowledge. Unjustified optimism is as much the enemy of science as is unreasoning credulity." (C. Singer, *A History of Biology,* 1959.) Through these published proceedings, the whole symposium is now made available to interested scientists everywhere. Proceedings of subsequent symposia on this subject will chronicle the rapid rise of effective biological control of soil-borne plant pathogens.

►

Preface

►

The Agricultural Board of the Division of Biology and Agriculture of the National Academy of Sciences–National Research Council established in 1958 a Committee on Biological Control of Soil-Borne Plant Pathogens to stimulate work in that field. The Committee consisted of:

W. C. Snyder, Chairman (University of California)
K. F. Baker, Cochairman (University of California)
R. R. Baker (Colorado State University)
F. E. Clark (U. S. Department of Agriculture)
A. W. Dimock (Cornell University)
W. A. Kreutzer (Colorado State University)
J. D. Menzies (U. S. Department of Agriculture)
L. I. Miller (Virginia Polytechnic Institute)
Z. A. Patrick (Canada Department of Agriculture)

The Committee decided that its purpose would best be discharged by organizing an international symposium to: (1) stimulate research on the important problems in the biological control of soil microorganisms; (2) bring together active investigators of the world in this and related fields for discussions aimed at synthesizing and unifying the underlying concepts, and to consider needed future work; (3) assemble the scattered basic information on the biology of soil microorganisms, to evaluate, and to publish the papers and discussions in a reference volume that would constitute a basic work in this new field.

In the preparation of the program for the symposium the Committee sought the advice of a number of scientists in various parts of the world: T. C. Broyer, N. T. Flentje, S. D. Garrett, P. H. Gregory, H. Katznelson, A. Kerr, L. W. Koch, P. J. Kramer, A. Newsam, G. S. Pound, J. T. Presley, G. Stotzky, J. H. Warcup, and the faculty of the Department of Plant Pathology, Berkeley.

To facilitate discussion between active leaders in this and related fields, participation was by invitation. In addition, announcement of the symposium was published in *Nature, Science, Phytopathology*, and the *American Institute of Biological Sciences Bulletin*, so that any interested scientists could arrange for an invitation.

The 310 participants (listed on pages 525-535) from 24 countries represented most of the world laboratories active in this field. Of those attending, 20% were from 23 foreign countries, and 80% from 37 states of this country.

Invitations for authors, discussants, and chairmen were issued in May-July, 1962, and papers were due in March, 1963. Most authors revised their manuscripts following presentation and discussion of the papers at the symposium. The above Committee served as an Editorial Board, concerning itself primarily with subject matter. Mrs. Mary Rubo, formerly Agricultural Publications Editor, University of California, edited the papers for form and style, prepared the manuscript for the printer, and indexed the volume.

The symposium was held in the Student Union Building of the Berkeley campus of the University of California, April 7 to 13, 1963.

Abridgements of 41 published papers by 44 authors were presented orally, each followed by a general discussion. Of the 27 hours of sessions, 56% were spent in formal papers, and 44% in discussion. There were 287 questions or comments by 97 participants (31% of those attending), and the extent and enthusiasm of discussion participation was exceptional. Nearly all discussion periods were terminated because of time, and numerous questions or comments that could not be presented from the floor were submitted in writing for the proceedings. The presentation abridgements of the papers led to a few queries or comments which became unnecessary with the full text; these have been deleted here. More than 3200 references are cited.

Comments were written on a card by the questioner and the speaker immediately after presentation, and from these, supplemented in a few cases by a tape recording, concise summaries of the discussions were prepared (A. R. Weinhold and K. F. Baker, *Science*, 14: 1474, 1964).

The Style Manual for Biological Journals, published by the American Institute of Biological Sciences, was followed in preparing the book for publication. As recommended in the *Manual*, the *Chemical Abstracts* system of abbreviations for journal titles is used in citations.

WILLIAM C. SNYDER
KENNETH F. BAKER
Berkeley, California
April 6, 1964

Acknowledgments

As with all such large conferences, many agencies and interested people contributed in various ways to make possible the meeting and the published proceedings.

The Symposium was supported by grants from the National Science Foundation, the National Institutes of Health, and the Agricultural Research Service of the United States Department of Agriculture, and administered by the Agricultural Board of the National Academy of Sciences–National Research Council. Additional funds were made available by a number of universities and agricultural experiment stations in this country and abroad, and by the United States Department of Agriculture, to cover in whole or in part the expenses of speakers, discussants, or chairmen representing them. Mayor C. B. Hutchison, an international figure in scientific agriculture, welcomed participants to the City of Berkeley.

The University of California, the Department of Plant Pathology, and University Extension, Berkeley, contributed personnel and facilities to make the Symposium and preparation of the Proceedings possible.

The Committee on Local Arrangements consisted of the following: W. C. Snyder, K. F. Baker, R. V. Bega, C. M. Olsen, J. R. Parmeter, Jr., M. N. Schroth, T. A. Toussoun, A. R. Weinhold, and S. Wilhelm. They were ably assisted by Patricia Abramovitz, J. V. Alexander, J. A. Bourret, T. Bowman, Flora A. Coach, R. J. Cook, Patricia J. Cove, K. L. Downes, Bonnie J. Eidman, N. T. Flentje, Sara A. Ford, M. O. Garraway, C. C. Gill, W. D. Harris, Luise Healey, Katherine Isaeff, C. I. Kado, W. J. Kaiser, Ming-tan Lai, R. G. Linderman, Anne L. Maino, R. W. Meyer, P. R. Miller, R. Muñoz, S. M. Nash, Barbara O'Meara, R. E. Reichle, J. E. Sagen, S. H. Smith, Jane Suman, D. S. Teakle, J. P. Thompson, G. L. Vertrees, and T. Watanabe.

The National Science Foundation made possible the publication of this volume by a partial support grant. The University of California Press, and particularly Mr. Ernest Callenbach, have been most coöperative and helpful in bringing this whole project to fruition. Mrs. Mary Rubo provided thought, experience, judgment, and effort beyond the call of duty in preparing the manuscript for the publisher. Katharine C. Baker and C. M. Olsen prepared illustrations for the printer. R. E. Reichle and C. M. Olsen checked some of the references. Dr. Frank L. Campbell, Dr. Paul F. Sharp, and Mr. R. E. Krauss, as officers of the National Academy of Sciences–National Research Council, were most helpful in implementing the activities of the Committee before, during, and after the Symposium.

Authors, discussants, and summarizers are to be especially commended for promptness and thoroughness in the preparation of their manuscripts, and for their coöperation in conforming to suggested standards.

►

Chairmen of Symposium Sessions

►

Martin Alexander, Department of Agronomy, Cornell University, Ithaca, New York (Wednesday morning, April 10)

Kenneth F. Baker, Department of Plant Pathology, University of California, Berkeley, California (Monday morning, April 8)

A. W. Dimock, Department of Plant Pathology, Cornell University, Ithaca, New York (Thursday afternoon, April 11)

George H. Hepting, Southeastern Forest Experiment Station, U. S. Department of Agriculture, Asheville, North Carolina (Friday afternoon, April 12)

Arthur Kelman, Department of Plant Pathology, North Carolina State College, Raleigh, North Carolina (Friday morning, April 12)

A. G. Norman, Department of Botany, University of Michigan, Ann Arbor, Michigan (Tuesday morning, April 9)

Dennis Parkinson, Department of Botany, University of Liverpool, Liverpool, England (Thursday morning, April 11) (now: Department of Biology, University of Waterloo, Waterloo, Ontario, Canada)

William C. Snyder, Department of Plant Pathology, University of California, Berkeley, California (Monday morning, April 8)

Roy A. Young, Department of Botany and Plant Pathology, Oregon State University, Corvallis, Oregon (Monday afternoon, April 8)

George A. Zentmyer, Department of Plant Pathology, University of California, Riverside, California (Tuesday afternoon, April 9)

Contents

PART I

◀

INTRODUCTION

▶

A Landmark in Biology

VICTOR R. BOSWELL—*Crops Research Division, Research Station, United States Department of Agriculture, Beltsville, Maryland.*

▶

One does not need to be either a plant pathologist or a soil microbiologist to appreciate the significance of this First International Symposium on Factors Determining the Behavior of Plant Pathogens in the Soil. It is evidence of the growing momentum of research in a vital field. Research in microecology as an approach to certain plant-disease problems is by no means new but it has been much too long neglected, almost ignored, except by a chosen few. Those few, by their vision and their scholarly accomplishments through the years, have kept before us the great potentials of using microscopic living things to help solve problems that involve other living things. An important by-product of this symposium should be an improved popular awareness of the work you biologists are doing, and of why much more such work needs to be done.

There probably is no more difficult, urgent, and profitable area of research in agricultural biology today than that of soil microecological phenomena in relation to plant disease. Probably also no area of research is less popular, less glamorous, among investigators and agencies that are impelled to try to produce spectacular results in a hurry. But we face problems of increasing urgency in this area. Why has the challenge of these soil-borne plant-disease problems been picked up by so few investigators and agencies?

Preoccupation with the nonliving components of the environments of organisms has too often tended to becloud our awareness of the living components and their importance. Indeed, it seems that for a long time the living components of the soil were largely forgotten by practitioners and researchers alike, as possible means of controlling certain plant diseases caused by soil-borne pathogens. Biological control through the development of resistant hosts quite properly has been given a great deal of attention, and with many notable successes. But if the search for disease resistance is not successful, and no industrial chemical or physical treatment is available for economically controlling a soil-borne pathogen, the disease generally goes uncontrolled. The problem is laid aside as unfinished business. Why is the microecological approach so rarely tried on a substantial basis? Is it too slow, too expensive, or just too hard? In view of the stakes to be won, and of some of man's efforts today, none of those terms seems to be applicable.

There is nothing wrong with man's desire to study "space" and to search for life beyond the earth. But his fascination for outer space and possible forms of extraterrestrial life should not be allowed to eclipse the greater importance of studying *extensively* the life that lies within those few inches of earth immediately beneath his feet. Can there be any doubt that what man can learn about subsurface terrestrial life is far more necessary to his welfare in the foreseeable future than what he may learn of extraterrestrial life? Is it well that man should reach for the moon before he has really tried very hard to understand the goings-on of the myriad life in the soil on which he stands? Wisely or not, he may reach the moon before he understands very much about the microlife of the soil, because he will have made a much greater effort to reach the moon.

When substantial intellectual and material resources are devoted to these microecological problems on a continuing basis, valuable results are produced. The work is slow, difficult, and expensive, but no more so than much other work of basic and practical importance that is far better supported. We who participate in this symposium and the agencies we represent have no greater responsibility than to promote popular understanding and appreciation of this problem area, to stimulate the interest of students in it, and to foster the expansion of sound research in it.

May this symposium be recognized as a landmark in a great renaissance of interest and research in microecological balance in relation to soil-borne plant disease, and in the development of more enduringly profitable and wiser farming practices.

Toward Biological Control of Soil-Borne Plant Pathogens

S. D. GARRETT—*Botany School, University of Cambridge, England.*

By the term biological control, we clearly imply control of a disease through some biological agency; by the term biological agency, we are bound to mean a living microorganism or macroorganism other than the diseased or damaged plant acting as host and the pathogen or pest causing the disease or damage. This interpretation of the term is supported both by its general usage by entomologists, who first introduced it, and by its more recent employment by plant pathologists. A more formal definition can therefore be proposed to comprehend both naturally occurring and artificially contrived biological control, as follows. Biological control of plant disease may be defined as any condition under which, or practice whereby, survival or activity of a pathogen is reduced through the agency of any other living organism (except man himself), with the result that there is a reduction in incidence of the disease caused by the pathogen. Biological control can be brought about either by introduction or by augmentation in numbers of one or more species of controlling organisms, or by a change in environmental conditions designed to favour the multiplication and activity of such organisms, or by a combination of both procedures.

Next we should consider the genesis of the idea of biological control of soil-borne plant diseases, and the early history of its development. I had nothing to do with the origin of this idea and indeed it took some years to reach me and then to sink in, but I joined in the general excitement of these new developments and attempted to take part in them—an attempt that I have been making, on and off, ever since. The job of the historian is to pinpoint, so far as he can, significant events that have determined important trends and developments, and this applies equally well to the history of science. Credit for discovery has almost always gone, and perhaps rightly, not to the man who first suggested an idea without adequate supporting evidence, but to the one who was able to convince his contemporaries of its rightness and importance.

A demonstration that the activity of a plant pathogen could be inhibited by an accumulation of its own metabolic products was furnished as early as 1908 by Potter (1908). Neither he nor anyone else, however, then followed up the implications of this discovery. I have already attempted (Garrett, 1956) to suggest a possible reason for this earlier neglect by plant pathologists of the microbiological factor in the en-

vironment of plant pathogens, but it will suffice here to say that their awakening seemed to be triggered off by a paper from Sanford (1926), in which he suggested that the control of potato scab by green manuring was a *biological control*, due to an increase in the populations of certain saprophytic bacteria that multiplied upon the organic material. It is important to note, however, that Sanford was not merely reiterating at a more opportune time the suggestions of earlier workers such as Hartley (1921); these suggestions had not gone beyond a general idea of inoculating either soil or plants with selected, "antagonistic" saprophytes. Sanford had, in fact, proposed not one but two concepts, the second of which was original at least in this particular context, and had integrated them into a concise hypothesis of biological control, as follows: (1) saprophytic microorganisms can control the activity of plant pathogens; (2) the microbiological balance of the soil can be changed by altering soil conditions; in particular, the addition of fresh organic material will promote the activity and multiplication of saprophytes, which both by their competition for nutrients and for oxygen, and by their excretion, will depress the activity and multiplication of the pathogens. Sanford's hypothesis had the three merits of being easy to understand, of explaining and collating earlier observations, and of being open to experimental test.

The results of such a test were not long in coming; in the following year, Millard and Taylor (1927) reported control of scab, in potatoes grown in sterilized soil and inoculated with *Streptomyces scabies*, through simultaneous inoculation of the soil with *S. praecox*, a vigorous saprophytic species. Sanford and Broadfoot (1931) then provided experimental evidence for Sanford's original hypothesis, by showing that infection of wheat seedlings by *Ophiobolus graminis* in sterilized soil could be completely suppressed by the antagonistic action of various individually coinoculated species of fungi and bacteria (Fig. 1). The impact of Sanford and Broadfoot's paper was soon reinforced by an extremely original and elegant demonstration from another Canadian worker, Henry (1932), that the influence of soil temperature upon the development of the take-all disease in glasshouse trials could be strongly affected by interactions between the pathogen and other soil microorganisms (Figs. 2, 3). I still think, as I thought then, that this work of Henry's has been one of the greatest single feats of intellectual and

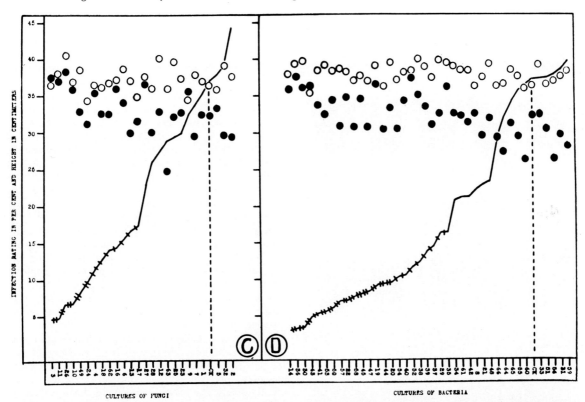

Fig. 1. The effect of 66 cultures of bacteria and fungi on the pathogenicity of *Ophiobolus graminis* on Marquis wheat seedlings. (C) Cultures of fungi. (D) Cultures of bacteria. Solid and barred line indicates the infection rating; double-barred part indicates control; single-barred part, intermediate control; solid part, no control. Black dot = average height of plants, culture plus *O. graminis;* black circle = average height of plants, culture alone. (G. B. Sanford and W. C. Broadfoot. Sci. Agr. 11: 512-528. 1931.)

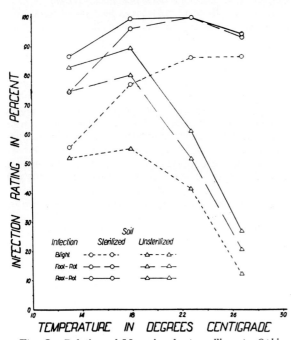

Fig. 2. Relation of Marquis wheat seedlings to *Ophiobolus graminis* at different soil temperatures in sterilized and unsterilized soil. (A. W. Henry. Can. J. Res. 7: 198-203. 1932.)

experimental analysis yet to have been performed in the field of root-disease investigation. My own earliest tribute to Henry's work (Garrett, 1934*b,c*) can be justly described as "the sincerest form of flattery" of which any young man is capable.

Last but not least, California played a prominent part in the early history of this new venture, the development of which belonged so largely to the North American continent. In 1930, Fawcett (1931) lent to this fresh departure both his personal prestige as an eminent plant pathologist, and that of his official position as President of the American Phytopathological Society, by devoting his presidential address to the subject "The importance of investigations on the effects of known mixtures of organisms." Shortly after this, one of Fawcett's research students, R. Weindling, published the first of a brilliant series of papers on the parasitism by *Trichoderma viride* of other soil fungi (Weindling, 1932, 1934, 1937, 1941; Weindling and Emerson, 1936; Weindling and Fawcett, 1936). This series of papers is now too well known to require further comment from me, except to say that I have never known which to admire the more—Weindling's original discovery of this phenomenon, or the pertinacious way in which he followed it up until he had thoroughly elucidated it. His achievement stimulated a great volume of further work on the

Fig. 3. Relative amount of blighting of Marquis wheat seedlings in sterilized and unsterilized soil kept at different temperatures, following inoculation with *Ophiobolus graminis*. Pots left to right: check; 2 pots of unsterilized soil; 2 pots of sterilized soil. (A. W. Henry. Can. J. Res. 7: 198-203. 1932.)

production of antibiotics by soil fungi, and interest in *T. viride* shows no signs of waning.

EVIDENCE FOR THE SIGNIFICANCE OF ANTIBIOTIC PRODUCTION IN NATURAL SOIL.—For a number of years, there was a considerable controversy amongst soil microbiologists as to whether antibiotic production played any significant part in the microbial economy of the soil. The strongest argument against activity of antibiotics in natural (i.e., unsterilized) soil lay in the difficulty of detecting any significant quantity by the current methods of soil analysis. Against this, Brian and others (Brian, 1949; Garrett, 1956) had argued that if antibiotics were an effective agent in competition between soil microorganisms in natural soil, then the site of competition in which they would be most likely to operate would be freshly colonized substrates of plant or animal tissue, and that the range of the antibiotic effect would be measurable in terms of microns rather than of larger units. Furthermore,

the existence of antibiotics had to be regarded as ephemeral, in view of their demonstrable inactivation in soil, through physical adsorption onto soil colloids (in which state, however, as Pramer and Starkey, 1962, have shown, they need not necessarily be inactivated), chemical inactivation (e.g., through an unfavourable pH) and microbial decomposition. The concentration of an antibiotic at any particular soil site at any one time was therefore thought to be governed by the excess of production over inactivation. None of us who advanced such arguments concerning the strictly localized activity and ephemeral nature of antibiotics in the soil found, therefore, any occasion for surprise in the fact that gross methods of soil analysis had hitherto failed to detect significant quantities of antibiotics. In arguing thus, I myself was largely recapitulating views I had expressed 20 years earlier (Garrett, 1936), in considering the possible effects of respiratory carbon dioxide in limiting the rate of ectotrophic spread of *Ophiobolus graminis* along wheat roots. Here, as I had pointed out, one was not concerned with the general concentration of carbon dioxide in the soil, as revealed by gross analyses, but with the local concentration at the root surface. This is, I believe, a general principle of importance for soil microbiologists. Gross analyses of soil for gas concentrations, levels of microbial and plant nutrients, pH values, and antibiotic concentrations reveal merely the mean values; individual values at particular sites or microhabitats may depart from the mean value by factors of a high order. Most soil microbiologists would probably now concede that antibiotic production is of some significance in the soil. Such general considerations apart, Wright (1956), working in Brian's laboratory, has since been able to detect significant amounts of gliotoxin when wheat straw buried in unsterilized soil was inoculated with a spore suspension of a gliotoxin-producing strain of *Trichoderma viride*.

At this point, it is relevant to consider evidence for the existence of a general fungistatic effect inhibiting spore germination in natural soil. Simmonds, Sallans, and Ledingham (1950) reported that unsterilized soil inhibited germination of the conidia of *Helminthosporium sativum;* later, Chinn (1953) demonstrated that this inhibiting effect could be overcome by addition of 2% soybean meal to the soil, providing a nutritive stimulus. Dobbs and Hinson (1953) reported a similar effect with spores of various fungi mounted on purified cellulose film buried in unsterilized soil; inhibition of spore germination could be overcome by a concentration of glucose as low as 0.1%. These observations have been confirmed by Jackson (1958a,b), working with a range of both Nigerian and English soils. The Dobbs and Hinson hypothesis has recently been tested by Lingappa and Lockwood (1961), whose results suggest that the "generalized soil fungistasis" is likely to be in part an artifact of the techniques for its demonstration. These authors were unable to detect any toxic substances in the soil, and concluded that part of the effect was due to production of antibiotics by microorganisms growing on the surface of the assay media. However, they also suggested that individual, living fungal spores serve as substrates, through excreted products having some nutrient value, and that this stimulates growth of bacteria and actinomycetes at the spore surface; production of fungistatic substances by these microbes is postulated as sufficient to inhibit spore germination in the absence of a sufficient substrate stimulus. This recalls an earlier observation by Thornton (1953) on Rossi-Cholodny slides of something like a "hyphasphere" of actinomycete hyphae growing closely around the hyphae of *Rhizoctonia solani*. It seems likely that this explanation put forward by Lingappa and Lockwood for the "generalized soil fungistasis" is substantially correct; it is certainly in keeping with general ideas on the ephemeral existence of most antibiotics in the soil.

Having argued the case for the significance of antibiotic production in the soil, I now wish to enter a caveat against the uncritical postulation of antibiotic effects that is all too common in the literature, and, I will hasten to add, of which I have been guilty before learning from repeated mistakes. Every soil microbiologist should keep constantly in mind the simple fact that the commonest cause of death in a microorganism, in whole or in part, is straight starvation. I will give merely a single example. If Rossi-Cholodny slides are buried in soil to which 1% of fresh plant material has been added, then after a few days a copious growth of fungal hyphae will be found covering the slides. A week or more later, most of the hyphae will be empty and outlined by the clustering of bacteria; still later, even the hyphal cell walls will be found to have disappeared. In the past, these observations have frequenty been interpreted by supposing that bacteria have attacked and killed the living fungal hyphae. Sometimes, maybe, such a thing does indeed happen. But it seems much more probable that the primary cause of death is autolysis through starvation or old age, which can also be observed (albeit at a slower tempo) in pure cultures, as Park (1957) has pointed out. Such autolysis is particularly marked amongst the Oomycetes, and in some species can lead to death of pure cultures in a few weeks after inoculation, if oospores are not produced (Geach, 1936). On the Rossi-Cholodny slides, other microorganisms of course accelerate this autolysis of fungal hyphae from starvation, through their competition for a limited supply of nutrients; it must further be conceded that bacteria may hasten the death of moribund and weakening fungal hyphae, and that they are largely responsible for the ultimate decomposition and assimilation of what remains.

If our visualization of microbial relations as they occur in the soil had been confined to a reading of the innumerable papers on antagonism between microorganisms in petri-dish experiments, most of us would now be asking ourselves the question, how do microorganisms manage to survive and thrive in the soil, in spite of the common occurrence of other organisms having antagonistic and parasitic properties? Yet it is an indisputable fact that most root-infecting fungi manage to spread, indefinitely if not unhindered, over the root systems of their host plants in most soils. Yet more remarkable and difficult to explain, perhaps, is the fact that some highly specialized root parasites, which are known to be susceptible to antibiotics in vitro, are able to survive merely as vegetative mycelium in infected field-crop residues buried in the soil, commonly for a year and sometimes for periods of up to 3 years. For the last 12 years at Cambridge, we have been studying the saprophytic behaviour of root-infecting fungi in the soil.

Our collective findings, recently summarized (Garrett, 1963), suggest a possible answer to the question just propounded. We have found that, in saprophytic competition for a suitable substrate in the soil, the success of a particular fungus will be conditioned as much by the *inoculum potential* at which it happens to be present at the surface of the substrate as by its intrinsic *competitive saprophytic ability*. Amongst cereal foot- and root-rot fungi, for instance, we have found that *Ophiobolus graminis*, *Helminthosporium sativum*, and *Cercosporella herpotrichoides* are all poor competitive saprophytes. Yet, if their inoculum potential be sufficiently high by comparison with that of other soil fungi present at the surface of the substrate, all these fungi can achieve saprophytic colonization of some 90% substrate units (Butler, 1953a,b; Lucas, 1955; Macer, 1961a). This quantitative aspect of saprophytic competition cannot be ignored. Secondly, under favourable conditions, *O. graminis* can survive for about 1 year, *H. sativum* for 2 years, and *C. herpotrichoides* for 3 years in infected cereal residues buried in the soil (Butler, 1953c, 1959; Macer, 1961b).

These latter observations on saprophytic survival can, I believe, find a simple explanation in what was previously said about the effect of inoculum potential on saprophytic colonization. For experiments on saprophytic survival, we have started off with the fungus in a condition of pure culture in the pieces of wheat straw employed for the test; in naturally infected straw, the fungus is similarly almost in pure culture, because it has colonized the plant tissues in its parasitic phase, ahead of all competitors. A fungus in this condition can be described as possessing maximum inoculum potential, so far as the resources of the substrate and its own capacity for utilizing them are concerned. The primary parasite thus established in the tissues has at first an overwhelming superiority in inoculum potential over later invaders for further saprophytic exploitation of the substrate. For the periods of longevity of the primary parasites quoted above (1-3 years), it seems that this initial advantage of a high inoculum potential must often be self-perpetuating. Microscopic observation of wheat straw originally occupied by *Ophiobolus graminis* shows a continued slow mycelial development of this fungus within the tissues (Garrett, 1940). If such a primary parasite is itself unable to decompose cellulose, it may benefit from a limited invasion of the tissues by other organisms that can do so, inasmuch as it is so placed as to be able to take a share of the breakdown products. Thus Macer (1961b) found that *Cercosporella herpotrichoides* was virtually unable to use even so easily available a form of cellulose as sodium carboxymethylcellulose, yet this fungus can survive for 3 years in buried, infected wheat straw. Such a colonization of the plant tissues by cellulose decomposers coming in later must to some extent be controlled and limited by the condition that the primary parasite has already utilized most of the more easily available substrate materials. This suggestion is supported by Macer's further observation that wheat straw occupied by *C. herpotrichoides* lost weight more slowly when buried in soil than did straw previously uncolonized; moreover, the unoccupied straw developed a more varied fungal flora, after burial in the soil, than did straw previously colonized by *C. herpotrichoides*.

From the evidence summarized above, we can conclude that the outcome of saprophytic competition between two or more microorganisms will be strongly affected by their respective inoculum potentials. This condition will apply not only to competition for colonization of a virgin substrate; it will also continue to apply to saprophytic survival of an organism on an already colonized substrate. In the case of an antibiotic-producing microorganism, its inoculum potential will determine the share of a finite substrate that it is able to secure; this in turn will determine the concentration of antibiotic that it produces, and hence its scope for further aggression. In the laboratory microbiologists have succeeded in isolating for detailed study the activities of antibiotic-producing organisms, including parasitic activities. We still have to determine the scope of such activities within the microbial economy of the soil, but it has now become possible to visualize the kind of way in which spectacular laboratory demonstrations of isolated phenomena can be reconciled with the less dramatic course of events in nature.

METHODS PROPOSED FOR BIOLOGICAL CONTROL.—*Inoculation of soil or plant tissues with antagonistic microorganisms.*—The earliest method of biological control to be proposed was naturally inoculation of soil or plant tissues with antagonistic microorganisms, but its possible applications are limited. It is an axiom of ecology that the flora and fauna of a habitat will be selected by the environmental conditions from amongst the species currently available. The balance of the flora and fauna can be upset only temporarily by augmenting artificially the population of a species already present. This statement applies even more strongly to the particular case of microbial ecology, in which the former equilibrium is more quickly restored, owing to the much shorter generation time of microorganisms. The truth of this generalization was demonstrated early by Weindling and Fawcett (1936) when they showed that protection of citrus seedlings against *Rhizoctonia solani* through soil inoculation with *Trichoderma viride* could be achieved most easily by acidifying the soil, and thereby making con-

ditions suitable for the establishment of *T. viride* at a higher population level. When this had been done, soil inoculation with *T. viride* sometimes gave increased control of seedling disease; in the absence of soil acidification, however, even heavy inoculation with this fungus was ineffective.

This conclusion that the microbial balance of the soil can be altered only temporarily by inoculation may seem to be at variance with many examples of successful biological control of introduced insect pests and weed plants. Such control was successful because the insects employed for biological control were not already present in the territories into which they were introduced. Not all such introductions have succeeded in their purpose, but there is at least a chance that a newly introduced insect or higher animal may be more successful in its new habitat than the indigenous species occupying the appropriate ecological niche; sometimes, indeed, an introduced animal may find its appropriate ecological niche not merely invadable but actually vacant in the new territory. Unfortunately, the requisite conditions for biological control of microbial pathogens are less easily satisfied. The soil microflora is a remarkably cosmopolitan one; as Stanier (1953) has explained, two reasons can largely account for this: (1) the soil environment, though widely variable over the earth's surface, is yet less variable in its extremes of temperature and humidity than is the aerial environment inhabited by terrestrial animals and plants; (2) owing to the efficiency of their dormant stages, most soil microorganisms are remarkably successful in surviving periods that are lethal to the vegetating organism.

Thus it follows that most species of microorganisms that could thrive in a particular soil are there already, and so it is difficult to find exotic species suitable for introduction. Prospects for inoculation of living plant tissues are perhaps somewhat brighter, even though they too may have to depend on employment of indigenous rather than of introduced microorganisms. I will give merely a single example from direct experience. My colleague at Cambridge, John Rishbeth, has been seeking methods for preventing colonization of freshly exposed stump surfaces, after the felling of pine trees, by basidiospores of *Fomes annosus*. One of the methods that has given good control has been inoculation of the stump surface immediately after felling by spore suspensions of another basidiomycete, *Peniophora gigantea*. *P. gigantea* is an indigenous species, and is the most effective natural competitor of *F. annosus* in pine-stump colonization in East Anglia (Rishbeth, 1952, 1963). Surprisingly enough, it now seems increasingly probable that this method of biological control can be made as cheap and trouble-free for foresters as the chemical protectants earlier tested by Rishbeth (1959). One factor contributing strongly to this favourable prognosis has been Rishbeth's (1963) success in developing a process for producing tablets from dried suspensions of *P. gigantea* oidia.

Modification of the soil environment.—Modification of the soil environment is a group of methods designed in full accordance with the ecological principle that the soil population at any time will be determined by habitat conditions, and that the population can therefore be changed in any desired direction by making an appropriate change in soil conditions. Chief attention has so far been paid to exploring the effects of various kinds of organic amendments, and especially those of green manures and dry crop residues, such as can be made available for ploughing into the soil during normal farming practice. As already remarked, control of potato scab by green manuring led Sanford (1926) to propose his theory of biological control by organic manuring. I shall restrict my discussion to the effects of organic amendments, but we must remember that other soil conditions will modify the sequence of microbial changes induced by manuring. Furthermore, other soil conditions can sometimes be so modified as to induce (or to increase the degree of) biological control, as was first demonstrated by Weindling and Fawcett (1936). As originally elucidated by Weindling (1934), the parasitism of *Trichoderma viride* on other fungi is probably mediated by one or other of its antibiotics (Fig. 4), gliotoxin

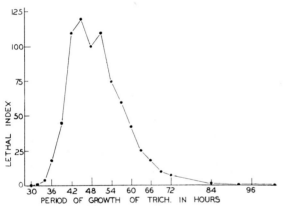

Fig. 4. Lethal indices obtained during the life cycle of *Trichoderma viride*. (R. Weindling. Phytopathology 24: 1153-1179. 1934.)

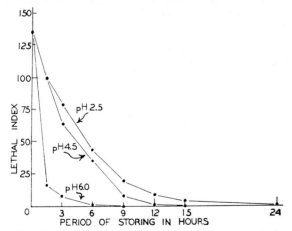

Fig. 5. Influence of pH on the deterioration of the lethal principle of *Trichoderma viride*. Filtrates kept aerobically at 24°C. (R. Weindling. Phytopathology 24: 1153-1179. 1934.)

(Weindling and Emerson, 1936) and viridin (Brian and McGowan, 1945). Both antibiotics are stable only in acid solution (Fig. 5), and this is evidence for mediation of parasitism through antibiotic action; a dependence upon acid conditions for lethal activity against other soil fungi is consistently demonstrated by isolates of *T. viride* secured quite at random (Aytoun, 1953).

It is now firmly established that a number of diseases can be controlled by the ploughing in of fresh organic material of suitable composition. Potato scab, *Phymatotrichum* root rot of cotton and other crops, and take-all of cereals can all be controlled in this way, though successful control depends on the right choice of amendment and the degree of control varies from one soil to another. More recently, root- and foot-rot diseases of snap beans (*Phaseolus vulgaris*) caused by *Rhizoctonia solani* and by *Fusarium solani* f. *phaseoli*, respectively, have been added to the list of diseases that can be thus controlled (Davey and Papavizas, 1960; Papavizas and Davey, 1960; Snyder, Schroth, and Christou, 1959).

Much of the control thus obtained can doubtless be described as biological control. It is essential to remember, however, that any organic amendment is going to affect development of a root disease in three distinct ways: (1) by a *direct effect* on activity of the parasite on the root systems of the growing crop; (2) by a *direct effect* on survival of the parasite from one host crop to the next; and (3) by an *indirect effect* on activity of the parasite on the roots of the growing crop through the medium of host resistance, chiefly through liberation of plant nutrients during the course of decomposition. Control of a disease through direct effects 1 and 2 can often be ascribed to biological control, but control through indirect effect (3) cannot be thus ascribed. In actual field practice, control of disease through effect 1 is likely to preponderate over control through effect 2, because limitation of disease development during the growing season also reduces the amount of inoculum left behind in the soil after harvest.

It is not difficult to analyse experimentally the effects of organic manuring upon these three components of disease development, i.e. activity and survival of the parasite and resistance of the host. In my study of the take-all disease of cereals published over the years 1934-1948, I came to the following conclusions: (1) The parasitic activity of *Ophiobolus graminis* is largely determined by its rate of ectotrophic growth over the host root system, and this seems to be governed chiefly by the concentration of respiratory carbon dioxide at the root surface; organic manuring will contribute to disease control as far as it retards diffusion of carbon dioxide away from the root, through a raising of the general concentration of this gas in the soil atmosphere. (2) The survival of *O. graminis* in infected stubble is largely dependent upon the supply of soluble nitrogen diffusing into the infected stubble from the surrounding soil; organic amendments low in nitrogen will take up available nitrogen from the soil during decomposition and will therefore reduce the longevity of *O. graminis*. (3) Organic manures that release nitrogen in decomposition will promote field resistance of the cereal crop to take-all, because nitrogen (and also phosphate in phosphate-deficient soils) greatly increases the rooting capacity of the cereal plant. Clark (1942) was the first to direct attention to this component in the action of organic manures upon the take-all disease. It has fortunately been possible to resolve all these different requirements into a unified scheme for effective control of take-all through crop husbandry (Garrett, 1950).

Control of *Phymatotrichum* root rot of cotton through heavy dressings of organic manure was originally established by King, Hope, and Eaton (1934). Their findings were confirmed by Mitchell, Hooton, and Clark (1941), who further demonstrated that, in addition to any indirect or microbiological effect, the organic material exercized a direct effect upon the sclerotia of *Phymatotrichum omnivorum*, which it caused to germinate in the absence of any host-root stimulus. The germination and dissipation of sclerotia induced in this way by organic material must contribute to control of the disease, but can scarcely be described as biological control. Nor can it be assumed that applications of fresh organic material to the soil will always help to eliminate sclerotia of root-infecting fungi, either through biological control or by stimulating spontaneous germination of sclerotia and dissipation of their reserves. Working in my laboratory with *Helicobasidium purpureum*, causing violet root rot of sugar beet, carrot, and other crops, Valder (1958) could detect no effect of 1% additions of grassmeal or peameal to the soil upon longevity of its sclerotia. His most important finding was that acid soils encouraged spontaneous germination of sclerotia, and that sclerotium populations were therefore shorter-lived in acid than in neutral or alkaline soils.

Control of potato scab by green manuring has often been successful, and sometimes spectacularly so, but there have also been some failures, indicating that we need to know more about the mechanics of this control method before it can be regarded as reliable. In Great Britain, for instance, the first crop of potatoes taken after ploughing up old grassland during the Second World War was often severely scabbed (Moore, 1943). In the United States, Ken Knight (1941) found in field trials over 3 years that green manures of blue grass and alfalfa produced significant increases in scabbing. A different approach to this problem has been made by Menzies (1959), who reported from a survey of potato scab in central Washington that the older irrigated lands were almost scab-free, whereas new land brought under irrigation during the preceding 15 years was generally infested by *Streptomyces scabies*. Such differences could be seen even in adjacent fields. Soil analyses showed that the older farmed areas were somewhat lower in lime content and pH value, and somewhat higher in organic content, than the new areas. Both of these changes in the soil of the older areas would have tended to reduce scab, but Menzies considered that such quantitative changes in the soil and its microflora were insufficient to explain the virtual disappearance of *S. scabies* as a parasite, and he therefore postulated a qualitative change in the soil microflora. Thus he found that scab was controlled both in a 50:50 mixture of old and new soils, and in new soil to which 1% of old soil together with 1% of alfalfa meal had been added. These observations by Menzies parallel, to quite a remarkable degree, the early history of the take-all disease of cereals in South Australia (Garrett, 1934a).

Attempts at biological control through organic amendments have at least a chance of success against soil-borne diseases caused by specialized parasites. Such attempts are obviously not going to be successful against primitive parasites, if the pathogen is a vigorous saprophyte able to colonize competitively the particular type of organic material that is added to the soil. Thus tropical species of *Rosellinia* can be seen to develop vigorously in surface litter under the shade of plantation crops, and removal of this litter is advocated as a control measure. Again, in a recent symposium on control of southern blight of peanuts, Garren (1961), Harrison (1961) and other speakers all agreed that *Sclerotium rolfsii* can colonize such fresh organic material as weeds ploughed into the soil adjacent to the peanut rows, and advocated deep ploughing of surface litter before preparation of land for the crop. It is well to remember, however, that green weeds ploughed into the soil are at first still alive and that any fungus colonizing such material is behaving as a weak parasite rather than as a saprophyte. Nevertheless, it seems probable from observations such as those of Thompson (1940) on compost heaps in Malaya that *S. rolfsii* also behaves as a vigorous saprophyte in competitive colonization of old, dead plant tissues.

Notwithstanding what I have just said, some primitive plant pathogens that have a phase as free-living saprophytes in the soil can be temporarily controlled through application of fresh organic material. My former research associate, I. D. Blair, showed that *Rhizoctonia solani* could grow as a saprophyte through unsterilized resting soil, devoid either of living roots or of fresh organic material, for an apparently indefinite period (Blair, 1943). In studies with Rossi-Cholodny slides, Blair demonstrated that the growth of *R. solani* through unsterilized soil was checked by incorporation of 1% of finely divided organic amendments such as dried grass, alfalfa, or wheat straw. At that time, Blair was unable to determine the substrates in resting soil on which *R. solani* was subsisting. I have recently gone back to this problem, and found that the three random isolates of *R. solani* tested were all strong decomposers of filter-paper cellulose in pure culture (Garrett, 1962). A further test with one of these isolates showed it to be a vigorous competitive colonizer of cellulose buried in unsterilized soil. If the ecological niche of *R. solani* as a saprophyte in soil is that of a cellulose decomposer, then it is reasonable to expect that its saprophytic activity would at first be suppressed by addition of fresh plant material to the soil, owing to the initial flare up of saprophytic sugar fungi as the pioneer colonizers.

Extensive data about the behaviour of *Rhizoctonia solani* have been provided by Papavizas and Davey (1960, 1961; Davey and Papavizas, 1960) from their study of control of the *Rhizoctonia* disease of snap beans (*Phaseolus vulgaris*) by the use of organic amendments. In an earlier paper (Papavizas and Davey, 1959), these authors had reported that short lengths of mature, dry buckwheat stem provided a saprophytic substrate particularly favourable for competitive colonization by *R. solani* in naturally infested soil, and that this technique provided a reliable method for assessing populations of the fungus. The method was therefore used to determine the direct effect of these organic amendments on the activity of *R. solani*; in every instance, the effect of a treatment on incidence of bean root rot was closely paralleled by its effect on competitive saprophytic colonization of the buckwheat substrate units by *R. solani*. This finding indicates that the effects of the organic amendments on the disease were due to a direct biological control of *R. solani*, rather than to an indirect effect on the disease through the medium of host-plant resistance.

Concerning the possible mechanism of this biological control, Davey and Papavizas (1963) have produced data that largely confirm the explanation originally suggested by Blair (1943), viz. that the activity of *Rhizoctonia solani* is temporarily checked (1) by an increase in carbon dioxide content of the soil atmosphere (2) by a scarcity of available nitrogen in the soil solution. Both effects are produced by rapid decomposition of nitrogen-poor organic matter in the soil. Whereas Blair had tested the response of *R. solani* to a reduction of the carbon dioxide content of the soil atmosphere during decomposition of organic material, Papavizas and Davey (1962) followed the alternative approach of enriching the carbon dioxide content by continuous passage of preformed gas mixtures through the soil. Both sets of results agree well enough with the data provided by Durbin (1959) on the sensitivity of different groups of *R. solani* isolates to carbon dioxide.

Some suggestive data on the effect of nitrogen content of the organic amendment are given in Table 3 of the paper by Davey and Papavizas (1963); these refer to an amendment of cellulose powder adjusted to a range of C:N ratios varying from 400 down to 5 through addition of graded doses of ammonium nitrate. Maximum inhibition of competitive saprophytic colonization of buckwheat stem segments by *Rhizoctonia solani* occurred in those soils receiving amendments adjusted to C:N ratios within the range 100-40. A lower degree of inhibition was provided by amendments having either higher (400 and 200) or lower (20, 10 and 5) C:N ratios. This result can be explained by postulating that nitrogen exerts two distinct and opposite effects upon the activity of *R. solani*, the first being predominant down to C:N ratio 40, and the second coming into action at C:N

ratios of 20 and below. The first, or inhibitory, effect can be attributed, as Davey and Papavizas have pointed out, to the effect of nitrogen in increasing rate of decomposition of the organic material, and hence in promoting a more rapid output of carbon dioxide. This increase in carbon dioxide output can be expected to follow closely the trend in total microbial numbers, which in Table 4 of this paper by Davey and Papavizas can be seen to have increased steadily from C:N 400 down to C:N 5. At C:N 20, however, the second or stimulatory effect (with respect to *R. solani*) of nitrogen comes in, and the total depressing effect of the organic amendment upon the fungus suddenly becomes sharply reduced. This can be ascribed to the presence of available nitrogen that can be directly absorbed by the mycelium of *R. solani*, thus removing the disability of nitrogen starvation suffered by the fungus in the presence of the organic amendment adjusted to higher C:N ratios. The change has come precisely where we might have predicted it, i.e., in the region of C:N 20. The C:N ratio of fallow soils and of microbial substance is generally around a value of 10-12; making some allowance for carbon consumed in respiration during the assimilation of organic material, we should expect that materials having a C:N ratio of 20 or less would liberate some nitrogen during decomposition.

Such an effect of the C:N ratio of organic amendments in biological control would be likely to vary quite widely with different fungi, according to their relative sensitivity to accumulated carbon dioxide, on the one hand, and to a scarcity of nitrogen, on the other. With a fungus relatively insensitive to carbon dioxide, a more effective check would be provided by nitrogen scarcity following amendments of high C:N ratio than by carbon dioxide accumulation associated with amendments of lower C:N ratios. According to Snyder, Schroth, and Christou (1959), control of the foot- and root-rot disease of snap beans due to *Fusarium solani* f. *phaseoli* was obtained only with amendments of high C:N ratio, such as corn stover (C:N 60), barley straw (C:N 80) and pinewood shavings (C:N up to 400). Green barley hay and green tops of soybean and alfalfa (C:N 16) actually increased incidence of the disease; addition of ammonium nitrate (0.3%) to mature barley straw eliminated the effect of the straw in biological control.

Apparent discrepancies with these conclusions will appear unless a distinction is made between the effects of organic amendments upon parasitic or saprophytic *activity* of a pathogen, on the one hand, and their effects upon its saprophytic *survival* in infected or colonized plant tissues, on the other. Thus in my own studies on *Ophiobolus graminis*, already summarized, I concluded that carbon dioxide was one of the chief factors affecting parasitic activity, whereas soil nitrogen was undoubtedly the chief factor determining length of saprophytic survival. Similarly, Papavizas and Davey (1962) found that concentrations of carbon dioxide that strongly depressed both parasitic and saprophytic activity of *Rhizoctonia solani* were without effect on saprophytic survival of this fungus.

Mediation of biological control by selective chemical or heat treatments of soil or plant tissues.—I have already pointed out that inoculation of unsterilized soil with a selected "antagonistic" microorganism is unlikely to produce more than a transient change in the soil population. This prognosis does not necessarily apply, however, to the very different conditions obtaining in sterilized or selectively treated soil. The difficulties of inoculation can, moreover, be avoided by an alternative procedure, which is partial sterilization by some agent so chosen as to favour selective survival or recolonization of the treated soil by a microorganism having the desired antagonistic properties. Such a proposal was in effect made by Bliss (1951), as a result of some unexpected observations during an investigation of carbon disulphide fumigation of the soil for elimination of *Armillaria mellea* from infected citrus roots. Whilst plating out samples of root tissue recovered from fumigated soil to determine if *A. mellea* had survived, Bliss regularly isolated *Trichoderma viride* from root samples in which *A. mellea* was no longer viable. Secondly, Bliss found that the maximum kill of *A. mellea* as a result of fumigation was not manifested at once, but was sometimes not complete until some 24 days after fumigation. Bliss therefore suggested that the killing of *A. mellea* was due not to a direct fungicidal action of carbon disulphide, but to the lethal effect of a soil population of *T. viride* much augmented by the selective action of fumigation on the soil fungus flora. Further evidence put forward by Bliss in support of his hypothesis was as follows: (1) *A. mellea* was not killed by carbon disulphide when fumigated in sterile soil. (2) The fungus was killed if infected root segments were buried in a culture of *T. viride* grown on autoclaved soil.

These findings by Bliss have been followed up by Darley and Wilbur (1954) at Riverside and by ourselves at Cambridge (Evans, 1955; Garrett, 1957, 1958; Saksena, 1960; Moubasher, 1963). Since I have already discussed our own work in a recent book (Garrett, 1963), it will suffice to summarize our main conclusions here. Firstly, we agree with Darley and Wilbur in attaching more importance than did Bliss to the direct fungicidal effect of carbon disulphide upon *A. mellea*, though Bliss was working with concentrations of carbon disulphide that did not appear to be directly fungicidal to *A. mellea,* at least under his particular conditions. We have evidence, however, that under appropriate conditions there is an indirect microbiological effect as well, due to dominance of *T. viride* in the treated soil and its lethal activity against the mycelium of *A. mellea.* This can be expressed by saying that *T. viride* may carry on and finish off what direct fungicidal action of the fumigant has begun. Secondly, we have found that the inoculum potential of *T. viride* that develops in the fumigated soil determines the degree of its lethal action on *A. mellea*; we have obtained near 100% kill of *A. mellea* only with a pure culture of *T. viride* on sterilized soil. Thirdly, we find it impossible to ascribe the dominance of *T. viride* in

fumigated soil wholly to its degree of fumigant tolerance. By comparison with a selected range of soil fungi that we have tested, *T. viride* possesses only a moderate degree of fumigant tolerance. But it is a much faster grower than other soil fungi possessing fumigant tolerance of a similar or higher order. We have therefore ascribed its dominance in fumigated soil to its combination of a moderate but sufficient degree of fumigant tolerance with an exceptionally high growth rate in recolonization of the soil after fumigation.

Such massive recolonization of fumigated soil by *Trichoderma viride* is likely to occur only under soil conditions optimum for its activity; these are: (1) a fairly high soil temperature (20°C or above); (2) good soil aeration, and therefore a medium to low soil moisture content (25-40% moisture-holding capacity in our experiments); and (3) an acid soil. With respect to the third condition, Lily and Saksena (Lily, 1961) have recently found that in an Indian soil of alkaline reaction, the place of *T. viride* as a dominant recolonizer after fumigation with carbon disulphide was taken by *Penicillium nigricans.* They were further able to control the balance between *T. viride* and *P. nigricans* as dominants by suitable adjustment of soil pH.

The breadth of variation in the fungus flora of fumigated soils is illustrated by the results of Martin, Baines, and Ervin (1957) in a study of several fumigants, including D-D, carbon disulphide, chloropicrin, ethylene dibromide, and Vapam, injected into field plots of a number of soil types. The disturbance in the fungus flora persisted for as long as 3 years. Twenty different species were listed as becoming dominant in one or more soils, but *Trichoderma viride* was stated to be favoured by fumigation much more often than any other species. Richardson (1954) had earlier found that *T. viride* and *Penicillium* spp. were preferentially favoured by thiram treatment of soil, and that the beneficial effect of treatment against damping-off of seedlings by *Pythium ultimum* persisted for longer than did the chemical itself in the soil.

A similar method of biological control applied to living host tissues is illustrated by the recent work of Rishbeth (1959) and his search for a chemical protectant for freshly exposed pine-tree stumps against invasion by the basidiospores of *Fomes annosus*. Previous work by Rishbeth and his associates (Meredith, 1959, 1960) had shown that the still-living tissues of the stumps were strongly selective for the pathogen *F. annosus*, and for a small number of harmless, weak parasites, such as *Peniophora gigantea* and *Stereum sanguinolentum*. Rishbeth therefore sought for chemical treatments that would destroy this dangerous selectivity of the stump tissues for *F. annosus* and permit colonization by harmless saprophytes instead. Any treatment that kills the living host tissues is likely to promote this result, but the most promising chemicals were found to be disodium octaborate, ammonium sulphamate, and urea. All three treatments favoured colonization of the stump surface by mould fungi in place of the basidiomycetes colonizing untreated stumps; ammonium sulphamate and urea encouraged a particularly vigorous growth of moulds, partly, perhaps, through their nitrogen content (Kreutzer, 1963).

Heat treatment of soil also can be employed as a method for changing the microflora. Warcup (1951) found that short heat treatments of soil in laboratory containers were useful for isolation of heat-resistant fungi that were too slow in growth to be isolated by standard cultural methods. In horticultural practice, however, control of soil temperature at anything short of that of flowing steam (i.e. 100°C) has hitherto been unavailable. This deficiency has now been remedied by Baker and Olsen (1960), who have demonstrated that steam can be accurately adjusted to any desired temperature for soil treatment, by admixture with air in calculated proportion. Low-temperature steam is cheaper to use, and also results in a lower degree of post-steaming toxicity to seedlings and delicate plants. Last but not least, it offers an opportunity for controlling precisely the degree of selective soil treatment effected by the heat treatment. Further research on this new method should be very rewarding. As a result of Baker's pioneer use of aerated steam in California, this method is now coming into commercial practice in Australia (Baker, 1962).

Selective and nonselective effects of the root systems of higher plants.—An outstanding example of the use of higher plant species for biological control of soilborne pathogens is the employment of decoy crops. A decoy crop for any particular pathogen may be defined as a crop the roots of which will stimulate germination of the dormant propagules of that pathogen, without themselves being sufficiently susceptible to permit a fresh crop of dormant propagules to be produced. In this line of research, nematologists have taken and maintained the lead, though White (1954) has succesfully employed *Datura stramonium* as a decoy planting against *Spongospora subterranea* on potatoes in Tasmania.

The most efficient and agriculturally acceptable kind of decoy crop is likely to be an immune or highly resistant variety of the crop plant itself. Thus Cole and Howard (1962) have studied in field plots the effects of planting potatoes bred from *Solanum tuberosum* spp. *andigena* on the egg population of *Heterodera rostochiensis* in the soil. Reduction of the egg population resulting from the growing of these resistant potato varieties was about 80% per year; after 4 years, the egg population was reduced to about 1% of its original value. These results agree well with others obtained in the Netherlands (Huijsman, 1957), and in Germany (Möller, Rothacker and Stelter, 1959; Goffart, 1960; McBeth and Taylor, 1944).

Nonselective effects of crop plants that can be employed for biological control result from the uptake of soil nutrients by the growing crop, and two examples of this effect will suffice. Vanterpool (1940, 1952) has summarized the results of his outstanding study of browning root rot of cereals on the Canadian prairies. The root rot is caused by various species of *Pythium*, but the underlying first cause was shown to be a deficiency of phosphate. Unlike the great majority of root diseases, browning root rot was most severe on cereals taken after fallow—an effect that Vanterpool showed to be due to aggravation of the phosphate deficiency by excess nitrogen that had accumulated over the fallow period. This effect could be avoided by replacing the fallow with a crop, though it is other changes (chiefly correction of soil phosphate deficiency) in husbandry that have resulted in the virtual disappearance of this disease from the Canadian prairies.

My second example concerns the take-all disease of cereals; a catch crop can be grown in Great Britain in autumn between consecutive spring-sown crops of wheat or barley, with the object of keeping available soil nitrogen down to the minimum and hence in starving *Ophiobolus graminis* of the nitrogen that it requires for prolonged survival in the infected stubble (Garrett and Buddin, 1947; Garrett and Mann, 1948). For this purpose, the "Chamberlain system" of undersowing consecutive spring-sown cereals with a suitable legume, or legume-grass mixture, is now in regular use. If a leguminous crop is growing under reasonably good conditions of illumination, it absorbs more soluble nitrogen from the soil than it excretes into it, and hence the over-all effect *whilst the crop is growing* is to deplete the soil of nitrate. Only under poor light conditions does a legume fail to photosynthesise enough carbohydrate to balance the nitrogen that its nodules fix and its roots absorb.

PROSPECTS FOR BIOLOGICAL CONTROL.—Once upon a time, oracles enjoyed a reputation for supernatural wisdom; insofar as these utterances were usually obscure or ambiguous, we can concede that this reputation was frequently justified by the event. Rather similarly, the proverbs current in most languages can be associated together in contradicting couples. Nevertheless, most scientists would subscribe to the truth embodied in the saying that "history repeats itself," which is merely tantamount to a belief in an ordered universe. Both collectively and individually, we as scientists know that history in the shape of our experiments can be made to repeat itself, provided that we know and understand all the conditions that are effectively operating to control the course of events. This proviso, however, is the difficulty, and an intractable one it can be. Some of the conditions effectively controlling the course of events in an experiment may be unknown and even unguessed at; one can control only the known and understood. Today, it would be accepted as a truism to declare that the microbiological factor is the most important one in the environment of root-disease fungi and other soil-borne pathogens. Yet less than 40 years ago, this factor was unrecognised, or at least ignored, by almost all root-disease investigators. No wonder, then, that I, and no doubt other workers of the same period, can still remember experimental results that I did not understand, could not repeat, and dared not publish.

History does repeat itself, then, provided that the same combination of effective conditions recurs. Imperfect as our knowledge and interpretation of history may be, it still provides the only basis for prophesy. Fortunately for us as microbiologists, microorganisms are far less complex than human beings, and prediction is to that degree less difficult. The past history of attempts at biological control is thus our safest guide to prospects for the future. The lessons that we have learnt from many disappointments can be summed up quite briefly. Biological control is a problem, or rather an endless series of individual problems, in applied microbial ecology. Nothing far short of fairly complete knowledge and comprehension of each ecological situation will enable us to control soil-borne diseases through biological agencies. There are no short cuts to biological control; that is the mistake that many of us have made in the past and that some of us, no doubt, will make again in the future.

Biological control cannot be separated from the whole subject of disease control, which involves eventually a complete knowledge of the biology and epidemiology of a disease, and of the ecology of the crop plant. That is why I applaud the far-sighted wisdom of the organizers of this symposium, in taking for our discussions the whole subject of control of soil-borne pathogens and matters related thereto. I am reminded of the story, no doubt apocryphal, of the farmer who on his deathbed told his son that there was treasure buried on his land, though he refused to disclose its whereabouts. For a number of years afterwards, the son occupied all his spare time by digging and redigging all the land as opportunity offered. No treasure was found, but the yield of the son's crops (so the story goes) went up steadily as a result of this thorough cultivation. Eventually he somehow learnt, or came to realize, that no gold lay under the surface of his soil; it was the soil itself that was the "treasure." This is a moral story, and it has a moral for us. The prospect of achieving biological control was the lure that gave many of us an exciting quest in the first place, and kept us experimenting in spite of repeated disappointments. In due course, some of us half forgot what we had first set out to find, because we found so much else of interest and value on the way. Christopher Columbus was the prototype of every successful scientist; behind each one is an exciting hypothesis, and a wrong hypothesis often provides as much motive power as the right one.

Despite what I have just said, however, I now believe that eventual prospects for biological control are brighter than ever before, partly because we can at last comprehend the magnitude of the problems to be solved. Just before I left Cambridge for Berkeley, recent developments in the work of one of my own colleagues (Rishbeth, 1963) caused me hurriedly to revise a rather gloomy prognosis I had written only a year earlier. It is my earnest hope that similar developments elsewhere will cause even my warnings to become out of date before these words go out of print.

LITERATURE CITED

AYTOUN, R. S. C. 1953. The genus *Trichoderma*; its relationship with *Armillaria mellea* (Vahl. ex Fries) Quél. and *Polyporus schweinitzii* Fr., together with preliminary observations on its ecology in woodland soils. Trans. Proc. Botan. Soc. Edinburgh 36: 99-114.

BAKER, K. F. 1962. Principles of heat treatment of soil and planting material. J. Australian Inst. Agr. Sci. 28: 118-126.

BAKER, K. F., and C. M. OLSEN. 1960. Aerated steam for soil treatment. (Abstr.) Phytopathology 50: 82.

BLAIR, I. D. 1943. Behaviour of the fungus *Rhizoctonia solani* Kühn in the soil. Ann. Appl. Biol. 30: 118-127.

BLISS, D. E. 1951. The destruction of *Armillaria mellea* in citrus soils. Phytopathology 41: 665-683.

BRIAN, P. W. 1949. The production of antibiotics by microorganisms in relation to biological equilibria in soil. Symp. Soc. Exptl. Biol. 3: 357-372.

BRIAN, P. W., and J. C. McGOWAN. 1945. Viridin: a highly fungistatic substance produced by *Trichoderma viride*. Nature (London) 156: 144.

BUTLER, F. C. 1953a. Saprophytic behaviour of some cereal root rot fungi. I. Saprophytic colonization of wheat straw. Ann. Appl. Biol. 40: 284-297.

BUTLER, F. C. 1953b. Saprophytic behaviour of some cereal root rot fungi. II. Factors influencing saprophytic colonization of wheat straw. Ann. Appl. Biol. 40: 298-304.

BUTLER, F. C. 1953c. Saprophytic behaviour of some cereal root rot fungi. III. Saprophytic survival in wheat straw buried in soil. Ann. Appl. Biol. 40: 305-311.

BUTLER, F. C. 1959. Saprophytic behaviour of some cereal root rot fungi. IV. Saprophytic survival in soils of high and low fertility. Ann. Appl. Biol. 47: 28-36.

CHINN, S. H. F. 1953. A slide technique for the study of fungi and actinomycetes in soil with special reference to *Helminthosporium sativum*. Can. J. Botany 31: 718-724.

CLARK, F. E. 1942. Experiments toward the control of the take-all disease of wheat and the Phymatotrichum root rot of cotton. U. S. Dept. Agr. Tech. Bull. 835, 27 p.

COLE, C. S., and H. W. HOWARD. 1962. The effect of growing resistant potatoes on a potato-root eelworm population—a microplot experiment. Ann. Appl. Biol. 50: 121-127.

DARLEY, E. F., and W. D. WILBUR. 1954. Some relationships of carbon disulfide and *Trichoderma viride* in the control of *Armillaria mellea*. (Abstr.) Phytopathology 44: 485.

DAVEY, C. B., and G. C. PAPAVIZAS. 1960. Effect of dry mature plant materials and nitrogen on *Rhizoctonia solani* in soil. Phytopathology 50: 522-525.

DAVEY, C. B., and G. C. PAPAVIZAS. 1963. Saprophytic activity of *Rhizoctonia* as affected by the carbon-nitrogen balance of certain organic soil amendments. Soil Sci. Soc. Am. Proc. 27: 164-167.

DOBBS, C. G., and W. H. HINSON. 1953. A widespread fungistasis in soils. Nature (London) 172: 197.

DURBIN, R. D. 1959. Factors affecting the vertical distribution of *Rhizoctonia solani* with special reference to CO_2 concentration. Am. J. Botany 46: 22-25.

EVANS, E. 1955. Survival and recolonization by fungi in soil treated with formalin or carbon disulphide. Trans. Brit. Mycol. Soc. 38: 335-346.

FAWCETT, H. S. 1931. The importance of investigations on the effects of known mixtures of organisms. Phytopathology 21: 545-550.

GARREN, K. H. 1961. Control of *Sclerotium rolfsii* through cultural practices. Phytopathology 51: 120-124.

GARRETT, S. D. 1934a. Factors affecting the severity of take-all. I. The importance of micro-organisms. J. Agr. S. Australia 37: 664-674.

GARRETT, S. D. 1934*b*. Factors affecting the severity of take-all. II. Soil temperature. J. Agr. S. Australia 37: 799-805.

GARRETT, S. D. 1934*c*. Factors affecting the pathogenicity of cereal foot-rot fungi. Biol. Rev. Cambridge Phil. Soc. 9: 351-361.

GARRETT, S. D. 1936. Soil conditions and the take-all disease of wheat. Ann. Appl. Biol. 23: 667-699.

GARRETT, S. D. 1940. Soil conditions and the take-all disease of wheat. V. Further experiments on the survival of *Ophiobolus graminis* in infected wheat stubble buried in the soil. Ann. Appl. Biol. 27: 199-204.

GARRETT, S. D. 1950. Some problems of intensive cereal cultivation. J. Inst. Corn and Agr. Merchants 1950: 147-151.

GARRETT, S. D. 1956. Biology of root-infecting fungi. Cambridge University Press, London and New York. 293 p.

GARRETT, S. D. 1957. Effect of a soil microflora selected by carbon disulphide fumigation on survival of *Armillaria mellea* in woody host tissues. Can. J. Microbiol. 3: 135-149.

GARRETT, S. D. 1958. Inoculum potential as a factor limiting lethal action by *Trichoderma viride* Fr. on *Armillaria mellea* (Fr.) Quél. Trans. Brit. Mycol. Soc. 41: 157-164.

GARRETT, S. D. 1962. Decomposition of cellulose in soil by *Rhizoctonia solani* Kühn. Trans. Brit. Mycol. Soc. 45: 115-120.

GARRETT, S. D. 1963. Soil fungi and soil fertility. Pergamon Press, Oxford. 165 p.

GARRETT, S. D., and W. BUDDIN. 1947. Control of take-all under the Chamberlain system of intensive barley growing. J. Minist. Agr. (London) 54: 425-426.

GARRETT, S. D., and H. H. MANN. 1948. Soil conditions and the take-all disease of wheat. X. Control of the disease under continuous cultivation of a spring-sown cereal. Ann. Appl. Biol. 35: 435-442.

GEACH, W. L. 1936. Root rot of grey peas in Tasmania. J. Council Sci. Ind. Res. Australia 9: 77-87.

GOFFART, H. 1960. Populationsveränderungen des Kartoffelnematoden (*Heterodera rostochiensis* Woll.) beim Anbau nematodenresistenter und nematodenanfälliger Kartoffelsorten unter Berücksichtigung des Auftretens agressiver Biotypen. Nematologica, Suppl. II.

HARRISON, A. L. 1961. Control of *Sclerotium rolfsii* with chemicals. Phytopathology 51: 124-128.

HARTLEY, C. 1921. Damping-off in forest nurseries. U.S. Dept. Agr. Dept. Bull. 934, 99 p.

HENRY, A. W. 1932. The influence of soil temperature and soil sterilization on the reaction of wheat seedlings to *Ophiobolus graminis*. Can. J. Res. 7: 198-203.

HUIJSMAN, C. A. 1957. Veredeling van der aardappel op resistentie tegen *Heterodera rostochiensis* Wollenweber. Mededel. Stichting Plantenveredeling, Wageningen, 14.

JACKSON, R. M. 1958*a*. An investigation of fungistasis in Nigerian soils. J. Gen. Microbiol. 18: 248-258.

JACKSON, R. M. 1958*b*. Some aspects of soil fungistasis. J. Gen. Microbiol. 19: 390-401.

KENKNIGHT, G. 1941. Studies on soil actinomycetes in relation to potato scab and its control. Michigan Agr. Expt. Sta. Tech. Bull. 178, 48 p.

KING, C. J., C. HOPE, and E. D. EATON. 1934. Some microbiological activities affected in manurial control of cotton root rot. J. Agr. Res. 49: 1093-1107.

KREUTZER, W. A. 1963. Selective toxicity of chemicals to soil microorganisms. Ann. Rev. Phytopathol. 1: 101-126.

LILY, K. 1961. Ecological studies on soil fungi. Ph.D. Thesis, Univ. Saugar, India.

LINGAPPA, B. T., and J. L. LOCKWOOD. 1961. The nature of the widespread soil fungistasis. J. Gen. Microbiol. 26: 473-485.

LUCAS, R. L. 1955. A comparative study of *Ophiobolus graminis* and *Fusarium culmorum* in saprophytic colonization of wheat straw. Ann. Appl. Biol. 43: 134-143.

MACER, R. C. F. 1961*a*. Saprophytic colonization of wheat straw by *Cercosporella herpotrichoides* Fron and other fungi. Ann. Appl. Biol. 49: 152-164.

MACER, R. C. F. 1961*b*. The survival of *Cercosporella herpotrichoides* Fron in wheat straw. Ann. Appl. Biol. 49: 165-172.

MARTIN, J. P., R. C. BAINES, and J. O. ERVIN. 1957. Influence of soil fumigation for citrus replants on the fungus population of the soil. Soil Sci. Soc. Am. Proc. 21: 163-166.

MCBETH, C. W., and A. L. TAYLOR. 1944. Immune and resistant cover crops valuable in root-knot-infested peach orchards. Proc. Am. Soc. Hort. Sci. 45: 158-166.

MENZIES, J. D. 1959. Occurrence and transfer of a biological factor in soil that suppresses potato scab. Phytopathology 49: 648-652.

MEREDITH, D. S. 1959. The infection of pine stumps by *Fomes annosus* and other fungi. Ann. Botany (London) [N.S.] 23: 455-476.

MEREDITH, D. S. 1960. Further observations on fungi inhabiting pine stumps. Ann. Botany (London) [N.S.] 24: 63-78.

MILLARD, W. A., and C. B. TAYLOR. 1927. Antagonism of microorganisms as the controlling factor in the inhibition of scab by green manuring. Ann. Appl. Biol. 14: 202-215.

MITCHELL, R. B., D. R. HOOTON, and F. E. CLARK. 1941. Soil bacteriological studies on the control of Phymatotrichum root rot of cotton. J. Agr. Res. 63: 535-547.

MÖLLER, K-H., D. ROTHACKER, and H. STELTER. 1959. Stand und Methodik der Nematodenresistenzzüchtung auf der Grundlage von *Solanum tuberosum* subsp. *andigenum* in der Deutschen Demokratischen Republik. T. B. Deut. Akad. Landwiss. (Berlin) 20: 65.

MOORE, W. C. 1943. Diseases of crop plants: a ten years review (1933-42). Minist. Agr. (London) Bull. 126.

MOUBASHER, A. H. 1963. Selective effects of fumigation with carbon disulphide on the soil fungus flora. Trans. Brit. Mycol. Soc. 46: 338-344.

PAPAVIZAS, G. C., and C. B. DAVEY. 1959. Isolation of *Rhizoctonia solani* Kuehn from naturally infested and artificially inoculated soils. Plant Disease Reptr. 43: 404-410.

PAPAVIZAS, G. C., and C. B. DAVEY. 1960. Rhizoctonia disease of bean as affected by decomposing green plant materials and associated microfloras. Phytopathology 50: 516-522.

PAPAVIZAS, G. C., and C. B. DAVEY. 1961. Saprophytic behaviour of Rhizoctonia in soil. Phytopathology 51: 693-699.

PAPAVIZAS, G. C., and C. B. DAVEY. 1962. Activity of Rhizoctonia in soil as affected by carbon dioxide. Phytopathology 52: 759-766.

PARK, D. 1957. Behaviour of soil fungi in the presence of bacterial antagonists. Trans. Brit. Mycol. Soc. 40: 283-291.

POTTER, M. C. 1908. On a method of checking parasitic diseases in plants. J. Agr. Sci. 3: 102-107.

PRAMER, D., and R. L. STARKEY. 1962. Determination of streptomycin in soil and the effect of soil colloidal material on its activity. Soil Sci. 94: 48-54.

RICHARDSON, L. T. 1954. The persistence of thiram in soil and its relationship to the microbiological balance and damping-off control. Can. J. Botany 32: 335-346.

RISHBETH, J. 1952. Control of *Fomes annosus* Fr. Forestry 25: 41-50.

RISHBETH, J. 1959. Stump protection against *Fomes annosus*. II. Treatment with substances other than creosote. Ann. Appl. Biol. 47: 529-541.

RISHBETH, J. 1963. Stump protection against *Fomes annosus*. III. Inoculation with *Peniophora gigantea*. Ann. Appl. Biol. 52: 63-77.

SAKSENA, S. B. 1960. Effect of carbon disulphide fumigation on *Trichoderma viride* and other soil fungi. Trans. Brit. Mycol. Soc. 43: 111-116.

SANFORD, G. B. 1926. Some factors affecting the pathogenicity of *Actinomyces scabies.* Phytopathology 16: 525-547.

SANFORD, G. B., and W. C. BROADFOOT. 1931. Studies of the effects of other soil-inhabiting micro-organisms on the virulence of *Ophiobolus graminis.* Sci. Agr. 11: 512-528.

SIMMONDS, P. M., B. J. SALLANS, and R. J. LEDINGHAM. 1950. The occurrence of *Helminthosporium sativum* in relation to primary infections in common root rot of wheat. Sci. Agr. 30: 407-417.

SNYDER, W. C., M. N. SCHROTH, and T. CHRISTOU. 1959. Effect of plant residues on root rot of bean. Phytopathology 49: 755-756.

STANIER, R. Y. 1953. Adaptation, evolutionary and physiological: or Darwinism among the micro-organisms. p. 1-20. *In* E. F. Gale and R. Davies [ed.], Adaptation in micro-organisms, Symp. Soc. Gen. Microbiol., 3rd, Cambridge University Press, London.

THOMPSON, A. 1940. Notes on plant diseases in 1939. Malayan Agr. J. 28: 400-407.

THORNTON, R. H. 1953. Features of growth of *Actinomyces* in soil. Research (London) 6: no. 6.

VALDER, P. G. 1958. The biology of *Helicobasidium purpureum* Pat. Trans. Brit. Mycol. Soc. 41: 283-308.

VANTERPOOL, T. C. 1940. Present knowledge of browning root rot of wheat with special reference to its control. Sci. Agr. 20: 735-749.

VANTERPOOL, T. C. 1952. The phenomenal decline of browning root rot (*Pythium* spp.) on the Canadian prairies. Sci. Agr. 32: 443-452.

WARCUP, J. H. 1951. Soil-steaming: a selective method for the isolation of ascomycetes from soil. Trans. Brit. Mycol. Soc. 34: 515-518.

WEINDLING, R. 1932. *Trichoderma lignorum* as a parasite of other soil fungi. Phytopathology 22: 837-845.

WEINDLING, R. 1934. Studies on a lethal principle effective in the parasitic action of *Trichoderma lignorum* on *Rhizoctonia solani* and other soil fungi. Phytopathology 24: 1153-1179.

WEINDLING, R. 1937. Isolation of toxic substances from the culture filtrates of *Trichoderma* and *Gliocladium.* Phytopathology 27: 1175-1177.

WEINDLING, R. 1941. Experimental consideration of the mold toxins of *Gliocladium* and *Trichoderma.* Phytopathology 31: 991-1003.

WEINDLING, R., and O. H. EMERSON. 1936. The isolation of a toxic substance from the culture filtrate of *Trichoderma.* Phytopathology 26: 1068-1070.

WEINDLING, R., and H. S. FAWCETT. 1936. Experiments in the control of *Rhizoctonia* damping-off of citrus seedlings. Hilgardia 10: 1-16.

WHITE, N. H. 1954. The use of decoy crops in the eradication of certain soil-borne plant diseases. Australian J. Sci. 17: 18-19.

WRIGHT, JOYCE M. 1956. The production of antibiotics in soil. III. Production of gliotoxin in wheat straw buried in soil. Ann. Appl. Biol. 44: 461-466.

► DISCUSSION OF S. D. GARRETT PAPER

L. I. Miller:

What methods are most satisfactory in distinguishing between the death of a fungus on a buried slide due to an antibiotic effect, as contrasted to that caused by starvation of the fungus?

S. D. Garrett:

This can't be done, and it is necessary to devise other types of experiments to find out what is happening.

H. Katznelson:

Conceding that there is competition for nutrients, do you think that competition for accessory growth factors and vitamins would be severe enough in soil to reduce the inoculum potential or infectious ability of an auxotrophic plant pathogen or even seriously to influence its survival?

S. D. Garrett:

I know of no evidence to support this suggestion. My own view is that most soils provide what is necessary in the way of accessory growth factors or vitamins.

C. H. Driver:

Referring to Dr. Rishbeth's work on inhibition of *Fomes annosus* by *Peniophora gigantea* in fresh pine stumps, my observations on PDA and malt-agar media show that when these organisms are grown together, there is no reaction similar to antibiosis. But I have observed, as has Dr. Rishbeth, some evidence of reduction of root-infection potential by *F. annosus* in the presence of *P. gigantea* in a pine stump. What are your comments in this respect?

S. D. Garrett:

Dr. Rishbeth's observations suggest that biological control of *Fomes annosus* by *Peniophora gigantea* during colonization of the pine-stump surface is effected by some mechanism of competition other than antibiosis. If the proportion of spores of *P. gigantea* is equal to (or even somewhat lower than) that of *F. annosus* in a mixed inoculum, *F. annosus* is completely suppressed. *P. gigantea* grows very vigorously in the tissues of fresh pine stumps.

L. F. Johnson:

Dr. Garrett, are you optimistic about the future of biological control? Do you think that this method might eventually compare with other control measures in the field of plant pathology?

S. D. Garrett:

Yes, but there are no shortcuts to biological control. We have to elucidate the microbiological situation very thoroughly before we can be sure that control will work consistently.

Also, many promising methods of biological control have been "killed" by the discovery that control could be effected in simpler and cheaper ways, as by rotation, fertilizer practice, and adjustments in crop husbandry. This has happened with the take-all disease of cereals, and to some extent with *Phymatotrichum* root rot of cotton.

D. Pramer:

The advent of antibiotics provided us with a convenient and dramatic explanation for observed antagonistic phenomena, but evidence to support this explanation was not obtained readily. It is true that even in the outstanding work of Dr. Joyce Wright, it remained necessary to inoculate with *Trichoderma,* if gliotoxin production was to be obtained on straw buried in natural soil. One can readily visualize discontinuous microenvironments in a body of soil in which antibiotic production may occur. The amounts formed would be small, however, and their influence would be limited to the immediate area. There is, I believe, a lack of convincing evidence to support the thesis that antibiotics produced under natural conditions are capable of exerting a significant and generalized, rather than restricted and generally inconsequential, effect.

S. D. Garrett:

I certainly admit that the fact that Dr. Joyce Wright inoculated with *Trichoderma viride* the wheat straw that she buried in unsterilized soil could be held to weaken her claim that this demonstrated *natural* production of antibiotics in the soil. But I have already suggested that significant antibiotic production in natural soil is both local and ephemeral, i.e. that it occurs during colonization of fresh substrates. If Dr. Wright had analyzed a sufficiently large number of microhabitats in the soil, I have no doubt that she would have found a few in which antibiotic production was active at time of sampling. Inoculation with *T. viride* was a device to dispense with analysis of the large number of samples otherwise necessary.

F. E. Clark:

I was especially interested in the emphasis that you chose to place on the factor of starvation, or shortage of food material, in the soil ecology. Some of the recent papers dealing with the importance of fungistasis and antibiosis in soil have in a sense implied that there is no shortage of food materials in the soil or in the soil solution. I do not question the occurrence of fungistasis, nor of the importance of pH or temperature or other factors; nevertheless, I do want to emphasize what several other microbiologists have stated elsewhere, namely, that there are many microorganisms in soil and that they are nearly always hungry.

S. D. Garrett:

I agree completely with Dr. Clark's comments. I have no doubt that if a visitor from the planet Mars were to view this city of Berkeley, he might find it difficult to believe that there could be any shortage of houses, not realizing that nearly all of them at any one time might be completely occupied, and therefore not available.

PART II

◄

THE SOIL MICROORGANISMS

►

The Soil Microflora—Its Nature and Biology

ALAN BURGES—*The Hartley Botanical Laboratories, University of Liverpool, England.*

►

ORGANISMS PRESENT.—Sooner or later practically all organisms or their reproductive structures reach the ground and become incorporated in the soil. Although most of the organisms die and decay, a small proportion are capable either of continuing growth in the soil for a while or of remaining in a dormant condition for varying lengths of time. In addition there are a number of organisms which appear to have soil as their natural habitat. In considering the microorganisms found in the soil one can make a preliminary grouping into (1) those which carry out most of their life in the soil, (2) those which primarily attack living plant or animal material but can continue growing in the soil at least for a time, and (3) those which are in the soil by accident, usually in the form of a resting propagule, which may remain dormant for varying lengths of time. Because there are these different ecological groups of organisms it is virtually impossible to define accurately what is meant by a soil organism.

Fungi.—In considering the fungi that have been isolated from soil one may use as a preliminary basis the book published by Gilman in 1945. Summarising the information regarding the species listed there, we find that some 200 phycomycetes, 32 ascomycetes, and 385 imperfect fungi are recorded as having been isolated from soil, making somewhat over 600 species in all. At the time Gilman collected this information on soil fungi little was published on the occurrence of basidiomycetes in the soil. It is now known, principally from the work of Warcup (1959) and Warcup and Talbot (1962) that a number of basidiomycetes grow actively in the soil and can be isolated and subsequently identified. There is little doubt that if we were to list the basidiomycetes known to occur in soil or which could reasonably be assumed to be soil organisms, we would have to add several hundred species to Gilman's lists. If, for the moment, consideration is restricted to Gilman's information, it is found that more than half of the recorded species belong to some ten genera, of which *Penicillium, Fusarium, Mucor,* and *Aspergillus* contain by far the major part of these species. Examination of the published species lists by very many authors show that the genera *Absidia, Acrostalagmus, Alternaria, Aspergillus, Botrytis, Cephalosporium, Chaetomium, Cladosporium, Cylindrocarpon, Fusarium, Mucor, Penicillium, Rhizopus, Stemphylium, Trichoderma, Verticillium,* and *Zygorhynchus* occur repeatedly and might reasonably be regarded as

the genera that are most commonly and characteristically isolated from soil. Such species lists, however, are very much a reflection of the techniques used (Warcup, 1960; Durbin, 1961). Many of the authors who have carried out work of this kind have utilised either a dilution-plate technique or some form of soil plate. These techniques predominantly favour species which have a fast growth rate, which spore abundantly, and which are very tolerant of the nature of the substrate on which they grow. If special techniques such as those designed to isolate aquatic phycomycetes are used or if special substrates, such as hair, are added to the soil, one can readily isolate a number of species from specialised groups that do not appear in species lists obtained by other techniques. There is not yet sufficient evidence to interpret such results and to decide how many of the species isolated were growing actively in the soil and how many were merely there as resting propagules.

Bacteria and actinomycetes.—When we turn to the bacteria, the problems are in some ways more simple, curiously enough because of the great difficulties associated with the taxonomic identification of bacteria. There is nothing comparable in the literature on soil bacteria to the many species lists published on soil fungi. Most studies on soil bacteria have been concerned either with the counting of the total flora or of certain categories such as spore-formers or anaerobes or else with the examination of the physiological groups and their relative abundance and activity. It is very difficult to provide information of the taxonomic kind that is so readily available for the fungi or the algae. Some indication of information of this kind can be obtained from *Bergey's Manual* (Breed, Murray, and Smith, 1957). Of the genera listed, above 50 have species which are regarded as having soil as their natural habitat. *Bergey* gives approximately 1,600 species of bacteria; of these, approximately 250 are recorded as having been isolated from soil. As Clark (1964) has pointed out, however, if we consider also species associated with mud or pond water or occurring in association with plant debris in the soil, the proportion of species associated with the soil becomes very much greater, and half or more of the genera recorded in *Bergey* might be regarded as having close association with the soil. With regard to the actinomycetes, the family Streptomycetaceae can be said, in broad terms, to be almost entirely made up of soil forms.

Algae.—Many algae occur in the soil but there is not yet sufficient information available to make generalisations of any great value. The majority of unicellular freshwater green or blue-green species appear to be capable of growing on the surface of moist soils (John, 1942). In addition most soils contain characteristic populations of diatoms. An examination of a number of papers published on soil algae shows that nine genera of the Cyanophyta, twenty-four genera of the Chlorophyta, nine of the Chrysophyta, and seven of the Bacillariophyta could be regarded as genera which characteristically have species occurring in the soil. Only a single genus of the Rhodophyta (*Porphyridium*) has been recorded from the soil.

The distribution of algae in a soil is often puzzling. Algae are dependent on light for the formation of their complex organic carbon compounds by photosynthesis; nevertheless quite a number of the algae are capable of carrying out heterotrophic growth when an elaborated carbon source is available. Despite this the present evidence suggests that heterotrophic growth of algae does not occur frequently in normal soils. Undoubtedly where very rich effluents enter the soil, particularly where there is sewage contamination, some of the normally pigmented flagellates appear to grow heterotrophically, but in most soils the algae are probably carrying out an autotrophic existence dependent on light. One might expect, therefore, that they would be fairly firmly restricted to the surface of the soil, but this is not always so. Frequently the maximum numbers of algae occur a centimetre or so below the surface of the soil. This may perhaps be a compromise between the maintenance of adequately moist conditions and light of sufficient intensity to keep the algal metabolism above the compensation point. Frequently algae can be recovered from considerable depths in the soil where virtually no light penetrates. These algae have presumably been washed down and although they are still viable are almost certainly not increasing their body weight but are gradually respiring away their reserves. No reliable evidence on this is available, however. The increased numbers of green algae in the rhizosphere as compared with those in the surrounding soil also await an adequate explanation (Katznelson, 1946). Algae appear to have a very great capacity for maintaining their viability. Stored soils maintained air-dry under laboratory conditions appear to retain a viable algal flora for sometimes as much as 20 years. The important study on the algae of the soils of Breckland carried out by John (1942) was based entirely on samples which had been collected some years earlier and stored in the laboratory at normal room temperatures.

ESTIMATION OF NUMBERS.—*Bacteria.*—Attempts to estimate the number of individuals of the various kinds of microorganisms in the soil run into many difficulties. In the case of the bacteria, one can define what is meant by an individual bacterium, and it might seem at first glance feasible to take the soil, disperse it in such a manner that the individual bacterial cells are separated from one another, and then transfer a portion of this suspension to a suitable nutrient medium. Each viable bacterium might then be expected to grow and give rise to a colony which could subsequently be counted and perhaps identified. By such means it would be theoretically possible to obtain an accurate estimate of the number of bacterial cells in a given weight of soil capable of growing on the medium chosen. The practical difficulties associated with such a procedure are very great indeed, however, and a tremendous amount of effort (Brierly, Jewson, and Brierly, 1927; James and Sutherland, 1939) and thought has gone into the improvement of the techniques and the statistical consideration of the results obtained. To begin with, soil is an extremely heterogeneous system, so that collecting the initial samples for examination represents a complex statistical sampling problem in itself. After a sample is obtained that might be regarded as representative of the soil from which it came, there is a major difficulty of getting adequate dispersal of the soil and of the bacteria. Most bacteria do not appear to exist in the soil as individual, isolated cells. A very high proportion of them occur as colonies of various size. Moreover, these colonies are usually closely associated with the organic material on which they are growing, and are often enveloped in mucilage. In general, the bacteria do not occur freely distributed in the soil solution but are closely attached to soil particles (see Fig. 1) or are embedded in the soil organic matter. Even with the use of dispersing agents it is clear that we cannot yet approach a situation in which the bacteria are completely dislodged from the soil particles and become distributed in the suspension as individual cells. If we could estimate the degree of clumping of the bacteria, this might not perhaps be so serious, but such evidence as we have at the moment suggests that even in the same soil the degree of clumping or dispersion can be very greatly affected by the physical condition of the soil and by treatments such as drying or freezing. Having prepared a suspension, this is then added to an appropriate nutrient medium and the viable cells allowed to grow. Here again difficulties arise; there is clearly a very great deal of interaction between the developing colonies. Some species clearly have an inhibiting action on neighbouring colonies, others a stimulating one. Often we do not detect any obvious interaction but are simply conscious of an awkward arithmetical discrepancy in our results. For instance, if we take a series of dilutions, each differing from the other by a factor of 10, one might anticipate that the number of colonies occurring per petri dish would correspondingly alter by a factor of 10. This is rarely so (Dr. E. Grossbard, personal communication). Experience with a particular soil often enables an investigator to select a dilution which appears to give least interaction between the developing colonies. In general, workers aim to have not more than 100 colonies of bacteria per plate. Even altering the dilution by a factor of 4 will often produce as much as

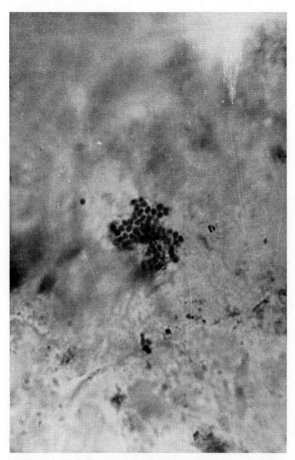

Fig. 1. Discrete colonial pattern of bacteria on the surface of a quartz grain in a consolidated sand-dune soil under *Pinus nigra*. Photograph kindly supplied by T. R. G. Gray.

a 25% difference in the estimate of the bacterial population obtained. The choice of the medium is again a matter which profoundly influences the result. Rich media are particularly prone to favour special groups and to give anomalous counts. On the other hand, many bacteria have requirements for specialised growth substances. Perhaps the most successful general media are those which have a very low level of available nutrient but of a very diverse nature, for instance, soil-extract agar. The final count obtained is, at the best, an estimate which has only a moderate degree of reliability. Many of the statistical treatments of the counts of soil bacteria give a false sense of security in the accuracy of the method. This is often due to an inappropriate use of statistical techniques and a disregard of the many sources of error and degrees of freedom involved.

It is possible to make a direct count of the bacteria in the soil by using some kind of microscopical investigation. This may be done by spreading a known volume of soil onto a slide, staining and counting the bacteria observed. Such a method, however, is extremely inaccurate and greatly underestimates the total number of organisms. One can reduce the errors involved in such techniques by the adoption of the ratio method, developed by Thornton and Gray (1934), in which soil is mixed with a known number of recognisable particles and then a count made of the ratio of added particles to bacteria. Jones and Mollison (1948) have developed a technique in which a soil suspension is made and after the addition of agar a small sample is allowed to solidify in a haemocytometer cell. The small agar block is then dried to form a film which is subsequently stained, and the organisms in a number of fields counted. This method has the great advantage that it gives information regarding the total number of organisms in the suspension and the degree of clumping of the individual bacteria. It is, however, still subject to difficulties associated with releasing the bacteria, particularly from organic matter or mineral particles to which they were attached.

Direct counts normally are greatly in excess of the counts obtained by culture techniques. This discrepancy has recently been considered by Clark (1964), who has pointed out that the discrepancy is least in soils to which fresh organic matter has recently been added and is greatest in soils which have reached a situation in which most of the readily fermentable organic material has disappeared. This situation might perhaps be likened to the comparison of a young culture in the logarithmic stage in the laboratory from which one can obtain cultures from most, if not all, individual cells, and an old culture where, if an attempt is made to obtain colonies from the individual cells, we find that a very large proportion of the bacteria are either dead or moribund and the number of colonies obtained will represent only a fraction of the total cells known to be present in the culture. In some soils the direct count may be as much as 100 times that obtained by dilution-plate methods. It might perhaps be thought, therefore, that since we are isolating only one tenth of the organisms present in the soil that the species isolated are very atypical of the flora as a whole. At the moment there is not sufficient evidence to give a definite answer to the questions raised by such considerations. In discussing the general nature of the bacterial flora Clark has pointed out that the coryneform bacteria, and particularly the forms grouped under *Arthrobacter*, frequently account for some 65% of the total bacterial flora. Sporing bacteria frequently account for a further 25%, leaving all the other forms together to make up the remaining 10%. The various genera associated with nitrogen fixation such as *Rhizobium*, *Clostridium*, and *Azotobacter*, and those concerned with oxidation of ammonia and nitrite numerically comprise a negligible fraction of the soil bacterial population.

Fungi.—Estimation of fungal numbers has, in addition to all those difficulties raised during the discussion of bacteria, the added problem that in a dilution count one is almost invariably counting only the fungal spores; virtually none of the colonies arises from fungal hyphae. While undoubtedly an estimate of the numbers of fungal spores present gives some measure of the previous level of physiological activity of the species concerned, it is much more important to know the actual amount of hyphae present. The most successful method available to date for estimating the length of hyphae present in the soil is that devised by Jones and Mollison (1948), already referred to. The total length of hyphae can be estimated by direct observation on soil sections (Burges and Nicholas, 1962) (Figs. 2, 3, and 4) but subsequent investigations have

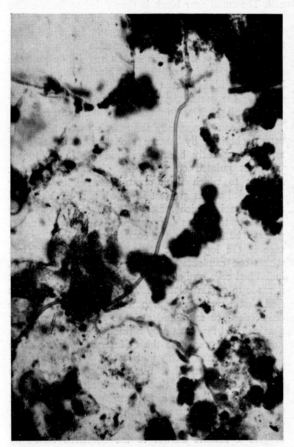

Fig. 2. Extended hyphal pattern of a fungus in the A_1 horizon of an iron-humus podzol under *Pinus sylvestris*. Organic matter mainly derived from faecal pellets. Photomicrograph of soil section embedded in polymeric resin.

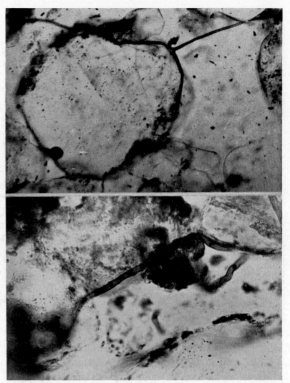

Figs. 3 and 4. The relation between fungal hyphae and the mineral and organic components of the soil. Photomicrographs of sections of an iron-humus podzol under *Pinus sylvestris,* embedded in polymeric resin. **Fig. 3** (upper). Typical hyphal pattern in the A_2 horizon. Many hyphae closely appressed to quartz grains with occasional strands crossing pore spaces. **Fig. 4** (lower). Hyphae associated with amorphous organic matter in the A_1 horizon.

indicated that considerable underestimates arise in the use of this technique because so many of the hyphae are embedded in more or less opaque organic material. Direct measurement of fungal hyphae in soil sections may estimate as little as one fifth of the total hyphae present. The soil-section technique, however, does give a great deal of information concerning the precise location of the hyphae which is, of course, lost in the Jones and Mollison technique.

Actinomycetes.—Estimates of actinomycete numbers are subject to the same kind of errors that we encounter when attempting to estimate the numbers of fungi.

Algae.—Soil algae have not yet been investigated sufficiently to consider in any detail the quantitative estimation of their numbers. Forms of dilution tech-

niques have been used, particularly those associated with the "probable number" method. Again we are faced with the difficulty of recognising what is an individual; this is particularly so in relation to the filamentous forms, which can readily fragment, and to many of the semicolonial forms in the Chlorophyta and Cyanophyta.

MEASUREMENT OF ACTIVITY.—In animal ecology a great deal of use is made of the concept of biomass. In its simplest terms the biomass of any particular species is the product of the number of individuals of that species and the average weight of one individual. There have been attempts to calculate the biomass of the various constituents of the soil microbiological population. In the case of bacteria one can obtain an approximation by taking the volume of an individual bacterium and multiplying this by an average specific gravity and then by the number of bacteria estimated per gram of soil. Such studies indicate that in an agricultural soil which contains about 3×10^9 bacteria per gram these will account for about 3 tons wet weight of bacteria per acre (Russell, 1950). The estimation of the biomass of fungi or of actinomycetes is very much more difficult. Even if such estimates could be obtained there is the very real problem of deciding how much of the fungal hyphae is filled with active cytoplasm and thus might have a relatively high physiological activity and how much is highly vacuolate or perhaps even void of cytoplasm (Figs. 5 and 6).

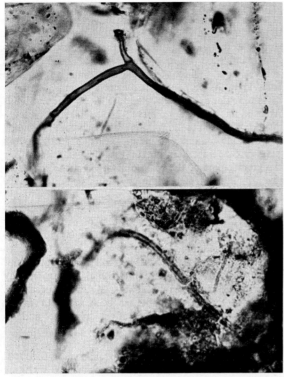

Figs. 5 and 6. Death of hyphae in soil. Photomicrographs of sections of an iron-humus podzol under *Pinus sylvestris,* embedded in polymeric resin. **Fig. 5** (upper). Death of part of the hyphal system of a fungus in the A$_2$ horizon. **Fig. 6** (lower). Remnants of hypha in B$_2$ horizon, presumably long dead and, in absence of soil animals and lysing bacteria, partly mummified by humic acid.

From time to time various workers have attempted to estimate the over-all biological activity in a soil by determining the oxygen uptake or the carbon dioxide output of a given volume of soil. There is a renewed interest in such measurements at the present time. Often these are referred to as measurements of "soil respiration," and if both oxygen uptake and carbon dioxide output is known then one can calculate respiratory quotients for the soil or for particular horizons within the soil. There are many objections to the expression "soil respiration," yet such a term serves a very useful purpose. It must be remembered, however, that a measure of oxygen uptake for the soil as a whole can be a very inaccurate measure of biological activity since it represents merely the sum of a very wide range of processes taking place simultaneously. These could vary considerably, particularly if there were some balancing mechanism, and yet the over-all activity might show little indication of change. Several workers have made attempts to inactivate different groups of soil organisms individ-

ually and in this way obtain a measure of the respiratory contribution of the group being studied. Simultaneous estimations of oxygen uptake and carbon dioxide output allow respiratory quotients to be calculated. In the upper layers of pine litter the respiratory activity is usually very high (Parkinson and Coups, 1963) and the oxygen uptake and carbon dioxide output ratios indicate that the predominant substrate being respired is carbohydrate in nature. At the base of the organic layer, in the H horizon, the respiratory quotients are appreciably below 1, suggesting that less oxygenated substrates are being utilised. In considering the results obtained by soil respiratory experiments, it is important to consider carefully the basis on which the measurements are made. If the gaseous exchange is related solely to the weight or volume of soil, this may give a somewhat misleading picture. Parkinson and Coups have shown that appreciable differences are found in the relative activity of the different horizons of a podzol according to whether the results of gaseous exchange are related to a given volume of soil or to the amount of organic matter present within that soil horizon.

In the early studies on soil respiration relatively large samples of soil were taken, often consisting of 500 to 5,000 g, and the gaseous exchanges measured. Sometimes techniques were employed in which a continuous stream of air was passed over or through the soil and the carbon dioxide produced absorbed in some convenient measuring device. More recently workers have used small samples, usually of 1-5 g, and have estimated the respiratory activity over a relatively short period of a few hours in a Warburg apparatus. There have been a number of specially modified flasks which have been designed for this type of work.

DISTRIBUTION AND ECOLOGY.—Any form of sampling of the soil population shows that both in number of individuals and in number of species, the upper layers of the soil are very much more heavily populated than the lower horizons. Apart from the changes in numbers of individuals, there are often well-marked differences in the vertical distribution of species. Some are characteristically surface organisms, others occur in the deeper layers of the soil, and it is often possible to determine a well-marked zonation in a profile (Burges, 1963a). In general the dispersion of microorganisms in the soil appears to be highly efficient, and if a large number of replicate samples are taken it is found that the species which are most abundant are usually very efficiently dispersed throughout the soil, despite the fact that many of these, when they reproduce, form their spores in dense masses. The dispersal is attributed very largely to the activity of soil animals; frequently this appears to be simply because microorganisms adhere to the surface of the animal and are carried with it through the soil (Hutchinson and Kamel, 1956). Movement of soil water perhaps is also important in the vertical movement of the spores and small organisms (Burges, 1950; Hepple, 1960).

A number of attempts have been made to place the study of soil microorganisms on a firm ecological basis (Burges, 1963*b*). Some European workers have sought in the soil a series of communities and have attempted to carry out the equivalent of a phytosociological survey and a characterisation of the communities involved (Sappa, 1955; Domsch, 1960). While such studies are undoubtedly important and may well lead to a profounder understanding of the interaction of the various microorganisms in the soil, the information so far available is too slight to provide any help to the understanding of soil communities in relation to agricultural soils. It is, in fact, virtually impossible at the present time to characterise a soil by its microbiological flora, yet it is very clear that the microorganisms in the soil have their characteristic ecological preferences just as have the higher plants and higher animals.

BREAKDOWN OF PLANT DEBRIS.—Both the nature and activity of soil microorganisms is very considerably affected by the annual increment of organic matter coming from leaves, branches, etc., aboveground, and from roots and root exudates belowground. The extent of the additional organic matter varies greatly. In a hardwood forest it may be of the order of only 1 or 2 tons per year on each acre. Coniferous forests normally have a much higher rate of organic addition; figures varying from 3 to 9 tons per acre are usually quoted (Ovington, 1962). Tropical rain forests can greatly exceed this, and some estimates are as high as 60 tons per acre per year. In a young plantation or young grass sward the organic matter falls to the ground and lies on the surface for a long time, so that for the first few years there is a steady increase in the amount of organic matter in the litter. For pine forests it is usually at least 15 or 20 years before an equilibrium situation is approached. At this stage decomposition approximately balances the rate of addition of organic matter. In forests of *Pinus sylvestris* in England it takes at least 8 or 9 years for an individual needle to become sufficiently decomposed so that it is no longer recognisable as an individual needle (Kendrick, 1959). It is not surprising, therefore, that a period of appreciably more than 10 years is required before an equilibrium situation in the litter layers is reached. In some broad-leaved forests, equilibrium may be reached very much earlier, and perhaps only a matter of a year or two is required once the trees have reached even approximately adult size. Sometimes the leaves may disappear quickly and no obvious litter is found. This may be due to rapid decomposition on the surface or it may be due to the incorporation of the fallen leaves into the mineral soil by the action of soil animals, particularly earthworms.

Very few estimates are available concerning the annual addition of organic matter to the soil by the death of roots. Those which have been made suggest that the annual increment from roots is perhaps about half or a little more, of the annual increment from the aboveground parts. In perennial plants most of the root increment comes from the death of small feeder roots, which may have a life of only a few months.

In addition to the falling of leaves and branches or to the death of roots, organic matter is added to the soil from the plant system either by leaching from the leaves or by exudation from the roots. At the moment we have no reliable evidence to estimate the extent of such accretions. Certainly quite a high proportion of the minerals can be leached from the leaves during the latter stages of their life before they have fallen from the trees. Exudates from the roots have a profound influence on the soil microflora but we are not yet in a position to place this on a quantitative basis in terms of pounds per acre. Present work indicates that the extent of the release of organic materials from roots is greatly affected by environmental conditions. Drought followed by rain appears to release considerable amounts of amino acids, especially from grasses. Some workers are of the opinion that by far the greater part of the release of organic material from roots is the outcome of injury or disturbance to the plant.

Detailed knowledge of the microbiological successions involved in the decomposition of organic matter in the soil is still very limited. Most workers who have been interested in this problem have tended to confine their investigations to a small number of groups of organisms. For instance the fungal succession may be followed or the bacterial or the animal succession. It is rare that an attempt has been made to follow the complete disintegration of a substrate and to define which steps are carried out by different groups of organisms.

The complexities of such studies are well illustrated by summarising the changes which occur in pine needles in the litter layers of a *Pinus sylvestris* forest (Kendrick and Burges, 1962). Infection of the needles takes place before they are shed from the tree. Not only are saprophytic organisms involved, but frequently parasites or invaders of moribund tissue also become well established before the needles fall.

Once the needle reaches the ground it is immediately subject to invasion by species characteristic of the litter, but organisms which invaded the needle while it was still on the tree may continue their activity for some time after the needle has fallen. In the litter studies at Delamere, Cheshire, England, once the needle has fallen to the ground it is invaded by at least three principal fungi. Two of these, *Helicoma* and *Sympodiella*, form superficial networks on the surface of the needle; the other, *Desmazierella*, attacks the internal tissues of the needle. The extent of the internal mycelium is largely determined by the previous attack of leaf parasites, such as *Lophodermium* and *Fusicoccum*. After a burst of vegetative activity the saprophytic fungi produce conidiophores and spores. In the case of *Desmazierella*, conidiophores project through the stomata and give rise to a large number of external conidiophores. This wave of sporing occurs some 6 months or so after the needle falls, and is immediately followed by a considerable activity on the part of small animals, mainly mites and Collembola. These eat the spores and much of the superficial mycelium; one can readily see in the faecal pellets of these animals short lengths of hyphae, apparently devoid of their cytoplasmic contents, and spores which often appear to be relatively undamaged (Fig. 7). A year later a second crop of conidiophores is produced with a second wave of spore production. This in turn is followed by renewed animal activity and a further grazing of the hyphae. Not all of the tissue is effectively invaded by fungi. Considerable portions of the needle and of the heavier bits of litter appear to be completely free from microbiological attack.

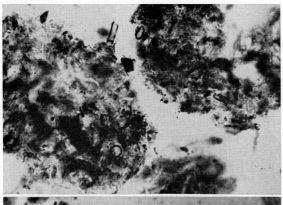

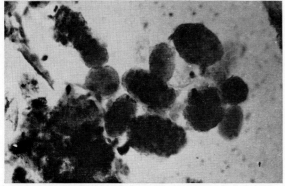

Figs. 7 and 8. The effect of soil animals on the decomposition of organic matter and the disintegration of hyphal systems. Photomicrographs of sections of an iron-humus podzol under *Pinus sylvestris,* embedded in polymeric resin. **Fig. 7** (upper). Faecal pellets in A horizon, presumably from orabatid mites. **Fig. 8** (lower). Disintegrating faecal pellets releasing spores and hyphal fragments in A horizon.

As needles get buried by the fall of other needles, the microenvironment becomes moister and apparently the tissues soften. Tunnelling by Collembola and mites occurs and both invaded and uninvaded tissue is eaten. During this phase much of the mesophyll is destroyed, leaving the outer shell of the needle with its thick, tough cuticle, and the vascular strands with their associated lignified tissues.

At this stage a number of other fungi become important, particularly the basidiomycetes. Histological examination shows that active decomposition of cellulose and of lignin occurs next. The fungi involved at this stage, particularly the basidiomycetes, have a much more extensive mycelium, which tends to matt the individual needles together. It has not been possible to determine any fruiting of the basidiomycetes directly associated with this phase of the decomposition but, as would be expected, there is the normal production of basidiomycete fruit bodies, particularly in the early autumn each year. The invasion by basidiomycetes is terminated by a considerable increase in animal activity, and both the remains of the needles and of the fungi are converted to a dark mass of faecal pellets, which accumulate at the junction of the litter and of the mineral soil. In the field this layer looks almost amorphous, but examination under the microscope reveals that it is a mass of faecal pellets (see Fig. 8) in various stages of disintegration and highly dispersed fragments of fungal hyphae, spores, and exoskeletons of the meiofauna. In this layer various species of *Mortierella, Trichoderma, Penicillium,* etc. are active, and it can be demonstrated that a number of these fungi are capable of decomposing the chitinous remains which form a relatively large proportion of the organic material in this horizon (Gray and Bell, 1963).

In this succession the major organisms are fungi and small animals. Bacteria appear to play relatively little part. This is perhaps because the general pH of the litter is low, usually between pH 3.0 and 4.0, and perhaps certain of the phenolic materials in pine litter act as efficient inhibitors to many species of bacteria. A small number of actinomycetes are present, but we have not yet been able to get any indication of how active they are in the breakdown processes.

In a typical mass of composting litter or composting straw with a pH higher than about 6.0, bacteria play an extremely active part and very large populations are involved. Many of these are capable of attacking the carbohydrates available and, one assumes, quantitatively play a considerable part in the disorganisation of the leaf and stem debris. Decomposition of the fungal hyphae, which are formed in very large numbers in the early stages of the decomposition, is also not restricted to the activity of other fungi or to small animals. Many bacteria are very active chitin splitters, and direct examination with a microscope often shows fungal hyphae apparently being lysed by an epiphytic population of bacterial cells.

CHEMICAL PROCESSES IN THE SOIL.—*Decomposition of organic residues.*—The decomposition of organic residues in the soil presents problems of very great biochemical complexity. If one considers the very large number of chemical substances which can be found in any one species of plant and remembers that when the plant falls to the ground each of these substances becomes available for utilisation by microorganisms which will, during their growth, form a new range of substances in their body material and their excreted metabolic products, it will readily be appreciated that the task of following the biochemical changes involved is virtually impossible unless one is content to restrict the investigation either to broad fractions of the material or to a few well-characterised compounds. In general it may be said that the decomposition of organic matter added to the soil proceeds in the following general pattern. Water-soluble compounds and particularly the sugars disappear first; protein is hydrolysed very easily and disappears usually within a matter of days or weeks. These initial stages are followed by the disappearance of the simpler polysaccharides, particularly starch and pectins; the decomposition of cellulose and lignin follows at a much later stage. Little is known about the decomposition of the cutin and suberin materials of plant debris, yet these often form a considerable proportion by dry weight of the initial material added. It seems that such material decomposes relatively slowly and is often still present in considerable amounts when most of the cellulose and lignin fractions have disappeared. The above pattern of sequential decomposition is subject to many variations, particularly where there is high moisture or low oxygen. Similarly, in highly acid soils, there is reason to believe that the general pattern is altered. Handley (1954) suggests that under conditions in which mor humus develops, the phenolic materials of the plant debris tan the protein, which then forms a protective coat on the cellulose. This protected cellulose residue may then remain relatively unattacked for a very long period. Saitô (1957) in Japan has shown that during the breakdown of beech litter the decomposition of lignin may precede the decomposition of the cellulose. During the initial phases of the decomposition, carbon is lost as carbon dioxide and a certain amount of water-soluble minerals are leached out into the soil, but usually the nitrogen is locked up by the microorganisms associated with the initial stages of decomposition. Again, as a broad generalisation, it may be said that carbon loss as carbon dioxide continues until the carbon:nitrogen ratio is of the order of 10 to 1. At this stage carbon and nitrogen loss tend to follow hand in hand. Little is known about the decomposition in the soil of what may be termed the secondary plant products, compounds such as tannins, anthocyanins, and flavones, which sometimes occur in very large quantities. During the decomposition of debris underneath *Acacia mollissima* (the tanbark wattle) in Eastern Australia, the tannin fraction disappears very rapidly soon after the bark falls to the ground and softens.

The breakdown of the plant and animal material is carried out by a very wide range of microorganisms and small animals. The ultimate residues which become incorporated into the amorphous soil organic matter quantitatively represent only a very small fraction of the total amount of organic matter which was originally added to the soil. This is a point of considerable importance because any particular fraction in the soil might perhaps have come from a compound present in the original plant material in only very small amounts indeed, but over the years, if the compound resists decomposition, it may accumulate and form an important fraction of the soil organic matter.

The biochemical processes involved in the decomposition and utilisation of the relatively simple poly-saccharides and their derivatives are fairly straightforward. In the case of starch it can be demonstrated that many microorganisms release enzymes which will hydrolyse the starch and give the parent sugar. Pectins are attacked by extracellular enzymes which hydrolyse the pectin chain, releasing the galacturonic acid units, and demethylate the carboxyl side groups. The decomposition of cellulose is apparently similar to this. Extracellular enzyme preparations can be obtained which will break down various modified celluloses either to cellobiose and then glucose or directly to glucose. However, convincing enzymatic breakdown in vitro of "native" cellulose is lacking. When we come to the more complex compounds, such as lignin and humic acid, we cannot get evidence for any comparable hydrolysis of the linkages forming the main structure of the molecule. Knowledge in the case of both of these substrates is considerably handicapped by our ignorance concerning their basic chemical structure.

Decomposition of humic acid.—The present views on humic acid may be summarized and will give some indication of what problems might be involved in the decomposition of substrates of this kind. Humic acid, using the term in its broad sense, is one of the most widespread and abundant of organic materials in the soil. Although it can be extracted and, to some extent, purified by relatively simple laboratory techniques, the nature of its molecule is such that one cannot readily characterise the humic acids from different soil types. Recently we have been able to show that by the use of a reduction with sodium amalgam high yields of phenols can be obtained which on chromatography give a characteristic phenol pattern for each of the types of soils—a podzol, a chernozem, and a rendzina—which we have studied.

Such work confirms the widely accepted view (Kumada, Suzuki, and Kazuyuki, 1961) that humic acid is essentially produced by the oxidative polymerisation of a mixture of phenols to give a very large molecule, whose chemical properties are primarily associated with surface carboxylic acid groups. Several sources can be suggested for the original phenols that go into the formation of humic acid. Some phenolic plant constituents may be leached out of the residues relatively unchanged. Substances such as lignin may be decomposed (Henderson, 1960) and during their decomposition release phenolic products. Microorganisms may synthesise phenolic metabolic products from nonphenolic substrates such as sugars or celluloses. The relative proportion of the individual phenols from these different sources may vary considerably from one soil to another; thus the final polycondensate may differ from soil to soil in the same way that one finds different clays. In our informal discussions on the nature of humic acid we have suggested that one may be faced with a humic acid chemistry analogous to that of clay chemistry, with the various phenolic moieties forming a network which might be compared with a clay lattice.

During the last few years it has been demonstrated

that a wide range of fungi are capable of decomposing humic acid under laboratory conditions. Most of these fungi are basidiomycetes but some of them are ascomycetes such as *Xylaria* and *Ustulina* (Latter and Burges, 1960; Hurst, Burges, and Latter, 1962). In the laboratory successful decomposition has been obtained only under highly aerobic culture conditions and when an accessory source of energy is supplied. Some evidence is available to show that the amount of humic acid decomposed is directly proportional to the amount of glucose utilised. An examination of the fungi capable of decomposing humic acid has shown that ability to decolourise humic acid is correlated with the ability to reduce an aromatic carboxyl group first to the aldehyde and then to the alcohol (Hurst, Burges, and Latter, 1962). Infrared examination of humic acid undergoing decomposition by fungi has demonstrated that the characteristic absorption peak associated with the carboxyl is lost in the partially attacked humic acid (Hurst, 1963). It would seem therefore that there are some grounds for believing that the initial stage in the decomposition of the humic acid is a reduction of the carboxyl to an alcohol group, a reaction which under laboratory conditions is an energy-demanding reaction. The reduction of the aldehyde to the alcohol in cell-free preparations requires the addition of reduced diphosphopyridine nucleotide (DPNH) or reduced triphosphopyridine nucleotide (TPNH). It was the recognition that microorganisms possibly utilise a reductive cleavage of the humic acid that led us to reinvestigate chemical reductions as a means of degrading humic acid.

Many of the organisms which decompose humic acid also decompose lignin and we are, at the moment, investigating the possibility that lignin decomposition is also energy-demanding, at least in its initial step. Much of the field evidence is consistent with such a hypothesis.

Microbial attack on solid substrates.—The decomposition of these complex organic residues raises a number of particularly interesting problems associated with enzyme action. Most of our traditional knowledge of enzymes has been concerned with systems in which there is a soluble substrate, and therefore substrate concentration can be varied; and with enzymes that are either in a soluble condition or that are dispersed adequately so that they approximate to soluble enzymes. With such systems the biochemist has worked out an elaborate analysis of the enzyme kinetics of the enzyme–substrate relations.

During the decomposition of materials in the soil, extracellular enzymes which act on a soluble substrate such as a sugar are sometimes concerned, but much more often solid substrates such as cellulose, lignin, or humic acid are involved. In the breakdown of a carbohydrate or a pectin, extracellular enzymes released by the microorganisms diffuse to the substrate and cause a relatively simple hydrolytic cleavage of the insoluble molecule, giving rise to water-soluble fragments which can then diffuse away from the site

of the decomposition and become absorbed by microorganisms in the vicinity. Where a substrate such as lignin or humic acid is concerned, the situation appears to be very different. As yet there is no convincing evidence of any extracellular enzyme that is capable of decomposing the substrates. Several possible explanations might be put forward to account for the way such materials decompose. In the case of humic acids, it might be possible for the organisms to release something which would bring the humic acid into solution; this could be accomplished by decreasing the hydrogen-ion concentration so that a soluble salt was formed, which might then diffuse to the fungal hypha and decomposition take place. Alternatively, some kind of dispersion might be obtained, as can be achieved with such substances as ethylenediamine tetracetic acid (EDTA). It is difficult, however, to see such a system working in the case of lignin or humin. There is a possibility that the fungus would need to secrete both the enzyme system and an accessory material such as TPNH before decomposition could proceed. Such a system one imagines would be efficient only for a relatively short range and would be particularly subject to interference from other organisms in the environment.

During the decomposition of the organic matter the carbon is released as carbon dioxide. Most of this is returned directly to the air but a small proportion is perhaps washed away in the leaching water.

Nitrogen transformations.—The fate of the nitrogen fraction differs considerably from one soil to another. In some acid soils it seems that the amino acids present in the fallen material are deaminated fairly rapidly and the ammonia released is either absorbed rapidly by the roots or microorganisms or is complexed with the organic matter in the soil, to be released subsequently when these organic complexes are decomposed. In many forest systems which have reached a stable situation this nitrogen conservation may be very efficient indeed, and almost 100% of the nitrogen that is released is reabsorbed by the plant cover. In soil conditions where a wide range of organisms associated with the nitrogen cycle are present, the ammonia which has been released by the deamination of the proteins may be oxidised via nitrite to nitrate. Here again it will be available for reabsorption by plant roots or perhaps first by microorganisms and then subsequently be released again and become available for absorption by roots. Nitrate appears to be less easily held by organic complexes and is much more susceptible to leaching. In addition, soil microorganisms are available which are capable of decomposing the nitrate and of releasing nitrogen either in the form of the free gas or in one of its oxides. Losses by leaching or by denitrification can at times make serious inroads in the general nitrogen level in the soil.

In contrast to such losses there may be accessions of nitrogen from symbiotic fixation by rhizobia or related organisms or by free-living forms such as *Azotobacter*.

Recently there has been a renewed interest in the possibility that many microorganisms other than the well-known *Azotobacter* and *Clostridium* are capable of fixing at least small amounts of nitrogen. The use of isotopically labelled gaseous nitrogen has demonstrated beyond doubt that yeasts (Metcalfe and Chayen, 1954) and some filamentous fungi, at least under laboratory conditions, can fix atmospheric nitrogen. Evidence is also available to suggest that some fungi can convert ammonia to nitrate (Schmidt, 1954; Eylar and Schmidt, 1959). The quantitative aspect of such activities, however, has not been adequately investigated, and at the moment we do not know whether these other organisms play any significant part in the quantitative turnover of nitrogen in the soil.

Sulphur transformations.—Organic residues contain appreciable quantities of combined sulphur, much of this in the form of sulphur-containing amino acids. The decomposition of these in the soil is of considerable interest, as is the ultimate fate of the sulphur concerned (Starkey, 1950). Some of it is clearly released and oxidised to form sulphates, a certain amount becomes locked up in complex soil organic materials; for instance, most extracted humic acids contain something like 0.2 to 0.4% sulphur. Even in humic acids which have been subjected to fairly prolonged acid hydrolysis to free them from complexed amino acids, it is still possible to obtain reasonable yields of sulphur in analyses.

Mineral cycles.—The fate of the other mineral constituents varies greatly. Most plants contain moderate amounts of sodium. On their death this sodium is released and is normally leached away very rapidly. Potassium, on the other hand, may be released equally as quickly but is frequently trapped by soil microorganisms in litter layers or in the layers rich in organic matter. In soils with a pronounced litter layer it is sometimes possible to demonstrate an accumulation of potassium in the intermediate layers of the litter; this is presumably due to the activity of microorganisms, particularly fungi. The subsequent breakdown of the fungal hyphae leads to the release of potassium, which then becomes mobile and available for absorption by plant roots lower down the profile. Magnesium and phosphate behave in a comparable way (Burges, 1956). As with the nitrogen, in the mature forest system the conservation of the minerals can be very efficient indeed; this is particularly true of many of the tropical forests in which the soil system may be so efficient that virtually no minerals escape into the leaching water (Milne, 1936).

SUGGESTIONS FOR FUTURE WORK.—Any recommendations for future work will obviously be influenced by the writer's own interests and knowledge, but there are some fields in which the need for further work is clear and in which there is every promise of useful results.

As regards the species lists of organisms present, there is still much to be done. This is particularly true in relation to soil bacteria, where identification is dependent on a large number of biochemical tests. Here we will have to await some simplification of the procedures that will enable very large numbers of isolates to be tested and characterised. As regards the fungi, it is probable that we have gone very nearly as far as is profitable using dilution or soil-plate techniques, and that very much greater use will have to be made of hyphal-isolation techniques such as that developed by Warcup and Talbot (1962). I think there is very little doubt that the biggest gap in our knowledge of soil fungi at the moment is associated with the identification of the sterile isolates and the hitherto unisolated Basidiomycetes that undoubtedly occur in abundance in most, if not all, soils.

So far our knowledge of the utilisation of substrates in the soil is very largely dependent on laboratory tests. In any particular soil it may be possible to demonstrate that ten or fifteen organisms present are capable of decomposing cellulose. Yet, if cellulose is added to the soil, only one or two species out of those potentially capable will invade and attack the cellulose. An understanding of the factors that determine the outcome of such competitions is of outstanding importance in soil microbiology. Perhaps in the first place this work should be developed by using simplified model systems so that we could determine what kind of factors may be involved. In this way we may get some idea of what we should look for in the natural system.

The third major task is to put some quantitative measure on the various processes involved. Because of the great interest in nitrogen transformations, the complex picture of all the possible interactions has a great appeal; but in any particular soil there may be only a few of the possible reactions taking place and the quantitative changes involved may differ very greatly. It would seem that the same kind of a problem arises, perhaps in an even more complex fashion, in other transformations. This is particularly true in what might be termed the carbon cycle. The measurement of the part played by different organisms or groups of organisms in each step of these transformations would be a major contribution, not only to soil microbiology but to pedology as a whole.

LITERATURE CITED

BREED, R. S., E. G. D. MURRAY, and N. R. SMITH. 1957. Bergey's manual of determinative bacteriology. Baillière, Tindall & Cox Ltd., London. 1094 p.

BRIERLEY, W. B., S. T. JEWSON, and M. BRIERLEY. 1927. The quantitative study of soil fungi. Proc. Intern. Congr. Soil Sci., 1st, 3: 48-71.

BURGES, A. 1950. The downward movement of fungal spores in sandy soil. Trans. Brit. Mycol. Soc. 33: 142-147.

BURGES, A. 1956. The release of cations during the decomposition of forest litter. Trans. Intern. Congr. Soil Sci., 6th, Paris. II. 48: 741-745.

BURGES, A. 1963a. Problems in soil microbiology. Trans. Brit. Mycol. Soc. 46: 1-14.

BURGES, A. 1963b. Importance de l'écologie dans la mycologie des sols. Ann. Inst. Pasteur 105: 3-18.

BURGES, A., and D. P. NICHOLAS. 1961. Use of soil sections in studying amount of fungal hyphae in soil. Soil Sci. 92: 25-29.

CLARK, F. E. 1964. Bacteria in soil. *In* A. Burges and

F. Raw [ed.], Soil biology, Academic Press, London. (In press.)

DOMSCH, K. H. 1960. Das Pilzspektrum einer Bodenprobe. Arch. Mikrobiol. 35: 181-195, 229-247, 310-339.

DURBIN, R. D. 1961. Techniques for the observation and isolation of soil micro-organisms. Botan. Rev. 27: 522-560.

EYLAR, O. R., and E. L. SCHMIDT. 1959. A survey of heterotrophic micro-organisms from soil for ability to form nitrite and nitrate. J. Gen. Microbiol. 20: 473-481.

GILMAN, J. C. 1945. A manual of soil fungi. The Collegiate Press, Ames, Iowa. 392 p.

GRAY, T. R. G. and T. F. BELL. 1963. The decomposition of chitin in an acid soil. p. 222-230. *In* J. Doeksen and J. van der Drift [ed.], Soil organisms. North-Holland Publ. Co., Amsterdam.

HANDLEY, W. R. C. 1954. Mull and mor formation in relation to forest soils. For. Comm. (H. M. Stationery Office, London) Bull. 23, 115 p.

HENDERSON, M. E. K. 1960. Studies on the physiology of lignin decomposition by soil fungi. p. 286-296. *In* D. Parkinson and J. S. Waid [ed.], Ecology of soil fungi, Liverpool University Press, Liverpool.

HEPPLE, S. 1960. The movement of fungal spores in soil. Trans. Brit. Mycol. Soc. 43: 73-79.

HURST, H. M. 1963. Aromatic acid-reducing systems in fungi. p. 121-128. *In* J. B. Pridham [ed.], Enzyme aspects of phenolic compounds, Pergamon Press, London.

HURST, H. M., A. BURGES, and P. LATTER. 1962. Some aspects of the biochemistry of humic acid decomposition by fungi. Phytochemistry 1: 227-231.

HUTCHINSON, S. A., and MUSTAPHA KAMEL. 1956. The effect of earthworms on the dispersal of soil fungi. J. Soil Sci. 7: 213-218.

JAMES, N., and M. SUTHERLAND. 1939. The accuracy of the plating method for estimating the number of bacteria and fungi from one dilution and one aliquot of a laboratory sample of soil. Can. J. Res. Sec. C, 17: 97-108.

JOHN, R. P. 1942. An ecological and taxonomic study of the algae of British soils. 1. The distribution of the surface-growing algae. Ann. Botany (London) [N.S.] 6: 323-349.

JONES, P. C. T., and J. E. MOLLISON. 1948. A technique for the quantitative estimation of soil organisms. J. Gen. Microbiol. 2: 54-69.

KATZNELSON, H. 1946. Rhizosphere effect of mangels on certain groups of soil micro-organisms. Soil Sci. 62: 343-354.

KENDRICK, W. B. 1959. The time factor in the decomposition of coniferous leaf litter. Can. J. Botany 37: 907-912.

KENDRICK, W. B., and A. BURGES. 1962. Biological aspects of the decay of *Pinus silvestris* leaf litter. Nova Hedwig 4: 313-342.

KUMADA, K., A. SUZUKI, and A. KAZUYUKI. 1961. Isolation of anthraquinone from humus. Nature (London) 191: 415.

LATTER, P., and A. BURGES. 1960. Experimental decomposition of humic acid by fungi. Trans. Intern. Congr. Soil Sci. (7th, Madison, Wisc. 1960) 2: 643-647.

METCALFE, G., and S. CHAYEN. 1954. Nitrogen fixation by soil yeasts. Nature (London) 174: 841-842.

MILNE, G. 1937. Essays in applied pedology. E. African Agr. J., July 1937.

OVINGTON, J. D. 1962. Concept of the forest ecosystem. Adv. Ecol. Res. 1: 103-192.

PARKINSON, D., and E. COUPS. 1963. Microbial activity in a podzol. p. 167-175. *In* J. Doeksen and J. van der Drift [ed.], Soil organisms, North-Holland Publ. Co., Amsterdam.

RUSSELL, E. J. 1950. Soil conditions and plant growth. 8th ed. Rev. by E. W. Russell. Longmans, Green & Co., London. 635 p.

SAITÔ, T. 1957. Chemical changes in beech litter under microbiological decomposition. Ecol. Rev. 14: 209-216.

SAPPA, F. 1955. La microflora del ferreno quale elemento strutturale delle comunita vegetali. Allionia 2: 293-345.

SCHMIDT, E. L. 1954. Nitrate formation by a soil fungus. Science 119: 187-189.

STARKEY, R. L. 1950. Relations of micro-organisms to transformations of sulfur in soils. Soil Sci. 70: 55-65.

THORNTON, H. G., and P. H. H. GRAY. 1934. The number of bacterial cells in field soils as estimated by the ratio method. Proc. Roy. Soc., Sec. B, 115: 522-531.

WARCUP, J. H. 1959. Studies on Basidiomycetes in soil. Trans. Brit. Mycol. Soc. 42: 45-52.

WARCUP, J. H. 1960. Methods for isolation and estimation of activity of fungi in soil. p. 3-21. *In* D. Parkinson and J. S. Waid [ed.], The ecology of soil fungi, Liverpool Univ. Press, Liverpool.

WARCUP, J. H., and P. H. B. TALBOT. 1962. Ecology and identity of mycelia isolated from soil. Trans. Brit. Mycol. Soc. 45: 495-518.

▶ DISCUSSION OF N. A. BURGES PAPER

W. C. Snyder:

Is it possible to make any generalization as to which group of the soil flora may be *the* dominant group, biologically speaking?

N. A. Burges:

This will change very much from one soil to the other. I don't really think one should talk about dominance. It is a fundamental error to look at this as a fungal succession or a bacterial problem; it must be looked at as an ecological problem.

M. Alexander:

To extend Professor Burges' comments on the microflora of soil as related to biological control, I should like to emphasize the need for further definitive work on the biochemical aspects of the interrelations between components of the microflora. Preconceived ideas on the basis of pure culture investigations on antibiosis, competition, mycolysis, etc., must not alter the line of direct approach to biochemical investigations of those control mechanisms which are actually operative in nature. The microbiologist needs only to reflect on the poor state of knowledge about the physiological and nutritional basis of competition, the mechanism of mycolysis, and the reason that some fungi are susceptible and others resistant to such action, and the identity of organisms responsible for the toxic substances found in the soil.

N. A. Burges:

I would agree very strongly that more work is needed on the physiology of organisms in their *natural* environment.

J. L. Harley:

I was interested in the statement that you had shown active chitin breakdown in some soil layers.

I would like to ask by which method you estimated chitin breakdown, what were the end products of breakdown, and what kinds of organisms are involved.

N. A. Burges:

The work was carried out by Dr. T. Gray and Mr. T. Bell using strips of chitin from *Sepia*. These were placed in the soil in the same way as Tribe's cellophane strips. These chitin strips also contain protein. In addition, powdered, purified chitin was incorporated in agar and cleared zones observed. No chemical work on the products of the breakdown was done.

V. W. Cochrane:

Is the reduction of the carboxyl groups of humic acid by pyridine nucleotide-linked enzymes envisaged as an extracellular process?

N. A. Burges:

We can only speculate on this. The first step seems to be the adsorption of humic acid onto the hyphal wall. If this is re-extracted, infrared spectra show that the carboxyl absorption peak has disappeared. This could be interpreted as the reduction occurring outside the hyphal protoplasm. It is possible that pinocytosis occurs and that the processes are internal, and that when we re-extract the humic acid we are extracting "internal" humic acid.

At present, we cannot produce any evidence to support either one or the other of the above ideas.

The Soil Fauna—Its Nature and Biology

D. KEITH McE. KEVAN—*Department of Entomology, Macdonald College of McGill University, Ste. Anne de Bellevue, Quebec.*

The purpose of this paper is to introduce the soil fauna to those who are not especially familiar with it, and, in a very small compass, to try to indicate some of the principal features concerning its study. To some extent the task is lightened by the fact that certain aspects, such as the role of soil animals in the transmission of plant diseases, the part played by nematodes as plant pathogens, and the interrelation between nematodes and zoopagous and other parasitic fungi will be treated by other contributors. On the other hand, the virtual elimination of these topics from the present discussion makes it less easy to relate the subject to the general theme of the symposium.

Perhaps, at the outset, it would be advisable to indicate what is implied by the terms soil and fauna. From the zoologist's point of view, soil is the mineral substrate in which plants can take root, together with the dead organic matter which may be incorporated and the decomposing organic remains which lie immediately above it (the litter layer). It is impossible for the zoologist to think of the soil fauna without regard for the litter layer, for many soil animals are found both in it and below it, often moving from one to the other. So far as the term fauna is concerned, it is proposed here to exclude the soil Protozoa and other Protista, since these fall more within the province of the microbiologist and the problems concerning them are quite different from those that concern the Metazoa.

THE GROWTH OF SOIL ZOOLOGY.—The scientific study of the soil fauna has only recently developed into a discipline of its own, though observations on soil animals started a very long time ago and may perhaps be said to have begun when G. White (1789), writing in 1770, expressed his opinions concerning earthworms and mole-crickets. Thereafter they continued in a piecemeal fashion until comparatively recent times. Among the early landmarks of soil zoology are the observations of Darwin (1840, 1881) on earthworms, and of early Scandinavian authors, culminating in the works of Müller (1879, 1884), who considered the role of various invertebrates in humus formation. Several studies on earthworms, and a few on other groups, were published during the latter part of the nineteenth and the first years of the twentieth century, but *general* studies of the soil fauna may perhaps be said to have begun with Diem's (1903) pioneer investigation of certain Swiss alpine soils.

During the first half of the present century, possibly the most far-reaching general studies on the soil fauna were those of Bornebusch (1930) and Forsslund (1945), although it might appear invidious not to refer to numerous other publications from A. E. Cameron (1913) to Strenzke (1949). Some of these, like that of Frenzel (1936), were of considerable magnitude. The reader, however, is referred to reviews (Kühnelt, 1950, 1957, 1961, 1963; Kevan, 1955a, 1960, 1961, 1962) for discussion of such works, as well as to more recent literature. It was during this period, also, that Joffe (1936) and, more particularly, Kubiëna (1948) drew the attention of pedologists to the important role of animals (other than earthworms) in soil formation. At the end of the half century, a treatise by Gilyarov (1949) appeared. This was very largely entomological, written from a phylogenetic point of view and thus in a rather different category from previous publications in the field.

It may, perhaps, be argued that it was the opening of the second half century that heralded soil zoology as a discreet discipline, for it was in that year that Kühnelt (1950) summarized in a single volume, *Bodenbiologie,* the greater part of what was known about soil animals, and Franz (1950) published his *Bodenzoologie,* in which he emphasized the practical implications of the study of the soil fauna. All but simultaneously Delamare Deboutteville (1951), in a large work, concentrated attention on the influence of animals in tropical soils (he was by no means the first to work in the field), Hartmann (1951) based his classification of forest soils on the activities of animals, and Drift (1951) published another large research work in the tradition of Bornebusch. Ever since, research on the soil fauna has been pursued with vigour by an increasing number of investigators. Symposia devoted exclusively to soil animals have also been held in a number of places (Kevan, 1955a; International Congress of Soil Science, Paris, 1956; International Congress of Zoology, London, 1959; International Congress of Entomology, Vienna, 1962; Murphy, 1962; Bodenzoologisches Kolloqium, Görlitz, 1962), the most recent having been held in the Netherlands in 1962 (Doeksen and Drift, 1963) and it is planned to hold another in Romania in 1964. (There was also a soil-fauna symposium at Kiev in 1962, but as yet I have no details except those given by Gilyarov, 1962.)

Apart from the separately published symposia referred to above, books largely or wholly devoted to soil zoology include Lawrence (1953), Eglitis (1954), Nosek (1957), Farb (1959), Kevan (1962), Delamare Deboutteville and Rapoport (1962-63), Schaller (1962), Dunger (1964), Gilyarov (1964), and new editions of *Bodenbiologie* (Kühnelt, 1957, 1961), and *Bodenzoologie* (Franz, in press). A small work on a limited aspect by Kipenvarlitz (1961) has also appeared in book form. Texts on animal ecology, which have long paid scant attention to soil animals, have also given increasing recognition to the soil fauna, and some of them (Tischler, 1955; Macfadyen, 1957, 1963; Balogh, 1958) lay heavy emphasis upon it. Some major works on plant ecology (e.g. Hartmann, 1952) and pedology (Kubiëna, 1953; Handley, 1954; Wilde, 1954; Russell, 1957) and even the occasional elementary zoology text (Moment, 1958) now devote appreciable space to the subject. There is thus plenty of readily available literature to aid the student on his way.

THE COMPOSITION OF THE SOIL FAUNA.—*Animals other than arthropods.*—Before considering the groups of animals that constitute the soil fauna, it would be as well to indicate which should be included by the term, for it is not possible to restrict this to those animals that pass virtually their entire lives underground. By so doing, we would exclude a large number of important forms, particularly (although by no means only) among the insects. We therefore include animals that pass one or more *active* stages wholly, or largely, in soil or litter, but exclude species which occur there only in a passive stage, such as egg, cyst, or pupa, or that use the earth only for hibernation, aestivation, or temporary shelter. Many animals, however, especially very small ones, may be equally at home in soil and in fresh water, or in soil and in certain habitats above ground. Many other anomalies exist—aerial insects with subterranean larvae (e.g. many flies, beetles, or some moths), or species that alternate from shoot to root as a normal part of their life cycle (e.g. some aphids or gall-wasps)—and in such cases we regard only the subterranean phases as soil animals (Drift, 1951). For those who wish to have available a rapid survey of the very many orders and suborders of soil animals, illustrated keys exist (Kevan, 1955b; Dunger, 1964) but, for precise identification, specialist works are required. Some of these are referred to in an earlier paper (Kevan, 1955b) and by Kühnelt (1963). For Palearctic insect larvae, see Gilyarov (1964).

Nearly all of the animal phyla that are not purely marine are represented to a greater or lesser extent in the soil, where the diversity and abundance of animal life is much greater than might be thought. But apart from free-living Protozoa, which are not considered here, the dominant soil animals are either nematodes (the most abundant in terms of individuals) or arthropods (the most numerous in terms of species). In certain soils, however, annelid worms (earthworms and enchytraeids), although few in species, constitute a high proportion of the biomass.

Vertebrates are represented by a number of species of mammals, particularly root-feeding rodents (e.g. pocket gophers such as *Geomys*, various mole-rats such as *Bathyergus* and *Stalacopus*, and rodent-moles such as *Spalax*) and carnivorous insectivores (e.g. true moles such as *Talpa* and *Scalopus*), whose burrow systems may be locally important in soil formation (Joffe, 1936). A few wormlike reptiles (amphisbaenid lizards and typhlopid or uropeltid snakes) and amphibia (Gymnophiona) are also true denizens of the soil in warmer parts of the world, but their importance is small.

Gasteropod molluscs (slugs and snails) may contribute a fair proportion of the biomass in some, mostly moist, environments, but their importance in soil formation is also small. Most feed on moribund or decaying vegetation. Some, such as the keeled slugs (*Milax*), are more confined to the soil than others, such as the field slugs (*Agriolimax*). A number (e.g. those just mentioned) may be pests of growing crops; a few, such as *Testacella*, which feeds mainly on earthworms, are carnivorous. The European needle-snail, *Cecilioides acicula*, is a true soil form, living deep down where it browses on fungal hyphae.

Annelid worms include perhaps the most familiar members of the soil fauna, the earthworms, as well as their more numerous but less well-known relatives, the pot-worms or Enchytraeidae. Almost all soil annelids belong to the subclass Oligochaeta (primarily an aquatic group), although some other groups are occasionally found. Earthworms are often thought of as all belonging to the family Lumbricidae, but this is only partly true, even in northern temperate regions. Other families, particularly the Megascolecidae, also include earthworms—such as *Pheretima hupeiensis*, the "Oriental" earthworm introduced into the United States. Each of the many species of earthworm has its own peculiar requirements, feeding and burrowing habits. Several species may occur together, a fact usually overlooked in pedological studies in spite of the universally appreciated importance of these animals in soil formation. Even the classical work of Darwin, already referred to, suffered from this defect. Enchytraeidae are largely aquatic, but some species are very abundant in certain soils, especially in raw humus (Overgaard Nielsen, 1955; O'Connor, 1957). They resemble pale diminutive earthworms, but they do not burrow. Their food is discussed by Forsslund (1945) and O'Connor (1957). They are often associated with decaying roots, but it is unlikely that they are ever the cause of damage. Their classification is in a chaotic state, except for the European species, which have recently been revised by Overgaard Nielsen and Christensen (1959).

In spite of the pre-eminent position afforded by pedologists to the annelid earthworms, the Nematoda are undoubtedly the dominant worms in the soil if factors other than bulk and pedological effects are considered. Nematodes constitute one of the largest and most ubiquitous groups of the Animal Kingdom, a fact which is scarcely apparent from the average university zoology curriculum. Even the use (or misuse) of the terms "nematology" and "nematologist" frequently indicates general lack of appreciation of how diverse nematodes are. The titles of a recent excellent monograph by Thorne (1961), and of the various international "nematology" symposia (e.g. Symposium International de Nematologie, 1961) do nothing to correct the growing impression that "nematology" means the study of a few species associated with higher plants—which is far from the truth. A better perspective can be gained from Chitwood and Chitwood (1950) or Hyman (1951) and from a recent, excellent symposium (Sasser and Jenkins, 1960), although the last is biased towards "plant" nematology.

Most nematodes are free-living, and a large proportion of the known species are found in soil. Most of the comparatively small number of plant-parasitic species and many of those parasitic in animals (both vertebrate and invertebrate) spend much of their time in the soil. Most nematodes are of microscopic proportions except for older stages of the majority of the more intensively studied parasites of vertebrates. Although many nematodes can survive drought in a state of anabiosis or as eggs or cysts, all require a fluid environment in order to remain active, even if this merely consists of a thin film of moisture surrounding a soil particle. It is, therefore, not surprising that species and even whole genera of soil nematodes are also found in mud beneath fresh water, but the soil also has its own peculiar, rich nematode fauna (Mikoletzky, 1922; Goodey, 1951, 1963).

Nematodes differ considerably in their alleged food requirements. Some are said to feed on diatoms and other algae or on protozoa, many (including the free-living stages of many animal and plant parasites) apparently feed on bacteria, some consume fungi, and others, like *Mononchus,* are voracious predators of small animals (including other nematodes and rotifers). Many species, e.g. of *Rhabditis* and *Plectus,* are said to be saprophagous, but it is doubtful if this is often strictly the case; such forms, in most instances, probably feed upon decay microorganisms and their liquified products rather than directly upon the matter in which they are found (Overgaard Nielsen, 1949; Sachs, 1950). Many species associated with plant roots may obtain their nourishment in a similar fashion, and it is a matter for further investigation to determine whether such species are directly responsible for significant plant injury, aggravate existing injury, render the plants more vulnerable to root rots and other diseases, are capable of transmitting diseases, or are quite harmless or even beneficial.

Various other groups of "worms" are also found in soil (see Kühnelt, 1950, 1957, 1961; Kevan, 1955a, 1962), notably the predominantly aquatic Rotatoria or rotifers, and Platyhelminthes or flatworms (Turbellaria only). Both groups are found mainly in rather moist situations and, with the exception of some of the larger Turbellaria (the land planarians), require to be immersed in water, like the nematodes, in order to remain active. Some can, however, withstand drought by means of resistant eggs and cysts. Some soil rotifers, like *Eucentrum,* are predacious on small nematodes, protozoa, and motile protophyta, others browse on bacteria and algae, and some feed upon plant debris (Overgaard [Nielsen], 1948). They are all microscopic and may be locally very abundant, but soil forms have been little studied; most species occur in fresh water also. Minute turbellarians may be relatively abundant in very rich, damp soils (Reisinger, 1954), but otherwise they are few in numbers. Land planarians are commoner in the tropics and subtropics where species many centimetres long occur, but smaller species are also found in temperate regions (e.g. *Rhynchodemus*). Almost all turbellarians are carnivorous, feeding upon whatever animals they can cope with, but some of the smallest species feed upon diatoms.

Arthropods.—The phylum Arthropoda includes more known species of animals (mostly of insects) than all other groups of living organisms together; hence it is scarcely surprising that it contains also the greatest diversity of soil-inhabiting species. Nevertheless the number of arthropod groups that predominate in the soil is comparatively small. Some large groups of arthropods, like the flies, beetles, and mites, include great numbers of soil-inhabiting forms; other large groups, such as the crustaceans and moths, are poorly represented in the soil. Some groups of moderate size are predominantly soil dwellers (e.g. the centipedes, millipedes, termites, and springtails) and others are not (e.g. the thrips and caddis-flies). Certain small groups (e.g. Symphyla, Diplura, Protura, Pauropoda, and Zoraptera) are found almost exclusively in soil and litter, whereas other small groups (e.g. snake-flies) are seldom found in such habitats.

The most abundant soil arthropods are the mites (Arachnida; Acarina), and the springtails (Collembola). Also very important are the millipedes (Diplopoda) and certain orders of insects, particularly termites (Isoptera) where they occur, fly larvae (Diptera), beetles and their larvae (Coleoptera), and ants (Hymenoptera; Formicoidea). Other groups of lesser importance, which may nevertheless be conspicuous, are woodlice (terrestrial isopod Crustacea), centipedes (Chilopoda), cutworms and other caterpillars (Lepidoptera), root-feeding bugs such as cicadas, aphids, and scale insects (Hemiptera-Homoptera), burrowing crickets (Orthoptera), and spiders (Araneida). Protura and Pauropoda are minute arthropods which may be locally very numerous. Many other groups of both larger and smaller size are also represented to a varying degree, but space does not permit their mention, and the reader is referred to general works (Kühnelt, 1950, 1957, 1961; Lawrence, 1953; Kevan, 1955a, 1962; and Delamare Deboutteville and Rapoport, 1962-63; and Gilyarov, 1964).

Most biologists are fairly familiar with the more

important insect orders mentioned (some, but by no means very many of whose soil-inhabiting species are well known as crop pests), and even, in rather more general terms, with the millipedes. In the interests of brevity, therefore, I shall pass over these well-known forms and comment upon the less familiar microarthropods. Soil-inhabiting Diptera, chiefly European, are treated by Brauns (1954, 1955); for strictly soil Coleoptera the reader is referred to Coiffait (1958); for termites to Snyder (1949, 1956, 1961), Griffin (1951), Schmidt (1955), and Harris (1961). Gilyarov (1949, 1964) considers many groups of soil insects and some of the microarthropods. North American millipedes have recently been covered synoptically by Chamberlin and Hoffman (1958). Many groups of South American arthropods are treated in Delamare Deboutteville and Rapoport (1962-63).

The term microarthropod is not, perhaps, a very satisfactory one since many of the true insects, such as minute flies and beetles, are small enough to qualify for inclusion and a few species among those which are included are rather large. By microarthropods, however, we usually mean arthropods that are not insects, or at least not true insects, whose length seldom exceeds a millimetre or two and is frequently much less. They include the Acarina (mites), the Collembola, the Protura, the Pauropoda, and for convenience (although they are somewhat larger), the Diplura and the Symphyla. These groups have little in common except that they are all predominantly soil dwellers, whereas the majority of true insects, which we have excluded, are not. Mites and Collembola, being present in astronomical numbers in many soils, merit further consideration, but the members of the other groups, being less abundant (though no less interesting), will have to be passed over. For recent general works on mites, the reader is referred to Baker and Wharton (1952), Stammer (1957, 1959, 1963), Hirschmann (1957—), Baker et al. (1958), T. E. Hughes (1959), Balogh (1961), and Evans, Sheals, and MacFarlane (1961). With the exception of Hughes, however, these are mainly taxonomic. The more recent general works on Collembola are those of Stach (1947—), Salmon (1951, 1956), Maynard (1951), and Gisin (1960). Again these are very largely taxonomic, but they all include numerous references to other literature. A useful general reference (particularly as a literature review) for nonsystematic aspects of the Collembola (and of Thysanura, Diplura, and Protura) is that of Paclt (1956).

Like the nematodes, the mites constitute one of the most successful, ubiquitous, and yet neglected animal groups. As with the nematodes, the vertebrate- and plant-feeding species, as well as those associated with stored products, and a few predatory and aquatic forms, have received much attention, whereas the majority of mites have been but little studied. Most mites are probably free-living, soil- and litter-inhabiting species; they are legion, outnumbering all other groups of soil arthropods together by more than three to one (Evans, 1955). Perhaps a greater proportion of mite species than of insects are predatory.

In litter and humus some of the most abundant species of mites belong to the Sarcoptiformes or Cryptostigmata. These include the pale, soft-bodied Acaridiae (some species of which are familiar in stored foodstuffs), and the dark, hard-bodied Oribatei. Both of these groups feed principally on dead organic matter (mainly of plant origin), on moribund vegetation, or on fungi. A few Acaridiae attack living plant tissues below ground level, e.g. the bulb mite, *Rhizoglyphus echinopus*, but they are usually associated with previous injuries and may help to disseminate rot organisms. A species of *Caloglyphus* eats animal remains and is itself preyed upon by other mites (Rohde, 1959). Oribatei are especially important in the comminution of plant remains and thus in humus formation. Many consume fungal hyphae and spores; several others are known to live within small twigs, leaf petioles, and conifer needles (Jacot, 1939), feeding on the softer tissues or upon fungi or other causative organisms of decay. Schuster (1956, 1958) sheds considerable light on the feeding habits of soil Oribatei; they have been shown to feed on plant remains, fungi, microorganisms, and often upon animal remains. Oribatei may be more important in disseminating plant diseases (such as root rots) than has previously been suspected; they are already well known to harbour cysticercoids of certain tapeworms that parasitize herbivorous domestic animals.

Other characteristic soil mites are the Mesostigmata, which are leathery, often rather flattened, and comparatively swift-moving. Many species are probably predators on other microarthropods, nematodes, and enchytraeids; others are parasitic or epizoic on other animals, or feed on dead animal remains, including carrion, and on faecal matter. In these latter habitats it is possible that they feed on decay microorganisms or fluids produced by them, rather than directly on the pabulum. The likelihood of their transmitting plant diseases may be small, although the phoretic association some of them (like certain nematodes) may have with insects might enable them to disseminate certain pathogens passively over considerable distances. More species probably feed on microorganisms, etc., than has generally been thought.

The last major order of soil mites, the Trombidiiformes, constitutes a very large and diverse group, best known by the foliage-feeding Tetranychidae, or spider-mites, and the medically important Trombiculidae, or chigger-mites. Few species of the former family are associated with the soil, but the latter group (except in the parasitic larval stage) spend most of their time there (and the same is true of the related, arthropod-parasitizing Trombidiidae). The predominating trombidiiform mites in the soil are the Tarsonemoidea, many of which are extremely minute, a little-studied group the majority of which are perhaps predatory. Some species seem to feed on plant or animal remains; *Tarsonemus laticeps*, the bulb-scale mite, is one which attacks living plant tissues. The Trombidiiformes also include the wormlike foliage- and bud-inhabiting gall mites (Eriophyidae), some of which are proven plant-virus vectors. One or two of these, like *Aceria tulipae*, which transmits wheat-streak and wheat-spot mosaics in North America (Slykhuis, 1960), may be to some extent associated with underground parts of plants, but they are not really soil mites. Dissemination of soil-borne plant pathogens by other trombidiiform mites is, however, not improbable.

Turning now from the mites to the Collembola, or springtails, we encounter yet another rather neglected group. Not so numerous in most soils as the mites, they nevertheless constitute the bulk of the remaining arthropod soil fauna. As a group they are more predominantly soil-inhabiting than the mites, although a fairly large number of species live above ground (e.g. most of the globular species, or Symphypleona). The springtails, most of which are of elongate form (Arthropleona), are six-legged and have usually for this reason been placed among the insects, although they do not seem to be very closely related to them. A few species are reasonably well known, but the biology of the majority has been little studied. What little is known of soil-inhabiting forms shows that individual species, even if closely related, may have quite different food and environmental requirements. Some have a fairly general diet of decaying leaves, while others rarely eat anything but fungi; some ingest humus (see Poole, 1957, 1959; Sharma and Kevan, 1963*a,b,c*). A few species consume the faeces of larger soil animals or dead animal remains; predatory Collembola are few (see Murphy and Doncaster, 1957; and Sharma and Kevan, 1963*a*, for references) and those that are do not appear to be exclusively, or even habitually, so. Collembola are of considerable importance in the comminution of organic residues and in humus formation (Dunger, 1956).

To conclude this rather sketchy review of the composition of the soil fauna, it should be pointed out that much of the available information is fragmentary and that much of what has been said is based on generalizations which may in future prove unsatisfactory. Sound taxonomy and far more biological studies on individual species are needed.

CATEGORIES OF SOIL-INHABITING ANIMALS.—Several methods of classifying the soil fauna, other than according to systematic arrangement have been devised (see Haarløv, 1960; Kevan, 1962). One such method commonly used is arbitrary arrangement according to size. The terms macrofauna and microfauna are often employed and usually imply only that the animals can or cannot readily be seen with the naked eye. It is preferable, however, to restrict "microfauna" more or less to forms less than 100 microns in length (mainly nematodes, rotifers, small turbellarians, and tardigrades), and "macrofauna" to those that may be measured in centimetres (vertebrates, earthworms, many molluscs, and larger arthropods). Between these size ranges lies the "meiofauna" or "mesofauna" (many enchytraeid worms and the smaller molluscs and arthropods).

Kühnelt (1955) (followed by Kevan, 1962), adopts three basic divisions: "Water fauna" (animals requiring free water, even if only a thin film, in which to swim), virtually the same as the microfauna (above); "burrowers" (animals capable of making their own channels through the soil), including in large part, but not entirely, the macrofauna; and the remainder, including most, but not quite all of the meiofauna (exceptions being ants and termites, which can burrow). These three basic categories may be subdivided under a number of subsidiary headings (Kevan, 1962) which need not concern us here, but the large, rather unsatisfactory third category is divided by Kühnelt (1959, 1961, 1963) into what he calls, in his most recent work, "litter inhabitants" and "inhabitants of microcaverns." If microcaverns include also the small cavities in litter fragments, the subdivision is reasonably satisfactory, for almost all the microarthropods fall into the latter group and the great majority of the larger animals (nonburrowing macrofauna) are unable to penetrate below the litter layer. Haarløv (1960) adopts much the same classification, which he bases on means of locomotion; he states that all other systems are, so far, less satisfactory.

The soil fauna may also be classified on other ecological criteria into epedaphon (inhabitants of the soil surface which may frequently enter the soil), hemiedaphon (inhabitants of the litter and fermentation layers), and euedaphon (inhabitants of the deeper, largely mineral layers). The members of these three categories are increasingly more specialized morphologically or physiologically for life in the soil, and their study has provided interesting examples of the development of "life-forms," e.g., in the Collembola (Krausse, 1928; Gisin, 1943; Schaller, 1950; Delamare Deboutteville, 1951) and Oribatei (Klima, 1956). Trophic relations form another possible basis for classification.

The food requirements of soil animals are almost as varied as those of animals living in other habitats and their choice of food quite as selective. Lindquist (1941) discusses food preferences in molluscs, and Dunger (1962) compares food selection mostly among the invertebrate macrofauna; evidence for this among microarthropods is also given, for example, by Murphy (1952), Schuster (1956), Poole (1957), Wallwork (1958), and Sharma and Kevan (1963*b,c*).

"Primary" feeders, i.e. those that feed directly upon vegetable matter, include truly phytophagous animals (from rodents, through certain molluscs and many insects—such as whitegrubs, wireworms, root maggots, aphids, and cicadas—and mites to nematodes) which consume living, or at least undecomposed parts of green plants, whether these be roots or leaves that have fallen to the ground. They also include "low primaries," feeding on decaying plant material, such as wood (e.g., termites, many beetles, fly maggots and even some nematodes) or other dead vegetation (e.g. molluscs, earthworms, enchytraeids, termites, crickets, many other insects, millipedes, woodlice, springtails, mites, and some nematodes). It is, however, often difficult to determine whether such animals are truly saprophagous or whether their actual nutritional requirements are provided by the fungi and other microorganisms ingested with the material upon which they appear to feed. Some species undoubtedly obtain nourishment from dead vegetation, even though this may be through the good offices of an intestinal microflora. Relatively few soil animals ingest more than very small quantities of mineral matter with their food; but earthworms, millipedes, many termites, and apparently some Collembola do so, voiding the mineral particles, considerably altered by passage through their intestines, after extracting the nutrients from the humus fraction. Many of the earthworms, of course, literally eat their way through soil and some millipedes may ingest up to 25% mineral matter (Romell, 1935; Drift, 1951).

"Secondary" feeders, i.e. those that obtain their food from plants secondhand, are those which prey upon or parasitize primary feeders—e.g. moles, carnivorous insects such as ants, many beetles, and some fly larvae, centipedes, all arachnids other than many mites, planarians, many rotifers, some tardigrades, and many nematodes. Secondary feeders also include fauna that feed on fungi and bacteria, which obtain their nourishment from dead or living organic matter (e.g. large numbers of mites and Collembola, numerous small beetle and fly larvae, some termites and ants, a few molluscs and Dermaptera, and many nematodes). Of special interest are certain Protura that feed upon mycorrhiza (Sturm, 1959). "Low secondaries," as they are sometimes called, devour either the remains of other animals or their faeces. Necrophagous soil animals include many beetles and their larvae, fly maggots, mites, some Collembola, and even a few molluscs and nematodes. Coprophagous species that consume the droppings of vertebrates consist mainly of certain lumbricid earthworms and Enchytraeidae, termites, beetles, flies, some Collembola and mites, and some nematodes; but the vast quantities of faeces of invertebrates also support a very diverse fauna of small insects, Collembola, mites, and nematodes. However, many of the small animals in carrion, dung, and faecal pellets, especially among the nematodes, probably feed on microorganisms and not directly upon the pabulum. Führer (1961), for example, showed that the oribatid mite *Pseudotritia ardua* is attracted only to rotting roots infected by certain bacteria upon which it presumably feeds.

There are, of course, also, as in any animal community, "tertiary" and "quaternary" feeders that devour the others in succession.

THE NUMBERS OF ANIMALS IN THE SOIL.—Space does not permit us to consider the various means by which populations of soil animals are sampled and extracted from their environment for study, so that the reader must be referred to the literature on the subject (reviewed by Kevan, 1955a, 1962; Kühnelt, 1961, 1963) and, more especially, to Murphy (1962) and Macfadyen (1962a). Suffice it to say that the techniques involved are almost as diverse as the fauna itself, including hand-sorting, sifting, repellence by heat or chemicals, funnels and various related devices, flotation, centrifugation, elutriation, and numerous other methods. There is no easy way. No one method

will cope with even a fraction of the fauna and all methods are very time-consuming. One cannot simply "plate out" a sample of soil and hope to learn anything. One should not be hypercritical of the efforts of the "gadgeteers" who seem to spend more time perfecting techniques than obtaining information, for comparisons of different methods of extraction have shown widely differing results under different conditions—see, for example, Macfadyen (1962a,b) and Satchell and Nelson (1962). Where quantitative data are required, the method giving statistically the most valid results is naturally to be desired.

Since many species of soil animals occur in aggregated populations and do not have a random distribution, probably the most satisfactory method of taking samples before extraction is the "paired-sample" technique suggested by R. D. Hughes (1962). Statistical methods are also discussed by several other authors in Murphy (1962). One of the greatest stumbling blocks in the study of populations of soil animals, however, is that so few of the species can be identified with certainty until much critical taxonomic work is done and experience gained. Closely related species may differ considerably in their biology, and, unless the facts are first determined and the species distinguished from one another, even the most careful statistical analyses may produce quite unreliable results.

In order to give some idea of the numbers of animals that may be present in soil, and by way of reassuring sceptics of their importance, the following estimates from Stöckli (1946) as modified by Macfadyen (1957) for fauna beneath one square metre of European grassland are given (see also Fig. 1):

Earthworms (Lumbricidae):	30-2,000
Pot-worms (Enchytraeidae):	200-20,000
Slugs and snails (Mollusca):	100-8,500
Millipedes and centipedes (Diplopoda and Chilopoda):	900-1,700
Woodlice (Isopoda):	100-400
Spiders (Araneida):	180-840
Beetles and larvae (Coleoptera):	500-1,000
Fly maggots (Diptera):	1,000 approx.
Ants (Hymenoptera):	200-500
Springtails (Collembola):	10,000-40,000
Mites (Acarina):	20,000-120,000
Nematodes (Nematoda):	1.8-120 million

The upper limits indicated are not maximal and the figures would differ considerably in different habitats. In woodland soils, enchytraeids may number up to 270,000 or even much more per square metre (O'Connor, 1955, 1957), mites up to 400,000, Collembola up to 200,000 (Nef, 1957). No less than 834,500 arthropods per square metre are recorded by Murphy (1953) from cultivated heathland. The estimated number of animals, excluding nematodes and protozoa, may total well over 1½ million per square metre, although figures of this kind should be treated with some reservation since they are necessarily based on very small samples. The aggregated nature of the distribution of many soil animals is also well established—by Sat-

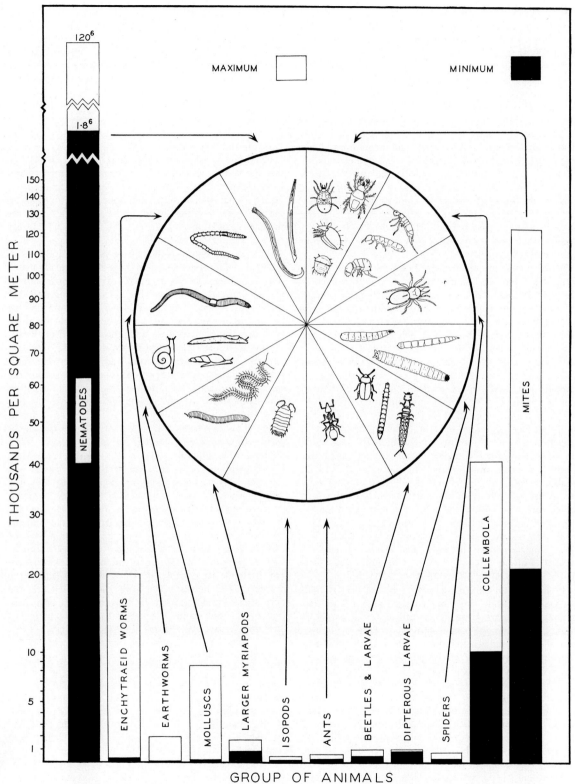

Fig. 1. Numbers of animals per square meter in soil of a European grassland, based on the estimates of Stockli (1946) modified by Macfadyen (1957) and plotted on a logarithmic scale. Such figures are only indications, since they are mostly calculated from small samples. Of the groups shown, spiders and centipedes are wholly carnivorous and ants predominantly so; beetles, fly maggots, mites, and nematodes range widely in their diet according to species; the remaining groups feed largely on decaying organic matter, many Collembola being also closely associated with fungi and other microorganisms.

chell (1955) for earthworms, by Overgaard Nielsen (1954, 1955) for Enchytraeidae, and by Murphy (1955) for mites. Seasonal fluctuations may also be very great (Witkamp and Drift, 1961).

Larger animals, as might be expected, are generally fewer than smaller ones, and populations of different size groups follow the usual "pyramid of numbers" (Park, 1950). Numbers also fall off rapidly with depth, the bulk of the nonburrowing fauna living in the top 30 cm and the majority of these at about half this depth. Earthworms, symphylids, and nematodes, however, are all known from depths of over 2 metres. Protura may also be found at considerable depths. Much of the fauna may be largely absent from the upper regions in times of excessive cold or heat. In spite of the very large number of animals present in the soil, it would appear from Haarløv's (1955, 1960) results that the available *Lebensraum* is far from completely occupied.

More important than mere numbers, however, are figures for biomass, since they give a better idea of the actual amount of living animal protoplasm present in soil. As examples of such figures (although different soils vary enormously) we may take those tabulated by Nef (1957; see also Kevan, 1962), which compare raw humus under spruce (a comparatively poor soil) with mull under deciduous woodland (a much richer soil). It was estimated that there were 95.86 g of animals per square metre in the mull, and 28.82 g in the raw humus. Microorganisms and fungi may constitute a higher proportion of the total biomass of the soil, but the animals form no mean proportion. In the mull, about two thirds of the biomass was made up of earthworms—a figure which is not dissimilar from that given much earlier by Bornebusch (1930) —about 10% by nematodes and just under 20% by arthropods. In the raw humus soils, earthworms were scarce, but about one third of the animal biomass consisted of enchytraeids and nearly half of arthropods; the rest was mainly made up of nematodes. The total animal biomass in such soils was not much less than that of the "non-earthworms" in mull. Nef's estimates were based on Bornebusch's (1930) figures.

In terms of respiratory activity—a measure of food consumption and thus of energy release—animals undoubtedly figure large in the utilization of available resources. Using the same sources of data as above, Nef (1957) indicates that in a mull soil, animals may consume nearly 50 mg of oxygen per hour per square metre at 13°C. A little over 20% of this was used by earthworms (relatively little as compared with their biomass), slightly less by nematodes, and rather more by mites alone; Collembola were the other large oxygen consumers, using about half that respired by mites; other arthropods and enchytraeids each consumed about two thirds as much as Collembola. In raw humus, Nef's figures show that, where earthworms were absent, total respiration was only slightly less than for the non-earthworm fauna of mull soil—which is in agreement with the figures for biomass. Nematode activity was somewhat reduced (to about one seventh of the total oxygen consumption), but enchy-

traeid activity was quadrupled (to just over one third). Mites consumed about the same amount of oxygen in raw humus as in mull soil, and thus maintained their premier position, but their relative importance was greatly enhanced—to the extent of using almost 40% of the oxygen used by the whole fauna. Collembola used only about a quarter as much as mites, for they were much less numerous than in mull. Small insects, however, were more prevalent, so that the total activity of these two groups together was about the same in the two types of soil.

From the foregoing figures, therefore, it will be seen that the soil fauna cannot be dismissed as unimportant. It is estimated by Nef, in fact, that soil animals require a quantity of nutrients approximately equal to that provided by the litter produced annually by the surface vegetation.

SOIL AS AN ENVIRONMENT FOR ANIMAL LIFE.—*The physical environment.*—Something has already been said regarding the food, mode of life, and numbers of soil animals, and we have thus introduced the subject of ecology. As in all other environments, the factors influencing the fauna may be divided into those that are physicochemical and those that are biotic.

Soil structure and texture are naturally very important environmental factors, particularly for burrowing animals, since their ability to burrow and the rate of burrowing are affected, the one by structure (or arrangement of particles) and the other by texture (or relative proportions of particles of different sizes). This has been well demonstrated for the earthworm *Allolobophora terrestris* by Guild (1955). With nonburrowing animals, one of the most critical factors is pore space, or the size of the microcaverns in the soil. Obviously if these are very small, only the very smallest animals will be able to enter them, but it is nevertheless truly amazing how small are the crevices into which even comparatively large animals can squeeze by virtue of their extensibility—in the case of slugs, such as *Milax* spp.—or their contractability—Manton's (1958) experiments with *Peripatus* are particularly notable in this regard. Usually the deeper one penetrates the soil, the smaller are the pore spaces, and this may lead to a distinct stratification of the meiofauna according to maximum, if not minimum size (Weis-Fogh, 1948). Haarløv (1955, 1960) considers in detail the distribution of microarthropods in relation to depth and soil structure.

Pore space is also very important for the aquatic microfauna. Their small size may permit them to enter the smallest of crevices, but they may be prevented from inhabiting them because of insufficient aeration. H. R. Wallace (1956), for example, found that the emergence of the nematode, *Heterodera schachti,* from eggs was apparently controlled by aeration. Gilyarov (1947) notes that vertical migration of rather larger animals may be limited by lack of oxygen at greater depths. At moderate depths, however, unless there is waterlogging or an unusual accumulation of organic matter, oxygen lack is not usually a limiting factor. Gaseous exchange with the surface is rapid, although slower in clay than in sandy soils (Burges, 1958). Even when nonaquatic soil animals (meiofauna) become trapped by water they can usually survive within small air-bubbles, later repaying any oxygen debt which may result, or even using the bubbles as physical gills (Wittasek, 1947, as cited by Kühnelt, 1961, 1963).

The composition of the soil air is of some importance to certain soil animals. Brief reference has already been made to oxygen requirements, but other gases may sometimes be of importance. The tolerance for carbon dioxide by termites is well known. Larger burrowing insect larvae may also be very tolerant of a saturated carbon dioxide atmosphere (Kupka and Schaerffenberg, 1947). Certain beetle larvae are actually attracted to concentrations of this gas produced by plant roots (Klingler, 1957, 1958). Mites and Collembola normally found in decomposing materials are now also considered by Moursi (personal communication, 1960, 1961; cited by Kühnelt, 1963) to favour carbon dioxide and nitrogen concentrations; but they are killed by small quantities of hydrogen sulphide or ammonia.

Moisture content, as one might expect, is of vital importance to the soil fauna. Absolutely dry conditions are rare except near the surface of deserts, and the soil atmosphere is frequently saturated. Usually at least some free water is present in the form of a thin film surrounding the soil particles. If such a film is not continuous, however, the dispersal of members of the aquatic microfauna may be severely restricted, as was demonstrated by H. R. Wallace (1955, 1956) for the nematodes *Heterodera schachti* and *Ditylenchus dipsaci*. Such nematodes also were believed to migrate further in a thin water film than a thick one, presumably because of a reduction in the proportion of oxygen in the water resulting from the lesser air-water interface in the latter.

Many air-breathing animals require very moist conditions in which to survive (or at least remain active), even if they are not subaquatic. Earthworms and enchytraeids, for example, are among those that need at least small amounts of free water to prevent desiccation, and much of the remaining soil fauna probably needs a near-saturated atmosphere. There are, however, marked differences in the moisture requirements of closely related forms, as shown by Riha (1951) for oribatid mites and by Blower (1955) for various myriapods. Perttunen (1953) and Barlow (1957, 1958) have studied the effects of humidity on certain millipedes. Overgaard Nielsen (1959) and Kühnelt (1960) discuss the effects of unsaturated air on soil animals. On the whole, the smallest meiofauna are the least drought-resistant and the most liable to suffer from excess moisture, for they are more readily immobilized by surface tension. Normal flooding does not seem to affect air-breathing soil animals unduly because they can usually escape drowning by taking refuge in trapped air pockets, but a rising water table (Kühnelt, 1955), or the formation of subterranean dew resulting from a sharp drop in temperature (Gilbert, 1955), may be lethal. Schaerffenberg (1942), however, indicates that elaterid beetle larvae may be drowned by summer floods but not by winter floods.

Temperature is probably of less importance to soil animals than it is to surface-dwelling species, not because they are insensitive to temperature changes, but because soil is an excellent insulator. Temperatures may vary throughout the year, especially in the upper layers, but, except in the immediate vicinity of the surface, they are seldom very high and fluctuations are rarely sudden or drastic. As temperatures change, there is ample time for many species to migrate to greater depths to avoid adverse effects. Migration of soil fauna in response to temperature is referred to by Handschin (1929) and Dowdy (1944). Temperature tolerance varies in different species inhabiting the same soils (Sharma and Kevan, 1963c). Some species (notably mites and Collembola) favour cool rather than warm conditions. Many soil animals at high latitudes or elevations are extremely resistant to cold and breed at very low temperatures—several species of Collembola, mites, and nematodes remain active in the soil in the depth of Canadian winter (observations at Macdonald College), whether a good insulating snow cover is present or not. For most soil fauna, however, low temperatures result in a reduction of activity. Unusually cold winters may reduce the soil fauna considerably (Bro Larsen, 1949).

Acidity and salinity are other factors influencing the soil fauna, especially the larger members. Earthworms are usually considered to be intolerant of acid conditions, but species vary in this respect (Satchell, 1955a), some, particularly among the Megascolecidae, actually seeming to prefer acid conditions (Hallsworth, 1955). It is also a fallacy that arthropods with heavily calcified integuments, such as woodlice and millipedes, or shell-bearing molluscs necessarily favour calcareous soils (Thiele, 1959). Saline soils, unless they be salt-marshes with a semimarine fauna, are usually very poorly populated by macrofauna, but Schuster (1958) found the microarthropods (especially oribatid mites and Collembola) to be little affected by salinity.

The biotic environment.—Biotic factors that affect the soil fauna may act indirectly. For example, variations in the organic matter present affect physical structure and texture of the soil; or living and dead roots may provide channels by which nonburrowing animals may penetrate the soil as well as provide them with food. Chemical secretions produced by fungi or even the physical nature of their hyphae may render certain soils intolerable (e.g., for earthworms) or, by depressing plant growth, may affect the food supply. Bornemissza (1957) has shown that the products of decaying carrion seriously depress the normal soil fauna. In contrast to the depressant effects, plant roots may produce attractant substances which stimulate some oligophagous animals, as is well known in the case of the root exudates of certain Solanaceae that stimulate the hatching of eggs of the potato root eelworm, *Heterodera rostochiensis*. The attraction of carbon dioxide produced by roots for certain beetle larvae has already been referred to. Root-nodule bacteria and mycorrhiza may enhance plant growth and thus the fauna that depends on it. The composition of the surface vegetation also influences the soil fauna by affecting the type of litter available (see Murphy, 1955), and may also influence distribution by providing more or less attractive oviposition sites for species with surface-living adults, e.g., elatrid beetles (Fox, 1959).

Food supply is one of the most significant of the biotic factors affecting life in the soil, as elsewhere. Although our knowledge of what particular species of soil animals eat is rather fragmentary, we have already seen that some depend on living plants, that a very large number consume dead or dying plant remains, that some are coprophagous, and that a few specialized species feed on carrion or other animal remains. There are also large numbers of species that are dependent on the fungi or microorganisms of decay and a few that may depend upon mycorrhiza.

Predators and parasites depend on the abundance of all the foregoing animals and are in turn an important biotic factor regulating animal populations in the soil. Predators range from vertebrates (including many species which do not themselves spend much, if any, time in the soil, e.g. toads, anteaters, and scratching birds) that attack the macrofauna, down to the myriads of predatory nematodes and other water animals that attack only other members of the water fauna. Metazoan parasites of soil animals, excluding very many inquilines or brood parasites inhabiting formicaries and termitaries, fall mainly into three categories: parasitic insects (chiefly minute endoparasitic wasplike Hymenoptera, but including some flies and a few unusual beetles, etc.); mites of several groups (nearly all ectoparasitic, many of them mere body scavengers); and nematodes (whose parasitic associations with the host vary enormously, but almost all of which are endoparasites).

A comprehensive discussion of parasitic and predatory arthropods attacking soil animals is beyond the limits of this paper, but Clausen (1940) gives an account of entomophagous insects in general, including some information on soil forms. Franz (1956-1961) lists most of the recent literature.

Nematodes infesting soil animals (other than vertebrates) are fairly numerous. Some *Rhabditis* species are found in earthworms, for example, and other species in molluscs. Soil insects harbour a wide range of nematode parasites and semiparasites, the best known of which include *Neoaplectana* (especially in scarabaeid-beetle and bibionid-fly larvae), *Mermis* in earwigs, and other mermithid genera in ants. General reviews of insect-parasitizing nematodes (including soil forms) are given by Steinhaus (1949) and Welch (1962, 1963). Franz (1956-1961) also lists most of the recent relevant titles. Predatory and parasitic nematodes attacking other nematodes are covered by Dollfus (1946), and some reference is also made to them by Christie (1960). H. R. Wallace (1963) briefly reviews the Metazoa, including nematodes, that attack plant-parasitic nematodes.

Besides Metazoa, parasites of soil insects also include fungi and many other microorganisms. Most of these are included in the general reviews and literature lists of Steinhaus (1946, 1949, 1957, 1963), Smith and Rivers (1956), Franz (1956-1961), K. M. Hughes (1957), Bucher (1960), Thomson (1960), Weiser (1961), and others. Stammer (1956) discusses the various natural enemies of bibionid larvae, including microbial infections. Hurpin and Vago (1958) give a very comprehensive account of the diseases that affect cockchafer (*Melolontha melolontha*) larvae. Surany (1960) reviews the diseases of rhinoceros beetles (*Oryctes* spp.). H. R. Wallace (1963) discusses the microorganisms attacking plant-parasitic nematodes.

Examples of fungi infecting soil insects are: *Empusa* sp. on leatherjackets (Müller-Kögler, 1957); *Entomophthora forficuli* on the European earwig (Crumb, Eide, and Bonn, 1941); *E. aphidis* on subterranean aphids (Harper, 1958); *Massospora cicadina* on the nymphs of periodic cicadas (Speare, 1921); *Cordyceps ravenelii* on scarabaeid-beetle larvae (see Steinhaus, 1949; Hammond, 1961); *Metarrhizium anisopliae*, the green muscardine fungus found on many hosts such as the European earwig (Crumb, Eide, and Bonn, 1941) and scarabaeid-beetle larvae (see Steinhaus, 1949; Nirula, 1957); *Sorosporella agrotidis* on cutworms (Speare, 1917); and *Spicaria* spp., also on cutworms. The minute Laboulbeniales also include species epiphytic on soil insects and mites. Several authors in Steinhaus (1963) review the fungous diseases of insects, including soil-inhabiting species. Fungi that attack nematodes include species of *Stylopage* (adhesive), *Arthrobotrys, Dactylaria,* and *Dactylella* (trappers) and *Acrostalagmus* and *Harposporium* (endozoic); they are reviewed by Dollfus (1946), Duddington (1955, 1957, 1962), and others, and will be considered further by contributors to this symposium.

Protozoa endozoic in the soil fauna include *Monocystis lumbricis*, a universally known gregarine found in earthworms, *Eimeria schubergi* (another "textbook" species), a coccidian affecting centipedes, *Gregarina cetoniae* and *G. longa*, gregarines from scarabaeid larvae and leatherjackets respectively (see Steinhaus, 1949), and the microsporidians *Plistophora melolonthae* and *Stempellia amasiae* from scarabaeid grubs (Krieg, 1955) and bibionid larvae (Stammer, 1956); some Haplosporidia also attack soil arthropods. Some authors in Steinhaus (1963) review the protozoan parasites of insects, including soil-inhabiting species. Numerous protozoa associated with free-living and plant-parasitic nematodes are referred to by Dollfus (1946), and further references are made to some of them elsewhere in this symposium. (See also H. R. Wallace, 1963.)

Among bacterial diseases of the soil fauna may be mentioned spring disease of cutworms (*Pseudomonas septica*), cutworm septicemia (*Bacterium noctuarum*) and the milky diseases (*Bacillus popilliae* and *B. lentimorbus*) of scarabaeid larvae, notably Japanese beetle, *Popillia japonica* (see Steinhaus, 1949; Dutky, 1963). Another bacterial disease of this beetle was found by Dutky (1937) to be transmitted by a parasitic nematode of the genus *Neoaplectana*. *Bacillus fribourgensis* parasitizes cockchafer larvae (Wille,

1956). Bacteria associated with nematodes are reviewed by Dollfus (1946), but there seems to be no confirmation of pathogenicity.

Rickettsiae pathogenic in soil insects include *Rickettsiella tipulae* in leatherjackets (Müller-Kögler, 1958) and blue disease of white grubs (see, for example, Dutky and Gooden, 1952; Wille and Martignoni, 1952; Hurpin, 1962; Krieg, 1963).

Virus infections (granuloses, both nuclear and cytoplasmic, and polyhedroses) are also known in a few soil insects, particularly cutworms (Paillot, 1936, 1937; see also Bergold, 1963; Huger, 1963; Smith, 1963) and tipulid larvae (Rennie, 1923; Smith and Xeros, 1954; see also Aizawa, 1963; Smith, 1963); iridescent virus also occurs in the latter (Xeros, 1954; see also Smith, 1963); histolytic virus diseases also occur in scarabaeid larvae (see Smith, 1963). Even nematodes have once been reported as suffering from virus diseases (Loewenberg, Sullivan, and Schuster, 1959).

HUMAN ACTIVITIES AND THE SOIL FAUNA.—Man, as a kind of superbiotic factor, affects the soil fauna by cultivation, drainage, irrigation, industrial pollution, the application of fertilizers and plant protection chemicals, cultural pest control, and various other means. Literature covering this topic may be found in more comprehensive works (Kevan, 1962; Kühnelt, 1961, 1963), but one form of human activity ought to be briefly commented upon: the deliberate attempt to interfere with the composition of the soil fauna by means of biological agents other than human—in short, biological control. Many potential agents for this purpose have been found among the predators, parasites, and pathogens. Although many of these have been used, sometimes with considerable success, against surface-dwelling animals, attempts to use them against the soil fauna have been few and successes even fewer. General accounts of the subject as applied to nematodes are given, for example, in Steinhaus (1949, 1963), Sweetman (1958), Clausen (1956), Bucher (1958), Tanada (1959, 1961), Angus and Heimpel (1960), and J. W. MacB. Cameron (1963); and most of the recent literature is listed by Franz (1956-1961). Nematological aspects are covered elsewhere in this symposium and by H. R. Wallace (1963).

Vertebrates are not usually considered very promising as biological control agents, but the South American giant toad, *Bufo marinus*, has been introduced into various tropical countries against scarabaeid larvae and mole-crickets, apparently with some success. Shrews (*Sorex cinereus*) have recently been introduced into Newfoundland from the Canadian mainland to control the larch sawfly, *Pristiphora erichsoni* (MacLeod, 1962), but neither of these are strictly soil animals.

Large predatory insects used with some success against Japanese-beetle larvae in the United States are the wasps *Tiphia vernalis* and *T. popilliavora* (Clausen, 1956; Langford, 1962); and another wasp, *Scolia ruficornis*, is being tried against rhinoceros beetle (*Oryctes*) in Fiji (Simmonds, 1959a,b). Comparatively few introductions of parasitic insects have proved useful against soil insects except against the inactive stages of some surface pests, but the introduction into North America of the tachinid fly *Bigonicheta setipennis* has helped to control the European earwig in some areas (Clausen, 1956).

The position of nematodes as biological-control agents against insects has been reviewed recently by Rühm (1957) and Welch (1962, 1963). Welch points out that, because of their moisture requirements, nematodes are more likely to prove of value against soil-inhabiting insects than against other species of insects. The best known of such nematodes is *Neoaplectana glaseri*, which became successfully established in the eastern United States in larvae of Japanese beetle (Glaser, McCoy, and Girth, 1940; Langford, 1962). *N. glaseri* has also been tried against pasture beetles in New Zealand without much success, probably because soil conditions were too dry, and against rhinoceros beetle in Fiji (Hoy, 1955). Larvae of the latter live in rotting vegetation so that chances for the success of the parasite are greater against this beetle. Certain neoaplectanids may transmit bacterial diseases in insects, and one (so far unnamed, but referred to as "DD136" along with other organisms in the complex) has been shown to produce infection in many kinds of insects (Dutky, 1959). This nematode can be mass-produced and used in a spray, and Welch (1962) reports promising experiments in Ontario, using it against cabbage root maggot *Hylemya* (*Erioischia*) *brassicae*. Nematodes have one particular advantage over insects as biological-control agents, and that is that they are little affected by most insecticides.

Protozoa have not so far been used against soil insects, and fungi have not proved promising in the few attempts that have been made against soil pests. Fox and Jaques (1958) report one unsuccessful attempt to reduce the numbers of wireworms with the often-tried *Metarrhizium anisopliae*.

The use of bacteria to control soil insect pests is best known by the comparative success achieved against Japanese beetle in the eastern United States by the mass application of spores of *Bacillus popilliae* and *B. lentimorbus* (R. T. White, 1948; Steinhaus, 1949; Polivka, 1956; Langford, 1962). Another species of *Bacillus* has also been used against European cockchafers (Hurpin, 1959). Dutky (1963) reviews this subject. *Bacillus thuringiensis* is now widely used as a commercial "insecticide," but it does not seem to have had much success against soil pests. Other microbial pathogens such as rickettsiae and viruses may prove of value in future soil-insect-pest control (see various authors in Steinhaus, 1963). The possibilities of the biological control of soil-inhabiting nematodes will be considered elsewhere in this symposium.

It should be made clear that the deliberate introduction of natural enemies is not the only way in which biological control may be attempted. Even judicious application of pest-control materials as suggested by Solomon (1953) or any other method of manipulating the environment to favour naturally occurring control agents at the expense of what man regards as undesirable animals should be considered a form of biological control. Some studies that show the effects of human activities on natural populations are those of Baudissin (1952), M. M. H. Wallace (1954), Satchell (1955b), Sheals (1955, 1956), Baring (1956a,b), Read (1960), Edwards and Dennis (1960), and Hartenstein (1960). Investigations aimed at finding out what effects naturally occurring populations of parasites and predators actually have on soil pests—such as that of Wright, Hughes, and Worrall (1960) in respect of the cabbage root fly—are fundamental to our understanding of the potentialities of biological control and are all too few.

INTERACTION BETWEEN SOIL FAUNA AND SOIL MICROFLORA.—The role that animals play in the breakdown of litter and in soil formation is not completely understood, but it is undoubtedly very significant (see Kühnelt, 1950, 1957, 1961, 1963; Stöckli, 1950; Drift, 1951; Kevan, 1955; Schuster, 1956; Dunger, 1956, 1958; Nosek, 1957; Nosek and Ambrož, 1957; Witkamp and Drift, 1961; Kevan, 1962). Its importance was indicated, from a pedological point of view, long ago by Müller (1879, 1884) and has been stressed more recently by Kubiëna (1948, 1953, 1955) and Hartmann (1951, 1952). According to Kubiëna (1955), there would appear to be no substitute for animals in mixing and binding the particles of highly developed humus soils.

Clearly one of the most important roles of the soil fauna is the comminution of humus particles and litter. This comminution results in an ever-increasing surface area upon which fungi and other microorganisms can act. Witkamp and Drift (1961) note that the larger animals are more important in mechanical than in chemical breakdown. Lignous material, which cannot be digested by animals, requires the action of fungi to soften it (Jacot, 1939; Winston, 1956) before animals can fragment it and ultimate decomposition can take place (Birch and Clark, 1953). Comminuting animals are mainly arthropods; those breaking down wood are mostly rather larger forms such as millipedes, dipterous and coleopterous larvae, and, of course, termites. The frass and faeces produced by these (except in the special case of termites), and the fungi that attack wood, are in turn consumed by microarthropods whose progressively smaller frass, faeces, and remains provide a milieu for other microorganisms. There is therefore an inseparable association between the soil fauna and the microflora.

Translocation of plant remains from the litter layer to lower horizons is probably also of very great significance in the breakdown of fragments, since the latter environment appears to be more favourable for microbial activity (Macfadyen, 1957). Earthworms and millipedes are among the most important of the fauna bringing about a mixing of organic and mineral particles. Soils worked by them are said by Kollmansperger (1956) to contain about two thirds more bacteria than unworked soil (attributable, in part, to the production of a tilth providing the bacteria with better living conditions). Kollmansperger also reported greater resistance by plants grown in such soils to fungal attack. Very few species of bacteria appear to be affected by passage through earthworms (Day, 1950).

The reciprocal influence of the microflora on the soil fauna has already been referred to. The chief role played by the microflora is undoubtedly the provision of food, but the microflora also include innumerable saprophytic species that decompose animal remains, as well as parasitic and "predacious" fungi and species that produce attractant or repellent or even antibiotic substances.

In connection with the interrelation between soil fauna and microflora, it should perhaps be pointed out that simply because certain animals are known to feed on fungi or bacteria, this does not necessarily mean that they do so indiscriminately, nor is there any reason to suppose that they will select the most abundant species (either beneficial or harmful from an anthropocentric point of view). This has already been indicated for bacteriophagous protozoa (Cutler and Crump, 1935; Russell, 1950). Some species of termites and ants feed very largely on fungi, but only on "domesticated" forms which they "cultivate" and which are not found except in association with these insects. Work in progress in our department indicates that some Collembola that feed on fungi digest only hyphae, the spores passing out more or less undamaged with the faeces. Passage of spores through animals may help to activate them; see Dr. Sussman's paper in this symposium. Dissemination of fungi through the soil by microarthropods (or nematodes) may thus be encouraged by the soil fauna, as was suggested by Hinson (cf. Burges, 1958). Possibly Protura that feed upon mycorrhiza (Sturm, 1959) also carry them from root to root. Führer's (1961) observations on the attraction of the oribatid mite *Pseudotritia ardua* to certain bacteria suggests that mites may assist in the dissemination of bacteria.

INTERRELATION BETWEEN THE SOIL FAUNA AND PLANT PATHOGENS.—The transmission of soil-borne plant pathogens by soil microarthropods appears to be a distinct possibility. That larger animals, such as maggots of the bean-seed fly or seed-corn maggot, *Hylemya* (*Delia*) *cilicrura* may disseminate the bacterium *Erwinia carotovora*, which causes rot of potato plants, was indicated many years ago (Leach, 1926). Other pathogens carried by soil insects and slugs are mentioned in Leach (1940) and later authors, but more attention to the microarthropods will doubtless show that these also play a very significant role. Enchytraeid worms, millipedes, and woodlice are often associated with rotting plant roots (though they may not themselves initiate the injury), and they, too, may disseminate the organisms that cause root rots. Bacteria that cause diseases may also be transported considerable distance in the gut of earthworms, since, as previously indicated, bacteria are mostly unaffected by such a sojourn (Day, 1950). In recent years it has been shown that various plant viruses can be transmitted by root aphids (McLean, 1962) and soil nematodes such as *Xiphinema* (see elsewhere in this symposium), and possibly by some soil mites, cf. *Aceria tulipae* (p. 37). Many nematodes are carried by insects, and some may possibly be plant-parasitic. The subject of animal transmission of plant pathogens, however, will be dealt with in another contribution to this symposium and need not be further considered here.

The only hopeful signs so far of controlling soil-borne plant pathogens by means of soil animals are in the field of biological control of nematodes, and this field will be dealt with by another contributor. But, so far as I am aware, the possible use of animals in their biological control offers very little encouragement (see Christie, 1960). It seems to me that any animal that favoured a plant pathogen as food would be more likely to spread it than to control it, even though it is true that one can prevent a petri plate from becoming overgrown with certain fungi by the introduction of colonies of certain Collembola and that slugs may consume fungal sclerotia. I fear that studies on biological control of non-animal plant pathogens must be indirect—i.e. the estimation of the importance of members of the soil fauna as vectors of disease, coupled with the study of the natural enemies of such vectors, with the ultimate object of eliminating or reducing their numbers by whatever means possible and encouraging species that may disseminate micro-organisms beneficial to man.

LITERATURE CITED

AIZAWA, K. 1963. The nature of infections caused by nuclear-polyhedrosis viruses. vol. 1, p. 381-412. *In* E. A. Steinhaus [ed.], Insect pathology, an advanced treatise, Academic Press, New York, London.

ANGUS, T. A., and A. M. HEIMPEL. 1960. The bacterial control of insects. Proc. Entomol. Soc. Ontario 90 (1959): 352-358.

BAKER, E. W., J. H. CAMIN, F. CUNLIFFE, T. A. WOOLLEY, and C. E. YUNKER. 1958. Guide to the families of mites. Contrib. Inst. Acarology, Dept. Zool., Univ. Maryland, No. 3, 242 p. College Park, Maryland.

BAKER, E. W., and G. W. WHARTON. 1952. An introduction to acarology. The Macmillan Company, New York. 465 p. 1 pl.

BALOGH, J. 1958. Lebensgemeinschaften der Landtiere, ihre Erforschung unter besonderer Berücksichtigung der zoologischen Arbeitsmethoden. Verlag der Ungarischen Akademie der Wissenschaften, Budapest; Akademie-Verlag, Berlin. 560 p.

BALOGH, J. 1961. Identification keys of world oribatid (Acari) families and genera. Acta Zool. Acad. Sci. Hungar. 7: 234-344.

BARING, H. H. 1956a. Die Wirkung insektizider Ganzflächenbehandlung auf die Mesofauna des Ackerbodens. Mitt. Biol. Bundesanstalt Land- Forstwirtsch. Berlin-Dahlem 85: 60-65.

BARING, H. H. 1956b. Die Milbenfauna eines Ackerbodens und ihre Beeinflussung durch Pflanzenschutzmittel. Z. Angew. Ent. 39: 410-444.

BARLOW, C. A. 1957. A factorial analysis of distribution in three species of diplopods. Tijdschr. Ent. 100: 349-426.

BARLOW, C. A. 1958. Distribution and seasonal activity in three species of diplopods. Arch. Neerl. Zool. 13: 108-133.

BAUDISSIN, F. VON. 1952. Die Wirkung von Pflanzenschutzmitteln auf Collembolen und Milben in verschiedenen Böden. Zool. Jahrb. Abt. Syst. 81: 47-90.

BERGOLD, G. H. 1963. The nature of nuclear-polyhedrosis viruses. vol. 1, p. 413-456. *In* E. A. Steinhaus [ed.], Insect pathology, an advanced treatise, Academic Press, New York, London.

BIRCH, L. C., and D. P. CLARK. 1953. Forest soil as an ecological community with special reference to the fauna. Quart. Rev. Biol. 1: 13-36.

BLOWER, J. G. 1955. Millipedes and centipedes as soil animals. p. 138-151. *In* D. K. McE. Kevan [ed.], Soil zoology, Butterworths Scientific Publications, London: Academic Press, New York.

BODENZOOLOGISCHES KOLLOQUIUM. 1962. Vorträge zum "Bodenzoologischen Kolloquium," am 6 und 7 April 1961 in Staalichen Museum für Naturkunde, Görlitz [East Germany] Abt. Ber. Naturkundemus, Görlitz, 37: 131-193.

BORNEBUSCH, C. H. 1930. The fauna of forest soil (Skovbundens Dipreverden). Forsth. Forsøgsv. Danm. 11: 1-224.

BORNEMISSZA, G. F. 1957. An analysis of arthropod succession in carrion and the effect of its decomposition on the soil fauna. Australian J. Zool. 5: 1-12.

BRAUNS, A. 1954. Terricole Dipterenlarven. Untersuchungen zur angewandte Bodenbiologie. Musterschmidt Wissenschaftlicher Verlag, Göttingen, Frankfurt, Berlin. vol. 1, 179 p.

BRAUNS, A. 1955. Puppen terricoler Dipterenlarven. Untersuchungen zur angewandte Bodenbiologie. Musterschmidt Wissenschaftlicher Verlag, Göttingen, Frankfurt, Berlin. vol. 2, 156 p.

BRO LARSEN, E. 1949. The influence of the severe winters of 1939-42 on the soil fauna of Tipperne. Oikos 1: 186-207.

BUCHER, G. E. 1958. General summary and review of utilization of disease to control insects. Proc. X. Intern. Congr. Ent., Montreal, 1956, vol. 4, p. 695-701.

BUCHER, G. E. 1960. Potential bacterial pathogens of insects and their characteristics. J. Insect Pathol. 2: 172-195.

BURGES, A. 1958. Micro-organisms in the soil. Hutchinson, London. 188 p.

CAMERON, A. E. 1913. General survey of the insect fauna of the soil within a limited area near Manchester; a consideration of the relationships between soil insects and the physical conditions of their habitat. J. Econ. Biol. 8: 159-204.

CAMERON, J. W. MACB. 1963. Factors affecting the use of microbial pathogens in insect control. Ann. Rev. Entomol. 8: 265-286.

CHAMBERLIN, R. V., and R. L. HOFFMAN. 1958. Checklist of the millipeds of North America. U. S. Natl. Mus. Bull. 212: 1-236.

CHITWOOD, B. G., and M. B. CHITWOOD. 1950. An introduction to nematology. rev. ed. G. Chitwood and Monumental Printing Co., Baltimore. 213 p.

CHRISTIE, J. R. 1960. Biological control—predaceous nematodes. p. 466-68. *In* J. N. Sasser, and W. R. Jenkins [ed.], Nematology: fundamentals and recent advances with emphasis on plant parasitic and soil forms, University of North Carolina Press, Chapel Hill, N. C.

CLAUSEN, C. P. 1940. Entomophagous insects. McGraw-Hill Book Co., New York, London. 688 p.

CLAUSEN, C. P. 1956. Biological control of insect pests in the continental United States. U. S. Dept. Agr. Tech. Bull. 1139, 151 p.

COIFFAIT, H. 1958. Les coléoptères du sol. Vie et Milieu, Suppl. 7, 204 p.

CRUMB, S. E., P. M. EIDE, and A. E. BONN. 1941. The European earwig. U. S. Dept. Agr. Tech. Bull. 766, 76 p.

CUTLER, D. W., and L. M. CRUMP. 1935. Problems in soil microbiology. Longmans, Green and Co., London. 104 p.

DARWIN, C. R. 1840. On the formation of mould. Trans. Geol. Soc. London (2), 5: 505-509.

DARWIN, C. R. 1881. The formation of vegetable mould through the action of worms, with observations on their habits. J. Murray, London. 326 p.

DAY, G. M. 1950. Influence of earthworms on soil microorganisms. Soil Sci. 69: 175-184.

DELAMARE DEBOUTTEVILLE, C. 1951. Microfaune du sol des pays tempérés et tropicaux. Vie et Milieu, Suppl. 1, 360 p.

DELAMARE DEBOUTTEVILLE, C., and E. RAPOPORT [ed.] 1962-63. Biologie de l'Amerique australe. 2 vols. Étude sur faune du sol. Editions du Centre National de la Recherche Scientifique, Paris.

DIEM, K. 1903. Untersuchungen über die Bodenfauna in den Alpen. Jahrb. Naturwiss. Ges. St. Galen, 1901-2: 1-234.

DOEKSEN, J., and J. VAN DER DRIFT. 1963. Soil organisms. Proceedings of the Colloquium on soil fauna, soil microflora and their relationships, Oosterbeek, the Netherlands, September 10-16, 1962. North-Holland Publishing Company, Amsterdam. 453 p.

DOLLFUS, R. P. 1946. Parasites (animaux et végétaux) des helminthes: hyperparasites, ennemis et prédateurs des helminthes parasites et des helminthes libres; essai de compilation méthodique. Encycl. Biol. Paris. vol. 27, Paul Lechevalier, Paris. 482 p., 1 pl.

DOWDY, W. W. 1944. The influence of temperature on vertical migration of invertebrates inhabiting different soil types. Ecology 25: 449-460.

DRIFT, J. VAN DER. 1951. Analysis of the animal community in a beech forest floor. Meded. Inst. Toegep. Biol. Onders. Nat. 9: 1-168.

DUDDINGTON, C. L. 1955. Inter-relations between soil microflora and soil nematodes. p. 284-301. *In* D. K. McE. Kevan [ed.], Soil zoology, Butterworths Scientific Publications, London; Academic Press, New York.

DUDDINGTON, C. L. 1957. The friendly fungi. A new approach to the eelworm problem. Faber and Faber, London. 188 p.

DUDDINGTON, C. L. 1962. Predacious fungi and the control of eelworms. vol. 1, p. 151-200. *In* J. D. Carthy, and C. L. Duddington [ed.], Viewpoints in biology, Butterworths Scientific Publications, London.

DUNGER, W. 1956. Untersuchungen über Laubstreuzersetzung durch Collembolen. Zool. Jahrb., Abt. Syst. 84: 75-98.

DUNGER, W. 1958. Über der Veränderung der Fallaubes im Darm von Bodentieren. Z. Pflanzenernähr. Düng. Bodenk. 82: 174-193.

DUNGER, W. 1962. Methoden zur vergleichende Auswerkung von Fütterungsversuchen in der Bodenbiologie. Abhandl. u. Ber. Naturkundemus. Görlitz 37: 143-162.

DUNGER, W. 1964. Tiere im Boden. Neue Boehm-Bücherei no. 327. A. Ziemsen Verlag, Wittenberg Lutherstadt. 265 p.

DUTKY, S. R. 1937. Investigation of the diseases of the immature stages of the Japanese beetle. Doctoral Thesis, Rutgers Univ., New Brunswick, New Jersey. (Not seen, cited by F. Welch, 1963).

DUTKY, S. R. 1959. Insect microbiology. Advanc. Appl. Microbiol. 1: 175-200.

DUTKY, S. R. 1963. The milky diseases. vol. 2, p. 75-115. *In* E. A. Steinhaus [ed.], Insect pathology, an advanced treatise, Academic Press, New York and London.

DUTKY, S. R., and E. L. GOODEN. 1952. *Coxiella popilliae*, n. sp., a rickettsia causing blue disease of Japanese beetle larvae. J. Bacteriol. 63: 743-750.

EDWARDS, C. A., and E. B. DENNIS. 1960. Some effects of aldrin and DDT on the soil fauna of arable land. Nature (London) 188: 767.

EGLITIS, V. K. 1954. Fauna pochv Latviiskoĭ SSR Akademiya Nauk, Latviiskoĭ, SSR, Riga, 261 p.

EVANS, G. O. 1955. Identification of terrestrial mites. p. 55-61. *In* D. K. McE. Kevan [ed.], Soil zoology, Butterworths Scientific Publications, London; Academic Press, New York.

EVANS, G. O., J. G. SHEALS, and D. MACFARLANE. 1961. Terrestrial acari of the British Isles. An introduction to their morphology, biology and classification (Introduction and biology). Trustees of the British Museum, London. 219 p.

FARB, P. 1959. Living earth. Harper and Brothers, New York. 178 p., 8 pl.

FORSSLUND, K. H. 1945. Studier över det lägre djurlivet i nordsvensk skogsmark. Medd. Skogsförsöksanst. 34 (1): 1-283.

FOX, C. J. S. 1959. Influence of vegetation on distribution of wireworms, *Agriotes* spp., in grassland: a progress report. Ann. Rept. Entomol. Soc. Ontario 89 (1958): 47-49.

FOX, C. J. S., and R. P. JAQUES. 1958. Note on the green-muscardine fungus, *Metarrhizium anisopliae* (Metch.) Sor., as a control for wireworms. Can. Entomologist 90: 314-315.

FRANZ, H. 1950. Bodenzoologie als Grundlage der Bodenpflege. Akademie-Verlag, Berlin. 316 p.

FRANZ, H. (In press.) Ibid., 2d edition.

FRANZ, J. M. 1956. Bibliographie concernant la lutte biologique [I.] Entomophaga 1: 107-112.

FRANZ, J. M. 1957. Bibliographie über biologische Bekämpfung II. Ibid. 2: 293-311.

FRANZ, J. M. 1958. Idem III. Ibid. 3: 333-364.

FRANZ, J. M. 1959. Idem IV. Ibid. 4: 315-343.

FRANZ, J. M. 1960. Idem V. Ibid. 5: 295-335.

FRANZ, J. M. 1961. Idem VI. Ibid. 6: 277-329.

FRENZEL, G. 1936. Untersuchungen über die Tierwelt des Wiesenbodens. G. Fischer, Jena. 130 p.

FÜHRER, E. 1961. Der Einfluss von Planzenwurzeln auf die Verteilung der Kleinarthropoden im Boden, untersucht an *Pseudotritia ardua*. Pedobiologia 1: 99-112.

GILBERT, O. 1955. Further discussion. p. 21. *In* D. K. McE. Kevan [ed.], Soil zoology, Butterworths Scientific Publications, London; Academic Press, New York.

GILYAROV (GHILAROV), M. S. 1947. Distribution of humus, root systems and soil invertebrates within the soil of the walnut forests of the Ferghana mountain range. Compt. Rend. Acad. Sci. URSS. 55: 49-52.

GILYAROV, M. S. 1949. Osobenosti pochvȳ kak sredȳ obitaniya i ee znachenie v évolutzii nasekomȳkh. Akademiya Nauk SSSR, Moskva, Leningrad. 279 p.

GILYAROV, M. S. 1962. Simpozium po pochvennoĭ faune v Kieve. Pochvoveddenie 9, 1 p.

GILYAROV, M. S. [ed.] 1964. Opreditel' obitayushchikh v pochve lichinok nasekomȳkh, Akademiya Nauk, SSSR, Moskva. 919 p.

GISIN, H. 1943. Ökologie und Lebensgemeinschaften der Collembolen in schweizerischen Excursionsgebiet Basels. Rev. Suisse Zool. 50: 131-224.

GISIN, H. 1960. Die Collembolen Europas. 312 p. Museum d'Histoire Naturelle, Gèneve.

GLASER, R. W., E. E. McCOY, and H. B. GIRTH. 1940. The biology and economic importance of a nematode parasitic in insects. J. Parasitol. 26: 479-495.

GOODEY, T. 1951. Soil and fresh water nematodes. Methuen, London; Wiley, New York. 389 p.

GOODEY, T. [and J. B. GOODEY]. 1963. Idem. 2d rev. ed. 576 p. + 5 folders.

GRIFFIN, F. J. 1951. Bibliography of the Isoptera (termites) 1758-1949. J. Soc. Bibliogr. Nat. Hist. 2: 261-368.

GUILD, W. J. McL. 1955. Earthworms and soil structure. p. 83-98. *In* D. K. McE. Kevan [ed.], Soil zoology, Butterworths Scientific Publications, London; Academic Press, New York.

HAARLØV, N. 1955. Vertical distribution of mites and Collembola in relation to soil structure. p. 167-179. *In* D. K. McE. Kevan [ed.], Soil zoology, Butterworths Scientific Publications, London; Academic Press, New York.

HAARLØV, N. 1960. Microarthropods from Danish soils: Ecology, phenology. Oikos, Suppl. 3. 176 p.

HALLSWORTH, E. G. 1955. Foreword. p. v-vii. *In* D. K. McE. Kevan [ed.], Soil zoology, Butterworths Scientific Publications, London; Academic Press, New York.

HAMMOND, G. H. 1961. Observations on infections of white grubs, *Phyllophaga* spp. by *Cordyceps ravenelii* Berk. & Curt. in eastern Canada. Can. Field Nat. 75: 41-42.

HANDLEY, W. R. 1954. Mull and mor formation in relation to forest soils. Forest Commiss. Bull. (London) 23, 115 p.

HANDSCHIN, E. 1929. Die Temperatur als Faktor lokaler Tierwanderung in Boden. Verhandl. Naturforsch. Ges. Basel 40: 486-504.

HARPER, A. M. 1958. Notes on behaviour of *Pemphigus betae* Doane (Homoptera: Aphididae) infected with *Entomophthora aphidis* Hoffr. Can. Entomologist 90: 439-440.

HARRIS, W. V. 1961. Termites: their recognition and control. Longmans, London. 187 p., 28 pl., 1 fold. tab.

HARTENSTEIN, P. C. 1960. The effects of DDT and malathion upon forest soil microarthropods. Ecology 42: 190-194.

HARTMANN, F. 1951. Der Waldboden, Humus-, Boden- und Wurzeltypen als Standortsanzeiger. Österreiches Produktivatäts Zentrum, Wien. 151 p.

HARTMANN, F. 1952. Forstökologie—Zustandserfassung und standortsgemässe Gestaltung der Lebensgrundlagen des Waldes. Georg Fromme & Co., Wien. 461 p. + 1 fold. tab.

HIRSCHMANN, W. [ed.] 1957–. Gangsystematik der Parasitiformes. Acarologie. Fürth, Bayern. (6 parts in 5 Folgen published to date).

HOY, J. M. 1955. The use of bacteria and nematodes to control insects. New Zealand Sci. Rev. 13: 56-58.

HUGER, A. 1963. Granuloses of insects. vol. 1, p. 531-575. *In* E. A. Steinhaus [ed.], Insect pathology, an advanced treatise, Academic Press, New York, London.

HUGHES, K. M. 1957. An annotated list and bibliography of insects reported to have virus diseases. Hilgardia 26: 597-629.

HUGHES, R. D. 1962. The study of aggregated populations. p. 51-55. *In* P. W. Murphy [ed.], Progress in soil zoology, Butterworths Scientific Publications, London.

HUGHES, T. E. 1959. Mites or the Acari. Athlone Press, University of London, London. 225 p.

HURPIN, B. 1959. Les maladies du ver blanc (*Melolontha melolontha* L.) et essai d'utilisation d'une maladie laiteuse indigène. Phytiatrie-Phytopharm. 8: 85-90.

HURPIN, B. 1962. Observations pathologiques sur les maladies à rickettsies des larves de Scarabaeidae. Verhandl. XI. Intern. Kongr. Entomol., Wien, 1960, 2: 875-880.

HURPIN, B., and C. VAGO. 1958. Les maladies du hanneton commun (*Melolontha melolontha* L.) (Col. Scarabaeidae). Entomophaga 3: 285-330.

HYMAN, L. H. 1951. Class Nematoda. vol. 3, p. 197-455. *In* The invertebrates, McGraw-Hill Book Co., New York, Toronto, London.

INTERNATIONAL CONGRESS OF ENTOMOLOGY. 1962. Symposium IX, Bodenarthropoden Verhandl. XI. Intern. Kongr. Ent., 1960. vol. 3, p. 148-174.

INTERNATIONAL CONGRESS OF SOIL SCIENCE. 1956. Biologie du sol. Rapp. VI. Congr. Intern. Sci. Sol, Paris, 1956. *C* (Commiss. III): 5-476.

INTERNATIONAL CONGRESS OF ZOOLOGY. 1959. The fauna of soil. Proceedings of the XV. Congress, London, 1958. p. 349-366.

JACOT, A. P. 1939. Reduction of spruce and fir litter by minute animals. J. Forestry 37: 858-860.

JOFFE, J. S. 1936. Pedology. Rutgers University Press, New Brunswick, New Jersey. 575 p. + 1 fold. map.

KEVAN, D. K. McE. 1955a. [ed.]. Soil zoology: Proceedings of the University of Nottingham Second Easter School in Agricultural Science. Butterworths Scientific Publications, London; Academic Press, New York. 512 p.

KEVAN, D. K. McE. 1955b. Identification of soil and litter inhabiting animals. Ibid. p. 23-28.

KEVAN, D. K. McE. 1955c. A practical key to the orders and suborders of soil and litter inhabiting animals. Ibid. p. 452-488.

KEVAN, D. K. McE. 1960. Soil entomology. Ann. Soc. Entomol. Québec 4 (1958): 33-46.

KEVAN, D. K. McE. 1961. Soil entomology in Canada—a review of recent and current work. Ann. Soc. Entomol. Québec 6 (1960): 19-45.

KEVAN, D. K. McE. 1962. Soil animals. H. F. and G. Witherby, London; Philosophical Library, New York. 237 p., 5 pl. (A revised reprint is in press.)

KIPENVARLITZ, A. F. 1961. Izmenenie pochvennoĭ faunȳ nizinnȳkh bolot pod vliyaniem melioratzii i selskokhozyaĭstvennogo osboeniya. Sel'khozgiz, Belorusskoĭ, SSR, Minsk, 199 p.

KLIMA, J. 1956. Strukturklassen und Lebensformen der Oribatiden. Oikos 7: 227-242.

KLINGLER, J. 1957. Über die Bedeutung des Kohlendioxyds für die Orientierung der Larven von *Otiorrhynchus sulcatus* F., *Melolontha* und *Agriotes* im Boden. Mitt. Schweiz. Entomol. Ges. 30: 317-322.

KLINGLER, J. 1958. Die Bedeutung der Kohlendioxyd-Ausscheidung der Wurzeln für die Orientierung der Larven von *Otiorrhynchus sulcatus* F. und anderer bodenbewohnender phytophager Insektenarten. Mitt. Schweiz. Entomol. Ges. 31: 205-269.

KOLLMANSPERGER, F. 1956. Lumbriciden in humiden und ariden Gebieten und ihre Bedeutung für die Fruchtbarkeit des Bodens. Rapp. VI. Congr. Intern. Sci. Sol, Paris, 1956, *C*: 293-297.

KRAUSSE, A. 1928. Zur Terminologie der edaphischen Biozönosen. Intern. Entomol. Z. 22: 110-111.

KRIEG, A. 1955. Über Infektionskrankheiten bei Engerlingen von *Melolontha* spec. unter besonderer Berücksichtigung einer Mikrosporidien-Erkrankung. Zentb. Bakteriol., Parasitenk., Abt. II, 108: 535-538.

KRIEG, A. 1963. Rickettsiae and rickettsioses. vol. 1, p. 577-617. *In* E. A. Steinhaus [ed.], Insect pathology, an advanced treatise, Academic Press, New York, London.

KUBIËNA, W. L. 1948. Entwicklungslehre des Bodens. Springer Verlag, Wien. 215 p.

KUBIËNA, W. L. 1953. The soils of Europe. Illustrated diagnosis and systematics. Issued under the auspices of the Consejo Superior de Investigacione Cientificas, Madrid. T. Mirby, London. 317 p.

KUBIËNA, W. L. 1955. Animal activity in soils as a decisive factor in establishment of humus forms. p. 73-82. *In* D. K. McE. Kevan [ed.], Soil zoology, Butterworths Scientific Publications, London; Academic Press, New York.

KÜHNELT, W. 1950. Bodenbiologie mit besonderer Berücksichtigung der Tierwelt. Herold, Vienna. 368 p.

KÜHNELT, W. 1955. An introduction to the study of soil animals. p. 3-22. *In* D. K. McE. Kevan [ed.], Soil zoology, Butterworths Scientific Publications, London; Academic Press, New York.

KÜHNELT, W. 1957. Biologia del suelo. (Transl. E. Humbert.) (2nd ed. of Kühnelt, 1950.) Consejo Superior de Investigaciones Cientificas, Madrid. 267 p.

KÜHNELT, W. 1959. Über die Herkunft der Bodentierwelt des Festlandes. Proc. XV. Intern. Congr. Zool., London, 1958: 353-360.

KÜHNELT, W. 1960. Der Wasseraushalt des Bodens als entscheidener Faktor für seine Tierische Besiedlung. Verhandl. Deutsch. Zool. Ges. 1960: 307-315.

KÜHNELT, W. 1961. Soil biology: with special reference to the Animal Kingdom. (Transl. N. Walker.) (3d ed. of Kühnelt, 1950.) Faber and Faber, London; Rodale Books Inc., Emmaus, Pennsylvania. 397 p.

KÜHNELT, W. 1963. Soil-inhabiting Arthropoda. Ann. Rev. Entomol. 8: 115-136.

KUPKA, E., and B. SCHAERFFENBERG. 1947. Untersuchungen über die Kohlensäureresistenz und den Sauerstoffverbrauch bei einigen Bodentieren. Österr. Zool. Z. 1: 345-363.

LANGFORD, G. S. 1962. The control of the Japanese beetle in Maryland through biological control methods with observations on effects of soil disturbance. Verhandl. XI. Intern. Kongr. Ent., Wien, 1960, 2: 700-702.

LAWRENCE, R. F. 1953. The biology of the cryptic fauna of forests with special reference to the indigenous forests of South Africa. A. A. Balkena, Cape Town and Amsterdam. 408 p.

LEACH, J. G. 1926. The relation of the seed-corn maggot (*Phorbia fuscipes* Zett.) to the spread and development of potato blackleg in Minnesota. Phytopathology 16: 149-176.

LEACH, J. G. 1940. Insect transmission of plant diseases. McGraw-Hill Book Co., New York and London. 615 p., 1 pl.

LINDQUIST, B. 1941. Experimentelle Untersuchungen über die Bedeutung einiger Landmollusken für die Zersetzung der Waldstreu. Kgl. Fysiograf. Sällskap. Förh., Lund, 11: 144-156.

LOEWENBERG, J. R., T. SULLIVAN, and M. L. SCHUSTER. 1959. A virus disease of *Meloidogyne incognita incognita*, the southern root knot nematode. Nature (London) 184 (Suppl. 24): 1896.

MACFADYEN, A. 1957. Animal ecology: aims and methods. Sir Isaac Pitman and Sons Ltd., London and Toronto; Pitman Publishing Corporation, New York. 264 p.

MACFADYEN, A. 1962a. Soil arthropod sampling. vol. 1, p. 1-34. *In* J. B. Cragg [ed.], Advances in ecological research, Academic Press, London and New York.

MACFADYEN, A. 1962b. Control of humidity in three funnel-type extractors for soil arthropods. p. 158-168. *In* P. W. Murphy [ed.], Progress in soil zoology, Butterworths Scientific Publications, London.

MACFADYEN, A. 1963. Animal ecology: aims and methods. 2nd ed. Sir Isaac Pitman and Sons, London and Toronto; Pitman Publishing Corporation, New York, 344 p., 6 pl.

MACLEOD, C. F. 1962. Introduction de la musaraigne à Terre-Neuve. Rapp. Ann. Dir. Ent. Path. Forest. Québec, 1962: 14.

MANTON, S. M. 1958. Habits of life and evolution of body design in Arthropoda. J. Linn. Soc. (London) (Zool.) 44 (and Bot. 56): 58-72, 2 pl.

MAYNARD, E. A. 1951. A monograph of the Collembola, or springtail insects of New York State. Comstock Pub. Co., Ithaca, New York. 333 p., 29 pl.

MCLEAN, D. L. 1962. Transmission of lettuce mosaic virus by a new vector, *Pemphigus bursarius*. J. Econ. Entomol. 55: 580-583.

MIKOLETZKY, H. 1922. Die freilebenden Erd-Nematoden. Arch. Naturgesch. 1921A (8/9), 650 p.

MOMENT, G. B. 1958. General zoology. Houghton Mifflin (Boston), Cambridge, Massachusetts. 631 p.

MOURSI, A. A. M. 1961. Die Wirkung von Kohlendioxyd, Stickstoff, Ammoniak und Schwefelwasserstoff auf das Verhalten und die Verbrietung von Bodenarthropoden. Doctoral Thesis, Universität, Wien. (Not seen; cited by Kühnelt, 1963.)

MÜLLER, P. E. 1879. Studier over Skovjord, som bidrag til skovdyrkingens theori. I. Om bøgemuld og bøgemor paa sand og ler. Tidsskr. Skovbr. 3: 1-124.

MÜLLER, P. E. 1884. Idem. II. Om muld og mor i egeskove og paa heder. Tidsskr. Skovbr. 7: 1-232.

MÜLLER-KÖGLER, E. 1957. Über eine Mykose der Larven von *Tipula paludosa* Meig. durch *Empusa* sp. Z. Pflanzenkrankh. 64: 529-534.

MÜLLER-KÖGLER, E. 1958. Eine Rickettsiose von *Tipula paludosa* Meigen durch *Rickettsiella tipulae* nov. spec. Naturwissenschaften 45: 248.

MURPHY, P. W. 1952. Soil faunal investigations. p. 130-134. *In* Forestry Commission, London. Rept. Forest Res. 1951.

MURPHY, P. W. 1953. The biology of forest soils with special reference to the mesofauna or meiofauna. J. Soil Sci. 4: 155-193.

MURPHY, P. W. 1955. Ecology of the fauna of forest soils. p. 99-124. *In* D. K. McE. Kevan [ed.], Soil zoology, Butterworths Scientific Publications, London; Academic Press, New York.

MURPHY, P. W. [ed.]. 1962. Progress in soil zoology. Butterworths Scientific Publications, London. 398 p.

MURPHY, P. W., and C. C. DONCASTER. 1957. A culture method for soil meiofauna and its application to the study of nematode predators. Nematologica 2: 202-214.

NEF, L. 1957. État actuel des connaissances sur le rôle des animaux dans la decomposition de litières des forêts. Agricultura (2) 5: 245-316.

NIRULA, K. K. 1957. Observations on green muscardine

fungus in populations of *Oryctes rhinoceros* L. J. Econ. Entomol. 50: 767-770.

NOSEK, J. 1957. Poznamky k ekologii pudny faunỹ s hlediska biologie pudy. Slovenskej Akadémie Vied v Bratislava. 154 p.

NOSEK, J., and Z. AMBROŽ. 1957. Le faune du sol et l'activité microbienne de sol forestier. J. Forest. Suisse 1957 (10/11): 11-14, 2 pl.

O'CONNOR, F. B. 1955. Extraction of enchytraeid worms from coniferous forest soil. Nature (London) 175: 815-816.

O'CONNOR, F. B. 1957. An ecological study of the enchytraeid worm population of a coniferous forest soil. Oikos 8: 161-199.

OVERGAARD [NIELSEN], C. 1948. An apparatus for qualitative extraction of nematodes and rotifers from soil and moss. Nat. Jutland. 1: 271-277.

OVERGAARD NIELSEN, C. 1949. Studies on the soil microfauna. II. The soil inhabiting nematodes. Oikos 2: 1-131 + 31 p. of tables.

OVERGAARD NIELSEN, C. 1954. Studies on Enchytraeidae. II. The microdistribution of Enchytraeidae. Oikos 5: 167-178.

OVERGAARD NIELSEN, C. 1955. Survey of a year's results obtained by a recent method for the extraction of soil-inhabiting enchytraeid worms. p. 202-214. *In* D. K. McE. Kevan [ed.], Soil zoology, Butterworths Scientific Publications, London; Academic Press, New York.

OVERGAARD NIELSEN, C. 1959. Soil fauna and the moisture regime of its environment. Proc. XV. Intern. Congr. Zool., London, 1958, p. 349-351.

OVERGAARD NIELSEN, C., and B. CHRISTENSEN. 1959. The Enchytraeidae: critical revision and taxonomy of European species (Studies on Enchytraeidae VII). Nat. Jutland. 8-9: 1-160.

PACLT, J. 1956. Biologie der primär flügellosen Insekten. G. Fischer, Jena. 258 p.

PAILLOT, A. 1936. Contribution à l'étude des maladies à ultravirus des insectes. Ann. Epiphyt. Phytogénét. 2: 341-379.

PAILLOT, A. 1937. Nouveau type de pseudo-grasserie observé chez les chenilles d'*Euxoa segetum*. Compt. Rend. 205: 1264-1266.

PARK, O. 1950. Community organization: metabolism. p. 495-528. *In* W. C. Allee, et al. Principles of animal ecology. Saunders Co., Philadelphia and London.

PERTTUNEN, V. 1953. Reactions of diplopods to the relative humidity of the air. Investigations on *Orthomorpha gracilis, Iulus terrestris,* and *Rhizophyllum sabulosum*. Ann. Soc. Zool. Botan. Fenn. 16: 1-69.

POLIVKA, J. B. 1956. Effectiveness of milky disease in controlling Japanese beetle in Ohio. J. Econ. Entomol. 49: 4-6.

POOLE, I. B. 1957. Soil Collembola in a Douglas fir plantation. p. 109-111. *In* Forestry Commission, London. Rept. Forest Res. 1956.

POOLE, I. B. 1959. Studies on food of Collembola in a Douglas fir plantation. Proc. Zool. Soc. London 132: 71-82.

READ, D. C. 1960. Effect of soil treatments of heptachlor and parathion on predators and parasites of root maggots attacking rutabagas on Prince Edward Island. J. Econ. Entomol. 53: 932-935.

REISINGER, E. 1954. Edaphische Kleinturbellarien als bodenkundliche Leitformen. Carinthia II, 174: 105-123.

RENNIE, J. 1923. Polyhedral disease in *Tipula paludosa* (Meig.). Proc. Roy. Phys. Soc. Edinburgh, A, 20: 265-267.

RIHA, G. 1951. Zur Ökologie der Oribatiden in Kalksteinböden. Zool. Jahrb., Abt. Syst. 80: 407-450.

ROHDE, C. J. 1959. Studies on the biologies of two mite species, predator and prey, including some effects of gamma radiation on selected developmental stages. Ecology 40: 572-579.

ROMELL, L. G. 1935. An example of myriapods as mull formers. Ecology 16: 67-71.

RÜHM, W. 1957. Nematoden und biologische Bekämpfung der Insekten. Nematologica, Suppl. 2: 349-354.

RUSSELL, E. J. 1950. Soil conditions and plant growth.

8th ed. rev. by E. W. Russell. Longmans Green, London. 635 p.

RUSSELL, E. J. 1957. The world of the soil. Collins, London. 237 p.

SACHS, H. 1950. Die Nematodenfauna der Rinderexkremente. Zool. Jahrb., Abt. Syst. 79: 209-272.

SALMON, J. T. 1951. Keys and bibliography to the Collembola. Zool. Publ. Victoria Univ. Coll. Wellington 8, 82 p.

SALMON, J. T. 1956. Idem. First supplement. Ibid. 20, 35 p.

SASSER, J. N., and W. R. JENKINS [ed.]. 1960. Nematology: fundamentals and recent advances with emphasis on plant parasitic and soil forms. University of North Carolina Press, Chapel Hill, North Carolina. 480 p.

SATCHELL, J. E. 1955a. Some aspects of earthworm ecology. p. 180-201. *In* D. K. McE. Kevan [ed.], Soil zoology, Butterworths Scientific Publications, London; Academic Press, New York.

SATCHELL, J. E. 1955b. The effects of BHC, DDT and parathion on soil fauna. Soils Fertilizers 18: 279-285.

SATCHELL, J. E., and J. M. NELSON. 1962. A comparison of the Tullgren-funnel and flotation methods of extracting Acarina from woodland soil. p. 212-216. *In* P. W. Murphy [ed.], Progress in soil zoology, Butterworths Scientific Publications, London.

SCHAERFFENBERG, E. 1942. Der Einfluss von Humusgehalt und Feuchtigkeit auf die Frasstätigkeit der Elateridenlarven. Anz. Schäldlingskunde 18: 133-136.

SCHALLER, F. 1950. Biologische Beobachtungen an humusbildenden Bodentieren, insbesondere an Collembolen. Zool. Jahrb., Abt. Syst. 78: 506-525.

SCHALLER, F. 1962. Die Unterwelt des Tierreiches. Verständl. Wiss. No. 78, 126 p. Springer-Verlag, Berlin, Göttingen, Heidelberg.

SCHMIDT, H. 1955. Die Termiten. Ihre Erkennungsmerkmale und wirtschaftliche Bedeutung. Akademische Verlagsgesellschaft, Leipzig. 309 p.

SCHUSTER, R. 1956. Der Anteil der Oribatiden an den Zersetzungsvorgängen im Boden. Z. Morphol. Ökol. Tiere 45: 1-33.

SCHUSTER, R. 1958. Ökologischfaunistische Untersuchungen an bodenwohnenden Kleinarthropoden (speziell Oribatiden) des Salzlachengebietes im Seewinkel. Sitzber. Akad. Wiss. Wien (1) 168: 27-78.

SHARMA, G. D., and D. K. McE. KEVAN. 1963a. Observations on *Istotoma notabilis* (Collembola: Isotomidae) in eastern Canada. Pedobiologia 3(1): 34-47.

SHARMA, G. D., and D. K. McE. KEVAN. 1963b. Observation on *Folsomia similis* (Collembola, Isotomidae) in eastern Canada. Pedobiologia 3(1): 48-61.

SHARMA, G. D., and D. K. McE. KEVAN. 1963c. Observations on *Pseudosinella petterseni* and *Pseudosinella alba* (Collembola: Entomobryidae) in eastern Canada. Pedobiologia 3(1): 62-74.

SHEALS, J. G. 1955. The effects of DDT and BHC on soil Collembola and Acarina. p. 241-252. *In* D. K. McE. Kevan [ed.], Soil zoology, Butterworths Scientific Publications, London; Academic Press, New York.

SHEALS, J. G. 1956. Soil population studies. I. The effects of cultivation and treatment with insecticides. Bull. Entomol. Res. 47: 803-822.

SIMMONDS, H. W. 1959a. Interim report on *Scolia ruficornis* in Fiji. So. Pacific Comm. Quart. Bull. 9: 28-30.

SIMMONDS, H. W. 1959b. Further note on *Scolia ruficornis* in Fiji. So. Pacific Comm. Quart. Bull. 9: 43.

SLYKHUIS, J. T. 1960. Current status of mite-transmitted plant viruses. Proc. Entomol. Soc. Ontario 90 (1959): 22-30.

SMITH, K. M. 1963. The cytoplasmic virus diseases. vol. 1, p. 457-497. *In* E. A. Steinhaus [ed.], Insect pathology, an advanced treatise, Academic Press, New York, London.

SMITH, K. M., and C. F. RIVERS. 1956. Some viruses affecting insects of economic importance. Parasitology 42: 235-242.

SMITH, K. M., and N. XEROS. 1954. An unusual virus disease of dipterous larvae. Nature (London) 173: 866-867.

SNYDER, T. E. 1949. Catalog of the termites (Isoptera) of the world. Smithson. Inst. Misc. Collections 112, 490 p.

SNYDER, T. E. 1956. Annotated subject-heading bibliography of termites 1350 B.C. to A.D. 1954. Smithson. Inst. Misc. Collections 130, 306 p.

SNYDER, T. E. 1961. Supplement to the annotated subject-heading bibliography of termites 1958 to 1960. Smithson. Inst. Misc. Collections 143 (3), 137 p.

SOLOMON, M. E. 1953. Insect population balance and chemical control of pests. Chem. Ind. (London) 1953: 1143-1147.

SPEARE, A. T. 1917. *Sorosporella uvella* and its occurrence in cutworms in America. J. Agr. Res. 8: 189-194.

SPEARE, A. T. 1921. *Massospora cicadina* Peck, a fungus parasite of the periodical cicada. Mycologia 13: 72-82.

STACH, J. 1947–. The apterygotan fauna of Poland in relation to the world fauna of this group of insects. Acta Mon. Mus. Hist. Nat., Krakow (9 vols. to date).

STAMMER, H. J. 1956. Die Parasiten der Bibioniden. Proc. XIV. Intern. Congr. Zool., Copenhagen, 1953: 349-358.

STAMMER, H. J. 1957. Tyroglyphidae und Tarsonemini 1. vol. 1, p. 1-384. *In*: H. J. Stammer [ed.], Beiträge zur Systematik und Ökologie Mitteleuropäischer Acarina. Akademische Verlagsgesellschaft, Geest und Portig K.-G.

STAMMER, H. J. 1959. Tyroglyphidae und Tarsonemini 2. vol. 1, p. 385-389. Ibid.

STAMMER, H. J. 1963. Mesostigmata 1. vol. 2, 804 p. Ibid.

STEINHAUS, E. A. 1946. Insect microbiology: an account of the microbes associated with insects and ticks with special reference to the biologic relationships involved. Comstock Pub. Co., Inc., Ithaca, New York. 763 p.

STEINHAUS, E. A. 1949. Principles of insect pathology. McGraw-Hill Book Co., New York, Toronto, London. 757 p.

STEINHAUS, E. A. 1957. Microbial diseases of insects. Ann. Rev. Microbiol. 11: 165-182.

STEINHAUS, E. A. [ed.]. 1963. Insect pathology, an advanced treatise. 2 vols. Academic Press, New York and London.

STÖCKLI, A. 1946. Die biologische Komponente der Vererdung der Gare und der Nährstoffpufferung. Schweiz. Landwirtsch. Monatsh. 24: 3-19.

STÖCKLI, A. 1950. Die Ernährung der Pflanze in ihrer Abhängigkeit von der Kleinlebewelt des Bodens. Z. Pflanzenernähr. Düng. Bodenk. 48: 264-279.

STRENZKE, K. 1949. Die biozönotischen Grundlagen der Bodenzoologie. Z. Pflanzenernähr. Düng. Bodenk. 45: 245-262.

STURM, H. 1959. Die Nahrung der Proturen. Naturwissenschaften 46: 90-97.

SURANY, P. 1960. Diseases and biological control in rhinoceros beetles, *Oryctes* spp. (Scarabaeidae, Coleoptera). S. Pacific Comm. Tech. Paper 128, 62 p.

SWEETMAN, H. L. 1958. The principles of biological control: interrelation of hosts and pests and utilization in regulation of animal and plant populations. W. C. Brown Co., Dubuque, Iowa. 560 p., 1 pl.

SYMPOSIUM INTERNATIONAL DE NEMATOLOGIE, VIe. 1961. Résumés de Communications. Ministère de l'Education Nationale et de la Culture et du Ministère de l'Agriculture, Gand, Belgium. 127 p.

TANADA, Y. 1959. Microbial control of insect pests. Ann. Rev. Entomol. 4: 277-302.

TANADA, Y. 1961. Bacterial control of insect pests. J. Agr. Vet. Chem. 2: 114-116, 157-159.

THIELE, H. U. 1959. Experimentelle Untersuchungen über de Abhängigkeit bodenbewohnender Tierarten vom Kalkgehalt des Standortes. Z. Angew. Entomol. 44: 1-21.

THOMSON, H. M. 1960. A list and brief description of the Microsporidia infecting insects. J. Insect Pathol. 2: 346-385.

THORNE, G. 1961. Principles of nematology. McGraw-Hill Book Co., New York, Toronto, London. 553 p.

TISCHLER, W. 1955. Synökologie der Landtiere. Fischer, Stuttgart. 414 p.

WALLACE, H. R. 1955. The influence of soil moisture on the emergence of larvae from cysts of the beet eelworm,

Heterodera schachtii Schmidt. Ann. Appl. Biol. 43: 477-484.

WALLACE, H. R. 1956. The effect of soil structure on the emergence of larvae from cysts of the beet eelworm. Nematologica 1: 145-146.

WALLACE, H. R. 1963. The biology of plant parasitic nematodes. Edward Arnold Ltd., London. 280 p., 9 pl.

WALLACE, M. M. H. 1954. The effect of DDT and BHC on the populations of the Lucerne flea, *Sminthurus viridis* (L.) (Collembola), and its control by predatory mites, *Biscirus* spp. (Bdellidae). Australian J. Agr. Res. 5: 148-155.

WALLWORK, J. D. 1958. Notes on the feeding behaviour of some forest soil Acarina. Oikos 9: 260-271.

WEISER, J. 1961. Die Mikrosporidien als Parasiten der Insekten. Monograph. Angew. Entomol. 17, 169 p.

WEIS-FOGH, T. 1948. Ecological investigations on mites and collemboles in the soil. Nat. Jutland. 1: 137-270 + tables.

WELCH, H. E. 1962. Nematodes as agents for insect control. Proc. Entomol. Soc. Ontario 92 (1961): 11-19.

WELCH, H. E. 1963. Nematode infection. vol. 2, p. 363-392. *In* E. A. Steinhaus [ed.], Insect pathology, an advanced treatise. Academic Press, New York, London.

WHITE, G. 1789. The natural history and antiquities of Selborne. (Various editions.) B. White & Son, London.

WHITE, R. T. 1948. Application of milky disease spore dust with a commercial fertilizer. J. Econ. Entomol. 41: 113-114.

WILDE, S. A. 1954. Forest humus: its genetic classification. Trans. Wisconsin Acad. Sci. 43: 137-167.

WILLE, H. 1956. *Bacillus fribourgensis* n. sp., Erreger einer "milky disease" im Engerling von *Melolontha melolontha* L. Mitt. Schweiz. Entomol. Ges. 29: 271-283.

WILLE, H., and M. E. MARTIGNONI. 1952. Vorläufige Mitteilung über einen neuen Krankheitstypus beim Engerling von *Melolontha vulgaris* F. Schweiz. Z. Allgem. Pathol. Bakteriol. 15: 470-474.

WINSTON, P. W. 1956. The acorn microsere with special reference to arthropods. Ecology 37: 120-132.

WITKAMP, M., and J. VAN DER DRIFT. 1961. Breakdown of forest litter in relation to environmental factors. Plant Soil 15: 295-311.

WITTASEK, S. 1947. Ökologische Untersuchungen an Kleinarthropoden von Verlandungsböden. Doctoral Thesis, Universität, Wien. (Not seen; cited by Kühnelt, 1963.)

WRIGHT, D. W., R. D. HUGHES, and J. WORRALL. 1960. The effect of certain predators on the numbers of cabbage root fly [*Erioischia brassicae* (Bouché)] and on the subsequent damage caused by the pest. Ann. Appl. Biol. 48: 756-763, 1 pl.

XEROS, N. 1954. A second virus disease of the leatherjacket, *Tipula paludosa*. Nature (London) 174: 562-563.

► DISCUSSION OF D. K. McE. KEVAN PAPER

H. Katznelson:

Could you give us some idea of actual numbers of mites and Collembola in different soils? What depth of soil sampling is implied for numbers per square metre?

D. K. McE. Kevan:

Examples have been given in the paper. Even higher figures of well over a million arthropods (mostly microarthropods) per square metre are given by Forsslund (1945) for spruce-pine-birch "mor" in Sweden. The same author (*Medd. Statens Skogsforskningsinst.* 37 (7): 49-51, 1948) records 2.3 million. There is considerable variation, however, with different soil types. (A range of further examples will be found in Kevan, 1962, cited in the paper.) In expressing populations in terms of square metres (rather than by cubic measure), depths of less than 30 cm are implied since most of the fauna is found above this depth, and most of that in the upper 15 cm.

R. Mankau:

Can one make the assumption that the manipulation of soil in agricultural operations reduces the number (especially qualitatively) of soil fauna in arable soils and therefore the general importance of soil fauna in the biology of arable soils?

D. K. McE. Kevan:

It is very true of the larger fauna in arable soils that manipulation reduces numbers—if by manipulation one means mechanical operations such as ploughing, discing, etc. (Much of the information on this point is briefly summarized in Kevan, 1962.) Arable land has, in general, a poorer fauna than uncultivated land, although grassland is not *necessarily* poorer than woodland (especially as regards nematodes). Microarthropods, as well as macroarthropods, are less numerous in cultivated soils than in undisturbed ones, but one should not generalize since the season at which the operations take place has a direct bearing upon the effect produced. Also, the effects on the microfauna and meiofauna may be less drastic than might be anticipated because in many soils structure is not lost and the microcaverns still exist in the soil fragments, which can continue to harbour small animals in a sufficiently humid atmosphere for their survival. Since I am not certain under any circumstances what is the general importance of soil fauna, I would not like to assume that, because the number of animals is reduced, any importance they may have is also reduced, although this would be the implication.

W. B. Mountain:

Is there much evidence for evolution toward root parasitism in the soil microfauna other than the nematodes?

D. K. McE. Kevan:

Other than the nematodes the microfauna are nearly all carnivorous, particle, or microbial feeders. In microarthropods, I would say, from the little we know, that morphological evolution specifically towards root-feeding has not occurred widely. Some microarthropods (e.g. a few mites) doubtless feed on living roots and we have the example of Sturm's observations (cited in the text) on the dependence of certain Protura on ectotrophic mycorrhiza. There are certain specialized Collembola whose mouthparts are modified into piercing instruments which we believe may be used for penetrating roots; thus paralleling the minority of nematodes similarly adapted. It is possible that certain Collembola use these specialized mouthparts principally for piercing fungal hyphae or even other animals. Among the insects there is a range of specific root-feeders of all sizes, for example, certain gall-wasps, aphids, phylloxeras, and root maggots; but they do not differ fundamentally from related forms that feed on the aerial parts of plants or on debris.

M. I. Timonin:

The enormous insect population in the soil deserves the special attention of plant pathologists and soil microbiologists. For example, fossorial insects belonging to the genus *Scaptocoris* secrete a volatile chemical compound toxic to many soil-borne pathogenic fungi. These insects are inhabitants of tropical soil. However, in Canada we also find pentatomids that secrete volatile compounds toxic to *Fusarium, Rhizoctonia,* and *Pythium.*

D. K. Mc.E. Kevan:

I am aware of the work to which Dr. Timonin refers, but I would point out that *Scaptocoris* is a rather peculiar heteropteran bug and the group to which it and the pentatomids belong is poorly represented in soil. Some fossorial Pentatomoidea of the family Cydnidae (of which *Scaptocoris* is a member) may be considered to be soil insects although not so highly specialized in this regard as the genus referred to, but their numbers are few. Most, incidentally, are plant feeders, so that they would not appear to be very satisfactory agents for biological control of plant pathogens. *Scaptocoris* itself is of considerable economic importance in Central America.

Comparatively few groups of insects are known to produce appreciable amounts of volatile chemicals, the Heteroptera and the Pentatomoidea, in particular, being especially noted for this. Some ants, beetles, and cockroaches also produce such substances, although I do not know if they are fungicidal. Millipedes also produce volatile chemicals and it may well be that the other soil arthropods do the same. Further investigation of this whole subject from the point of view of toxicity to fungi might profitably be undertaken.

C. G. Dobbs:

Can you give us any information on the part played by the small soil animals in the mixing and movement of small soil particles and their microbial content in the soil on a micro scale? Which animals are most likely to be active in this respect? Has any work been done on this subject by the soil zoologists?

D. K. McE. Kevan:

Since the question refers particularly to the microscale, I would refer to the publications of Gisin (Prisma, 2: 144-147, 184-187, 1947) and Dunger (1958, cited in the paper), who show that Collembola may ingest minute mineral soil particles. This has also been confirmed at Macdonald College. Few, if any, mites prob-

ably ingest much in the way of mineral particles since their mouthparts are presumably unsuited to this. As Dr. Burges has illustrated in his talk, and as is well known, mites may ingest spores and minute fragments of fungal hyphae. Collembola will do the same. The spores, at least, will probably, in some cases, pass undigested through the gut of the arthropods and remain viable; dispersal would then take place. To my knowledge, no work has been done by zoologists specifically on the transportation of microorganisms by the soil fauna. Such work is urgently required. I would also suggest that minute dipterous larvae—especially Fungivoridae (Mycetophilidae)—should be investigated in this connection.

L. W. Boyle:

Has the role of termites in control of sclerotia of pathogenic fungi been evaluated? Termites have frequently been observed to eat sclerotia of *Sclerotium rolfsii.*

D. K. McE. Kevan:

Not so far as I am aware. Some species of termite are particularly fond of fungi and some, as is well known, may cultivate "fungus gardens," the produce of which forms a significant part of their diet. Such fungi appear to be peculiar to termitaria. Termites which do not cultivate fungi will also feed on "wild" fungi, so that this feeding upon sclerotia would not seem to be remarkable. From the point of view of biological control of *Sclerotium,* I think it would not be a particularly popular idea to encourage termites any more than it would be to encourage slugs—which, according to Dr. K. Kreitlow, may feed voraciously on the sclerotia of *Helminthosporium!*

W. D. Thomas, Jr.:

Could the soil fauna carry microorganisms antagonistic to pathogens, such as mites carrying *Penicillium* and *Sclerotinia* spores into areas which have been infested with *Rhizoctonia* and *Fusarium* through intensive cultivation, and thus aid in dispersal of fungi parasitic on pathogenic fungi?

D. K. McE. Kevan:

Dr. Thomas has brought up a valuable point. I have postulated that microarthropods may conceivably carry plant pathogens from one place to another. We do not know how they do so. It may be equally correct to suggest that fungi, such as *Trichoderma,* attacking pathogenic fungi may be similarly transported and that the fauna might possibly aid in *natural* biological control as suggested. I doubt, however, whether fauna attacking pathogenic fungi could be *utilized* for the purpose of controlling such pathogens.

Growth and Reproduction of Soil Microorganisms in Relation to Substrate

J. H. WARCUP—*Department of Plant Pathology, Waite Agricultural Research Institute, University of Adelaide, South Australia.*

It has been said that biological control of soil-borne diseases is essentially a problem in applied microbial ecology (Garrett, 1958). But while it is well established that soil contains a large population of diverse organisms, detailed knowledge of microbial ecology in soil is generally lacking.

It is considered that many soil microorganisms are cosmopolitan in their distribution and that there is nothing in microbial ecology corresponding to the broad zones into which the vegetation of the world is divided. On the other hand, local diversity is great, since "microbial environments are microenvironments, hundreds or even thousands of which lie concealed from the gross ecological eye in any gram of soil" (Stanier, 1953). Garrett (1955) considered that a new picture of the distribution of many soil microorganisms is slowly emerging and suggested that soil should be considered as a three-dimensional pattern of substrates each of which passes in turn through successive phases of colonization, exploitation, and exhaustion. He also stressed that a succession of microorganisms does not improve but rather depletes the capacity of a habitat to support further plant life, so that the end point of such a succession is not a persisting climax, as with higher plants, but zero. Members of the soil fauna also deplete a habitat though they may not colonize it.

While such generalized concepts have been widely discussed and the importance of specific substrates for microbial growth in soil has been emphasized, direct experimental evidence of microbial growth or succession on a substrate, or of the interrelations of organisms occupying a common habitat in soil, is meagre. Much information has been obtained on occurrence of organisms in "the soil," but such information is too imprecise to further understanding of microbial ecology (Chesters, 1949, 1960; Garrett, 1951).

There are problems concerned with the study of substrates, with determining what organisms are present on a substrate in soil, with the difficulty of differentiating between resting and active phases of organisms, and with measuring, in some sense, their activity. Some of the difficulties are those inherent in investigating soil because of its opacity, its heterogeneous nature, and its complex structure. A major problem has been the differentiation of active and inactive portions of the microbial population. This difficulty is twofold: that of differentiating between active and inactive species in a complex population; and that of differentiating between growing and resting phases of a single organism, for instance, between active and resting phases of a nonsporing bacterium or between active mycelium and a variety of inactive spores of a fungus. Most existing isolation methods are inadequate for distinguishing between active and resting structures of fungi in soil (Warcup, 1960), and the position with other groups is very similar. Further, there is usually great difficulty in interpretation owing to the complexity of natural substrates, particularly in relation to the smallness of the microhabitats that may be inhabited by individual microorganisms.

The aim of this contribution is to consider what is known of growth and reproduction of microorganisms in relation to substrates in soil. Since many members of the soil fauna, particularly the larger ones, do not grow or reproduce on substrates in soil in the same sense as do members of the soil flora, the discussion is, in general, limited to the latter group. Fungi are considered in most detail because in recent years the ecological aspects of soil mycology have attracted much attention.

TYPES AND DISTRIBUTION OF SUBSTRATES IN SOIL.—The soil population, apart from algae and autotrophic bacteria, is supported by the decomposition of many different kinds of organic matter, such material forming substrates for microbial life in soil.

Types of organic matter.—The organic matter in soil comes from several different sources. In a broad sense the organic layers on the surface of mineral soil are here included as part of the soil complex. Some microorganisms may use living tissue, plant or animal, for food, but the majority decompose nonliving organic matter. Nonliving organic matter in soil consists of the remains of dead plants and animals and their excretory products in various stages of decomposition, the final stage being humus. In addition the cells of microbes themselves serve as organic substrates for succeeding generations of microorganisms. In fact any organic compound that is synthesized biologically may be subject to decomposition, either rapidly or slowly, by the soil inhabitants; many compounds synthesized by the organic chemist are also decomposed (Bollen, 1961).

The diversity of materials that enter soil means that the number and variety of organic compounds available for microbial decomposition are enormous. A host of organic acids, polysaccharides, lignins, aromatic and aliphatic hydrocarbons, sugars, alcohols, amino acids, proteins, lipids, and other compounds undergo attack in soil. In the laboratory much work has been carried out on the ability of various organisms to decompose different compounds, interest being concentrated on the decomposition of the more resistant material added to soil.

Since each individual organism has a complex of enzymes which permit it to oxidize only a certain array of compounds, knowledge of these is of value in ecological studies. While there is an increasing store of knowledge on microbial nutrition, with few exceptions this knowledge has yet to be applied to decomposition of complex natural substrates in soil. Care needs to be taken in transposing laboratory results to the field. It cannot be implicitly assumed that an organism able to carry out a decomposition in a test tube will carry out the same reaction in soil. While organisms take the path of least resistance and a fungus which can decompose cellulose will grow on a simple sugar if it is present, this does not necessarily mean that in the highly competitive environment of the soil the organism would be able to establish itself when soluble carbohydrate is available. Nevertheless, pure-culture studies of decomposition by an organism do indicate its potential for growth.

Because a large part of the plant material added to soil is cellulosic, the decomposition of this carbohydrate has attracted considerable attention. Decomposition of cellulose in soil is slow. Relatively few animals appear to have the ability to attack cellulose and most of those that do are dependent on the cellulolytic activity of symbiotic microorganisms. The cellulose-utilizing population includes aerobic and anaerobic bacteria, fungi, actinomycetes, and certain protozoa. In contrast to bacteria, relatively few of which attack cellulose, many fungi can decompose cellulose. The heterogeneity of the cellulose-decomposing microflora permits attack over a wide range of environmental conditions, with or without oxygen, in acid or alkaline soils, at various moisture levels, and at temperatures ranging from near freezing point to the top of the thermophilic range.

Many microorganisms—fungi, actinomycetes, aerobic and anaerobic bacteria—are able to use hemicelluloses for growth. More microbial species are capable of using hemicelluloses than cellulose, and in general the rate of decomposition of these substances is also faster.

Another abundant constituent of plant tissues is lignin. This is rather slowly decomposed in soil and less is known about its microbiology and decomposition than is known about cellulose. There are difficulties in assaying for lignin and in isolating a suitable purified lignin for use as a microbiological substrate. Lignin probably never occurs free; it is especially plentiful in woody plants and is often mixed with cellulose to a greater or lesser degree. As the lignin content of plants increases, the ability of microorganisms in the soil to decompose them decreases. The main lignin destroyers are Basidiomycetes (Waksman, 1938), but several species of *Pseudomonas* present in soil have now been shown to destroy lignin (Sørensen, 1962).

Chitin is the most common polysaccharide whose basic unit is an amino sugar. It occurs in the cell walls of many fungi; also a substantial quantity becomes incorporated into soil in the form of insect remains. Chitin-utilizing microorganisms in soil include actinomycetes, bacteria, and some fungi. The storage polysaccharides such as starch are readily broken down by many animals and microorganisms, as also are pectins and proteins. Aromatic compounds in soil seem to be decomposed mainly by bacteria, though fungi may be important in the breakdown of certain aromatic humus constituents.

While simple organic compounds occur, particularly during decomposition of residues or in association with the growth of plants, most natural substrates for microbial growth in soil are complex, rarely being composed of a single substance.

Distribution of organic matter in soil.—Besides the chemical composition of organic matter, its distribution in soil, i.e. the way in which the organic and inorganic constituents of soil are mixed or combined with one another, is of particular importance in gaining an understanding of microbial ecology. Such information is necessary to obtain a picture of the size and extent of soil microhabitats. With soil animals these may vary with the organism being considered. It is probable that the same applies to members of the soil microflora: size of microhabitat and effect of soil texture may be very different for a bacterium than for a filamentous fungus. Certainly the effect of soil texture on the biology of members of the microflora has been rather neglected, though this factor is well appreciated by soil zoologists (Murphy, 1955).

The distribution of organic matter in soil may be considered on a broad scale in relation to types of vegetation and climatic and soil zones, or on a microscale in relation to the distribution of organic materials within a profile.

The quantity of organic material varies from soil to soil. Some sandy soils may contain less than 1% whereas peats may contain as much as 60-95% organic matter. Field observations suggest that there are at least two well-marked forms of soil organic matter, the *mull* and *mor* of Müller.

In a mull soil such as a forest brown earth, apart from loose plant debris lying on the surface, the decomposed plant material is well incorporated in the surface layers of soil and there is no sharply differentiated organic zone. Often this type of soil contains numerous earthworms and is rich in animal life. A typical mor on a podzol contrasts strongly with the above. The fallen plant debris forms a thick layer with a clear disjunction from the mineral soil, which is usually sandy. Animal life is not abundant and earthworms are characteristically absent from mor soils. The organic matter on the surface can usually be separated into layers which are often designated, from the surface downwards, as the litter (L), the fermentation (F), and the humification (H) layers (Hesselman, 1926). Many of the factors which influence the development of mull and mor have been considered by Handley (1954).

Mull and mor are usually considered as extremes of a series of humus forms. By microscopic examination of thin sections of humus formations, Kubiëna has correlated the progress of humification, the transformation of different substances of plant and animal origin into humic materials, with activity of soil invertebrates and presence of their excreta in the soil. In this way he has defined some 30 humus forms (Kubiëna, 1953).

Grassland soils (prairie, chernozem, and chestnut soils) resemble brown forest soils in that the organic matter is well distributed throughout the profile. Grasses differ from forest trees in that they translocate much of the organic matter they synthesize into the soil as roots. Grass roots are extensive and fine and their decomposition in situ gives organic matter at considerable depth.

On a microscale, the nonliving part of soil is composed of four major components—mineral particles, organic matter, water, and air. These provide the environment in which soil microorganisms are found; the organic matter also serves as the major energy source for the population. Solid materials occupy only about half the volume of a soil, the remainder being composed of pores filled with air and water, both essential for much microbial life. The size of individual pores and the total pore space depend on the texture of the soil, its structure, and the presence or absence of burrowing animals. In clay soils the pores are generally small; in sandy soils the pores are larger, but total pore space is less than in soils containing many fine particles. Most soils also have at least some of their individual particles clustered into aggregates and the channels between these contribute to total soil porosity.

Thus soil is a series of larger channels and fine pores filled with air and water and bounded by solid surfaces, and its fundamental properties depend on the geometry of this interconnecting network, on the behaviour of water in the spaces, on the properties of the bounding surfaces, and on the mechanisms which supply nutrients to surfaces and to water (Russell, 1961). These channels and pores in soil provide much of the living space of microorganisms, and the distribution of organic matter in relation to the pores influences growth, sporulation, and dissemination.

It can be seen that the number of possible substrates and microhabitats present in different soils, under different vegetations, in different climatic zones, is legion. While there is much incidental information on microbial growth in soil, few substrates have been studied in any detail.

METHODS OF STUDY.—While techniques for investigation of several different groups of organisms in soil have recently been reviewed (Warcup, 1960; Durbin, 1961; Murphy, 1962), the methods available for study of the occurrence and growth of microorganisms on natural substrates in soil are here examined in some detail, for it cannot be overemphasized that the experimental data obtained and the interpretations made depend in the main on the techniques used to derive them. As cautioned by Durbin (1961), it is of great importance that an investigator be aware of the limitations of the methods available. Many of the methods for studying microorganisms on substrates in soil have been adapted from those used to study organisms in soil itself and are subject to the same limitations.

In general there have been two different approaches to the study of microorganisms in soil. The first is by microscopic examination of soil or substrates or such materials as glass or nylon, after they have been placed in soil; the second is by isolation of organisms, either directly or by cultural techniques. For ecological studies both approaches have major disadvantages. Direct observation gives information on the location and form of microbes in soil but the majority cannot be identified because cell or mycelium morphology is insufficient for identification and sporing structures are rarely encountered. On the other hand cultural methods, particularly dilution-plating methods, are selective and allow only a portion of the flora present to develop, are indirect, and usually fail to discriminate between currently active organisms and inactive ones. The contrast between the two approaches has been epitomized by Garrett (1952): "With the plate count one identifies what one cannot see (i.e. in situ), whereas with the direct method one sees what one cannot identify." Recognition of these difficulties has led to much work on isolation techniques in relation to study of active organisms in soil. The most promising approaches are those which combine direct observation with isolation techniques.

In ecological studies with soil microorganisms, another problem, and a rather neglected one, is that of sampling the soil in such a way that the natural substrate pattern is not immediately lost. Thus the procedure, often adopted, of taking samples at random, bulking them, and thoroughly mixing to obtain a "representative" sample completely destroys the substrate pattern of the soil. Such a sampling procedure may be used in compiling species lists, may indicate the frequencies of species in different soils, horizons, or under different soil treatments, and may be necessary where the soil is to be used for laboratory experiments, but gives little information on such questions as distribution, growth, sporulation, and methods of dispersal. Even with single samples, substrate patterns are easily lost unless soil blocks are carefully collected or soil is examined, as by Kubiëna, in situ. Examinations of soil blocks and of soil in situ are both rather neglected techniques which seem capable of yielding much useful information on the biology of soil organisms.

Direct observation methods.—The most direct approach to the study of microorganisms occurring on substrates in soil is that of Kubiëna (1938) who, using a microscope equipped with a normal incidence illuminator, examined organisms in situ. His observations were necessarily confined to naturally or artificially exposed soil surfaces and were most successful with the larger members of the soil population. He was also able to show that fungi growing in or fruiting on organic matter in soil can be isolated from their actual habitats and that some can be identified in situ on their substrates. He noted, however, that certain fungi had reduced types of fructifications in soil, for instance *Gliocladium* had *Hyalopus*-like fructifications, suggesting that caution ought to be exercised in identifying organisms solely by their fruiting bodies in soil.

Soil surfaces need not always be examined in the field; examination may be done on freshly exposed surfaces in the laboratory (Warcup, 1957). With soils which fracture readily, clods or soil blocks broken apart in the hands will provide successive freshly exposed surfaces for examination.

Soil Sections.—Kubiëna (1938) used a thermolabile plastic material to prepare sections of soil, but his method has not been followed extensively. Haarløv and Weis-Fogh (1955) impregnated soil with agar for sectioning. An undisturbed sample of soil was soaked in a hot, 2% aqueous solution of agar, cooled, hardened in alcohol, and sectioned as thinly as the largest mineral particles would allow (100-750 μ). Alexander and Jackson (1955) adapted standard mineralogical techniques to prepare sections of soil. The method involved impregnation with a synthetic resin and final preparation of sections by cutting, grinding, and polishing. Hepple and Burges (1956) and Burges and Nicholas (1961) have used a similar method but with different resins. Sections 50-100 μ in thickness may be obtained. Minderman (1956) treated soil with hydrofluoric acid to dissolve the sand grains before preparing sections. Sections as thin as 7.5–10 μ were obtained.

These methods are of use in studying microorganisms in their natural relations to soil structure and substrate, although the methods which involve desiccation before embedding have been criticized (Haarløv and Weis-Fogh, 1955) because desiccation changes the texture of the organic layers. Because of the small quantity of soil which may be examined and the labour involved in preparing sections, they are perhaps best applied to selected sites rather than to soil collected at random.

Soil Staining.—Conn (1918) seems to have been the first to stain soil suspensions. He prepared an infusion of soil (1:9) in dilute gelatin, spread 0.1 ml of this across a slide and stained the preparation with rose bengal.

A more recent staining procedure is that of Jones and Mollison (1948). They incorporated a soil suspension in melted and cooled 1.5% agar. A drop of the agar suspension is placed on a haemocytometer slide with a depth of 0.1 mm and a coverslip added. The film obtained is floated off on sterile water to a microscope slide, allowed to dry, then stained with phenolic aniline blue and made into a permanent mount.

Bunt and Tchan (1955) described a differential staining technique where, by use of erythrosin and methyl green, colloidal particles in the soil appear green while protozoa are stained pink with purple nuclei.

Staining methods allow organisms, particularly bacteria, to be seen and counted, but their relation to soil structure is, in general, lost.

Slide or Burial Techniques.—A different approach but still predominantly an observational one, is that of the burial methods such as Rossi-Cholodny slides. Rossi (1928) pressed a clean microscope slide against a freshly exposed soil surface so that soil particles and microbial colonies adhered to the slide. After removal and staining, the soil-impression slides depicted microorganisms as they actually occurred in the soil at that time. He also buried slides in soil for different periods. This latter method was perfected by Cholodny (1930), who first brought it to the attention of most workers, and it has become known as the Rossi-Cholodny or contact slide method. It has become the most widely used in-situ method. The technique is applicable to both qualitative and quantitative investigations (Blair, 1945). It has also been used to study microorganisms on substrates; for instance, Starkey (1938) studied the occurrence of microorganisms in relation to plant roots by letting roots grow against buried slides.

It should be noted that there is an essential difference between soil-impression slides and Rossi-Cholodny slides. The former indicate occurrence at the time of examining a soil surface, the latter provide a surface for microbial growth after the soil has been disturbed. There is strong circumstantial evidence that fungal growth on buried slides may be influenced by the disturbance of the soil in burying the slides (Sewell, 1959b).

The impression slides of Brown (1958a) follow Rossi in that slides are pressed against a soil surface and not incubated in soil. Brown, however, smeared slides with nitrocellulose thinned to a suitable consistency with amyl acetate to aid retention of soil on the slide.

Instead of glass slides, Waid and Woodman (1957) buried nylon mesh in soil. After periods of burial up to several months the gauze was removed and examined.

Observation Boxes.—Another type of observation method is provided by the observation box (Dean, 1929; Linford, 1942; Parkinson, 1957; Sewell, 1959c). Pieces of glass, slides, or coverslips are incorporated into the side of a box containing soil in which plants may be growing, permitting microscopic examination at a high magnification under reflected light.

Isolation methods.—Most workers have used isolation methods to study microorganisms in soil because these, in general, allow subsequent identification of the organisms. While some organisms may be easily cultured from soil, there are very real difficulties connected with the isolation of others. The diversity of microorganisms, their widely differing number of propagules present in soil, their differing ability to grow on agar media, combine to make isolation of some a difficult procedure. If one is interested in specific organisms all others can be treated as "contaminants" and selective media or methods used as aids to isolation. In more general studies of wide groups of organisms this approach, however, is rarely successful.

It must be emphasized how dependent is the apparent composition of the fungal flora of a soil on the isolation methods used. This may be illustrated by comparison

TABLE 1. Fungi obtained from Urrbrae loam (wheat-field soil) by different isolation methods

| | | | Method of isolation | | | | |
| | | | Isolations from | | | | |
	Dilution plates*	Soil plates*	Hyphae*	Rhizo-morphs†	Sclerotia‡	Fruc-tifications‡	Total number of species
Phycomycetes	18	17	11	0	0	11	26
Ascomycetes (b) Discomycetes	0	0	0	0	3	4	5
(b) all others	8	10	3	0	1	5	18
Basidiomycetes	0	0	8	8	7	12	30
Fungi Imperfecti	81	60	16	0	2	24	95
Sterile mycelia	29	23	59	1	2	0	85
Total number of species	136	110	97	9	15	56	—

* Warcup, 1957.
† Warcup, 1959.
‡ Unpublished data 1961-1962.

of data from three experiments during which fungi were isolated from wheat-field soil at Adelaide (Table 1 and Fig. 1). While not strictly comparable in that, although on the same soil, the experiments were carried out in different years, the data do show the marked influence of method on the fungal flora obtained and how, in particular, soil-dilution plates and Warcup soil plates neglect many mycelial fungi, including Discomycetes and Basidiomycetes.

Isolation from Soil.—Various physical, chemical, and biological methods have been used to obtain separation of different microorganisms from soil (Durbin, 1961). The classical and most widely used isolation method is the soil-dilution-plate method (Waksman, 1927; Johnson et al., 1959). The merits and limitations of this method have been widely discussed, particularly in relation to fungi. Because of their complex mycelial thallus and variety of reproductive structures, fungi pose a more difficult problem in interpretation than do single-celled organisms. It is generally accepted that most of the colonies obtained on soil-dilution plates are derived from spores (Warcup, 1960). This means that the method is of little use in detecting fungal activity except in an indirect way.

While many isolation procedures, including soil dilution, are indirect (i.e. the nature of the propagules being isolated is not known), more direct methods have been devised. Casida (1962) has described a method for the direct isolation and growth of individual vitally stained microorganisms that have been observed in soil preparations. The soil is stained with acridine orange and mounted on agar so that individual cells, including bacteria, can be picked up with a micromanipulation tool while the organism is being viewed with an ultra-violet fluorescence microscope.

Fungal hyphae, rhizomorphs, and sclerotia may be isolated directly from soil (Warcup, 1960); even with dilution plates the origin of colonies developing on the plates may be determined (Warcup, 1955). Many direct methods for isolation of nematodes and other members of the soil fauna are known (Murphy, 1962).

Isolation from Organic Materials.—Examination of microorganisms occurring on substrates in soil, except in surface litter, often necessitates separation of organic debris from the mineral fraction. Several types of method have been used for separating debris from soil. Most employ washing, usually with sieves of varying sizes to retain the debris, but sedimentation and centrifuging are also used. Simmonds (1930) described a continuous-flow washing apparatus for plant material from soil. Chesters (1948) used a method by which organic debris could be isolated by counter-current washing with sterile water, and Parkinson and Williams (1961) devised a series of washing boxes for the same purpose. Washing not only isolates organic substrates from soil but also removes the majority of the surface contaminants from the material. Harley and Waid (1955) introduced the refinement of plating out samples of the wash water obtained during serial washing to check the efficiency of the washing process. They found that most detachable units were removed in the first washes and that after about ten washes a low, fairly constant number was obtained.

The techniques applicable to surface litter more closely resemble those in use for isolating pathogenic

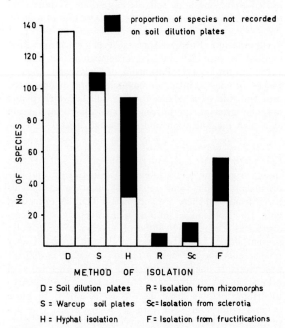

Fig. 1. Comparison of isolation methods, showing the number of fungi obtained and the proportion of species different from those isolated on soil-dilution plates.

organisms from plants, because the organic material can be collected directly in recognizable fractions and can be surface-sterilized if necessary for isolation of organisms within the material. Plant roots may be handled in a similar way.

It is perhaps surprising that washing has been so frequently used to isolate roots or organic materials from soil and so few attempts have been made to isolate such substrates directly from soil without the use of water. There are several conditions in which direct isolation, though perhaps slower, is preferable to washing. After the initial microbial attack, decomposing leaves become very fragile and if washed free from soil usually disintegrate into small fragments together with free vascular tissues so that the path of decomposition is difficult to follow. Such partially decomposed leaves may often be removed whole from soil if picked up directly with fine forceps. Similar stages occur in the decomposition of other plant material in soil.

In a study in Adelaide of the occurrence of microorganisms on the dead bodies and cast exuviae of soil Collembola, it has been found that washing these substrates from soil results in contamination from bacteria and fungal spores so that it is difficult to isolate the organisms initially present. Collembola picked direct from soil have a simpler, more constant flora, and direct observation shows the presence of much of this as mycelium and fructifications.

Gregory and Lacey (1962) noted that dry air removes spores of Streptomycetaceae in preference to bacteria and have used an Andersen sampler (Andersen, 1958) to obtain actinomycetes from mouldy hay; such a method may hold promise in soil studies.

Isolated debris may be examined microscopically, placed in a moist chamber for growth and sporulation of the organisms present, or plated on an agar medium. For ease of study large pieces are often cut into smaller ones, roots often being cut into segments 1-2 mm long. A difficulty in isolation from roots or other larger fragments is that on plating out such materials usually only the faster-growing species survive, overgrowing any other organisms present. Stover (1953) macerated banana roots in a Waring blender, and reported a greater range of fungi by this technique than from plating root segments. For examination of small individual roots, I (Warcup, 1959) used a root-fragmentation method and isolated many slower-growing nonsporing fungi; fragmentation of some roots, however, may reduce the number of organisms obtained owing to release of toxic materials (Clarke and Parkinson, 1960). Dropkin, Smith, and Myers (1960) have successfully macerated tomato roots with enzyme preparations for recovery of viable nematodes. Such a technique may be of interest for isolation of microorganisms, though the period of maceration (4-6 hr) may be rather long. With some fungi, including plant pathogens, it may be more advantageous to keep roots or debris in a moist chamber to obtain growth or sporulation than to plate out on agar (Taubenhaus and Ezekiel, 1930; Butler, 1953).

Addition of Substrates to Soil.—Besides isolation from natural materials from soil, several general tech-

niques have been devised in which a substrate for microbial growth is placed in soil. Such methods have been used to follow colonization of a sterile or nonsterile substrate, or to follow competition between a pure culture and the soil microflora. Sadasivan (1939) followed the colonization of pieces of wheat straw by *Fusarium culmorum,* and the Madras school has exploited this technique in studying soil-borne pathogenic fungi. Garrett and his colleagues have used inoculated straw buried in soil to follow persistence of soil-borne pathogens (Garrett, 1956a). Instead of adding materials to soil, colonization of root tissues may be followed by excising shoots and leaving roots to become moribund and to decay naturally (Chesters, 1960).

An interesting approach is that of Tribe (1957, 1961), who buried pieces of cellophane attached to coverslips in soil. After different periods of time and at different stages of decomposition of the cellophane, the coverslips are removed and examined microscopically. Griffin (1960) placed hair in soil and studied its colonization by a succession of microorganisms by direct examination and by plating methods. Many natural substrates have been added to soil as baits (Durbin, 1961) but usually to obtain selective isolation of a particular organism rather than to study general microbial colonization.

EXAMINATION OF SOME SUBSTRATES IN SOIL.—Few of the many different substrates in soil have been investigated in any detail; fewer still have been examined in situ, i.e. in relation to soil structure and environment, information on which is necessary to obtain a detailed ecological picture of microbial growth in soil. This section, while far from exhaustive, outlines some investigations on microbial substrates and illustrates problems associated with their study.

Litter.—While the organic matter of natural soils usually reaches its maximum value on and in the surface layers, this region is often neglected in soil microbiological studies. Much work, however, has been carried out on forest litter, particularly in relation to the formation of mull and mor.

Saitô (1956, 1957, 1958, 1960), both by direct observation and by plating methods, studied microbiological decomposition in the L and F layers of beech litter. The L layer consisted of freshly fallen leaves and brown leaves only slightly subject to microbial attack, since surface leaves were liable to dry out rapidly and thoroughly. In the F layer, where moisture was more constant, many leaves turned yellow after attack by Basidiomycetes and bacteria. Infected leaves became thinner without losing their structure, then mouldy from overgrowth of basidiomycete mycelia. Later, growth of other organisms was seen and leaves gradually became transformed into amorphous debris. Not all leaves in the same layer became infected by Basidiomycetes and decomposition did not always take place uniformly throughout a leaf. Four Basidiomycetes, including two species of *Collybia* and a *Mycena,* fruited on the site. Plating techniques failed to record Basidiomycetes but showed that species of *Penicillium, Absidia, Trichoderma,* and *Mucor ramannianus* were widespread throughout the litter horizons.

Saitô found that in yellow, basidiomycete-infected leaves there was a marked loss of lignin followed by a rise in the quantity of water-soluble substances; attack on cellulose was slower than on lignin. He considered that the filamentous moulds were active on the water-soluble materials initially present in the leaves and on these materials liberated later during lignin breakdown. Although bacterial numbers were high when basidiomycete mycelia were young and vigorous, they rose further when mycelia underwent lysis.

Witkamp and van der Drift (1961) have given an interesting general picture of litter decomposition under slash oaks mixed with birch, alder, and poplar near Arnhem, Netherlands. The maximum litter fall occurred in October-November when temperatures were still about 10°C. At this time there was an active population in the soil. Rossi-Cholodny slides showed rapid accumulation of mycelium, bacterial numbers were high, and Basidiomycetes fruited in maximum number. After November loss of weight of wooden sticks in soil, and carbon dioxide production of soil, declined rapidly under the influence of decreasing temperatures. In December-January, mycelium and the concentration of fungal propagules recorded by plating increased to reach a maximum. From then on, all microbial activity was low, presumably because of low temperatures. Nevertheless, during the first 4 months of the year the amount of litter at a mull site decreased at a relatively rapid rate. This reduction was probably caused by attack by great numbers of enchytraeids which moved on the wet leaves, by earthworms, by several species of slugs and snails, and by larvae of the caddis fly, *Enoicyla pusilla* Burm., which were numerous and took an active part in disintegration of litter.

With rising temperatures in May bacterial and fungal numbers and mycelial growth increased but animal numbers decreased. The decomposition of cellulose and wood also increased. Often in late May a dry period occurred and the microflora and fauna minimized their activity in and also directly under the litter. In the mineral soil, which was still moist, the decomposition of wood and production of carbon dioxide by microorganisms and plant roots increased. With the start of summer rains in late July or August all groups increased their activity again.

Plant residues.—It is well known that addition of plant residues to soil greatly stimulates the microbial population and may have important consequences on soil structure, immobilization of nitrogen, occurrence of soil-borne pathogens, and the growth of crops. A voluminous literature has arisen on all aspects of the decomposition of crop residues; only a few are mentioned here. The effects, both chemical and biological, of stubble mulching in contrast to ploughing has attracted much attention (McCalla, 1953; Patterson, 1960; Norstadt and McCalla, 1960). Decomposition of residues at the surface usually proceeds more slowly than with those buried in soil (Parker, 1962); Newman and

Norman (1943) earlier showed that materials introduced into subsurface soil decompose much less rapidly than those in surface soil. The ability of root-infecting fungi to survive in or to colonize residues has been investigated by many workers (Garrett, 1956a), but usually without detailed study of other organisms present or of the course of decomposition.

Our knowledge of the microorganisms responsible for the decomposition of plant residues is not as extensive as might be expected. Those studies made by the soil-dilution-plate technique have undoubtedly failed to record many nonsporing mycelia present in residues, as work on root parasites in debris has long indicated.

Some results obtained in Adelaide on early stages of decomposition of wheat straw (chaff) illustrate the effect of the isolation method on the records obtained of organisms. Dilution plates of soil with straw recorded high counts of *Mucor, Penicillium,* and bacteria, as compared with nonamended soil. Isolation from straw itself after washing and fragmentation yielded *Fusarium, Mortierella, Pythium, Rhizoctonia solani, Waitea circinata,* and several sterile mycelia, including T322, an unidentified discomycete. Hyphal isolation showed that there was a zone of profuse mycelial activity around the layer of residues. Some species found as mycelium in soil were not isolated from straw. Direct microscopic examination of soil blocks containing the straw layer showed fructifications of *Rhizopus, Actinomucor, Coemansia, Mortierella,* and sclerotia of *Waitea* and T322. Fructifications were not confined to residues but occurred in worm tunnels and other cavities up to 5-8 mm away; some fructifications, notably of *Coemansia,* did not arise from straw but always occurred in the larger air spaces nearby. Although *Mucor* was very abundant on dilution plates as compared with *Rhizopus, Actinomucor,* and *Mortierella,* its fructifications were not easily seen because the sporangiophores were fragile and most had collapsed. Collembola, mites, enchytraeids, earthworms, and some insect larvae also occurred in the decomposition layer.

Soil animals.—Apart from the group of predacious fungi which attack nematodes or protozoa, comparatively little attention has been paid to animal tissues, residues, or faeces as substrates for microbial growth in soil. This is perhaps surprising, particularly with groups such as mites and Collembola, which may occur in soil in high number; similarly, cast insect exuviae often occur in sufficient number to provide adequate material for study of organisms able to use this source of chitin in soil. There have been incidental observations, particularly of species of *Aspergillus* and *Penicillium* fruiting on dead soil animals (Warcup, 1957; Sewell, 1959b), but little systematic study of the decomposition of members of the soil fauna has been made.

Insect parasites such as *Entomophthora* (Miller, Giddens, and Foster, 1957; Griffin, 1960) and *Beauveria bassiana* have been isolated from soil itself; the latter was of frequent occurrence in certain profiles (Sewell, 1959a; Brown, 1958b; Christensen, Whittingham, and Novak, 1962). Little is known, however, of the biology of these fungi in soil. The observation that these fungi may parasitize certain soil arthropods and insects and sporulate abundantly thereon suggests that in soil as aboveground, these organisms may be primarily parasites (Warcup, unpublished data).

The predacious fungi form a well-marked ecological group, united by their habit of capturing and consuming minute animals, although taxonomically they are much more diverse (Duddington, 1957). Knowledge of these fungi has been particularly due to the studies of Drechsler (1941), who isolated many predacious fungi from leaf mould. They are also widely distributed in soil, but since most observations on predacious fungi have been made from agar culture, there is little direct evidence of their activity in this habitat. Capstick, Twinn, and Waid (1957) showed, however, that a small proportion of free-living nematodes isolated directly from forest litter were infected with various predacious fungi. Cooke (1961) has studied the behaviour of nematode-destroying fungi during the decomposition of organic matter in soil. Fungi also attack nematode eggs, and van de Laan (1956) has investigated the fungi which attack eggs in the cysts of *Heterodera rostochiensis* and kill the larvae within.

Griffin (1960) studied the colonization of hair by fungi in soil in the laboratory. Although hair had been used as a bait for keratinolytic fungi, no previous study of its general colonization in soil had been made. Besides keratin, hair contains traces of many other substances (Bollinger and Gross, 1952). Griffin found that many fungi sporulated on the surface of hair so that direct observation could be used as a check on isolation data. Initial colonizers were often fusaria, certain penicillia, and various members of the Mucorales; these were overlapped or followed by a second group, including *Chaetomium cochliodes, Gliocladium roseum, Humicola* species, and certain other penicillia; the final group comprised keratinolytic fungi such as *Keratinomyces ajelloi* and *Microsporum gypseum*. Many fungi sporulated profusely as they passed their peak of activity and then survived as dormant spores, the hyphae remaining, at least initially, as empty tubes. In others, however, much of the protoplasm of the colony was probably destroyed by direct parasitism of a succeeding fungus. While the great majority of keratinophilic fungi have been obtained from agricultural and garden soils, Pugh and Mathison (1962) found *Arthroderma curreyi* and *Ctenomyces serratus* to be common in salt-marsh and sand-dune sites. Mathison has suggested that keratinolytic fungi compete successfully with other fungi on a wide range of protein substrates, particularly fibrous proteins.

The excrement of soil invertebrates and insects provides an important substrate for further decomposition, but has been little studied. Mite and enchytraeid droppings, which constitute a large fraction of some natural humus forms (Kubiëna, 1955), appear to be very slowly decomposed.

Microbial structures.—Microbial structures themselves may provide substrates for other microorganisms. Bacteria are attacked by many predators, including myxobacteria, Protozoa, and Myxomycetes. Many bacteria feed on fungal hyphae, as has often been noted on Rossi-Cholodny slides. Actinomycetes may cause lysis of fungal hyphae and bacterial cells; on the other hand, some bacteria and fungi lyse actinomycetes (Thornton and Skinner, 1960). Fungi may parasitize other fungi; the behaviour of *Trichoderma viride,* in particular, has attracted much attention.

Cellophane.—Although cellophane is not a natural material, the studies of Tribe (1957, 1960a,b, 1961) on its decomposition in soil are of considerable interest. Cellophane is a pure regenerated cellulose. Its advantages as a substrate are its simplicity and its transparency, which render it excellent for microscopic examination. Tribe has used cellophane with advantage to make a biological analysis of a decomposition, to show the presence, growth, coexistence, and succession of diverse microorganisms on a substrate; also to follow their influence on the substrate and on soil properties.

Tribe has shown that relatively few fungi in a soil are capable of attacking cellulose film, also that many of these are species which are not recorded in soil-dilution-plate studies. The fungi attacking cellophane differed markedly from soil to soil. In England some alkaline soils gave *Botryotrichum piluliferum (Chaetomium piluliferum;* see Daniels, 1961), *Chaetomium, Humicola grisea,* chytrids, and occasionally *Stachybotrys. Stysanus* was common in a chalk soil and *Oidiodendron* in an acid soil. A brown forest soil in Canada yielded *Rhizoctonia, Humicola, Botryotrichum,* and chytrids. Some fungi grew on the surface of the film, others were notable for "rooting branches" in the thickness of the cellophane.

Tribe found that the primary colonizers of buried film were fungi. Chytrids were frequent early colonists but filamentous fungi appeared at the same time. After 2 to 4 weeks bacteria developed profusely around the mycelium and over the cellophane; bacteria were usually not prominent before fungal growth had occurred. Keynan, Henis, and Keller (1961) have pointed out, however, that *Cellvibrio* does not grow readily on cellophane, thus this substrate does not equally support all cellulose-decomposing microorganisms but favours fungi. Tribe reported that the bacteria invariably supported a population of nematodes and sometimes patches of amoebae. Nematodes were often parasitized by predacious fungi, which were the only fungi developing over the bacterial debris.

Frequently the microbial tissue and cellulose were consumed by soil animals. In acid sand, mites were the predominant organisms, but in neutral to alkaline soils Collembola and enchytraeid worms were found. Enchytraeid worms were often seen in the soil from the time of burial of the cellulose film, but did not attack it until it was partly replaced by microbial tissue. Went (1959) also found that after cellophane has been attacked by fungi, mites and springtails will start to eat it. Mites and Collembola produced well-defined faecal pellets which contained microbial cells; enchytraeid worms mixed the residues with a large proportion of soil and their excreta were difficult to recognize. Different pieces of film varied greatly in the time taken to decompose, even in one soil, and the rate of decomposition was greatly influenced by the organisms present. Bacteria alone had little effect, chytrids caused little damage unless present in high number, rooting fungi were more active, but a *Rhizoctonia* was able to reduce film to a mushy condition in 2 to 3 weeks. Further decomposition was dependent on the activity of soil animals.

Two major points emerge from consideration of these studies on decomposition of substrates in soil, whether they be laboratory studies such as those of Tribe or in-situ investigations. First, our ideas on the organisms active in a decomposition are often merely a reflection of the method used; and second, decomposition is typically a complex process involving many different microorganisms belonging to *both the microflora and microfauna.*

MICROBIAL GROWTH IN RELATION TO SUBSTRATE.—Organic materials available as food for microorganisms in soil vary from traces of substances in the soil solution or soil atmosphere to substrates as different as a bacterial cell and a large decomposing root system. Thus not only the chemical composition, but also the quantity of nutrient in different substrates may vary enormously. The difference in size and complexity of vegetative thalli suggests that the response of different microorganisms to a source of nutrient also varies widely. A quantity of food sufficient for growth and multiplication of a bacterium may be insufficient for germination of a fungal spore and quite inadequate to sustain extensive mycelial development. Some substances may also provide a substrate for respiration but not for growth (Foster, 1962).

The general nutritional level of soil, particularly in terms of readily decomposable materials, is usually considered to be very low except during those relatively isolated and sporadic periods when fresh plant materials or animal residues become available (Foster, 1949). This fact gives force to Winogradsky's (1949) classification of soil organisms into two groups, the autochthonous flora normally present in the vegetative phase and carrying on their biochemical processes more or less continuously, and a zymogenous flora normally in the resting phase but springing into activity when a suitable fermentable substrate is available and then subsiding. While examples of the zymogenous group, such as species of *Bacillus,* the cellulose-decomposing bacteria, and the "sugar fungi" (Burges, 1939), are well known, characterization of the autochthonous flora presents many problems. Substrates for the autochthonous flora are generally considered to be true humus materials and fatty residues from cuticular waxes, cutins, and similar substances (Burges, 1958). There is no reliable knowledge of the organisms which use humus. Bacteria and actinomycetes are involved in the decomposition of waxes and cutins. Actinomycetes in particular are considered to grow on highly resistant materials during the latter stages of decomposition and during humus disintegration (Waksman, 1960). Whether any fungi belong to the autochthonous group is not known; cer-

tainly some fungi seem to be normally present as hyphae in soil (Warcup, 1957; Burges, 1958), but nothing is known about their nutrition.

Bacteria are rarely free in the liquid phase in soil; most cells adhere to clay particles and humic matter. A large part of the population is probably segregated into definite colonies in favourable sites; however, single cells may occur in soil (Jones and Mollison, 1948). From perfusion studies, it has been found that nitrifying bacteria grow on the surface of soil crumbs at the sites where ammonium ions are held in base exchange (Quastel, 1955), but because of technical difficulties little is known of the occurrence of specific bacteria in relation to substrates in soil.

Irrespective of whether there is a clear distinction between autochthonous and zymogenous floras, a large number of organisms—bacteria, actinomycetes, and fungi—show a zymogenous pattern of growth in soil. The best-studied group is the fungi. Much work has indicated that soil contains a large number of inactive propagules of fungi; these include "resting hyphae," sclerotia, oospores, ascospores, chlamydospores, sporangiospores, and conidia, the last three groups being the most abundant and constituting the "soil spora" of Dobbs and Hinson (1953). The number of propagules varies markedly with the soil, its past history, and with the kinds of organisms present. In Urrbrae loam in Adelaide, the basidiomycete *Waitea circinata* may be present as 1-10 sclerotia per 500 g of soil, but at the other end of the scale certain *Penicillium* species are present relatively uniformly as $1\text{-}4 \times 10^4$ spores per g. It is now considered that the soil spora provides the bulk of the propagules in soil suspensions and hence on soil-dilution plates and that they are common on the surfaces of roots and other particles in soil (Warcup, 1960).

Since the conidia of many fungi occurring in soil are known to germinate even in distilled water, the presence of large numbers of ungerminated spores in soil may appear anomalous. Dobbs and Hinson (1953), however, reported a widespread inhibition of fungal spores in the organic layers of most soils. Failure of spores to germinate when in contact with soil has been observed in many types of soil in many parts of the world (Chinn, 1953; Hessayon, 1953; Park, 1955; Jackson, 1958a,b; Dobbs, Hinson and Bywater, 1960). The nature of the inhibitor is not known and it seems probable that several different kinds of inhibition and inhibitors may occur (Jeffreys and Hemming, 1953; Stevenson, 1956; Lingappa and Lockwood, 1961, 1962; Park, 1961).

While some sclerotia may be nutritionally independent, there is increasing evidence that spores and resting structures of fungi in soil germinate only when provided with an external source of nutrient. In some cases the response appears to be to specific substances, in other cases the response is more general. Known sources of nutrients are roots, germinating seeds, and decomposing plant and animal residues. Germination is also dependent on suitable pH, carbon dioxide concentration, temperature, oxygen and water supply, and the absence of inhibitors (Cochrane, 1958).

After germination, fungal growth is dependent upon a suitable substrate or a continuing supply of nutrients, particularly nitrogen; otherwise lysis of germ tubes takes place or the fungus forms a resting structure such as a chlamydospore and ceases further growth. Continuing growth is also dependent upon a suitable physical environment.

Lysis of young mycelia has been recorded by direct observation (Chinn, 1953; Novogrudsky, 1948; Park, 1955; Stevenson, 1956; Tribe, 1957). Such lysis may be a result of purely internal metabolic changes (autolysis), of contact with enzymes of other organisms, or of exposure to toxic materials. Autolysis is usually a consequence of nutrient deficiency, often nitrogen deficiency, but may occur if utilization of energy sources is prevented by oxygen lack, or as a result of accumulation of by-products that are toxic (Brian, 1960). There is ample evidence that lysis of fungi may be caused by other organisms.

The studies of Snyder and co-workers on *Fusarium solani* f. *phaseoli,* the bean root-rot pathogen, are of interest in connexion with questions on the germination and growth of fungi in soil. Direct examination has shown that *F. solani* f. *phaseoli* exists in soil as thick-walled chlamydospores, many of which are embedded in plant debris or particles of organic matter. Although chlamydospores will germinate in water, they were rarely observed to do so in unsterilized soil, even when the soil was saturated with water (Toussoun and Snyder, 1961). They germinated, however, when close to germinating bean seed and root tips. Mature roots had little effect on chlamydospore germination and growth when tested in soil. Exudation of amino acids and sugars was most abundant from germinating bean seeds and root tips, and only traces of exudate were detected from mature roots unless they were dried or injured. Solutions of aspartic acid, asparagine, glucose, and sucrose stimulated germination and growth of chlamydospores when tested in vitro. All these materials were identified as constituents of bean exudate (Schroth and Snyder, 1961). Chlamydospores also germinate near seed of several nonhosts of the fungus and around decomposing residues of barley and broccoli, and when water extracts of these residues are added to soil (Schroth and Hendrix, 1962).

Thus the data suggest that growth of *Fusarium solani* f. *phaseoli* in soil is limited to the rhizosphere of bean plants and possibly various nonhosts or other temporary supplies of nutrient. Toussoun, Nash, and Snyder (1960) also showed that it is necessary to provide the fungus with adequate nitrogen nutrition for growth and infection to proceed effectively. While saprophytic species of *Fusarium* may possibly grow more extensively in soil, it is probable that features in the growth cycle of *F. solani* f. *phaseoli* apply also to these species.

Actinomycete spores are also common in soil and have been observed directly (Kubiëna, 1938). Whether there is inhibition of germination of actinomycete spores in soil is not known. Gottlieb's (1960) observation that spores of *Streptomyces venezuelae* require an external energy source for germination suggests that actinomycetes may resemble fungi in this respect.

Direct examination indicates that different fungi exploit substrates and soil habitats in different ways. With *Phytophthora* there is doubt whether free hyphal growth occurs in soil (Hickman, 1958). Oospores occur in soil, often embedded in plant residues, and germination takes place by the formation of germ tubes which quickly give rise to sporangia (Legge, 1952).

That many soil-borne pathogens make limited free hyphal growth in soil has long been known and is a basis of separation between the ecological groups "soil-inhabiting" and "root-inhabiting" fungi, the latter making little free growth apart from their hosts (Garrett, 1956a). Many saprophytes, including species of *Penicillium* and *Aspergillus,* also do not normally grow extensively through soil, most growth occurring on or in a substrate.

Discussing growth patterns of fungi in soil, Burges (1960) outlined the *Penicillium* pattern as follows: "A small piece of substrate is densely colonized by the fungus. Spore production occurs heavily over the surface of the substrate, and there is no extension of the mycelium into the surrounding soil." Sewell (1959b), investigating fungi in a *Calluna*-heath soil, observed penicillia on few soil slides but in each case these fungi were confined to specific substrates, frequently animal remains, from which there was negligible mycelial spread but considerable sporulation. Sewell's observations substantiate this *Penicillium* pattern, but other data suggest that it is not applicable to all penicillia. For instance, *P. vermiculatum* is recorded as a parasite on fungal hyphae (Boosalis, 1956).

Data suggest that the growth of many common fungi is associated with specific substrates in soil and that such organisms make little free growth unless the level of available soluble nutrient is high, a comparatively rare event in natural soil. Many belong to the sugar fungi, which as a group are considered to be characterized by a high mycelial growth rate allied with a capacity for rapid germination of spores (Garrett, 1951). These fungi are likely to "flare up" wherever and whenever a suitable substrate becomes available. Between the exhaustion of one substrate and the appearance of the next, most species remain dormant in soil as spores.

Some fungi, particularly the higher Ascomycetes and Basidiomycetes with longer-lived mycelia, may make more extensive growth through soil and travel from substrate to substrate. Burges (1960) gives the basidiomycete pattern as: "The fungus colonizes the substrate with a long-lived mycelium and then migrates to other substrates or to a position where it will produce fruit-bodies by means of rhizomorphs or well-developed mycelial strands." This group is similar to Garrett's (1951) lignin fungi. Lignin, cellulose, and simpler compounds, if available, may be used by these fungi.

The studies of Garrett (1954, 1956b, 1960) have increased our knowledge of the growth of rhizomorph-bearing fungi and give information on the effect of size of food supply (inoculum potential) on rhizomorph production and ability to colonize fresh substrates. While few studies have been made on the extent of the vegetative thallus of Basidiomycetes in soil, the data of Grainger (1962) emphasize the contrast between the growth of certain Basidiomycetes and that of short-lived fungi such as *Penicillium*. Grainger excavated the rhizomorph system attached to fructifications of *Phallus impudicus* and found that in one case rhizomorph length was 55.5 ft with a volume of 124.6 cc.

While the rhizomorph pattern is probably general for many Basidiomycetes, other growth cycles are known. A species of *Omphalina* in wheat-field soil in Adelaide oversummers as sclerotia, which are produced abundantly in the late spring. In the following autumn when the soil becomes moist again the fungus returns to the mycelial phase by germination of sclerotia; only rarely are conditions suitable for formation of fructifications (Warcup and Talbot, 1962). Several other Basidiomycetes in this soil are present as sclerotia for much of the year. Their type of growth cycle has marked resemblances to that of some moulds.

Because of differences in ability to decompose different materials in complex substrates, fungi differ markedly in their utilization of substrates. Many sugar fungi grow quickly on a substrate then sporulate abundantly. Chlamydospores and sclerotia may be formed internally or externally, but conidia are more usually formed externally. Other fungi may survive within substrates as mycelium for long periods. Butler (1959) found that root-rotting fungi such as *Ophiobolus graminis, Helminthosporium sativum,* and *Curvularia ramosa* survived in infected straws for up to 2 years. The wood-rotting fungus *Fomes annosus* may survive in root systems for as long as 30 years (Rishbeth, 1951). It is interesting that Macer (1961) found not only that *Cercosporella herpotrichoides* survived with virtually undiminished vigour in straw buried for 3 years, but also that straws containing the fungus decomposed more slowly in soil than did noninfected ones. These extended periods suggest that in many cases the fungi are present as resting mycelium rather than growing actively.

Recently several workers have washed debris particles from soil and studied their fungal populations. It is noticeable that many of the fungi obtained, *Aphanomyces* and *Rhizoctonia* (Boosalis and Scharen, 1959), *Fusarium, Pythium,* and *Cylindrocarpon* (Parkinson and Kendrick, 1960; Parkinson and Williams, 1961; Nash, Christou, and Snyder, 1961) are organisms known to produce resting spores, oospores, sclerotia, or chlamydospores in decomposing tissues. More information is necessary before we can be sure that these fungi are active in decomposition of debris particles in soil.

The ecological groups such as sugar fungi and lignin fungi are useful concepts for highlighting the marked differences in growth patterns of fungi and their ability to utilize different substrates. Soils, however, contain a very wide range of organisms with many different growth patterns. Much more information on the substrates used by different organisms in natural soil is necessary. Further, while it is now possible to sketch an outline of the life of some sugar fungi, there are major gaps in our knowledge of the growth and activity of many other fungi in soil.

OCCURRENCE OF FRUCTIFICATIONS IN SOIL.—Several groups of microorganisms, myxobacteria, actinomycetes and Acrasieae, Myxomycetes, and fungi, may form fructifications in soil. Our knowledge of these structures in the field has been obtained mainly from collection from natural grassland or woodland sites rather than from arable soils. Furthermore, most information is of fructifications from the soil surface and little is known of sporulation within mineral soil itself (Burges, 1958).

Fungal fructifications.—The range of fructifications formed by soil fungi is very wide; they vary in size and complexity from simple scarcely differentiated conidiophores to the large complex sporophores of Ascomycetes and Basidiomycetes. Very little is known of the factors, internal or external, inducing reproduction, but it is probable that the factors inducing the formation of these widely different types of reproductive structures differ greatly and may be very distinct from those favouring maximum production of mycelium (Cochrane, 1960).

As we have already seen, cessation of growth may take place without sporulation, the hyphae either "resting," forming hyphal segments or chlamydospores, or dying. Some fructifications, particularly oospores, may be formed in plant tissues, others occur in larger cavities in soil. Sporulation may occur on bare ground or on litter or residues at the soil surface and may also occur within the mineral layers. Fructifications formed within soil vary from simple conidiophores which occur in soil pores to the complex fructifications of the Endogonaceae, Tuberales, and the subterranean Gasteromycetes, all of which may affect soil structure.

Physical factors, such as temperature, water content of substrate, humidity, pH, aeration, all influence sporulation although the mechanisms by which they do so are largely obscure. Waid (1962) has shown that some fungi require a higher concentration of oxygen for sporulation than for growth. Fructifications of larger fungi are often seasonal and many, though by no means all, fruit in autumn. According to Grainger (1946) and Wilkins and Harris (1946), autumn is the only season when soil temperature, moisture conditions, and nitrogen supply are simultaneously adequate to fulfill the requirements for formation of fruiting bodies.

Some fungi require light for sporulation; this varies from an absolute requirement for initiation or maturation of reproductive bodies, to a quantitative response such as an increase in the number of sporophores upon illumination. Light is an absolute requirement for the formation of many different types of reproductive organs including sporophores of certain Basidiomycetes, apothecia, perithecia, pycnidia, sporangia and conidia (Cochrane, 1958). The effect of light on sporulation of fungi occurring in soil has not been studied in any detail, but it is known that *Trichoderma viride* produces no or very few conidia in continuous darkness whereas light causes profuse sporulation (J. J. Miller and Reid, 1961) and that in *Fusarium* light brings about macrospore production (Snyder and Hansen, 1941; Carlile, 1956; Reid, 1958).

Microbial sporulation in an arable soil.—During examination of the activity of fungi in an arable field in Adelaide, many observations have been made on the occurrence of fungal and other fructifications in soil. Climatically the area has a hot, dry summer and a cool, wet winter, the marked seasonal incidence in rainfall causing great variation in soil moisture (Warcup, 1957). After onset of the autumn rains the field was cultivated and sown to wheat, which was harvested in early summer at the end of the rainy period.

After cultivation the surface of an arable field is highly complex with clods and fine soil, thus giving both exposed and protected surfaces. Many fungi have been found fruiting at the soil surface, particularly on the protected undersurfaces of larger clods (Fig. 2).

Fig. 2. Fructifications of *Hyphodontia nudiseta* on the undersurface of a clod from a ploughed field at the Waite Agricultural Research Institute, Adelaide, South Australia.

Fructifications obtained include those of species of *Mucor, Rhizopus, Absidia, Cephalosporium, Fusarium, Myrothecium, Trichoderma, Penicillium, Helicomyces, Helicosporium, Phymatotrichum,* and the Basidiomycetes *Physalacria* and *Peniophora,* all of which occur on residues; and the Basidiomycetes *Thanatephorus, Sistotrema, Oliveonia, Sebacina,* and *Peniophora,* which occur mainly on bare soil (Warcup and Talbot, 1962). The range of fungi fruiting at the surface is probably greater than recorded here since no detailed search for smaller fructifications has been made. Myxomycete fructifications may also occur on residues at the soil surface.

After heavy rain the loose surface becomes flattened and compacted and fructifications are more rarely noted in this zone. At the same time earthworm action, mainly by *Eisenia rosea* (Sav.) and *Allolobophora caliginosa* (Sav.) (Barley, 1959), produces a series of horizontal and vertical tunnels in the upper layer of the soil where the worms feed on plant residues and dung.

As noted by Guild (1955), the burrows are quite strongly constructed, the walls being cemented with ejected soil pressed into the soil interspaces and often darkly coloured owing to incorporation of organic matter in the soil. While worm activity decreases from midwinter onwards, the burrows, ant tunnels, and old root channels from the previous crop remain in the soil until it is ploughed again the following autumn. The tunnels range in diameter from 0.5 to 3 mm and together with the larger soil pores act as pathways for nonburrowing members of the soil fauna.

Direct microscopic examination of soil blocks has often revealed fungal sporulation in these tunnels (Fig. 3), sometimes on the remains of the soil invertebrates

Fig. 3. Mycelium and ascocarps of *Spiromastix* lining a root tunnel in natural soil.

that use them, sometimes on plant residues, on earthworm casts (both species make most of their casts belowground) and on mineral particles. It is interesting that sporulation on buried residues is often confined to those portions which abut on tunnels or other large cavities in the soil. Dobbs and Hinson (1960) consider that many moulds are able to spore in soil cavities of the order of 200 μ in diameter. Fungi noted sporulating on buried straws and roots include species of *Dinemasporium, Chaetomium, Periconia, Trichoderma, Gonytrichum, Brachysporiella,* and *Endophragmia.* Fructifications are usually confined to residues, but with some fungi hyphal growth may extend short distances from a residue allowing conidiophores to appear to arise directly from mineral particles. *Rhizopus arrhizus* on decomposing leaf material in the plough layer may scramble and sporulate a centimeter or more from the substrate. Many Phycomycetes and occasionally other fungi, such as *Penicillium, Verticillium,* and *Coprinus,* growing on relatively rich substrates—invertebrate remains, dung, seed—may grow and sporulate some distance from the substrate.

Kubiëna (1938) reported that, in general, there was a reduction in the size of fruiting structures with decrease in pore size in soil. He also noted that the dimensions of fructifications from soil were smaller than those recorded for the fungi grown in culture; this, however, could be an effect of low nutrient level in soil. One effect of pore size was seen in wheat-field soil. Sporangiophores of *Rhizopus* that formed in larger cavities were normal and straight while those formed in smaller cavities were coiled and springlike in appearance. A different effect, presumably related to low nutrient level, is that some fructifications in soil may be reduced in complexity as compared with those formed in culture. Conidiophores of *Cunninghamella* with but 1-2 conidia have been noted; similarly some penicillia may bear reduced penicilli.

Many of the fungi found fruiting in cavity systems occurred on cast exuviae or dead bodies of members of the soil fauna. The fungi included animal parasites, such as *Conidiobolus, Entomophthora,* and *Beauveria,* and many saprophytes, including *Absidia, Cunninghamella, Mucor, Penicillium, Aspergillus,* and several unidentified species. The fructifications of *Absidia* included both sporangia and zygospores. A *Verticillium* species was of interest in that it was one of the commonest fungi found fruiting in the soil; in contrast, from several hundred soil-dilution plates prepared from this soil it was recorded only twice. Scarcely a soil block examined during the period when the soil was moist failed to show this fungus. Particularly from remains and exuviae of Collembola, but also from spiders and some insects it produced long, trailing, verticillate conidiophores in tunnels and pores in soil. At times sporulation was dense enough to form a "web" across a tunnel. Besides sporulation on remains of species of *Hypogastrura,* spores were noted on living animals. The characteristic spores of *Endophragmia* were also found on Collembola and mites. Witkamp (1960) has also noted many fungal spores adhering to the bristles of oribatid mites.

Sporulation of fungi including several cleistothecial Ascomycetes occurred from mineral soil along tunnels. Whether such fructifications arose from concealed debris or whether the fungi were using organic substances in solution or more resistant materials in the soil is not known. As noted by Eriksson (1949) some aphyllophoraceous Basidiomycetes also produced fruit bodies more or less hypogeously in worm tunnels. Fructifications of *Dictyostelium mucoroides* have also been noted on several occasions, apparently arising from worm casts.

Besides fungi, actinomycete fructifications were common in soil cavities and tunnels. Actinomycete fructifications occurred as fine tufts of a few conidiophores which were very difficult to see without high-power microscopic examination; they also arose as small visible tufts, or as diffuse sheets of conidiophores, or occasionally fruited so densely as to resemble sporulation of a *Penicillium.* They occurred on plant and animal residues, on fungal hyphae, and on small "humus particles." Their abundance, particularly when the soil was drier, would suggest that they may be seriously underestimated in soil-dilution-plate counts. The presence of sporogeneous hyphae of actinomycetes in the minute air spaces between soil crumbs has been noted many times (Kubiëna and Renn, 1935; Starkey, 1938).

Thus direct observation may allow many fructifications to be seen, their occurrence relative to substrate may be noted, and they may be isolated and grown; but fructifications become virtually impossible to find if the soil is suspended in water. Spores are washed off, many sporophores collapse, and other structures, particularly cleistothecia, may trap air and float. Other fructifications, however, cannot be seen by direct examination; some are embedded in humus particles (Warcup, 1952, 1957) either after breakdown of plant tissue (Boosalis and Scharen, 1959) or through being surrounded by a considerable accumulation of bacterial cells and small mineral particles (Barton, 1958).

The presence of fructifications in soil, particularly at the soil surface, raises many interesting questions on the fate of the spores produced and on their possible dispersal by wind, rain, or by members of the soil fauna.

LITERATURE CITED

ALEXANDER, F. E. S., and R. M. JACKSON. 1955. Preparation of sections for study of soil micro-organisms. p. 433-440. *In* D. K. McE. Kevan [ed.], Soil zoology, Butterworths Scientific Publications, London; Academic Press, New York.

ANDERSEN, A. A. 1958. New sampler for the collection, sizing, and enumeration of viable airborn particles. J. Bacteriol. 76: 471-484.

BARLEY, K. P. 1959. The influence of earthworms on soil fertility. 1. Earthworm populations found in agricultural land near Adelaide. Australian J. Agr. Res. 10: 171-178.

BARTON, R. 1958. Occurrence and establishment of Pythium in soils. Trans. Brit. Mycol. Soc. 41: 207-222.

BLAIR, I. D. 1945. Techniques for soil fungus studies. New Zealand J. Sci. Technol., A, 26: 258-271.

BOLLEN, W. B. 1961. Interactions between pesticides and soil microorganisms. Ann. Rev. Microbiol. 15: 69-92.

BOLLIGER, A., and R. GROSS. 1952. Nitrogenous compounds in the aqueous extract of vertebrate keratinous structures. Australian J. Exptl. Biol. Med. Sci. 30: 399-408.

BOOSALIS, M. G. 1956. Effect of soil temperature and green manure amendment of unsterilized soil on parasitism of *Rhizoctonia solani* by *Penicillium vermiculatum* and *Trichoderma* sp. Phytopathology 46: 473-478.

BOOSALIS, M. G., and A. L. SCHAREN. 1959. Methods for microscopic detection of *Aphanomyces euteiches* and *Rhizoctonia solani* and for isolation of *Rhizoctonia solani* associated with plant debris. Phytopathology 49: 192-197.

BRIAN, P. W. 1960. Antagonistic and competitive mechanisms limiting survival and activity of fungi in soil. p. 115-129. *In* D. Parkinson and J. S. Waid [ed.], The ecology of soil fungi, Liverpool University Press, Liverpool.

BROWN, J. C. 1958a. Fungal mycelium in dune soils estimated by a modified impression slide technique. Trans. Brit. Mycol. Soc. 41: 81-88.

BROWN, J. C. 1958b. Soil fungi of some British sand

dunes in relation to soil type and succession. J. Ecol. 46: 641-664.

BUNT, J. S., and Y. T. TCHAN. 1955. Estimation of protozoan populations in soils by direct microscopy. Proc. Linn. Soc. N.S. Wales 80: 148-153.

BURGES, A. 1939. Soil fungi and root infection. Brotéria 8, fasc. 2: 64-81.

BURGES, A. 1958. Micro-organisms in the soil. Hutchinson & Co., London. 188 p.

BURGES, A. 1960. Dynamic equilibria in the soil. p. 185-191. *In* D. Parkinson and J. S. Waid [ed.], The ecology of soil fungi, Liverpool University Press, Liverpool.

BURGES, A., and D. P. NICHOLAS. 1961. Use of soil sections in studying amount of fungal hyphae in soil. Soil Sci. 92: 25-29.

BUTLER, F. C. 1953. Saprophytic behaviour of some cereal root-rot fungi. Ann. Appl. Biol. 40: 284-311.

BUTLER, F. C. 1959. Saprophytic behaviour of some cereal root-rot fungi IV. Saprophytic survival in soils of high and low fertility. Ann. Appl. Biol. 47: 28-36.

CAPSTICK, C. K., D. C. TWINN, and J. S. WAID. 1957. Predation of natural populations of free-living nematodes by fungi. Nematologica 2: 193-201.

CARLILE, M. J. 1956. A study of the factors influencing non-genetic variation in a strain of *Fusarium oxysporum.* J. Gen. Microbiol. 14: 643-654.

CASIDA, L. E. 1962. On the isolation and growth of individual microbial cells from soil. Can. J. Microbiol. 8: 115-119.

CHESTERS, C. G. C. 1948. A contribution to the study of fungi in the soil. Trans. Brit. Mycol. Soc. 30: 100-117.

CHESTERS, C. G. C. 1949. Concerning fungi inhabiting soil. Trans. Brit. Mycol. Soc. 32: 197-216.

CHESTERS, C. G. C. 1960. Certain problems associated with the decomposition of soil organic matter by fungi. p. 223-238. *In* D. Parkinson and J. S. Waid [ed.], The ecology of soil fungi, Liverpool University Press, Liverpool.

CHINN, S. H. F. 1953. A slide technique for the study of fungi and actinomycetes in soil, with special reference to *Helminthosporium sativum.* Can. J. Botany 31: 718-724.

CHOLODNY, N. 1930. Über eine neue Methode zur Untersuchung der Bodenmikroflora. Arch. Mikrobiol. 1: 620-652.

CHRISTENSEN, M., W. F. WHITTINGHAM, and R. O. NOVAK. 1962. The soil microfungi of wet-mesic forests in southern Wisconsin. Mycologia 54: 374-388.

CLARKE, J. H., and D. PARKINSON. 1960. A comparison of three methods for the assessment of fungal colonization of seedling roots of leek and broad bean. Nature (London) 188: 166-167.

COCHRANE, V. W. 1958. Physiology of fungi. John Wiley and Sons, New York. 524 p.

COCHRANE, V. W. 1960. Spore germination. vol. 2, p. 169-202. *In* J. G. Horsfall and A. E. Dimond [ed.], Plant pathology, an advanced treatise, Academic Press, New York and London.

CONN, H. J. 1918. The microscopic study of bacteria and fungi in soil. New York Agr. Exp. Sta. (Geneva, N. Y.) Tech. Bull. 64, 20 p.

COOKE, R. C. 1961. The ecology of nematode-trapping fungi in the soil. Ann. Appl. Biol. 50: 507-513.

DANIELS, J. 1961. *Chaetomium piluliferum* sp. nov., the perfect stage of *Botryotrichum piluliferum.* Trans. Brit. Mycol. Soc. 44: 79-86.

DEAN, A. L. 1929. Root-observation boxes. Phytopathology 19: 407-412.

DOBBS, C. G., and W. H. HINSON. 1953. A widespread fungistasis in soils. Nature (London) 172: 197.

DOBBS, C. G., and W. H. HINSON. 1960. Some observations on fungal spores in soil. p. 33-42. *In* D. Parkinson and J. S. Waid [ed.], The ecology of soil fungi, Liverpool University Press, Liverpool.

DOBBS, C. G., W. H. HINSON, and J. BYWATER. 1960. Inhibition of fungal growth in soils. p. 130-147. *In* D. Parkinson and J. S. Waid [ed.], The ecology of soil fungi, Liverpool University Press, Liverpool.

DRECHSLER, C. 1941. Predaceous fungi. Biol. Rev. Cambridge Phil. Soc. 16: 265-290.

DROPKIN, V. H., W. L. SMITH JR., and R. F. MYERS. 1960. Recovery of nematodes from infected roots by maceration. Nematologica 5: 285-288.

DUDDINGTON, C. L. 1957. The predacious fungi and their place in microbial ecology. Symp. Soc. Gen. Microbiol. 7: 218-237.

DURBIN, R. D. 1961. Techniques for the observation and isolation of soil microorganisms. Botan. Rev. 27: 522-560.

ERIKSSON, J. 1949. Notes on *Corticium muscicola* Bres. and its taxonomical position. Svensk Botan. Tidskr. 43: 310-315.

FOSTER, J. W. 1949. Chemical activities of fungi. Academic Press, New York. 648 p.

FOSTER, J. W. 1962. Hydrocarbons as substrates for microorganisms. Antonie van Leeuwenhoek J. Microbiol. Soc. 28: 241-274.

GARRETT, S. D. 1951. Ecological groups of soil fungi: a survey of substrate relationships. New Phytologist 50: 149-166.

GARRETT, S. D. 1952. The soil fungi as a microcosm for ecologists. Sci. Progr. (London) 40: 436-450.

GARRETT, S. D. 1954. Function of the mycelial strands in substrate colonization by the cultivated mushroom, *Psalliota hortensis.* Trans. Brit. Mycol. Soc. 37: 51-57.

GARRETT, S. D. 1955. Microbial ecology of the soil. Trans. Brit. Mycol. Soc. 38: 1-9.

GARRETT, S. D. 1956a. Biology of root-infecting fungi. Cambridge University Press, London and New York. 292 p.

GARRETT, S. D. 1956b. Rhizomorph behaviour in *Armillaria mellea* (Vahl) Quél. II. Logistics of infection. Ann. Botany (London) [N.S.] 20: 193-209.

GARRETT, S. D. 1958. Inoculum potential as a factor limiting lethal action by *Trichoderma viride* Fr. on *Armillaria mellea* (Fr.) Quél. Trans. Brit. Mycol. Soc. 41: 157-164.

GARRETT, S. D. 1960. Rhizomorph behaviour in *Armillaria mellea* (Fr.) Quél. III. Saprophytic colonization of woody substrates in soil. Ann. Botany (London) [N.S.] 24: 275-285.

GOTTLIEB, D. 1960. The physiology of the actinomycetes. Intern. Congr. Microbiol., 6th Congr. (Rome) 5: 122-136.

GRAINGER, J. 1946. Ecology of the larger fungi. Trans. Brit. Mycol. Soc. 29: 52-63.

GRAINGER, J. 1962. Vegetative and fructifying growth in *Phallus impudicus.* Trans. Brit. Mycol. Soc. 45: 147-155.

GREGORY, P. H., and M. E. LACEY. 1962. Isolation of thermophilic actinomycetes. Nature (London) 195: 95.

GRIFFIN, D. M. 1960. Fungal colonization of sterile hair in contact with soil. Trans. Brit. Mycol. Soc. 43: 583-596.

GUILD, W. J. McL. 1955. Earthworms and soil structure. p. 83-98. *In* D. K. McE. Kevan [ed.], Soil zoology, Butterworths Scientific Publications, London; Academic Press, New York.

HAARLØV, N., and T. WEIS-FOGH. 1955. A microscopical technique for studying the undisturbed texture of soils. p. 429-432. *In* D. K. McE. Kevan [ed.], Soil zoology, Butterworths Scientific Publications, London; Academic Press, New York.

HANDLEY, W. R. C. 1954. Mull and mor formation in relation to forest soils. Forest. Comm. Bull. [H. M. Stationery Office, London] 23, 115 p.

HARLEY, J. L., and J. S. WAID. 1955. A method of studying active mycelia on living roots and other surfaces in the soil. Trans. Brit. Mycol. Soc. 38: 104-118.

HEPPLE, S., and A. BURGES. 1956. Sectioning of soil. Nature (London) 177: 1186.

HESSAYON, D. G. 1953. Fungitoxins in soil. II. Trichothecin, its production and inactivation in unsterilized soil. Soil Sci. 75: 395-404.

HESSELMAN, H. 1926. Studier över barrskogens humustäcke, dessegenskaper och beroende av skogsvarden. Medd. Statens Skogsförskningsinst. 22: 169-552.

HICKMAN, C. J. 1958. Phytophthora—plant destroyer. Trans. Brit. Mycol. Soc. 41: 1-13.

JACKSON, R. M. 1958a. An investigation of fungistasis in Nigerian soils. J. Gen. Microbiol. 18: 248-258.

JACKSON, R. M. 1958b. Some aspects of soil fungistasis. J. Gen. Microbiol. 19: 390-401.

JEFFERYS, E. G., and H. G. HEMMING. 1953. Fungistasis in soils. Nature (London) 172: 872.

JOHNSON, L. F., E. A. CURL, J. H. BOND, and H. A. FRIBOURG. 1959. Methods for studying soil microflora-plant disease relationships. Burgess Publishing Co., Minneapolis. 178 p.

JONES, P. C. T., and J. E. MOLLISON. 1948. A technique for the quantitative estimation of soil micro-organisms. J. Gen. Microbiol. 2: 54-69.

KEYNAN, A., Y. HENIS, and P. KELLER. 1961. Factors influencing the composition of the cellulose-decomposing microflora on soil crumb plates. Nature (London) 191: 307.

KUBIËNA, W. L. 1938. Micropedology. Collegiate Press, Ames, Iowa. 243 p.

KUBIËNA, W. L. 1953. The soils of Europe. Cons. Sup. Investig. Cient. Madrid. 318 p.

KUBIËNA, W. L. 1955. Animal activity in soils as a decisive factor in establishment of humus forms. p. 73-80. In D. K. McE. Kevan [ed.], Soil zoology, Butterworths Scientific Publications, London; Academic Press, New York.

KUBIËNA, W., and C. E. RENN. 1935. Micropedological studies of the influence of different organic compounds upon the microflora of the soil. Zentbl. Bakteriol. Parasitenk., Abt. II, 91: 267-292.

LAAN, P. A. VAN DER. 1956. [Investigations on fungi predacious on the cyst contents of the potato root eelworm, *Heterodera rostochiensis* Wollenw.] Tijdschr. Plantenziekten 62: 305-321.

LEGGE, B. J. 1952. Use of glass fibre material in soil mycology. Nature (London) 169: 759-760.

LINFORD, M. B. 1942. Methods of observing the soil flora and fauna associated with roots. Soil Sci. 53: 93-103.

LINGAPPA, B. T., and J. L. LOCKWOOD. 1961. The nature of the widespread soil fungistasis. J. Gen. Microbiol. 26: 473-485.

LINGAPPA, B. T., and J. L. LOCKWOOD. 1962. Fungitoxicity of lignin monomers, model substances, and decomposition products. Phytopathology 52: 295-299.

McCALLA, T. M. 1953. Microbiology studies of stubble mulching. Nebraska Agr. Expt. Sta. Bull. 417, 14 p.

MACER, R. C. F. 1961. The survival of *Cercosporella herpotrichoides* Fron in wheat straw. Ann. Appl. Biol. 49: 165-172.

MILLER, J. H., J. E. GIDDENS, and A. A. FOSTER. 1957. A survey of the fungi of forest and cultivated soils of Georgia. Mycologia 49: 779-808.

MILLER, J. J., and J. REID. 1961. Stimulation by light of sporulation in *Trichoderma lignorum* (Tode) Harz. Can. J. Botany 39: 259-262.

MINDERMAN, G. 1956. The preparation of microtome sections of unaltered soil for the study of soil organisms in situ. Plant Soil 8: 42-48.

MURPHY, P. W. 1955. Ecology of the fauna of forest soils. p. 99-123. In D. K. McE. Kevan [ed.], Soil zoology, Butterworths Scientific Publications, London; Academic Press, New York.

MURPHY, P. W. [ed.] 1962. Progress in soil zoology. Butterworths Scientific Publications, London. 398 p.

NASH, S. M., T. CHRISTOU, and W. C. SNYDER. 1961. Existence of *Fusarium solani* f. *phaseoli* as chlamydospores in soil. Phytopathology 51: 308-312.

NEWMAN, A. S., and A. G. NORMAN. 1943. The activity of subsurface soil populations. Soil Sci. 55: 377-391.

NORSTADT, F. A., and T. M. McCALLA. 1960. Influence of stubble mulching on organic matter and nitrogen content of the soil. Agron. J. 52: 477-479.

NOVOGRUDSKY, D. M. 1948. The colonization of soil bacteria on fungal hyphae. Mikrobiology (USSR) (English transl.) 17: 28-35.

PARK, D. 1955. Experimental studies on the ecology of fungi in soil. Trans. Brit. Mycol. Soc. 38: 130-142.

PARK, D. 1961. Morphogenesis, fungistasis and cultural staling in *Fusarium oxysporum* Snyder and Hansen. Trans. Brit. Mycol. Soc. 44: 377-390.

PARKER, D. T. 1962. Decomposition in the field of buried and surface applied cornstalk residue. Soil Sci. Soc. Am. Proc. 26: 559-562.

PARKINSON, D. 1957. New methods for the qualitative and quantitative study of fungi in the rhizosphere. Pédologie 7, no. spéc. (Symp. Méth. et Microbiol. Sol), p. 146-154.

PARKINSON, D., and W. B. KENDRICK. 1960. Investigations of soil micro-habitats. p. 22-28. In D. Parkinson and J. S. Waid [ed.], The ecology of soil fungi, Liverpool University Press, Liverpool.

PARKINSON, D., and S. T. WILLIAMS. 1961. A method for isolating fungi from soil microhabitats. Plant Soil 13: 347-355.

PATTERSON, H. D. 1960. An experiment on the effects of straw ploughed in or composted on a three course rotation of crops. J. Agr. Sci. 54: 222-230.

PUGH, G. J. F., and G. E. MATHISON. 1962. Studies on fungi in coastal soils. III. An ecological survey of keratinophilic fungi. Trans. Brit. Mycol. Soc. 45: 567-572.

QUASTEL, J. H. 1955. Soil metabolism. Proc. Roy. Soc. (London), Ser. B, 143: 159-178.

REID, J. 1958. Studies on the fusaria which cause wilt in melons II. The effect of light, nutrition, and various chemicals on the sporulation of certain fusarial isolates, and preliminary investigations on the etiology of wilting of the muskmelon Fusarium. Can. J. Botany 36: 507-537.

RISHBETH, J. 1951. Observations on the biology of *Fomes annosus,* with particular reference to East Anglian pine plantations II. Spore production, stump infection, and saprophytic activity in stumps. Ann. Botany (London) [N.S.] 15: 1-21.

ROSSI, G. M. 1928. L'exame microscopio e bacteriologio diretto del Terreno agrario. Nuovi. Ann. Agr. 7: 457-470.

RUSSELL, E. W. 1961. Soil conditions and plant growth. 9th ed. Longmans, Green & Co., London. 688 p.

SADASIVAN, T. S. 1939. Succession of fungi decomposing wheat straw in different soils, with special reference to *Fusarium culmorum*. Ann. Appl. Biol. 26: 497-508.

SAITÔ, T. 1956. Microbiological decomposition of beech litter. Seitaigaku Kenkyu 14: 141-147.

SAITÔ, T. 1957. Chemical changes in beech litter under microbiological decomposition. Seitaigaku Kenkyu 14: 209-216.

SAITÔ, T. 1958. The characteristic features of fungi taking part in the decomposition of beech litter. Sci. Rept. Tôhoku Univ., 4th Ser., 24: 73-79.

SAITÔ, T. 1960. An approach to the mechanism of microbial decomposition of beech litter. Sci. Rept. Tôhoku Univ., 4th Ser., 26: 125-131.

SCHROTH, M. N., and F. F. HENDRIX, JR. 1962. Influence of nonsusceptible plants on the survival of *Fusarium solani* f. *phaseoli* in soil. Phytopathology 52: 906-909.

SCHROTH, M. N., and W. C. SNYDER. 1961. Effect of host exudates on chlamydospore germination of the bean root rot fungus, *Fusarium solani* f. *phaseoli*. Phytopathology 51: 389-393.

SEWELL, G. W. F. 1959a. Studies of fungi in a Calluna-heathland soil. I. Vertical distribution in soil and on root surfaces. Trans. Brit. Mycol. Soc. 42: 343-353.

SEWELL, G. W. F. 1959b. Studies of fungi in a Calluna-heathland soil. II. By the complementary use of several isolation methods. Trans. Brit. Mycol. Soc. 42: 354-369.

SEWELL, G. W. F. 1959c. Direct observation of *Verticillium albo-atrum* in soil. Trans. Brit. Mycol. Soc. 42: 312-321.

SIMMONDS, P. M. 1930. A washing device for isolation work with plant material. Phytopathology 20: 911-913.

SNYDER, W. C., and H. N. HANSEN. 1941. The effect of light on taxonomic characters in Fusarium. Mycologia 33: 580-591.

SØRENSEN, H. 1962. Decomposition of lignin by soil bacteria and complex formation between autoxidized lignin and organic nitrogen compounds. J. Gen. Microbiol. 27: 21-34.

STANIER, R. Y. 1953. Adaptation, evolutionary, and physiological: or Darwinism among the micro-organisms. Symp. Soc. Gen. Microbiol. 3: 1-14.

STARKEY, R. L. 1938. Some influences of the development of higher plants upon the microorganisms in the soil. VI. Microscopic examination of the rhizosphere. Soil Sci. 45: 207-249.

STEVENSON, I. L. 1956. Antibiotic activity of actinomycetes in soil as demonstrated by direct observation techniques. J. Gen. Microbiol. 15: 372-380.

STOVER, R. H. 1953. Measurement of colonization and survival of soil fusaria in detached plant tissue. Nature (London) 172: 465.

TAUBENHAUS, J. J., and W. N. EZEKIEL. 1930. Studies on the overwintering of Phymatotrichum root rot. Phytopathology 20: 761-785.

THORNTON, H. G., and F. A. SKINNER. 1960. The interaction of actinomycetes with other micro-organisms in soil. Intern. Congr. Microbiol. 6th Congr. (Rome) 5: 174-190.

TOUSSOUN, T. A., S. M. NASH, and W. C. SNYDER. 1960. The effect of nitrogen sources and glucose on the pathogenesis of *Fusarium solani* f. *phaseoli*. Phytopathology 50: 137-140.

TOUSSOUN, T. A., and W. C. SNYDER. 1961. Germination of chlamydospores of *Fusarium solani* f. *phaseoli* in unsterilized soils. Phytopathology 51: 620-623.

TRIBE, H. T. 1957. Ecology of micro-organisms in soils as observed during their development upon buried cellulose film. Symp. Soc. Gen. Microbiol. 7: 287-298.

TRIBE, H. T. 1960a. Aspects of decomposition of cellulose in Canadian soils I. Observations with the microscope. Can. J. Microbiol. 6: 309-316.

TRIBE, H. T. 1960b. Aspects of decomposition of cellulose in Canadian soils II. Nitrate nitrogen levels and carbon dioxide evolution. Can. J. Microbiol. 6: 317-323.

TRIBE, H. T. 1961. Microbiology of cellulose decomposition in soil. Soil Sci. 92: 61-77.

WAID, J. S. 1962. Influence of oxygen upon growth and respiratory behaviour of fungi from decomposing ryegrass roots. Trans. Brit. Mycol. Soc. 45: 479-487.

WAID, J. S., and M. J. WOODMAN. 1957. A method of estimating hyphal activity in soil. Pédologie, 7, no. spéc. (Symp. Méth. et Microbiol. Sol) p. 155-158.

WAKSMAN, S. A. 1927. Principles of soil microbiology. Baillière, Tindall and Cox, London. 897 p.

WAKSMAN, S. A. 1938. Humus: origin, composition, and importance in nature. 2nd ed. rev. Williams and Wilkins Co., Baltimore, Md. 526 p.

WAKSMAN, S. A. 1960. The biology of the actinomycetes and their economic importance. Intern. Congr. Microbiol. 6th Congr. (Rome) 5: 1-12.

WARCUP, J. H. 1952. Effect of partial sterilization by steam or formalin on damping-off of Sitka spruce. Trans. Brit. Mycol. Soc. 35: 248-262.

WARCUP, J. H. 1955. On the origin of colonies of fungi developing on soil dilution plates. Trans. Brit. Mycol. Soc. 38: 298-301.

WARCUP, J. H. 1957. Studies on the occurrence and activity of fungi in a wheat-field soil. Trans. Brit. Mycol. Soc. 40: 237-262.

WARCUP, J. H. 1959. Studies on Basidiomycetes in soil. Trans. Brit. Mycol. Soc. 42: 45-52.

WARCUP, J. H. 1960. Methods for isolation and estimation of activity of fungi in soil. p. 3-21. *In* D. Parkinson and J. S. Waid [ed.], The ecology of soil fungi, Liverpool University Press, Liverpool.

WARCUP, J. H., and P. H. B. TALBOT. 1962. Ecology and identity of mycelia isolated from soil. Trans. Brit. Mycol. Soc. 45: 495-518.

WENT, J. C. 1959. Cellophane as a medium to study the cellulose decomposition in forest soils. Acta Botan. Neerl. 8: 490-491.

WILKINS, W. H., and G. C. M. HARRIS. 1946. The ecology of the larger fungi V. An investigation into the influence of rainfall and temperature on the seasonal production of fungi in a beech wood and a pine wood. Ann. Appl. Biol. 33: 179-188.

WINOGRADSKY, S. N. 1949. Microbiology du sol; problèmes et méthodes. Masson et Cie, Paris. 861 p.

WITKAMP, M. 1960. Seasonal fluctuations of the fungus flora in mull and mor of an oak forest. Thesis Wageningen nr. 46 Inst. Toegepast Biol. Onderz in de Natuur.

WITKAMP, M., and J. VAN DER DRIFT. 1961. Breakdown of forest litter in relation to environmental factors. Plant Soil 15: 295-311.

► DISCUSSION OF J. H. WARCUP PAPER

G. W. F. Sewell:

Would you comment upon the relation between the sporulation of fungi in soils after drying and rewetting and the suggestion that nutrient shortage is more likely to be limiting to growth than fungistatic factors.

J. H. Warcup:

I might mention that although there is a burst of growth and sporulation of microorganisms in Urrbrae loam following wetting of soil after the opening rains, sporulation may occur without drying and wetting. While nutrient shortage is important, it and fungistatic factors are perhaps complementary in limiting fungal growth in soil.

Z. A. Patrick:

We are all familiar with the so-called characteristic flora of the rhizosphere. Do you believe that a similar flora exists around the soil litter, which could be referred to as the "littersphere"?

J. H. Warcup:

During early stages of decomposition, released materials may stimulate microbial growth around and in the decomposing material. I think, however, that this system has differences from the rhizosphere and would hesitate to use the term littersphere.

K. F. Baker:

In view of your findings that fungi develop on faunal residues, might this not be another mechanism by which the fauna affect plant pathogens? The fungi growing on such residues might produce toxins which could be inhibitory to plant pathogens.

J. H. Warcup:

It is possible that such toxins might be formed, although there is no evidence on this point. It is likely to be on a microscale, however, rather than a general one.

D. Pramer:

Will you provide us with details of how you peer into a worm hole, and give us your opinion of the buried-slide technique as a technique for gaining an insight into the relations between soil organisms and their environment?

J. H. Warcup:

Details of major channels, including worm tunnels, may be seen by examination of soil blocks. Buried-slide techniques show the microbial growth that occurs after slides are buried. A complication is that there is good evidence that the disturbance in burying the slide may allow growth which would not have occurred had the soil remained undisturbed.

D. W. Burke:

Your remarks and those of previous speakers have emphasized the complex relations and ephemeral nature of most microbiological phenomena in the soil. Furthermore, those of us who have attempted microbiological controls of root diseases in the field, are acutely aware of the sensitivity of such control measures to environmental fluctuations. Our greatest problem in the utilization of soil microbiological phenomena in control of root diseases appears to be one of stabilizing particular phenomena or populations. What are your ideas for the solution of this problem?

J. H. Warcup:

Microbial populations may be markedly changed by soil treatments—soil steaming, fumigation, etc. The problem is to keep the organisms in the active phase. For instance, *Trichoderma viride* may grow abundantly in soil after fumigation. But after initial growth the fungus sporulates. These spores may remain in the soil for some time but may not be active.

Dispersal of Soil Microorganisms

J. M. HIRST—*Plant Pathology Department, Rothamsted Experiment Station, Harpenden, England.*

▶

When I mentioned this title to soil microbiologists the two most frequent reactions have been pity or the question "Do soil microorganisms disperse?" In seeking an answer I shall concentrate on the fungi, mentioning other groups only to illustrate particular processes or important differences. Many niceties of definition will be left to the reader, thereby avoiding the need to explain precisely what is meant by an "individual" among microorganisms, what they must do to earn the "soil" prefix, or what constitutes "dispersal."

The difficulties and the pedantry to be avoided are best illustrated by questions. Is *Cladosporium herbarum* less worthy to be called a soil fungus because it also abounds in litter and is probably the commonest constituent of the air spora in temperate latitudes? As a colony grows, its centre may die and the periphery fragment, or even saltate, and enter widely different habitats. Have the parts been dispersed and are they separate individuals? Does colonization of a new host through root contact imply dispersal or is it necessary that a new discrete infection should be established although it may only be on the next root hair? Is the sclerotium less important to the dispersal of a *Sclerotinia* than the ascospores subsequently produced from its apothecium?

Whatever definition of "dispersal" was chosen would not alter the fact that this is a topic which seldom excites soil microbiologists. They seem eager both to belittle the ability of their organisms to spread and to show how nearly ubiquitous they may become. My task is to reconcile these contradictory attitudes by attempting to show how soil organisms manage to reach places where they can prosper, yet without seeming to move. Obligate parasites of the foliage of annual plants, like *Puccinia graminis* on wheat, must disperse or die. If they are to prosper they must go far, often, and in large numbers so there is little difficulty in tracing their movements. Seldom does such a necessity confront the rather anonymous autochthonous fungi living deep in soils, where the physical environment and the nutrient supply are fairly constant. Herein lies the fundamental difference, that the soil environment *continues* in a way the air cannot. No organisms live suspended in air so, for example, aerial saprophytes, must disperse to their substrates; whereas substrates are often brought to soil organisms by leaf fall, the death of a nearby root, by soil animals, cultivations, or in many other ways. The success which soil organisms can achieve merely by waiting lessens their dependence on distribution but requires that they be numerous, widespread, and instantly ready to grow quickly and compete with their neighbours.

Effective dispersal must result in organisms being where they can prosper. It is obvious that soil microorganisms do this both by moving and by waiting—they disperse both in space and time. At some risk of overlapping with the following paper I shall mention both processes to stress their equality and frequent interdependence in helping organisms to exploit their substrates and find new ones. To avoid confusion or the need for new terms I shall specify "dispersal in time" where applicable, so that "dispersal" can retain its traditional connotation of spatial scattering.

Planning this paper has proved difficult not only because there have been very few attempts to review the pertinent literature (Garrett, 1939a) but also because of enormous voids in our knowledge. Every elementary textbook is crammed with mentions of possible transport by wind, water, animals, seeds, and machines, and to repeat many would make tiresome reading. By contrast, quantitative data are too rare, particularly concerning soil saprophytes, to justify any conclusions of the relative importance and frequency of dispersal by various means. I shall try to compromise by quoting only enough references to outline the characteristics of various units and means of dispersal and to allow some discussion of the patterns and detection of dispersal.

UNITS OF DISPERSAL.—The units of dispersal, or "propagules," for want of a less ugly yet equally comprehensive term, take many and diverse forms. Sometimes the propagules are whole organisms dispersed singly, as in Protozoa, Algae, and free-living nematodes. Much more often successful dispersal leading to establishment requires groups acting together, as is usual in viruses, bacteria, Myxomycetes, some fungi, and cyst-forming nematodes. Groups may be needed to enhance enzymic capability or ensure the associated dispersal of sexes or compatible mating groups. The greatest variety of fragmentary propagules occurs among fungi, where the individual organisms are so difficult to distinguish. Simplest among these propagules are hyphal fragments, which Warcup (1955) showed could function as transplants. Some are quite resistant, for many hyphal fragments, mostly conidiophores, were alive when caught from the air by Pady and Kramer (1960). Hyphal fragments must be poorly adapted to all but the least discriminatory means of dispersal because their size and shape are determined by other factors. As all microorganisms are by definition small, it is not surprising there is an inverse relation between the size and the number of their propagules. Many of the larger units are resistant, presumably because they contain stored nutrient and have thick walls, but it by no means follows that small ones must be short-lived. The importance of propagules to dispersal in space and time are major themes of my paper and the next, but propagules also have important genetical functions, and these are often neglected by students of dispersal. Details of the methods are scarcely our concern here, but it is important to recognize that propagules are a vital means of distributing genetic diversity within populations and so may aid establishment in new hosts or substrates. "Dispersal" as interpreted here may then be effected without the movement of whole organisms. Some microorganisms are dispersed in the haploid state and some in the diplophase. Fusions of migrant propagules in what seem bisexual systems are common in lower fungi, but others exhibit much more complex mating systems. Some involve fertilization like the spermatization of flexuous hyphae of rust fungi, but others result only in asexual diploidization or the formation of hetero-karyons. Microconidia, about which we know so little, are important in some of these processes. Like other migrant diploidizing propagules, they are often so simplified that little but the nucleus remains. This may be little of a handicap because their establishment does not demand ability to grow competitively or overcome host resistance other than intrinsic incompatibility. From the viewpoint of dispersal, they are of interest mainly as examples of successful, precise, often vectored, dispersal to extremely minute targets and because of the challenge from the extreme difficulty of detecting their movements and effects.

Ignorance about the production and presentation of propagules is less excusable than ignorance of their genetical importance. Some improvement in knowledge can fortunately be expected because the distribution of organisms within soil particles is now a fashionable study. But insistence on "representative sampling" to provide reproducible estimates of average population of soil microorganisms long obscured the true heterogeneity of soil and hence the need for local dispersal within it.

Nutritional control of sporulation is important, but as spores are frequent in soil, their formation cannot be subject to any general inhibition. The zonation of propagules within small clods (Dobbs and Hinson, 1960) suggests that the environment is important. Indeed the soil surface is often an inhospitable environment for growth and sporulation unless covered with litter or shaded by dense foliage or unless the weather is dull and wet (Geiger, 1950). These exceptions are obviously important and it must be admitted that we do not know how important the soil surface is as a source of spores. Casual observation in fine

weather suggests that it is seldom a prolific one, but we may not have looked hard enough, at the right times, or with the right methods to find the spores. Sporulation certainly is important on projecting organic matter, which differs widely from the mineral soil in such things as specific heat, and moisture and nutrient content (Glynne, 1953; Cox and Cock, 1962). Growth and sporulation of fungi on the soil surface must depend on the ability to switch rapidly between growth and resistance, as demonstrated by the fungal components of lichens growing on bare rock, an even less hospitable environment. Conditions within the soil environment fluctuate much less rapidly and violently, but there water films often prevent sporulation; and the discovery that branching is affected by water or temperature changes (Robertson, 1958; D. H. Lapwood, unpublished) suggests that constant environments may not be optimal.

THE MEANS OF DISPERSAL.—Plant pathogens will be emphasized unduly in this section; this perhaps needs no apology in this symposium, but such imbalance is at present inevitable. Dispersal studies require both a concern for the whereabouts of the organism and convenient means of recognizing its movements, and both seem lacking for soil saprophytes. No doubt this partly reflects the fact that, as substrates or organisms become more nearly ubiquitous, it becomes progressively more difficult to show that dispersal has occurred and less essential to find out how.

The soil environment offers so many obstacles that it is legitimate to question the value of soil-borne spores to spatial dispersal. There should be ample opportunity for downward transport but, if unrestricted, its usefulness is doubtful, for the chance of propagules becoming re-established would be small. Lateral movement seems more promising, but the means are few and the range small unless the many obstacles in soil can be avoided by propagules rising to the surface. Pathogens, litter fungi, and many Basidiomycetes are notable for improving their chance of dispersal by liberating propagules into turbulent air. It is necessary to distinguish dispersal between separated soils from that within single soils. Much spread within soil occurs over the minute distances separating microenvironments (Stanier, 1953), and may be so frequent that, like the individual frames of a motion picture, the intervening dispersal, in time or space, can easily pass unnoticed so long as it continues repeatedly.

Dispersal in time.—I wish to trespass as little as possible into "dormancy," the topic of the next paper, but having been impressed by the equal contributions dispersal in space and time make to the success of soil microorganisms, it seems worthwhile making a plea that we should consider them not as unrelated but as complementary processes.

Propagules that survive for long periods or through adverse conditions are usually specialized, but all need some ability to be inactive or resist the environment even if only briefly during transport. Lower fungi offer many examples of dispersal between soils being achieved only by resistant spores that are concurrently dispersing the fungus in time; the same is true of the inactive colonies of other organisms that are transported in seed, other propagating material, or in debris of plants. Survival in and dispersal by animal vectors is important for some pathogens (Harrison, 1961; Campbell, 1962) and infection of alternative host plants, often weeds, is a common means of surviving the absence of host crops, important in practice but of little theoretical interest.

Saprophytes must be dispersed in time by similar means but perhaps the most widespread and important is fungistasis (Dobbs, Hinson, and Bywater, 1960; Jackson, 1961). Whatever its causes, this phenomenon provides a large, well-distributed, tactical reserve of fungi able to colonize new substrates quickly. It offers a good example of dispersal in time, with a cause which is at least partly exogenous and an end stimulus. It seems reasonable to suppose that it may have two functions in dispersal: first as a means of inactive survival, automatically ended when favourable conditions recur; second as a means of preventing the precocious germination of spore masses before they have been dispersed. The first has parallels in the dormancy of some weed seeds, and the second resembles the self-inhibition of spores of aerial parasites (Allen, 1957; Shepherd and Mandryk, 1962).

Active movement.—Motility.—The ability of nematodes to orient themselves assists migration through the pore spaces of the soil, and they are the most motile of the soil microorganisms. They have some ability to migrate towards higher moisture content and optimal temperatures but tactic responses to gravity, light, and soil texture are doubtful (Peters, 1953; Wallace, 1959, 1960, 1961). It is probable that annual migrations are measured in inches and are greatest towards roots (Endo, 1959; Bird, 1959; Harrison and Winslow, 1961). Many fungi form zoospores but their range is so small (Esmarch, 1927) that motility is chiefly important for finding infection sites (Goode, 1956; Zentmyer, 1961; Dukes and Apple, 1961). The motility of *Rhizobium trifolii* also would not take it far in soil (Thornton and Gangulee, 1926).

Growth.—Only fungi and, perhaps, actinomycetes can grow to new microenvironments, but the speed with which they do and the distance they go are unknown, presumably because growth is so difficult to trace through soil. Occasionally it becomes visible, as in the centrifugal extension of "fairy-rings" (Shantz and Piemeisel, 1917; Bayliss Elliott, 1926; Parker-Rhodes, 1955a), where it also allows the number and extent of colonies to be measured. The establishment of pathogens in susceptible crops might be expected to offer good opportunities and it does allow colonies to be counted (Stover, 1962, Fig. 8), but the rate of extension is confused by the root growth of the host.

Many pathogens that are weak saprophytes cannot grow far from the roots of their host. For practical purposes it seems safe to assume that hyphae spread from infected roots only to uninfected ones that are adjacent or in contact, although in experiments infective range can be shown to depend on food supply (Scott, 1956a, b; Stover, 1962). Rhizomorphs of *Armillaria mellea* behave similarly in experiments (Garrett, 1956) and in plantation crops (Napper, 1932; Wallace, 1935; Marsh, 1952). Plainly, active saprophytes are better able to grow in soil (Garrett, 1944; Grainger, 1962), but their speed and range of growth have rarely been measured and information obtained from the colonization of buried substrates seldom seems applicable to unaltered soil.

Host roots aid dispersal in other ways besides mycelial growth, but spread is always limited by their extent. Related oak species form root grafts through which *Ceratocystis fagacearum* spores can move (Kuntz and Riker, 1950). Root contact was also claimed to lead to the exchange of rhizosphere floras (Pugh, 1962) and to the transmission of potato virus X (Roberts, 1948). Uninjured roots may attract pathogens, stimulate their germination (Buxton, 1957) or hatching (Shepherd, 1962), and so complete dispersal by assisting establishment.

Passive movement.—By Air.—The problems organisms must solve before they can suspend particles in air have been described recently and comprehensively by Gregory (1961). To be carried by turbulent air, spores must first traverse the laminar airflow boundary layer. Coprophilous fungi achieve this by a diversity of discharge mechanisms and agarics drop spores into turbulent air from raised fructifications (Ingold, 1953). Kelly and Pady (1953) suggested that much of the air spora originated from soil, but Gregory (1961) doubted this origin because of the difficulties of "take-off" from soil and because most of the soil fungi represented were saprophytes also able to live above-ground. Conidial and slime-spored fungi from soil probably become air-borne only as a result of rain (see below) or of dust dispersal. Dispersal on dust "rafts" is one of the most important means of bacterial dispersal (Bourdillon, Lidwell, and Lovelock, 1948) and must surely apply to fungi and yeasts contained in or cemented to soil particles. In dry weather, wind, cultivations, or any other disturbance easily raises dust, not only from light sand and peat soils, but also from clay soils in moist climates on a few days in most years. Wind erosion (Jacks and Whyte, 1939; Bennett, 1939) and wind-formed loess and Sahara soils (Nicot, 1960) show the potential magnitude of dust dispersal.

I have found no information about fungi being dispersed in wind-blown soils, but spores must go as far as nematode cysts and these have been found in blown soil at the edge of fields (Chitwood, 1951; White, 1953). Probably they go a great deal farther, for organic matter is separated from mineral soils by the wind and blown farther than the heaviest soil particles, which travel close to the ground and therefore encounter frequent obstacles (Bagnold, 1954). The smallest particles, presumably including fungus spores, behave as aerosol particles. On March 29, 1953, when peat soils were being blown, a spore trap operating in an apple orchard at Wisbech, Cambridgeshire, recorded many thousands of particles per cubic metre of air although the nearest peat soils were at least 10 miles away.

Once the difficulties of take-off have been overcome, aerosol particles are at the mercy of physical processes. It then makes little difference to the dispersal of propagules of equal terminal velocity whether they were projected into the air from an ascus, survived the evaporation of a splash droplet, or were remnants of some dust storm. The distance to which a single particle may be carried is theoretically almost limitless, but the chance that any one will go far and establish itself is minute. Gregory (1962) endeavoured to clarify this by estimating the "probable flight range" or 50% deposition point and "escape fraction" of air-borne spores. The former ranged from 4 m with large spores, liberated 10 cm aboveground in low turbulence, to 850 m with medium spores released 1 m aboveground in high turbulence. The proportion escaping from the local deposition plume and available to be dispersed long distances might commonly be as high as 10%.

Many fungi seem not to have spores dispersed in the air but some of these may be Fungi Imperfecti being spread by unrecognized perfect stages. Dispersal under such an alias may help to explain the occurrence in lists of fungi, cultured from dry air, of genera such as *Fusarium* and *Phoma* the asexual spores of which undoubtedly become air-borne only with difficulty (Richards, 1956; Pady, 1957). Systematic culturing of unidentified ascospores might well be profitable. The difficulty of relating asexual to sexual forms is increased when the sexual stage appears only several years after the death of the host, as in *Rosellinia necatrix* and *Eutypa armeniacae* (Carter, 1957). Soil microbiologists have, justifiably, stressed that even when spore take-off, transport, and deposition are demonstrated, this is still not evidence that it leads to infection (Garrett, 1939*a*). Yet too often, by successive misquotation, careful reports of failure to infect in limited experiments have become accepted as established negatives. Improved knowledge of infection conditions makes it desirable to re-examine these questions, for among the important pathogens affected are *Fomes, Armillaria, Ganoderma, Corticium, Helicobasidium,* and *Ophiobolus graminis,* which I shall use as an example.

In South Australia, Samuel and Garrett (1933) found it difficult to explain the epidemiology of *Ophiobolus graminis* without involving spread and infection by ascospores. The disease was serious in the second crop on newly reclaimed land (Oort, 1936). After rain Gregory and Stedman (1958) measured up to 3,700 ascospores per cubic metre of air ½ m over wheat stubble at the time when winter wheat was emerging. In later experiments, Garrett (1939*b*) got no infection on wheat seedlings growing in unsterile soil even when each seedling was inoculated with a suspension containing 80,000 ascospores; but the same methods infected seedlings grown in sterile soil. No doubt Garrett was right to conclude that microbial competition in unsterile soil prevented infection but his experiment cannot prove that ascospores do not infect in other conditions. Padwick (1939) calculated that Garrett diluted

the heaviest dose of ascospores with 13,000 times their volume of water and so some nutrients or growth stimulants might have been removed from the spores.

In 1956, Dr. G. A. Salt and I tested the infectivity of air-borne ascospores to wheat seedlings. Up to now no attempt has been made to repeat the test, which was apparently successful. Despite the deficiencies of this simple experiment the results are worth mentioning here, not to further any claim, but to provoke fuller investigation of this and similar problems. On October 8, 1956, a box (15 × 9 × 3 in) of unsterile loam-sand mixture containing 50 wheat seedlings, about 1 in high, and bearing terminal guttation drops, was exposed to the ascospores from 200 wetted straws bearing perithecia of *Ophiobolus graminis*. To exclude any danger of infected fragments falling on the box, the straws were wetted before they were placed in the wind tunnel (Gregory, 1951). Exposure lasted for 3 hr at 2 mph with the seedlings approximately 2 m downwind of the straws. About 26 ascospores per sq cm were deposited on the soil between the seedlings and heavier deposition would be expected on the coleoptiles, which would act as small cylindrical traps. The box and a similar control not exposed to ascospores were lightly watered and left outside until early March, when they were put in an unheated glasshouse until May 29. All plants in the exposed box then had runner hyphae on some roots and 70% had blackened roots, whereas the box not exposed to ascospores had no runner hyphae or black roots. The possibility of mycelial spread in the exposed box prevents estimation of how many plants were infected by ascospores. It seems reasonable to allow air-borne ascospores a chance to deposit and infect in their own fashion. The application of aqueous spore suspensions to soil known to be highly competitive and antagonistic may not reproduce natural inoculation; indeed Garrett (1942) suggested the possibility of infection through the coleoptile.

There was similar controversy about the ability of basidiospores to establish root-disease fungi such as *Fomes annosus* or mycorrhizal fungi. But by finding favourable substrates and using natural inoculation methods, both have been shown to be possible (Rishbeth, 1951*a,b*; Robertson, 1954; Meredith, 1959).

By Water.—Growth and spore discharge of many microorganisms are favoured by moisture. Spores suspended in air can be trapped in falling raindrops but the subsequent effects rainwater has on dispersal are less well known. The first raindrops to wet spore-bearing surfaces may shake them, and for about a millisecond each drop may cause rapid radial air movement in front of the spreading splash. These air movements disrupt the laminar boundary layer and can disperse many litter fungi. This process probably operates on the soil surface and may contribute to the smell of freshly wetted soil (Hirst and Stedman, 1963).

After surface water films are established, splash dispersal may become important (Faulwetter, 1917; Gregory, Guthrie, and Bunce, 1959). Heavy rain splashes soil on to the lower part of plants (Rose, 1960) and can lead to infection by bacteria and fungi that have overwintered in or on soil (Glynne, 1953; Renfro, 1959). Splash dispersal is particularly important for slimy spores that become cemented to their substrates on drying (Dobbs, 1939) but may carry whole perithecia (Dixon, 1961) or unwettable spores on the outside of droplets (Davies, 1961; Jarvis, 1962). Preliminary tests, made with Mr. O. J. Stedman, suggest that the number of splash products from bare soil increases as soil wetness increases, and that most products are redeposited within a metre of the impact point. But some drops, the proportion depending on wind velocity and relative humidity, evaporate and their solid contents then behave as air-borne particles. Quite a different mechanism, able to lift heavy particles over short distances, operates when raindrops fall into the specialised splash cups of the Nidulariaceae and *Polyporus conchifer* (Brodie, 1951a,b).

As the texture and moisture content of soils determine whether rainwater will run off or percolate, they also help to decide the movement of spores. Nicot (1960) showed that spores are rapidly carried through coarse sands by percolating water, but spores do not move readily in all soils (Burges, 1950). Continuous fast percolation may be necessary to maintain movement because drainage causes menisci to retreat into interstitial pore spaces and presses mucilaginous spores against mineral particles, where they adhere. Watering equivalent to heavy rain was needed to wash *Phytophthora infestans* spores through packed soil columns (Zan, 1962). In crops, most infected potato tubers occur near the surface, but there may be many at least 7 in below the crest of the ridge. The penetration of spores to these depths could be down soil cracks and potato stems to the tuber zone (Lacey, 1962).

Many soil fungi have spherical or elongate spores; few are filiform or of complex shapes or have ornamentation. Analogy with Wallace's (1959) conclusion that inactive filiform nematodes do not percolate suggests that the spore shapes of soil fungi might be adapted towards movement in soil. Certainly most of them differ greatly from Ingold's (1959) "stream spora." The three-dimensional complexity of these spores seems highly adapted towards adhesion to obstacles and congregation in scum and foam (Webster, 1959). Differences between the behaviour of different spherical spores are usually attributed to differences in the ease with which they are wetted (Burges, 1950). Electron micrographs show that spores of many soil fungi are less ornamented than air-borne spores and wettable spores are often slime covered. Resistance to wetting is usually attributed to waxy surfaces. But conidia of *Aspergillus fumigatus* and *Penicillium restrictum*, both difficult to wet, have characteristically spiny and sculptured walls, and their structure is not visibly altered by wax solvents.

In considering migration with percolating water, we should not omit to mention that possibly in undisturbed soils it may be advantageous for fungi to remain in the horizon that contains their nutrients, and even in cultivated soils unlimited leaching would usually be unprofitable.

Percolating water obviously has less chance of dispersing microorganisms laterally over considerable distances than run-off water. The load of propagules will be greatest when the soil is being eroded in the catchment area, but although propagules may be common in drainage-channel water (Cooke, 1954, 1956), their chance of reestablishment is small unless they are redistributed over soil or crops by flooding or irrigation. The best evidence of movement in floods comes from work with nematodes (Chitwood, 1951; Thompson, Roebuck, and Cooper, 1959), but there are numerous examples of lateral spread in wet soils both for nematodes (Beaumont and Staniland, 1941; Ducharme, 1955; E. B. Brown, 1957) and fungi (Hickman, 1958; Colhoun, 1958). Glasshouse water supplies have also been found to be contaminated with fungi (Bewley and Buddin, 1921) and tobacco-necrosis virus (Smith, 1937).

By Man, Animals, and Other Vectors.—The influence of man on the above means of dispersal has sometimes been important but usually indirect. In the means now to be discussed it is direct and often indispensable. Quantitative confirmations of man's participation are rare, except for the introduction of exotic pathogens or interceptions in quarantine inspections (Hant, 1946; Moore, 1953; McCubbin, 1954). No doubt similar movements of soil saprophytes exist but may be of less importance; for both means depend chiefly on trade in plants, to which soil is often only incidental.

Other animals must transport organisms adhering to them in dust or mud, and activities like leaf burial or casting by arthropods and earthworms must regularly move microorganisms through soil (Murphy, 1953; Satchell, 1958). Occasionally, very specific and directed relations occur as with the attraction of flies to Phallaceae (Fulton, 1889). The fact that specialized fungal pathogens of animals and man are now so widespread in soils (Ajello, 1956) perhaps indicates how effectively the movement of their hosts has assisted their dispersal. Although insects may be most active in dispersal aboveground, they are also important below (Bonde, 1939; Leach, 1940) and seem to have been responsible for moving most of the propagules caught in the slide-traps buried in soil by Dobbs and Hinson (1960). Insects also make dispersal effective by wounding roots sufficiently to aid the entry of pathogens.

Fungus propagules are eaten by both wild and domesticated mammals. Usually, as with sclerotia or resting spores on fodder plants, they are incidental to the diet (Gibbs, 1931; Leach and Mead, 1936; J. G. Brown, 1937; Colhoun, 1958), and the transmission of these is usually inefficient and negligible more than 48 hours after feeding. Coprophilous fungi are no more important to their vectors but are more closely adapted to this mode of dispersal because many are stimulated to germinate by conditions in the gut. The propagules are sometimes part of the diet (Diehl, 1939; Dowding, 1955) but even then some are likely to escape digestion and to be dispersed.

Nematodes are often synergistic to other pathogens (Fielding, 1959) or introduce pathogens to new hosts (Metcalfe, 1940), sometimes with very specific vector relations with viruses (Hewitt, Raski, and Goheen, 1958; Harrison, 1961; Raski and Hewitt, 1962). Recently zoospores of *Olpidium* spp. have been proved important as vectors of lettuce-big-vein virus and tobacco-necrosis virus (Grogan et al., 1958).

Transmission on Clothing, Implements, or Machines. —This type of transmission is often mentioned but seldom measured perhaps because it is difficult to prevent and its means impossible to enumerate. Certainly it can be important with viruses and bacteria such as *Corynebacterium sepedonicum,* which are spread on cutting knives and planting machinery.

Cultivations move plant debris, disturb microenvironments, and obliterate soil horizons. Cultivations in one and in two directions at right angles produced different patterns of spread of *Verticillium* wilt in hop gardens (Keyworth, 1942). Weather decides if machines move soil as dust or mud and therefore how many organisms are transported, how well they survive, and where they will be deposited. Sugar-beet eelworm was found at 19 of 144 roadside loading points and in washings at processing factories (Petherbridge and Jones, 1944). Similar transport was recorded in Chitwood's (1951) account of the spread of *Heterodera rostochiensis,* recorded in Long Island, New York, in one of the best-documented case histories of the spread of a newly introduced pathogen. There was an abnormally large chance of infestation in all the scattered fields cropped by the owner of the field where the first discovery was made. Within some fields there was good evidence of spread by cultivation, for infection spread 400 ft in a direction contrary to that of drainage. About 5 gal of soil containing some 32,000 cysts were recovered from a tractor and 180 cysts from dirt off a pair of boots. Dry mud may stick on implements for months and allow eventual dispersal over a large area or distance.

Machines can create dust aerosols fine enough to travel as far as air-borne spores, but the majority of propagules, deposited close to the machine, will extend the infected areas or start new ones. Exposure of a few nutrient petri plates for 2 min on the soil 12 yds downwind from a small rotary cultivator which made 4 passages across a dry fallow, yielded 62 colonies including 15 recognizable genera, mostly of soil fungi. Simultaneous exposures the same distance upwind yielded only 12 colonies of 4 genera (Fig. 1). Some machines spread root pathogens without disturbing soil, for example, forage harvesters spread *Verticillium* wilt in alfalfa, partly by wounding and inoculating and partly by spreading debris on which the fungus forms spores (Isaac, 1957; Kreitlow, 1962).

With Seed and Plant Propagating Material.—All groups of soil microorganisms and viruses (Lister and Murant, 1961) may be seedborne. Many fungi dispersed with seed have been listed by Noble, de Tempe, and Neergaard (1958). It is surprising to note that they include fungi like *Plasmodiophora brassicae* (Colhoun, 1958), *Phytophthora infestans* on tomato seed (Boyd, 1935), and *Rhizoctonia solani* (Baker, 1947). When seeds are plated on nutrient media many saprophytes grow, particularly with seeds of short plants where seeds may become contaminated by splashed soil particles. The newly discovered viruses of cultivated mushroom (Hollings, 1962) are transmissible with hyphae and so could easily be spread in commerce with diseased spawn; perhaps they may also be the first to be shown to be transmitted by spores.

Demand for propagating material certified as healthy perhaps reflects the importance of this means of dispersal. The sometimes high proportion of seed potatoes visibly diseased is further evidence of dispersal both in time and space.

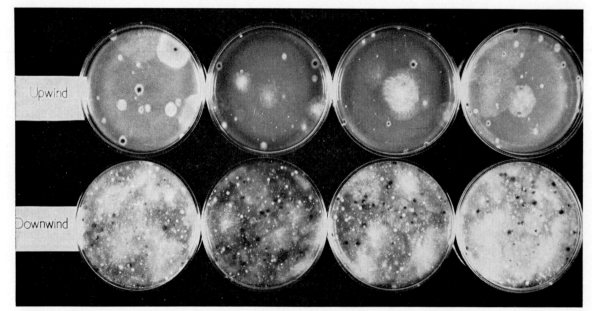

Fig. 1. Colonies growing on potato-dextrose-agar plates exposed approximately 12 yd upwind or downwind of a small rotary cultivator making 4 passages across dry fallow soil during a 2 min exposure; Harpenden, 27 June, 1962.

With plant debris.—Dispersal of fungi in crop debris occurs during cultivations, notably with *Verticillium* spp. (Keyworth, 1942; Isaac, 1957), when root crops are fed to stock or when crop residues are moved after harvest. Dung or mixed composts develop such unique floras that, if properly rotted, they rarely seem important in dispersing pathogenic soil organisms; but special composts can be infective, particularly when improperly made (Sewell and Wilson, 1961; Sewell, Wilson, and Martin, 1962).

DISCUSSION.—My first step in preparing this paper was to tabulate the fungi mentioned in one textbook of plant pathology. I hoped this might help me to discard the bias of an aerobiologist. Of approximately six hundred fungal species, almost five hundred could be excluded for my subject as chiefly parasitic aboveground. The small number of root pathogens does not imply they are less important or variable; on the contrary, it gives some indication that many have wide host ranges and that the specialized forms we know as pathogens are often morphologically indistinguishable from others. Of the group of "soil-borne" and "possibly soil-borne" species, almost half had propagules that might be spread by air, and almost half might be spread by water. Other means of dispersal were suggested for about a quarter, and in only a tenth were there no known propagules potentially capable of distribution. At least among this group of soil fungi the potentiality for spread is great; but how often is the potentiality achieved and then establishment accomplished?

Those who have studied the dispersal of soil microorganisms will already have realized that there is a wealth of possible means, many of which are obvious and make trite reading, others so unusual that for reviewers they develop the attractions of collector's pieces. By contrast, quantitative information is so scarce as to be almost nonexistent. If this paper were intended to evaluate dispersal in terms of range, frequency, and importance, it could not be anything but a failure for lack of measurements. Only if it encourages extra work and provides a guide to what might be done will it be worthwhile.

The evidence of dispersal.—The importance of Stanier's (1953) concept of soil as a matrix of discrete, transient microenvironments was recognized by Garrett (1955), who stressed that successive cycles of "colonization, exploitation and exhaustion" were separated either by inactivity or spread. It is therefore normal, indeed essential, that within soils both saprophytes and parasites must disperse both in time and space. The frequency, brevity, or shortness of the individual stages do nothing to diminish the importance of the process, although they may often disguise it. Motility, growth, disturbance, percolation, and transport by the soil fauna provide ample means of spread, and almost all soil organisms can adopt inactive forms.

Few organisms can be truly ubiquitous in soils but many are widespread. It is inconceivable that they all originated everywhere, so gradual dispersal is the only

feasible explanation. That dispersal occurs continuously there is no doubt, for it can be detected both in action and by its effects. The Agaricaceae provide one of the best illustrations. They are difficult to isolate from soils, even to find by searching for sporophores (Parker-Rhodes, 1955b) during their brief periods of fructification (Wilkins and Harris, 1946). Nevertheless, throughout late summer and autumn, air-borne basidiospores are numerous in England (Gregory and Hirst, 1957; Hamilton, 1959), can establish root diseases and mycorrhizal infection (Rishbeth, 1951a,b; Robertson, 1954), and presumably explain the regularity with which typical agaric floras establish themselves in young forests. It is interesting to recall that among the 310 species of fungi which between the eruption of 1883 and 1934 recolonised Krakatau across at least 40 km of sea, there were 150 Hymenomycetes (together with 10 Discomycetes, 56 Pyrenomycetes, 9 Gasteromycetes, 2 Uredinales and 51 Fungi Imperfecti) (see Bisby, 1943).

Doubt concerning the importance of dispersal often arises from the sharply defined boundaries of experimental plots, and the success of crop rotations or quarantine restrictions in controlling root diseases. Similarly, disease gradients are less obvious with root than with foliage pathogens, and patches of diseased plants increase more slowly. The failure of some propagules to infect in experiments designed to test this ability has also been accepted as evidence that these are rarely, if ever, functional. These doubts will be resolved only after much progress has been made in improving detection methods, in understanding dispersal types and patterns, and in estimating the frequency and range of completed dispersal.

Detection of dispersal.—It is generally admitted that no sampling methods are yet reliably quantitative, nonselective, or suitable for all groups of organisms. The problems are so many and difficult that it is no disparagement to consider aims before any improvements can be suggested. At present one of the most urgent needs is an "absolute" standard against which other methods could be judged and detection thresholds calculated. Measurement of number is unsatisfactory as a measure of prevalence, particularly when fragmentation during sampling may increase it or many of the propagules may have been inactive. Even supposing that activity could be measured accurately, it would be a thoroughly unsuitable parameter for dispersal studies. Mutually exclusive organisms, substrates, and environments make any universal method almost certainly unattainable. Therefore most progress is likely to come from applying several specialized and selective methods to similar samples. The development of selective methods of extraction (Ledingham and Chinn, 1955; Watson, 1960; Chinn, Sallans, and Ledingham, 1962), quantitative baiting techniques (Tsao, 1960; Lacey, 1962), highly specialized media or incubation conditions (Lingappa and Lockwood, 1962; Gregory and Lacey, 1962) can improve the sensitivity with which particular organisms can be detected. Reducing the number of unwanted colonies in these ways offers a temporary amelioration of the constraint of the petri plate, from which it is to be hoped microbiology will soon escape.

These are all methods for estimating populations rather than changes in populations; they are the normal methods of soil microbiology, but can reveal dispersal only through changes between successive estimates.

Two other methods widely used by epidemiologists studying foliage diseases are mapping and interception. Drawbacks of mapping are discussed below but there seem many untested opportunities for intercepting soil microorganisms during dispersal. To some extent the method is used in the colonization of buried substrates or slide traps and by examining seeds and propagating material. Measurement of air dispersal of basidiospores has already been mentioned, and it is comparatively easy to do because the spores are highly characteristic and numerous. Success with many (or most) soil organisms spreading through air awaits improved methods for catching splashes and culturing catches. Comparison of the propagules and the resulting colony is the only way to assess and expose the possibility of dispersal of Fungi Imperfecti under the alias of perfect stages. Progress could be made with extraction or culture of propagules from percolating or drainage water and by removing propagules from such agents of dispersal as machines, soil insects, and migratory animals (Pugh and Mathison, 1962). To evaluate interceptions it would be necessary to define the minimum units able to establish organisms, information which would also be valuable for understanding dispersal patterns and designing methods able to reveal the presence of organisms very soon after arrival.

Patterns and signs of dispersal.—Two extreme dispersal patterns can usefully be distinguished by their different efficiencies, ranges, and results. "Imperative dispersal," which must be repeated for the organism to survive, is usually the means whereby the organism exploits its habitat. It is typically thorough, often frequent and specialized, and may employ many agencies, including the growth of the host. There are many intermediates between this and the other extreme of "capricious dispersal," which is occasional and, although it may spread an organism, is not necessary for it to survive. Because it must operate at greater ranges than imperative dispersal and need not succeed, it is less frequent and can use less efficient methods. But the area, time, and number of propagules are so enormous that eventually it will be successful—this is a game of chance, imperative dispersal a game of skill.

Harvest, fire, and cultivations may all obliterate the aerial environment. Although they cause profound changes belowground, they seldom necessitate the complete re-establishment of the flora. Even dead host plants remain only briefly aboveground before they get incorporated into litter or soil where their residues may remain for many years. Temporary absence or inactivity of hosts usually presents little difficulty to root pathogens, but foliage parasites *must* resort to perennial alternate or alternative hosts, to seed, or to resistant forms that temporarily contaminate soil. Epidemiologists studying foliage diseases therefore become conversant with the signs of introduction and spread. The occurrence of rusted wheat plants around a barberry bush, or of blighted potatoes around an initial source of *Phytophthora infestans*, are good evidence of introduction. No doubt foci often occur belowground, but unless they produce foliage symptoms their development is difficult to study. Furthermore, unlike foliage diseases, the presence of groups of plants with diseased roots may not imply recent introduction of the pathogen.

The distribution of *Xiphinema diversicaudatum* in Geesecroft Wilderness at Rothamsted (Harrison and Winslow, 1961) may be an example of a persistent relic population. Spread into this naturally regenerated wood seems to have started from an old hedgeline where woody plants and lack of cultivation probably preserved vestiges of a population once more widespread under natural climax forest before the advent of agriculture. Such persistent vestiges may be rare, but relic populations are often important in the epidemiology of root pathogens. Among plantation crops root diseases may come from preceding crops or jungle (see Garrett, 1939a), and foci of infection do not necessarily imply introduction but may come from increased growth or sporulation after the death of a partially resistant host plant. Most crop rotations have been determined partly by the extent root pathogens are able to disperse in time either in resistant forms or on alternative hosts. The amount and distribution of relics is a major factor determining the speed and severity of disease increase when susceptible hosts are reintroduced.

Fungi have such a propensity for exchanging genetic material through hyphal anastomoses (Pontecorvo and Sermonti, 1954; Buxton, 1956) that nuclear migration and parasexual recombination can provide variation within vegetative populations. If pathogenicity can be controlled at a few loci, it is reasonable to question whether pathogens always need to arrive from elsewhere or whether they can be synthesized or originate entirely by genetic recombination in microorganisms already in soils (Bawden, 1957; Nelson, 1961). The existence of such pathogenic variants would be manifested only by planting susceptible crops on which they could multiply preferentially.

Ability to forecast the start of foliage-disease epidemics is useful to agriculture and horticulture. Meteorological forecasting of apple scab or potato late blight implies that the pathogen is present, will disperse and infect hosts *whenever* simple phenological and meteorological criteria are satisfied. Such methods have been little used with soil fungi other than for empirical estimates of the probability of severe foot-rots in cereal rotations. Predicting imperative dispersal seems feasible and would be valuable for estimating how existing populations would increase. There must be few root diseases about which we know the essential parameters of host susceptibility, pathogen supply, competition, and environmental effects well enough to design an accurate method of forecasting severity. Further, the lack of effective chemical or biological controls, other than crop rotation, provide little incentive to seek predictions. Capricious dispersal is even more difficult to predict and in my opinion only empiricism can succeed until much more is known about all the means of dispersal and their efficiency. Few propagules are distributed randomly and only some obey the physical rules of diffusion. The movement of many would be very directional, depending on vectors or rare sequences of coincidence.

Theoreticians, with mathematical ability that most of us can only envy, will no doubt be tempted to design models of these methods of dispersal, as they have done for others. While welcoming their interest we must strive to ensure that, in the course of their intellectually satisfying work, they are not tempted to diverge entirely from the ways in which the organisms really operate. Inevitably models portray averages; equally inevitably every occasion of dispersal is peculiar, involving unique combinations of biological processes and often requiring exceptional weather. In aerobiology, although more is known of the rules, dispersal models have not provided more valuable information than observation, and distant dispersal seems likely to be controlled by meteorological processes not yet included in any models.

Frequency of dispersal.—The effect of dispersal depends as much on its frequency as on its means. Dating the frequent rapid dispersal between microenvironments is unimportant, but it is vital for assessing the importance of local and distant extension and how this is related to season, weather, production, and reception.

Few organisms can have such frequent opportunities for dispersal as the inhabitants of tidal mud flats, where the surface is usually disturbed four times daily. By contrast the opportunities for successful dispersal will obviously be few with those soil-borne viruses whose spread requires the coexistence, not only of host and pathogen, but also two sexes of the nematode vector; or for the establishment of *Fomes annosus* if it must wait for a pine tree to die or be felled. Though interesting and important, occurrences of this rarity are ill suited for quantitative experiments on the number and range of successful dispersals. An example will simplify discussion of such a diffuse subject. The epidemiology of take-all disease of wheat (*Ophiobolus graminis*) will be compared with potato late blight (*Phytophthora infestans*), a long established favourite of epidemiologists.

Blight starts each year from minute sources, usually thought to be relics of former epidemics in seed or culled tubers. It can be estimated that the progeny of each relic annually infects between one and ten million plants (van der Zaag, 1956; Hirst and Stedman, 1960). Observations over a 10-year period at Rothamsted suggest that this multiplication is achieved by an average of 7 successful dispersal occasions before "outbreak," when the disease is first found in crops, and about 20 later occasions involving such massive doses that plants are killed.

Comparable evidence of the abilities of *Ophiobolus graminis* are scanty, but under conditions favourable to the fungus, results reported by Wehrle and Ogilvie (1956) suggest that about 50 plants become infected by mycelial spread from single diseased plants scattered through a small plot of otherwise healthy wheat. Analysing the increase in percent plants infected in spring between the first and second wheat crops in rotation experiments suggests that this figure is of the right order and, even allowing for multiple infection, it would be safe to assume that multiplication varies between tenfold and hundredfold each year.

There is no evidence that *Ophiobolus graminis* is able to survive saprophytically other than in infected roots or stubble, and rotation experiments show that, in the absence of alternative grass hosts, infectivity decreases greatly within a single year (Garrett, 1942). Although a maximum plant-to-plant spread of up to 5 ft per season has been reported (Wehrle and Ogilvie, 1956), the fungus cannot grow beyond the root zone of its hosts, so that at harvest abrupt changes of infectivity are inevitable at the boundaries of an experimental plot that has grown a succession of susceptible crops. It is the persistence of such boundaries when wheat is again grown on both sides that gives the impression of dispersal being unimportant. The line of demarcation might be blurred by mycelial spread, by cultivations spreading infected stubbles, or perhaps by air-borne ascospores (although in experiments stubble and emerging crops seldom coexist, assuming these are true requirements). My colleague Mr. D. B. Slope tells me that the spread between the guard rows of contiguous plots is common but it does not happen when a cultivated path separates plots by about 2 feet. By analogy with other organisms, spread of infected stubble and roots by cultivations would be expected to cross such boundaries and presumably does, for although first crops after fallow breaks seldom have more than 1% plants infected, 1 to 5 repetitions are usually sufficient, at Rothamsted, to ensure severe infection.

Let us assume that ascospores can infect germinating seedlings, for they occur in the air after rain during several weeks in the year (Gregory and Stedman, 1958; R. H. Gregory, personal communication) and concentrations up to 3,700 ascospores per cubic metre of air have been measured. Sampling for *Phytophthora infestans* revealed a similar duration and up to a maximum of 14,000 spores per cubic metre of air. Both fungi therefore seem prolific, but if *Ophiobolus graminis* ascospores do infect they will lead to only one infection cycle per year, in contrast to at least 20 cycles by *P. infestans*.

Ophiobolus graminis seems certain to spread by mycelial growth, probably by disturbance of relics, and possibly by ascospores. Taking the season's growth as a unit, each method operates only once per season. If potato blight was similarly limited, it would reach only the stage of minute foci of perhaps ten infected plants per square kilometre. The conclusion must be that the rate of multiplication decides our ability to detect spread. Intensive spring sampling of experimental plots for foot and root fungi (Glynne, 1951) involved examination of the plants from approximately 0.3% of the area, or about one plant per square yard.

Laborious though this sampling is, it gives a high threshold level for detection (Hirst, 1959) and a small probability of finding new foci before there has been a large increase in the number of plants infected. The first wheat crops after two nonsusceptible crops usually have less than 1% of plants infected or about 3 per square yard. Allowing for increased infection through mycelial spread, this suggests that establishment in the crop can rarely be so high as one per square yard. Thus sampling designed to determine the percentage of plants infected is nowhere near sensitive enough to detect the initial infections early enough to determine whether they originated from relics or perhaps from ascospores. Clearly this is a problem demanding improved methods before useful estimates of dispersal are possible.

The moral of the preceding example is that effective dispersal is likely to be rare (often much less frequent than the relic populations which may disguise it). At such low rates of subsequent multiplication it seems doubtful if we would even yet be aware that *Endothia parasitica* or *Peronospora tabacina* had reached Europe or *Puccinia polysora* was in Africa. But the soil and many of its inhabitants have the advantages of durability. Although many of the processes described here are slow, inefficient, and require improbable coincidences to bring them to fruition, this in no way invalidates them. The dispersal of soil microorganisms can often succeed at extremely low efficiencies, almost by mistakes; and, because they are such masters of the waiting game their success must be judged not only in terms of annual crops but on historical or geological time scales, on which the recolonization of Krakatau is only a brief interlude. Bisby (1943) struck just the right note when considering the fungi in the relatively young soils of Manitoba. He pointed out that since the retreat of the last glacier there has been an opportunity of "not more than 25,000 years."

LITERATURE CITED

AJELLO, L. 1956. Soil as a natural reservoir for human pathogenic fungi. Science 123: 876-879.

ALLEN, P. J. 1957. Properties of a volatile fraction from uredospores of *Puccinia graminis* var. *tritici* affecting their germination and development. I. Biological activity. Plant Physiol. 32: 385-389.

BAGNOLD, R. A. 1954. The physics of blown sand and desert dunes. Methuen, London. 265 p.

BAKER, K. F. 1947. Seed transmission of *Rhizoctonia solani* in relation to control of seedling damping-off. Phytopathology 37: 912-924.

BAWDEN, F. C. 1957. The role of plant hosts in microbial ecology. Symp. Soc. Gen. Microbiol. 7: 299-314.

BAYLISS ELLIOTT, J. S. 1926. Concerning 'fairy rings' in pastures. Ann. Appl. Biol. 13: 277-288.

BEAUMONT, A., and L. M. STANILAND. 1941. The spread of eelworm in commercial narcissus plantings. Ann. Appl. Biol. 28: 135-141.

BENNETT, H. H. 1939. Soil conservation. McGraw-Hill Publishing Co. Ltd., New York. 939 p.

BEWLEY, W. F., and W. BUDDIN. 1921. On the fungus flora of glasshouse water supplies in relation to plant disease. Ann. Appl. Biol. 8: 10-19.

BIRD, A. F. 1959. The attractiveness of roots to the plant parasitic nematodes, *Meloidogyne javanica* and *M. hapla*. Nematologica 4: 322-335.

BISBY, G. R. 1943. Geographical distribution of fungi. Botan. Rev. 9: 466-482.

BONDE, R. 1939. The role of insects in the dissemination of potato blackleg and seed-piece decay. J. Agr. Res. 59: 889-917.

BOURDILLON, R. B., O. M. LIDWELL, and J. E. LOVELOCK. 1948. Studies in air hygiene. Med. Res. Council, Spec. Rept. Ser., No. 262, H. M. Stationery Office, London. 356 p.

BOYD, O. C. 1935. Evidence of the seed-borne nature of late blight (*Phytophthora infestans*) of tomatoes. Phytopathology 25: 7.

BRODIE, H. J. 1951a. The splash-cup dispersal mechanism in plants. Can. J. Botany 29: 224-234.

BRODIE, H. J. 1951b. The splash-cups of *Polyporus conchifer*. Can. J. Botany 29: 593-596.

BROWN, E. B. 1957. Lucerne stem eelworm, a serious threat to lucerne growing. Agriculture (London) 63: 517-520.

BROWN, J. G. 1937. Relation of livestock to the control of sclerotinosis of lettuce. Phytopathology 27: 1045-1050.

BURGES, A. 1950. The downward movement of fungal spores in sandy soil. Trans. Brit. Mycol. Soc. 33: 142-147.

BUXTON, E. W. 1956. Heterokaryosis and parasexual recombination in pathogenic strains of *Fusarium oxysporum*. J. Gen. Microbiol. 15: 133-139.

BUXTON, E. W. 1957. Some effects of pea root exudates on physiologic races of *Fusarium oxysporum* Fr. f. *pisi* (Linf.) Snyder & Hansen. Trans. Brit. Mycol. Soc. 40: 145-154.

CAMPBELL, R. N. 1962. Relationship between the lettuce big-vein virus and its vector *Olpidium brassicae*. Nature (London) 195: 675-677.

CARTER, M. V. 1957. *Eutypa armeniacae* Hansf. & Carter, sp. nov., an airborne vascular pathogen of *Prunus armeniaca* L. in Southern Australia. Australian J. Botany 5: 21-35.

CHINN, S. H. F., B. J. SALLANS, and R. J. LEDINGHAM. 1962. Spore populations of *Helminthosporium sativum* in soils in relation to the occurrence of common root rot of wheat. Can. J. Plant Sci. 42: 720-729.

CHITWOOD, B. G. 1951. The golden nematode of potatoes. U. S. Dept. Agr. Circ. 875, 48 p.

COLHOUN, J. 1958. Club root disease of crucifers caused by *Plasmodiophora brassicae* Woron. Commonwealth Mycol. Inst. Kew, Surrey, Phytopathological Paper No. 3, 108 p.

COOKE, W. B. 1954. Fungi in polluted water and sewage. III. Fungi in a small polluted stream. Sewage Ind. Wastes 26: 790-794.

COOKE, W. B. 1956. Potential plant pathogenic fungi in sewage and polluted water. Plant Disease Reptr. 40: 681-687.

COX, J., and L. J. COCK. 1962. Survival of *Cercosporella herpotrichoides* on naturally infected straws of wheat and barley. Plant Pathol. 11: 65-66.

DAVIES, R. R. 1961. Wettability and the capture, carriage and deposition of particles by raindrops. Nature (London) 191: 616-617.

DIEHL, W. W. 1939. *Endogone* as animal food. Science 90: 442.

DIXON, P. A. 1961. Spore dispersal in *Chaetomium globosum* (Kunze). Nature (London) 191: 1418-1419.

DOBBS, C. G. 1939. Sporangial drops in the Mucoraceae. Nature (London) 143: 286.

DOBBS, C. G., and W. H. HINSON. 1960. Some observations on fungal spores in soil. p. 33-42. *In* D. Parkinson and J. S. Waid [ed.], The ecology of soil fungi, Liverpool University Press, Liverpool.

DOBBS, C. G., W. H. HINSON and J. BYWATER. 1960. Inhibition of fungal growth in soils. p. 130-147. *In* D. Parkinson and J. S. Waid [ed.], The ecology of soil fungi, Liverpool University Press, Liverpool.

DOWDING, E. S. 1955. *Endogone* in Canadian rodents. Mycologia 47: 51-57.

DUCHARME, E. P. 1955. Sub-soil drainage as a factor in the spread of the burrowing nematode. Proc. Florida State Hort. Soc. 68: 29-31.

DUKES, P. D., and J. L. APPLE. 1961. Chemotaxis of zoospores of *Phytophthora parasitica* var. *nicotianae* by plant roots and certain chemical solutions. Phytopathology 51: 195-197.

ENDO, B. Y. 1959. Responses of root-lesion nematodes *Pratylenchus brachyurus* and *P. zeae* to various plants and soil types. Phytopathology 49: 417-421.

ESMARCH, F. 1927. Untersuchungen zur Biologie des Kartoffelkrebses. Angew. Botan. 9: 88-124.

FAULWETTER, R. C. 1917. Wind blown rain, a factor in disease dissemination. J. Agr. Res. 10: 639-648.

FIELDING, M. J. 1959. Nematodes in plant disease. Ann. Rev. Microbiol. 13: 239-251.

FULTON, T. W. 1889. The dispersion of the spores of fungi by the agency of insects, with special reference to the Phalloides. Ann. Botany (London) 3: 207-237.

GARRETT, S. D. 1939a. Soil-borne fungi and the control of root disease. Commonwealth Bur. Soil Sci. (Harpenden), Tech. Commun. 38, 64 p.

GARRETT, S. D. 1939b. Soil conditions and the take-all disease of wheat. IV. Factors limiting infection by ascospores of *Ophiobolus graminis*. Ann. Appl. Biol. 26: 47-55.

GARRETT, S. D. 1942. The take-all disease of cereals. Commonwealth Bur. Soil Sci. (Harpenden) Tech. Commun. 41, 40 p.

GARRETT, S. D. 1944. Root disease fungi. Chronica Botanica Co., Waltham, Mass. 177 p.

GARRETT, S. D. 1955. Microbial ecology of the soil. Trans. Brit. Mycol. Soc. 38: 1-9.

GARRETT, S. D. 1956. Rhizomorph behaviour in *Armillaria mellea* (Vahl) Quél. II. Logistics of infection. Ann. Botany (London) [N.S.] 20: 193-209.

GEIGER, R. 1950. The climate near the ground. Harvard University Press, Cambridge, Mass. 482 p.

GIBBS, J. G. 1931. Club root in cruciferous crops. New Zealand J. Agr. 42: 193-198.

GLYNNE, MARY D. 1951. Effects of cultural treatments on wheat, and on the incidence of eyespot, lodging, take-all and weeds. Ann. Appl. Biol. 38: 665-688.

GLYNNE, MARY D. 1953. Production of spores by *Cercosporella herpotrichoides*. Trans. Brit. Mycol. Soc. 36: 46-51.

GOODE, P. M. 1956. Infection of strawberry roots by zoospores of *Phytophthora fragariae*. Trans. Brit. Mycol. Soc. 39: 367-377.

GRAINGER, J. 1962. Vegetative and fructifying growth in *Phallus impudicus*. Trans. Brit. Mycol. Soc. 45: 147-155.

GREGORY, P. H. 1951. Deposition of air-borne *Lycopodium* spores on cylinders. Ann. Appl. Biol. 38: 357-376.

GREGORY, P. H. 1961. The microbiology of the atmosphere. Leonard Hill Ltd., London. 251 p.

GREGORY, P. H. 1962. The dispersal distance problem. Pollen et Spores 4: 348.

GREGORY, P. H., E. J. GUTHRIE, and M. E. BUNCE. 1959. Experiments on splash dispersal of fungus spores. J. Gen. Microbiol. 20: 328-354.

GREGORY, P. H., and J. M. HIRST. 1957. The summer air-spora at Rothamsted in 1952. J. Gen. Microbiol. 17: 135-152.

GREGORY, P. H., and M. E. LACEY. 1962. Isolation of thermophilic actinomycetes. Nature (London) 195: 95.

GREGORY, P. H., and O. J. STEDMAN. 1958. Spore dispersal in *Ophiobolus graminis* and other fungi of cereal foot rots. Trans. Brit. Mycol. Soc. 41: 449-456.

GROGAN, R. G., F. W. ZINK, W. B. HEWITT, and K. A. KIMBLE. 1958. The association of *Olpidium* with the big-vein disease of lettuce. Phytopathology 48: 292-297.

HAMILTON, E. D. 1959. Studies on the air spora. Acta Allerg. Kobenhavn 13: 143-175.

HANT, N. R. 1946. Destructive plant diseases not yet established in N. America. Botan. Rev. 12: 593-726.

HARRISON, B. D. 1961. Soil-borne viruses. vol. 1, p. 401-406. *In* Recent Adv. Botany (9th Intern. Botan. Congr. Montreal), University of Toronto Press, Toronto.

HARRISON, B. D., and R. D. WINSLOW. 1961. Laboratory and field studies on the relation of arabis mosaic virus to its nematode vector *Xiphinema diversicaudatum* (Micoletzky). Ann. Appl. Biol. 49: 621-633.

HEWITT, W. B., D. J. RASKI, and A. C. GOHEEN. 1958.

Nematode vector of soil-borne fanleaf virus of grapevines. Phytopathology 48: 586-595.

HICKMAN, C. J. 1958. *Phytophthora*—plant destroyer. Trans. Brit. Mycol. Soc. 41: 1-13.

HIRST, J. M. 1959. Spore liberation and dispersal. p. 529-538. *In* C. S. Holton et al. [ed.], Plant pathology, problems and progress 1908-1958. University of Wisconsin Press, Madison, Wisc.

HIRST, J. M., and O. J. STEDMAN. 1960. The epidemiology of *Phytophthora infestans*. II. The source of inoculum. Ann. Appl. Biol. 48: 489-517.

HIRST, J. M., and O. J. STEDMAN. 1963. Dry liberation of fungus spores by raindrops. J. Gen. Microbiol. 33: 335-344.

HOLLINGS, M. 1962. Viruses associated with a die-back of cultivated mushroom. Nature (London) 196: 962-965.

INGOLD, C. T. 1953. Dispersal in fungi. Clarendon Press, Oxford. 197 p.

INGOLD, C. T. 1959. Submerged aquatic hyphomycetes. J. Quekett Microscopy Club 5: 115-130.

ISAAC, I. 1957. Wilt of lucerne caused by species of *Verticillium*. Ann. Appl. Biol. 45: 550-558.

JACKS, G. V., and R. O. WHYTE. 1939. The rape of the earth. Faber & Faber Ltd., London. 313 p.

JACKSON, R. M. 1961. Soil fungistasis and the rhizosphere. p. 169-176. *In* D. Parkinson and J. S. Waid [ed.], The ecology of soil fungi, Liverpool University Press, Liverpool.

JARVIS, W. R. 1962. Splash dispersal of spores of *Botrytis cinerea* Pers. Nature (London) 193: 599.

KELLY, C. D., and S. M. PADY. 1953. Microbiological studies of air over some non-arctic regions of Canada. Can. J. Botany 31: 90-106.

KEYWORTH, W. G. 1942. Verticillium wilt of the hop (*Humulus lupulus*). Ann. Appl. Biol. 29: 346-357.

KREITLOW, K. W. 1962. Verticillium wilt of alfalfa. A destructive disease in Britain and Europe not yet observed in the United States. U. S. Dept. Agr. A.R.S. 34-20, 15 p.

KUNTZ, J. E., and A. J. RIKER. 1950. Root grafts as a possible means for local transmission of oak wilt. (Abstr.) Phytopathology 40: 16.17.

LACEY, J. 1962. The activity of *Phytophthora infestans* (Mont.) de Bary in soil. Ph.D. Thesis University of Reading. 226 p.

LEACH, J. G. 1940. Insect transmission of plant diseases. McGraw-Hill Publishing Co. Ltd., New York and London. 615 p.

LEACH, L. D., and S. W. MEAD. 1936. Viability of sclerotia of *Sclerotium rolfsii* after passage through the digestive tract of cattle and sheep. J. Agr. Res. 53: 519-536.

LEDINGHAM, R. J., and S. H. F. CHINN. 1955. A flotation method for obtaining spores of *Helminthosporium sativum* from soil. Can. J. Botany 33: 298-303.

LINGAPPA, Y. E., and J. L. LOCKWOOD. 1962. Chitin media for selective isolation and culture of actinomycetes. Phytopathology 52: 317-323.

LISTER, R. M., and A. F. MURANT. 1961. p. 56. *In* C. H. Cadman, Virology, 8th. Ann. Rept. Scottish Hort. Res. Inst. Invergowrie.

MARSH, R. W. 1952. Field observations on the spread of *Armillaria mellea* in apple orchards and in a blackcurrant plantation. Trans. Brit. Mycol. Soc. 35: 201-207.

McCUBBIN, W. A. 1954. The plant quarantine problem. Ejnar Munksgaard, Copenhagen. 255 p.

MEREDITH, D. S. 1959. The infection of pine stumps by *Fomes annosus* and other fungi. Ann. Botany (London) [N.S.] 23: 455-476.

METCALFE, G. 1940. *Bacterium rhaponticum* (Millard) Dowson, a cause of crown-rot disease of rhubarb. Ann. Appl. Biol. 27: 502-508.

MOORE, W. C. 1953. International trade in plants and the need for healthy planting material. J. Roy. Hort. Soc. 78: 453-462.

MURPHY, P. W. 1953. The biology of forest soils with special reference to the mesofauna and meiofauna. J. Soil Sci. 4: 155-193.

NAPPER, R. P. N. 1932. Observations on the root disease of rubber trees caused by *Fomes lignosus*. J. Rubber Res. Inst. Malaya 4: 5-33.

NELSON, R. R. 1961. Evidence of gene pools for pathogenicity in species of *Helminthosporium*. Phytopathology 51: 736-737.

NICOT, J. 1960. Some characteristics of the microflora in desert sands. p. 94-97. *In* D. Parkinson and J. S. Waid [ed.], The ecology of soil fungi, Liverpool University Press, Liverpool.

NOBLE, M., J. DE TEMPE, and P. NEERGAARD. 1958. An annotated list of seed-borne diseases. Commonwealth Mycol. Inst. Kew, Surrey. 163 p.

OORT, A. J. P. 1936. The eyespot disease of cereals caused by *Cercosporella herpotrichoides*. Tijdschr. Plantenziekten 42: 179-210.

PADWICK, G. W. 1939. Note on the limitation of infection of wheat by ascospores of *Ophiobolus graminis* Sacc. A possible explanation. Ann. Appl. Biol. 26: 723-825.

PADY, S. M. 1957. Quantitative studies of fungus spores in the air. Mycologia 49: 339-353.

PADY, S. M., and C. L. KRAMER. 1960. Kansas aeromycology. VI. Hyphal fragments. Mycologia 52: 681-687.

PARKER-RHODES, A. F. 1955a. Fairy-ring kinetics. Trans. Brit. Mycol. Soc. 38: 59-72.

PARKER-RHODES, A. F. 1955b. Statistical aspects of fungus forays. Trans. Brit. Mycol. Soc. 38: 283-290.

PETERS, B. G. 1953. Vertical migration of potato root eelworm. J. Helminthol. 27: 107-112.

PETHERBRIDGE, F. R., and F. G. W. JONES. 1944. Beet eelworm (*Heterodera schachtii* Schmidt) in East Anglia, 1934-1943. Ann. Appl. Biol. 31: 320-332.

PONTECORVO, G., and G. SERMONTI. 1954. Parasexual recombination in *Penicillium chrysogenum*. J. Gen. Microbiol. 11: 94-104.

PUGH, G. J. F. 1962. Studies on fungi in coastal soils. I. *Cercospora salina* Sutherland. Trans. Brit. Mycol. Soc. 45: 255-260.

PUGH, G. J. F., and G. E. MATHISON. 1962. Studies on fungi in coastal soils. III. An ecological survey of keratinophilic fungi. Trans. Brit. Mycol. Soc. 45: 567-572.

RASKI, D. J., and W. B. HEWITT. 1962. Plant-parasitic nematodes as vectors of plant viruses. Phytopathology 53: 39-47.

RICHARDS, M. 1956. A census of mould spores in the air over Britain in 1952. Trans. Brit. Mycol. Soc. 39: 431-441.

RISHBETH, J. 1951a. Observations on the biology of *Fomes annosus* with particular reference to East Anglian pine plantations. II. Spore production, stump infection and saprophytic activity in stumps. Ann. Botany (London) [N.S.] 15: 1-21.

RISHBETH, J. 1951b. Observations on the biology of *Fomes annosus*, with particular reference to East Anglian pine plantations. III. Natural and experimental infection of pine and some factors affecting the severity of the disease. Ann. Botany (London) [N.S.] 15: 221-246.

RENFRO, B. L. 1959. Local dissemination of *Phoma herbarum* var. *medicaginis*. (Abstr.) Phytopathology 49: 548.

ROBERTS, F. M. 1948. Experiments on the spread of potato virus X between plants in contact. Ann. Appl. Biol. 35: 266-274.

ROBERTSON, N. F. 1954. Studies on the mycorrhiza of *Pinus sylvestris*. I. The pattern of development of mycorrhiza roots and its significance for experimental studies. New Phytologist 53: 253-283.

ROBERTSON, N. F. 1958. Observations of the effect of water on the hyphal apices of *Fusarium oxysporum*. Ann. Botany (London) [N.S.] 22: 159-173.

ROSE, C. W. 1960. Soil detachment caused by rainfall. Soil Sci. 89: 28-35.

SAMUEL, G., and S. D. GARRETT. 1933. Ascospore discharge in *Ophiobolus graminis* and its probable relation to the development of whiteheads in wheat. Phytopathology 23: 721-728.

SATCHELL, J. E. 1958. Earthworm biology and soil fertility. Soils Fertilizers 21: 209-219.

SCOTT, M. R. 1956a. Studies of the biology of *Sclerotium cepivorum* Berk. I. Growth of the mycelium in soil. Ann. Appl. Biol. 44: 576-583.

SCOTT, M. R. 1956b. Studies of the biology of *Sclerotium cepivorum* Berk. II. The spread of white rot from plant to plant. Ann. Appl. Biol. 44: 584-589.

SEWELL, G. W. F., and J. F. WILSON. 1961. Machine picking in relation to progressive *Verticillium* wilt of hop. I. A study of the infectivity of machine-picked hop waste. Rept. E. Malling Res. Sta. 1960: 100-104.

SEWELL, G. W. F., J. F. WILSON, and D. G. MARTIN. 1962. Machine picking in relation to progressive *Verticillium* wilt of the hop. II. The effect of composting on the infectivity of machine-picked hop waste. Rept. E. Malling Res. Sta. 1960-61: 102-106.

SHANTZ, H. L., and R. L. PIEMEISEL. 1917. Fungus fairy rings in eastern Colorado and their effect on vegetation. J. Agr. Res. 11: 191-245.

SHEPHERD, A. M. 1962. The emergence of larvae from cysts in the genus *Heterodera*. Commonwealth Agr. Bur., Farnham Royal. 87 p.

SHEPHERD, C. J., and M. MANDRYK. 1962. Auto-inhibitors of germination and sporulation in *Peronospora tabacina* Adam. Trans. Brit. Mycol. Soc. 45: 233-244.

SMITH, K. M. 1937. Further studies on a virus found in the roots of certain normal-looking plants. Parasitology 29: 86-95.

STANIER, R. Y. 1953. Adaptation in micro-organisms. p. 1-20. *In* Third Symp. Soc. Gen. Microbiol. Cambridge University Press, London.

STOVER, R. H. 1962. Fusarial wilt (Panama disease) of bananas and other *Musa* species. Commonwealth Mycol. Inst. Phytopathol. Paper 4, 117 p.

THOMPSON, H. W., A. ROEBUCK, and B. A. COOPER. 1949. Floods and the spread of potato root eelworm. J. Minist. Agr., London, 56: 109-114.

THORNTON, H. G., and N. GANGULEE. 1926. The life cycle of the nodule organism *Bacillus radicicola* (Beij.), in soil and its relation to the infection of the host plant. Proc. Roy. Soc. (London), Ser. B, 99: 427-451.

TSAO, P. H. 1960. A serial dilution end-point method for estimating disease potentials of citrus phytophthoras in soil. (Abstr.) Phytopathology 48: 398-399.

WALLACE, G. B. 1935. Armillaria root rot in East Africa. E. African Agr. J. 1: 182-192.

WALLACE, H. R. 1959. Movement of eelworms. IV. The influence of water percolation. Ann. Appl. Biol. 47: 131-139.

WALLACE, H. R. 1960. Movement of eelworms. VI. The influence of soil type, moisture gradient and host plant roots on the migration of the potato root eelworm *Heterodera rostochiensis*. Ann. Appl. Biol. 48: 107-120.

WALLACE, H. R. 1961. The orientation of *Ditylenchus dipsaci* to physical stimuli. Nematologica 6: 222-236.

WARCUP, J. H. 1955. Isolation of fungi from hyphae present in the soil. Nature (London) 175: 953.

WATSON, R. D. 1960. Soil washing improves the value of the soil dilution and the plate count method of estimating populations of soil fungi. Phytopathology 50: 792-794.

WEBSTER, J. 1959. Experiments with spores of aquatic hyphomycetes. I. Sedimentation, and impaction on smooth surfaces. Ann. Botany (London) [N.S.] 23: 595-611.

WEHRLE, V. M., and L. OGILVIE. 1956. Spread of take-all from infected wheat plants. Plant Pathol. 5: 106-107.

WHITE, J. H. 1953. Wind-blown dispersal of potato eelworm. Nature (London) 172: 686-687.

WILKINS, W. H., and G. C. M. HARRIS. 1946. The ecology of the larger fungi. V. An investigation into the influence of rainfall and temperature on the seasonal production of fungi in a beechwood and in a pinewood. Ann. Appl. Biol. 33: 179-187.

ZAAG, D. E. VAN DER. 1956. Overwintering and epidemiology of *Phytophthora infestans,* and some new possibilities of control. Tijdschr. Plantenziekten 62: 89-156.

ZAN, K. 1962. Activity of *Phytophthora infestans* in soil in relation to tuber infection. Trans. Brit. Mycol. Soc. 45: 205-221.

ZENTMYER, G. A. 1961. Chemotaxis of zoospores for root exudates. Science 133: 1595-1596.

► DISCUSSION OF J. M. HIRST PAPER

C. W. Emmons:

The methods of studying spore dispersal used by Dr. Hirst need to be more widely known and used in medical mycology. "Vital Statistics of the United States" lists 350-450 deaths per year from mycoses. Many times this number of mild fungal infections occur. In parts of the San Joaquin Valley most of the residents, particularly agricultural workers, have been infected at some time by *Coccidioides.* Nearly all the systemic mycoses are caused by fungi which are normally saprophytes in soil or organic waste. These mycoses are not contagious and man is infected when he inhales spores dispersed (probably) usually by air currents, from these sites of saprophytic growth.

G. Stotzky:

Water falls on the earth as drops. What are the energetics involved several inches below the soil surface in moving microorganisms from one site to another by means of water? Many of our soil-borne pathogens are not on the soil surface, they are several inches below in decaying roots. Are they dispersed by water?

J. M. Hirst:

That is a very interesting question. It is in fact akin to the pressures that are generated by waves smashing against rocks on the seashore, when enormous atmospheric pressure cracks and blasts the rocks apart. I see no reason why falling raindrops, which have fairly high energies, shouldn't do this on a microscale.

Survival of Microorganisms in Soil

DAVID PARK—*Department of Botany, University of Manchester, England.*
(Now: The Botany Department, The Queen's University, Belfast, North Ireland.)

The microorganisms we have with us now have become adapted to survive under present conditions. Survival of the species is the important end in organic evolution, but is brought about through survival of individuals. For plant pathogens it is this more immediate aspect of survival that concerns the plant pathologist. Not many natural habitats provide microorganisms with any great degree of continuity of conditions, and an important problem for the species is the bridging of any discontinuities in its environment; this includes discontinuities in the supply of hosts. With crop plants the position of pathogens differs from that with plants in nature. In some crops artificial culture is continuous or near continuous, either spatially or in time, and the immediate survival problem for the pathogen is thereby solved. Agricultural or horticultural techniques arrange some degree of discontinuity between related host crops. This discontinuity may, nevertheless, be less than that which exists in nature, and, therefore, the attributes evolved by pathogens for bridging natural gaps are often more than adequate for bridging those in artificial plant culture. Problems of disease control are in direct proportion to the ease with which a pathogen can transfer from one crop to another, either in space or time.

The pathologist has three courses open to him: he may seek ways to reduce the severity of disease once a plant or crop is infected, he may seek ways to prevent infection once the pathogen has reached the surface of the host, or he may seek to prevent any contact between pathogen and host. There are several reasons why the third approach is the most desirable, and it can be achieved by interfering with the normal mechanisms of the pathogen for overcoming its environmental discontinuities. The transfer mechanisms that pathogens have adopted are related to the types of discontinuities that they face. These fall into two categories, spatial and temporal. Spatial transfer from one crop to another distant but contemporary crop is the subject of the preceding paper. Fungal and virus pathogens are notably successful at this type of dispersion. However, in these two groups some important pathogens have solved their problems by temporal rather than spatial spread. Nematodes are of limited mobility even at best, and host finding is normally by persistence in soil. Plant-pathogenic bacteria, as opposed to animal pathogens, are also mainly without any special adaptation to spatial dispersal, although there are important exceptions.

While the mechanisms of continuity are related to the type of discontinuity, the situations are not necessarily exclusive. Thus spatial dispersal structures such as fungal conidia may survive for long periods in soil (Caldwell, 1958) and, conversely, resting bodies such as eelworm cysts may be aerially disseminated (H. W. Thompson, 1959). Some pathogens combine temporal and spatial mechanisms of transfer, as the teliospore followed by sporidia in the Uredinales. There is a general concurrence, however, between the means and the actual need. In spatial dispersal small size of propagule is likely to be an advantage for ease of carriage, and large numbers of propagules deal with dilution at a distance from the source. In temporal dispersal (or persistence) numbers are of smaller importance, but large size may be an advantage.

Just as studies of the mechanisms, phases, and agents of spatial dispersal are important in the control of diseases caused by pathogens possessing those mechanisms, so, if duration of survival of pathogens in soil is to be reduced, it is important to understand the mechanisms of survival in the absence of the crop host. The difficulties may, of course, be greater in view of the greater technical and visual opacity of the matrix.

SURVIVAL IN PURE CULTURE.—In most forms of laboratory culture, microorganisms develop fairly quickly and usually complete their active growth fairly soon. Concurrently with this situation many species require for their maintenance in culture collections fairly frequent subculturing. This relation in some microorganisms between cessation of growth and loss of viability implies that inactive structures do not stay alive very long. Zan (1962) states that most sporangia of *Phytophthora infestans* lose viability in 3-4 weeks. On the other hand, many microorganisms continue to survive after the phase of "staling" is reached, and special structures may assist in such survival. Thus Nelson and Wilhelm (1958) describe conditions where conidia of *Verticillium albo-atrum* survived less than 3 days but where microsclerotia could survive for 6 months. Some continued activity may take place in pure culture even after the period of rapid growth has ceased and a conventional state of staling or apparent cessation of activity has been reached (Park, 1961).

Microorganisms of some sorts may in relatively unfavourable conditions survive by making a low level of growth to balance the death that occurs.

The duration of survival in pure culture has in many organisms been shown to be sensitive to environmental factors like temperature, pH, and relative humidity. It is probable that such factors affect the condition of the protoplasm. The lyophil process for preserving cultures of microorganisms acts by its effects on the protoplasm, and mineral oil added to cultures affects metabolism so as to give a longer viability. One expects factors such as these to be active in respect of survival in soil as well as in culture. The nature of the culture substratum may also be important, and autoclaved soil has been recommended as a culture medium for retention of stock cultures in an unchanged condition for longer periods than is usual with more commonly used media (Bakerspigel, 1953). Soil may be effective in this way because of its colloidal properties, which confer some protection on resting structures. Mucilaginous substances similar to those in which some conidia are produced are said (Gottlieb, 1950) to help prolong viability under adverse conditions, and the mucous capsule of some nonmotile soil bacteria is said to be protective in function during survival (Bissett, 1952). In this connection it is of interest that Warcup (1957) has pointed out the importance of humus particles as a site of origin of fungus colonies from soil.

Grindle and Good (1961) have shown that it is not only the conditions to which structures are exposed that govern their survival, but also the rate of transfer to those conditions. Germinating spores of fungi are considered very sensitive to low humidities and high temperatures, and yet were found to survive well if taken to these conditions quickly, to avoid the abnormal metabolism that occurred during a slow transference. Organisms growing under unfavourable conditions and with a lower rate of metabolism may thus be better placed to withstand some sorts of adverse factors.

Cultural studies can be of much assistance in indicating those conditions that might extend survival and those that might reduce it. It might also be of more than academic interest to know how the factors act on the protoplasm to produce their effects, and in what way it is altered. In cultural studies one distinction that should be given more consideration than it has received is that between loss of viability and loss of infectivity with age. Last (1960) has shown that loss of infectivity of a population of spores of a fungal pathogen may occur before any change of viability is detected by germination on agar.

Features Inimical to Survival in Soil.—Agencies known to be active in the reduction of viability in soil are not necessarily effective under all conditions, and their action may be dependent upon particular environmental circumstances or be limited to certain pathogens only, or to pathogens only in certain habitats or phases of activity.

Physical and chemical agencies can in appropriate sites contribute to the eradication of pathogens from soil. High temperature, radiation, desiccation, flooding, anaerobiosis, and toxic chemicals are examples. Most of these would act in pure culture as well as in soil. Of more especial interest here are the effects peculiar to field soil with its mixed population. Rosen and Weetman (1940) found that survival of fungal resting spores in nature might be shorter than that in comparable laboratory studies. This phenomenon is partly attributable to the variety of the natural population of microorganisms, which can accentuate the effects of adverse physicochemical conditions. Thus Stover (1955) found that anaerobic conditions were more toxic to *Fusarium oxysporum* in nonsterile than in sterile soil. Laboratory studies of the sort advocated in the foregoing section would need to be supplemented to show their applicability to field conditions.

In discussing the operation of factors inimical to microorganisms in soil it is important to recognise the distinction between activity in soil and survival in soil, and the fact that some adverse agencies cause loss of viability in the active phase of growth while others affect the inactive phase of the pathogen. During the ecological succession of microorganisms in soil, species commonly produce resting stages after their phase of activity is over, so that survival may continue longer than activity. If resting spores are experimentally added to soil and their fate followed, a decline in numbers usually occurs. Such studies are subject to criticism in that sometimes the added spores are not native to the soil, and usually, in order to facilitate observation, the structures are added in numbers considerably in excess of those that occur naturally. The ecologist accustomed to a natural balance would expect the observed decline, but would not necessarily read into it proof of eradication in a natural state, merely interpreting it as a shift away from an artificially high population. In some studies of natural successions, however, where isolation techniques have included the resting structures, it has been shown that a similar decline in numbers does occur under natural conditions following the microorganisms' burst of activity (Pugh, 1958; Caldwell, 1963). In the soil environment then there is a natural decline in the viability of resting structures, as well as in the activity of a species.

Lack of nutrients, one possible cause of death, may develop if the pathogen is not always in contact with its special environment. In soil the mechanism is closely connected with true competition from other microorganisms. Many microorganisms, however, are able to withstand starvation conditions relatively well. The fact that mixed cultures have rigours additional to those of pure culture implies not only the removal of nutrients, but also the positive contribution of some adverse effect by the other organisms. Nevertheless nutrient deficiency and true competition are possible agents leading to death and they may, in addition, intensify the effect of other more potent agencies. It is clear that these two agencies could only operate against pathogens during the active phase; inactive resting structures, which have no demands for nutrients, cannot be deprived.

Antibiosis, the production by microorganisms of chemicals toxic to others, seems to be established as one of the causes of lack of survival in soil. Much discussion has centred on whether the chemicals might be fairly complex antibiotics of specific nature or substances of more general antibiotic action. Both types probably occur and are active in different positions and situations in soil (Park, 1960; Brian, 1960). It is probable that the more general type of antibiosis is responsible for the widespread general soil fungitoxicity that has attracted much attention. There seems to be no reason why pathogens of groups other than fungi should not be affected similarly. Under optimal conditions the soil fungitoxicity can cause death and lysis of cells, but the intensity of its action is influenced by the presence of other substances, and some materials may ameliorate its action (Park, 1955; Jackson, 1958a). Under some circumstances it may be fungistatic (Jackson, 1958a) and could conceivably assist in survival rather than help in eradication (Dobbs and Hinson, 1953). Toxic chemicals in soil may also originate from higher plants and from animals. Examples have been found affecting pathogenic fungi (Timonin, 1941) and nematodes (Darpoux, 1960; Timonin, 1961).

Parasitism and predation also contribute to the disappearance of microorganisms from soil. Fungi may be parasitized by other fungi (Drechsler, 1938; Godfrey, 1957) or by bacteria (Drechsler, 1938; Mitchell and Alexander, 1961), or preyed upon by mites (Smith, 1960) or by nematodes (Franklin, 1959). Pathogenic nematodes are parasitized by bacteria, microsporids, and fungi (Darpoux, 1960) and preyed upon by protozoa, fungi, arthropods, and by other nematodes (Duddington, 1956; Darpoux, 1960). These influences are universal in that they affect both active and inactive phases of the pathogens, except as some resting stages might be resistant to the digestive juices of the prospective predators (Gregg, 1957; Smith, 1960).

Senescence of inactive stages may be expected to occur in soil as in culture and thus account for a progressive decline in the populations of those pathogens unable to multiply in the absence of the host. Relatively little is known about this phase, nor whether it might occur in soil at the same rate as in culture. As described in the previous section, this phase is influenced by external factors. But while continued lack of activity of a population of resting stages may lead to a gradual decline of numbers through senescence, there is the converse situation that reversion to activity under the wrong sort of conditions may lead to an even more rapid disappearance. Chinn and Ledingham (1961) have described "germination lysis" as a factor in the disappearance of spores of fungi from soil. Germination lysis would seem to be stimulation of inactive spores to activity followed by their death caused by the normal soil fungitoxic factor; thus it is the action of the normal soil antagonism upon the active rather than the inactive phase. This is in effect a restatement of Bremer's (1924) conclusion that in the absence of the host a pathogen is likely to survive longest under conditions least favourable to germination, a conclusion that has been supported by observation of various diseases. Noble (1924) with *Urocystis tritici*, Glynne (1926) with *Synchytrium endobioticum*,

Macfarlane (1952) with *Plasmodiophora brassicae*, and White (1954) with *Spongospora subterranea* are among those who have experimented with the "decoy" method of eradication, whereby inactive resting structures are stimulated into activity and thus exposed to the hazards of antagonism without being presented with the opportunity for the effective infection of a suitable host. Similar approaches have been made for nematodes (Darpoux, 1960). Resistant bacterial spores also, a few minutes after stimulation to germinate, become sensitive to factors that previously did not affect them (Henderson, 1955). It should in this connection be remembered that it may be more difficult to stimulate resting structures to activity in soil than it is in culture, since the limits for germination are narrower when other factors are not optimal (Cochrane, 1960). Mitchell, Hooton, and Clark (1941) and Clark (1942) have described how improving the soil conditions by tilling promoted germination of the pathogen *Phymatotrichum omnivorum* and limited survival of the fungus.

W. R. Thompson as long ago as 1929 in his very helpful paper on biological control pointed out that in natural eradication physical and chemical agents will be more important where conditions are relatively unfavourable for activity, and that biological agents will be more important where conditions are generally favourable. Evidence accumulated since then goes to support Thompson's conclusion.

DURATION OF SURVIVAL.—Estimates of the extent of survival of some pathogens in nonsterile soil vary from low values like the 4 weeks for *Didymella lycopersici* (Hack and Williams, 1960) to the "indefinite" survival claim for *Phytophthora erythroseptica* by Cairns and Muskett (1933). Between these extremes lies a whole range of values that depends upon the species, and sometimes variety, of pathogen concerned, the soil type and local environment, the cropping history of the site, the cultivation treatments given, and sometimes the methods used by the observer. Consequently different values may be found in the literature for a single disease organism. Zybina (1929) gave 7 years as a practical rotation period for flax in connection with wilt caused by *Fusarium oxysporum* f. *lini* in Russia, but Barker (1923) in the United States concluded that 10-12 years was probably the minimum for profitable culture. These values for useful rotation periods might be compared with the 50-year survival period of *F. oxysporum* f. *lini* in the absence of flax recorded by Houston and Knowles (1949). Total eradication, of course, is not necessary before a crop may with some profit be grown on the land again, but in some diseases low levels of survival may have a great significance. *F. oxysporum* f. *cubense* may survive upwards of 40 years in infested soils that have been abandoned and still infect banana plants introduced (Stover and Waite, 1954), but only occur at levels undetectable by plating (Rishbeth, 1955). Such findings indicate the importance of technique, and of type of cropping.

Species of the same genus may differ widely in ability to survive in soils. Zan (1962) found the maximum persistence period of *Phytophthora infestans* in nonsterile soil to be 77 days, *P. capsici* will survive for 5 months in moist soil (Critopoulos, 1955), whereas for *P. parasitica* var. *nicotianae* 3-year rotation is necessary for crops to be reasonably free from disease (Valleau, 1951). That this variation exists in a genus of considerable morphological uniformity should emphasize that care needs to be taken in translating structural data into behavioural conclusions. In the genus *Verticillium* also, species may differ widely in ability to survive in nonsterile soil. Isaac (1953) describes how some species disappear quickly, whereas others continue to survive in soil.

Sclerotia have been regarded as adaptations not so much to survival as to successful infection (Garrett, 1956); yet such bulky structures might be expected to have survival value in soil. Coley-Smith (1959) records that the sclerotia of *Sclerotium cepivorum* may persist in field soil for many years. Yet even with such massive bodies the actual soil conditions may be important in determining the period of survival. The sclerotia of *Phymatotrichum omnivorum* can persist for more than 5 years in moderately moist soils, but in air-dry soil do not survive many days (King and Eaton, 1934; Taubenhaus and Ezekiel, 1936). Those of *Rhizoctonia solani,* on the other hand, may survive at least 6 years in air-dry soil (Gadd and Bertus, 1928), which is longer than they do in moist soil (Palo, 1926).

Records of long periods of survival of nematodes are available. Taylor (1953) gives examples of 28 and 39 years. Some bacterial pathogens can survive for long periods in soil in the absence of any host (Stakman and Harrar, 1957) but few details are known. There are records of the survival of viruses in soil in the absence of host plants for periods of 9 years (McKinney, 1946).

STRUCTURES INVOLVED IN SURVIVAL.—It was stated earlier that there is a general distinction between structures that are dispersed in space and those that remain viable for long periods in the soil, and to some extent this distinction can be attributed to the different properties required for the two processes. The soil matrix, although it allows some movement of even nonmotile spores (Burges and Fenton, 1953; Park, 1959), does not allow of efficient spatial dissemination. Moreover, for aerial dissemination small mass is an advantage, and, while large mass is not necessarily an advantage for long-continued viability of resting spores, bulk is often associated with resting structures in soil, possibly (Garrett, 1956) to provide a sufficient inoculum potential for infection of hosts arriving subsequently at that site. The question of inoculum potential is, of course, much more important in connection with soil-borne than with air-borne pathogens, and viability alone is not sufficient to ensure ecological survival. Survival in nature can only be effective if subsequent colonization of a substratum is to occur, and it is at this stage that inoculum potential applies. Diseases caused by soil-borne pathogens start in a habitat that is closed in the ecological sense, and consequently, by analogy with Salisbury's arguments for higher plants, larger bodies will contribute to success in colonization. Dis-

eases caused by air-borne pathogens usually start in an open habitat and therefore inoculum potential is of smaller significance; a spore can be small and yet effective. Yet, despite these divergent conditions and requirements for the two types of transference to another substratum or host, and despite the fact that mycologists tend to think of large spores as being resting spores, there is no completely exclusive differentiation of function, and all types of structures found in fungi may assist in long-term survival in soil.

Any spore of large size, having a thick wall and resulting from sexual fusion is without proof commonly assumed to aid long-term survival. In plant pathogens at least such structures only exceptionally function in long-term survival. Legge (1952) has given a neat and direct demonstration that the oospores of *Phytophthora* spp. may remain viable and undamaged in soil for a considerable time, and Barton (1958) has shown that the ability of *Pythium mamillatum* to form oospores in a field soil is correlated with its ability to survive in that soil. It did not survive in nonsterile soils in which it did not form oospores. The effective resting stages of the obligate parasites *Synchytrium endobioticum*, *Plasmodiophora brassicae*, and *Urocystis tritici* are also thick-walled and are associated with the sexual process. Ascomycetes may produce ascospores in soil, and Warcup (1951*b*) has shown that some of these can tolerate very severe conditions and subsequently appear on isolation plates. In fact some are more easily isolated after subjection to rigorous conditions.

A majority of pathogens do not produce such sexual stages. Nevertheless some have fairly large and apparently resistant structures. Examples have already been given of sclerotia, the mycelial organs of mass storage that assist in long-term survival. Chlamydospores are single-celled mycelial modifications that may also serve in survival. The production of chlamydospores by some fungi has been correlated with their soil habitat (Park, 1954). Warcup (1955, 1957) states that species of *Fusarium* appearing on soil plates arise mainly from chlamydospores or from humus particles. Tousson and Snyder (1961) have discussed physiological differences between conidia and chlamydospores of *F. solani* f. *phaseoli*, the conidia germinating easily in soil, the chlamydospores germinating only under conditions likely to lead to host infection. Thus chlamydospores would here appear to have a higher degree of adaptation to survival in soil. Newcombe (1960), working with *F. oxysporum* f. *cubense*, found that some conditions which adversely affected survival of the fungus in soil did so by inhibiting formation of chlamydospores and by stimulating conidia present to germinate under conditions where mycelium might not effectively colonize. In soil, structures other than chlamydospores may become converted into chlamydospores. Chlamydospores may originate by the modification of conidia added to soil (Park, 1955); or conidia may germinate briefly to give rise to chlamydospores (Jackson, 1957, 1958*b*; Nash, Christou, and Snyder, 1961) and thus alter their potentialities for survival in soil. The sporangia of Phycomycetes may become modified into gemmae or chlamydospores, with an increase in survival potentiality. Mycorrhizal fungi of the endotrophic sort, which may persist in soil in the absence of the symbiont, have been recorded in soil as germinating from thick-walled resting spores resembling chlamydospores (Gerdemann, 1955; Dowding, 1959; Mosse, 1959).

Caldwell (1958) showed by direct observation that ordinary conidia of an imperfect fungus can survive for at least 1 year in soil. Warcup (1955) found evidence that many fungi appearing on soil isolation plates do so from conidia, and suggests that in soil conidia may be more generally implicated in survival than has often been thought. Most of the conidia found appear to be viable (Warcup, 1951a). Phycomycetes may also survive by means of asexual structures. Barton (1958) cites sporangia as one of the sources of persistence in soil of *Pythium mamillatum*. Zan (1962), on the other hand, has described the extremely short period of viability even in culture of the sporangia of *Phytophthora infestans*. He states that the sporangia may produce germ tubes that can survive in soil for longer periods even though germinating spores are often considered particularly susceptible to adverse factors. From this discussion it should be evident that dispersal structures may be involved in efficient survival, and such bodies ought not to be overlooked in any study of this phenomenon.

The early controversy on whether fungi occur in soil as mycelium or as spores has lost its qualitative character but still persists in a quantitative form; it is recognized now that both spores and mycelium can occur in soil, yet it can still be stated, for instance (Lockwood, 1959), that survival of fungi is mostly by resting structures, not by mycelium; and indeed for some pathogens there is good support for this statement (Stover, 1958a, for *F. oxysporum;* Scott, 1956, for *Sclerotium cepivorum*). But there is also evidence that resting structures and mycelium need not be discordant states. Garrett (1938) describes resting mycelium of *Ophiobolus graminis,* and Warcup's (1957) studies indicate clearly that viable mycelium is not uncommon in soil and that some of it occurs in a resting condition. Pady and Kramer's (1960) work showed viable, though brown and thick-walled, hyphae to be present in the atmosphere and indicates that hyphae in an inactive condition may be relatively resistant to some adverse factors. Nicot (1960) records that dark sterile mycelium of dematiaceous and sphaeropsidaceous fungi are present in desert soils; this would indicate tolerance to intense conditions of desiccation and insolation. J. C. Brown (1958a), in investigating fungal ecology in dune soils, found a general correspondence between the fungal population of a soil as determined by plating, and the amount of mycelium appearing on impression slides, indicating that a portion of the fungal population was present as mycelium. Agnihothrudu (1955) states that in the rhizosphere and on the surface of the root, fungi are present as active mycelia rather than as spores.

Special modifications of mycelium may confer resistance and survival ability on fungi. Sclerotia have already been mentioned in this context. Rhizomorphs may perform a similar function, as in *Armillaria mellea* (Garrett, 1959). Even less complex organizations such as hyphal strands may be significant in persistence in soil, as in *Phymatotrichum omnivorum* (McNamara, Wester, and Gunn, 1934). Small aggregations such as the bulbils of the dark imperfect fungi (Nicot, 1960) or the microsclerotia of *Verticillium* (Isaac and MacGarvie, 1962) may give increased powers to retain viability.

Skinner (1951), using an indirect method, concludes that actinomycetes are present in soil, and presumably persist there, as spores rather than as mycelium or mycelial fragments. Pfennig (1958), using a direct method for observation of actinomycetes, reaches a similar conclusion, and adds that the spores include both aerial-mycelial spores and chlamydospores. These structures remain inactive in the general soil matrix, but may develop into mycelium after a reduction of the soil toxicity or on contact with a nutrient substratum.

Some species of bacteria persist in soil as active cells. These constitute the autochthonous flora of Winogradsky. Other bacterial species produce spores that are extremely resistant to adverse conditions, but this process has been thought to be an adaptation to aerial dispersal rather than to persistence (Bissett, 1952), a conclusion supported by the fact that spore formation in these bacteria is not favoured by adverse conditions but on the contrary requires quite specific conditions. Thimann (1955) states that spore-forming bacteria are relatively infrequent in soil. It would thus appear that spores are not the main means of bacterial survival. It is probable that the bacterial resting cells, rather than spores, are concerned in the long-term retention of viability in soil. The resting cell is a spherical or subspherical cell, nonflagellated, and formed like fungal chlamydospores directly from the trophic cell, not within it. The resting cell is in a condition of reduced vitality, and may be enclosed in a cyst (Bissett, 1952). In addition, it must be realized that in soil, bacteria rarely occur as single cells, but survive as microcolonies, each of these being a pure culture, probably surrounded by a mucilaginous capsule and often embedded in humic material (Thimann, 1955). The importance of such materials in survival has been mentioned in an earlier section.

Nematodes survive in soil simply as active animals utilizing reserves in the absence of the host, or as eggs. The eggs may be more durably enclosed in cysts, namely the body wall of the female animal, which forms a tough resistant structure containing embryonated eggs (Fenwick, 1959).

Some viruses are able to persist in soil. The account by Cadman in this symposium gives details of these and of the mechanics of their survival.

INDUCED FORMATION OF RESTING STRUCTURES.—Some of the structures listed in the foregoing section require for their formation a certain amount of prior activity of a fairly specialized kind. This is particularly true of the sexual stages, and there may be in these examples difficulties in the way of any immediate response to suddenly changed conditions in which resting structures could be useful. But many of the resting stages connected with sexual activity are produced at a time of year or stage of host-crop growth that will benefit the pathogen and when the production of dispersal spores would no longer confer any great advantage. There seems in this respect to have been some permanent adaptation during evolution to the benefit of the long-term interests of pathogens.

Some of the other structures without any such dependence on previous morphological or nuclear steps may be very rapidly formed from the trophic stages. In some such examples there seems to be a relation between the onset of unfavourable conditions and the development of the resistant structure which may have considerable biological advantages for the pathogen. This immediate stimulation may also apply to some of the sexual stages. Barton (1958) reports that a soil in which *Pythium mamillatum* survived stimulated the production of oospores as well as that of resting sporangia, whereas a soil in which the fungus did not survive gave no such stimulus. Arrilaga (1935) similarly found that reproduction of *Phytophthora citrophthora* in culture was stimulated by antagonism from *Diaporthe citri* (= *Phomopsis citri*), resulting in increased production of chlamydospores and sporangia, and also in oogonial development that had not previously been reported.

Sewell (1959), by an ingenious direct observation of tomato roots in soil infected with *Verticillium alboatrum*, demonstrated that sporulation occurred only after the death of the root. Garrett (1946), working with *Helicobasidium purpureum*, showed similarly that sclerotia are produced during the postparasitic phase. This behaviour compares well biologically with the sporulation of such air-borne pathogens as *Stereum purpureum* after death of the host parts bearing them.

From pure-culture studies there has been evidence that unfavourable conditions promote the production of chlamydospores from either mycelia (McClary, 1952) or conidia (Moore, 1924). There are also indications that natural soil or other antagonisms might act as a stimulus to both sorts of transformation. Koch (1934) found that *Dibotryon morbosum* produced chlamydospores from mycelium only near certain bacteria or near *Trichothecium roseum*, or on addition of strong acids or copper compounds. Venkat Ram (1952) found chlamydospore production in *Fusarium solani* to be stimulated by bacterial contamination of the cultures. Bywater (1959) and Park (1959) have reported that soil stimulates the production of chlamydospores by fungal mycelium and conidia. Wilhelm (1954) similarly found that conidia of *Verticillium albo-atrum* may on stimulus from soil become transformed into either chlamydospores or microsclerotia.

Some sclerotia seem, like some spores, to be dependent upon suboptimal conditions for production. Matsumoto (1921) got production of sclerotia in *Rhizoctonia solani* only at lower glucose levels. Townsend (1957), using a variety of species able to produce sclerotia, found that initiation depended upon good nutrition, but that no maturation occurred until growth

was checked, either by nutrient exhaustion or from other causes. Sanford (1956) found that sclerotia of *R. solani* developed best where antagonism might be expected to be greatest, or else on relatively inert and inhospitable substrata.

King, Loomis, and Hope (1931) record the germination of sclerotia to produce further and younger sclerotia. This process is in some ways comparable with the conversion of conidia to chlamydospores, or with the repeated emergence of zoospores in the Saprolegniales. It could if it were to occur in soil delay degeneration and senility, allowing the retention of viability perhaps longer than might be possible without the phenomenon.

Just as sclerotia may have their development stimulated by antagonistic and inhospitable conditions, so may rhizomorphs and hyphal strands (Butler, 1957; Valder, 1958). While these structures appear to be more directly connected with spatial distribution of fungi, they may, as already indicated, play a part in temporal survival. Here again there is an example of the production of a stage conferring increased chances of viability being initiated by conditions under which it might be most useful to the pathogen.

The L-forms of bacteria may be induced by treatment of cultures with antibiotics (Vilas, Tejerima, and Rubio, 1954; Vadász and Juhász, 1955) or by exposure to other unfavourable factors (Hawker et al., 1960).

There is then a certain amount of evidence that soil may favour the production of structures conducive to the survival in it of microorganisms during uncongenial periods. There is, however, a little contrary evidence that antibiotics from soil microorganisms (Bilai, 1956); or soil extracts may inhibit the production of spores from mycelium by some fungi under certain circumstances (Stover, 1958b). Studies of the natural features of the environment which may influence sporulation in either a positive or a negative direction may be profitable in designing treatments for the artificial manipulation of survival.

MODES OF SURVIVAL IN SOIL.—Pathogens in the absence of the crop host may survive in soil in several different ways (Fig. 1). This survival may come about by continued activity and growth, either parasitically on other hosts or saprophytically on available dead material; or it may come about by the pathogen's entering upon an inactive phase of the life-cycle, which may involve either a passive inactivity imposed by the environment, or a positive dormancy governed by the physiology of the resting structure. These different methods and their variations may have different implications for disease relations and can profitably be considered here. In any study of survival of a specific pathogen, the detection of the precise mode of survival should be one of the aims.

The persistence of a pathogen, and possibly its multiplication, on alternative hosts or nonsusceptible carrier hosts, has a serious effect on control measures based on rotation. Linford and Vaughan (1925) conclude that *Aphanomyces euteiches* could survive for 10 years under apparently nonsusceptible crops, and they

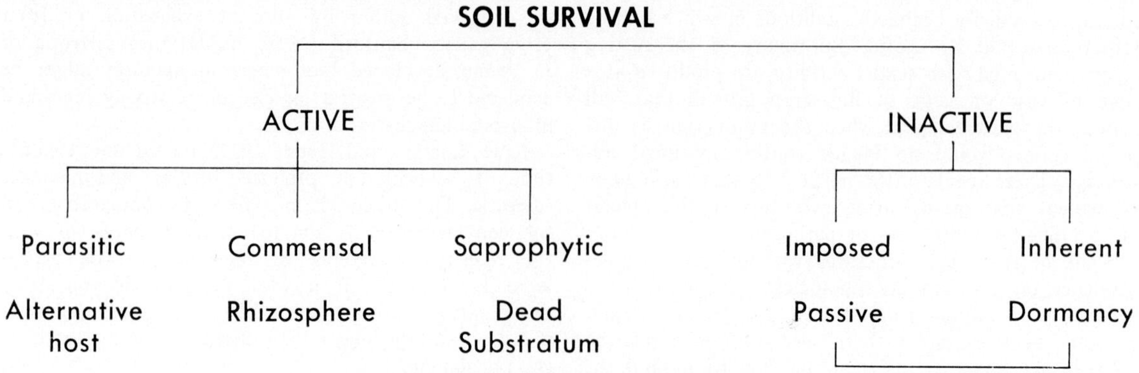

SOIL SURVIVAL

```
                                    SOIL SURVIVAL
                                         |
                  +----------------------+----------------------+
                  |                                             |
               ACTIVE                                        INACTIVE
                  |                                             |
        +---------+---------+                            +------+------+
        |         |         |                            |             |
    Parasitic  Commensal  Saprophytic                 Imposed       Inherent

    Alternative  Rhizosphere   Dead                    Passive       Dormancy
      host                   Substratum                   |             |
                                                          +------+------+
```

Fig. 1. Modes of survival of pathogens in soil.

presumed that oospores conferred this longevity. Linford (1927), however, produced evidence that the pathogen was not restricted to pea but could infect some other legumes and some grasses without these hosts showing much sign of infection. Young (1926), in an extensive series of observations, showed that under his somewhat artificial conditions common pathogenic fungi were able to infect many kinds of plants not normally subject to their attack. This shows that fungi may under some circumstances become parasitically active on unexpected hosts, and this could extend their period of survival. An organism that, in respect of pathogenesis, has a limited host range may yet have a wide range of hosts upon which it can be parasitic and that may help in survival. Armstrong and Armstrong (1948) state that wilt fusaria may occur without producing symptoms in the tissues of "resistant varieties" of the usual host, and also in many other species of plants that show no symptoms of infection. Waite and Dunlap (1953) also indicate such a situation for *Fusarium oxysporum* f. *cubense*. Gordon (1959), in a survey of *Fusarium* species, found that many of the potential plant pathogens were not uncommon on plants other than the usual crop hosts, and emphasized that this method of overwintering and spread could be important. Not only may one pathogen be able to associate with the living tissues of a range of plants, but correspondingly a single weed of cultivated soil may harbour, without showing definite symptoms, a large variety of potential pathogens. Wilhelm (1956) lists nine economically important pathogens surviving in this way on a single weed species.

Pathogens other than fungi may similarly be carried by noncrop hosts with or without detectable symptoms. A number of solanaceous species are hosts for *Heterodera rostochiensis* (Jones, 1959), and cereal root eelworm may be carried by ryegrass in pastures. A number of nematodes have an even wider host range, being described by Pitcher (1959) as fairly catholic in tastes, and are consequently widely distributed.

The rhizosphere phenomenon in which a quantitatively and qualitatively different microbial population exists near roots in soil may be significant here. Some of the fungi characteristic of the rhizosphere and rhizoplane regions may be pathogens. Buxton (1957) and Jackson (1957) are among those who have shown

that the rhizosphere of healthy plants may support potential fungal pathogens without the latter's necessarily infecting the plant. Soil fungi of only moderately high competitive saprophytic ability, which fall between true soil inhabitants and soil invaders, may typically occur in this site. Such fungi might be ill-equipped to withstand the full effect of the soil antagonism and yet be able to tolerate only a certain degree of host resistance. A niche close to the host would be indicated, and such microorganisms from such a position would be well placed to infect when the host resistance for some reason is low. *Pythium* spp. (Barton, 1961), *Fusarium oxysporum* (Park, 1959) and *F. solani* f. *phaseoli* (Schroth and Hendrix, 1962) are probably fungi of this sort, being restricted as saprophytes to a pioneer role in the colonization of dead tissues, but being common and persistent inhabitants of the root-surface region of healthy plants.

There is evidence that some soil fungi and at least one mycorrhizal fungus (Downie, 1943) may be present on living leaves before these are added to the soil litter at leaf-fall. A situation parallel to that in the rhizosphere may exist with leaves, and allow the persistence of some soil fungi.

The extent of active saprophytic survival and its stage on dead material is one basis of the ecological grouping of soil fungi (Garrett, 1956). Those fungi that on death of the host survive saprophytically for only a short period, being succeeded by more successful saprophytes, are described as root-inhabiting fungi. They are defined as having a declining saprophytic phase which effectively limits the survival of the fungus in soil. The relation between this and competitive saprophytic ability is discussed later in this paper. These fungi are unable to continue activity in the absence of another host plant, and this limitation is directly due to the activities of other soil organisms: in pure culture root-inhabiting pathogens can exist saprophytically for long periods. Only if the colonized host parts take a long time to die or if they are massive and therefore only slowly colonized from the soil is the survival of the pathogen extended sufficiently to allow infection of a subsequent crop. Taubenhaus and Ezekiel (1930) describe how roots of cotton infected with *Phymatotrichum* may pass through the winter still alive and so support the fungus, although it is unable to survive in roots subject to any decay.

Fungi with slightly more tolerance for soil antagonism than these root-inhabiting pathogens are those rhizosphere pathogens discussed above, which apart from being able to survive in a plant's root region, are restricted to the pioneer colonization of dead substrata. In habitats where recently dead materials are fairly continuously provided, such microorganisms may survive actively and multiply in the absence of any host. But in an ecologically closed habitat (e.g. heath and certain types of woodland), where uncolonized materials are only infrequently added to soil, these pathogens do not survive. There exists therefore the possibility of control of such pathogens away from their hosts by the addition to the soil of already colonized (e.g. composted) material.

Typical soil-inhabiting root-infecting fungi survive successfully in field soil in the absence of a host and colonize decomposable materials normal to the soil. These pathogens may survive in the soil as saprophytes for unlimited periods, but would nevertheless seem to depend on the addition to the soil of organic materials of the right sort for their activity and hence multiplication. Little is known about the relation between the sort of substrates added, the organisms colonizing, and the stage of succession at which individual organisms colonize. More information is needed about the detailed ecology of specific saprophytic niches before any deliberate attempt can be made to control the pathogenic microorganisms that occupy them. By analogy with the situation of the pioneer colonizers, it might be expected that the relatively early stages in the ecological succession would be appropriate for pathogens, but some seem to be more akin to Winogradsky's autochthonous flora in being able to survive actively in soil for very long periods without organic additions to the soil, and they may occupy a late stage in the succession on the decomposing substrata. Blair (1943) describes how *Rhizoctonia solani* in its growth through soil does better when no organic materials have been recently added.

There is the possibility that in soil an organism may continue to be active for a period in the absence of any external supply of nutrients, by utilizing its own stored reserves. Fungi are known to do this in culture but there is no good example from soil. All plant nematodes, however, have a soil phase (Jones, 1959). While the nonparasites have their whole life history in this phase, other nematodes have the free-living period reduced to a very short preparasitic larval stage comparable to the preinfection germ-tube phase of fungal parasites. Between these extremes is a range that includes the vagrant species. These are fully mobile in the adult stage and are capable of some existence away from the hosts and can even overwinter on their reserves in the absence of a host (Taylor, 1953).

Survival in soil without growth and activity occurs by the structures listed earlier. These structures may lack activity because of some inherent dormancy or because of an imposed inactivity as a result of an unfavourable environment. Dormancy (Gottlieb, 1950; Cochrane, 1960) is the condition in which the structure is at first unable to resume activity even under conditions that subsequently favour germination. Thus a period intervenes during which no resumption of activity is normally possible, but after this period dormancy no longer exists and the condition that remains is identical with that present from the first in an inactive but not dormant structure. Thus biologically, apart from the initial lag endurancy during which no development is possible, there is no fundamental difference between the two conditions in respect of survival in soil. Indeed in many examples it is difficult to know whether a stimulus to germination is a result of breaking dormancy by counteracting an internal inhibition, or a result of counteracting the external inhibition imposed from without by the general soil toxicity.

Host exudates frequently stimulate inactive structures in soil to germinate. Barton (1957) showed this with fungal spores, and Rolfe (1959) with eelworm cysts. The response may be specific, the only effective stimulation being that from plants capable of being parasitized, as shown for sclerotia of *Sclerotium cepivorum* by Coley-Smith (1959); or the relation may be less perfect, whereby nonhosts may promote germination. This condition is common for eelworm cysts (Jones, 1959; Rolfe, 1959; Winslow, 1955). Stimulation may be even less specific, particularly where inactivity is primarily imposed by soil antagonism, and may even be provided by dead organic matter that can counteract soil toxicity (Clark, 1942). This process can result in the disappearance of a pathogen as a result of "spontaneous" germination in the absence of the host (Valder, 1958). Burke (1954) describes an interesting example of how a soil that is apparently unfavourable to fungal activity may promote survival of the fungus. Conidia of the pathogen *Fusarium solani* f. *phaseoli* buried in one soil germinated to give fairly extensive mycelium with relatively late formation of few and small chlamydospores. In another soil conidia germinated to give very short germ tubes, each soon producing a large terminal chlamydospore. In both soils lysis of mycelium eventually took place, and the soil that had given least activity retained greatest infectivity.

The situation in which activity is promoted under conditions unsuitable for successful infection or colonization of a substratum leads to the possibility of decoy methods of biological control, namely of eradicating or reducing the amount of a pathogen in soil by applying an appropriate stimulus to germination. Decoy methods might be used for dormant structures or for those inhibited by external conditions. As was emphasized earlier, the distinction between the two conditions might not be easy to make. Furthermore, in soil the distinction may not have any great significance, as the following consideration helps to show. One advantage of dormancy in a population of spores is that the effect is not uniform and termination of the dormant period is spread out through the population. This results in an initial period of total dormancy, followed by a more or less extended period during which successive sections of the population arrive at a condition ready for germination and capable of infecting should a host present itself. The process then is well suited to certain types of discontinuous habitat in that it increases the chance of the organism's being able to take advantage of the appropriate conditions when these appear. In soil, however, this function of spreading the germination in a population is unnecessary since even nondormant structures are held in inactivity in the absence of stimulus from organic materials. When a substratum presents itself, germination occurs as a result of its arrival. Thus dormancy, while it may occur in soil, is biologically more appropriate to aerial surroundings and to organisms of discontinuous habitats surviving in nontoxic environments.

SITE OF SURVIVAL.—Soils are more or less heterogeneous and some organisms survive better in some sites than in others. The greater the heterogeneity in a soil the greater the number of different niches and hence the number of species that might survive. Parkinson and Kendrick (1960) have demonstrated a type of study that analyses the different microhabitats in soil, and the different fungi that occur there.

Cultivation of soil, by providing a greater heterogeneity, allows a greater number of fungi to survive (England and Rice, 1957). In addition, cultivation provides conditions qualitatively different from those in natural soils and there is evidence that some pathogens—e.g. *Pythium* spp. (Barton, 1958) and *Fusarium oxysporum* (Park, 1963)—are more characteristic of cultivated soils than of natural soils. The survival of some pathogens is correlated closely with the type of covercrop, as was shown for *Rhizoctonia solani* (Sanford, 1952), and cultivation may affect survival in this way by affecting the availability of appropriate sites for survival. These sites may be diseased plant parts or apparently healthy parts. Propagative bodies like potato tubers (Chamberlain, 1935) and seeds, as well as vegetative plant parts, may appear sound and yet carry pathogens. Waid (1957) and Peterson (1958) have shown that roots of healthy plants may support viable fungal colonists that are rare even in the rhizosphere. Within the roots of one species there may be site differentiation for fungal species according to age and distance from the root surface.

In addition to living plants providing special sites, the debris of dead plants may provide places more favourable than the soil matrix. Anwar (1949) for *Helminthosporium sativum* in barley stubble, Blair (1952) and Macer (1961) for *Cercosporella herpotrichoides* in wheat straw, Stover (1953) and Venkata Ram (1953) for *Fusarium* spp. in colonized plant materials, all show survival in these materials at the same time as loss of viability in the soil matrix. Stakman and Harrar (1957) list plant debris and insects as favourite sites for the survival in soil of plant-pathogenic bacteria. Lucas (1955) showed that even within dead materials different sites may exist, and that the morphology of an individual piece of straw may influence the species colonizing it. After some decomposition of colonized materials in soil some species may disappear (Blair, 1952), while others, both fungi (Warcup, 1957) and bacteria (Strugger, 1948), continue to find a spe-

cially favourable site for survival in the resulting humus. It has already been suggested that this may be due in part to protection afforded by organic stuff, and Record and Taylor (1953) indicate that organic matter may help to protect bacterial cells against adverse conditions.

There is thus a good deal of evidence that organic material may assist in the survival of pathogens. It is, however, possible that other microorganisms survive as well or better in the mineral soil matrix than in organic matter. Thom (1927) describes hyphae closely attached to the soil mineral particles, and Dobbs and Hinson (1960) found fungi arising on isolation plates from mineral fragments. Rishbeth (1955) describes the survival of *Fusarium oxysporum* f. *cubense* for only a short period in infected plant material but for many years in soil.

Hawker (1957), in her review of survival of fungi in relation to ecological factors, states that one of the special modes of survival of some fungi is through colonization of unusual habitats. Numbers of these may exist in soils, providing special and characteristic sites for survival of certain species by being unfavourable to the majority of microorganisms in the soil. J. C. Brown (1958b) describes some fungal species as being consistently present in the apparently inhospitable conditions of the fore-dunes of a sand-dune system. Such microorganisms escape the intense competition of more generally favourable habitats by having developed a tolerance for extremes of physicochemical conditions.

Sites for survival outside the soil itself must also be considered, and the addition of fungi to soil via colonized plant materials falling on the soil has been mentioned. Man-made additions to cultivated soils may also carry an inoculum of pathogens surviving outside the soil. Bewley and Buddin (1921) describe the presence of pathogens in soil irrigation water, and Cooke and Kabler (1957) found others in sewage effluent used as an irrigation additive.

COMPETITIVE SAPROPHYTIC ABILITY AND SURVIVAL.—The method of survival of a plant pathogen in the absence of its host, whether as an active saprophyte or as inactive structures, affects the duration of survival and also the way in which environmental conditions influence that duration. Thus an organism surviving as inactive bodies may possibly have a long survival period, but one which, even under the most favourable conditions, is limited in length by the maximum retention of viability by those structures. Unfavourable conditions may reduce viability and hence the survival period. Organisms that are, on the other hand, able to exist as active saprophytes may under appropriate conditions survive indefinitely in soil.

For some pathogens the effect of the environment on duration of survival may be inversely related to its effect for the soil population generally, a shift favourable to the soil microbia's reducing the population and survival of the pathogen.

Garrett (1956) discusses in detail the importance of the competitive saprophytic ability of a pathogen to its ability to survive in soil as a saprophyte. Since soil and soil habitats do not provide pure-culture conditions but are open to colonization by numbers of microorganisms in the soil population, organisms of low competitive saprophytic ability, which may be efficient pathogens and also able to grow vigorously as saprophytes in pure culture, are unable to withstand successfully the antagonism from common soil saprophytes and thus fail to maintain their population effectively in soil. Organisms of high competitive saprophytic ability are effective colonizers and utilizers of appropriate substrata in soil even in the presence of antagonism from other microorganisms and from the background soil toxicity. Many of the most effective soil saprophytes are obligately saprophytic, but some are facultative parasites. These latter are often economically important pathogens not because of efficiency in parasitic properties but because their high competitive saprophytic ability causes difficulties in controlling their presence and numbers in soil. *Fusarium culmorum* is such a pathogen. At the other extreme are those pathogens which while culturally classed as facultative saprophytes, have such a low competitive saprophytic ability that in soil they may be what Garrett (1956) has aptly called ecologically obligate parasites. *Ophiobolus graminis* is a pathogen of this type.

Between these extremes there probably exists a whole series of forms, but our detailed knowledge is insufficient to allow us to delimit intermediate categories. More detailed research on this system would be useful, and more comparative studies of pathogens from this viewpoint are desirable, with the aim of being able to place any pathogen on a scale of competitive saprophytic abilities.

It is, of course, also necessary to know the conditions under which the best degree of competitive saprophytic ability is exhibited. Griffiths and Siddiqui (1961) have shown that relatively small environmental variations may reverse the outcome of a soil antagonism. This sort of information could be very relevant to the theory and practice of biological control. Even a rough ranking of pathogens into broad categories could be useful. Garrett (1944) emphasizes that some pathogens of relatively low competitive saprophytic ability have, after death of the host crop, a shorter period of survival under conditions more favourable to microbial activity generally. Earlier Garrett (1939) had concluded that biological control was probably best applied to soil invaders, i.e. pathogens that we now know to be of low competitive saprophytic ability, rather than to soil inhabitants.

For soil inhabitants of high competitive saprophytic ability, a determination of the range within which their expression is best would indicate the directions in which useful control methods might be found.

VARIATION AND SURVIVAL IN SOIL.—An initial heterogeneity in a population of a pathogen has a survival value for the species, increasing the chances of its survival in soil and of its subsequently infecting a host. The characters, variation in which might increase duration of survival, include resistance to adverse factors,

sensitivity to soil toxicity, reaction to germination stimulus, and host range.

Heterogeneity in characters of this sort is known to occur. Thus Toussoun and Snyder (1961) found that the conidia and chlamydospores of a pathogen had different physiological properties in respect of behaviour in soil. MacFarlane (1952) found that *Plasmodiophora brassicae* has some spores that germinate spontaneously some months after formation, and some that continue to be inactive in the absence of any host stimulus. Isaac and MacGarvie (1962) present evidence suggesting that among the cells of the microsclerotia of *Verticillium* spp. there exists a division of function, some germinating sooner and more easily than others.

In the multicellular condition there is an advantage in heterogeneity in addition to that of large storage of reserves for long duration and for massive infection. The mechanism could be operative in some multicellular spores. A heterokaryotic condition in resting structures might confer a similar advantage by the different nuclei present, which affect the cytoplasm even during cryptobiosis, allowing in smaller space a cytoplasmic heterogeneity similar to that existing in the multicellular condition.

Variation in host range, which is known to occur in all the groups of pathogens, can be extended by mutation and thus increase a pathogen's chances of successfully terminating its period of survival in the absence of a specific host.

Of the normal mechanisms of variation in microorganisms, mutation has been mentioned, and is unique in that it can occur during the inactive phase (Fig. 2).

VARIATION MECHANISM

Inactive Survival		Active Survival
+	Mutation	+
−	Hybridisation	+
−	Heterokaryosis	+
−	Parasexuality	+
−	Differential Cytoplasmic Inheritance	+

Fig. 2. Potential mechanisms of variation of pathogens in soil, and their applicability during active and inactive modes of survival.

The other normal mechanisms found in microorganisms —namely hybridization during the sexual process, and differential cytoplasmic inheritance, in which daughter cells may differ from each other and from the mother cell (Briault, 1956; Hughes, 1956), and also the additional fungal mechanisms of variation through hetero-karyosis (Jinks, 1952; Buxton, 1954) and the para-sexual cycle (Pontecorvo, 1949)—all these depend upon activity for their occurrence and therefore, if they are operative in soil—and the evidence for this is as yet controversial—produce an effect proportional to the amount of activity that takes place during survival in soil. And, although mutation can occur in an inactive population, growing and dividing cells exhibit a proportionately greater amount. Pathogens able to survive in soil in an active form have, therefore, greater potentialities for variation than those pathogens surviving by inactive resting structures. That the degree of variation in a soil population varies with the amount of growth it makes is confirmed by the results of Nash, Christou, and Snyder (1961).

It has been disputed that some pathogens exhibit any variation in field soil. Miller (1946) has suggested that many of the variants and even species descriptions of pathogens are based on cultural variants derived by manipulation from more uniform wild-type populations. This view has been challenged (e.g. Subramanian, 1951), and there is good evidence that variation in a species does occur in natural soils and that it can be economically important (Borlaug and Christensen, 1941). Moreover Grossbard (1954) has shown that a fungus can "mutate" after inoculation into soil, and with a greater frequency than when in artificial culture.

In soil the background antagonism is not highly favourable for growth. There is, however, some suggestion that during antagonised growth certain variations might be specifically induced. Thus Christensen and Davies (1940) found that a bacterial contamination of cultures of *Helminthosporium sativum* resulted in an increase in the production of genetical variants by the fungus. Wiltshire (1932) investigated a similar contamination of *Stemphylium* that caused inhibition of growth, which was followed by the production of variants able to grow and that conformed with the generic characters of *Alternaria*. The change was reversible. W. Brown and Wood (1953) found that 2,3,5,6-tetrachloronitrobenzene (TCNB) stimulated the production of tolerant saltants in *Botrytis cinerea*. In fungi (Isaac and Abraham, 1959) and bacteria (Goodlow, Mika, and Braun, 1950) an old culture medium may increase the rate of production of saltants. Thus the marginal growth conditions in soil may favour the production of certain genetical variant forms.

Provided that variability is maintained in the soil population, a host root faces the prospect of selecting from the available pool an appropriate pathogenic strain or combination of nuclei (Buxton, 1954; Pontecorvo, 1949). Sanford (1941) describes in *Rhizoctonia solani* a preinfection phase of inhibited massing hyphae at the host surface. Such an ectotrophic phase is a characteristic feature of some soil-borne pathogens (Garrett, 1956) and could provide a situation in which selection for the appropriate pathogenic combination can develop.

INOCULUM POTENTIAL AND THE HALF-LIFE CONCEPT.—For a single propagule, survival ceases at a given time and one can legitimately quote a period of duration of survival. But for a population of such structures there is, under pure-culture conditions, a distribution of survival times about a mean. Under conditions where an adverse environment causes death or disappearance of such structures at a rate more rapid than the inherent one, then this effect will probably be random, resulting in a normal distribution curve for the over-all rate of loss of viability. Given such a situation, if the number of viable propagules is plotted against time, a sigmoid curve is obtained, and the later section of it conforms more or less to a declining logarithmic curve. Yarwood and Sylvester (1959) have developed this concept and shown that for a population total longevity can have no precise meaning. The value obtained for duration of survival of any pathogen in any particular conditions depends upon (1) the size of the initial population, and (2) the sensitivity of the method used for detecting its residual presence. The development of methods sensitive to low number of pathogens in soil is consequently of great value in survival studies.

The gradual decline of a population is linked in significance with the concept of inoculum potential for host infection (Garrett, 1956). For structures such as sclerotia and rhizomorphs, the required inoculum potential for infection is a function of their size or mass, but for smaller structures such as spores their number at the host surface is important. If, with time, the numbers of small propagules of a pathogen in soil fall to low levels, then they may become ecologically inviable, in that they may be incapable of causing any significant infection. A mechanism controlling such a situation has not been described, but Padwick (1939) and Darling and McArdle (1959) have demonstrated situations in which spores present in low numbers were at a considerable disadvantage in germination as compared with those at higher concentrations. A further significance of low soil populations is that they may be able to infect but not cause disease at economically important levels. This could allow crop production and persistence of the pathogen, but if repeated too frequently might allow the pathogen to build up its population to a level at which disease could become serious.

Despite the general comment that high populations with their high inoculum potential give disease more easily, there are examples in which infection can be caused by very low numbers of a pathogen in soil. Rishbeth (1955) cites *Fusarium* wilt of banana developing in soil containing 2 spores per g, and Maloy and Burkholder (1959) state that a 20% level of infection of bean with root rot occurred in soil with a pathogen population as low as 0.1 spore per g. Many common plating methods of detecting pathogens in soil are insensitive to numbers below 100-1,000 spores per g, whereas lower numbers are probably important in the ecology of survival. Moreover, numerous studies of declining populations in soil have traced them to the point of no further detection, yet the further decline can be predicted to occur much more slowly than that observed in the initial stages (Fig. 3). Consequently

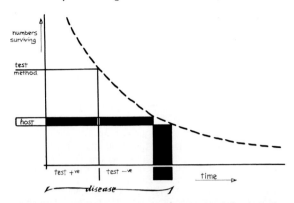

Fig. 3. Survival of pathogens at potentially infective inoculum levels beyond the range of sensitivity of commonly used detection methods.

not only may total eradication take long periods, but also the periods for reduction in pathogen numbers to population levels allowing economical crop production may be extended beyond those forecast on the basis of relatively insensitive detection methods.

METHODS.—As pointed out, many methods at present used for detection and estimation of numbers of pathogens in soil are so insensitive as to be of limited value. In addition to host infection being possible at population levels too low to be detected by normal plating, some resting structures fail to develop on dilution plates although they can germinate in the presence of the host (Isaac, 1954) and cause disease.

Because of these difficulties workers have sometimes found it more convenient to use artificially high numbers inoculated into soil to follow the effects of various factors on establishment or eradication. The results from such high levels may not necessarily reflect what occurs at more natural levels, since not only has the pathogen a higher inoculum potential, but also environmental effects on decline through negative feedback systems will be accentuated. With other pathogens even very high levels may not allow detection by normal plating methods. *Fusarium coeruleum* at 10^6 spores per g (Park, unpublished data) and *Thielaviopsis basicola* at 1.4×10^5 spores per g (Papavizas and Davey, 1961) cannot be isolated by general plating. For reasons such as these, special methods selective for particular pathogens have advantages. By favouring the investigated organism and preferably hindering development of other microorganisms, appropriate methods may allow large quantities of inoculum to be used and therefore low numbers in soil to be detected (Park, 1963). Such methods, by reducing antagonism on plates, might allow pathogens of low competitive saprophytic ability to appear where they might otherwise be inhibited.

Such special and sensitive methods have been defined for some pathogens (Chinn and Ledingham, 1958, and Chinn, Ledingham and Sallans, 1960, for *Helminthosporium sativum*; Nadakavukaren and Horner, 1959, for *Verticillium* spp.; Park, 1963, for *Fusarium oxysporum*; Singh and Mitchell, 1961, for *Pythium* spp.)

and enable population studies to be made at natural levels. Where relatively large structures are involved as with eelworm cysts and fungal sclerotia (Rogers, 1936; Leach and Davey, 1938), physical separation may be used to determine soil populations. These methods can assist, not only in experimental investigation of the biology of disease, but also in forecasting the disease potential of the soil and in checking the efficacy of any control system used.

With organisms for which no culture or counting method is available then host tests or baiting tests may be used.

FUTURE RESEARCH.—The aspects discussed in this section are those thought to be important to an understanding of the subject. For no one pathogen is there comprehensive information on many of these aspects. This paper serves therefore to indicate deficiencies in our knowledge, and consequently lines of research that could be usefully followed. For each soil-borne pathogen it would be ideal to have information on each of the following points.

1. The structures by which survival occurs in soil.
2. The conditions affecting the duration of survival of these structures in pure culture, and those affecting their germination.
3. As 2, but in soil instead of pure culture.
4. The factors contributing to the production and inhibition of production of the durable stages.
5. The precise microhabitats in soil in which activity and survival occurs.
6. The host range and the effect of nonsusceptible crops on survival.
7. The relative degree of competitive saprophytic ability and the conditions under which it is highest and lowest, together with the precise mode of survival in soil.
8. The exact substrates saprophytically utilized in soil and the stage of succession on them.
9. Methods of detecting, if necessary specifically, the pathogen in soil at low population levels.

Information on these points would contribute toward a more scientific basis for biological control of soilborne pathogens.

LITERATURE CITED

AGNIHOTHRUDU, V. 1955. State in which fungi occur in the rhizosphere. Naturwissenschaften 18: 515-516.
ANWAR, A. A. 1949. Factors affecting the survival of *Helminthosporium sativum* and *Fusarium lini* in soil. Phytopathology 39: 1005-1019.
ARMSTRONG, G. M., and J. K. ARMSTRONG. 1948. Nonsusceptible hosts as carriers of wilt fusaria. Phytopathology 38: 808-826.
ARRILAGA, J. G. 1935. The nature of the inhibition between certain fungi parasitic on *Citrus*. Phytopathology 25: 763-775.
BAKERSPIGEL, A. 1953. Soil as a storage medium for fungi. Mycologia 45: 596-604.
BARKER, H. D. 1923. A study of wilt resistance in flax. Minnesota Agr. Expt. Sta. Tech. Bull. 20, 42 p.
BARTON, R. 1957. Germination of oospores of *Pythium mammillatum* in response to exudates from living seedlings. Nature (London) 180: 613-614.

BARTON, R. 1958. Occurrence and establishment of *Pythium* in soils. Trans. Brit. Mycol. Soc. 41: 207-222.

BARTON, R. 1961. Saprophytic activity of *Pythium mamillatum* in soils. II. Factors restricting *P. mamillatum* to pioneer colonization of substrates. Trans. Brit. Mycol. Soc. 44: 105-118.

BEWLEY, W. F., and W. BUDDIN. 1921. On the fungus flora of glasshouse water-supplies in relation to plant diseases. Ann. Appl. Biol. 8: 10-19.

BILAI, V. I. 1956. Volatile antibiotics in fungi of the genus *Trichoderma*. Microbiology (U.S.S.R.) (Engl. transl.) 25: 458-465.

BISSET, K. A. 1952. Bacteria. Livingstone Ltd., London. 123 p.

BLAIR, I. D. 1943. Behaviour of the fungus *Rhizoctonia solani* Kühn in the soil. Ann. Appl. Biol. 30: 118-127.

BLAIR, I. D. 1952. Parasitism and saprophytism among soil pathogens. Rept. Sci. Congr. Roy. Soc. New Zealand, 1951: 45-46.

BORLAUG, N. E., and J. J. CHRISTENSEN. 1941. Variation in *Fusarium lini*. Phytopathology 31: 4.

BREMER, H. 1924. Untersuchungen über Biologie und Bekämpfung des Erregers der Kohlhernie, *Plasmodiophora brassicae* Woronin. 2 Mitteilung. Kohlhernie und Bodenazidität. Landwirtsch. Jahr. Schweiz 59: 673-685.

BRIAN, P. W. 1960. Antagonistic and competitive mechanisms limiting survival and activity of fungi in soil. p. 115-129. *In* Proc. Symp. Ecol. Soil Fungi (Liverpool, 1958), Liverpool University Press, Liverpool.

BRIAULT, P. L. 1956. Cytoplasmic changes associated with adaptation and differentiation. Nature (London) 178: 1223-1224.

BROWN, J. C. 1958a. Fungal mycelium in dune soils estimated by a modified impression slide technique. Trans. Brit. Mycol. Soc. 41: 81-88.

BROWN, J. C. 1958b. Soil fungi of some British sand dunes in relation to soil type and succession. J. Ecol. 46: 641-664.

BROWN, W., and R. K. S. WOOD. 1953. Ecological adaptations in fungi. *In* Adaptation in microorganisms, Symp. Soc. Gen. Microbiol. 3: 326-336.

BURGES, A., and E. FENTON. 1953. The effect of CO_2 on the growth of certain soil fungi. Trans. Brit. Mycol. Soc. 36: 104-108.

BURKE, D. W. 1954. Pathogenicity of *Fusarium solani* f. *phaseoli* in different soils. Phytopathology 44: 483.

BUTLER, G. M. 1957. The development and behaviour of mycelial strands in *Merulius lacrymans* (Wulf.) Fr. I. Strand development during growth from a food-base through a non-nutrient medium. Ann. Botany (London) [N.S.] 21: 523-537.

BUXTON, E. W. 1954. Heterocaryosis and variability in *Fusarium oxysporum* f. *gladioli* (Snyder & Hansen). J. Gen. Microbiol. 10: 71-84.

BUXTON, E. W. 1957. Differential rhizosphere effects of three pea cultivars on physiologic races of *Fusarium oxysporum* f. *pisi*. Trans. Brit. Mycol. Soc. 40: 305-317.

BYWATER, J. 1959. Infection of peas by *Fusarium solani* var. *martii* forma 2 and the spread of the pathogen. Trans. Brit. Mycol. Soc. 42: 201-212.

CAIRNS, H., and A. E. MUSKETT. 1933. Pink rot of the potato. Ann. Appl. Biol. 20: 381-403.

CALDWELL, R. 1958. Fate of spores of *Trichoderma viride* Pers. ex Fr. introduced into soil. Nature (London) 181: 1144-1145.

CALDWELL, R. 1963. Observations on the fungal flora of decomposing beech litter in soil. Trans. Brit. Mycol. Soc. 46: 249-261.

CHAMBERLAIN, E. E. 1935. Fungi present in the stem-end of potato tubers. New Zealand J. Sci. Tech. 164: 242-246.

CHINN, S. H. F., and R. J. LEDINGHAM. 1958. Application of a new laboratory method for the determination of the survival of *Helminthosporium sativum* spores in soil. Can. J. Botany 36: 289-295.

CHINN, S. H. F., and R. J. LEDINGHAM. 1961. Mechanisms contributing to the eradication of spores of *Hel-*

minthosporium sativum from amended soil. Can. J. Botany 39: 739-748.

CHINN, S. H. F., R. J. LEDINGHAM, and B. J. SALLANS. 1960. Population and viability studies of *Helminthosporium sativum* in field soils. Can. J. Botany 38: 533-539.

CHRISTENSEN, J. J., and F. R. DAVIES. 1940. Variation in *Helminthosporium sativum* induced by a toxic substance produced by *Bacillus mesentericus*. Phytopathology 30: 1017-1033.

CLARK, F. E. 1942. Experiments towards the control of take-all disease of wheat and the *Phymatotrichum* root rot of cotton. U.S. Dept. Agr. Tech. Bull. 835, 27 p.

COCHRANE, V. W. 1960. Spore germination. *In* J. G. Horsfall, and A. E. Dimond [ed.], Plant pathology, an advanced treatise, Academic Press, New York and London.

COLEY-SMITH, J. R. 1959. Studies on the biology of *Sclerotium cepivorum* Berk. III. Host range; persistence and viability of sclerotia. Ann. Appl. Biol. 47: 511-518.

COOKE, W. B., and P. W. KABLER. 1957. Plant disease fungi in sewage polluted water. Publ. Health Rept. (U.S.) 72: 651-654.

CRITOPOULOS, P. D. 1955. Foot rot of tomato caused by *Phytophthora capsici*. Bull. Torrey Botan. Club 82: 168-182.

DARLING, W. M., and M. MCARDLE. 1959. Effect of inoculum dilution on spore germination and sporeling growth in a mutant strain of *Aspergillus amstelodami*. Trans. Brit. Mycol. Soc. 42: 235-242.

DARPOUX, H. 1960. Biological interference with epidemics. *In* J. G. Horsfall and A. E. Dimond [ed.], Plant pathology, an advanced treatise, Academic Press, New York and London.

DOBBS, C. G., and W. H. HINSON. 1953. A widespread fungistasis in soils. Nature (London) 172: 197-199.

DOBBS, C. G., and W. H. HINSON. 1960. Some observations on fungal spores in soil. p. 33-42. *In* Proc. Symp. Ecol. Soil Fungi (Liverpool, 1958) Liverpool University Press, Liverpool.

DOWDING, E. S. 1959. Ecology of *Endogone*. Trans. Brit. Mycol. Soc. 42: 449-457.

DOWNIE, D. G. 1943. Source of the symbiont of *Goodyera repens*. Trans. Proc. Botan. Soc. Edinburgh 33: 383-390.

DRECHSLER, C. 1938. Two hyphomycetes parasitic on oospores of root-rotting oomycetes. Phytopathology 28: 81-103.

DUDDINGTON, C. L. 1956. The predacious fungi: Zoopagales and Moniliales. Biol. Rev. 31: 152-193.

ENGLAND, C. M., and E. L. RICE. 1957. A comparison of the soil fungi of a tall grass prairie and of an abandoned field in central Oklahoma. Botan. Gaz. 118: 186-190.

FENWICK, D. W. 1959. The genus *Heterodera*. p. 61-64. *In* Plant nematology, H.M. Stationery Office, London.

FRANKLIN, M. T. 1959. Plant parasitic nematodes of the genus *Aphelenchoides* Fischer, 1894. p. 71-77. *In* Plant nematology, H.M. Stationery Office, London.

GADD, C. H., and L. S. BERTUS. 1928. *Corticium vagum* B. & C.—the cause of a disease of *Vigna oligosperma* and other plants in Ceylon. Ann. Roy. Botan. Gardens, Peradeniya, 11: 27-49.

GARRETT, S. D. 1938. Soil conditions and take-all disease of wheat: III. Decomposition of the resting mycelium of *Ophiobolus graminis* in infected wheat stubble buried in the soil. Ann. Appl. Biol. 25: 742-766.

GARRETT, S. D. 1939. Soil-borne fungi and the control of root disease. Imp. Bur. Soil Sci. Tech. Commun. 38, 54 p.

GARRETT, S. D. 1944. Root disease fungi. Chronica Botanica Co., Waltham, Mass. 177 p.

GARRETT, S. D. 1946. A study of violet root rot: factors affecting production and growth of mycelial strands in *Helicobasidium purpureum* Pat. Trans. Brit. Mycol. Soc. 29: 114-127.

GARRETT, S. D. 1956. Biology of root-infecting fungi.

Cambridge University Press, London and New York. 292 p.

GARRETT, S. D. 1959. *Armillaria* root disease in orchards. Agriculture (London) 66: 331-335.

GERDEMANN, J. W. 1955. Relation of a large soil-borne spore to phycomycetous mycorrhizal infections. Mycologia 47: 619-632.

GLYNNE, MARY D. 1926. The viability of the winter sporangium of *Synchytrium endobioticum* (Schilb.) Perc., the organism causing wart disease in the potato. Ann. Appl. Biol. 13: 19-36.

GODFREY, R. M. 1957. Studies of British species of *Endogone*. II. Fungal parasites. Trans. Brit. Mycol. Soc. 40: 136-144.

GOODLOW, R. J., L. A. MIKA, and W. BRAUN. 1950. The effect of metabolites upon growth and variation of *Brucella abortus*. J. Bacteriol. 60: 291-300.

GORDON, W. C. 1959. The occurrence of *Fusarium* species in Canada. VI. Taxonomy and geographic distribution of *Fusarium* species on plants, insects and fungi. Can. J. Botany 37: 257-290.

GOTTLIEB, D. 1950. The physiology of spore-germination in fungi. Botan. Rev. 16: 229-257.

GREGG, M. 1957. Germination of oospores of *Phytophthora erythroseptica*. Nature (London) 180: 150.

GRIFFITHS, E., and M. A. SIDDIQUI. 1961. Some factors affecting occurrence of *Fusarium culmorum* in the soil. Trans. Brit. Mycol. Soc. 44: 343-353.

GRINDLE, M., and H. M. GOOD. 1961. Effects of drying on the viability of germinated and germinating conidia of *Monilinia fructicola* (Wint.) Honey. Trans. Brit. Mycol. Soc. 44: 549-558.

GROSSBARD, E. 1954. The improvement in antibiotic activity of *Aspergillus clavatus* after sojourn in nonsterile soil. Antibiot. Ann. 1953-54: 141-146.

HACK, J., and P. H. WILLIAMS. 1960. The effect of certain soil treatments on *Didymella* stem-rot of tomatoes. II. Laboratory investigations. Ann. Appl. Biol. 48: 236-244.

HAWKER, L. E. 1957. Ecological factors and the survival of fungi. *In* Microbial ecology; Symp. Soc. Gen. Microbiol. 7: 238-258.

HAWKER, L. E., A. H. LINTON, B. F. FOLKES, and M. J. CARLILE. 1960. An introduction to the biology of microorganisms. Edward Arnold, London. 452 p.

HENDERSON, D. W. 1955. The Microbiological Research Department, Ministry of Supply, Porton, Wilts. Proc. Roy. Soc. (London), Ser. B, 143: 192-202.

HOUSTON, B. R., and P. F. KNOWLES. 1949. Fifty year survival of flax *Fusarium* wilt in the absence of flax culture. Plant Disease Reptr. 33: 38-39.

HUGHES, W. H. 1956. Bacterial variation to sensitivity: an example of individuality in micro-organisms. Nature (London) 177: 1132-1133.

ISAAC, I. 1953. Studies in the interactions between species of *Verticillium*. Ann. Appl. Biol. 40: 623-629.

ISAAC, I. 1954. Studies in the antagonism between *Blastomyces luteus* and species of *Verticillium*. Ann. Appl. Biol. 41: 305-310.

ISAAC, I., and G. H. ABRAHAM. 1959. Saltation and zonation formation in *Verticillium lateritium*. Can. J. Botany 37: 801-814.

ISAAC, I., and Q. D. MACGARVIE. 1962. Germination of resting bodies in *Verticillium* species. Nature (London) 195: 826-827.

JACKSON, R. M. 1957. Fungistasis as a factor in the rhizosphere phenomenon. Nature (London) 180: 96-97.

JACKSON, R. M. 1958a. An investigation of fungistasis in Nigerian soils. J. Gen. Microbiol. 18: 248-258.

JACKSON, R. M. 1958b. Some aspects of soil fungistasis. J. Gen. Microbiol. 19: 390-401.

JINKS, J. L. 1952. Heterokaryosis—a system of adaptation in wild fungi. Proc. Roy. Soc. (London), Ser. B, 140: 83-99.

JONES, F. G. W. 1959. Ecological relationships of nematodes. p. 395-411. *In* C. S. Holton et al. [ed.] Plant

pathology: problems and progress 1908-1958, University of Wisconsin Press, Madison, Wisc.

KING, C. J., and E. D. EATON. 1934. Influence of soil moisture on the longevity of cotton root rot sclerotia. J. Agr. Res. 49: 793-798.

KING, C. J., H. F. LOOMIS, and C. HOPE. 1931. Studies on sclerotia and mycelial strands of the cotton root rot fungus. J. Agr. Res. 42: 827-840.

KOCH, L. W. 1934. Investigations of black knot of plums and cherries. II. Occurrence and significance of certain fungi associated with *Dibotryon morbosum* (Schw.) T. & S. Sci. Agr. 15: 80-95.

LAST, F. T. 1960. Longevity of conidia of *Botrytis fabae* Sardiña. Trans. Brit. Mycol. Soc. 43: 673-680.

LEACH, L. D., and A. E. DAVEY. 1938. Determining the sclerotial population of *Sclerotium rolfsii* by soil analyses and predicting losses of sugar beets on the basis of these analyses. J. Agr. Res. 56: 619-651.

LEGGE, B. J. 1952. Use of glass fibre material in soil mycology. Nature (London) 169: 759.

LINFORD, M. B. 1927. Additional hosts of *Aphanomyces euteiches,* the pea root rot fungus. Phytopathology 17: 133-134.

LINFORD, M. B., and R. E. VAUGHAN. 1925. Root rot of peas. Some ways to avoid it. Wisconsin Agr. Ext. Serv. Circ. 188, 12 p.

LOCKWOOD, J. L. 1959. Lysis of non-soil, soil-invading and soil-inhabiting fungi by soil. Phytopathology 49: 544.

LUCAS, R. L. 1955. A comparative study of *Ophiobolus graminis* and *Fusarium culmorum* in saprophytic colonization of wheat straw. Ann. Appl. Biol. 43: 134-143.

MACER, R. C. F. 1961. The survival of *Cercosporella herpotrichoides* Fron. in wheat straw. Ann. Appl. Biol. 49: 165-172.

MACFARLANE, I. 1952. Factors affecting the survival of *Plasmodiophora brassicae* Wor. in the soil and its assessment by a host test. Ann. Appl. Biol. 39: 239-256.

MALOY, O. C., and W. H. BURKHOLDER. 1959. Some effects of crop rotation on the *Fusarium* root rot of bean. Phytopathology 49: 583-587.

MATSUMOTO, T. 1921. Studies on the physiology of the fungi. XII. Physiologic specialization in *Rhizoctonia solani* Kühn. Ann. Missouri Botan. Garden 8: 1-62.

MCCLARY, D. O. 1952. Factors affecting the morphology of *Candida albicans*. Ann. Missouri Botan. Garden 39: 137-164.

MCKINNEY, H. H. 1946. Soil factors in relation to incidence and symptom-expression of virus diseases. Soil Sci. 61: 93-100.

MCNAMARA, H. C., R. E. WESTER, and K. C. GUNN. 1934. Persistent strands of the cotton root rot fungus in Texas. J. Agr. Res. 49: 531-538.

MILLER, J. J. 1946. Cultural and taxonomic studies on certain fusaria. Can. J. Res., Sec. C, 24: 188-223.

MITCHELL, R., and M. ALEXANDER. 1961. The mycolytic phenomenon and biological control of *Fusarium* in soil. Nature (London) 190: 109-110.

MITCHELL, R. B., D. R. HOOTON, and F. E. CLARK. 1941. Soil bacteriological studies on the control of *Phymatotrichum* root rot of cotton. J. Agr. Res. 63: 535-547.

MOORE, E. S. 1924. The physiology of *Fusarium coeruleum*. Ann. Botany (London) 38: 137-161.

MOSSE, B. 1959. The regular germination of resting spores and some observations on the growth requirements of an *Endogone* sp. causing vesicular-arbuscular mycorrhiza. Trans. Brit. Mycol. Soc. 42: 273-286.

NADAKAVUKAREN, M. J., and C. E. HORNER. 1959. An alcohol agar medium selective for determining *Verticillium* microsclerotia in soil. Phytopathology 49: 527-528.

NASH, S. M., T. CHRISTOU, and W. C. SNYDER. 1961. Existence of *Fusarium solani* f. *phaseoli* in soil. Phytopathology 51: 308-312.

NELSON, P. E., and S. WILHELM. 1958. Thermal death range of *Verticillium albo-atrum*. Phytopathology 48: 613-616.

NEWCOMBE, M. 1960. Some effects of water and anaerobic conditions on *Fusarium oxysporum* f. *cubense* in soil. Trans. Brit. Mycol. Soc. 43: 51-59.

NICOT, J. 1960. Some characteristics of the microflora in desert sands. p. 94-97. *In* Proc. Symp. Ecol. Soil Fungi, (Liverpool, 1958) Liverpool University Press, Liverpool.

NOBLE, R. J. 1924. Studies on the parasitism of *Urocystis tritici,* the organism causing flag smut of wheat. J. Agr. Res. 27: 451-489.

PADWICK, A. W. 1939. Note on the limitation of infection of wheat by ascospores of *Ophiobolus graminis* Sacc. A possible explanation. Ann. Appl. Biol. 26: 823-825.

PADY, S. M., and C. L. KRAMER. 1960. Kansas aeromycology. VI. Hyphal fragments. Mycologia 52: 681-687.

PALO, M. A. 1926. *Rhizoctonia* disease of rice. Philippine Agriculturist 15: 361-375.

PAPAVIZAS, A. C., and C. B. DAVEY. 1961. Isolation of *Thielaviopsis basicola* from bean rhizosphere. Phytopathology 51: 92-96.

PARK, D. 1954. Chlamydospores and survival in soil fungi. Nature (London) 173: 454-456.

PARK, D. 1955. Experimental studies on the ecology of fungi in soil. Trans. Brit. Mycol. Soc. 38: 130-142.

PARK, D. 1959. Some aspects of the biology of *Fusarium oxysporum* Schl. in soil. Ann. Botany (London) [N.S.] 23: 35-49.

PARK, D. 1960. Antagonism—the background to soil fungi. p. 148-159. *In* Proc. Symp. Ecol. Soil Fungi (Liverpool, 1958). Liverpool University Press, Liverpool.

PARK, D. 1961. Morphogenesis, antagonism and cultural staling. Trans. Brit. Mycol. Soc. 44: 377-390.

PARK, D. 1963. The presence of *Fusarium oxysporum* in soils. Trans. Brit. Mycol. Soc. 46: 444-448.

PARKINSON, D., and W. B. KENDRICK. 1960. Investigations of soil microhabitats. p. 22-28. *In* Proc. Symp. Ecol. Soil Fungi (Liverpool, 1958). Liverpool University Press, Liverpool.

PETERSON, E. A. 1958. Observations on the fungi associated with plant roots. Can. J. Microbiol. 4: 257-265.

PFENNIG, N. 1958. Beobachtungen des Wachstumsverhaltens von Streptomyceten auf Rossi-Cholodny-Aufwuchsplatten im Boden. Arch. Mikrobiol. 31: 206-216.

PITCHER, R. S. 1959. *Pratylenchus* spp. and other migratory soil nematodes. p. 77-87. *In* Plant nematology. H.M. Stationery Office, London.

PONTECORVO, G. 1949. The origin of virulent strains as recombinants from non-virulent strains, and the kinetics of epidemics. p. 376. *In* Proc. 4th Intern. Congr. Microbiol. (Copenhagen, 1947).

PUGH, A. J. F. 1958. Leaf litter fungi found on *Carex paniculata* L. Trans. Brit. Mycol. Soc. 41: 185-195.

RECORD, B. R., and R. TAYLOR. 1953. Some factors influencing the survival of *Bacterium coli* on freeze-drying. J. Gen. Microbiol. 9: 475-484.

RISHBETH, J. 1955. *Fusarium* wilt of bananas in Jamaica. I. Some observations on the epidemiology of the disease. Ann. Botany (London) [N.S.] 19: 293-328.

ROGERS, C. H. 1936. Apparatus and procedure for separating cotton root rot sclerotia from soil samples. J. Agr. Res. 52: 73-79.

ROLFE, S. W. H. 1959. Cereal root eelworm. p. 95-100. *In* Plant nematology, H.M. Stationery Office, London.

ROSEN, H. C., and L. M. WEETMAN. 1940. Longevity of urediospores of crown rust of oats. Arkansas Agr. Exp. Sta. Bull. 391, 20 p.

SANFORD, G. B. 1941. Studies on *Rhizoctonia solani* Kühn. V. Virulence in steam-sterilized and natural soil. Can. J. Res., Sec. C, 19: 1-8.

SANFORD, G. B. 1952. Persistence of *Rhizoctonia solani* Kühn in soil. Can. J. Botany 30: 652-664.

SANFORD, G. B. 1956. Factors influencing formation of sclerotia by *Rhizoctonia solani.* Phytopathology 46: 281-284.

SCHROTH, M. N., and F. F. HENDRIX, JR. 1962. Influence of non-susceptible plants on the survival of *Fusarium solani* f. *phaseoli* in soil. Phytopathology 52: 906-909.

SCOTT, M. R. 1956. Studies of the biology of *Sclerotium cepivorum* Berk. I. Growth of the mycelium in soil. Ann. Appl. Biol. 44: 576-583.

SEWELL, G. W. F. 1959. Direct observation of *Verticillium albo-atrum* in soil. Trans. Brit. Mycol. Soc. 42: 312-321.

SINGH, R. S., and J. E. MITCHELL. 1961. A selective method for isolation and measuring the population of *Pythium* in soil. Phytopathology 51: 440-444.

SKINNER, F. A. 1951. A method for distinguishing between viable spores and mycelial fragments of actinomycetes in soils. J. Gen. Microbiol. 5: 159-166.

SMITH, G. 1960. Industrial mycology. Edward Arnold Ltd., London. 398 p.

STAKMAN, E. C., and J. G. HARRAR. 1957. Principles of plant pathology. Ronald Press Co., New York. 581 p.

STOVER, R. H. 1953. Measurement of colonization and survival of soil fusaria in detached plant tissues. Nature (London) 172: 465.

STOVER, R. H. 1955. Flood-fallowing for eradication of *Fusarium oxysporum* f. *cubense.* III. Effect of oxygen on fungus survival. Soil Sci. 80: 397-412.

STOVER, R. H. 1958a. Studies on *Fusarium* wilt of bananas. II. Some factors influencing survival and saprophytic multiplication of *F. oxysporum* f. *cubense* in soil. Can. J. Botany 36: 311-324.

STOVER, R. H. 1958b. Studies on *Fusarium* wilt of bananas. III. Influence of soil fungitoxins on behaviour of *F. oxysporum* f. *cubense* in soil extracts and diffusates. Can. J. Botany 36: 439-453.

STOVER, R. H., and B. H. WAITE. 1954. Colonization of banana roots by *Fusarium oxysporum* f. *cubense* and other soil fungi. Phytopathology 44: 689-693.

STRUGGER, S. 1948. Fluorescence microscope examination of bacteria in soil. Can. J. Res., Sec. C, 26: 188-193.

SUBRAMANIAN, C. V. 1951. Is there a wild type in the genus Fusarium? Proc. Natl. Inst. Sci. India 17: 403-411.

TAUBENHAUS, J. J., and W. N. EZEKIEL. 1930. Recent studies on *Phymatotrichum* root rot. Am. J. Botany 17: 554-571.

TAUBENHAUS, J. J., and W. N. EZEKIEL. 1936. Longevity of sclerotia of *Phymatotrichum omnivorum* in moist soil in the laboratory. Am. J. Botany 23: 10-12.

TAYLOR, A. L. 1953. The tiny but destructive nematodes. *In* Plant diseases, Yearbook Agr. (U.S. Dept. Agr.) 1953: 78-82.

THIMANN, K. V. 1955. The life of bacteria. Macmillan Co., New York. 775 p.

THOM, C. 1927. Present and future studies of soil fungi. Trans. 1st Intern. Congr. Soil Sci. 3: 39-47.

THOMPSON, H. W. 1959. Potato root eelworm. p. 89-95. *In* Plant nematology, H.M. Stationery Office, London.

THOMPSON, W. R. 1929. On natural control. Parasitology 21: 269-281.

TIMONIN, M. I. 1941. The interaction of higher plants and soil micro-organisms. III. Effect of by-products of plant growth on activity of fungi and actinomycetes. Soil Sci. 52: 395-408.

TIMONIN, M. I. 1961. The interaction of plant, pathogen and *Scaptocoris talpa* Champ. Can. J. Botany 39: 695-703.

TOUSSON, T. A., and W. C. SNYDER. 1961. Germination of chlamydospores of *Fusarium solani* f. *phaseoli* in unsterilized soils. Phytopathology 51: 620-623.

TOWNSEND, B. B. 1957. Nutritional factors influencing the production of sclerotia by certain fungi. Ann. Botany (London) [N.S.] 21: 153-166.

VADÁSZ, J., and I. JUHÁSZ. 1955. Plasma globules of *Salmonella enteritidis* arising under the influence of penicillin, and their reversion to the original bacillary forms. Nature (London) 176: 168-169.

VALDER, P. L. 1958. The biology of *Helicobasidium purpureum* Pat. Trans. Brit. Mycol. Soc. 41: 283-308.

VALLEAU, W. D. 1951. Longevity of tobacco black shank fungus in the soil in the absence of tobacco. Plant Disease Reptr. 35: 453-454.

VENKAT[A] RAM, C. S. 1952. Soil bacteria and chlamydospore formation in *Fusarium solani*. Nature (London) 170: 889.

VENKATA RAM, C. S. 1953. Sensitivity of *Fusarium vasinfectum* to antagonistic microorganisms in the soil. Phytopathology 43: 482.

VILAS, L., A. TEJERIMA, and M. RUBIO. 1954. Présence des bactéries du sol sons leur forme L et leur forme filtrable. Trans. 5th Intern. Congr. Soil Sci. 3: 141-150.

WAID, J. S. 1957. Distribution of fungi within the decomposing tissues of ryegrass roots. Trans. Brit. Mycol. Soc. 40: 391-406.

WAITE, B. H., and V. C. DUNLAP. 1953. Preliminary host range studies with *Fusarium oxysporum* f. *cubense*. Plant Disease Reptr. 37: 79-80.

WARCUP, J. H. 1951a. Ecology of soil fungi. Trans. Brit. Mycol. Soc. 34: 376-399.

WARCUP, J. H. 1951b. Soil steaming as a selective method for isolation of ascomycetes from soil. Trans. Brit. Mycol. Soc. 34: 515-518.

WARCUP, J. H. 1955. On the origin of colonies of fungi developing on soil dilution plates. Trans. Brit. Mycol. Soc. 38: 298-301.

WARCUP, J. H. 1957. Studies on the occurrence and activity of fungi in a wheat field soil. Trans. Brit. Mycol. Soc. 40: 237-259.

WHITE, N. H. 1954. The use of decoy crops in the eradication of certain soil-borne plant diseases. Australian J. Sci. 17: 18-19.

WILHELM, S. 1954. Aerial microsclerotia of *Verticillium* resulting from conidial anastamosis. Phytopathology 44: 609-610.

WILHELM, S. 1956. A sand culture technique for the isolation of fungi associated with roots. Phytopathology 46: 293-295.

WINSLOW, R. D. 1955. The hatching responses of some root eelworms of the genus *Heterodera*. Ann. Appl. Biol. 43: 19-36.

WILTSHIRE, S. P. 1932. A reversible *Stemphylium-Alternaria* saltation. Ann. Botany (London) 46: 343-351.

YARWOOD, C. E., and E. S. SYLVESTER. 1959. The half-life concept of longevity of plant pathogens. Plant Disease Reptr. 43: 125-128.

YOUNG, P. A. 1926. Penetration phenomena and facultative parasitism in *Alternaria, Diplodia,* and other fungi. Botan. Gaz. 81: 258-279.

ZAN, K. 1962. Activity of *Phytophthora infestans* in soil in relation to tuber infection. Trans. Brit. Mycol. Soc. 45: 205-221.

ZYBINA, S. P. 1929. [Experimental work in the study of flax diseases in the Nijni-Novgorod government in 1927-8.] Morbi Plantarum, Leningrad 18: 67-100. *Abstr. in* Rev. Appl. Mycol. 8: 785-786.

▶ DISCUSSION OF DAVID PARK PAPER

G. H. Hepting:

Since basidiospores are often thin-walled and ephemeral, would spores such as those of *Fomes annosus* be likely to drop through the air and filter through a couple of inches of soil and still survive to infect a root, in view of the vicissitudes these spores would encounter?

S. D. Garrett:

Dr. John Rishbeth at Cambridge has investigated the possibility of protecting exposed surfaces of pine stumps against infection by *Fomes annosus* through covering the stump surfaces with a layer of soil. Much to his surprise, Rishbeth found that the basidiospores of *F. annosus* could survive for several months in soil and thereafter cause infection of pine-stump surfaces.

D. Pramer:

You mentioned in passing that colloids are capable of influencing survival; will you elaborate on your statement? What system did you have in mind? Can you offer some explanation for this effect?

D. Park:

My references to this fact were intended to indicate its relevance to soil conditions, and its implications regarding different microhabitats in soil. To explain the mechanism is outside both my competence and the scope of my contribution.

N. A. Burges:

Dr. Douglas of the Department of Inorganic Chemistry at the University of Liverpool has shown that a number of organic colloids—particularly polysaccharides—used during lyophilisation of bacteria very greatly increases the viability.

A. Kelman:

Do you have an explanation for the remarkable survival ability of a few plant-pathogenic bacteria although they do not form spores or other known resistant stages and do not compete well with other soil microorganisms as saprophytes? This would seem to differ from the concept that survival is dependent upon successful competitive saprophytic ability and formation of dormant resting structures.

D. Park:

Spores are not the only means by which bacteria can persist in soil. Resting cells and filterable stages are structures that may confer resistance to antagonism, but I do not know that these have yet been looked for in bacterial plant pathogens.

K. A. Grossenbacher:

Colloidal material was said to have significant effect on survival. Only organic material was referred to. What of inorganic colloidal material?

D. Park:

The literature that I know on this subject makes reference only to organic materials.

N. A. Burges:

We have no direct evidence of humic acid prolonging viability but it will alter the growth form and perhaps in that way lead to prolonged viability. *Mucor rammanianus* in the presence of humic acid becomes closely septate and forms short cells, densely filled, which may act as chlamydospores.

K. W. Kreitlow:

Would you care to comment on the capacity of antagonistic organisms to attack sclerotia in relation to their survival in soil?

D. Park:

Inactive sclerotia in soil may be subject to antibiosis and predation, and may also be parasitised by other microorganisms. Their longevity may be reduced by any of these means.

N. T. Flentje:

Dr. K. F. Baker and I, with assistance from Dr. Warcup, have been examining the survival of different strains of *Rhizoctonia* in Urrbrae loam held at 18% moisture (just below field capacity) and at a temperature range of 18°-25°C. The soil was subjected to treatment at the following temperatures in aerated steam for 30 minutes: 120°, 130°, 140°, 150°, 160°F. and unheated. The strains were introduced as washed mycelial mats.

One strain appears to have survived as active vegetative mycelium for nearly 2 years in all treatments, whereas other strains, including those which formed sclerotia, appear to have completely died out. The work is being repeated using other soils.

Dormancy of Soil Microorganisms in Relation to Survival

ALFRED S. SUSSMAN—*Department of Botany, University of Michigan, Ann Arbor.*

▶

Although the vegetative stages of some microorganisms survive astonishingly well through adverse circumstances, the standards of survivability usually are set by dormant cells. Such dormant stages, therefore, present the major challenge to those who would control soil microorganisms. Furthermore, since most microorganisms utilize spores as the vehicle for their dormancy, this paper will stress such stages, although I recognize that rhizomorphs, sclerotia, and other vegetative structures occasionally may possess a form of dormancy (Hawker, 1957).

Before entering into the role of dormant organisms in survival, let us define dormancy. I consider it to be *any reversible interruption of development.* Viewed in this way, dormancy can be of two types, which I have called "exogenous" and "constitutive" (Sussman, 1964). Exogenous dormancy is *that condition wherein development is delayed because of unfavorable chemical or physical circumstances in the environment.* Dr. Park, in his paper at this symposium, has referred to this kind of dormancy as being the "inactive" state of an organism, and workers with higher plants call it "quiescence" when they speak of the effect of cold upon buds and other organs.

On the other hand, constitutive dormancy is *the condition wherein development is delayed owing to an innate property of the dormant stage, such as a barrier to the penetration of nutrients, a metabolic block, or the production of a self-inhibitor.* Consequently, this state corresponds to the "dormant" condition as used by Park, and to the condition of "rest" in certain seeds.

Having discussed in a general way the forms that dormancy can take, what role does it play in the survival of organisms in soil?

LONGEVITY.—Earlier I stated that the standards of survivability are usually set by dormant stages, that is, by spores. What evidence is there for this assumption? The recent review of Menzies (1963) is a treatment of this subject and Tables 1 and 2 provide a selected list of pathogens and some other organisms about which records of longevity exist. The many microorganisms found to survive in culture for longer than 10 years include bacteria and representatives of each of the major groups of fungi. Judging from the resistance of some ascospores to heat (Lingappa and Sussman, 1959), it is lack of data, rather than inherent evanescence, that accounts for the absence of ascomycetes on this list. Moreover, it is likely that many of the data in Table 1 are minimum estimates, for germination was still obtained in many of the cases listed.

Several stages other than spores are to be found on this list, including vegetative bacteria, gemmae, sclerotia, and, in the case of *Ustilago nuda,* mycelium of surprising persistence in barley seeds. This instance is not exceptional because *Phytophthora infestans* is known to overwinter and to survive several weeks of hot weather in stems of potatoes (Hickman, 1958), and some powdery mildews are capable of overwintering in the buds of host plants (Yarwood et al., 1954). Moreover, Zimmerman (1925) and Hawker (1957) review several cases where viable mycelium of parasites has been found in the host after winter; and Wahl (1961) lists several pathogenic genera where rhizomorphs, or sclerotia, are the main reproductive structures that survive in nature. Furthermore, the production of spores is no guarantee of longevity, as the data in Table 1 reveal. Also, several entomophthoraceous species are notoriously evanescent (Hesseltine, Bradle, and Benjamin, 1960).

Nevertheless, in the majority of cases for which records exist, spores are the surviving element for microorganisms. Furthermore, recent data assembled by Hesseltine, Bradle, and Benjamin (1960) demonstrate that only 32, out of the 363 cultures tried, failed to survive lyophilization. Of these exceptions, more than half had no spores when lyophilized. In fact, their conclusion is, "Spores, or mycelial structures functioning as spores must be present before lyophilization, especially in the Fungi Imperfecti."

But, it may be argued, the evidence for the greater survivability of spores stems largely from laboratory experiments, rather than from studies of natural habitats. Others have discussed the difficulties in distinguishing between spores and vegetative cells from soil so I shall note merely that the techniques are imperfect and require that we accept such data with reserve. According to McKeen and Wensley (1961), maintenance of several pathogenic fusaria in nature as the "wild types" is due to their survival in the form of dormant propagules. Furthermore, the work of Borut (1960) with the fungi of desert soils argues strongly for a pre-eminent role of spores in survival. This study revealed that most of the fungi found in such habitats sporulate intensively, or possess resistant resting organs of other kinds. Furthermore, the optimum for the

TABLE 1. Longevity of certain spores and vegetative stages and the conditions under which they survive

Organism	Stage	Longevity	Conditions of storage	Reference
Bacillus anthracis	Spores	47 yr	Sealed vials & test tubes	Bosco, 1960*a*
Clostridium sporogenes	Spores	46 yr	In alcohol	Bulloch, 1928
65 strains of non-spore-forming bacteria	Vegetative	16-48 yr	Room temp. in dark	Bosco, 1960*b*
Eberthella typhosa	Vegetative	28 mo	In ice cream (—20°C)	Prucha and Brannon, 1926
Rhizobium meliloti	Vegetative	30-45 yr	Autoclaved soil	Jensen, 1961
Hemitrichia clavata	Spores	75 yr	Herbarium collection	Erbisch, 1963*
Lycogala flavofuscum	Spores	68 yr	Herbarium collection	Erbisch, 1963*
Peronospora schleideni	Oospores	3-4 yr	Dry	McKay, 1935
Endoconidiophora fagacearum	Ascospores	232 days	24°C, 10% relative humidity	Merek and Fergus, 1954
Endothia parasitica	Ascospores	1 yr	Dry in bark	Anderson and Rankin, 1914
Omphalia flavida	Gemmae	26 hr	Dry air	Buller, 1931*b*
Cronartium ribicola	Basidiospores	5-6 days	Air-dried	Spaulding and Rathbun-Gravett, 1926
C. ribicola	Aeciospores	8 wk	—	Spaulding, 1922
Puccinia triticina	Teliospores	2 yr	5°-7°C	Prasada, 1948
P. triticina	Uredospores	44 days	—8° to —9°C, on plant	Abe, 1933
Tilletia foetida	Basidiospores	25 yr	Herbarium	Fischer, 1936
T. foetida, T. caries	Basidiospores	22 yr	Room temp.	Kendrick and Holton, 1960
Ustilago nuda	Mycelium	11 yr	In barley seed	Porter, 1955
Psilocybe natans	Basidiospores	9 yr	Herbarium	McKnight, 1960†
Schizophyllum commune	Fruit body and spores	35 yr	0.1 mm Hg and 3 wk at —190°C	Bisby, 1945
Verticillium albo-atrum	Microsclerotia	13 yr	In field or culture	Wilhelm, 1955

* F. Erbisch, personal communication, 1963.
† K. H. McKnight, personal communication, 1963.

TABLE 2. Longevity of various organisms other than microorganisms

Organism	Stage	Longevity	Conditions of storage	Reference
Insects:				
Polypedilum vanderplanki	Larvae	11 hr	Dry at 68.5°C	Hinton, 1951
Eburia quadrigeminata	Larvae	40 yr	Dry wood	Hinton, 1953
Nematodes:				
Anguina tritici	Larvae	28 yr	Dried	Steiner and Albin, 1946
Tylenchus polyhypnus	Larvae and mature females	39 yr	Dried	Goodey, 1923
Phanerogams:				
Several legumes	Seeds	Up to 90 yr	Dried	Turner, 1933
Nelumbo nucifera	Seeds	800-1,000 yr (?)	In peat	Ohga, 1923; Chaney, 1951
Rumex crispus, Oenothera biennis, Verbascum blattaria	Seeds	80 yr	In soil	Darlington and Steinhauser, 1961
Viruses				
Nuclear polyhedrosis	—	20 yr	Sealed tubes	Steinhaus, 1960
Tobacco mosaic	—	52 yr	Dried leaves	Spector, 1956
Sugar-beet curly top	—	8 yr	Plant tissue	Spector, 1956

sporulation of all the species tested was 4°-10°C higher than for growth, suggesting that selective advantages accrue to those fungi in the desert which produce spores in response to an increase in temperature, that is, to an increase in the rigor of the environment. The isolation of increased numbers of spore formers from steamed soils (Warcup, 1957) also argues for the durability of such cells.

To conclude this section: a large amount of data from laboratory experiments suggest that resistant propagules like spores confer survivability upon micro-organisms. To set these data in perspective, Table 2 provides information on the longevity of other organisms. Of interest to pathologists are the data on insects, nematodes, and viruses, in which survival for long periods of time has been observed in several cases. These figures are to be compared with those for the lotus, living seeds of which have been dated at 800-1,000 years.

What is the maximum time microorganisms can survive? Sneath recently (1962) attempted to answer this question by surveying the survivors among the microorganisms present on plant roots in the collections of some British herbaria. Few fungi and actinomycetes survived over 50 years under these conditions. On the other hand, species of *Bacillus* survived for much longer periods of time. According to his calculations, a kilogram of soil would be sterilized after about 1,000 years, an order of resistance theoretically equivalent to that of the lotus seed.

SURVIVABILITY.—Having discussed the role of spores in longevity, we will now consider the factors which contribute to their success in filling this role. The factors listed below are those whose interaction I consider to determine survivability in microorganisms:

> *Resistance to deleterious agents
> *Nutritional status and capacity
> *Timing
> Degradative capacity
> Rapidity of growth
> Mutational capacity
> Disseminability

These are not original with me although one or two may not have been generally applied to this question before. Not all of the above factors are of equal importance for all organisms, but a favorable combination would seem to be required for survivability to be great. Therefore, it is these attributes of dormant creatures to which the biologist must turn in order to control such resourceful adversaries. It is obvious, however, that only a few of these characteristics lend themselves to the control of spores and these are starred in the list given above. I propose, in the remainder of this paper, to deal with some of the opportunities for control presented through the manipulation of these factors involved in survivability. Let us consider the first of these next.

Resistance to deleterious agents.—Data are available which reveal that dormant spores are more resistant to irradiation and extremes of temperature than are vegetative stages (Halvorson and Sussman, 1963), but I will stress resistance to chemicals at this time and will deal with the response to temperature in a later section.

Resistance to Chemicals: Studies in Soil.—Chemical treatments of several kinds have resulted in the enrichment of spore-forming bacteria in soil (Crump, 1953; McKeen, 1954; Allison, 1951). Fumigation of soil has been shown to shift the balance in favor of spore-forming fungi, as well. Thus, Wensley (1953) found that several ascomycetes, whose development usually is suppressed by penicillia and aspergilli, could be recovered from soil after treatment with methyl bromide, propane-propene, and ethylene dibromide. Ascosporic species of *Penicillium, Aspergillus, Chaetomium,* and *Thielavia* are remarkably resistant to carbon disulfide as well as to the above fumigants. Recent experiments by J. H. Warcup (personal communication) have revealed that ethanol-treated soil has yielded ascomycetes whose propagules may require heat-activation before growth can occur.

Another aspect of resistance to chemicals concerns the response to lytic factors. That spores of some fungi are destroyed when in contact with raw soil has been shown by Lingappa and Lockwood (1961), in contrast to the greater longevity of these cells in autoclaved soil. This is the case for conidia of *Glomerella cingulata, Fusarium oxysporum,* and *Penicillium frequentans.* Similar results have been reported by Subramanian (1950) and by Park (1955), so that this phenomenon appears to be well recognized. On the other hand, the data on longevity reported previously suggest that some propagules resist lysis over long periods of time. Our own experiments have shown that the melanized coat of *Neurospora* ascospores is very durable when exposed to soil, and it is possible that such structures in other spores and mycelia may serve a similar purpose.

Yet some fungi which do not possess resistant spores are remarkably well adapted to survive treatment with chemicals. This is true of *Trichoderma viride,* which tolerates soil fumigants to a remarkable degree (Warcup, 1957). Even sterile types of fungi have been recovered from chemically fumigated soils by Wensley (1953), so that while spores undoubtedly do help fungi to survive under such conditions, they are not always essential.

Resistance to Chemicals: Culture Studies.—As was mentioned above, dormant spores can be divided into two types, according to the nature of the restraints upon their development. If the physiological properties of these classes of spores differ, control measures may have to be adjusted to fit these properties. Therefore, I should like to compare certain characteristics of the two types which may serve as examples of the kind of differences which were discussed above. Let me stress that I don't claim any generality for this illustration: the organism isn't even a pathogen! I present it merely as a guide to what might be done with other organisms.

Inasmuch as permeability is at the core of many aspects of biological control, I have chosen to compare the effect of anions and cations upon the ascospores and conidia of *Neurospora.* The former are extremely resistant spores, about $25\,\mu$ in length, and require a heat shock or chemical treatment before germination can occur. Conidia of *Neurospora,* on the other hand, are more sensitive to heat (Lingappa and Sussman, 1959), are much smaller, and do not require any special treatment in order to germinate. Consequently, the ascospore serves as an example of a constitutively dormant cell, whereas the conidia might be considered to illustrate exogenous dormancy. Table 3 provides the comparison between the permeability of ascospores and conidia. It is clear that the dormant ascospores are relatively impermeable to all the cations used, whereas small anions are absorbed, but only when they do not exceed two carbon atoms in size. However, when germinating, the ascospores admit both cations and anions and they are killed almost immediately by toxic agents.

Conidia, on the other hand, appear to be freely permeable to most substances, so that chemical treatment should be an effective control technique. These differences are shown quantitatively in Table 4, wherein the dormant ascospores are shown to adsorb more than

TABLE 3. Comparison of the permeability characteristics of different stages in the life-cycle of *Neurospora*

| Ascospores of *N. tetrasperma* | | Conidia of: | |
Dormant	Germinating	*N. sitophila*	*N. crassa*
Cations like UO_2^{++}, Cu^{++}, Cd^{++}, Polymyxin-B taken up by cells without affecting respiration	Cations like UO_2^{++}, etc., inhibit respiration	Cations like Ag^+, Zn^{++}, Ce^{+++}, Cd^{++}, Hg^{++}, inhibit respiration, or stimulate depending upon concentration	—
Cations bound to cell wall of intact cell, as well as to isolated walls	As in dormant ascospores	Very little attachment of cations to wall; mostly bound on intracellular particles	Rb^+, K^+ and Na^+ bound intracellulary
Cations bound to dead cells	As in dormant ascospores	Uptake abolished by killing cells	Uptake abolished by metabolic inhibitors
Uptake of cations repressed by pretreatment with densely charged basic substances	As in dormant ascospores	Uptake affected variously depending on nature of pretreatment	Intracellular binding repressed by deoxycorticosterone
Acids larger than 2 carbon atoms enter slowly or not at all; glucose does not enter	Glucose and other sugars enter; acids taken up	Glucose and Krebs-cycle acids enter	—
References: Lowry, Sussman, and von Böventer-Heidenhain, 1957; Sussman, Holton, and von Böventer-Heidenhain, 1958	As in dormant ascospores	Kunkel, 1913; McCallan, Miller and Wood, 1954; Owens, 1955; Miller, 1956; Owens and Miller, 1957; Cochrane and Tull, 1958	Lester and Hechter, 1958, 1959

TABLE 4. Comparison of the toxicity of Ag^+ and Cu^{++} for conidia and ascospores of *Neurospora*

Toxicant	Organism	ED_{50} (germination) μg per g spores	Uptake, μg per g spores	Reference
Ag^+	Conidia (*N. sitophila*)	165	—	Miller, 1956
	Ascospores (*N. tetrasperma*)			
	Dormant	—	8,300*	} Lowry, Sussman, and Böventer-Heidenhain, 1957
	Germinating	216	—	
Cu^{++}	Conidia (*N. sitophila*)	1,650	—	McCallan, Miller, and Wood, 1954
	Ascospores (*N. tetrasperma*)			
	Dormant	—	2,730*	} Lowry, Sussman, and Böventer-Heidenhain, 1957
	Germinating	1,905	—	

* There is no measurable effect of the cation upon dormant ascospores.

40-fold more Ag^+ than would be necessary to kill 50% of the conidia of *Neurospora*, yet they are unharmed if the adsorbed mineral is removed before germination. These differences derive from the nature of the cell wall of the two types of cells. Thus, whereas the ascospores have a complex, three-layered wall (Lowry and Sussman, 1958) which adsorbs cations tenaciously, that of conidia is simpler and does not adsorb appreciably.

Implications for Control.—Control of organisms having spores with properties like those of conidia of *Neurospora* is a matter of using the right chemical agent. There would seem to be no special problem of permeability. By contrast, spores like ascospores of *Neurospora* present a challenge because of the impermeability of the dormant cell. Therefore, direct treatment of such cells by chemicals is unlikely to yield results unless the agent used remains attached to the walls long enough, in amounts large enough, to kill them when they germinate. That this may not be a hopeless endeavor is illustrated by the data in Fig. 1 and Table 5, which illustrate the adsorptive properties

of the walls of ascospores. As can be seen in Fig. 1, cationic substances like methylene blue are bound even to killed cells and to cells maintained at 4°C. Furthermore, the kinetics of uptake follow a typical Freundlich isotherm. We were interested in learning whether there are differences in the tenacity with which cations are bound, so we treated ascospores with various cations, after which we measured the time required for the adsorption of methylene blue. It is shown in Table 5 that substances like cobalt hexammine, hexol nitrate, protamine, and polymyxin-B are bound so tightly to the ascospores that they exclude methylene blue from the surface for hours. This is in comparison with untreated spores, which remove 50% of the dye in less than 90 seconds! The possibility toward which these data point is that cationic substances with high charge density may be effective toxicants for dormant spores with properties similar to those of *Neurospora* ascospores. Assuming that they are toxic, such compounds will have the important advantage of being concentrated on the cell surface, where they will remain until germination is triggered. A model for this kind of

TABLE 5. Effect of various substances upon the ability of ascospores of *Neurospora tetrasperma* to remove methylene blue from solution*

Substance used†	Concentration	Time for 50% dye uptake	Germination
Glycine, 0.01 M PO_4, pH 6.5	1×10^{-2} M	165 sec	+
Lysine	1×10^{-2} M	90 sec	+
Arginine	1×10^{-2} M	174 sec	+
Glycyl-glycine, 0.01 M PO_4, pH 6.5	1×10^{-2} M	104 sec	+
Glutathione, 0.01 M PO_4, pH 6.5	1×10^{-2} M	104 sec	+
Polymyxin-B SO_4, 0.01 M PO_4, pH 7.1	1×10^{-2} M	19 hr	—
Lysozyme, 0.01 M PO_4, pH 6.8 (incubated 12 hr)	1%	420 sec	+
Hyaluronidase, 0.1 M "Tris" buffer, pH 7.1	0.1%	150 sec	+
Protamine SO_4, 0.01 M PO_4, pH 7.9 (incubated 24 hr)	2%	21 hr	+
Protamine SO_4, 0.01 M PO_4, pH 7.9 (incubated 108 hr)	2%	36 hr	—
Bovine serum albumen, 0.1 M PO_4, pH 6.5	1%	128 sec	+
Fe^{+++}	1×10^{-2} M	32 min	—
Al^{+++}	1×10^{-2} M	40 min	—
H^+	1×10^{-2} M	108 sec	+
Th^{++++}	1×10^{-2} M	120 sec	?
$[Co(NH_3)_6]Cl_3$, 0.01 M PO_4, pH 7.9	1×10^{-2} M	22 hr	+
$[Co(NH_3)_6](NO_3)_3$, 0.01 M PO_4, pH 7.9	1×10^{-2} M	75 min	+
$[Co(NH_2CH_3CH_2NH_2)_3]Cl_3$, pH 7.9	1×10^{-2} M	144 sec	+
Hexol nitrate, 0.01 M PO_4, pH 7.9	1×10^{-2} M	20 hr	+

* From Sussman and Lowry, 1955.

† The spores were incubated in these compounds for 24 hours unless otherwise indicated.

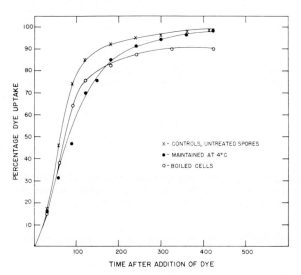

X – CONTROLS, UNTREATED SPORES
● – MAINTAINED AT 4°C
○ – BOILED CELLS

Fig. 1. Uptake of methylene blue by ascospores of *Neurospora tetrasperma* treated in various ways. Starting concentration of dye was 2×10^{-5} M. (A. S. Sussman and R. J. Lowry. J. Bacteriol. 70: 675-685. 1955.)

substance is polymyxin-B, which we have found to be extremely toxic, as well as binding strongly to the spore surface (Lowry and Sussman, 1956).

Other possibilities for control stem from the fact that some spores are more sensitive to certain chemicals than are vegetative stages. For example, the germination of spores of *Fusarium oxysporium* f. *lycopersici* and *F. roseum* is completely inhibited by a concentration of Phygon (3,3-dichloro-1,4-naphthoquinone) below 5 ppm. By contrast, the mycelium of these fungi will grow in 100-fold greater concentrations of this substance (Deep and Corden, 1961). Another instance is that of actidione, which is ten times more effective against spores of *Myrothecium verrucaria* than against mycelium (Walker and Smith, 1952). Similarly, it has been shown that mycelial fragments of *Verticillium* are much less sensitive to chlorogenic acid than are spores (McLean, Le Tourneau, and Guthrie, 1961). Another claim that fungus spores are more sensitive to fungicides is that of Domsch (1958). These studies, in which six different assay procedures were used, revealed that the differences in sensitivities were as great as 100-fold with *Pythium* sp., *Rhizoctonia solani,* and *Fusarium culmorum.* An interesting instance where survival value might accrue to the vegetative stage through enhanced resistance to chemicals is provided by Slotnick's (1959) work on *Bacillus.* In this case, out of eight actinomycin-D-resistant isolates of this organism, *all* were asporogenous. This is a possible means through which sterile organisms gain survivability in nature.

Nutritional status and capacity.—The second of the factors in survivability that I will consider is nutritional status and capacity. Although it is usually considered that prototrophy, or independence from special nutritional requirements, is an advantage to organisms, there are situations where metabolic incapacities confer advantages in survival. Thus, in *Ophiostoma multiannulatum,* Fries (1948) has shown that conidia of deficient mutants are more viable than those of unmutated

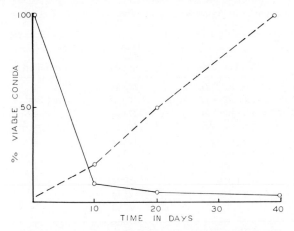

Fig. 2. Survival of Conidia of *Ophiostoma multiannulatum*. Solid line = percentage living conidia of all conidia; dotted line = percentage living mutant conidia of all living conidia. (N. Fries. Hereditas 34: 338-350. 1948.)

strains under circumstances where deficient media are employed (Fig. 2). These results parallel those of Macdonald and Pontecorvo (1953) with *Aspergillus nidulans,* in which spores of a biotin-requiring mutant died rapidly in a biotin-deficient medium but the introduction of a second mutation increased survival drastically. Such is the case in *Neurospora* as well; for the longevity of inositolless strains was extended 70-fold if a tryptophane requirement was added to that for the vitamin (Strauss, 1958).

On the other hand, the enhanced requirement by spores for a metabolite may work to the disadvantage of the organism. Thus, conidia of inositol- and pyridoxal-requiring strains of *Neurospora* die very rapidly when incubated on deficient media, whereas those that do survive fail to germinate (Lester and Gross, 1959). Consequently, it is likely that conidia of the inositol- and pyridoxal-requiring strains do not require the growth factor whereas vegetative stages do. Therefore, advantages in these cases accrue to those organisms whose spores cannot germinate in the absence of a growth factor for which they are deficient.

These considerations lead to a possible beneficial

effect of antibiotics upon some sensitive organisms. A model of this kind of interaction derives from the work of Strauss (1958), who found that ethionine prolonged the life of inositolless (suicide) strains of *Neurospora.* Thus, any means through which the germination of "suicide" strains of microorganisms could be reversibly delayed, in the absence of the needed metabolite, would enhance the chances for survival.

The inhibition of germination alone, however, cannot explain the long-term survival of dormant spores, for what is also needed is a mechanism for restricting metabolic activity to levels that permit the husbanding of endogenous reserves. In fact, the most generalized physiological effect of activation in a wide variety of spores is enhanced respiratory activity, underscoring the likelihood that lowered metabolism is characteristic of dormant spores. The reciprocal may also be true: Allen (1948) has reported that the evanescent sporidia of *Ustilago sphaerogena* have an endogenous Q_{O_2} of 75, which increases to 375 in the presence of sugar. These rates are to be compared with the value of 0.3 for dormant ascospores of *Neurospora* (Sussman, 1961*b*), which is not exceptional for other spores in the dormant state. Another role of a positive nature for antibiotics, as far as survival of spores is concerned, may be in reversibly lowering the respiratory rate of cells, thereby preserving their substrate and extending their viability.

Finally, the recent work of B. T. Lingappa and J. T. Lockwood (personal communication, 1963) reveals that the leakage of materials from spores may contribute to their downfall through the "widespread soil fungistasis" (Table 6). Thus, ascospores of *Neurospora* and washed spores of *Glomerella* resist the fungistatic principle, whereas the addition of peptone leads to failure to germinate. It is too early to be certain that the mechanism discussed above is an adequate explanation of these data. The work has to be done in more detail and with more organisms before it can be accepted, but it offers promising experimental leads.

Implications for control.—Where spores can be induced to germinate in the absence of a needed metabolite, as in the case of the "suicide" strains discussed above, killing will result. Another means of

TABLE 6. Effect of soils treated in various ways upon fungal spores*

Organism	Treatment	% Germination	
Neurospora tetrasperma, heat-activated ascospores	Water agar	80	
	Sterile soil	80	
	Natural soil	80	
	Natural soil + 0.5% peptone	0	
Puccinia glumarum, uredospores	Water agar	75	
	Sterile soil	75	
	Natural soil	40	
	Natural soil + 0.5% peptone	0	
Glomerella cingulata, conidia		*Washed*	*Unwashed*
	Water agar	98	85
	Sterile soil	98	98
	Natural soil	80	0
	Natural soil + 0.5% peptone	0	0

* Unpublished data of B. T. Lingappa and J. L. Lockwood.

accomplishing this is to induce spores which have fewer requirements than the mycelium to germinate. For example, basidiospores of *Tilletia caries* and *T. contraversa* will germinate in distilled water (Siang, 1956), and spores of *Isaria cretacea* require fewer vitamins than do the other stages in its growth (Taber and Vining, 1959). If the host is not available for infection, precocious germination may kill the organism, as in the case of fungi which respond to decoy plants.

If the low respiratory rate of dormant spores could be increased, in the absence of germination, their longevity might be drastically reduced. An interesting example of this kind of approach is provided by the work of Mandels (1963) with conidia of *Myrothecium verrucaria*. In this case, the endogeonous respiration is enhanced markedly by azide, diethyldithiocarbamate, and cyanide. Of course, these poisons probably are too general in effect to be useful in control, but uncouplers of respiratory from phosphorylative mechanisms in cells include phenols, tetracycline antibiotics, and other substances. Therefore, some among these may prove effective for inducing dormant organisms to squander their endogenous reserves precociously.

Timing.—In addition to the enhanced survivability imparted by resistance to chemical and physical factors in the environment, and by a favorable nutritional potential, spores can be considered to be timing devices which ensure that active growth occurs when conditions are most favorable. This type of ecological adaptation would confer advantage upon organisms whose environments undergo fluctuations in moisture, temperature, light, and other factors. Lees (1961) has proposed that diapause serves such a function in some insects, and it is likely that dormancy plays a similar role in microorganisms.

A simple model of a timing system is that in which there is an arresting device which must be overcome by an activator. In that which follows, I shall try to view dormancy within the framework of the mechanism through which development is arrested, as well as through the treatments which lead to the renewal of activity.

MECHANISMS OF ARREST.—*Exogenous factors.*—It is convenient to arrange this subject in terms of the types of restraints upon development. These include physical ones like extremes of temperature and humidity, which lead to types of exogenous dormancy like overwintering. This form of arrested development is, of course, one of the important controls which exist in nature and is common to many organisms. From the point of view of manipulation, however, this type of timing is of less interest than that which depends upon chemical restraints upon the organisms. Therefore, I shall concentrate upon the chemical mechanisms of exogenous dormancy.

It is almost a cliché to talk of the "widespread fungistasis" in soil because of its ubiquity and wide acceptance as a phenomenon. Furthermore, it has been recognized that this inhibitory effect probably plays a role in nature through the regulation of spore germina-

tion in soil (Garrett, 1956), thereby becoming a potentially important means through which exogenous dormancy is imposed. The mechanisms of this effect will be discussed by others so I will restrict my attention to its role in dormancy. In this connection, it is worth noting that although the spores of a large number of organisms are susceptible to the "widespread fungistasis," the ascospores of *Neurospora* germinate completely in untreated soil, and uredospores of *Puccinia glumarum* are only partially susceptible to inhibition (Table 6).

Another exogenous restraint upon spore germination is that produced by higher plants. Gäumann (1950) and Garrett (1956) review some of the inhibitory principles that contribute to the resistance of plants to pathogens and it has been suggested by several workers that where such inhibitors are fungistatic, they impose a type of dormancy upon spores which may have survival value for the microorganism.

Sensitivity to minerals in the soil affords another mechanism through which dormancy may be imposed. Thus, Cantino (1951) has shown that "cracking" of the sporangium of *Blastocladiella* is retarded by certain anions, and Duggar (1901) found that uredospores of *Puccinia helianthi* did not germinate in the presence of moderate amounts of ammonium nitrate.

Constitutive factors.—The fact that high concentrations of certain spores germinate less well than lower ones has led to the suggestion that self-inhibitors are present in these organisms. For example, Boyd (1952) has shown with *Fusarium coeruleum* that when a concentration of 2,000 conidia per field is used, only 1% germinate. Self-inhibitors may be present in a variety of organisms, including conidia of *Glomerella cingulata* (B. T. Lingappa and J. T. Lockwood, personal communication, 1963) and of *Erysiphe graminis* (Domsch, 1954), uredospores of *Puccinia graminis tritici* (Allen, 1955), and uredospores and aeciospores of *P. sorghi* and *P. purpurea* (Le Roux and Dickson, 1957). Another source of self-inhibitors may be those sporangia in which germination does not occur. For example, von Stosch (1935) showed that spores of *Didymium* did not germinate within the sporangia, even under high humidities. Therefore, control is probably exerted this way in other cases, although instances are known where spores do germinate within sporangia (Chamberlain and Allison, 1945; Schnathorst, 1959; R. Benjamin, personal communication, 1963).

The striking increases in respiratory rates which ensue upon the activation of dormant spores suggest that important metabolic changes occur at this time. Therefore, internal regulatory mechanisms are invoked to explain certain types of constitutive dormancy, as in the cases of *Neurospora* ascospores (Sussman, 1961*a*) and conidia of *Phycomyces blakesleeanus* (Rudolph, 1961).

MECHANISMS OF STIMULATION (ACTIVATION).—As was noted above, survival requires activation as a necessary concomitant of arrested development. Consequently, the activation process must be understood before control of such stages can be explained. Unfortunately, the mechanism through which dormancy is broken is only poorly understood in microorganisms, as well as in other creatures, as is evidenced by the paucity of detailed information on the subject (Grossowicz, Hestrin, and Keynan, 1961). Nevertheless, one approach to the problem of control is through the treatments that accomplish activation, and these will be reviewed below.

A variety of treatments have been used to break the dormancy of microorganisms including the following:

Temperature extremes
Temperature fluctuations
Drying and wetting
Light
Chemicals

Among these, only temperature extremes and chemical treatments will be discussed because by far the largest number of microorganisms respond to such activation treatments (Halvorson and Sussman, 1965).

Temperature extremes.—Heat shocks have been successfully applied to the dormant spores of bacteria (Powell, 1957), as well as to sporangia of *Phytophthora infestans* (Taylor et al., 1955) and to the ascospores of numerous ascomycetes (Halvorson and Sussman, 1965). Warcup's (1957) experiments on soil-steaming have shown that spore formers are enriched in soils treated in this manner. These experiments, and some later ones (J. H. Warcup, personal communication, 1963) suggest that heat activation of dormant ascospores, and of chlamydospores, may explain the results. The elimination of competing species through heating, however, must still be considered as a possible explanation of the effect.

Low-temperature activation has been found to be effective in aiding the germination of propagules of many pathogenic fungi. These include oospores of *Peronospora schleideni* (Blackwell, 1935), resting spores of *Physoderma* (Sparrow, 1957; Johns, 1958), sclerotia of *Claviceps purpurea* (Kirchoff, 1929), teliospores of *Puccinia glumarum* (Raeder and Bever, 1931), as well as the spores of many smuts (cf. Halvorson and Sussman, 1965).

Chemical treatment.—Various complex media have been used to stimulate the germination of microbial spores, including those from the sources listed below:

Plant extracts (seedlings, oils, leaf distillates,
  volatile wood products)
Diffusates from other microorganisms
Self-activators
Paraffin waxes
Soil extracts
Passage through animals

Therefore a wide range of materials has been used to elicit spore germination, including that of many pathogens. In the case of plant extracts, Garrett (1956) already has discussed the implications for control, from the standpoint of decoy and host plants. Related problems exist in plant-nematode interrelations so far as there are "enemy" and decoy plants (Seinhorst, 1961).

"Enemy" plants, that is, plants that can be infected but which the nematodes cannot leave, offer a potentially effective means of control, through which the longevity of the pathogen is curtailed.

A neglected area of investigation is one that I shall call "probiosis," that is, the production of stimulatory materials by organisms. For example, cultures of *Alternaria tenuis* or of *Stemphylium ilicis,* induce the germination of spores of *Tilletia brevicaule* and *T. secalis,* according to Gassner and Niemann (1955); and bacteria can overcome the action of the self-inhibitor in the sporangium of *Didymium,* according to von Stosch (1935). Perhaps microorganisms will be shown to serve as "decoys" in nature, if they induce germination of pathogens in the absence of the host.

Self-activators coexist with self-inhibitors in the case of rust spores (French and Weintraub, 1957) but their role is still not clear. Similarly, reports exist in the literature about the effectiveness of paraffin waxes and passage through animals as means of activating dormant cells. In the latter case, however, Buller (1931a) has argued that avoidance of competition by dung-inhabiting fungi like *Coprinus sterquilinus* could equally well explain this effect. The presence of stimulatory materials in soil extract is of interest in view of the stress placed upon fungistatic principles.

Known chemicals of many kinds have been found to be activators of fungal spores, as the data in Table 7 reveal for a selected list of pathogens. There is evidence that plant products like indole acetic acid, phenols, and organic acids are effective, as would be expected from the data on complex materials discussed above.

Implications for control.—Broadening the concept of decoy plants to include microorganisms may actually represent a kind of interaction to be found in nature but, to my knowledge, data are scarce. As for the possibility of manipulating natural environments, chemical and physical treatments of soils already have revealed that resistant stages may be selected for under some circumstances. Thus organic solvents like alcohols and ketones are known to activate certain microbial spores (Sussman, 1961a) and it will be interesting to determine which organisms appear after such treatments in soil. Also, a large number of other activating substances are known and can be studied in the same way, as Menzies (1963) has suggested. Such studies pertain to other soil-borne pathogens as well because the dormant cysts of nematodes, and the larvae and eggs of insects sometimes respond to chemical treatments of this kind.

Other aspects of survivability.—Most of the seven factors which are listed as influencing the survival of microorganisms (page 101) are discussed in Garrett (1956) and in other places. Therefore, it is not necessary to elaborate on the last four points, especially since they do not necessarily involve spores. The reasons why the last four items are included are given below.

Degradative capacity may be called "saprophytic

TABLE 7. Chemicals which break the dormancy of spores of pathogenic fungi

Organism	Stage	Treatment	Reference
Puccinia graminis f. *tritici*	Uredospore	2,4-Dinitrophenol, methyl naphthoquinone, coumarin	Allen, 1955
Puccinia graminis f. *tritici*	Uredospore	Aldehydes and ethanol, n-nonanal (most active)	French and Weintraub, 1957
Puccinia graminis f. *tritici*	Uredospore	Indole acetate, coumarin, protocatechuic acid, umbelliferone, daphnetin, o-coumaric acid	Van Sumere, et al., 1957
Puccinia graminis	Uredospore	Organic or inor. acids at pH 2.0	Sibilia, 1930
Melampsora occidentalis	Uredospore	Methyl p-hydroxybenzoate + Ni^{++} + chlortetracycline	Turel, 1955
Ustilago zeae	Spore	Indole acetate, α- or β-alanine, glutanate, niacinamide	von Güttenberg and Strutz, 1952
Ustilago maydis	Spore	Acetate, citrate, mineral acids, K^+	Leszcenko, 1928
Urocystis tritici	Spore	Benzaldehyde, Na stearate, salicylaldehyde, acetone, butyrate	Noble, 1924
Urocystis occulta	Spore	Benzaldehyde	Stakman, Cassell, and Moore, 1934; Ling 1940
Piricularia oryzae	Spore	Cholesterol, diosgenin, gitogenin, hecogenin, smilagenin	Weintraub, Miller, and Schantz, 1957

capacity," or "enzymatic potential" and involves the ability of an organism to degrade materials in its environment and use them for its growth. Therefore, the greater its degradative capacity, the better the chances for survival.

Rapidity of growth should perhaps be expanded to include germination. In any case, what is meant here is the ability of an organism to exploit the environment quickly. Through this means it might escape the effects of antibiotic producers and other competitors.

Mutational capacity: mutations work in both directions for a given process. Although there are cases where lower competitive saprophytic ability is engendered by mutation, the reverse mutation probably occurs also. In any event, the gene pool is the ultimate source of all inherited variation, so that the mutational capacity of an organism is an important determinant of its adaptability.

Disseminability aids in survival through three means: (1) escape from competitors; (2) accessibility of new substrates; and (3) provision of different gene pools from which new genetic combinations can result.

CONCLUSION.—Problems of a higher order of complexity are raised when extrapolation to nature is attempted. Thus it should not be forgotten that seven factors were listed as contributing to survivability in microorganisms, but I have discussed only three, and have not said much about their interaction. To illustrate this point, I will borrow from my work on *Neurospora* ascospores again. Their survival is fostered by great resistance to deleterious agents like temperature, by their impermeability and resistant wall, and by their independence from exogenous nutritional requirements. Moreover, they may evade the "widespread soil fungistasis" by germinating quickly and without releasing materials which sponsor the development of competitors; timing is accomplished by the use of heat plus chemicals like furfural. It would be difficult, if not impossible, to decide which of these talents are most

important to the survival of *Neurospora* in nature, but clearly all may contribute. Therefore, I believe these studies illustrate very well the need for integrating all the elements of the ecosystem which soil represents, in order that the interaction of its biological elements may be understood. But the need for concomitant studies in which the variables are isolated is emphasized as the means of providing the elements to be integrated.

LITERATURE CITED

ABE, T. 1933. On the relation of air humidity to germination and the effect of low temperature on the vitality of uredospores of some species of cereal rusts. Ann. Phytopathol. Soc. Japan 2: 505-512.
ALLEN, P. J. 1948. Growth and metabolism of the sporidial stage of *Ustilago sphaerogena*. Am. J. Botany 35: 799.
ALLEN, P. J. 1955. The role of a self-inhibitor in the germination of rust uredospores. Phytopathology 45: 259-266.
ALLISON, L. E. 1951. Vapour-phase sterilization of soil with ethylene oxide. Soil Sci. 72: 341-352.
ANDERSON, P. J., and W. H. RANKIN. 1914. Endothia canker of chestnut. New York Agr. Expt. Sta. (Geneva) Bull. 347, 34 p.
BISBY, G. R. 1945. Longevity of *Schizophyllum commune*. Nature (London) 155: 732.
Blackwell, E. 1935. Germination of resting fungal spores. Nature (London) 135: 546.
BORUT, S. 1960. An ecological and physiological study of soil fungi of the northern Negev (Israel). Bull. Res. Council Israel Sec. D, 8: 65-80.
Bosco, G. 1960a. Sulla capacita di sopravvivenza delle spore. Nuovi Ann. Igiene Microbiol. 11: 335-338.
Bosco, G. 1960b. Studio della sensibilita in vitro agli antibiotici da parte di microorganismi isolati in epoca pre-antibiotica. Nuovi Ann. Igiene Microbiol. 11: 227-240.
BOYD, A. E. W. 1952. Dry rot disease of potato. IV. Laboratory methods used in assessing variations in tuber susceptibility. Ann. Appl. Biol. 39: 322-329.
BULLER, A. H. R. 1931a. Researches on fungi. vol. 4. Longmans, Green & Co., London. 329 p.
BULLER, A. H. R. 1931b. Researches on fungi. vol. 6. Longmans, Green, & Co., London. 513 p.
BULLOCH, W. 1928. The viability of bacteria in anti-

septic solutions. Zentr. Bakteriol. Parasitenk., Abt. II, 106: 21-29.

CANTINO, E. C. 1951. Metabolism and morphogenesis in a new *Blastocladiella*. Antonie van Leeuwenhoek J. Microbiol. Serol. 17: 59-96.

CHAMBERLAIN, O. W., and J. L. Allison. 1945. The brown leaf spot on *Bromus inermis* caused by *Pyrenophora bromi*. Phytopathology 35: 241-248.

CHANEY, R. W. 1951. How old are Manchurian lotus seeds? Garden J., N. Y. Botan. Gardens 1: 137.

COCHRANE, V. W., and D. L. W. TULL. 1958. Uranium and spore respiration in *Neurospora sitophila*. Phytopathology 48: 623-628.

CRUMP, L. M. 1953. Partial sterilization of soil in the field. Rothamsted Exptl. Sta. Rept. 1952: 58.

DARLINGTON, H. T., and G. P. STEINBAUER. 1961. The eighty-year period for Dr. Beal's seed viability experiment. Am. J. Botany 48: 321-325.

DEEP, I. W., and M. E. CORDEN. 1961. Relative sensitivity of fungus spores and mycelium to toxic agents. p. 103-105. *In* Biological investigations for secondary school students, Am. Inst. Biol. Sci. Curriculum Study, Boulder, Colorado.

DOMSCH, K. H. 1954. Keimungsphysiologische Untersuchungen mit Sporen von *Erysiphe graminis*. Arch. Mikrobiol. 20: 163-175.

DOMSCH, K. H. 1958. Die Prüfung von Bodenfungiciden. I. Pilz-substrat-Fungicid-Kombinationen. Plant Soil 10: 114-131.

DUGGAR, B. M. 1901. Physiological studies with reference to the germination of certain fungous spores. Botan. Gaz. 31: 38-66.

FISCHER, G. W. 1936. The longevity of smut spores in herbarium specimens. Phytopathology 26: 1118-1127.

FRENCH, R. C., and R. L. WEINTRAUB. 1957. Pelargonaldehyde as an endogenous germination stimulator of wheat rust spores. Arch. Biochem. Biophys. 72: 235-237.

FRIES, N. 1948. Spontaneous physiological mutations in *Ophiostoma*. Hereditas 34: 338-350.

GARRETT, S. D. 1956. Biology of root infecting fungi. Cambridge University Press, London and New York. 292 p.

GASSNER, G., and E. NIEMANN. 1955. Synergistische und antagonistische Wirkung von Pilzen und Bakterien auf die Sporenkeimung verschiedener *Tilletia*-Arten. Phytopathol. Z. 23: 395-418.

GÄUMANN, E. A. 1950. Principles of plant infection. Authorized English ed. Crosby Lockwood and Son, Ltd., London. 543 p.

GOODEY, T. 1923. Quiescence and reviviscence in nematodes with special reference to *Tylenchus tritici* and *Tylenchus dispar*. J. Helminthol. 1: 47-58.

GROSSOWICZ, N., S. HESTRIN, and A. KEYNAN [ed.]. 1961. Cryptobiotic stages in biological systems. 5th Biology Conference, "Oholo." 1960. Elsevier Publ. Co., Amsterdam. 232 p.

GÜTTENBERG, H. Y. VON, and I. STRUTZ. 1952. Zur Keimungsphysiologie von *Ustilago zeae*. Arch. Mikrobiol. 17: 189-198.

HALVORSON, H. O., and A. S. SUSSMAN. 1965. Spores and dormancy in microbes. Harper and Bros., New York. (In press.)

HAWKER, L. E. 1957. Ecological factors and the survival of fungi. p. 238-258. *In* R. E. O. Williams and C. C. Spicer [ed.], Microbial ecology, 7th Symp., Soc. Gen. Microbiol., Cambridge University Press, London.

HESSELTINE, C. W., B. J. BRADLE, and C. R. BENJAMIN. 1960. Further investigations on the preservation of molds. Mycologia 52: 762-774.

HICKMAN, C. J. 1958. *Phytophthora*—plant destroyer. Trans. Brit. Mycol. Soc. 41: 1-13.

HINTON, H. E. 1951. A new chironomid from Africa, the larvae of which can be dehydrated without injury. Proc. Zool. Soc. London 121: 371-380.

HINTON, H. E. 1953. Some adaptations of insects to environments that are alternately dry and flooded, with some notes on the habits of the Stratiomyidae. Trans. Soc. Brit. Entomol. 11: 209-213.

JENSEN, H. L. 1961. Survival of *Rhizobium meliloti* in soil culture. Nature (London) 192: 682-683.

JOHNS, ROBERT M. 1958. A study of *Physoderma dulichii* Johns. Doctoral Thesis, Univ. of Michigan, Ann Arbor.

KENDRICK, E. L., and C. S. HOLTON. 1960. Differential longevity of teliospores of pathogenic races of *Tilletia caries* and *T. foetida*. Phytopathology 50: 51-54.

KIRCHOFF, H. 1929. Beiträge zur Biologie und Physiologie des Mutterkornpilzes. Zentr. Bakteriol. Parasitenk., Abt. II, 77: 310-369.

KUNKEL, O. 1913. The influence of starch, peptone, and sugars on the toxicity of various nitrates to *Monilia sitophila* (Mont.) Sacc. Bull. Torrey Botan. Club 40: 625-647.

LEES, A. D. 1961. Discussion. p. 224 *In* N. Grossowicz, S. Hestrin, and A. Keynan [ed.], Cryptobiotic stages in biological systems, 5th Biology Conference "Oholo." 1960. Elsevier Publ. Co., Amsterdam.

LEROUX, P. M., and J. G. DICKSON. 1957. Physiology, specialization and genetics of *Puccinia sorghi* on corn and of *Puccinia purpurea* on sorghum. Phytopathology 47: 101-108.

LESTER, H. E., and S. R. GROSS. 1959. Efficient method for selection of auxotrophic mutants of *Neurospora*. Science 129: 572.

LESTER, G., and O. HECHTER. 1958. Dissociation of rubidium uptake by *Neurospora crassa* into entry and binding phases. Proc. Natl. Acad. Sci. U.S. 44: 1141-1149.

LESTER, G., and O. HECHTER. 1959. The relationship of Na+, K+ and deoxycorticosterone in *Neurospora crassa*. Proc. Natl. Acad. Sci. U.S. 45: 1792-1800.

LESZCZENKO, P. 1928. Studies on the action of solutions of salts, alkalis, and acids on the spores of some pathogenic fungi. Trans. Phytopathol. Section. *In* Bydgoszcz State Inst. Agr. Sci. 6, 37 p. (Polish, with English summaries).

LING, L. 1940. Factors affecting spore germination and growth of *Urocystis occulta* in culture. Phytopathology 30: 579-591.

LINGAPPA, B. T., and J. T. LOCKWOOD. 1961. The nature of the widespread soil fungistasis. J. Gen. Microbiol. 26: 473-485.

LINGAPPA, Y., and A. S. SUSSMAN. 1959. Changes in the heat-resistance of ascospores of *Neurospora* upon germination. Am. J. Botany 46: 671-678.

LOWRY, R. L., and A. S. SUSSMAN. 1956. Physiology of the cell surface of *Neurospora* ascospores. II. Interference with dye adsorption by polymyxin. Arch. Biochem. Biophys. 62: 113-124.

LOWRY, R. J., A. S. SUSSMAN, and B. VON BÖVENTER-HEIDENHAIN. 1957. Physiology of the cell surface of *Neurospora* ascospores. III. Distinction between the adsorptive and entrance phases of cation uptake. Mycologia 49: 609-622.

LOWRY, R. J., and A. S. SUSSMAN. 1958. Wall structure of ascospores of *Neurospora tetrasperma*. Am. J. Botany 45: 397-403.

MACDONALD, K. D., and G. PONTECORVO. 1953. Starvation technique. *In* The genetics of *Aspergillus nidulans*. Adv. Genet. 5: 142-238.

MANDELS, G. R. 1963. Endogenous respiration of fungus spores in relation to dormancy and germination. Ann. N. Y. Acad. Sci. 102: 724-739.

McCALLAN, S. E. A., L. P. MILLER, and R. M. WEED. 1954. Comparative effect of fungicides on oxygen uptake and germination of spores. Contrib. Boyce Thompson Inst. 18: 39-68.

McKAY, R. 1935. Germination of resting spores of onion mildew (*Peronospora schleideni*). Nature (London) 135: 306-307.

McKEEN, C. D. 1954. Methyl bromide as a soil fumigant for controlling soil-borne pathogens and certain other organisms in vegetable seedbeds. Can. J. Botany 32: 101-108.

McKEEN, C. D., and R. N. WENSLEY. 1961. Longevity of

Fusarium oxysporum in soil tube culture. Science 134: 1528-1529.

McLean, J. G., D. J. Le Tourneau, and J. W. Guthrie. 1961. Relation of histochemical tests for phenols to *Verticillium* wilt resistance of potatoes. Phytopathology 51: 84-89.

Menzies, J. D. 1963. Survival of microbial plant pathogens in soil. Botan. Rev. 29: 79-122.

Merek, E. L., and C. L. Fergus. 1954. The effect of temperature and relative humidity on the longevity of spores of the oak wilt fungus. Phytopathology 44: 61-64.

Miller, L. P. 1956. Use of radioactive tracers in studying fungicidal action. p. 170-176. *In* Proc. Conf. Radioactive Isotopes in Agriculture, East Lansing, Michigan.

Noble, R. J. 1924. Studies on the parasitism of *Urocystis tritici* Koern., the organism causing flag smut of wheat. J. Agr. Res. 27: 451-489.

Ohga, I. 1923. On the longevity of the fruits of *Nelumbo nucifera*. Botan. Mag. (Tokyo) 37: 87.

Owens, R. G. 1955. Metabolism of fungus spores. I. Oxidation and accumulation of organic acids by conidia of *Neurospora sitophila*. Contrib. Boyce Thompson Inst. 18: 125-144.

Owens, R. G. 1955. Metabolism of fungus spores. II. Cytochrome oxidase, succinoxidase and pyruvate carboxylase systems in homogenates of conidia of *Neurospora sitophila*. Contrib. Boyce Thompson Inst. 18: 145-152.

Owens, R. G., and L. P. Miller. 1957. Intracellular distribution of metal ions and organic fungicides in fungus spores. Contrib. Boyce Thompson Inst. 19: 177-188.

Park, D. 1955. Experimental studies on the ecology of fungi in soil. Trans. Brit. Mycol. Soc. 38: 130-142.

Porter, R. H. 1955. Longevity of loose smut *Ustilago nuda* (Jens.) Kostr. in barley seed. Phytopathology 45: 637-638.

Powell, J. F. 1957. Biochemical changes occurring during spore germination in *Bacillus subtilis*. J. Appl. Bacteriol. 20: 349-358.

Prasada, R. 1948. Studies on the formation and germination of teliospores of rusts. I. Indian Phytopathol. 1: 119-126.

Prucha, M. J., and J. M. Brannon. 1926. Viability of *Bacterium typhosum*. J. Bacteriol. 11: 27-29.

Raeder, J. M., and W. M. Bever. 1931. Spore germination of *Puccinia glumarum* with notes on related species. Phytopathology 21: 767-789.

Rudolph, H. 1961. Weitere Untersuchungen zur Wärmeaktivierung der sporangiosporen von *Phycomyces blakesleeanus* III. Planta 57: 284-312.

Schnathorst, W. C. 1959. Spread and life cycle of the lettuce powdery mildew fungus. Phytopathology 49: 464-468.

Seinhorst, J. W. 1961. Plant-nematode inter-relationships. Ann. Rev. Microbiol. 15: 177-196.

Siang, W. N. 1956. Studies on the physiology and nutrition of *Tilletia caries* and *T. contraversa*. Res. Studies, State Coll. Washington 24: 291-306.

Sibilia, C. 1930. Ricerche sulle ruggini dei cereali II. La germinazione delle teleutospore di *Puccinia graminis* e *P. triticina*. Boll. Sta. Patol. Veg. 10: 164-190.

Slotnick, I. J. 1959. Asporogeny in *Bacillus subtilis* associated with development of resistance to actinomycin D. J. Bacteriol. 78: 893-895.

Sneath, P. H. A. 1962. Longevity of microorganisms. Nature (London) 195: 643-646.

Sparrow, F. K. 1957. Observations on chytridiaceous parasites of phanerogams. VI. Resting spore germination in *Physoderma* (*Urophlyctis*) *pluriannulatum*. Mycologia 49: 426-429.

Spaulding, P. 1922. Investigations of the white pine blister rust. U. S. Dept. Agr. Bull. 957, 100 p.

Spaulding, P., and A. Rathbun-Gravatt. 1926. The influence of physical factors on the viability of sporidia of *Cronartium ribicola* Fischer. J. Agr. Res. 33: 397-433.

Spector, W. S. 1956. Handbook of biological data. W. B. Saunders Co., Philadelphia. 584 p.

Stakman, E. C., R. C. Cassell, and M. B. Moore. 1934.

The cytology of *Urocystis occulata*. Phytopathology 24: 874-889.

Steiner, G., and F. E. Albin. 1946. Resuscitation of the nematode *Tylenchus polyhypnus* n. sp. J. Wash. Acad. Sci. 36: 97-99.

Steinhaus, E. A. 1960. The duration of viability and infectivity of certain insect pathogens. J. Insect Pathol. 2: 225-229.

Stosch, H. A. von. 1935. Untersuchungen über die Entwicklungsgeschichte der Myxomyceten. Sexualität und Apogamie bei Didymiaceen. Planta 23: 623-656.

Strauss, B. S. 1958. Cell death and "unbalanced growth" in *Neurospora*. J. Gen Microbiol. 18: 658-669.

Subramanian, C. V. 1950. Soil conditions and wilt disease in plants with special reference to *Fusarium vasinfectum* on cotton. Proc. Indian Acad. Sci., Sec. B, 31: 67-71.

Sussman, A. S. 1961a. The role of endogenous substrates in the chemical activation of ascospores of *Neurospora*. p. 198-213. *In* H. O. Halvorson [ed.], Spores II. Proc. 2d Allerton Park Spore Conference. Burgess Publ. Co., Minneapolis.

Sussman, A. S. 1961b. The role of trehalose in the activation of dormant ascospores of *Neurospora*. Quart. Rev. Biol. 36: 109-116.

Sussman, A. S. 1964. Dormancy in cryptogams. vol. 15. *In* A. Lang [ed.], Encyclopedia of plant physiology, Springer-Verlag, Berlin. (In press.)

Sussman, A. S., R. Holton, and B. von Böventer-Heidenhain. 1958. Physiology of the cell surface of *Neurospora* ascospores. Entrance of anions and non-polar compounds. Arch. Mikrobiol. 29: 38-50.

Sussman, A. S., and R. J. Lowry. 1955. Physiology of the cell surface of *Neurospora* ascospores: Cation binding properties of the cell surface. J. Bacteriol. 70: 675-685.

Taber, W. A., and L. C. Vining. 1959. Studies on *Isaria cretacea*. Nutritional and morphological characteristics of two strains and morphogenesis of the synnema. Can. J. Microbiol. 5: 513-535.

Taylor, C. F., J. J. Smoot, D. O. Quinn, R. A. Rohde, and E. S. Elliott. 1955. Effect of brief exposures at 40°C on germination of sporangia of *Phytophthora infestans*. Phytopathology 45: 673-675.

Turel, F. 1955. Influence of methyl-p-hydroxybenzoate, chlortetracycline, and certain trace metals on germination of uredospores of *Melampsora occidentalis* Jacks. Can. J. Microbiol. 1: 293-298.

Turner, J. H. 1933. The viability of seeds. Kew Bull. 6: 251.

van Sumere, C. F., C. van Sumere-de Preter, L. C. Vining, and G. A. Ledingham. 1957. Coumarins and phenolic acids in the uredospores of wheat stem rust. Can. J. Microbiol. 3: 847-862.

Wahl, I. 1961. Hypobiotic phenomena in fungi and their significance in plant pathology. p. 107-119. *In* N. Grossowicz, S. Hestrin, and A. Keynan [ed.], Cryptobiotic stages in biological systems, 5th Biology Conference "Oholo" 1960. Elsevier Publ. Co., Amsterdam.

Walker, A. T., and F. G. Smith. 1952. Effect of actidione on growth and respiration of *Myrothecium verrucaria*. Proc. Soc. Exptl. Biol. 81: 556-559.

Warcup, J. H. 1957. Chemical and biological aspects of soil sterilization. Soils Fertilizers 20: 1-5.

Weintraub, R. L., W. E. Miller, and E. L. Schantz. 1958. Chemical stimulation of germination of spores of *Piricularia oryzae*. Phytopathology 48: 7-10.

Wensley, R. N. 1953. Microbiological studies of the action of some selected soil fumigants. Can. J. Botany 31: 277-308.

Wilhelm, S. 1955. Longevity of the Verticillium wilt fungus in the laboratory and field. Phytopathology 45: 180-181.

Yarwood, C. E., S. Sidkey, M. Cohen, and V. Santilli. 1954. Temperature relations of powdery mildews. Hilgardia 22: 603-622.

Zimmerman, A. 1925. Sammelreferate über die Beziehungen zwischen Parasit und Wirtspflanze. Zentr. Bakteriol. Parasitenk., Abt. II, 65: 311-418.

► DISCUSSION OF A. S. SUSSMAN PAPER

G. Stotzky:

Can the longevity of spore survival in soil be correlated with the metabolic (respiratory) rate and stored food supply of the spores? If not, how do you account for the presumed longevity of spores in soil?

A. S. Sussman:

In general, longevity appears to vary inversely as the metabolic rate. As for the stored food supply, I have made the calculations for *Neurospora* ascospores but know of no data for any other spores. In this case, my calculations suggest that at 4°C the spores could survive for about 20 years, based upon the amount of endogenous substrate. Longevity is, of course, reduced at higher temperatures so that it is difficult to account for *Neurospora* spore survival for periods of time greater than 10 years. On the other hand, Table 1, in which the longevity of spores was listed, shows that no ascomycetes survived much beyond 10 years. Whether this is due to inherent evanescence in spores of this group, or to insufficient sampling, is not known.

K. F. Baker:

Do you have an explanation for the effect of heat in breaking dormancy in fungus spores?

A. S. Sussman:

I can speak only for the heat activation of *Neurospora* spores, but I believe the mechanism may have some generality. In these cells, the substrate in the dormant condition is lipid. As soon as activation is effected, however, trehalose is metabolized at an increasing rate. Therefore, an enzyme system which is responsible for the dissimilation of trehalose appears to become active after activation. But the simplest hypothesis that trehalose activity is present after activation, but not before, does not hold, since we have demonstrated such an enzyme even in dormant spores. Our present feeling is that activation brings enzyme and substrate into contiguity.

As for the generality of this mechanism, I can say only that the sugar trehalose is very widely distributed in the fungi and, in fact, is to these organisms what sucrose is to green plants. Furthermore, trehalose has been found to accumulate during fruiting in several fungi, and to be present in several types of spores. Therefore, it may prove to be involved in the dormancy of other organisms as well as *Neurospora*.

H. Katznelson:

Is there any evidence that microbial products in the soil increase leakage of substances from fungus spores, as Dr. Norman has shown for plant roots, using various antibiotics?

A. S. Sussman:

Yes, because in some work performed in Dr. Norman's laboratory, I found that polymyxin-B will induce the leakage of substances from *Neurospora* ascospores. This antibiotic is very toxic to these spores, and is bound to their surface. These data resemble those obtained with bacteria treated with polymyxin, according to Few and Shulman in England.

G. A. Zentmyer:

Is there any information on respiratory rates of oospores of *Phytophthora,* or survivability in this genus?

A. S. Sussman:

I know of no information on respiratory rates for oospores of *Phytophthora*.

C. Driver:

In the genus *Gelasinospora* there is a species complex that may be of interest to you in relation to heat treatment of ascospores for germination similar to *Neurospora*. I have found that the heterothallic strains in this case require heat treatment, whereas a homothallic strain of this species of *Gelasinospora* does not require heat treatment for germination.

A. S. Sussman:

This is a very interesting observation. I knew of Alexopolous' student's (Tylutki) findings on the response of *Gelasinospora* to furfural, but was unaware of the data you have obtained. These data could have very interesting genetic and evolutionary implications. For instance, what if the heat requirement for the activation of spores of heterothallic strains was a means of ensuring against the precocious germination of the spores, thereby making more certain that compatible strains would be approached? This situation could help to make outbreeding more likely.

D. Barbe:

In the case of uredospores of *Puccinia glumarum,* in natural soil to which 0.5% peptone had been added (shown in your Table 6), how was germination of the spores determined? Were the spores irreversibly inhibited, or were they still capable of germinating and infecting a host? This suggests another means by which heteroecious rusts, e.g. antirrhinum rust (*P. antirrhini*), may survive in the sporophytic phase, in the absence of any other host.

J. L. Lockwood:

Uredospores were placed on soil surfaces and incubated for 16 hours. Germination was determined by removing spores from soil surfaces by their adhesion to water agar dishes and incubating these. The recovered spores were viable, but their longevity was not determined, nor was their infectivity.

Summary and Synthesis of the Papers on the Soil Microorganisms

J. D. MENZIES—*Soil and Water Conservation Research Division, Agricultural Research Service, United States Department of Agriculture, Beltsville, Maryland.*

The preceding group of papers in this symposium was selected to give a background for more detailed consideration of the behavior of plant pathogens in soil. Throughout the Symposium, the possible application of the information to biological control of these disease-producing organisms will be implicit. It has been most appropriate, therefore, to have Garrett's presentation of the history, present status, and future prospects for biological control of root diseases, presented against the background of the complex microbiota that one hopes to manipulate.

Garrett recognized that past achievements in biological control of soil-borne diseases justified no more than modest optimism for future success. Although he remarked that he had been waiting 30 years for a symposium such as this, he apparently found little reason to change his opinion expressed in 1956 in his book, *Biology of Root-Infecting Fungi*, that "The first rush to demonstrate and exploit the possibilities for biological control of root disease has now been succeeded by a more sober effort to elucidate its mechanisms, without which no further advance is possible." The presentations on the complex populations and activities of the microflora and microfauna with which the pathogens are associated clearly emphasized the problems in ecological analysis that must be solved before these mechanisms can be understood and biological control can reach a practical level.

Because of the many authentic observations of spontaneous decrease of root diseases under circumstances pointing to biological mechanisms, it was natural to hope that a simple manipulation of some key factors would permit practical use of this natural control in agriculture. In practice, however, the situation has been found to be unusually complex. Although experimental laboratory or greenhouse studies have given high correlations between disease reduction and treatments such as specific green manures, certain crop sequences, or the presence of selected antagonists, it has seldom been possible to repeat these effects at other locations or at other times. This is perhaps most clearly illustrated in the case of antagonists selected for antibiotic effects against the pathogen in pure culture where, as Garrett notes, there has been too much uncritical hypothesizing on the possible extension of these phenomena to field conditions. The almost universal disappointment with attempts to extrapolate from laboratory to field have

made it clear that the most obviously correlated factors are usually not the controlling ones. The general recognition that significant progress now must wait on a much more thorough analysis of microecology of the soil was, in fact, the reason why this symposium was planned to cover all possible aspects of pathogen behavior in soil rather than specializing on biological control.

The papers of Burges and Kevan have provided an unusually complete coverage of both the microflora and microfauna of cultivated soils. Warcup's discussion re-emphasized the overriding importance of the energy-yielding substrate in controlling the activity of these organisms. Their populations generally are relatively stable, except for the rapid flushes of growth that follow the introduction of fresh substrates into the soil. It is during these sporadic periods of high activity that biological influences on the pathogens should be most pronounced. In the more quiescent intervals, all interactions are slowed down. Probably there are different biological-control processes operating under each condition, but which of these may be the most significant in the prolonged survival of pathogen inoculum in soil is unknown. At least it would seem necessary to study separately the effects occurring during rapid substrate turnover and those occurring when the microbiota is in the more usual state of semistarvation.

It was particularly instructive to microbiologically oriented biologists to hear Kevan's discussion of the role of arthropods, nematodes, and other microscopic animals in decomposing crop residue. This microfauna, in the process of ingesting organic material, must also ingest plant pathogens. In Kevan's view, however, fungus structures are not generally killed by passage through the animal gut, and even those microscopic animals that prefer fungus substances for food are probably more likely to disseminate pathogens than to digest them.

Hirst and Parks described dormancy and other methods of survival of soil microorganisms as a special type of dispersal, i.e. dispersal in time rather than space. In the soil environment, spatial dispersion is slow and not particularly valuable to the life of the species involved. A pathogen's ability to survive for long periods of time in the root zone of soil is of great importance, since the roots of the host plant grow to the pathogen propagule through the soil. If the pathogen is one that remains dormant until stimulated to grow and infect when contacted by host roots, its dormancy has served as an efficient dispersal mechanism. Conversely, a pathogen that survives only over winter in infested plant tissue has a poor dispersal mechanism because its perpetuation depends on its annually finding a host.

The various aspects of microbial dormancy, as reviewed by Sussman, are of critical importance not only to the pathogen, but to the saprophytes as well. The widely fluctuating nature of the food supply, either organic residue or host plants, and the long periods of food shortage, demand survival mechanisms that preserve the individual during periods of stress and release it for growth when food is available. One of the most intriguing possibilities in biological control of pathogens is the use of nonsusceptible crops to break dormancy. If the pathogen tends to die out in the absence of susceptible tissue, after it has been stimulated to germinate, the trap-crop method of control may be valuable. Such a process depends on the pathogen's being more selective about the host it attacks that about the stimuli that break its dormancy.

Those pathogens that persist in an inactive state between intervals of association with host plants are not under unusual stress when the general microbial activity in the soil is low. But when periodic additions of food supply stimulate this activity, such pathogens are probably exposed to greatly intensified adverse factors, particularly antibiosis and predation. The relatively mobile and omnivorous microarthropods, and possibly even the Protozoa, build up populations at such times that surely must ingest and destroy the dormant structures of pathogens, especially when the normal food supply becomes depleted. This process is obviously not sufficiently developed in nature to provide a level of biological control satisfactory to agriculture, but further research may show how to make it more effective.

This broad introductory look at the past efforts on biological control in the light of current knowledge on microbial ecology suggests why relatively little practical progress has been made. Researchers have tended to concentrate on the types of organisms they know best and which are easiest to study with the methods now available. In looking for biological-control processes, the fungi in particular, and bacteria to a lesser extent, have been studied critically, whereas the many other plant and animal forms have been neglected. Although such narrowly directed investigations may not have led directly to biological control, they have contributed to the rapidly developing understanding of the ecology of soil microorganisms in general, a subject which now appears to be a prerequisite to understanding the behavior of plant pathogens in soil.

PART III

◄

THE SOIL ENVIRONMENT

Physical Factors of the Soil as They Affect Soil Microorganisms

WILLIAM A. RANEY—*Soil and Water Conservation Research Division, Agricultural Research Service, United States Department of Agriculture, Beltsville, Maryland.*

There are four soil physical factors that affect microorganisms—moisture, temperature, aeration, and the mechanical strength of the soil. These factors in turn are profoundly influenced by the nature of the soil solids, by the meteorological characteristics of the environment, and by the crops and microbes that inhabit the environment. (Collis-George, 1962; Luthin, 1957; E. W. Russell, 1961; Shaw, 1952.)

Despite the heterogeneous arrangement of the solids, liquids, and gases in soil, there is a great deal of order in the structure and in the behavior of the soil constituents. The solids, which are largely inorganic, are dominated by three elements—silicon, aluminum, and oxygen.

In nearly every case, however, the external atoms of the solid constituents of the soil are oxygen atoms which have unshared electrons that are available for hydrogen-bridge bonds to organic molecules or to water. It is probably for this reason that water dominates all of the soil physical factors. It is generally impossible to change moisture without simultaneously influencing other properties.

SOIL MOISTURE.—The atomic structure of the water molecule itself markedly influences the behavior of water in the soil (Buswell and Rodebush, 1956; Hendricks, 1955). The six outer-shell electrons of the oxygen atom include two pairs and two single electrons. These four groups are tetrahedrally arranged around the oxygen atom. A hydrogen atom with its single orbital electron is bonded to oxygen at the sites of the two unpaired electrons to form water. The water molecule so formed is unsymmetrical, has a positive and a negative side, and is called a dipole. Hydrogen atoms which are bonded to oxygen in the dipolar water molecule can be bonded to other oxygen atoms that have exposed pairs of electrons. These are called bridge bonds.

Water in the liquid and solid form does not behave as single molecules. They are bonded together into polymers. In the solid form, all of the molecules are bonded together. Single water molecules exist only in water vapor. Energy is required to break the hydrogen bridges that bond water molecules into polymers.

Actually, when bridge bonds are formed heat is liberated, and when they are broken, heat is absorbed. As ice melts, about 8% of the bridge bonds are broken

and 80 cal of heat per g of ice are absorbed by the water molecules involved. To break all of the hydrogen-bridge bonds and convert the water to vapor, requires another 540 cal per g. In melting, there is a decrease in volume of water because of some relaxation of the rigid polymer structure.

When a surface containing oxygen or nitrogen is exposed, it is considered wettable because it is subject to formation of hydrogen-bridge bonds with water. Waxy surfaces, on the other hand, contain no atoms with external electron pairs and are not wettable.

Water is bonded in this fashion to soil particles but with much stronger attraction. Soil particles have a net negative charge and tend to behave as ions. The attraction between ions and water dipoles is about 10,000 times as great as that between water dipoles. These forces are inversely proportional to the square of the distance between seats of attraction; therefore, a terrific amount of energy must be expended in breaking all of the bonds and removing the last traces of water from soil particles.

Since these forces are proportional to film thickness or water content, they are useful in characterizing the soil moisture regime.

The forces of attraction between water molecules and surfaces that are wettable are called adhesive; those between only water molecules are called cohesive. Soil microorganisms, with their carbohydrate type of composition, have external oxygen atoms with unshared electrons. As a result, their surfaces are subject to hydrogen-bridge bond formation. Both adhesive and cohesive forces are operative at the surfaces of soil solids, soil microorganisms, and plant roots.

When forces of attraction between soil constituents, plant roots, or soil microorganisms and water are greater at one place than at another, water will flow to the locus of greater attraction. At equilibrium these forces are equal, though they may not be zero. When zero, the attractive forces are equal to gravitational forces, which tend to move water out of the soil. These forces are normally measured in terms of pressure. (L. A. Richards and Wadleigh, 1952; M. B. Russell, 1961).

Crop plants have their tops in the atmosphere, and when water is lost by transpiration, differential forces are set up between plant roots and tops causing water to flow to the tops. This sets up a deficit in the roots

115

which causes inflow from the soil solids and the soil microorganisms.

There is no such chain reaction with microorganisms, which are wholly within the soil. It is true that as new microbial tissue develops there is new surface area available for wetting, which causes moisture flow; but the amount of such tissue is relatively small and the volume of flow is quite small.

Moisture movement or transfer in soil takes place by two mechanisms, liquid flow and vapor diffusion. Liquid flow or mass movement results from pressure gradients and is more important where moisture films are quite thick. Diffusion is more important when moisture films are thin. There really is no sharp point where one process stops and the other begins.

The rate of absorption of solar energy by plant tops determines the rate at which hydrogen-bridge bonds are broken and water is turned into vapor. Moisture movement from the soil into plant roots to replace that lost by the tops usually becomes too slow to maintain turgid plant tissue when the force of attraction between soil and water exceeds about 15 atmospheres. Actual measurements are somewhere between 4 and 32 atmospheres, but film thicknesses are not greatly different and 15 atmospheres is a satisfactory average value. The moisture in soil at permanent wilting, which is generally used as the lower limit of availability to plants, represents a 15-atmosphere equilibrium value.

The microbe-energy relations have been less carefully examined. In a static system they can probably withstand higher moisture tensions than plants, but in a dynamic system where soil moisture changes are continuous they probably respond about like plants.

While soil microorganisms are not subject to transpiration, the force-field alteration by transpiring plants causes water to flow from microorganisms just as it does from soil particles. For this reason they are not independent of plants and soil solids so far as moisture is concerned. Furthermore, most of the microbial activity is near the surface of aggregates or clods. The first change that takes place when soils are drained is emptying of large pores. This would suggest that discontinuous moisture changes affect microbes long before there is an appreciable change in gross moisture content of soil.

As energy is absorbed by plants and soil, bonds broken, water lost by vaporization, and film thicknesses reduced, there is usually an increase in the salt concentration of the water films that remain. While there has been little attempt in the past to separate the consequences of forces involved, whether osmotic or from the soil matrix, there now appears to be ample evidence to question lumping them all together (Collis-George and Sands, 1962).

The higher osmotic concentration is usually less deleterious to the well being of plants and perhaps to pathogens too, than the reduced film thickness until toxic levels of salts are encountered.

SOIL AERATION.—Aerobic respiration is essential for the penetration and proliferation of soil by plant roots (M. B. Russell, 1952). When oxygen adjacent to the root is used, the resulting partial-pressure difference causes movement of oxygen toward the root. This movement is greatly affected by soil moisture. In the gas phase of soil, oxygen moves by diffusion more than 10,000 times as rapidly as through the liquid phase. This means that the capacity of soil to supply oxygen is increased as soil moisture dries out and film thicknesses are reduced. When soil is loosened by tillage operations, there is a reduction in surface area of soil particles per unit volume which gives the same net effect as a reduction in moisture content per unit volume.

When crop plants absorb water and there is flow of water to plant roots, oxygen dissolved in the water moves into the root both by mass flow along with the water and by diffusion within the liquid film. This suggests that soil-aeration conditions in terms of oxygen supplies are better when moisture movement is taking place than when soil-moisture conditions are at equilibrium. It thus becomes obvious that the chain reaction set off by absorption of solar radiation and conversion of water to vapor in leaves, has an influence on soil aeration, too.

In addition to increased energy supplies for the microorganisms from decaying root tissue, improved aeration in the proximity of roots of transpiring plants may explain increased number of microbes in the vicinity of roots.

Polarigraphic measurements of oxygen diffusion in moisture films have shown that oxygen delivery rates are increased as soils dry out from saturation to about 30% moisture on a volume basis. At lower moisture contents, film rupture and increased tortuosity of diffusion path, cause oxygen delivery rates in films to decrease. In these drier ranges, however, diffusion through the gas phase provides greater contribution to the total aeration picture.

Respiration processes, both aerobic and anaerobic, where oxygen supplies are of consequence also influence the oxidizing or reducing conditions. Aerobic respiration is usually associated with oxidizing conditions where outer-shell electrons are fewer than where anaerobic respiration and associated reducing conditions exist. These oxidizing or reducing conditions in turn influence the electron status of all surrounding atoms.

Where there is rapid respiration and thus a high oxygen demand, aeration may be inadequate, whereas it would be satisfactory for normal respiration rates. For this reason, turning under a covercrop or copious crop residues may cause a condition of poor aeration until microbial activity has proceeded to a point where most of the energy source is gone.

When plant materials are turned under in the field, they are not homogeneously mixed with the soil. Under these conditions, microbial activities can create gradients in oxygen supplies which cause oxygen transport to take place. Thus, conditions may be favorable for simultaneous activity by both aerobic and anaerobic microorganisms.

SOIL TEMPERATURE.—Thermal characteristics of soil are closely associated with soil moisture conditions, too

(S. J. Richards, Hagan, and McCalla, 1952). Since 1 cal is required to raise the temperature of 1 g of water 1°C, whereas only 0.2 cal per g per degree is required for the soil solids, the dominating influence of soil moisture content on the heat capacity is obvious. The heat conductivity of dry soil is low but increases as moisture content increases. When soils are saturated, so much heat is required because of the high heat capacity and the high heat conductivity that soils are slow to warm up.

When moist soil absorbs solar energy at the soil surface, hydrogen bridges that bond the water molecules together and to the soil are broken. Part of the water is vaporized and leaves the soil. This causes moisture deficits at the soil surface and initiates moisture flow toward the surface.

At the same time there is a higher temperature at the surface which sets the stage for heat flow to lower depths. It is thus obvious that temperature and moisture variations at the soil surface are much greater than those within the soil.

If the entire soil profile is dry and thermal conductivity low, there are excessive temperature fluctuations at the soil surface, with the dry soil acting somewhat like a thermal insulator for deeper layers. Fortunately, the thermal conductivity at moisture contents that are satisfactory for plant growth allows the entire root zone to be warmed in the spring. In like manner, a dry soil surface in the summer may assist in keeping deeper soil layers cooler than would be expected if thermal conductivity were not influenced by soil moisture.

When soil profiles are modified by placing thermal insulators (mulches) on the soil surface, the influence of incoming solar energy is markedly reduced, and cold, wet soils stay cold and wet longer in the spring.

Soil temperature is also influenced by evaporation. When soils are moist, large quantities of solar energy can be dissipated in evaporation of water. For this reason, irrigated areas are cooler than areas where moisture supplies are low and most of the energy is used to heat the soil and the air above it.

Soil temperature influences aeration conditions of the soil, too. As temperature is increased, oxygen supplying power is increased. If oxygen demand remained constant, aeration would be improved because of increase in diffusion rate with increase in temperature. Quite frequently, however, respiration rates are increased so that oxygen demand exceeds supply.

Microorganisms are more tolerant than plants to extremes of heat and cold. This may be due to *positional* protection. If those at the soil surface are killed by extremes of temperature or water, there are more at greater depths in the soil.

SOIL STRENGTH.—Perhaps the most difficult physical parameter to understand and appreciate is the mechanical strength of the soil.

When soils are dry they tend to be rigid and have high mechanical impedance. When wet they lose rigidity, unless the particles are spatially fixed by some cementing agent; for example, certain iron compounds, which dry irreversibly.

Mechanical impedance is also increased by compaction, which in turn influences moisture relations. Frequently, compaction results in sufficient decrease in pore sizes and continuity to limit both moisture retention and moisture flow. This subsequently influences thermal and aeration conditions.

It is highly probable that, in most cases, the secondary effects of mechanical impedance are of much greater consequence to plants and to microorganisms than are the primary effects. Changes in numbers of microorganisms result in such small changes in total volume of tissue that resistance of the soil to deformation is of little consequence. But root development and the synthesis of new tissue (which ultimately becomes an energy source for the microorganisms) may be retarded by compaction and thus markedly influence bacterial numbers.

INTERDEPENDENCE OF PHYSICAL PARAMETERS ON EACH OTHER.—The discussion of solids, liquids, and the thermal, aeration, and strength characteristics of soils has been limited largely to situations that would influence both crop plants and microorganisms, even though there are occasions where only one or the other is of consequence. Persistence of pathogens, pathogenic products, or antipathogens where no plants are involved is receiving increased attention.

In most cases, however, soil pathogens are of minor concern unless they adversely influence crop plants. Soil physical parameters become important only when they adversely affect the crop plants more than they adversely affect pathogens. However, there surely are situations where soil conditions that are more favorable for plants may actually be less favorable to the pathogens.

There is no set of specifications of soil physical conditions that are optimum for all organisms. Frequently the interactions between parameters may be of much greater consequence than the primary effects themselves.

POTENTIALS FOR PREDICTION OR CONTROL OF SOIL PHYSICAL FACTORS AFFECTING SOIL MICROORGANISMS. —Conventionally, soil moisture control has been effected largely through irrigation, drainage, or management practices, such as tillage or crop rotations, that enhance the intake and transmission of water by soil. Currently, however, there are encouraging possibilities for modification of evaporation rates, too. Advective energy can be reduced by wind modification with loose windbreaks; net radiation can be modified by changing the reflectance characteristics of the soil; and turbulent exchange of energy between crop canopy and the atmosphere can be increased by increasing canopy roughness. Since most of the energy in a cropped area is dissipated in evaporation of water, any reduction in such energy reduces the evaporative demand.

There are also chemical means for reducing evaporation. Most of these operate as barriers to outward diffusion of water, but others are effective because they increase diffusion path length sufficiently to impair evaporation. Such procedures invariably result in higher soil temperatures because the energy conserved in evaporation reduction is dissipated in heating the air and soil. In such instances, it is desirable to increase advection of the excess energy away from the treated area.

Moisture retention by a soil profile may be modified, too. In nearly every case this is accomplished by placing in the soil profile a layer of soil with adverse moisture-transmission characteristics.

Soil thermal properties may be modified by soil moisture control or by the same microclimatological procedures described for soil moisture. In addition, soil management practices, such as turning crop residues under rather than leaving them as insulative layers on the crop surface, cause cold soils to warm up faster in the spring.

Adequate soil aeration and soil strength may, for some time to come, be largely effected through water management coupled with good soil husbandry.

LITERATURE CITED

BUSWELL, A. M., and W. H. RODEBUSH. 1956. Water. Sci. Am. 94: 76.

COLLIS-GEORGE, N. 1962. Environment and the soil. J. Australian Inst. Agr. Sci. 28: 13-22.

COLLIS-GEORGE, N., and JOCELYN E. SANDS. 1962. Comparison of the effects of the physical and chemical components of soil water energy on seed germination. Australian J. Agr. Res. 13(4): 575-584.

HENDRICKS, S. B. 1955. Necessary, convenient, commonplace. Water. Yearbook Agr. (U.S. Dept. Agr.) 1955: 9-14.

LUTHIN, J. N. [ed.] 1957. Drainage of agricultural lands. Agron. Monograph 7. Am. Soc. of Agron., Madison, Wisc. 670 p.

RICHARDS, L. A., and C. H. WADLEIGH. 1952. Soil water and plant growth. Chap. 3, p. 73-252. *In* B. T. Shaw [ed.], Soil physical conditions and plant growth, Agron. Monograph 2, Academic Press, New York.

RICHARDS, S. J., R. M. HAGAN, and T. M. McCALLA. 1952. Soil temperature and plant growth. Chap. 5, p. 303-480. *In* B. T. Shaw [ed.], Soil physical conditions and plant growth, Agron. Monograph 2. Academic Press, New York.

RUSSELL, E. W. 1961. Soil conditions and plant growth. 9th ed. Longmans, Green and Co., London and New York. 688 p.

RUSSELL, M. B. 1952. Soil aeration and plant growth. Chap. 4, p. 253-301. *In* B. T. Shaw [ed.], Soil physical conditions and plant growth, Agron. Monograph 2, Academic Press, New York.

RUSSELL, M. B. 1961. Water in the ecosystem. Soil Sci. Soc. Am. Proc. 25: 451-455.

SHAW, B. T. [ed.] 1952. Soil physical conditions and plant growth. Agron. Monograph 2. Academic Press, New York. 491 p.

► DISCUSSION OF W. A. RANEY PAPER

A. D. McLaren:

Dr. Hirst and Dr. Warcup have introduced the concept of microenvironments. Dr. Raney has now discussed the subject on a molecular basis. Soil colloids have a negative charge and therefore attract H^+ ions. Thus, *Nitrobacter* grown in soil sterilized by an electron beam has a higher pH optimum than it has when grown in solution. This observation serves to introduce a concept of molecular environments in nature.

Does the concentration of salts, on drying soil, lead to elution of organic matter, which becomes a nutrient for microbes?

W. A. Raney:

There is probably no effect of soil drying on exudation of organic matter from roots as long as the osmotic concentration of the soil solution is below toxic levels. There are indications of exudates when roots grow into dry soils. Their nature is unknown.

A. Kerr:

The importance of the effect of root exudates on the activity of soil fungi, including pathogens, is now realized. Before these exudates can act, they must diffuse from the root, through soil. What soil physical factors would influence this diffusion?

W. A. Raney:

Diffusion of root exudates is dominated by soil temperature, by moisture-film thickness, and by moisture-film continuity.

G. Stotzky:

A correlation was established in Central America between rapid spread of fusarium wilt of banana and the absence of montmorillonoid-type clay minerals in the soil. (G. Stotzky, J. E. Dawson, R. T. Martin, and C. H. H. der Kuile, Science 133: 1483-1485, 1961.)

H. Burström:

Within what limits of soil water content do you have an increasing soil solution concentration upon drying the soil?

It is known from the literature, and we have confirmed, that in an ordinary humid soil the soil-solution concentration is practically constant between field capacity and wilting point.

W. A. Raney:

In arid regions, salinity levels are sometimes high enough to become serious when soil approaches the wilting point, whereas they are tolerable at higher moisture contents.

S. Wilhelm:

Has it been shown experimentally that a plant root can pull water from within soil microorganisms or from their surfaces, or is it assumed from physical considerations?

W. A. Raney:

Loss of water from microorganisms to plant roots in response to an energy gradient is assumed. The rate of such transfer would be quite slow.

G. Stotzky:

Isn't the water around microorganisms "structured" water, similar to that around colloidal particles (clay minerals), and held with such great tensions that it would be unavailable to plants?

W. A. Raney:

The extent to which water is oriented around clay minerals or microbial tissue is determined by the charge density at the surface. Thus, at equilibrium the film thickness would be different if surfaces had different charge densities. There is no sharp point where water attracted to surfaces becomes unavailable. At low moisture tensions, moisture could be oriented around a soil surface, yet available to plants.

A. Kerr:

Most fungi grow on a dry surface in an atmosphere of 99% R.H. A soil in equilibrium with an atmosphere of 99% R.H. is at wilting point. If supplied with nutrients, I believe most fungi can grow in soil at wilting point or higher moisture content, until oxygen becomes limiting.

S. D. Van Gundy:

A comment on the possible usefulness of oxygen diffusion rates in soil water films as a means of determining the availability of oxygen to plant roots and microorganisms in soils. The measurement of gaseous oxygen in soil pore spaces does not appear to be as critical an evaluation as diffusion rates in our studies on plant growth and on nematode movement, reproduction, and survival. The solubility and diffusion rates of oxygen in the water films surrounding soil particles are far less than in the air spaces betwen soil particles. Therefore, all the microorganisms and plant roots in the water films are in competition for this oxygen, which, under certain conditions, such as in compacted and waterlogged soils, may be in short supply.

M. I. Timonin:

In the spring, soil harbors an increasing microbial population. Could it be due to the higher oxygen content in the soil solution?

What is the temperature effect on the solubility of oxygen in soil solution?

W. A. Raney:

A burst of growth always follows rectification of adverse growing conditions. In spring, increased microbial activity probably results from more favorable temperature conditions, even though oxygen solubilities in the cold soil solution are greater than they would be later in the summer.

Chemical Factors of the Soil as They Affect Microorganisms

HOMER D. CHAPMAN—*Department of Soils and Plant Nutrition, University of California, Riverside.*

The purpose of this paper is to describe some characteristics of soils, emphasize their extreme variability, indicate by a few examples the effects of pH on the solubility of elements, list some of the interactions and soil conditions which affect the solubility, availability, or toxicity of elements to plants (and by implication, organisms), list some of the more commonly used availability tests for determining nutrient status of elements in soils, describe briefly some soil-plant-microorganism relations, and finally list plant diseases that are influenced by soil conditions and management practices. For the latter, I have drawn largely on papers and reviews by Wingard (1941), Walker (1946), Daines (1946), Kincaid (1946), McKinney (1946), McNew (1953), Garrett (1939), and Stover (1959).

SOIL CHARACTERISTICS AND VARIABILITY.—Soil is usually described as a three-phase system consisting of solid, liquid, and gas. The solid-phase components consist of both inorganic and organic entities of great variability. Included in the organic phase are the living organisms, whose enormous numbers and multiple kinds are well known.

Solid-phase components.—As a starting point for some of the data and discussion that follow, differences among soils from a simple textural point of view are shown in Table 1, where the proportions of sand, silt, clay, and organic matter in a few soils are presented.

TABLE 1. Variations in mechanical composition of soils*

Fraction	Sandy loam, %	Light loam, %	Heavy loam, %	Clay, %
Coarse sand	66.6	27.1	13.6	1.0
Fine sand	17.8	30.3	17.4	4.1
Silt	5.6	20.2	24.7	7.9
Clay	8.5	19.3	35.1	82.8
Organic matter	1.5	3.1	9.2	4.2
Total	100.0	100.0	100.0	100.0

* From G. W. Robinson. Soils, their origin, constitution and classification. Thomas Murphy & Co., London. 1932.

In addition to the infinite number of obvious gradations between these, an enormous number of chemical differences may occur between soils of more or less identical mechanical composition. Thus, while a soil type listed as fine sandy loam has definite meaning in regard to the proportions of sand, silt, and clay, soils of this or any other textural class may be widely different in chemical, mineralogical, physical, and biological properties.

Internal surface of soils.—Not well appreciated by many who deal with soils is the striking effect of particle-size distribution on internal surface. This is illustrated by the data of Table 2. In addition to showing the defined diameter limits for sand, silt, and clay fractions, the table gives the surface that would be exposed by a solid substance, e.g. a piece of gravel, in the shape of a cube 1 cm on a side were it subdivided into the aforementioned fractions. Subdivided into cubes of the dimensions of colloidal clay (0.5μ), surface would increase from 6 to 600,000 cm^2; or subdivided to give the sand, silt, and clay proportions of a heavy loam soil, it would have an internal surface of 72 ft^2; of this the clay fraction would account for about 98% and the coarser fraction (comprising 55% of the weight) would provide only 2%. One ft^3 of such a soil, considering it to contain 50% solids, would have an internal surface of 22.7 acres, or 1 acre-ft would have an internal surface of about 1,000,000 acres.

It is both the surface and the reactivity and variable properties of clay and colloidal clay which impart to soils such startling differences in characteristics as those, for example, in water retention and movement, swelling, shrinking, base exchange, pH, structure, aeration, and of course, growing out of these, a substrate of great diversity and complexity for the millions of organisms present.

Mineralogical make-up.—The mineralogical make-up of soils becomes increasingly complex as the proportion of clay increases. In sands, for example, quartz and other primary silicate minerals such as feldspars, micas, and hornblende dominate; whereas in clays, secondary clay minerals such as kaolin, montmorillonite, and hydrous micas are dominant, with primary minerals and quartz becoming very small or vanishing altogether.

The clay components of soil deserve additional description. They exist largely in crystalline form, vary greatly in ultimate particle size, and belong to several well-defined mineralogical groups. While it is common to find dominant forms, such as kaolinite or montmorillonite, depending on the parent minerals and the weathering processes involved, usually more than one clay mineral is found in a given soil. In addition to crystalline silicate clay minerals, oxides and hydrous

TABLE 2. Particle size and surface relations

Fraction	Diameter limits	Length of side	Area		Fraction, %	Surface, ft²	% Surface
			cm²	ft²			
			Surface exposed by subdivision of a cube 1 cm on a side		One cm³ broken down into fractions corresponding to a heavy loam		
Gravel	2 mm-3 in	1.0 cm	6.0	0.0065	—	—	—
Coarse sand	2.0-0.2 mm	1.0 mm	60	0.065	13.6	0.007	0.01
Fine sand	0.2-0.02 mm	0.1 mm	600	0.65	17.4	0.090	0.12
Silt	0.02-0.002 mm	0.01 mm	6,000	6.50	24.7	1.370	1.807
Clay	< 0.002 mm	0.001 mm	60,000	65.0	35.1	19.500	27.00
Colloidal clay	< 0.0005 mm	0.0001 mm (0.5 μ)	600,000	650	9.2	51.200	71.00
Upper limit of molecular sizes	0.000,001 mm (1.0 μμ)	1.0 μμ	60,000,000	65,000	—	—	—
Total	—	—	—	—	100	72.167	100.0

oxides, as well as traces of many other inorganic compounds, occur.

The silicate clays have a layered or a micalike structure. These layers of plates or flakelike wafers are held together with varying degrees of force, and in some of these clays, when wetted, the layers are pushed apart or swell and absorb water molecules between the plates. Thus in addition to the aforementioned large surface due to small particle size, there is a chemically reactive internal surface in some of the clay minerals.

The exterior and to some degree the internal surfaces of these platy minerals carry negative charges due to unsatisfied valences. These latter arise in part from oxygen atoms attached to aluminum ions in the crystal surface; and these charges attract hydrogen or basic cations such as calcium, magnesium, and sodium. These unsatisfied valences also may arise from replacement of trivalent aluminum ions by divalent magnesium ions in some minerals such as montmorillonite, leaving free valence or electrical charges which are satisfied by hydrogen or other ions.

In other minerals, four-valent silicon atoms may be replaced by trivalent aluminum ions, leaving unsatisfied negative valences. It is these loosely or semiloosely held cations on the surfaces of crystalline clays that account for the property of base exchange. The so-

called base-exchange capacity of a soil is determined in large measure by the amount as well as the kind of clay or clays which predominate. (Organic matter also carries exchangeable cations.) See Fig. 1 for a diagrammatic illustration of the platy structure and exchangeable base sites on the flat surfaces and edges.

Water of hydration is also held by these exchangeable ions, and as stated, water is also found between the plates of the clay crystal, or micelle as it is sometimes termed.

It is the varying kinds and number of adsorbed cations and attached water molecules which so greatly influence and alter soil properties such as swelling, shrinkage, granulation, soil structure, water movement, aeration, pH, buffer capacity, and many others.

Some of the chief clay minerals found in soil are kaolinite, montmorillonite, vermiculite, and illite. All of these arise from aluminum silicate minerals such as feldspars, micas, and hornblende.

Organic constituents.—The soil is sometimes referred to as a vast biochemical laboratory where the organic debris and remains of plants and organisms are constantly undergoing breakdown and change as a result of the activities of enormous numbers and kinds of organisms.

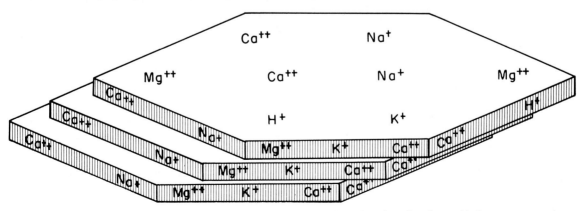

Fig. 1. Diagrammatic representation to show platy structure of clay minerals and exchangeable bases on exposed surfaces and edges.

In the course of the progressive breakdown of these constituents, many products are formed. Some of these are ammonia, nitrates, nitrites, sulfides, sulfates, phosphates, and gases such as methane, hydrogen, oxygen, carbon dioxide, water vapor, hydrogen sulfide; and others are transient organic constituents. A partial list of some toxic organic constituents that have been isolated from soils or plant roots or organisms is shown in Table 3. These consist primarily of acids, aldehydes,

TABLE 3. Some toxic organic constituents found in soils and plant residues*

Acids
  Benzoic acid; from soil
  trans-Cinnamic acid; from guayule roots
  p-Coumaric acid; from sugar-beet roots, fungi
  threo-9, 10-Dihydroxystearic acid; from soil, oak roots
  Ferulic acid; from plant residues
  p-Hydroxy benzoic acid; from soil, sugar-beet roots
  2-Methylisonicotinic acid; from soil

Aldehydes
  3-Acetyl-6-methoxybenzaldehyde; from desert shrub (*Encelia farinoso*)
  Benzaldehyde; occurs as amygdalin in plant tissue; rapidly oxidized in soil to benzoic acid
  Salicylaldehyde; isolated from soil
  Vanillin (4-hydroxy-3-methoxybenzaldehyde); isolated from soil

Amino acids, from soils, plants and fungi
  α-Alanine
  γ-Aminobutyric acid
  Aspartic acid
  Glutamic acid
  Glycine
  Leucine
  Trytophane

Coumarins; from plant roots
  Esculetin (6,7-dihydroxycoumarin); in plants as glucoside esculin
  Furano coumarins; from leaves of desert plants
  Scopoletin (6-methoxy-7-hydroxycoumarin); from roots of plants, potato tubers

Glycosides
  Amygdalin; from peach root bark, fruits of Rosacea
  Phlorizin; from root bark of apple trees
  Juglone; occurs in Juglandaceae family as 5-b-glucoside of 1, 4, 5, trihydroxy naphthalene

---

* From W. Moje. *In* H. D. Chapman [ed.], Plant and soil criteria for diagnosing nutrient status. Univ. of California, Div. Agr. Sci., Berkeley, California.

coumarins, and glycosides. In addition, there are the hormones, vitamins, antibiotics, and other compounds both beneficial and toxic.

The so-called humus materials have high base-exchange capacity, perhaps two to four times that of clays of an equivalent weight. They also have a high water-holding capacity. Therefore in terms of such functions as source of nutrients, structure, aeration, pH, base exchange, moisture retention, and energy source for microorganisms, plus direct and indirect effects on plants and organisms, the role of organic matter in soils is far reaching and of special significance to soil microorganisms.

The liquid phase of soils.—The moisture or soil solution of soils is a highly fluctuating entity. It is not only the chief source of moisture for plants and organisms, but the source or medium by which plants and organisms derive their needed nutrients. In the soil solution are not only the dissolved inorganic constituents, but also dissolved gases—oxygen, nitrogen, carbon dioxide—and of course, many microorganisms. The dissolved components of the soil solution are in a constantly shifting equilibrium with the solid phase, with the soil air, with the soil moisture, and as well, with soil-organism and plant-root activity. Variable forces bind water to soil particles as the moisture film decreases or increases in thickness around a soil particle.

Some idea of the variations in total inorganic salt content of the soil solution, as well as something of the range of variations for any given ion, is shown in Table 4. Since analyses are not included for soils of the humid regions, this table provides an incomplete picture of the great range in concentration of nutrients occurring in soils; and of course, in any one soil, as moisture content fluctuates from high to low, there will be great fluctuation in concentration as well. Moreover, the solution in close proximity to the solid phase will vary in composition from that farther away because of varying electrical forces, which change with distance from the soil interface. Rainfall, temperature, plant absorption, microbial activities, all bring about continued changes as well.

Chemical composition of whole soils.—To illustrate the variability in chemical composition of widely different soils, I have selected a few analyses showing macroelement composition (Table 5), and in Table 6, something as to the enormous variability of soils with respect to ultimate chemical composition.

The gaseous phase.—As a broad generalization, one can say that about one half of the volume of a soil is pore space occupied by water and soil air. The proportions of air and water fluctuate with the soil moisture, and in general the soil air can be regarded as occupying between 5 and 40% of the available pore space. In composition, soil air is generally saturated with moisture vapor, contains from 10 to more than a hundred times as much carbon dioxide as the air above the soil, and less oxygen and nitrogen, generally. In addition, there are the inert gases, and under anaerobic conditions there may be more or less methane, hydrogen sulfide, and hydrogen. Where ammonium fertilizers are used on alkaline soils, free ammonia gas may be temporarily present. Reduction of nitrates may yield oxides of nitrogen.

The quantity as well as composition of soil air will fluctuate with moisture, texture, depth, temperature, plant growth and cover, microbiological activity, structure, barometric pressure, winds, and other factors. The composition and quantity will also vary from point to point within the soil mass; it is quite possible to have local anaerobic zones existing temporarily in what is otherwise regarded as a well-aerated soil. For temporary periods following rain or irrigation or both, widespread anaerobic conditions may prevail.

Leather (1915) found the composition of soil air in

TABLE 4. Composition of displaced soil solution showing variability among some soils of semiarid regions*

Soil	Treatment	Moisture, %	pH	NO$_3$$^-$	HCO$_3$$^-$	Cl$^-$	SO$_4$$^{--}$	Ca^{++}	Mg^{++}	Na$^+$	K$^+$	Total
Hanford fine sandy loam	Cropped	16	7.4	116	83	0	438	189	71	33	16	946
	Fallowed	16	7.6	1,781	73	55	454	672	134	75	38	3,282
Imperial clay	Cropped	29.9	7.6	402	152	540	2,522	625	180	680	—	5,101
Imperial clay (saline soil)	Saline soil	34.8	7.2	4,090	109	40,650	1,570	11,400	2,995	11,000	113	71,927
Indio very fine sandy loam	Cropped	16.5	8.6	458	347	369	2,128	78	6	1,610	59	5,055
Superstition sand	Cropped	14.5	8.7	—	486	174	150	288	57	255	27	1,437
Reagan clay loam	Cropped	20.4	8.6	2,720	672	702	2,840	900	609	529	352	9,324

* Data from Burd and Martin (1924) and Reitemeier and Richards (1944).

TABLE 5. Some macroelement variations in soils (in % of dry soil)

Soil series and type	SiO$_2$	Al$_2$O$_3$	Fe$_2$O$_3$	TiO$_2$	CaO	MgO	K$_2$O	P$_2$O$_5$	Organic matter
Norfolk sandy loam	94.5	2.1	0.8	0.7	0.4	0.09	0.10	0.06	1.1
Carrington silt loam	73.5	9.1	4.3	0.6	0.9	0.71	2.03	0.24	4.9
Cecil clay	66.5	17.1	7.4	1.0	0.3	0.31	0.62	0.17	1.3
Stockton clay loam	63.5	14.3	7.9	1.2	2.3	1.81	0.78	—	—
Nipe clay (serpentine) 0-26 cm	3.3	18.5	63.0	0.8	0.12	0.33	0.06	—	—
Laterite	3.3	46.8	26.1	0.7	Nil	Nil	Nil	0.13	—

TABLE 6. Trace element variations in soils (in ppm of dry soil)*

Element	Extreme range	Usual range	Variation Extreme	Variation Usual
Silver	< 0.1–9.0	0.1–1.0	90 ×	10 ×
Arsenic	< 0.1–1000.0	1.0–50.0	10,000 ×	50 ×
Gold	0.1–6.0	0.1–0.3	60 ×	3 ×
Boron	< 0.2–1000.0	2.0–100.0	5000 ×	50 ×
Barium	8.0–33,700	100.0–3000.0	4,210 ×	30 ×
Cadmium	0.01–45.0	0.01–0.70	4,500 ×	70 ×
Cobalt	0.001–1000	1.0–40.0	1 × 10^6	40 ×
Chromium	< 0.01–35,800	5.0–1000.0	1 × 10^6	200 ×
Caesium	0.3–25.7	?	80 ×	?
Copper	< 1.0–14,000	2.0–100.0	1.4 × 10^3 ×	50 ×
Gallium	0.4–300.0	3.0–30.0	750 ×	10 ×
Germanium	0.1–10.0	—	100 ×	—
Mercury	—	0.03	—	—
Lanthanum	< 30.0–500.0	—	15 ×	—
Lithium	< 1.0–5,000	< 1.0–< 100.0	5,000 ×	100 ×
Manganese	1–70,200	200–3,000.0	1.7 × 10^5	15 ×
Molybdenum	0.1–224.0	0.2–5.0	224 ×	25 ×
Nickel	0.5–6,200.0	5.0–500.0	12,400 ×	100 ×
Lead	0.1–10,000	2.0–200.0	1 × 10^6 ×	100 ×
Radium	1–237 × 10^{-6}	1 × 10^{-6}	—	—
Rare earths	38–1,600	100–800	—	8 ×
Rubidium	0.2–2,000	20–500	2 × 10^5 ×	25 ×
Scandium	—	< 10–25	—	2.5 ×
Selenium	0.01–225	0.1–2.0	1 × 10^5 ×	20 ×
Tin	0.03–300	0.1–5.0	3 × 10^5 ×	50 ×
Strontium	0.10–5,000	50–1,000	50,000 ×	20 ×
Thorium	0.5–56	2–10	100 ×	5 ×
Titanium	80–150,000	1,000–10,000	1,000 ×	10 ×
Uranium	—	0.9–5.8 (?)	—	—
Vanadium	1–1,000	20–500	1,000 ×	25 ×
Zinc	6–30,000	10–300	5,000 ×	30 ×

* From D. J. Swaine. Commonwealth Bur. Soil Sci. (Gt. Brit.) Tech. Commun. 48. 1955.

TABLE 7. Effect of soil acidification on solubility of some soil constituents*

Soil	S added, g/kg	pH of soil 1:2.5 soil-water susp.	Composition of saturation extract, in me/1				
			Ca^{++}	Mg^{++}	K^+	Na^+	SO_4^{--}
Yolo clay loam	0	8.20	4.0	1.5	0.6	2.6	3.1
	0.24	8.00	5.2	2.3	0.5	1.5	7.5
	1.76	7.40	31.0	6.5	1.0	1.8	36.6
	3.13	5.70	30.3	18.3	1.4	2.3	46.8
	3.70	4.70	29.0	22.5	1.5	2.9	50.2

* Data from D. G. Aldrich, J. R. Buchanan, and J. R. Bradford. Soil Science 79: 427-439. 1955.

immediate proximity to plant roots where the temperatures were about 30°C, and air content varying from 5.5 to 25% by volume, to run as follows:

Nitrogen	73-85% by volume
Oxygen	2.2-13.8% by volume
Carbon dioxide	3.3-17.0% by volume
Methane	None
Hydrogen	0.0-1.4% by volume
Argon	0.9-1.1% by volume

The effect of soil aeration on microbial activities is being discussed by others and will not be covered here, save to stress its great importance and its extreme fluctuation and variability in soils.

Soil pH.—Probably no single characteristic of a soil is more significant than pH. As has been pointed out earlier, pH is primarily determined by the base-exchange components of the soil. The solubility and "availability" to plants (and organisms) of many chemicals in soils is strongly influenced by pH.

Some distinction must be made between soils that have become acid over a long period of soil formation and weathering, and those that have become acid by additions of sulfur, ammonium sulfate, or other chemicals. The initial effects of soil acidification are usually to increase the solubility of calcium, magnesium, sodium, and phosphorus, as well as zinc, manganese, boron, lithium, copper, iron, nickel, and other elements. Effects on the solubility of some of the aforementioned are shown in Tables 7 and 8.

TABLE 8. Relation of soluble phosphorus to pH in a soil differentially fertilized 28 years*

Fertilizer treatment	pH of soil	Soluble P,[†] ppm
Sodium nitrate	8.5	5.7
Check (irrigated only)	8.1	6.6
Covercrop	8.0	5.5
Calcium nitrate	7.8	4.5
Sodium nitrate and gypsum	7.6	9.5
Urea	7.1	6.9
Ammonium sulfate and lime	7.1	14.0
Calcium nitrate, sulfur, and covercrop	5.8	19.7
Ammoniun sulfate and covercrop	4.1	31.6
Ammonium sulfate	4.0	30.6

* Soluble in 0.5 M $NaHCO_3$ at pH 8.5; using a 1:10 soil-to-solution ratio.
† From: P. F. Pratt, R. B. Harding, W. W. Jones, and H. D. Chapman. Hilgardia 28: 381-420. 1959.

In soils which have become acid over a long period and where leaching has largely removed soluble products, soils are characteristically low in calcium, magnesium, sodium, potassium, boron, and in some cases zinc. Also, phosphorus tends to be converted to less available aluminum and iron forms. Because of large initial supplies in the soil, aluminum and as well manganese may be sufficiently solubilized to cause toxicity to plants and organisms. The increase in aluminum solubility with pH is shown by the data of Table 9.

TABLE 9. Relation of pH to soluble aluminum in displaced soil solution*

pH of solution	Soluble aluminum, ppm
7.33	0.21
7.23	0.00
5.78	1.00
4.64	0.74
4.50	1.60
4.35	10.0
4.30	17.5
4.06	96.0

* Data from O. C. Magistad. Soil Sci. 20: 181-255. 1925.

Iron solubility is also increased as soils become acid, and in certain soils one needs to look for possible nickel and chromium and lithium toxicity. Molybdenum availability tends to decrease in acid soils.

All of these effects may bring about not only primary deficiencies or toxicity effects or both, but may induce secondary unbalances in relation to plant nutrition. (See Table 10.)

Soil alkalinity, on the other hand, according to the degree and circumstances, usually decreases manganese, zinc, copper, and iron solubility and availability; may either increase or decrease phosphorus availability; usually increases molybdenum availability; and may decrease boron availability. Commonly one begins to look also for increased exchangeable sodium levels, increased salinity, and also free lime. Obviously, the degree of change in any of these depends on the inherent characteristics of the soil at the outset, the factors responsible for the changes, and the degree of acidity or alkalinity found.

FACTORS AFFECTING SOLUBILITY, AVAILABILITY, AND TOXICITY OF ELEMENTS IN SOILS.—A partial list of the soil conditions (including pH), practices, and changes which affect the solubility, availability, or toxicity of elements in soils is presented in Table 10.

Many of these are well known and established; others are not so well known. No attempt has been made to make a complete list. The specific references cited for most interrelations could be greatly expanded. It is likely that many of the interrelations or antagonisms which affect higher plants will likewise affect microorganisms. No two plant species, varieties, or strains are equally affected, and it is obvious that the same diversity of reaction will be obtained in the case of microorganisms. Space does not permit discussion of this broad subject, but a look at the table will suffice to show the many soil conditions and interrelations that increase or decrease solubility, availability, or toxicity.

The effects of one chemical or condition on the so-called availability of another chemical as affecting plants operate through a variety of mechanisms; some are purely chemical reactions in the soil, others operate through soil-plant interactions, others through biochemical reactions within the plants. For example, one mechanism is solubility or fixation by clays, either in positions not accessible to plant roots or so tightly held that replacing ions (hydrogen, for example) resulting from plant-root or organism respiration are insufficiently concentrated to displace the needed ion fast enough for plant needs; another mechanism is competition between higher plants and organisms for a given nutrient; another, competition for exchange sites on plant roots. Aeration, with all the chain of events that are tied to it, moisture availability, drought, and over-moist conditions are additional factors.

As to reactions within the plants, these can be of a type which take place within the root, e.g. poisoning of enzyme systems and prevention of normal movement; or reactions within other parts of the plant, such as blockage of vascular ducts and effects of chelating agents.

SOME SPECIFIC SOIL AND NUTRIENT CONDITIONS AFFECTING BIOLOGICAL ACTIVITIES IN SOILS.—In this section, I have elected to briefly describe and discuss a few more or less specific relations between substrate and organisms with which I have had some personal experience.

Nitrite accumulation in soil.—Some years ago, following the findings of W. P. Martin, Buehrer, and Caster (1943), we (Chapman and Liebig, 1952) made a rather extensive study of the circumstances under which nitrite accumulates in arable citrus soils. This work was carried out both in citrus orchards and under laboratory conditions. Our studies showed that substantial amounts of nitrite accumulate under neutral and alkaline soil conditions whenever a significant amount of ammonia or ammonium ion is present. Under winter soil conditions in southern California (where temperatures may stay in the 45° to 55°F range for some time), nitrites accumulate and may persist for several months before being converted to nitrate. The apparent basic reason is that the nitrobacter which converts nitrite to nitrate is more sensitive to free ammonia than the organisms which convert ammonia or ammo-

nium ions to nitrite. Low application rates of ammonium or ammonia-producing fertilizers (ammonia gas, urea, ammonium sulfate, and ammonium nitrate) do not produce much nitrite; whereas higher rates, especially of urea, do produce nitrite. Heavy application of manure, at nitrogen rates equivalent to those of urea, did not result in nitrite accumulation. This result with manure could be due to several factors: (1) the slower production of ammonia in the manure; (2) its immediate absorption by soil colloids; or (3) the simultaneous production of carbon dioxide.

In soils more acid than pH 7.0 (pH determined on a soil paste), very little nitrite accumulated irrespective of the nitrogen fertilizer used.

The persistence of nitrite was strongly related to soil temperatures. This probably means that the nitrite oxidizers are less active at temperatures under 50°F than the ammonia oxidizers. Our observations on this harmonize with those of Tyler and Broadbent (1960). They found that nitrite added to two soils incubated at 75° and 45°F, respectively, persisted longer at the lower than the higher temperature. These investigators also showed that nitrite reduced microbiological activity in soils.

Effects of ammonium sulfate.—It is well known that ammonium sulfate makes soils acid. Some years ago we noted that water penetration was being markedly impeded in the plots of our citrus fertilizer experiment where rather heavy rates of ammonium sulfate had been used for a number of years. We found (Aldrich, Parker, and Chapman, 1945) that these soils had become so acid that the ammonium was no longer being nitrified and had built up in the exchange complex of the soil. The ammonium, in turn, exerted a dispersing effect on the soil colloids, slowed water penetration, and led to salt buildup in the soil (owing to impaired permeability), and finally to tree deterioration.

Phosphate in relation to Thielaviopsis basicola *infection of citrus roots.*—In an outdoor water-culture experiment (Chapman and Brown, 1942) with bearing orange trees to determine the effects of variable phosphate supply on tree performance, three levels of phosphate were maintained—0.1, 1.50, and 5.00 meq of phosphate per liter. The trees had been transplanted bare-root from a citrus nursery. After about 5 months, we noted a black fungus infection on the citrus roots in the medium- and high-phosphate cultures. This fungus was identified as *Thielaviopsis basicola*.

The infection became progressively worse on the medium- and high-phosphate cultures, with a little even on the low-phosphate cultures. The pH of these solutions was being maintained at 5.0. We decided to reduce the pH on all cultures to 3.5. Soon after this change, healthy, fungus-free roots were produced in all cultures and they continued healthy until the experiment was terminated several years later. This experiment clearly demonstrated the influence of phosphate and the modifying influence of pH as related to citrus-root infection under solution-culture conditions.

TABLE 10. Soil conditions and practices which increase or decrease solubility, availability, or toxicity of various elements to plants

Element	Conditions or practices which *increase* solubility, availability, or toxicity		Conditions or practices which *decrease* solubility, availability, or toxicity	
	Condition or practice	Reference*	Condition or practice	Reference*
Aluminum	Soil acidity	Magistad, 1925	Soil alkalinity	Magistad, 1925
	Gypsum added to acid soils	Fried and Peech, 1946	Organic matter additions	Pierre, Pohlman, and McIlvaine, 1932
	KCl, and CaCl$_2$ additions to some soils	Ragland and Coleman, 1959	Phosphate fertilizer additions	Hartwell and Pember, 1918
Arsenic	Decreasing amounts of clay in soils	Crafts and Rosenfels, 1939	Ferrous sulfate additions	Vandecaveye, Horner, and Keaton, 1936
	Phosphate fertilizer increases solubility	Albert, 1932, 1933, 1934	Zinc sulfate additions	Thompson and Batjer, 1950
			Zinc chelate additions	Thompson and Batjer, 1950
			Organic matter additions	Vincent, 1939
			Increasing iron content of soils	Albert, 1932, 1933, 1934
Boron	Soil acidification	Aldrich, Buchanan, and Bradford, 1955	Overliming of soils	Midgley and Dunklee, 1940; and many others
	Use of irrigation water with more than 0.5 ppm B	Kelley and Brown, 1928	Potassium fertilizer additions	Reeve and Shive, 1943
	Use of fertilizers containing boron	Reeve and Shive, 1944	High nitrogen	Beckenbach, 1944
	Lack of sufficient potassium	Chapman and Brown, 1943	Low phosphate	Beckenbach, 1944
			Drought conditions	Morris, 1938; and others
			Calcium nitrate fertilizers; also organic matter	Cooper, Peynado, and Olsen, 1958
Calcium	Acidification of neutral or alkaline soils	Aldrich, Buchanan, and Bradford, 1955; and others	Increasing soil acidity	Swanson, Gainey, and Latshaw, 1924
			Increasing exchangeable sodium	Kelley, 1951
			Soluble aluminum, manganese, and hydrogen may reduce calcium absorption	Schmehl, Peech, and Bradfield, 1950
Chromium	Increasing soil acidity	Hamence and Taylor, 1948; W. O. Robinson, Edgington, and Byers, 1935; also Soane and Saunder, 1959	Additions of lime	Hamence and Taylor, 1948
	Soils derived from serpentine rocks are frequently high in chromium			
Cobalt	Increasing soil acidity	Ekman, Karlsson, and Svanberg, 1952	Molybdenum 2-25 ppm added to culture solutions	Millikan, 1947
			Phosphate additions	Beeson, Gray, and Hamner, 1948
			Lime additions	Wright and Lawton, 1954
Copper	Prolonged use of bordeaux sprays	Reuther and Smith, 1954	Organic matter additions to soils	Lucas, 1948
	Acidification of soils	Reuther, 1957	Lime additions to soil	Reuther and Smith, 1954
			Heavy nitrogen fertilization	Florida experience
			Heavy phosphate fertilization	Bingham and Martin, 1956; and Reuther and Smith, 1954
			Aluminum in culture solutions	Liebig, Vanselow, and Chapman, 1942
			Iron chelate additions	Stewart and Leonard, 1954

TABLE 10. (*Continued*)

Element	Conditions or practices which *increase* solubility, availability, or toxicity		Conditions or practices which *decrease* solubility, availability, or toxicity	
	Condition or practice	Reference*	Condition or practice	Reference*
Fluorine	Phosphate fertilizers usually carry some F	Common knowledge	Alkaline soil conditions	MacIntire et al., 1951; and others
	Soil acidification increases solubility	MacIntire et al., 1951; and others	Phosphate, calcium, and lime additions	
			Some clays fix soluble fluorine compounds	
Iron	Acidification of soils	Common knowledge	Liming of acid soils	Common knowledge
	Soil fumigation	J. P. Martin, Klotz et al., 1956	Phosphate fertilization under some conditions	Sideris and Krauss, 1934; and others
	Drying of soils where wet conditions have prevailed	Common knowledge	Low soil temperatures	Chapman, 1945
			Overmoist soil conditions will often produce Fe deficiency, especially in fruit trees	Common knowledge
			Zinc in excessive amounts	Chapman, Liebig, and Vanselow, 1939
			Bicarbonate ions	Wadleigh and Brown, 1952; and others
			Copper in excessive amounts	Anne and Dupuis, 1953; Reuther and Smith, 1954; and others
			Chromium (8-16 ppm in soln. culture)	Hewitt, 1953; Hunter and Vergnano, 1953
			Nickel additions	Hunter and Vergnano, 1952
			Poor soil aeration	Wallihan et al., 1961
			Manganiferous soils	Noted especially in Hawaii
			Potassium excess	Reuther and Smith, 1954
			Potassium deficiency	Chapman and Brown, 1947
			Magnesium excess and magnesium deficiency	Chapman (unpublished)
Lithium	Use of irrigation water containing lithium	Aldrich, Vanselow, and Bradford, 1951; Bradford (unpublished data)	Increasing calcium concentration in the nutrient medium	Jacobson, Moore, and Hannapel, 1960; Epstein, 1960
	Soil acidification	Aldrich, Buchanan, and Bradford, 1955		
Magnesium	Soil acidification	Common knowledge	Potassium fertilization	Numerous investigations
	Nitrogen fertilization	Boynton, 1947; and others	Ammoniacal fertilization	Mulder, 1951
	Phosphorus fertilization	Embleton et al., 1956; and others	Liming with non-magnesium-containing lime	Willis, Piland, and Gray, 1934
			High soluble calcium in nutrient medium	Stier, 1941
			Increases in exchangeable hydrogen in soils	Mulder, 1956; and others
			Sulfate additions to soils	Nicholas and Catlow, 1947
			Sodium salts	Carolus, 1935
Manganese	Soil acidification	Fried and Peech, 1946; and others	Citrus exposed to 2-3 ppb HF in air for several months showed manganese deficiencies patterns	Brewer, 1964
	Anaerobic conditions brought on by waterlogging	Bradfield, Batjer, and Oskamp, 1934	Ca, Mg, K, and Na through effects on pH	Marshall, 1944
	Increased phosphorus in soils	Bingham and Garber, 1960	Phosphorus deficiency	Chapman and Rayner, 1951

TABLE 10. (*Continued*)

Element	Conditions or practices which *increase* solubility, availability, or toxicity		Conditions or practices which *decrease* solubility, availability, or toxicity	
	Condition or practice	Reference*	Condition or practice	Reference*
			Soil alkalinity beyond pH 6.5	Leeper, 1947
			Soil organisms which oxidize manganous to difficult soluble oxides	Leeper, 1947
			Excessive potassium and calcium deficiency	Chapman (unpublished data)
			Organic matter additions	Sherman and Fujimoto, 1947
Molybdenum	Soil alkalinity increases availability	A. J. Anderson, 1956	Soil acidification decreases availability	A. J. Anderson, 1956
	Phosphate fertilization	Stout et al., 1951	High nickel?	Sato (unpublished data†)
	Some peat soils are high in Mo	Dunne and Jones, 1948	Copper corrects Mo excess in animal nutrition	Ferguson, Lewis, and Watson, 1943
	Poorly drained soils	Dye and O'Harra, 1959	Allophane strongly fixes molybdenum	Wells, 1956
			Sulfate additions to soil	A. J. Anderson, 1956
			Manganese additions to nutrient media	Mulder, 1954
Nitrogen	Increased potassium	Chapman and Liebig, 1940	High phosphate	Chapman, 1951; Lilleland, 1932
			High sulfate	Foote and McElhiney, 1937; W. W. Jones et al., 1963
			Addition of low nitrogen organic matter (microbial immobilization)	Common knowledge
Phosphorus	Acidification of neutral soils will temporarily increase phosphorus availability	Chapman, 1936; Pratt et al., 1959; and others	Copper additions to soils	Reuther and Smith, 1954
			Phosphorus usually less available in acid soils due to fixation in iron and aluminum forms	Common knowledge
	Adequate soil moisture	Cannell, Bingham, and Garber, 1960	Phosphorus in calcareous soils low in availability	Chapman, 1934, 1936
			Low soil temperatures	Common knowledge
			Fixation by certain clays	Murphy, 1939
Potassium	With some crops sodium may partially substitute for potassium	Common knowledge	High magnesium in soils	Stanford, Kelly, and Pierre, 1942
	Sod culture	Proebsting, 1953	High calcium in soils; liming	Stanford, Kelly, and Pierre, 1942; York, Bradfield, and Peech, 1953a,b
	Addition of organic mulches	Common knowledge	Prolonged cropping	Common knowledge
	Drying of soils	Attoe, 1947; and others	Leaching of very sandy soils and peat soils	Common knowledge
	Freezing and thawing	Batz, 1927	Fixation by certain types of clay minerals	Reitemeier, 1951
	Biological activity in soils	Common knowledge		
	Liming acid soils	Reitemeier, 1951		
Selenium	Selenium is more soluble or available in alkaline soils	Trelease and Beath, 1949; Lakin, 1961	Irrigation and drainage	General experience
			Sulfates inhibit Se absorption	Hurd-Karrer, 1933, 1934; and others
			Barium chloride	Ravikovitch and Margolin, 1959
			Se is less available and soluble in acid soils due apparently to formation of very insoluble compounds with iron hydroxide	Trelease and Beath, 1949

TABLE 10. (*Continued*)

Element	Conditions or practices which *increase* solubility, availability, or toxicity		Conditions or practices which *decrease* solubility, availability, or toxicity	
	Condition or practice	Reference*	Condition or practice	Reference*
Sodium	Increased per cent saturation of exchange complex in soils	Kelley, 1951	Increased calcium and/or magnesium in soil solution	Many investigations
	Plants vary markedly in ability to accumulate or exclude Na	Wybenga, 1957		
	Low levels of oxygen in root zone may contribute to increased accumulation	Smith, Reuther, and Specht, 1952; Pearson, Goss, and Hayward, 1957		
	High bicarbonate increases sodium accumulation	Wadleigh and Brown, 1952		
Sulfur	Use of irrigation water high in sulfate	Chapman, 1960; and many others	There is some but not conclusive evidence that high N may decrease sulfate absorption	Foote and McElhiney, 1937; Rasmussen and Smith, 1958; Chapman and Liebig, 1940; W. W. Jones et al., 1963
	Factors such as high water table which lead to capillary rise of soil solution and deposition of salts in soil surface	Kelley, 1951		
	Low or deficient N permits accumulation in citrus	Foote and McElhiney, 1937; W. W. Jones et al., 1963	High calcium in soil solution will decrease soluble sulfate if amounts of both exceed solubility product of calcium sulfate, but other salts will alter calcium sulfate solubility also	
Zinc	Soil acidification	Aldrich (unpublished data‡)	Soil alkalinity where calcium predominates	Jurinak and Thorne, 1955
	Soil fumigation	J. P. Martin and Pratt, 1958	Phosphate fertilizer	West, 1938; and others
	Alfalfa growth	Millikan, 1953	Clays with low Si/Mg ratios are said to fix Zn in forms not readily available to plants	Elgabaly, 1950
			Lime additions to soils	Lott, 1938; and others
			Nitrogen fertilization	Chapman, Vanselow, and Liebig, 1937; and others
			Molybdenum salts decreased Zn toxicity in culture solutions	Millikan, 1947

* In most cases many other citations might be given in support of the relation in question.
† K. Sato, Natl. Inst. Hort. Sci. Hiratsuka City, Kanagawa Pref., Japan, personal communication.
‡ D. G. Aldrich, unpublished data on file in the Dept. of Soils and Plant Nutrition, Univ. California, Riverside, 1955.

High-potassium–low-calcium in relation to brown-rot gummosis of citrus orange trees.—In another outdoor water-culture experiment (Chapman and Brown, 1942) with bearing navel orange trees on sour-orange rootstock, typical brown-rot gummosis (due to *Phytophthora parasitica*) developed near the bud union in the high-potassium–low-calcium nutrient solutions, but none appeared where the K:Ca ratio was lower. Malnutrition symptoms on both top and fruit had become manifest in the trees of the high-potassium series before the gummosis appeared. This seems to be a case of trees suffering from malnutrition displaying lowered resistance to organism invasion.

The citrus-replant problem.—More than 25 years ago, it became apparent that citrus replanted on soils previously cropped to this plant did not grow nearly as well as on comparable soils never planted to citrus.

In a series of investigations, J. P. Martin (1947, 1948a, b, 1950) showed that the primary cause was a buildup of organisms (various fungi and nematodes, primarily) which were detrimental to citrus roots. In the course of his studies, he found that the degree of growth depression on different soils varied widely.

In a recent study of 100 soils from citrus orchards, conducted in 3-gallon glazed pots in the greenhouse, and using sweet-orange seedlings, J. P. Martin, Harding, and Garber (1961) found that growth increases after fumigation varied from 0 to 211%. Citrus-root nematodes (*Tylenchulus semipenetrans*) were found in 93 of the nonfumigated old citrus soils dealt with, and *Phytophthora* spp. were found in 40. No assays were made for other detrimental fungi, but it can be safely concluded that one or more parasites detrimental to sweet-orange seedlings were present in all of the old citrus soils.

And yet, in spite of the presence of these organisms, responses to fumigation varied enormously from soil to soil. This means that in those soils where growth was just as good without fumigation as with it, some factors were operating to limit or offset the detrimental effect of the organisms. The question is, what were these factors? Martin, Harding, and Garber found, in general, that in the nonfumigated soils citrus growth was better in the *acid soils* than in the neutral or alkaline soils; in the fumigated soils, there was no relation of citrus growth to pH. This means that in acid soils there are factors either more favorable for plant growth or less favorable for the parasites, or a combination of the two. Of the factors favorable for plant growth, there were suggestions that absence of appreciable salt, greater availability of manganese, absence of sufficient replaceable sodium to affect growth, greater phosphorus availability, and less available potassium may have been operative. In addition, it may be that conditions were better for an antagonistic soil flora and perhaps less favorable for the detrimental organisms.

Calcium and aeration in relation to root rot of orange trees.—At the termination of a calcium-nutrition experiment with Washington Navel orange trees on Troyer citrange rootstock (carried on in outdoor water cultures for 7½ years), a striking qualitative relation between calcium supply and aeration came to light when we lifted the root systems out of the water cultures and examined them in some detail.

The containers were large, 700-liter capacity concrete conduit, which had been provided with concrete bottoms and painted on the interior with an asphaltum emulsion (Tree Seal). Continuous aeration was provided by inserting a plastic tube on one side to the bottom of the container, with an aeration rate of about 2 liters per min.

There were 24 trees in this experiment, and they were divided into 4 groups of 6 trees each. Four different calcium levels were maintained in these cultures —15, 20, 50, and 200 ppm. The levels were maintained reasonably constant. All cultures were maintained at pH levels varying from pH 3.8 to 4.5. The trees in the 15- and 20-ppm calcium solutions made significantly less growth, but at no time did they show acute calcium-deficiency symptoms. Root growth was less in these cultures and was more stubby and less branched than in the 50- and 200-ppm cultures.

The point of interest here, and the one I want to stress, is that in the low-calcium cultures there was little root rot in the side where the aerator was located, but a considerable amount in the interior of the root mass and on the side away from the aerator (see Fig. 2). On the other hand, in the high-calcium cultures, while root proliferation was also better on the side toward the aerator, there was much less root rotting on the interior and the side away from the aerator than in the low-calcium cultures (see Fig. 3).

These results suggest that roots of citrus trees under low calcium nutrition are less resistant to root-rotting organisms (Dr. J. P. Martin has found that the pre-

Fig. 2. Root system of low-calcium (20 ppm Ca) orange tree grown in nutrient solution: *A,* longitudinal view showing much greater root development on the side where the aerator was installed; *B,* transverse cut across the center of the root system showing considerable amount of root rotting (dark area) in the interior and on the side away from the aerator.

dominating fungus, under the pH 3.8 to 4.5 conditions that we maintain in our citrus water cultures, is *Fusarium solani*) than roots of trees well supplied with calcium.

Other soil-plant-disease relations.—In Table 11, I

have listed a number of plant diseases which are influenced to a greater or lesser degree by either soil conditions, nutrition, fertilization, or amendments. No attempt has been made to compile a complete list, and they are included in this paper only to indicate something of the variety of soil conditions and management practices which can to some degree increase or decrease disease. While there are quite a few cases of acid or alkaline soil conditions which exert a strong effect and in which high nitrogen may increase susceptibility and high potassium decrease susceptibility, there are many exceptions. This is understandable when it is realized that we are dealing with complex relations in which varying plant resistance, nutritional state, climatic factors, soil temperature, moisture, aeration, chemical state of the soil, organism variations and reactions, nonparasitic organisms, antibiotics, and other factors, all play a role in the final outcome.

This and other similar research illustrate the complexities of the problem. Plant growth and performance represent the final integration of all factors—soil, climate, heredity, insects, and disease—which play a role. The specific part played by soil organisms and the soil and plant factors, pro and con, which determine their specific influence are difficult to assess, but constitute a field in which continued research is needed.

DIAGNOSTIC TECHNIQUES.—*Availability tests for determining nutrient status of the soil.*—In Table 12, I have listed some of the more common chemical availability tests by which the status of the soil with respect to each element can be roughly evaluated. While these are standardized in terms of higher plants, they will be useful to investigators interested in relating nutrient conditions of the soil to microbiological activity.

Use of leaf analysis for determining nutrient status. —A substantial body of data is now at hand by which the current nutrient status of many different crops and, by inference, the soil conditions, can be appraised. With the cooperation of some twenty of my colleagues in the University of California, we have brought together much of the widely scattered literature of leaf analysis and other information of diagnostic value as well (Chapman, 1964).

While there are still many blind spots in existing information, and uncertainties with respect to interpretations, much useful information and tentative criteria are available for many crops and elements. The use of both soil and leaf analysis information will prove of considerable value in further investigations of the relation of soil and plant nutrient status to the many diseases, soil-borne and otherwise, affecting plants.

Fig. 3. Root system of high-calcium (200 ppm Ca) orange tree grown in nutrient solution: *A*, longitudinal view showing somewhat greater root development on the side where the aerator was installed, but not as pronounced as in the low-calcium culture (Fig. 2); *B*, transverse cut across the center of the root system showing much less root rotting (darker color) in the center than in the low-calcium cultures.

TABLE 11. Some examples of plant diseases influenced by soil condition, fertilization, and amendments*

Disease	Organism	Soil, management, or nutritional factors which have effects
Potato scab	*Streptomyces scabies*	1. In acid soils of pH 4.8 or less, scab not a problem; reactions of pH 5.0 to 5.2 are recommended 2. Infection aggravated by increasing either Ca or K when both present in adequate supply (Reported by McNew, 1953)
Angular leaf spot of tobacco	*Pseudomonas tabaci*	1. Potassium increases plant resistance by encouraging thicker cell walls, heavier cuticle and mechanical tissues 2. Nitrogen increases susceptibility 3. Balanced fertilizers of 4-10-6 or 6-2-3 are beneficial (Reported by McNew, 1953)
Take-all disease of wheat	*Ophiobolus graminis*	1. Disease decreased by adequate nutrition and nutritional balance; in Arkansas plots, 10 tons of manure or 400 lb of 4-8-3 reduced infection over control; from 80% on check to 45 and 7% respectively 2. Too much nitrogen in fall permits fungus to prolong its existence on infested stubble; therefore fall crops which absorb excess nitrogen or organic matter which encourages use of excess N by microorganisms are beneficial (Reported by NcNew, 1953)
Texas root rot	*Phymatotrichum omnivorum*	1. Favored in alkaline soils; reduced in acid soils 2. Phosphate fertilizers increase severity 3. Potassium deficiency slightly reduced disease 4. Adequate N fertilization decreases disease 5. Organic matter which encourages a microflora that destroys sclerotia is beneficial 6. High carbohydrate in roots of cotton decreases amount of infection (Reported by McNew, 1953)
Cotton wilt	*Fusarium vasinfectum*	1. Potassium deficiency favors disease 2. High potassium decreases disease 3. High nitrogen increases severity of disease 4. Ammonium salts more conducive to disease than nitrates (Reported by McNew, 1953)
Club root of cabbage	*Plasmodiophora brassicae*	1. Disease less on alkaline soils of pH 7.0 and above 2. Potassium deficiency lessens disease 3. Abundant fertilizer encourages disease 4. Ratio of Ca to K may be important—high Ca and low K lessening disease 5. Deficiency or excess of N favors disease 6. Disease becomes more severe on acid soils; probably related to less Ca supply (Reported by McNew, 1953) 7. Ca(OH)$_2$ in amounts to give a pH of 7.4 gave control (Chupp, 1928)
Peach and plum leaf lesions	*Xanthomonas pruni*	1. Leaf health and abscission decreased by application of ample N fertilizer (McNew, 1953)
Powdery mildew of cereals	*Erysiphe graminis*	1. Heavy N fertilization by decreasing cell wall thickness promotes disease; whereas K increases resistance 2. Boron and Mn deficiency increases disease (Reported by McNew, 1953)

TABLE 11. (*Continued*)

Disease	Organism	Soil, management, or nutritional factors which have effects
Cereal rusts	*Puccinia glumarum, P. graminis* and others	1. Susceptibility increased by N 2. Potassium salts increase resistance 3. Plant deficiencies of Ca, Fe, Mg, K, P, N, and S decrease amount of disease (Reported by McNew, 1953)
Tobacco mosaic virus	Virus	1. Nitrogen and P increase number of leaf lesions 2. Potassium decreases number of lesions (Spencer 1935*a,b*)
Cabbage yellows	*Fusarium oxysporum* f. *conglutinans* Wr. S. & H.	1. Increased K decreased disease; whereas increasing P and N increased disease using cabbage varieties of intermediate resistance. However, substrate temperature and host resistance were more important factors than nutrition (Walker, 1946)
Black root rot of tobacco	*Thielaviopsis basicola*	1. Disease strongly decreased by acid soil reaction (P. J. Anderson and Morgan, 1929).
Blossom end rot of tomato		1. Favored by low Ca condition and much less where Ca is ample (Geraldson, 1957)
Root rot of peas	*Aphanomyces eutiches*	1. Potassium chloride added to a K deficient soil decreased disease both in soils saturated for one week and at normal soil moistures (Wade, 1955; see also Geach, 1936)
Bacterial blight of lima bean	*Pseudomonas syringae*	1. Disease was markedly enhanced in plants grown in high N, low P, and low K nutrients, when compared to those grown in balanced solution (Thaung and Walker, 1957)
Wilt of carnations	*Fusarium* sp.	1. High N and low K encouraged disease development (Gasiorkiewicz, 1960)
Rhizoctonia brown patch of bent grass (*Agrostis palustris*)	*Rhizoctonia solani*	1. High N increased severity 2. Varying P and K did not affect 3. At high N, disease less at pH 4.0, than at pH 5.6 and 9.0 4. Moisture level in soil did not affect—ranging from field capacity to wilting percentage (Bloom and Couch, 1960)
Sclerotinia dollar spot of Kentucky blue grass (*Poa pratensis*)	*Sclerotinia homoeocarpa*	1. Disease decreased under low N or under low balanced nutrition 2. pH from 4.0 to 9.0 did not affect 3. Under water stress, disease greater (Couch and Bloom, 1960)
Big vein of lettuce	Virus	1. High soil moisture and low temperatures (45°-50°F) at night and 50°-60° during the day increases disease (McKinney, 1946)

* Most of these cases have been drawn from reviews, and no attempt has been made to list all the investigators who have contributed.

TABLE 12. Soil test methods and criteria for evaluating chemical soil conditions as related to plant growth

Element	Method and/or fraction and basis of expressing result	Low or deficient range	Ample or satisfactory range	Excess range	Crops to which applicable	Reference
Aluminum	Water-soluble; ppm Al in soil	—	—	0.56	Alfalfa	Fried and Peech, 1946
	Water-soluble; ppm Al in soil	—	—	1.90	Alfalfa	Schmehl, Peech, and Bradfield, 1950
	Exchangeable; meq Al in 100 g of soil	—	—	2.3	Alfalfa	Fried and Peech, 1946
	Exchangeable; meq Al in 100 g of soil	—	—	2.70	Alfalfa	Schmehl, Fried, and Bradfield, 1950
Arsenic	Water-soluble; in ppm soil	—	—	3.4-9.5	Alfalfa	Vandecaveye, Horner and Keaton, 1936
Boron	Hot-water-reflux soluble; ppm B in soil	< 0.5	> 0.5	—	General farm crops	Berger and Truog, 1940
	Hot-water-reflux soluble; ppm B in soil	—	—	1.3	Citrus	Penman and McAlpine, 1949
Bromine	Water-soluble; Br in ppm soil	—	—	38.0-83.0	Beans and cabbage	Stelmach, 1958
	Added to soil as $CaBr_2$; Br in ppm soil	—	—	15.0	Citrus	J. P. Martin, Helmkamp, and Ervin, 1956
Calcium	Exchangeble Ca as per cent of exchange capacity	< 23.0	42.0-55.0	—	Peanuts	Strauss and Grizzard, 1948
Chlorine	Water extract in meq Cl per 100 g of soil	0.003-0.005	—	—	—	Ozanne, 1958
Chromium	Solution cultures; concentration of Cr in ppm of solution	—	—	5.0-50.0	Corn	Scharrer and Schropp, 1935
Copper	0.1 N HCl extract in ppm Cu in soil	0.9-1.6	—	—	Apples	Bould et al., 1950
	Total Cu in Florida sandy soils	—	—	> 150.0	Citrus	Reuther and Smith, 1953
Fluorine	In solution cultures as ppm F	—	< 1.0	25.0	Citrus	Brewer et al., 1959
Iodine	In solution cultures as ppm I	—	—	0.5-1.0	—	Lewis and Powers, 1941
Lead	In solution cultures as ppm Pb	—	—	4.0	Barley	Scharrer and Schropp, 1936
Lithium	Li_2SO_4 applied to soil to give 2 ppm Li in soil	—	—	2.0	Citrus	Aldrich, Vanselow, and Bradford, 1951
Magnesium	Exchangeable Mg in meq/100 g of soil	< 0.5	—	—	Wheat and rye	Goto et al., 1953
	Exchangeable K/Mg in soil	> 0.4-0.5	—	—	Citrus	McColloch, Bingham and Aldrich, 1957

TABLE 12. (*Continued*)

Element	Method and/or fraction and basis of expressing result	Low or deficient range	Ample or satisfactory range	Excess range	Crops to which applicable	Reference
Manganese	Pretreatment of soil with 0.05% Quinal–50% alcohol mixture followed by extraction with 0.5 M calcium nitrate at pH 7.0; Mn expressed in ppm dry soil	2-18	20-50	—	Oats	L. H. P. Jones and Leeper, 1951
Molybdenum	Ammonium oxalate (pH 3.3) extractable Mo in ppm soil	0.04-0.12	—	—	—	Purvis and Peterson, 1956
Nickel	Exchangeable Ni by ammonium acetate extraction in ppm soil	—	—	11-70	—	Soane and Saunder, 1959
Nitrogen	Nitrate N produced by soil incubation in ppm N	< 20	80-100	—	Corn	Stanford and Hanway, 1955
Phosphorus	Extraction of soil with 0.5 M sodium bicarbonate of pH 8.5 for 30 min; expressed in ppm P in soil	5	6-10	—	Field	Olsen et al., 1954
Potassium	Exchangeable K in lb per acre Exchangeable K in lb per acre	0-200 < 100	> 325.0 < 200	— —	Sugarcane —	Baver, 1960 Bray, 1948
Selenium	Total Se in soil	< 2.0	—	30.0-324.0	Accumulator-type plants	Walsh and Fleming, 1952
Sodium	Exchangeable Na percentage in soil	—	< 4.0	> 10.0	Field and garden	Bernstein and Pearson, 1956; and many others
Sulfur	Morgan's Na-acetate-acetic-acid extract in ppm soil	< 3.0	—	—	Cotton, clover, tobacco	Jordan and Bardsley, 1958
Vanadium	Calcium vanadate added to a sandy soil in ppm	—	—	10.0	Citrus	Vanselow (unpublished data*)
Zinc	Soil extract with ammonium acetate-dithizone-carbon tetrachloride reagent; Zn in ppm soils	< 1.0 (in soils of pH 7.0 and higher)	2.5 (in soils of pH 6.0 or lower)	—	Many crops	Shaw and Dean, 1952

* A. P. Vanselow, unpublished data on file at the Dept. of Soils and Plant Nutrition, Univ. California, Riverside.

LITERATURE CITED

ALBERT, W. B. 1932. Arsenic toxicity in soils. S. Carolina Agr. Expt. Sta. Ann. Rept. 45: 44-46.

ALBERT, W. B. 1933. Arsenic toxicity in soils. S. Carolina Agr. Expt. Sta. Ann. Rept. 46: 44-45.

ALBERT, W. B. 1934. Arsenic solubility in soils. S. Carolina Agr. Expt. Sta. Ann. Rept. 47: 45-46.

ALDRICH, D. G., J. R. BUCHANAN, and J. R. BRADFORD. 1955. Effect of soil acidification on vegetative growth and leaf composition of lemon trees in pot cultures. Soil Sci. 79: 427-439.

ALDRICH, D. G., E. R. PARKER, and H. D. CHAPMAN. 1945. Effects of several nitrogenous fertilizers and soil amendments on the physical and chemical properties of an irrigated soil. Soil Sci. 59: 299-312.

ALDRICH, D. G., A. P. VANSELOW, and J. R. BRADFORD. 1951. Lithium toxicity in citrus. Soil Sci. 71: 291-295.

ANDERSON, A. J. 1956. Molybdenum as a fertilizer. Advan. Agron. 8: 163-202.

ANDERSON, P. J., and M. F. MORGAN. 1929. Soil reaction studies on the Connecticut tobacco crop. J. Am. Soc. Agron. 21: 156-158.

ANNE, P., and M. DUPUIS. 1953. Toxicity of copper with regard to some crop plants. Compt. Rend. 39: 58-60.

ATTOE, O. J. 1947. Potassium fixation and release in soils occurring under moist and drying conditions. Soil Sci. Soc. Am. Proc. (1946) 11: 145-149.

BATZ, B. 1927. The action of frost in the solubilization of phosphoric acid and potassium investigated by the seedling method of Neubauer. Z. Pflanzenernähr. Düng. Bodenk. 9(A): 346-363.

BAVER, L. D. 1960. Plant and soil composition relationships as applied to cane fertilization. Hawaiian Planters' Record 56(1): 1-153.

BECKENBACH, J. R. 1944. Functional relationships between boron and various anions in the nutrition of the tomato. Florida Agr. Expt. Sta. (Gainesville) Bull. 395, 34 p.

BEESON, K. C., LOUISE GRAY, and K. C. HAMNER. 1948. The absorption of mineral elements by forage crops. J. Am. Soc. Agron. 40: 553-562.

BERGER, K. C., and E. TRUOG. 1940. Boron deficiencies as revealed by plant and soil tests. J. Am. Soc. Agron. 32: 297-301.

BERNSTEIN, L., and G. A. PEARSON. 1956. Influence of exchangeable sodium on the yield and chemical composition of plants: I. Green beans, garden beets, clover and alfalfa. Soil Sci. 82: 247-258.

BINGHAM, F. T., and M. J. GARBER. 1960. Solubility and availability of micronutrients in relation to phosphorus fertilization. Soil Sci. Soc. Am. Proc. 24: 209-213.

BINGHAM, F. T., and J. P. MARTIN. 1956. Effects of soil phosphorus on growth and minor element nutrition of citrus. Soil Sci. Soc. Am. Proc. 20: 382-385.

BLOOM, J. R., and H. B. COUCH. 1960. Influence of environment on diseases of turf-grasses. I. Effect of nutrition, pH and soil moisture on Rhizoctonia brown patch. Phytopathology 50: 532-535.

BOULD, C., D. J. D. NICHOLAS, J. M. S. POTTER, J. A. TOLHURST, and T. WALLACE. 1950. Zinc and copper deficiency of fruit trees. Bristol Univ. (Long Ashton) Agr. Hort. Res. Sta. Ann. Rept. 1949: 45-49.

BOYNTON, D. 1947. Magnesium nutrition of apple trees. Soil Sci. 63: 53-58.

BRADFIELD, R., L. P. BATJER, and J. OSKAMP. 1934. Soils in relation to fruit growing in New York. Part IV. The significance of the oxidation-reduction potential in evaluating soils for orchard purposes. New York State Agr. Expt. Sta. (Ithaca) Bull. 592, 27 p.

BRADFORD, G. R. 1963. Lithium in California's water resources. California Agr. 17(5): 6-8.

BRAY, R. 1948. Correlation of soil tests with crop response to added fertilizers with fertilizer requirement. Chap. 2. *In* Diagnostic techniques for soils and crops, The American Potash Inst., Washington 6, D. C.

BREWER, R. F. 1964. Fluorine. Chap. 12. *In* H. D. Chapman [ed.], Plant and soil criteria for diagnosing nutrient

status. University of California, Division of Agricultural Sciences, Berkeley, Calif. (In press.)

BREWER, R. F., H. D. CHAPMAN, F. H. SUTHERLAND, and R. C. McCOLLOCH. 1959. Effect of fluorine additions to substrate on navel orange trees grown in solution cultures. Soil Sci. 87: 183-188.

BUCKMAN, H. O., and N. C. BRADY. 1960. The nature and properties of soils. The Macmillan Co., New York. 567 p.

BURD, J. S., and J. C. MARTIN. 1924. Secular and seasonal changes in the soil solution. Soil Sci. 18: 151-167.

CANNELL, G. H., F. T. BINGHAM, and M. J. GARBER. 1960. Effects of irrigation and phosphorus on vegetative growth and nutrient composition of tomato leaves. Soil Sci. 89: 53-60.

CAROLUS, R. L. 1935. The relation of potassium, calcium, and sodium to magnesium deficiency. Proc. Am. Soc. Hort. Sci. 33: 595-599.

CHAPMAN, H. D. 1934. The phosphate of southern California soils in relation to citrus fertilization. California Agr. Expt. Sta. Bull. 571, 22 p.

CHAPMAN, H. D. 1936. Effect of nitrogenous fertilizers, organic matter, sulfur, and colloidal silica on the availability of phosphorus in calcareous soils. J. Am. Soc. Agron. 28: 135-145.

CHAPMAN, H. D. 1945. Mineral nutrition of plants. Ann. Rev. Biochem. 15: 709-732.

CHAPMAN, H. D. 1951. Why so much nitrogen. California Citrograph 36(6): 223, 250-253.

CHAPMAN, H. D. 1960. Leaf and soil analysis in citrus orchards. California Agr. Exp. Sta. Manual 25, 53 p.

CHAPMAN, H. D. [ed.]. 1964. Plant and soil criteria for diagnosing nutrient status. University of California Division of Agricultural Sciences, Berkeley, Calif. (In press.)

CHAPMAN, H. D., and S. M. BROWN. 1942. Some fungal infections of citrus in relation to nutrition. Soil Sci. 54: 303-312.

CHAPMAN, H. D., and S. M. BROWN. 1943. Potash in relation to citrus nutrition. Soil Sci. 55: 87-100.

CHAPMAN, H. D., S. M. BROWN, and D. S. RAYNER. 1947. Effects of potash deficiency and excess on orange trees. Hilgardia 17: 619-650.

CHAPMAN, H. D., and G. F. LIEBIG, JR. 1940. Nitrate concentration and ion balances in relation to citrus nutrition. Hilgardia 13: 141-173.

CHAPMAN, H. D., and G. F. LIEBIG, JR. 1952. Field and laboratory studies of nitrite accumulation in soils. Soil Sci. Soc. Am. Proc. 16: 276-282.

CHAPMAN, H. D., G. F. LIEBIG, JR., and A. P. VANSELOW. 1940. Some nutritional relationships as revealed by a study of mineral deficiency and excess symptoms in citrus. Soil Sci. Soc. Am. Proc. (1939) 4: 196-200.

CHAPMAN, H. D., and D. S. RAYNER. 1951. Effect of various maintained levels of phosphate on the growth, yield, composition, and quality of Washington Navel oranges. Hilgardia 20: 325-358.

CHAPMAN, H. D., A. P. VANSELOW, and G. F. LIEBIG, JR. 1937. The production of citrus mottle-leaf in controlled nutrient cultures. J. Agr. Res. 55: 365-379.

CHUPP, C. 1928. Club root in relation to soil alkalinity. Phytopathology 18: 301-306.

COOPER, W. C., A. PEYNADO, and E. O. OLSEN. 1958. Response of grapefruit on two rootstocks to calcium additions to high-sodium, boron-contaminated and saline irrigation water. Soil Sci. 86: 180-189.

COUCH, H. B., and J. R. BLOOM. 1960. Influence of environment on diseases of turf-grasses. II. Influence of nutrition, pH, and soil moisture on Sclerotinia dollar spot. Phytopathology 50: 761-763.

CRAFTS, A. S., and R. S. ROSENFELS. 1939. Toxicity studies with arsenic in eighty California soils. Hilgardia 12: 177-200.

DAINES, R. H. 1946. Control of plant diseases by use of inorganic soil amendments. Soil Sci. 61: 55-66.

DUNNE, T. C., and L. T. JONES. 1948. Molybdenum for the prevention of "whiptail" in cauliflowers. J. Agr. W. Australia 25: 412-418.

DYE, W. B., and J. L. O'HARRA. 1959. Molybdensis. Nevada Agr. Expt. Sta. Bull. 208, p. 1-32.

EKMAN, P., N. KARLSSON, and O. SVANBERG. 1952. Investigations concerning the cobalt problem in Swedish animal husbandry. Acta Agr. Scand. 2: 103-130.

ELGABALY, M. M. 1950. Mechanism of zinc fixation by colloidal clays and related minerals. Soil Sci. 69: 167-173.

EMBLETON, T. W., J. D. KIRKPATRICK, W. W. JONES, and C. B. CREE. 1956. Influence of applications of dolomite, potash, and phosphate on yield and size of fruit and on composition of leaves of Valencia orange trees. Proc Am. Soc. Hort. Sci. 67: 183-190.

EPSTEIN, E. 1960. Calcium-lithium competition in absorption by plant roots. Nature (London) 185: 705-706.

FERGUSON, W. S., A. H. LEWIS, and S. J. WATSON. 1943. The Teart pastures of Somerset. I. The cause and cure of teartness. J. Agr. Sci. 33: 44-51.

FOOTE, F. J., and J. B. McELHINEY. 1937. Effect of available nitrogen in soil on sulfate and boron in lemon leaves. California Citrograph 22(8): 346, 347, 380.

FRIED, M., and M. PEECH. 1946. The comparative effects of lime and gypsum upon plants grown on acid soils. J. Am. Soc. Agron. 38: 614-623.

GARRETT, S. D. 1939. Soil-borne fungi and the control of root disease. Imp. Bur. Soil Sci. Tech. Commun. No. 38, 54 p.

GASIORKIEWICZ, E. C. 1960. Influence of nitrogen and potassium levels on the development of Fusarium systemic wilt of carnations. (Abstr.) Phytopathology 50: 636.

GEACH, W. L. 1936. Root rot of grey peas in Tasmania. J. Council Sci. Ind. Res. Australia 9: 77-87.

GERALDSON, C. M. 1957. Control of blossom-end rot of tomatoes. Proc. Am. Soc. Hort. Sci. 69: 309-317.

GOTO, Y., K. SHIGETA, T. ISHIHARA, and M. YAMAMOTO. 1953. Studies on the magnesium deficiency of crops (Part 2). Chemical relations in case of wheat and rye. Sci. Rept. Shiga. Agr. Coll., No. 5, p. 15-18 (Shiga Pref., Japan).

HAMENCE, J. H., and G. TAYLOR. 1948. Experiments on the toxicity of chrome-bearing fertilizer to plants including a brief survey of the literature on chromium toxicity. Fertiliser Feeding Stuffs J. 34: 449-453.

HARTWELL, B. L., and F. R. PEMBER. 1918. The presence of aluminum as a reason for the difference in the effect of so-called acid soil on barley and rye. Soil Sci. 6: 259-279.

HEWITT, E. J. 1953. Metal interrelationships in plant nutrition. I. Effects of some metal toxicities on sugar beet, tomato, oat, potato, and narrow stem kale grown in sand cultures. J. Exptl. Botany 4: 59-64.

HUNTER, J. G., and O. VERGNANO. 1952. Nickel toxicity in plants. Ann. Appl. Biol. 39: 279-284.

HUNTER, J. G., and O. VERGNANO. 1953. Trace element toxicities in oat plants. Ann. Appl. Biol. 40: 761-777.

HURD-KARRER, ANNIE M. 1933. Inhibition of selenium injury to wheat plants by sulfur. Science 78: 560.

HURD-KARRER, ANNIE M. 1934. Selenium injury to wheat plants and its inhibition by sulfur. J. Agr. Res. 49: 343-357.

JACOBSON, L., D. P. MOORE, and R. J. HANNAPEL. 1960. Role of calcium in absorption of monovalent cations. Plant Physiol. 35: 352-358.

JONES, L. H. P., and G. W. LEEPER. 1951. Available manganese oxides in neutral and alkaline soils. Plant Soil 3: 154-159.

JONES, W. W., T. W. EMBLETON, S. B. BOSWELL, M. L. STEINACKER, B. W. LEE, and E. L. BARNHART. 1963. Nitrogen control program for oranges and high sulfate and/or high boron. California Citrograph 48(4): 107, 128, 129.

JORDAN, H. V., and C. S. BARDSLEY. 1958. Responses of crops to sulfur on southeastern soils. Soil Sci. Soc. Am. Proc. 22: 254-256.

JURINAK, J. J., and D. W. THORNE. 1955. Zinc solubility under alkaline conditions in a zinc-bentonite system. Soil Sci. Soc. Am. Proc. 19: 446-448.

KELLEY, W. P. 1951. Alkali soils, their formation properties and reclamation. Am. Chem. Soc. Monogr. Ser. No. 111, 176 p. Reinhold Publishing Corp., New York.

KELLEY, W. P., and S. M. BROWN. 1928. Boron in the soils and irrigation waters of southern California and its relation to citrus and walnut cultures. Hilgardia 3(16): 445-458.

KINCAID, R. R. 1946. Soil factors affecting incidence of root knot. Soil Sci. 61: 101-109.

LAKIN, H. W. 1961. Selenium content of soils. p. 27-34. *In* Selenium in agriculture, U. S. Dept. Agr. Handbook 200.

LEATHER, J. W. 1915. Soil temperatures. India Dept. Agr. Mem., Chem. ser., IV, 2: 19-49.

LEEPER, G. W. 1947. The forms and reactions of manganese in the soil. Soil Sci. 63: 79-94.

LEWIS, J. C., and W. L. POWERS. 1941. Iodine in relation to plant nutrition. J. Agr. Res. 63: 623-637.

LIEBIG, G. F., JR., A. P. VANSELOW, and H. D. CHAPMAN. 1942. The effects of aluminum on copper toxicity as revealed by solution-culture and spectrographic studies of citrus. Soil Sci. 53: 341-351.

LILLELAND, O. 1932. Experiments in K and P deficiencies with fruit trees in the field. Proc. Am. Soc. Hort. Sci. 29: 272-276.

LOTT, W. L. 1939. The relation of hydrogen-ion concentration to the availability of zinc in soil. Soil Sci. Soc. Am. Proc. (1938) 3: 115-121.

LUCAS, R. E. 1948. Chemical and physical behavior of copper in organic soils. Soil Sci. 66: 119-129.

MacINTIRE, W. H., S. H. WINTERBURG, L. B. CLEMENTS, L. J. HARDIN, and L. S. JONES. 1951. Crop and soil reactions to applications of hydrofluoric acid. Ind. Eng. Chem. 43: 1800-1803.

MAGISTAD, O. C. 1925. The aluminum content of the soil solution and its relation to soil reaction and plant growth. Soil Sci. 20: 181-225.

MARSHALL, C. E. 1944. The exchangeable bases of two Missouri soils in relation to the composition of four pasture species. Missouri Agr. Expt. Sta. Res. Bull. 385, 60 p.

MARTIN, J. P. 1948a. Effect of fumigation, fertilization and various other soil treatments on growth of orange seedlings in old citrus soils. Soil Sci. 66: 273-288.

MARTIN, J. P. 1948b. Fungus flora of some California soils in relation to slow decline of citrus trees. Soil Sci. Soc. Am. Proc. (1947) 12: 209-214.

MARTIN, J. P. 1950. Effects of fumigation and other soil treatments in the greenhouse on the fungus population of old citrus soil. Soil Sci. 69: 107-122.

MARTIN, J. P., R. B. HARDING, and M. J. GARBER. 1961. Relation of soil properties and plant composition to growth of citrus seedlings in 100 nonfumigated and fumigated old citrus soils. Soil Sci. 91: 317-323.

MARTIN, J. P., G. K. HELMKAMP, and J. O. ERVIN. 1956. Effect of bromide from a soil fumigant and from $CaBr_2$ on growth and chemical composition of citrus plants. Soil Sci. Soc. Am. Proc. 20: 209-212.

MARTIN, J. P., L. J. KLOTZ, T. A. DeWOLFE, and J. O. ERVIN. 1956. Influence of some common soil fungi on growth of citrus seedlings. Soil Sci. 81: 259-267.

MARTIN, J. P., and P. F. PRATT. 1958. Fumigants, fungicides and the soil. Agr. Food Chem. 6: 345-348.

MARTIN, W. P., T. F. BUEHRER, and A. B. CASTER. 1943. Threshold pH value for the nitrification of ammonia in desert soils. Soil Sci. Soc. Am. Proc. (1942) 7: 223-228.

McCOLLOCH, R. C., F. T. BINGHAM, and D. G. ALDRICH. 1957. Relation of soil potassium and magnesium to magnesium nutrition of citrus. Soil Sci. Soc. Am. Proc. 21: 85-88.

McKINNEY, H. H. 1946. Soil factors in relation to incidence and symptom-expression of virus diseases. Soil Sci. 61: 93-100.

McNEW, G. L. 1953. The effects of soil fertility. p. 101-114. *In* Plant diseases. Yearbook Agr. (U. S. Dept. Agr.) 1953.

MIDGLEY, A. R., and D. E. DUNKLEE. 1940. The cause

and nature of overliming injury. Vermont Agr. Expt. Sta. Bull. 460, 22 p.

MILLIKAN, C. R. 1947. Effect of molybdenum on the severity of toxicity symptoms in flax induced by an excess of either Mn, Zn, Cu, Ni, or Co in the nutrient solution. J. Australian Inst. Agr. Sci. 13: 180-186.

MILLIKAN, C. R. 1953. Relative effects of zinc and copper deficiencies on lucerne and subterranean clover. Australian J. Biol. Sci. 6: 164-177.

MOJE, W. 1964. Organic soil toxins. Chap. 37. *In* H. D. Chapman [ed.], Plant and soil criteria for diagnosing nutrient status. University of California, Division of Agricultural Sciences, Berkeley, Calif. (In press.)

MORRIS, A. A. 1938. Some observations on the effects of boron treatment in the control of hard fruit in citrus. J. Pomol. Hort. Sci. 16: 167-181.

MULDER, E. G. 1951. The feeding of magnesium to agricultural crops, particularly in combination with fertilization with nitrogen. Landbouwk. Bur. Ned. Stikstofmeststoffen-Ind., p. 3-16. *Cited in:* Bibliog. Minor Elements, 4th ed., vol. 4, p. 78, 1955. Chilean Nitrate Educational Bur. Inc.

MULDER, E. G. 1954. Molybdenum in relation to growth of higher plants and organisms. Plant Soil 5: 368-415.

MULDER, E. G. 1956. Nitrogen-magnesium relationships in crop plants. Plant Soil 7: 341-376.

MURPHY, H. F. 1939. The role of kaolinite in phosphate fixation. Hilgardia 12(5): 342-382.

NICHOLAS, D. J. D., and E. CATLOW. 1947. Manurial experiments on vegetable crops. XII. Effects of farmyard manure and various fertilizer treatments on three varieties of potato. Bristol Univ. (Long Ashton) Agr. Hort. Res. Sta. Ann. Rept. 1947: 110-117.

OLSEN, S. R., C. V. COLE, F. S. WATANABE, and L. A. DEAN. 1954. Estimation of available phosphorus in soils by extraction with sodium bicarbonate. U. S. Dept. Agr. Circ. 939, 19 p.

OZANNE, P. G. 1958. Chloride deficiency in soils. Nature (London) 182: 1172-1173.

PEARSON, G. A., J. A. GOSS, and H. E. HAYWARD. 1957. The influence of salinity and water table on the growth and mineral composition of young grapefruit trees. Proc. Am. Soc. Hort. Sci. 69: 197-203.

PENMAN, F., and D. M. McALPINE. 1949. Boron poisoning in citrus. Victoria J. Dept. Agr. (Australia) 47: 181-189.

PIERRE, W. H., G. G. POHLMAN, and T. C. McILVAINE. 1932. Soluble aluminum studies: I. The concentration of aluminum in the displaced soil solution of naturally acid soils. Soil Sci. 34: 145-160.

PRATT, P. F., R. B. HARDING, W. W. JONES, and H. D. CHAPMAN. 1959. Chemical changes in an irrigated soil during 28 years of differential fertilization. Hilgardia 28: 381-420.

PROEBSTING, E. L. 1953. Certain factors affecting the concentration of N, P, K, Ca, and Mg in pear leaves. Proc. Am. Soc. Hort. Sci. 61: 27-30.

PURVIS, E. R., and N. K. PETERSON. 1956. Methods of soil and plant analyses for molybdenum. Soil Sci. 81: 223-228.

RAGLAND, J. L., and N. T. COLEMAN. 1959. The effect of soil solution aluminum and calcium on root growth. Soil Sci. Am. Proc. 23: 355-357.

RASMUSSEN, G. K., and P. F. SMITH. 1958. Effects of fertilizer rate, rootstock, and leaf age on the level of sulfur in citrus leaves. Proc. Am. Soc. Hort. Sci. 71: 241-247.

RAVIKOVITCH, S., and M. MARGOLIN. 1959. The effect of barium chloride and calcium sulfate in hindering selenium absorption by lucerne. Empire J. Exptl. Agr. 27: 235-240.

REEVE, E., and J. W. SHIVE. 1943. Potassium-boron relations in plants. Better Crops Plant Food 27(4): 14-16, 45-48.

REEVE, E., and J. W. SHIVE. 1944. Potassium-boron and calcium-boron relationships in plant nutrition. Soil Sci. 57: 1-14.

REITEMEIER, R. F. 1951. Soil potassium. Advan. Agron.

3: 113-164.

REITEMEIER, R. F., and L. A. RICHARDS. 1944. Reliability of the pressure-membrane method for extraction of soil solution. Soil Sci. 57: 119-135.

REUTHER, W. 1957. Copper and soil fertility. *In* Soil, Yearbook Agr. (U. S. Dept. Agr.) 1957: 128-135.

REUTHER, W., and P. F. SMITH. 1953. Effects of high copper content of sandy soil on growth of citrus seedlings. Soil Sci. 75: 219-224.

REUTHER, W., and P. F. SMITH. 1954. Toxic effects of accumulated copper in Florida soils. Soil Sci. Soc. Florida Proc. 14: 17-23.

ROBINSON, G. W. 1932. Soils, their origin, constitution and classification. Thomas Murby & Co., London. 390 p.

ROBINSON, W. O., G. EDGINGTON, and H. G. BYERS. 1935. Chemical studies of infertile soils derived from rocks high in magnesium and generally high in chromium and nickel. U. S. Dept. Agr. Tech. Bull. 471, 29 p.

SCHARRER, K., and W. SCHROPP. 1935. The action of chromic and chromate ions upon cultivated plants. Z. Pflanzenernährung Düng. Bodenk. 37:137-149.

SCHARRER, K., and W. SCHROPP. 1936. The effect of lead upon plant growth. Z. Pflanzenernährung Düng. Bodenk. 43: 34-43.

SCHMEHL, W. R., M. PEECH, and R. BRADFIELD. 1950. Causes of poor growth of plants on acid soils and beneficial effects of liming: I. Evaluation of factors responsible for acid-soil injury. Soil Sci. 70: 393-410.

SHAW, E., and L. A. DEAN. 1952. Use of dithizone as an extractant to estimate the zinc nutrient status of soils. Soil Sci. 73: 341-347.

SHERMAN, G. D., and G. K. FUJIMOTO. 1947. The effect of the use of lime, soil fumigants, and mulch on the solubility of manganese in Hawaiian soils. Soil Sci. Soc. Am. Proc. (1946) 11: 206-210.

SIDERIS, C. P., and B. H. KRAUSS. 1934. The effect of sulfur and phosphorus on the availability of iron to pineapple and maize plants. Soil Sci. 37: 85-97.

SMITH, P. F., W. REUTHER, and A. W. SPECHT. 1952. Seasonal changes in Valencia orange trees. II. Changes in microelements, sodium, and carbohydrates in leaves. Proc. Am Soc. Hort. Sci. 59: 31-35.

SOANE, B. D., and D. H. SAUNDER. 1959. Nickel and chromium toxicity of serpentine soils in Southern Rhodesia. Soil Sci. 88: 322-330.

SPENCER, E. L. 1935a. Effect of nitrogen supply on host susceptibility to virus infection. Phytopathology 25: 178-191.

SPENCER, E. L. 1935b. Influence of phosphorus and potassium supply on host susceptibility to yellow tobacco mosaic infection. Phytopathology 25: 493-502.

STANFORD, G., and J. HANWAY. 1955. Predicting nitrogen fertilizer needs for Iowa soils. II. A simplified technique for determining relative nitrate production in soils. Soil Sci. Soc. Am. Proc. 19: 74-77.

STANFORD, G., J. B. KELLY, and W. H. PIERRE. 1942. Cation balance in corn grown on high-lime soils in relation to potassium deficiency. Soil Sci. Soc. Am. Proc. (1941) 6: 335-341.

STELMACH, Z. 1958. Bromine retention in some soils and uptake of bromine by plants after soil fumigation. Soil Sci. 88: 61-66.

STEWART, I., and C. D. LEONARD. 1954. Chelates in the soil. Soil Sci. Soc. Florida Proc. 14: 47-52.

STIER, H. L. 1941. Are some of our cantaloupe troubles caused by nutrient deficiencies rather than by diseases. Trans. Peninsula Hort. Soc. *In* Bull. State Board Agr. Delaware 31(4): 88-90.

STOUT, P. R., W. R. MEAGHER, G. A. PEARSON, and C. M. JOHNSON. 1951. Molybdenum nutrition of crop plants: I. Plant Soil 3: 51-87.

STOVER, R. H. 1959. Growth and survival of root-disease fungi in soil. p. 339-355. *In* C. S. Holton et al., Plant pathology, problems and progress 1908-1958, University of Wisconsin Press, Madison, Wisc.

STRAUSS, J. L., and A. L. GRIZZARD. 1948. The effect of

calcium, magnesium, and potassium on peanut yields. Soil Sci. Soc. Am. Proc. (1947) 12: 348-352.

SWAINE, D. J. 1955. The trace-element content of soils. Commonwealth Bur. Soil Sci. (Gt. Brit.) Tech. Commun. 48, 157 p.

SWANSON, C. O., P. L. GAINEY, and W. L. LATSHAW. 1924. The calcium content of soil in relation to absolute reaction. Soil Sci. 17: 181-191.

THAUNG, M. M., and J. C. WALKER. 1957. Studies on bacterial blight of lima bean. Phytopathology 47: 413-417.

THOMPSON, A. H., and L. P. BATJER. 1950. Effect of various soil treatments for correcting arsenic injury of peach trees. Soil Sci. 69: 281-290.

TRELEASE, S. F., and O. A. BEATH. 1949. Selenium. Published by the authors, New York. 292 p.

TYLER, K. B., and F. E. BROADBENT. 1960. Nitrite transformation in California soils. Soil Sci. Soc. Am. Proc. 24: 279-282.

VANDECAVEYE, S. C., G. M. HORNER, and C. M. KEATON. 1936. Unproductiveness of certain orchard soils as related to lead arsenate spray accumulations. Soil Sci. 42: 203-215.

VINCENT, C. L. 1939. Problems in vegetables and small fruit production on toxic orchard soils of central Washington. Proc. Am. Soc. Hort. Sci. 37: 680-684.

WADE, G. C. 1955. *Aphanomyces* root rot of peas—the effect of a potassium fertilizer on the severity of the disease in a potassium deficient soil. J. Australian Inst. Agr. Sci. 21: 260-263.

WADLEIGH, C. H., and J. W. BROWN. 1952. The chemical status of bean plants afflicted with bicarbonate-induced chlorosis. Botan. Gaz. 113: 373-392.

WALKER, J. C. 1946. Soil management and plant nutrition in relation to disease development. Soil Sci. 61: 47-54.

WALLIHAN, E. F., M. J. GARBER, R. G. SHARPLESS, and WILMA PRINTY. 1961. Effect of soil oxygen deficit on iron nutrition of orange seedlings. Plant Physiol. 36: 425-428.

WALSH, T., and G. A. FLEMING. 1952. Selenium levels in rocks, soils, and herbage from a high selenium locality in Ireland. Trans. Intern. Soc. Soil Sci. Comm. II and IV. 1952, 2: 178-183.

WELLS, N. 1956. Soil studies using sweet vernal to assess element availability: II. New Zealand J. Sci. Tech. 37B: 482-502.

WEST, E. S. 1938. Zinc-cured mottle leaf in citrus induced by excess phosphate. J. Council Sci. Ind. Res. (Australia) 11: 182-184.

WILLIS, L. G., J. R. PILAND, and R. L. GRAY. 1934. The influence of magnesium deficiency on phosphate absorption by soybean. J. Am. Soc. Agron. 26: 419-422.

WINGARD, S. A. 1941. The nature of disease resistance in plants. Botan. Rev. 7:59-109.

WRIGHT, J. R., and K. LAWTON. 1954. Cobalt investigations on some Nova Scotia soils. Soil Sci. 77: 95-105.

WYBENGA, J. M. 1957. [A contribution to the knowledge of the importance of sodium for plant life.] Diss. Wageningen. (Original not seen; cited by W. Baumeister, Das Natrium als Pflanzennährstoff, Gustav Fischer Verlag, Stuttgart, Germany, 1960.)

YORK, E. T., JR., R. BRADFIELD, and M. PEECH. 1953a. Calcium-potassium interactions in soils and plants: I. Lime-induced potassium fixation in Mardin silt loam. Soil Sci. 76: 379-387.

YORK, E. T., JR., R. BRADFIELD, and M. PEECH. 1953b. Calcium-potassium interactions in soils and plants: II. Reciprocal relationship between calcium and potassium in plants. Soil Sci. 76: 481-491.

► DISCUSSION OF H. D. CHAPMAN PAPER

H. Katznelson:

So often in rhizosphere studies we find it hard to decide whether the effects obtained from soil treatment are due to the influence of treatment on the rhizosphere microflora itself or on the plant or on both. Consequently, is it not possible that in your work low calcium and poor aeration stimulated, or were favourable for, the root-rotting organisms that developed under these conditions?

Perhaps the problem can be at least partially resolved by conducting such experiments under aseptic conditions, if this can be done with citrus plants.

H. D. Chapman:

Yes, it is difficult to decide whether the root rotting under low calcium and poor aeration is due primarily to a stimulation of root-rotting organisms, reduced resistance of the plant, or a combination of the two. As you suggest, one way to resolve this and like questions is to conduct experiments under aseptic conditions. The indications from this experiment are that neither low calcium nor poor aeration by themselves were causal factors, but a combination of the two. My guess is that this situation decreased root resistance and opened the way to invasion by the organisms present.

D. F. Bateman:

When divalent ions are used to replace exchangeable ions in tissues of excised 1-week old bean hypocotyl, these tissues become more resistant to *Rhizoctonia* attack. Calcium is more effective than magnesium in

this respect; when sodium or potassium is used, susceptibility is increased. Hypocotyls were soaked for 3 hr in aqueous solutions of the chlorides of the indicated elements, then $\frac{1}{2}$ hr in water prior to inoculation. The effect probably involves the activity of the pectic enzyme of the fungus.

R. G. McMinn:

The influence of aeration and calcium level on the growth and degeneration of citrus roots shown by Dr. Chapman and the reduced susceptibility of bean hypocotyls to *Rhizoctonia* in the presence of increased calcium noted by Dr. Bateman seem to parallel some of the differences in occurrence of pole blight of western white pine in British Columbia, Canada. This decline disease, one characteristic of which is degeneration of root systems, is found more commonly on well podzolized soils than on weakly podzolized soils. A reduction in the amount of exchangeable calcium is normally associated with degree of podzolization. The relative importance of pathogens versus root growth per se in the development of this disease, however, has not been established.

R. G. Grogan:

Would you comment on biuret toxicity in relation to your previous discussion of nitrite toxicity?

H. D. Chapman:

Citrus is quite sensitive to biuret. We have noted this where urea containing more than 0.5% biuret is used as a foliar spray or in soil applications. Unfortunately, we were not conscious of the biuret question at the time we carried out our nitrite studies, but because of its known toxicity this compound could conceivably have had an adverse effect on nitrate-producing organisms and hence be one of the factors at work in the much greater nitrite buildup from the use of urea than from equivalent amounts of other ammonium-carrying or -producing compounds.

H. Burström:

How do you distinguish an effect of overmoistening of soil from oxygen deficiency?

H. D. Chapman:

I have usually equated overmoistening of the soil with oxygen deficiency and the chain of chemical reactions and biological activities which stem from lack of oxygen. The fact that we can grow citrus trees and, of course, most other plants in water cultures provided there is good aeration indicates that oxygen concentration in the soil solution is a critical factor. When, through accident or intent, the air supply is cut off from our citrus water cultures for a period of a day or two, root rotting sets in.

A. W. Dimock:

1. What organisms were associated with the rotted roots in the aeration tanks as illustrated by the slides?

2. Is it likely, after excessive irrigation under high temperatures, that oxygen may be sufficiently deficient to result in anaerobic respiration and autolytic breakdown of root hairs and epidermal cells, which might in turn permit invasion by weak pathogens?

H. D. Chapman:

1. Dr. Martin has tested our water cultures repeatedly and the only pathogen isolated has been *Fusarium solani.*

2. Yes, I think it is quite likely that under high-soil-temperature conditions oxygen deficiency can quickly occur under excessive irrigation, with resulting anaerobic respiration and autolytic breakdown of root hairs and epidermal cells, thus permitting invasion by weak pathogens.

M. Alexander:

Because L. Sequeira has recently reported upon the relation of nitrite toxicity during nitrification to a type of biological control of *Fusarium*, I believe it is necessary to point out that there is no threshold pH for nitrification such as that reported by Martin, Buehrer, and Caster at pH 7.7, rather there is a direct effect of soil pH on the ammonium-ammonia equilibrium, the free ammonia apparently acting as the inhibitor of *Nitrobacter* spp. The apparent "threshold" is concerned only with a shift in the chemical equilibrium to favor the inhibition of the nitrite oxidizers.

H. D. Chapman:

I agree that the ammonium-ammonia equilibrium is probably the important factor in nitrite accumulation.

W. C. Snyder:

Studies on the nutrition of plants using nutrient-culture techniques often seem to ignore the flora and fauna occurring in the culture solution. In view of the knowledge that the microorganisms on the surfaces of roots influence substances moving in and out of roots, and that their own metabolites may also enter roots, is it not possible that the microorganisms on roots in routine nutrient-culture tests have an important impact on the physiology of the plant, and therefore must be taken into account in the interpretation of nutrition studies?

H. D. Chapman:

I have no doubt that the flora and fauna occurring in water cultures, and particularly the organisms in the rhizosphere, have some influence on the physiology of the plant. We have found it difficult to grow citrus trees over long periods in water cultures unless the pH is maintained in the vicinity of pH 4. At pH 5 and higher, we have commonly gotten into trouble with *Phytophthora* spp., *Thielaviopsis basicola,* and other organisms. This is not to say, of course, that there are not plenty of organisms at pH 4. With suitable nutrition at this pH, however, the roots always look clean and bright, though they become somewhat suberized and brownish with age. We have been inclined, however, to ignore the possible role of organisms on metabolism and tree physiology so far as the principal items which we are trying to measure are concerned; namely, the effects of nutrient deficiencies and excesses on growth, visual symptoms, yield, fruit quality, and leaf analysis. We have found over the years that symptoms of deficiencies and excesses, as produced under our water-culture conditions, are identical with those seen in the field. Fruit-quality effects are the same and leaf-analysis values arrived at from our water-culture studies agree very well with those obtained under field conditions. Trees in our cultures also behave, in a macro way at least, the same as trees in soil; that is to say, they bloom at the same period; there is the same number of growth flushes; appearance, leaf sizes, density of foliage, amount of bloom, amount of fruit set, insect infestation, etc., all appear to be the same as with comparable trees on the same root stock growing in the same climatic environment. In the early years, trees in water cultures grow somewhat faster than when planted in soil. However, after about 5 years, the water-culture trees grow somewhat slower than in the field, though there are no specific top symptoms. There is a tendency for the root system in water cultures to become very dense in the course of time, and it is my belief that under the aeration conditions we have used, oxygen deficiency develops in the center of the root mass and this tends to slow down growth. Our usual practice is to make up new culture solutions at monthly intervals, but a few years ago we ran one experiment with a number of 14-year-old trees where we compared concentrations by solution analysis and appropriate adjustments. At the end of 3 years, we noted no difference between the trees which had been managed in the latter manner, as against those where the nutrient solution was made up fresh every month. In this experiment, the pH was maintained around 4. What we were trying to find out here was whether the old roots would slough off and produce toxins which were detrimental to the tree. I recognize that this single experiment, and as well the aforementioned observations, do not completely answer your question; nonetheless, we have developed a good deal of confidence in the kinds of conclusions which we attempt to draw from our water-culture experiments.

Z. A. Patrick:

1. You mention the citrus-replant problem. Would you or Dr. Martin give us some idea as to what you think is the cause of this condition?

2. Do you believe toxins are involved?

3. You mention that microorganisms are involved. What is their mode of action? Do they nibble at the roots?

J. P. Martin:

1. Our studies indicate that the development of feeder-root parasites in the soil is the most important cause of the citrus replant problem. These conclusions are based on the following observations: (*a*) reduced growth of replants is always associated with feeder-root decay; (*b*) inoculation of growth media, including soil, with such organisms as *Phytophthora* spp., *Thielaviopsis basicola, Tylenchulus semipenetrans, Fusarium solani,* or others isolated from citrus roots, has under one or more conditions reduced growth of citrus plants; (*c*) proper soil fumigation with a variety of chemicals may completely overcome the reduced growth condition of old citrus soils; (*d*) additions of citrus roots to soils does not reduce growth of citrus plants; (*e*) extracted toxic coumarin derivatives have reduced growth of citrus seedlings in sand but not in soil. (This latter work was carried out by Dr. William Moje of the Riverside station.)

Studies now in progress are designed to determine the influence of soil properties on the magnitude of the injury caused by the root parasites.

2 and 3. Several different types of organisms may attack citrus feeder roots. We in the Soils Department have not attempted to determine the mechanisms involved. Undoubtedly, destruction of a considerable percentage of the root surfaces by "nibbling" could be one factor. It is also highly probable that part of the feeding mechanisms may involve a "toxic" compound excreted by the organisms.

A study was undertaken to determine the influence of wide variations in soil exchangeable Ca, Mg, K, Na, and H-Al ratios on the kinds of fungi developing during decomposition of plant residues in soil. The study indicated that the type of residue applied exerted a greater effect on the fungus species becoming dominant and in the succession of dominant species than did the exchangeable cation ratios. High soil acidity and high exchangeable K or Na, however, did influence the kinds of fungi developing.

G. A. Zentmyer:

In studies of toxicity of nitrite to pathogen and host, we observed that low levels of nitrite (about 2 ppm) were more toxic to *Phytophthora cinnamomi* than to avocado roots. Development of root rot was greatly reduced by low levels of nitrite (2 ppm) in nutrient-solution tests. Nitrite toxicity to zoospores was increased as pH decreased. This could be considered as a form of biologic control.

G. C. Papavizas:

1. Do you have any evidence whether nitrites may accumulate in the rhizosphere of plants?

2. Is there any work done so far to distinguish between pH in the rhizosphere and that of soil away from the rhizosphere?

H. D. Chapman:

I cannot answer either of these questions, but I am under the impression that work has been carried out to determine pH in the rhizosphere.

A. D. Rovira:

The work of Dr. G. D. Bowen and myself on the inhibition of roots by nonpathogenic soil organisms has shown that inhibition of root growth is greatest when plants grow under adverse conditions of light, temperature, and nutrition.

H. D. Chapman:

Thanks for this observation. Our field observations over the years in citrus orchards, trying to account for the disappearance of feeder roots of citrus trees, have led many of us to believe that anything which tends to devitalize the tops of trees, such as climatic extremes, insect infestation, insecticidal damage, and nutrient deficiencies and excesses, will lower the vitality of citrus roots and thus open them to destructive influences by both pathogenic and nonpathogenic soil organisms. The difficulties of growing bearing citrus plants under sterile conditions have made it impossible to study this question in a more precise manner.

PART IV

◄

THE PLANT ROOT AND THE RHIZOSPHERE

The Anatomy of Plant Roots

FLORA MURRAY SCOTT—*Department of Botany, University of California, Los Angeles.*

The structure of the root, as described in current textbooks, is well known. On germination of the seed, the primary root appears with root cap, meristem, region of elongation, and root-hair zone. During later growth, secondary thickening may or may not take place. Lateral roots originate in the pericycle. The root system of the feeder roots of mature plants resembles that of the seedling. Adventitious roots which arise from stem, leaf, or cuttings are similar in structure.

Organisms which invade the roots from the soil enter in general through the younger roots, the primary system of the seedling, or the feeder roots of the full-grown plant. After entry their growth depends on their capacity to obtain the necessary food from the tissues invaded. In addition to the principal component, cellulose, the cell wall in the various tissues may contain mucilage, pectic substances or noncellulosic polysaccharides, lignin, cutin, and suberin, and the precursors of these compounds. All cells are interconnected at least in their early growth, and later in many tissues, by plasmodesmata. The invading organisms must therefore have the enzyme systems necessary for the breakdown of the compounds present in the wall, or the ability to obtain their food by diffusion. Since the pH of tissues may range from 3 to 8, the organism can select its path of growth (Small, 1929).

Since this symposium is concerned with pathogen invasion, I have limited this survey to the anatomy of the root-hair zone of soil-grown roots. I have emphasized certain features of root structure which appear to be significant, and which, so far as I know, are not discussed at length, if at all, in current textbooks.

EXTENT OF ROOT SYSTEMS.—The extent of the root systems of species which have been systematically measured has been discussed by Miller (1938). The total length may be measured in miles; the surface area of the root system in ryegrass, with its estimated 4 billion root hairs, measures 130 times that of the tops (Dittmer, 1937). The area and depth of soil penetrated by roots, important in agriculture, ecology, and soil conservation, has been intensively investigated (Cannon, 1911; Muller, 1946).

In young garden-grown seedlings of common dicotyledons such as castor bean (*Ricinus communis*), mustard (*Brassica nigra*), purslane (*Portulaca oleracea*), radish (*Raphanus sativus*), and squash (*Cucurbita pepo*), the main root system consists of taproot and numerous branching laterals, all of which develop secondary thickening. In these species, however, in addition, there is a wealth of fine filamentous roots about 1 mm in diameter, the longest of which are equal in length to the taproot and the longest laterals. These thicken but slightly and are covered throughout their length with living nucleated root hairs. They arise from the taproot or laterals, and resemble in general the roots described in the strawberry as transitory (Nelson and Wilhelm, 1937). When moribund, they are discolored, brownish, and shrunken. No abscission zone has been observed, but the epidermal and cortical cells around the emergent roots are effectively suberized. When the roots eventually decay and disappear, root scars remain evident on the surface of taproots and laterals until sloughed off during secondary thickening (Figs. 1, 2. 3).

In full-grown flowering and fruiting plants of these species, the roots penetrate deeply into the soil and are widespread. All terminate in a feeder system similar to that of the seedling, with the same wealth of root-hair-coated filamentous roots.

EPIDERMIS.—The surface of soil-grown roots is covered with an adherent layer of soil particles, in which fungal hyphae and bacteria are visible microscopically. An electron micrograph of a soil-grown mustard root with bacteria in situ is shown in the frontispiece. Epidermal cells, in general tabular in form, are piliferous or nonpiliferous (Cormack, 1962). The epidermal surface is covered with a film of mucilage, beneath which lies a cuticle. The cell wall consists of cellulose and pectic substances or noncellulosic polysaccharides. Epidermal protoplasts are connected through radial walls and through pits in the inner tagential walls to the cortical cells below. Plasmodesmata penetrate the outer tangential wall and appear to be anchored in the cuticle (Scott, Hamner, et al., 1958).

The coating of mucilage is generally thin, but in certain species it is conspicuous and distinctive (Leiser, 1959). In azalea and other members of the Ericaceae the root cap consists of but few cells and is sheathed in a mucilaginous thimble, which may extend into the region of elongation. In the smoke tree, a characteristic xerophyte of the southwestern desert washes, the long taproot and the laterals are coated with a thick layer of mucilage, which contracts and hardens as the sandy

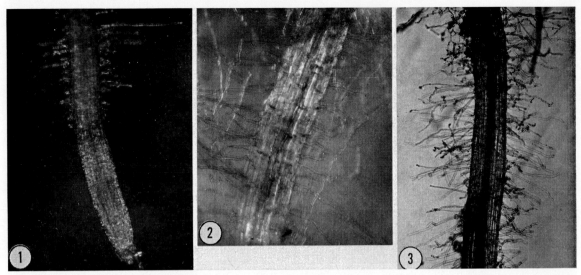

Figs. 1-3. Mustard, filamentous root, freshly dug from soil and floated in water; light micrographs. **Fig. 1.** Root tip, region of elongation and root-hair zone. Light is reflected from intercellular spaces in the cortex and from cell walls of the root hairs; semidark field. **Fig. 2.** Segment shows origin of root hairs in piliferous cells. Light is reflected from intercellular spaces in the cortex; semidark field. **Fig. 3.** Segment shows abundance and length of root hairs; ectotrophic hyphae visible.

soil dries out. But in the deeper sand, where some trace of hygroscopic water remains, the youngest zone of the taproot is still enclosed in a cylinder of mucilage about 2 mm thick (Reynolds, 1943).

The epidermis of the filamentous roots is similar to that of the main roots. Filamentous roots are covered throughout their length with living root hairs and therefore provide excellent material for study. Root hairs range in length from papillae to 2,000 µ.

Certain details of structure in epidermal cells are evident under the electron microscope. The microfibrillar pattern of the outer wall of the young epidermal cell, including the root hair, is a reticulum. The wall of the cell body is thickened by the deposition of successive lamellae, generally also reticulate. In contrast, in the root-hair zone the later fibrils are as a rule parallel and slightly helical in orientation (Dawes and Bowler, 1959). Interfibrillar spaces are filled with amorphous material, noncellulosic polysaccharides. Fragments of cuticle, isolated during ultrasonic treatment, resemble in ultraporous texture the cutin and suberin previously observed (Scott, Hamner, et al., 1958; Scott, Bystrom, and Bowler, 1962). Plasmodesmata, present in the outer wall, occur also in the root hairs. They appear as minute points on the hair surface. When removed during the preparation of material, solitary pores, or pits (groups of pores as defined in previous papers) remain. Plasmodesmata occur near the root-hair tip and at any point between tip and root-hair base (Scott, Bystrom, and Bowler, 1963). The epidermis of the monocotyledons onion (*Allium cepa*) and wheat (*Triticum aestivum*) is similar to that of the dicotyledons examined (Figs. 4, 5, 6).

CORTEX.—In the young emerging main root, the cortical cells are polyhedral and approximately isodiametric. During growth, the cells become cylindrical (Scott, Hamner, et al., 1956). A system of intercellular spaces develops, lined throughout with a lipid material termed here and in previous papers, suberin. These spaces are interconnected and form a reticulate continuum. The pits on the cylindrical walls are aligned in 5 or 6 vertical rows, but they remain randomly arranged over the entire area of the circular end wall (Scott, 1950; Scott and Lewis, 1954).

Fungal hyphae that invade the cortex and follow the intercellular space network presumably obtain the necessary food by diffusion. Haustorial species must penetrate through a lipid-coated wall into the living protoplast.

In filamentous roots, the cortex is comparatively narrow, but the intercellular spaces, suberin-lined, are

——————→

Figs. 4-12. Filamentous roots: electron micrographs of parts of cell walls of epidermis, cortex, endodermis, and xylem. **Fig. 4.** Mustard: epidermis, surface remains of mucilage and ultraporous cuticle on microfibrillar outer wall (× 13,300). **Fig. 5.** Wheat: epidermal outer and radial cell faces; microfibrillar pattern dominantly helical; hyphal perforation in central face (× 6,600). **Fig. 6.** Wheat: epidermis, root-hair tip with numerous plasmodesmata and pits:—arrows (× 6,600). **Fig. 7.** Wheat: cortical wall partially cleared, with scattered pits and plasmodesmata; overlap is part of suberin lining of intercellular space (arrow) (× 6,600). **Fig. 8.** Squash: endodermal cell flattened, radial wall with heavy Casparian strip (*CS*), tangential walls with pits (× 6,600). **Fig. 9.** Wheat: endodermal radial wall with part of Casparian strip (*CS*); marginal pits adjacent to tangential wall presumably related to characteristic wrinkling of isolated endodermal walls (× 5,300). **Fig. 10.** Radish: Casparian strip with central pit (× 6,600). **Fig. 11.** Wheat: endodermal tangential wall with scattered pits and plasmodesmata (× 6,600). **Fig. 12.** Radish: xylem, isolated spiral element, microfibrillar wall not yet completely suberized (× 3,300).

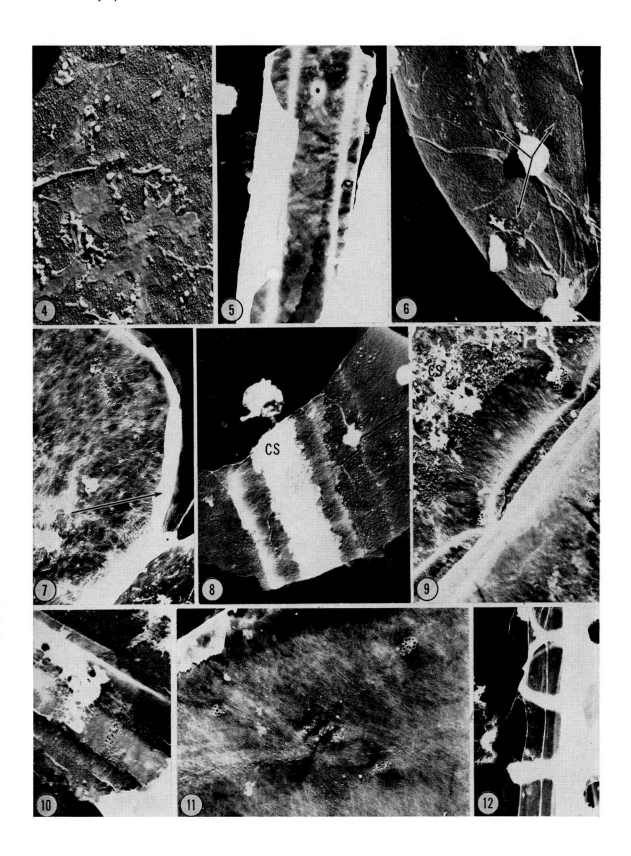

large and conspicuous and glisten brilliantly when fresh roots are immersed in water (Fig. 7).

ENDODERMIS.—In classic studies of the structure of the endodermis in relation to function, Priestley discussed a mechanism for the control of the entrance of solutes into the stele (Priestley and North, 1922). The recent intensive work of Van Fleet (1961) on the microchemistry of the endodermal region during differentiation demonstrates cytological variations which presumably affect, sooner or later, the paths of invading organisms. The endodermis consists of brick-shaped cells distinguished by the suberized and lignified Casparian strip. Passage cells occur in certain species. Pits are present on all cell faces. Minute intercellular spaces are observed at cell corners both inside and outside the endodermal cylinder, and the initiation of suberin in the Casparian strip may therefore be similar to the deposition of suberin lining the intercellular spaces.

The microfibrillar pattern of the young endodermal wall is a reticulum. During thickening, successive cellulose lamellae are deposited. The Casparian strip is defined early by deposition of amorphous material which masks the microfibrillar pattern. This masking begins along the margin of the Casparian strip, near the intercellular spaces. After differentiation, the inner surface of the strip resembles in texture the inner lining of xylem vessels, osmiophilic membrane, warty layer, or suberized lining (Wardrop, 1957; Liese, 1957; Scott, Sjaholm, and Bowler, 1960). The masking of pits in the Casparian strip explains the well-known pattern of plasmolysis in the endodermis. The protoplast remains firmly attached by plasmodesmata in the radial wall, while the plasmodesmata contract away from the outer and inner periclinal walls. The plasmodesmata within and at the limits of the Casparian strip presumably become firmly embedded in the lignin-suberin complex of this thickened region of the wall (Figs. 8, 9, 10, 11).

PERICYCLE.—The pericycle is the point of origin of branch roots. The details of the branching of filamentous roots has not been worked out in detail in any of the species observed at the present time.

STELE.—In the main and the filamentous roots, the xylem differentiates into annular and spiral elements and, later, into reticulate and pitted cells. In the transparent filamentous roots two or three spiral elements are visible near the root tip. Slight pressure on the older regions of these roots flattens the stele and reveals from six to eight or more reticulate and pitted

vessel elements. Xylem elements are in general long and slender. They range in length from $50\,\mu$ to $960\,\mu$, and from $4\,\mu$ to $25\,\mu$ in diameter. Vessel differentiation resembles that of *Ricinus* (Scott, Sjaholm, and Bowler, 1960). All living cells are interconnected by plasmodesmata (Scott, 1949). The walls of the xylem elements consist initially of cellulose. Wall thickening and lignification occur in various patterns. By the time of the death of the protoplast, the end walls of the individual elements of the vessel have disappeared, and the lengthy cylinder is lined with suberin and impregnated at least partially with the same material (Figs. 12, 13-19).

In the main roots, absorption is limited to the so-called primary region of the root, since during secondary thickening, the epidermis with its root hairs is sloughed off with the outer cortex. In contrast, the surface of the barely thickened filamentous roots remains covered with living nucleated root hairs, so that absorption may continue throughout their entire length, be it 20 cm or more. In the absorptive region of the root, the protoplasts of the xylem are in general nucleated and alive. This fact may be observed in fresh material, slender transparent filamentous roots, or main roots sectioned longitudinally and stained in neutral red or other aqueous stain (Figs. 20, 21). Ultrasonic treatment is effective in isolating individual elements complete with their protoplasts. Treatment of fresh roots with I_2-KI-H_2SO_4 indicates the degree of suberization of the walls in spiral and other vessels. While the wall consists only of cellulose or when the degree of lignification and suberization is still slight, the protoplasts of the elements are nucleated and intact.

It is therefore evident that, when solutes enter the root through the root-hair zone, they pass from living cells, endodermal, pericyclic, or parenchymatous, directly into xylem elements that still contain their living nucleated protoplasts. When the sap eventually reaches a moribund protoplast at a higher level in the older root, it flows upward as a unit of the transpiration stream in a suberized vessel devoid of protoplasmic content.

The differentiation of the phloem in the stele follows the typical pattern of sieve tubes and companion cells. The nacré consistency of the walls is evident in fresh material.

Young soil-grown roots of the gymnosperms *Pinus aristata* and *P. monticola* were examined under the light microscope. The root hairs, from papillae a few microns in length to those full grown, contain normal living protoplasm and nuclei. The root-hair walls are thicker than those of angiosperms of comparable age previously

$\longrightarrow$

Figs. 13-19. Xylem: various stages of cell-wall development. Electronmicrographs. **Fig. 13.** Radish: spiral element, "transection," part of internal suberized lining attached to spiral thickening ($\times$ 8,000). **Fig. 14.** Mustard: pitted element, young microfibrillar pattern dominantly reticular; pitted thickening outlined by beginnings of parallel microfibrillar orientation; pits and plasmodesmata evident in unthickened areas ($\times$ 9,600). **Fig. 15.** Mustard: pitted element during lignification; microfibrillar pattern and majority of pits masked by protoplasmic remain ($\times$ 5,000). **Fig. 16.** Mustard: pitted element, older, thickening cleared from outer wall except for small marginal overlap (O); microfibrillar inner wall reticular, partially impregnated; occasional pits and plasmodesmata still evident ($\times$ 8,000). **Fig. 17.** Mustard: pitted differentiating wall after removal of thickening; pits visible in unthickened areas ($\times$ 12,000). **Fig. 18.** Mustard: pitted element, older; impregnation almost completely masks microfibrillar pattern in outer wall; a few pits visible in end wall; microfibrillar pattern of inner wall reticular with pits and plasmodesmata ($\times$ 5,000). **Fig. 19.** Mustard: pitted element (Fig. 18) showing thickening in relation to microfibrillar pattern; pits and plasmodesmata evident; microfibrillar structure of outer wall still visible at upper left ($\times$ 16,000).

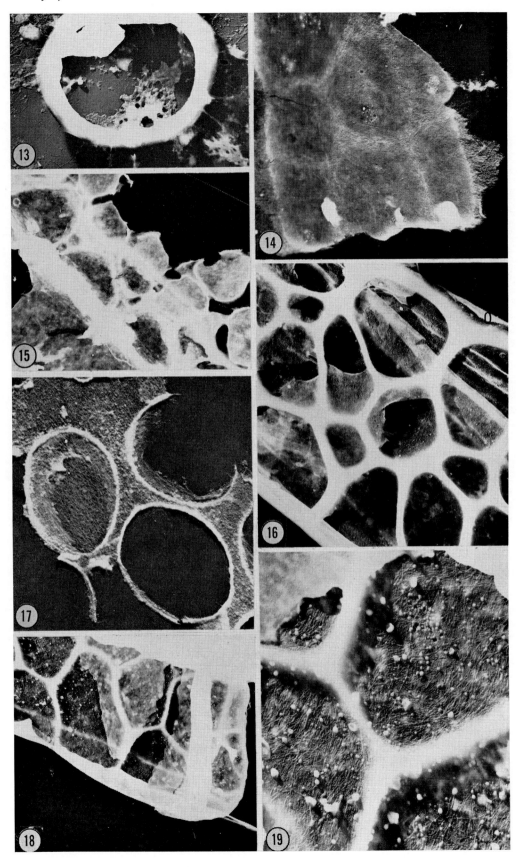

Figs. 20, 21. Radish, filamentous-root-hair zone, fresh material, slightly crushed and stained with neutral red, showing living protoplasts in xylem elements, the actual diameter of which ranges from 4 to 6 μ. The living root hairs on the epidermis are not in focus. (Fig. 20 from **F. M. Scott**. Science 199: 1009-1010. 1963. Copyright 1963 by the American Association for the Advancement of Science.)

examined. The roots were treated with I_2KI-H_2SO_4, a standard microchemical test for cellulose, and were observed during the entire test. The root-hair walls of both species of *Pinus* consist of a very fine pellicle of what appears to be mucilage, a clearly defined cuticle, and the structural wall of cellulose and noncellulosic polysaccharides. By the time the cellulose of the body of the epidermal cells and of the underlying cortical cells has disintegrated, the cellulose of the root-hair walls has also disappeared. The outline of the cuticle remains intact, in situ, attached to the cutinized outer epidermal wall. During the test, numerous fine protoplasmic strands appear anchored in the cellulose of the hair wall. It is expected that, under the electron microscope, the size and distribution of pits, if present as in the angiosperms, will be determined.

DISCUSSION AND SUMMARY.—The present survey deals with the structure of the root-hair zone of soil-grown roots in certain seedlings and of the feeder roots of the same flowering and fruiting plants.

The root-hair zone of the main root system of typical dicotyledons is limited in length and is sloughed off during secondary thickening. In the species examined the absorptive zone is supplemented by a wealth of filamentous roots, equal in length to the taproot and the longest secondaries. The pattern of the feeder roots in mature plants is similar to that of the seedling roots. The filamentous roots, 15 cm or more in length, are thickly covered from tip to origin with living nucleated root hairs.

The epidermis of the root in piliferous and nonpiliferous cells is covered with a film of mucilage and a layer of cutin, beneath which lies the cellulose-pectic framework of the cell wall. Pits and plasmodesmata occur in the outer wall and also in the wall of the root hairs. The plasmodesmata presumably transport the precursors of mucilage and cutin for the construction of the wall, and also function in the release of exudates into the soil in certain species. The "semipermeable membrane" responsible for the absorption of the necessary solutes is therefore a many-layered wall complex penetrated by living plasmodesmata.

One of the first visible reactions of a living tissue to

wounding is suberization (Priestley and Woffenden, 1922). During the growth of polyhedral isodiametric cells, plasmodesmata are broken and intercellular spaces appear. Intercellular spaces in the cortex and other tissues are lined with a lipid material (suberin). This suberin deposit may, therefore, be considered to be a normal reaction of the protoplasts to wounding.

Fungi which enter the root-hair zone may run through intercellular spaces and obtain food by diffusion through suberin-coated walls. If and when they enter living protoplasts, they necessarily possess enzyme systems capable of breaking through pitted walls covered or impregnated with one or more of the following substances: mucilage, cutin, suberin, cellulose, noncellulosic polysaccharides, and lignin.

The general opinion that xylem elements are devoid of contents in the root-hair zone is probably based on the study of sections about $10\,\mu$ thick, with well-stained cell walls, but with cells devoid of protoplasm and ergastic substances. Such sections are considered photogenic from the textbook standpoint. Since xylem elements in this region may measure $900\,\mu$ or more in length, the chances of observing a nucleus or traces of vacuolated protoplasm are decidedly slight. In the species observed, the majority of the xylem elements contain nucleated protoplasts interconnected with surrounding cells by plasmodesmata. The entrance of solutes into the living protoplasts is regulated by osmotic gradient. When the solutes eventually reach the moribund elements at a higher level in the older region of the root, they form the ascending transpiration stream contained within the suberized vessels.

I am not qualified to discuss the path of viruses within the plant. Pit diameter, plasmodesmatal number and thickness, which, so far as I know are undetermined, and the volume of water molecules surrounding each protein chain, must necessarily be considered. It is well known that cell turgor varies constantly, which causes visible changes in volume in the living cell. The increase in the surface area of the wall, including the pits, depends on loose microfibrillar structure and water content. In all living cells, the protoplasm is in a constant turmoil of visible movement. It appears possible that viruses, along with particles equally minute, may be swept along the plasmodesmata from cell to cell like brush in a fast-moving current.

ACKNOWLEDGMENTS.—The author is indebted to Barbara G. Bystrom, Department of Botany, and E. Bowler, College of Engineering, University of California, Los Angeles, for the illustrations and for constructive criticism.

This work was supported by a grant from the National Science Foundation (NSF-G-23387).

LITERATURE CITED

CANNON, W. A. 1911. Root habits of desert plants. Carnegie Inst. Wash. Publ. 131, 96 p.

CORMACK, R. G. H. 1962. Development of root hairs in angiosperms. Botan. Rev. 28: 446-464.

DAWES, C., and E. BOWLER. 1959. Light and electron microscope studies of cell wall structure of the root hairs of *Raphanus sativus*. Am. J. Botany 46: 561-565.

DITTMER, H. J. A. 1937. Quantitative study of roots and root hairs of a winter rye-plant (*Secale cereale*). Am. J. Botany 24: 417-420.

LEISER, A. 1959. Nutrition and root anatomy of Azalea (Rhododendron). Dissertation, University of California at Los Angeles.

LIESE, W. 1957. Zur Struktur der Tertiärwand bei den Laubhölzeren. Naturwissenschaften 44: 240-241.

MILLER, E. C. 1938. Plant physiology. McGraw-Hill, New York and London. 1201 p.

MULLER, C. H. 1946. Root development and ecological variations in guayule. U.S. Dept. Agr. Tech. Bull. 923, 114 p.

NELSON, P., and S. WILHELM. 1957. Some anatomic aspects of the strawberry root. Hilgardia 26: 631-642.

PRIESTLEY, J. H., and E. NORTH. 1922. The structure of the endodermis in relation to function. New Phytologist 21: 113-139.

PRIESTLEY, J. H., and L. M. WOFFENDEN. 1922. Causal factors in cork formation. New Phytologist 21: 252-268.

REYNOLDS, M. E. 1943. Anatomy of a xerophyte: *Dalea spinosa*. Dissertation. University of California at Los Angeles.

SCOTT, F. M. 1949. Plasmodesmata in xylem vessels. Botan. Gaz. 110: 492-495.

SCOTT, F. M. 1950. Internal suberisation of tissues. Botan. Gaz. 111: 378-394.

SCOTT, F. M., B. G. BYSTROM, and E. BOWLER. 1962. *Cercidium floridum* seed coat, light and electron microscope study. Am. J. Botany 49: 821-833.

SCOTT, F. M., B. G. BYSTROM, and E. BOWLER. 1963. Root hairs, cuticle and pits. Science 140: 63-64.

SCOTT, F. M., K. C. HAMNER, E. BAKER, and E. BOWLER. 1956. Electron microscope studies of cell wall growth in the onion root. Am. J. Botany 43: 313-324.

SCOTT, F. M., K. C. HAMNER, E. BAKER, and E. BOWLER. 1958. Electron microscope studies of the epidermis of *Allium cepa*. Am. J. Botany 45: 449-461.

SCOTT, F. M., and M. LEWIS. 1954. Pits, intercellular spaces and internal "suberisation" in the apical meristerms of *Ricinus communis* and other plants. Botan. Gaz. 114: 253-264.

SCOTT, F. M., V. SJAHOLM, and E. BOWLER. 1960. Light and electron microscope studies of the primary xylem of *Ricinus communis*. Am. J. Botany 47: 162-173.

SMALL, J. 1929. Hydrogen ion concentration in plant cells and tissues. Gebrüder Borntraeger, Berlin. 421 p.

VAN FLEET, D. S. 1961. Histochemistry and function of the endodermis. Botan. Rev. 27: 166-220.

WARDROP, A. 1957. Lignification of plants in relation to ruminant nutrition. Symposium Commonwealth Sci. Ind. Res. Organization, Melbourne. p. 18-48.

► DISCUSSION OF F. M. SCOTT PAPER

A. D. McLaren:

Is the mucilaginous layer synthesized by the root or by the rhizoplane organisms on the root? Protein molecules easily penetrate this layer but they do not enter root hairs (O. Bradfute and A. D. McLaren, Physiol. Plantarum, in press, 1964).

F. M. Scott:

The mucilaginous layer is part of the outer epidermal wall and is present in mist-grown as well as in soil-grown roots.

C. B. Davey:

What are the factors which affect the thickness of the mucilaginous layer? Recently, we have grown wheat seedlings under "ideal" nutritional conditions and the mucilaginous layer was quite thin. But when the seedlings were grown on soil crumbs which had been coated with iron to reduce the availability of nutrients, the mucilaginous layer was very pronounced. In fact, the roots appeared to have been smeared over the surface of the crumbs due to the abundance of the mucilage.

F. M. Scott:

I do not know details of this experimental work. Andrew Leiser (1959; cited in the paper) discussed this problem.

G. H. Hepting:

Mucilage is soluble in water; mucus is not. Which is the material covering the primary roots? Whether this material hydrates or not would make a big difference in fungus penetration.

F. M. Scott:

I do not know the exact chemical composition of mucilage. It appears to be variable, and consistency probably varies under varying conditions of plant growth.

H. Burström:

1. Can you tell how early the cuticle appears on root hairs?
2. Have you seen ectodesmata in transverse sections go right through the wall?
3. Do xylem vessels with living cytoplasm have intact transverse walls or not?

F. M. Scott:

1. Cuticle appears on youngest papillae of root hairs. It is clearly defined in living cells in *Vicia faba* and other roots examined.
2. The outer epidermal wall of the shoot consists of cuticle, noncellulosic polysaccharides, and principally of cellulose. In many species wax is present on the surface of the cuticle, as a rule in the form of wax rodlets, as shown by de Bary. In the young root, the same components are present, but wax has not been observed in any species examined. There is, however, always a surface film of mucilage.

I have not made longitudinal or transverse ultrathin sections of root hairs, some of them more than 1500 μ in length, nor of the root-hair zone of the species examined. But in electron micrographs of material cleared and treated ultrasonically, pits are evident in the microfibrillar network and plasmodesmata are still present in many pits (see Fig. 6 in this paper, wheat root hair). Similar pits are present in the root hairs of other species examined, *Raphanus sativus* (radish), *Cucurbita* (squash), and *Brassica nigra* (mustard) (Scott, Bystrom, and Bowler, Science 140: 63-64, 1963).

In a fragment of the outer epidermal wall of a non-piliferous cell in mustard to which bacteria of the rhizoplane are still attached, similar pits in the microfibrillar network are clearly evident (see frontispiece).

3. In xylem vessels observed in the root-hair zone, the transverse walls are intact.

A. D. Rovira:

A mucilaginous material occurs around the roots of oat roots grown aseptically in nutrient solution. This material is insoluble in cold water, soluble in hot water, and is an oligosaccharide comprising glucose and fructose units. Under nonsterile conditions microorganisms grow prolifically in this mucilage.

F. M. Scott:

In all roots examined by me and my students, mucilage occurred in films of varying thickness. I am interested to know that the chemical nature of mucilage is known to be an oligosaccharide, a suitable stratum for the growth of certain microorganisms. The solubility of this layer, as you have found, appeared to us to be variable.

S. Wilhelm:

Please comment on the possible significance of pores in root hairs. Are they large enough to serve for points of entry for zoospores or other stages of microorganisms?

F. M. Scott:

The diameter of pores in root hairs is about 0.2 μ or less. Plasmodesmata fill these pores but are partially removed by ultrasonic treatment (Scott, Bystrom, and Bowler, 1963, cited in this paper). In all roots examined, outer epidermal walls, including the living root hairs, are covered with mucilage and cuticle. I do not think that zoospores could enter. But many microorganisms can change shape from ellipsoidal to linear outlines. When change in cell volume is considered as seen in living cells, turgescent or flaccid, the diameter of pores and pits presumably can change significantly and therefore the volume of water molecules surrounding the protein chains in the plasmodesmata may also change.

T. Kommedahl:

Mention was made of staining of roots by humic acids, presumably in the absence of infection. Do you know what is stained?

F. M. Scott:

I have not observed roots of this type. I should think that humic acid accumulates in the cell walls. The components of the cell wall include mucilage, cutin, pectic substances, and cellulose, also interfibrillar material, presumably pectic in nature. Humic acids might also possibly be deposited in the plasmodesmata.

E. E. Trujillo:

Information has been obtained (E. E. Trujillo, Phytopathology 53: 162-166, 1963) on the significance of living xylem in the roots of bananas, with respect to the fusarium-wilt fungus penetration of banana vascular tissues. Living xylem was present in the banana root close to the apex and, as xylem maturation occurred, such elements became vacuolated and the protoplasm and nucleus of such elements finally disappeared. The living xylem was found to be a barrier against the advance of the pathogen. The pathogen was able to invade mature nonliving xylem readily. Therefore, it appears that although the living xylem is found in the roots, it is not present all over the vascular system.

The Physiology of Plant Roots

H. G. BURSTRÖM—*Department of Plant Physiology, University of Lund, Sweden.*

It is no easy task to anticipate what information about root physiology may be relevant to the topic of soil-borne infections. In many respects roots do not differ physiologically from other plant materials, and a general sketch of root physiology would embrace matters of common knowledge to every biologist, for example, the fundamentals of cell physiology including respiratory metabolism. A careful selection of such material is called for, which is either specific to root physiology or deemed to be of particular interest with regard to infections from the soil. It is, nonetheless, probably impossible to avoid burdening the treatise with information of no consequence on the infection problem.

I have ventured to select four loosely related subjects, namely: the composition of roots as nutrient substrates for microorganisms; changes in some pertinent properties of root systems under varying external conditions; the resistance offered by the root to an invasion from the soil; and the ability of the plant to endure mutilations of the root system, if such have occurred. In this last-mentioned connection it is necessary to pay attention also to the general importance of the root system for the plant as a unit.

A satisfactory treatment of these questions is complicated by the fact that our knowledge of roots growing in soil is very meager, because they are inaccessible for direct studies. Deductions have to be made from laboratory experience to specific conditions prevailing in the soil, and this leaves a wide margin for error. The relation between plant roots and soil microorganisms is, as a matter of fact, not so much a physiologic as an ecologic problem: physiology as it appears in a certain natural environment. Attention has been focused primarily on the fibrous roots, which are physiologically most active, most easily attacked by microorganisms, but—alas—also most difficult to study in natural habitats.

The following survey of these problems will appear somewhat rhapsodic, because I have to touch lightly upon several chapters of root physiology and come back to the same question from other related points.

THE ROOT AS A NUTRIENT MEDIUM.—Before entering a discussion on the chemical composition of the roots it may be appropriate to recall some of their general properties. It is easy to tell morphologically what a root is, and it has been described anatomically by Dr. Scott in her paper in this symposium, but it is more difficult to distinguish a root physiologically from a shoot part and tell what the salient features of a root are relevant to a soil-borne infection, without giving a broad survey of the whole field of plant physiology. Although the metabolic capacity of the root should be considered initially, I should prefer first to make some remarks on the chemical composition of roots with special regard to compounds of nutritional value to parasites.

Chemical composition.—In spite of the great number of plant analyses carried out, there is little information to be derived from the literature on the nutritive value of roots in general. Analyses usually refer to entire root systems, including old parts accumulating metabolites or excretions, and more than often they are based on storage roots of cultivated plants. Thus they do not show the composition of the young fibrous roots, where invasions from the soil are likely to occur. By and large, the young roots contain literally all sorts of useful, indifferent, and even for an invader detrimental organic compounds produced in plants, to which are added the mineral nutrients taken up directly from the soil. Some points should be emphasized and illustrated by a few figures.

Roots depend upon the leaves for the supply of carbohydrates; for carbon and energy they feed as heterotrophically as any parasitic fungus. In spite of this, it is wrong to assume that even the fibrous tips live in a state of carbohydrate shortage. It is true that occasional determinations of the contents of soluble sugars have given figures as low as 2% on a dry-weight basis, but also very high figures have been recorded. The variations are large, undoubtedly depending, among other things, on the actual growth and rate of consumption. It is also noticeable that depositions of starch are very common, for example, in the central cells of the calyptra and in the cortical parenchyma. This is an infallible sign of an ample carbohydrate supply.

The content of organic nitrogen seems to be more constant. Fibrous roots have been reported to have a rather high content of protein nitrogen, around 8% in the meristem, decreasing to a value of about 4% in the mature parts owing to dilution during growth (Brown, Reith, and Robinson, 1952). It could be mentioned by way of comparison that leaves usually contain 2 to 3% of protein on a dry-weight basis. The difference between leaves and roots certainly does not depend upon different cytoplasmic organization but rather upon smaller amounts of cell-wall depositions in the root. The fibrous roots could be regarded as substrates of a fairly high protein:carbohydrate ratio as compared with other plant parts, but are for analogous reasons lower in protein than bacteria and fungi.

There are some special trends also in the mineral-salt composition of roots. Reliable determinations on the fibrous roots from soil are difficult to obtain. Results from water-culture experiments may be misleading as far as the actual concentrations are concerned, but a comparison with leaf analyses reveals some characteristics of roots in this respect. Thus the ratio of the content of mineral nutrients in corn roots to that in leaves, on a dry-weight basis, was found to be, for nitrogen, 1.0; for sulfur, 1.0; for phosphorus, 0.5; for potassium, 0.3; for magnesium, 0.8; for calcium, 1.3; for manganese, 2.0; and for iron, 7.3. These elements, which are relatively abundant in roots, are slowly transported within the plant. Thus we find low concentrations of phosphorus and potassium, also of boron, but relatively high amounts of calcium and heavy metals in roots. Special features of roots are a high Ca:K ratio, as well as large depositions of heavy metals.

All these are average data and do not give any information concerning the distribution of the nutrients within the tissues and cells, which may be more important than the over-all contents for parasites living either inside cells or in the intercellular spaces between them. The nutrient conditions in these two locations must be very different, as mentioned in a later section. It is also possible that the actual concentrations of the nutrients are of less importance for the roots as substrates than the mode and rate of supply of nutrients to the roots. We should consider the dynamics of the root nutrition, not only the static picture.

There are three sources of the root constituents: the soil delivering mineral salts, the leaves providing certain organic compounds, and the synthetic capacity of the root itself. The last one may not be least important, owing to the strongly heterotrophic nature of the root parasites.

Synthetic capacity.—There are few parts of plant metabolism which cannot be carried out in the root, provided that appropriate conditions prevail. This goes so far that roots grown in the soil always form protochlorophyll in the tips in measurable amounts (Hejnowicz, 1958) just as dark-grown etiolated shoots do, and only illumination is required for roots to develop regular green chloroplasts and perform photosynthesis (Fadeel, 1963). This does occur in nature but, of course, not under ordinary conditions in darkness in the soil. Not only do the roots depend upon the leaves for the supply of carbohydrates, but the leaves deliver essential compounds of hormonal nature as well, which cannot be formed by the root. On the other hand, the roots readily take up nitrogen as nitrate from the soil and assimilate this into organic form, and synthesize protein themselves. In the organized plant there is a mutual interchange of nutrients and hormonal compounds between root and top.

The root system is obviously the main seat of the assimilation of inorganic nitrogen, which takes place in close connection with the uptake in the young fibrous roots (Burström, 1945a). In some instances, for example in fruit trees, the assimilation is entirely confined to the root. High accumulation of nitrate occurs only on habitats rich in soluble soil nitrogen, and the roots can then accumulate nitrate in considerable amounts without inconvenience to the plant; values up to 2 mmoles per g of dry matter have been recorded. From such high values the nitrate content can be of any value down to zero.

Little is known about the synthetic capacity of roots for secondary metabolites and of the root content of these substances; evidence here is mainly indirect. Extensive experiments carried out for the past 30 years on the cultivation of excised roots have revealed that roots may more or less completely lack the ability to synthesize essential metabolites. It is then inferred that they are able to form all other compounds: building stones, enzymes, and activators, required for normal development. We know what they cannot do, but less positively what they are able to do. Excised roots grown on artificial media are nearly always heterotrophic with regard to one or more of the common vitamins: thiamine, niacin, or pyridoxine (Street, 1959). They may also lack the capacity of forming tryptophane (Ferguson, 1963), which is of special interest not only for protein synthesis but also as a mother substance of the indole auxins. It is assumed that the same kinds of vitamin heterotrophy occurs in roots of intact plants. Natural vitamin deficiency is not known to occur in roots, but this does not mean that it does not. It is difficult to study such nutrient conditions of roots from natural habitats, and we cannot be sure that they do not differ from roots grown excised, or roots of intact plants from artificial water cultures raised under very different nutrient conditions. It is known, however, that deficiency of hormonal compounds can be produced in attached roots by artificial means such as defoliation and shading (Richardson, 1957). The compounds were in this case not identified, but so far as they were necessary for growth they belong to the generic group of rhizocalines. Otherwise, this seems to be an important point for infecting soil microorganisms, because bacteria and fungi are deficient in the same accessory growth compounds as roots; these compounds serve as vitamins to microorganisms but as hormones in the higher plants.

There are also secondary compounds that are easily produced in roots, such as coumarin derivatives, or are predominatingly synthesized there, for example alkaloids. The roots are the seat of synthesis of the nicotine and tropane derivatives in *Nicotiana, Atropa,* and *Datura,* of betain in *Beta,* and hordein in barley (Mothes and Romerke, 1958). These substances may be of no special importance for soil-borne infections, but they are certainly physiologically active, and we can expect roots to produce and contain a variety of such compounds, even if only a limited number of them have been studied with regard to the location of their formation and their actual content in fibrous roots.

Salt uptake.—The mechanism of salt uptake is well known and has been extensively discussed; therefore I will restrict myself to taking up one point only of this complex machinery. One component of the salt uptake, and indeed the very first step, is a passive diffusion of salts into the roots (Epstein, 1960). Where this diffusion takes place has been a controversial question, but at present all seem to agree to that it is mainly, perhaps entirely, confined to the cell walls, and also that it is a general phenomenon encountered in all plant tissues investigated (Fig. 1). The cell walls

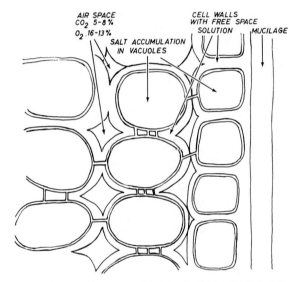

Fig. 1. Semidiagrammatic picture of the nutritive organization of the root surface with epidermis and cortex. Free space in the walls containing a dilute solution, salt accumulation in vacuoles, and aeration system enriched in carbon dioxide. Pits and plasmodesmata form cytoplasmic connections between cells traversing the free space.

form, as is well known, a continuous system in the root, because the cells retain their contact with each other during growth. The walls are also easily permeable to all diffusible solutes and thus form a continuous transport system around the less permeable outer cytoplasmic membranes. This space in the walls is called the free space, meaning that it is free to a diffusion and a mass movement of a solution. How far this free space extends inward in the root is a problem older than the concept of free space itself, which is a recent innovation. It was long maintained that the endodermis, owing to its peculiar cytologic organization, should form a rather impenetrable barrier around the stele and prevent a ready passage of solutes and also of invading microorganisms. Observations of the free-space ion uptake have shown this in a sense to hold true but not just in the way originally anticipated. Only in the outermost meristem, where there is yet no visibly differentiated endodermis, does the diffusion in

the walls stop at the endodermis level. Farther back, where the endodermis is suberized, it lets salts through (Lüttge and Weigl, 1962). This is, however, a metabolic, active transport, not a free diffusion. Then there is assumed to be a free space in the stele (Jackson and Weatherley, 1962), but whether these two free systems directly communicate is an open question. However that may be, the endodermis forms a barrier of some kind. Outside this layer there is the free space in the cortex containing a freely moving salt solution in direct contact with the salt solution in the external medium. It is accessible to this external medium to such an extent that it is filled by diffusion from the outside to a diffusion equilibrium in about 1 min (Pettersson, 1961). This forms a nutrient solution on one side bordering on the cytoplasm, from which it obtains leaking organic compounds, on another side bordering on the air-filled intercellular spaces providing oxygen. The very thin lipophilic film covering the cell-wall surface does not impede an exchange of oxygen. This free space is an excellently arranged nutrient medium, only a few (10 to 50) microns thick, flowing over a large surface in contact with an air phase and thus well aerated. The reason for this detailed description is that this free-space solution must be the nutrient medium for aerobic microorganisms invading the root and living intercellularly. For example, ectotrophic mycorrhiza should feed directly on the free-space solution. The solution ought to be buffered to the favorable pH of 5 to 6 (Burström, 1945*b*).

I will come back to the passively moving salt solution in connection with the functional aspects of the roots. The rest of the salt-uptake mechanism is probably of no particular interest in this connection; it will suffice to mention that we have a metabolic accumulation of salts in the vacuole to high concentrations especially of potassium, by a mechanism which is probably common to all cells of higher plants, and microorganisms as well.

Incorporation of large-molecular matter.—Fairly large molecules can be incorporated into the root in the normal process of uptake, for example the common antibiotics such as terramycin and streptomycin, with molecular weights up to 600. It has been advocated that even much larger molecules can pass into the root. According to McLaren, Jensen, and Jacobson (1960), the protein lysozome of a molecular weight of about 15,000 is taken up by undamaged roots under some circumstances. The suggested mechanism is pinocytosis, known from protozoa. It implies that the cytoplasm forms pockets on the outer side, probably from the endoplasmic reticulum. These pockets enclose portions of the external medium including solutes and bodies which happen to be at hand (Fig. 2). A cell can in this way incorporate indiscriminately all sorts of bodies regardless of their nature, even if they have no affinity for the cell system. If this is to be verified as a common procedure, it is necessary to determine how large molecules can be taken up. If it is very common it is surprising that roots have not been shown convincingly to incorporate humus compounds

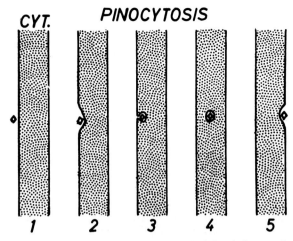

Fig. 2. Schematic picture of the principle of pinocytosis for uptake of a large molecule compound. 1, particle near external surface; 2, particle in pocket of the cytoplasm; 3, pocket closed; 4, particle carried through cytoplasm in artificial "vacuole"; 5, particle released to vacuole. $Cyt =$ cytoplasm.

from the soil, although earlier much work was done along such lines.

The diameter of a lysozome molecule is of the magnitude of 2 mμ. It should be noticed that the smallest virus particles have diameters of 15 to 25 mμ, so that there is at present no ground for assuming a passage of viruses into undamaged roots by some such mechanism.

It is of some importance in this connection that the occurrence of plasmodesmata on root surfaces has been doubted (Franke, 1961). We know that inside the plant these are the pathways for the migration of viruses and they must let through all bodies up to the virus size. Regardless of whether large bodies enter by way of pinocytosis or through plasmodesmata, they must be able to pass through cutinized wall layers where such occur. This would detract from the value of both these postulated mechanisms.

Loss of compounds.—Another aspect of the exchange of compounds between root and soil is exudation of matters (Starkey, 1958). The different kinds of exudates and their importance for the soil microorganisms will be dealt with by Dr. Rovira in his paper in this symposium. I will only make some remarks on the different kinds and mechanisms of exudation which might occur in roots and their bearing on the nutrient conditions inside the root. An exudation can be mediated by the free-space solution or bypass this space, and this is of some importance for the distribution of solutes within the root cells.

It has been definitely established with mineral salts that compounds accumulated in the vacuole diffuse out through the cytoplasm to the free space. There is a continuous loss counteracted by the active accumulation. Such a leakage simply must occur if there is a diffusion gradient and the cytoplasm is to some extent permeable to the solute. The same holds true of organic compounds. It is thus hardly surprising that

exudates have been detected comprising all sorts of organic compounds; soluble carbohydrates and nearly all amino acids (Buxton, 1962), together with a wide array of other compounds of the most divergent nature, although in minute quantities only. It may well be said that investigators have found what they have been looking for, or compounds responding to the particular assay method employed.

If this exudation takes place by way of the free space, this latter must contain a rather full spectrum of diffusible organic nutrients, adding to the nutritive value of the free-space solution. It is true that the concentration must be low, but if the compounds are consumed by a parasite the losses from the cells would presumably be speeded up.

As far as mineral nutrients are concerned, it has been shown in some instances that plants can lose considerable amounts of their salts by way of the roots to the soil; salts also move from the leaves right down the stem and are exuded. This is probably a sign of aging or extremely unfavorable external conditions, being a passive flow, comparable to a reversal of the transpiration stream. Generally, passive exudation is most pronounced under unfavorable conditions (Grineva, 1962), for example with oxygen deficiency and a reduced respiration. This is understandable since the compounds are retained in the root by a metabolic expenditure of energy. We can thus hardly regard such a wholesale loss as normal or of particular interest, except in special cases.

There are, however, very efficient modes of active secretion of both inorganic and organic compounds located in the vacuole or the cytoplasm and bypassing the free spaces. They require certain definite anatomic structures. Salts may be accumulated in such amounts in leaf cells that the salt solutions are squeezed out osmotically (Helder, 1956). This is most obvious in halophytes, and there are reasons to assume that such secretions are mediated by plasmodesmata on the leaf surfaces. An example of the excretion of an organic compound is the loss of sugars common in nectaries, which are glands of a specific structure. The secretion evidently goes directly from the cytoplasm through pores in the cell walls to the outside, and it is supposed to be of the same nature as the sugar secretion into the sieve elements of the phloem (Lüttge, 1962). There are no indications of glandular structures in the outer walls of roots. The anatomic prerequisites for an active exudation seem to be lacking. We have to assume that exudation depends mainly upon a slow passive leakage through the free space.

On the other hand, all compounds given off from healthy roots are not exudates of this kind. Ecologically not distinguishable from the exudation proper, but from an internal nutritional view of no consequence, are exudates resulting when dying cells or parts of the root deliver their contents to the soil. As will be discussed later on, a large-scale dying of root tips is a normal phenomenon, and furthermore even a living root loses calyptra cells and may shed epidermis at the metacutis formation; there are disrupted cortical cells around the base of every lateral root, and the whole cortex may be shed at the onset of secondary growth. This must not be confused physiologically with a true exudation, but it certainly delivers cell constituents to the soil.

Internal atmosphere.—The composition of the internal atmosphere should also be considered. The gas phase of the intercellular spaces is at atmospheric pressure, containing the ordinary 78% nitrogen, but an increased content of carbon dioxide and correspondingly less oxygen. It is difficult to determine these concentrations accurately in tissues, especially in such delicate parts as fibrous roots. Determinations of bulky subterranean plant parts have given figures of 2 to 5% or occasionally up to 16% carbon dioxide and correspondingly less oxygen, or values between 19 and 5%. Determinations have been carried out on fibrous roots of wheat plants by a recently devised method (Fadeel, 1963), showing 8% carbon dioxide in the most actively growing zone 10 mm from the tip, and 5% in the mature part. This is a considerable accumulation, but it still leaves 13 to 16% of oxygen in the air spaces.

These intercellular spaces of the root stand in open communication with those of the stem and by means of the stomata with the free atmosphere. This is important for the functioning of the root. It was earlier deduced from the anatomic structure and has been verified experimentally that the roots are supplied with oxygen by these channels. This does not make them independent of the soil aeration, but contributes to the oxygen supply to the root system. It may be of special interest for root infections that even in a poorly aerated medium, for example in a waterlogged soil, the plant roots carry on a strictly aerobic metabolism and offer an aerobic substrate for parasites. This also holds true for such a cultivated plant as rice seedlings.

So much for the intercellular spaces. It is still more difficult to estimate the redox conditions in the inner parts of cells, but they are assumed to be lower in oxygen tension. The reason is, of course, the respiratory consumption of oxygen, causing a gradient from the surface to the interior of the cell. Only the meristematic root tip is living under more clearly anaerobic conditions. The tissues of the root tip are dense, the intercellular spaces minute, and they have been reported in instances to contain a considerable excess of carbon dioxide, probably rendered possible by a low permeability together with the poor aeration (Burström, 1959). As soon as cell elongation begins and intercellular spaces are widened, respiration increases(Eliasson, 1955) and metabolism runs strictly aerobically.

INFLUENCE OF EXTERNAL CONDITIONS.—The extent and properties of the root system are liable to be influenced by variations of the external soil conditions, such as temporary variations within one habitat and particularly differences between localities.

A satisfactory interpretation of the action of each individual edaphic factor on the properties of the roots is difficult and sometimes impossible, for two reasons. First, the study of roots from natural habitats, espe-

cially the chemical composition of fibrous roots, meets with obvious technical difficulties, and we cannot always draw conclusions about field conditions from artificial laboratory experiments. Second, different chemical and physical soil factors are interrelated in such a way that we can seldom isolate one from another, and even with regard to the most fundamental soil properties we cannot give unequivocal answers to questions relating to the real cause of an observed change in plant response. The following survey must for this reason be restricted to a brief review of selected ecologic factors and recorded root responses without definite explanations of the causal relations in every instance.

Of importance for the function of the plant is the size of the root system relative to that of the shoot, or the root:top ratio expressed on a weight basis. Root and top depend upon each other; the root furnishes the top with water, mineral salts, and certain metabolites produced in the root, the shoot delivers to the root carbohydrates, hormones, and other metabolic products. This is no voluntary partnership but a case of hard competition for the necessary compounds. We may even be justified in regarding the two parts as growing and developing independently of each other according to the amounts of nutrients each part can appropriate from the environment and from its competitor. There is an equilibrium between root and shoot development, and under a given set of external conditions the ratio between root and shoot growth for a certain species is fairly constant (Rogers and Booth, 1960). This is the reason why infections or mutilations of one part will also affect the other, as we shall see later. Attention will here be directed to ecologic factors causing changes in root growth or in the root:top ratio.

Water supply.—Three main factors are responsible for the root:top ratio, namely the water conditions, the light, and the nitrogen supply. Of these the water factor is the most important, but also the one most difficult to interpret. The reason is that waterlogging of a soil also means decreased oxygen supply, just as drought also implies a good aeration. It is difficult to isolate the water factor experimentally and study its effect on root properties. It has even been suggested that water itself cannot limit root growth as long as the roots grow at all, but that the apparent water effects depend upon oxygen or mineral-nutrient supply. The water factor itself can hardly influence the chemical composition of the root either. Water conditions are not uniform in a soil; they may vary locally in the microenvironment of the root, and also between layers of different physical texture. By and large, the abstruse water factor has a profound influence on the roots. In a dry soil, or even in a dry layer of a soil, root elongation is favored but branching is reduced, so that the root rapidly extends over a large distance (Stålfelt, 1960). High soil water content, on the contrary, gives short and richly branched roots. The root weight may increase or decrease, but in any case drought causes a reduced top growth and a high root:top ratio. An excess of water increases top growth and decreases top:root ratio until oxygen deficiency eventually limits the development of all parts of the plant.

Light and nitrogen supply.—The reason why light and nitrogen supply will be considered under one heading is not the direct connection which exists, but that they together regulate the balance between carbohydrates and protein, which has far-reaching consequences for the general properties of the root system and its development.

Illumination of the shoot has, of course, its paramount importance by way of the photosynthesis. Increasing light will increase carbohydrate, its delivery to the root, and consequently the root:top ratio by favoring the root growth (Kozlowski, 1949) (Fig. 3).

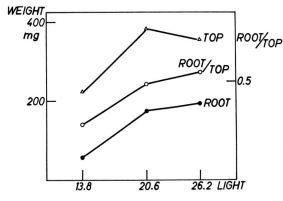

Fig. 3. Influence of light on root:top ratio in *Impatiens*. (A. P. Hughes and G. C. Evans. New Phytologist 61: 154-174. 1962.)

This is directly counteracted by an ample nitrogen supply to the roots.

Nitrogen is taken up as nitrate by higher plants from the soil and readily assimilated. This is done at the expense of carbohydrates delivered from the shoot. An increased supply of nitrogen draws on the available carbohydrates, the protein content increases, and less carbohydrate is available for other purposes. This is still more true of plants taking up ammonia directly. Nitrate is partly stored as such without reduction, but ammonia is assimilated by most plants, the excess not utilized for protein synthesis being accumulated as amides, which means a greater consumption of carbohydrates than with nitrate nutrition.

In any case, high nitrogen supply causes changes in the properties of the roots as well as of the whole plant, which may be of importance for the ability of the plant to withstand or endure infections from the soil. I will mention some of the consequences of an increased nitrogen supply, without trying to evaluate their relative merits in this respect. The immediate result of the nitrogen assimilation is the increased ratio of proteins to carbohydrates. This means a considerable change in the chemical composition and the value of the root as a nutrient medium (to invaders). Such a shift in the C:N ratio is for analogous reasons also caused by a low light intensity, and has been suggested

as a factor in the development of mycorrhizas (Björkman, 1942).

Another consequence of the impaired carbohydrate status is that less is available for cell-wall synthesis. The cell walls become weaker and their mechanical strength is reduced, and probably also the strength of the entire roots, because this is known to be the result of overfeeding shoots with nitrogen. This is mainly a change in the quantity of wall substance laid down, since the composition of the wall, as revealed by the ratio between the main components pectins, hemicellulose, and cellulose undergoes rather small variations even under extreme nitrogen nutrition (Burström, 1958) (Table 1).

TABLE 1. Composition of cell walls of fibrous roots of young wheat plants*

Treatment	Root length, cm	Grams in 100 cm root		
		Pectins	Hemi-cellulose	Cellulose
High N	7	0.56	0.46	1.39
Medium N	15	0.39	0.37	0.96
Low N	20	0.45	0.50	1.20
Low Ca	5	1.04	0.90	2.45
Herbicide inhibition	2	4.70	2.90	6.10

* From H. Burström. Fysiogr. Sällsk. (Lund) Förh. 28: 53-64. 1958.

The increased nitrogen supply also leads to striking morphologic alterations in that the root:shoot ratio decreases. This holds true over the whole range of nitrogen supply whether it is in excess as a nutrient or within the deficiency range (Fig. 4). The reason for this is not quite clear; it may be because of the comparatively smaller amounts of carbohydrates available in the roots, or an improved transport of mineral nutrients from the root to the top which follows from a high nitrate content, or probably a combination of both. However this may be, the serious implication for the plant is that concomitantly the transpiration in-

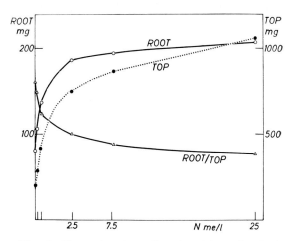

Fig. 4. Top and root growth and root:top ratio of oats in relation to nitrogen supply. (H. Burström. Svensk. Bot. Tidskr. 28: 157-263. 1934.)

creases (Biedle, 1958). Combined with a reduced root system, this means a much increased strain on the capacity of the roots to supply water. Thus it is reasonable to assume that all other things being equal, a high nitrogen supply should render the plant as a whole more sensitive to encroachments upon the root system by endangering its water-supplying capacity.

Oxygen and carbon dioxide tensions.—As already mentioned, a difficulty in evaluating the importance of the oxygen tension under field conditions is that we cannot easily distinguish between oxygen deficiency and water excess, or between good oxygen supply and drought. There is also often an inverse relation between oxygen and carbon dioxide in the soil, but carbon dioxide increases more than oxygen decreases, owing to the activity of microorganisms with a high respiratory quotient. Thus it is necessary to keep effects of oxygen and carbon dioxide apart. In laboratory experiments with aerated water cultures the oxygen supply can be carefully controlled, but variations in carbon dioxide tensions must also be avoided. It is possible under such conditions to arrive at some understanding of the oxygen and carbon dioxide effects separately.

Carbon dioxide in concentrations exceeding 10% is an efficient inhibitor of root growth, and such concentrations may well occur in the soil atmosphere. Complete cessation of growth requires much higher carbon dioxide contents than those realized in nature. These effects do not necessarily depend upon changes in the respiration, because both oxygen deficiency and carbon dioxide excess are reported to decrease the permeability to water directly (not by mediation of metabolism) and hence to decrease the water uptake by the plant (Glinka and Reinhold, 1962). If roots of plants are artificially exposed to high concentrations of carbon dioxide, the tops may wilt within an astonishingly short time, indicating that water uptake has completely stopped.

Notwithstanding the difficulties of isolating oxygen-supply effects, it is obvious that the soil oxygen requirement of different species varies considerably, both as regards the minimum requirement and the lowest oxygen tension allowing maximal growth response (Carr, 1961) (Fig. 5). The minimum requirement has been recorded to be as low as 0.5% or for the rice plant even 0.2%; roots do not survive below these values. Normal root growth may be obtained at 8 to 10% but growth may increase up to 40% oxygen, which quantity is never available in nature. This tallies well with figures recorded of the critical oxygen tension, or the lowest one giving maximal respiration. It is normally found between 10 and 30% (Lemon and Wiegand, 1962). The evaluation is complicated by the fact that the requirement is temperature-dependent, and the tolerance to extreme values depends upon the time the roots are subjected to the adverse conditions. Nevertheless, roots of tomato and conifers are reported to be oxygen-exacting, whereas water plants, of course, tolerate low oxygen contents. These differences certainly do not depend upon physiologic differences of the respiratory systems, since all roots are strictly

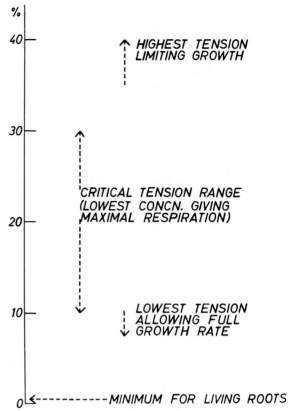

Fig. 5. Diagram showing the sensitivity of roots to external oxygen tension.

aerobic; rather it is a matter of morphologic differences. Species with root systems tolerating a low external oxygen concentration are evidently those which are equipped with richly developed intercellular spaces supplying oxygen from the shoots to the roots. As previously mentioned, such a supply is probably normal in all plants (cf. Barber, Ebert, and Evans, 1962) but has been little evaluated quantitatively.

Anatomic adaptation must also be considered in this connection. All anatomic and morphologic structures conducive to the ecologic adaptation of plants are highly modifiable, as also are those related to the oxygen conditions. A temporary flooding of a soil may adversely affect roots developed with a more favorable aeration of the medium, whereas the same species raised under conditions of poor aeration may have developed a rich system of intercellular spaces permitting better internal oxygen supply. It is for this reason impossible to state that a certain condition is unfavorable for a certain plant species; it depends to some degree on its development and adaptation. The effects of oxygen must be explained in rational terms as an influence on cellular metabolism and growth. Without greatly changing the over-all growth, a prolonged exposure at 5% oxygen may cause profound changes in the cytologic differentiation and enzyme chemistry (Siegel, Rosen, and Renwick, 1962). The leading cytologic feature is that oxygen shortage causes a reduction of suberization and lignification of tissues.

Mineral nutrient conditions.—Among the overwhelming mass of data available from practical husbandry on mineral-nutrient contents of crops, there is hardly any information on the fibrous roots. There are no systematic records of how the composition of these roots changes under the influence of varying nutrient supply. It is not easy either to draw conclusions from water-culture experiments or from the behavior of tops in this respect. Their contents of mineral nutrients are well known and the more or less regular increase in shoot content of mineral nutrients with manuring has been mapped out in some detail. We also know from studies with water cultures that increasing the supply of mineral elements may increase the mineral content of roots as well, but mainly at high concentrations not likely to occur in the soil. At low external concentrations it is not necessarily so: an increased nutrient supply may result mainly in an increased growth, or the active accumulation will turn out to be a function more of the total amounts available than the actual concentrations in the medium. It is certainly a gap in our knowledge of the mineral nutrition in the field that we are so ignorant of the properties of the growing fibrous root tips. We cannot predict for certain the salt distribution within the cells either. We should expect the free-space solution to resemble the external medium, which it does in a solution culture. It is not necessarily so in the soil, where the bulk of the mineral nutrients are adsorbed on colloidal particles, and the actual concentration of the soil solution is of secondary importance for salt uptake. It has also been advocated on rather good evidence that the uptake from a soil may bypass the free solution and go directly by an exchange from soil to root colloids (Jenny, 1961). We have, as a matter of fact, no idea of the composition and changes of concentrations of the free-space solutions of roots from soil.

The mineral-salt status of a cell determines the content of one group of organic constituents of the cell, which has hitherto been omitted, that is the di- and tri-carboxylic acids of the respiratory cycle. The difference between cations and anions retained in the cell after the uptake, the assimilation of parts of nitrate and sulfur, and the binding of phosphate in esters are balanced by carboxylic acids, in the instances analyzed primarily malic acid, secondarily smaller amounts of citric acid. The organic acid content of the cell sap is in this way regulated directly by the mineral-salt uptake, and this holds true for all parts of the plant. The remaining excess of cations, and concomitantly the organic acid content, can vary within wide limits, so that the cell sap is nicely buffered, in the recorded instance (Table 2) to a pH value of around 6 or 6.5. This renders the pH of the cell practically independent of the external acidity. The mechanism is also worthy of attention with regard to the metabolic value of the organic acids.

All external factors influencing the salt uptake may thus change the content of organic acids. One factor is the carbonate or bicarbonate content of the soil, which is assumed to be responsible for acid formation by carboxylation and induced iron deficiency on calcareous

TABLE 2. Influence of mineral nutrition on the malic acid content and pH of the sap of wheat roots*

External salt	pH in solution	pH in sap	Malic acid, me/ml
$KHCO_3 + CO_2$	7.4	6.25	0.140
K_2SO_4	3.6	6.07	0.120
$CaCO_3 + CO_2$	6.8	6.54	0.110
$CaSO_4$	5.4	6.32	0.036
$(NH_4)_2CO_3 + CO_2$	5.5	6.55	0.096
$(NH_4)_2SO_4$	2.9	5.89	0.044

* From H. Burström. Arkiv. Botan. 32a(17): 1-18. 1945.

soils. Another is the oxygen supply. Part of the salt uptake, namely the active accumulation, is oxygen-dependent, since it is connected with respiration. An impoverished aeration causes a decreased active uptake of salts; a shortage of unused anions and an increase of malic acid also has been experimentally verified (Dubinina, 1961) as a sign of reduced oxygen tension.

THE RESISTANCE OF THE ROOT TO INFECTIONS.—The extensive problem of the mode of entrance of parasites into the plant and the different kinds of resistance are well known to every pathologist. I must restrict myself here to some brief remarks on physiologic properties of roots conducive to the susceptibility to infections and leave out of consideration the whole pathologic side.

Recalling the anatomic structure of roots, we find that fibrous roots occupy a small part of the root system in all perennials and dicotyledonous annuals. The root tissues differentiate and mature rapidly and the epidermis and cortex are often destroyed and shed early. Even before that, these parts are probably characterized by a very slow metabolism. They are not very active. Growth with accompanying syntheses takes place in the tip and near the center of the axis around the border between cortex and stele. It seems likely that the peripheral tissues for physiologic reasons should offer little active metabolic resistance to an invading parasite. Mechanical resistance has to be considered, however.

Pathways of infection.—The root system can be compared with a filter rod dipping in the soil (Fig. 6). Water is sucked through the root system by means of the transpiration stream, and mineral nutrients generally follow the water. Everybody knows what happens when a cut flower is placed in water: it continues to transpire and take up water. It is also known that under such circumstances plants are not long-lived for several reasons. It is easy to establish that nothing will prevent microorganisms from entering the plant with the water through the opened conducting channels. Common mold and bacterial infections will be found in the stem. This shows that the root system prevents microbes from entering the plant. The root system offers a resistance to the water stream (S. O. Falk, unpublished data), probably due to the nature of the root surface and the high viscosity of the cell constituents (Kramer, 1940). To an even greater extent

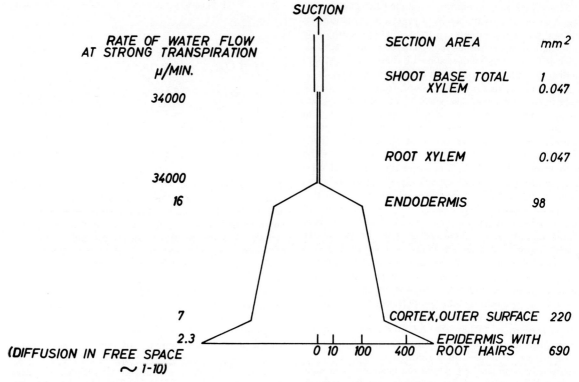

Fig. 6. Diagrammatic picture of the rate of water flow through the roots of a 5-day-old wheat plant. Linear scale on the abscissa is the (surface)$^{-2}$.

it keeps back microorganisms. Fig. 6 visualizes diagrammatically the streaming in a root. Running at a high speed in the vessels, water is slowly drawn through the very much larger outer epidermal surface with its root hairs, leaving some dissolved compounds and entirely excluded microorganisms stuck on the surface.

The rate of the stream is of some interest. The comparison of the root with a filter rod is inadequate in one respect. Water is not sucked from the surrounding soil to the root. The rate of flow at the root surface is of the same low order of magnitude as a diffusion. As a matter of fact, all movements of water and solutes from the soil through the cortex up to the endodermis are not more rapid than a diffusion of solutes in a dilute solution, although the stream is directed by the transpiration, with the plant transpiring vigorously. This is of some importance. First because soil microbes cannot be passively sucked to the root and accumulated on the root surface, and second because a diffusion in all directions inside the cortex is possible in spite of the directed stream. This is technically called a mass movement, but it is so slow that it does not prevent a diffusion in the opposite direction, which is a prerequisite of, for example, the exudation of compounds already mentioned. If, however, ruptures occur in the epidermis and cortex, they may serve as entrance paths for invasions from the soil (Kern, 1959).

Root damage occurs regularly and on a large scale. All microbes unable to dissolve the wall or to puncture it mechanically have to enter through macro- or microscopic wounds; as mentioned, not even the smallest

viruses are likely to enter directly through the undamaged cell wall. The most common ruptures are those where lateral roots emerge. They leave an open wound, which is not healed by the plant. Another important source of root mutilation is a large-scale regular dying of fibrous root tips in a seasonal rhythm. As an example may be mentioned conditions recorded for *Pinus sylvestris* (Kalela, 1955). It was found in a natural community that the length of the finest roots was about doubled from May to July and decreased to the original figure again in October (Fig. 7). Still more striking

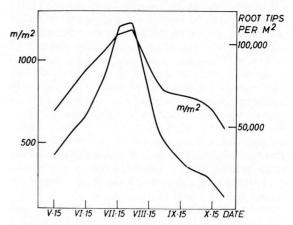

Fig. 7. Seasonal variation in amount of roots of *Pinus sylvestris* in the field. Total root length (m per m² and number of root tips per m². (E. K. Kalela. Acta Forest. Fennica 65: 1-41. 1955.)

was the variation in number of root tips, reaching a peak in July nearly four times the spring and fall values. This is then repeated annually. Similar conditions are found in herbs, for example tomato (Hudson, 1960), with a reduction of the number of tips to one half at the time fruiting begins. The cause of the seasonal changes is not known; both attacks of parasites and unfavorable external conditions have been suggested (Heikurainen, 1955). Whatever the cause, the dead tips must leave numerous open wounds where invasion can take place.

Parasites are also able to enter right through the undamaged root in different ways, either by mechanical rupturing of the cell wall, a mode of entrance only open to fungi, or a chemical dissolution of the wall. The resistances are thus also of either chemical or mechanical nature.

Antibiotics.—It goes without saying that regardless of the mode of entrance of the parasite, a most efficient resistance is offered by antibiotics. Little is known of the occurrence and accumulation of antibiotics in roots, least of all fibrous roots. What we know is not based on systematic studies from a physiologic point of view but rests on scattered observations only. Induced formation of antibiotics occurs and is dealt with in the paper by Dr. Cruikshank in this symposium. It is well known that the occurrence and the activity of antibiotics are very specific for the plant producing them and for their actions against microorganisms. It has earlier been mentioned that fibrous roots generally have a high capacity of synthesis, and some compounds known to be produced have antibiotic properties. They deserve to be mentioned even if we have no clear picture of how widespread the compounds are.

The most efficient and common antibiotics are phenols and quinone derivatives (Schwarze, 1958) of various types, some of which are known to be produced in roots. Coumarin derivatives occur (Goodwin and Pollock, 1954), and scopoletin belongs to the decidedly antibiotic compounds. A group of phytotoxic compounds denoted as inhibitor β is common; it also comprises unsaturated lactones; but the effect on microorganisms is unknown. Different anthocyanin and flavanone derivatives have been found in fibrous roots and are reported to act as uncouplers of phosphorylation (Stenlid, 1961). Flavanone derivatives, together with other strong antibiotics, are especially common in the periderm and xylem. The wood of conifers contains such antibiotics as tropolones with seven-membered carbon rings. The deposition of such compounds has been studied very little in roots, but we may assume that these secondary anatomical parts, known to have the same structure in roots and stems, also contain the same substances.

It has already been mentioned that alkaloids are often produced in roots, but in spite of the strong physiologic action of the compounds they are of varying and sometimes doubtful value as antibiotics against fungi and bacteria. Nicotine may prevent infections but other alkaloids do not seem to have any antibiotic value at all. All effects of alkaloids are specific for different organisms, but we can generally say that alkaloid production in roots is no insurance against infections.

Even if we thus know that certain antibacterial and antifungal substances are produced in roots, we cannot evaluate their practical importance unless we know in what amounts they occur and under what conditions they are formed. With regard to the very common occurrence of mycotrophy, it may be readily concluded that fibrous roots generally are devoid of efficient protection by antifungal substances.

Mechanical Resistance.—The strongest mechanical resistance is offered by suberized periderm, mainly developed in roots of perennials, but weakly so in annual roots. A direct entrance is possible in the periderm only through lenticels, and they are rare in roots or sometimes nearly absent. The strengthening occurring in most annual roots is a suberization of cortical layers leading to the formation of a metacutis. Suberization of all kinds is modifiable, always stronger on surfaces exposed to air than on those developing submersed or in a moist substrate (Kramer, 1950). The decisive factor is in point of fact the oxygen tension. Oxygen deficiency and water excess will generally lower the mechanical resistance the root may offer to a parasite.

If not suberized, the cell walls on the root surface have the ordinary structure of an amorphous matrix of pectins and hemicellulose enclosing a rigid skeleton of cellulose microfibrils. The resistance to an invasion by strictly mechanical forcing of the wall must mainly be offered by the cellulose skeleton, less so by the plastic amorphous components. It then also follows that a chemical dissolution of the cellulose must take place in order to make the wall permeable to an invasion. Fungi attacking the cellulose of higher plants are known to produce cellulase, but it is probably of little or no actual importance. The dissolution of cell walls depends upon the parasite, and as is well known, quite a number of bacteria and fungi produce cellulase often as an adaptive enzyme. Generally it seems that the resistance of the nonsuberized root surface rests mainly on the cellulose component.

Cellulose amounts to as much as 40% of the wall matter in the root, and it may vary somewhat with the external conditions (Table 1). As already mentioned, a high nitrogen supply will cause a low amount of wall substance and especially a reduction of the cellulose content. Otherwise growth can be considerably reduced by nutritional or other soil factors with rather small changes in the amount of wall substance formed and the composition of the walls (Burström, 1958). This means that unfavorable conditions reducing root growth tend to give rather thick cell walls but with rather small changes in their percentage composition. The nitrogen supply is the main natural factor changing the amount of cellulose and the mechanical strength of the cell walls.

EFFECT OF MUTILATION OF THE ROOT SYSTEM.— Assuming that an infection from the soil cannot be prevented and the parasite attack leads to mutilations of the roots, the question arises how extensive a damage the plant can endure. This is one final practical aspect of root infection from the soil. In order to answer this question it is first necessary to recall why plants require roots and what physiologic functions the root system has. Apart from the obvious fact that a plant devoid of roots would lose its foothold, there are three functions to recognize: the synthetic capacity, the salt uptake, and the water uptake. The question is how indispensable the roots are for these processes, and how much of the root system can be impaired without reducing the yield or jeopardizing the life of the plant.

A striking feature of fibrous roots is that they are so organized that the active centers are located in the interior, around endodermis, pericycle, and the primary stele. The peripheral parts, epidermis and cortex, occupying two thirds of the sectional area, are less important.

It has been found by artificial operations that roots can grow without an epidermis (Burström, 1949) and take up salts for a limited period with the whole cortex removed (Branton and Jacobson, 1962). Small and superficial woundings may thus offer no other disadvantage to the plant than permitting microbes to enter.

Plant species may also have the ability to counteract a destruction of roots by the formation of adventitious roots. They are usually produced from the shoot bases as a hormonally regulated process induced by the loss of the primary root system. It has been demonstrated in water cultures that severed root systems can be wholly replaced by adventitious roots of equal or even greater capacity (Humphries, 1958b). No rules can be given for the conditions under which this occurs in the field, but the time at which the primary root system is damaged is of particular importance.

The synthesizing capacity of roots has already been touched upon, especially that of nitrogen compounds. There is not much to be added, because there are to my knowledge no elucidative studies of what a partial loss or inactivation of the root system quantitatively means for the syntheses. It is a rather important function of the roots under ordinary conditions in certain species, but since probably all shoots are capable of assimilating nitrogen if nitrate is available, the roots are certainly not indispensable for this purpose. Extensive experience from tissue culture work has taught that unorganized callus tissues can produce normally organized shoots virtually without roots (cf. Miller, 1961). Not too far-reaching conclusions can be drawn from these results, however, because the shoots are auxoheterotrophic under these conditions, requiring auxin and kinetin as vitamins. As a matter of fact, we do not know to what extent the roots are indispensable as sources of compounds for the plant under normal conditions.

We are a little better informed about the salt-uptake function. The salt transport to the shoot is mediated by the transpiration stream. It is a matter of considerable controversy whether the salt transport from the root is only a passive mass flow with the water

or whether it involves metabolically controlled steps. For the present purposes there is no reason to distinguish between different mechanisms of solution flow; we need only consider the composition of the bulk solution streaming upwards in the xylem. The concentration varies, of course, and may attain values higher than that of the external solution if this is very dilute, which it generally should be in the soil, but otherwise it may be lower, standing in a fairly good relation to the external concentration (Russel and Barber, 1960; Kihlman-Falk, 1961). The roots not only contain mechanisms of accumulating salts but offer a resistance to the flow of salts as well. If the root system is cut off, water flows directly into the opened vessels and salts follow into the shoot. Perennial leaves have been kept alive accumulating salts for years in this way. As long as transpiration is going on, the salt uptake is not impeded, and for this purpose the root system should certainly be dispensable for the plant.

A practical point in connection with damages of the root system is the seasonal variation in salt uptake and salt requirements. Most nutrients are taken up rapidly by ordinary crop plants during the beginning of the season up to the time of flower induction and may then slow down or stop altogether. The total demand for a certain nutrient may also be entirely satisfied by this early uptake. It is known from the agricultural literature that the salt uptake at later stages usually is of little if any importance to the plant development, except for nitrogen, which may be required continuously throughout the vegetation period. There are, of course, pronounced differences between species in this respect. By and large, during a considerable part of the growing season, the plant can do fairly well without roots as far as the mineral nutrient supply is concerned.

The water supply to the plant is the crucial point in the function of the root. The effect of reducing the root system on the water uptake has been studied in experiments of different kinds (Gračanin, 1962), which showed that species react very differently to a root severing or inactivation. Several methods have been employed: part of the root system cut off, branches of the root system inactivated by drying in air, or the roots raised more or less above the water level. The operations uniformly show that regardless of the method, reduction of the root system decreases water uptake and concomitantly transpiration, considerably in some species, less in others (Fig. 8).

The influence of the amount of roots on the transpiration helps us understand the function of the root. It is not evident that transpiration should be curtailed, because it could go on even if water uptake was impeded, under an increasing water deficit and eventual wilting of the plant. This does not occur; on the contrary, the impression is that the magnitude of the transpiration is determined by the extension of the functioning root system even in water cultures. With complete excision of roots, the conducting vessels are sometimes blocked by excreted colloidal matter of necrotic origin, but in other instances this explanation fails and we must assume that there is a high resist-

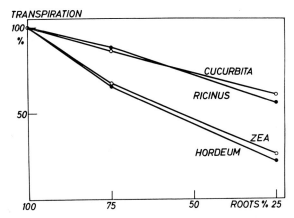

Fig. 8. Relation between reduction of size of root system and transpiration in four species. (M. Gračanin. Fac. Sci. Nat. Univ. Skopje, Yugoslavia. p. 39-64. 1962.)

ance to water somewhere in the root (S. O. Falk, unpublished data). The funnel-type function of the root (Fig. 6) would thus be necessary in order to secure a sufficiently wide entrance surface. The importance of this function is apparent in the soil (Parker, 1949), where local water supply is limited and streaming of water is of minor importance. These relations can scarcely be studied accurately under field conditions, but it can be concluded by analogy that in nature the size of the root system is decisive for the water supply.

Even under favorable weather conditions, tops of plants often suffer from a temporary water deficit in the daytime; therefore it could be suspected that an inactivation of parts of the root system would markedly influence top growth, and this is what actually takes place. Under a given set of external conditions the ratio of root to top growth may be kept nearly constant. There is obviously a delicate balance between the capacities of the two parts. Consequently a mutilation of the root system would be expected to reduce top growth and yield, and this has been verified in long-term experiments (Humphries, 1958a). With barley in water cultures an excision of one half the root system reduced top growth by 20% and yield by one half. In spite of the great extension of the root system and the amazingly large contact surface between plant roots and soil—in a classic example for a single rye plant estimated to as much as nearly 700 m²—the root systems are not overabundant, and mutilations of even limited range may seriously affect the plant. This ought to be most noticeable under unfavorable conditions when great demands are made on the roots. It could be inferred that such conditions as temporary drought and mineral-nutrient disorders, increasing the strain on the root system, ought to make the plant more susceptible to root damage.

We cannot apply stringent conclusions from the scanty experience of laboratory experiments and tests under carefully controlled field conditions to ordinary fields or natural habitats. The living conditions are too different; it is hardly possible to interpret field obser-

vations satisfactorily. For example, it has been shown with ryegrass (Vose, 1962) that high-yielding strains in the field have an extensive root system, whereas there is no difference between high and low-yielding strains in water culture with excess of both water and nutrients. Obviously some nutrient factor is utilized more easily by the high-yielding strain, favoring root extension and plant growth. There is under ecologic conditions often some nutrient deficiency and usually, at least temporarily, a water deficiency with increased demands on the roots. In a dense mixed community, conditions are further aggravated by the interaction and competition between individual plants. The root system of a plant individual is greatly reduced under such conditions. It has been reported that grass plants growing isolated may produce ten times more roots than in a closed community, with only a meager 15% increase in top production. Under such conditions, which are those normally encountered in the field, the strain on the roots must be very great, and any kind of mutilation of the roots, mechanically by animals or by infectious parasites, may become serious to the plant. We have no clear idea of what further mutilation and root reduction the plant could endure under such field conditions, and we must cautiously refrain from predictions based on favorable and idealized laboratory experiments.

These concluding remarks are also meant to indicate what kind of research is needed for a better understanding of the root-microbe relation in the soil. Further, we need to devise methods of studying chemical activity and exchange of compounds in roots under conditions at least resembling those the plant encounters in natural habitats.

LITERATURE CITED

BARBER, D. A., M. EBERT, and N. T. S. EVANS. 1962. The movement of 15O through barley and rice plants. J. Exptl. Botany 13: 397-403.

BIEDLE, R. 1958. Der Einfluss der Mineralstoffe auf die Transpiration. vol. 4, p. 328-426. *In* A. Lang [ed.], Encyclopedia of plant physiology, Springer Verlag, Berlin.

BJÖRKMAN, E. 1942. Über die Bedingungen der Mykorrhizabildung bei Kiefer und Fichte. Symbolae Botan. Upsalensis 6: 2-19.

BRANTON, D., and L. JACOBSON. 1962. Iron transport in pea plants. Plant Physiol. 37: 539-545.

BROWN, R., W. S. REITH, and E. ROBINSON. 1952. The mechanism of plant cell growth. Symp. Soc. Exptl. Biol. 6: 329-347.

BURSTRÖM, H. 1934. Über antagonistische Erscheinungen bei der Kationenaufnahme des Hafers. Svensk. Botan. Tidskr. 28: 157-263.

BURSTRÖM, H. 1945a. The nitrate nutrition of plants. Ann. Agr. Coll. Sweden 13: 1-86.

BURSTRÖM, H. 1945b. Studies on the buffer systems of cells. Arkiv Botan. 32A(7): 1-18.

BURSTRÖM, H. 1949. Studies on growth and metabolism of roots. I. The action of n-diamylacetic acid on root elongation. Physiol. Plantarum 2: 197-209.

BURSTRÖM, H. 1958. The influence of growth regulators on the composition of the cell wall. Fysiogr. Sällsk. (Lund) Förh. 28: 53-64.

BURSTRÖM, H. 1959. Formation of intercellularies in root meristems. Physiol. Plantarum 12: 371-385.

BUXTON, E. W. 1962. Root exudates from banana and

their relationship to strains of the Fusarium causing Panama wilt. Ann. Appl. Biol. 50: 269-282.

CARR, D. J. 1961. Chemical influences of the environment. Encycl. Plant Physiol. 16: 737-794.

DUBININA, I. M. 1961. Metabolism of roots under various levels of aeration. Plant Physiol. (U.S.S.R.) (Engl. translation) 8: 395-406.

ELIASSON, L. 1955. The connection between the respiratory gradient and the growth rate in wheat roots. Physiol. Plantarum 8: 374-388.

EPSTEIN, E. 1960. Spaces, barriers, and ion carriers; ion absorption by plants. Am. J. Botany 47: 393-399.

FADEEL, A. A. 1963. Assimilation of carbon dioxide by chlorophyllous roots. Physiol. Plantarium 16: 870-888.

FERGUSON, J. D. 1963. The continuous culture of excised wheat roots. Physiol. Plantarum 16: 585-595.

FRANKE, W. 1961. Tröpfchenausscheidung und Ektodesmenverteilung in Zwiebelschuppenepidermen. Planta 57: 266-283.

GLINKA, Z., and L. REINHOLD. 1962. Rapid changes in permeability of cell membranes to water brought about by carbon dioxide and oxygen. Plant Physiol. 37: 481-486.

GOODWIN, R. H., and B. M. POLLACK. 1954. Studies on roots. I. Am. J. Botany 41: 516-520.

GRAČANIN, M. 1962. Über die Rolle des Wurzelsystems in der Wasserversorgung der Pflanzen. Fac. Sci. Nat. Univ. Skopje, Yugoslavia, 1: 39-64.

GRINEVA, G. M. 1962. Excretion by plant roots during brief periods of anaerobiosis. Plant Physiol. (U.S.S.R.) 8: 549-552.

HEIKURAINEN, L. 1955. Über Veränderungen in den Wurzelverhältnissen der Kiefernbestände auf Moorböden im Laufe des Jahres. Acta Forest. Fennica 65 (2): 1-70.

HEJNOWICZ, Z. 1958. Protochlorophyll in root tips. Physiol. Plantarum 11: 878-888.

HELDER, R. J. 1956. The loss of substances by cells and tissues (salt glands). vol. 2, p. 468-488. *In* A. Lang [ed.], Encyclopedia of Plant Physiology. Springer-Verlag, Berlin.

HUDSON, J. P. 1960. Relations between root and shoot growth in tomato. Sci. Hort. 14: 49-54.

HUGHES, A. P., and G. C. EVANS. 1962. Plant growth and the aerial environment II, New Phytologist 61: 154-174.

HUMPHRIES, E. C. 1958a. Effect of removal of a part of the root system on the subsequent growth of the root and shoot. Ann. Botany (London) [N.S.] 22: 251-257.

HUMPHRIES, E. C. 1958b. The effect of removal of the root-system of barley on the production of ears. Ann. Botany (London) [N.S.] 22: 417-422.

JACKSON, J. E., and P. E. WEATHERLEY. 1962. The effect of hydrostatic pressure gradients on the movement of sodium and calcium across the root cortex. J. Exptl. Botany 13: 404-413.

JENNY, H. 1961. Plant-root-soil interactions. p. 665-694. *In* M. Zarrow [ed.], Growth in living systems, Proc. Intern. Symp. on Growth (Purdue Univ., 1960), Basic Books, New York.

KALELA, E. K. 1955. Die Veränderungen in den Wurzelverhältnissen der Kiefernbestände im Laufe der Vegetationsperiode. Acta Forest. Fennica 65: 1-41.

KERN, H. 1959. Parasitismus und Symbiose. Allgem. Handb. Pflanzenphysiol. 11: 429-446.

KIHLMAN-FALK, E. 1961. Components in the uptake and transport of high accumulative ions in wheat. Physiol. Plantarum 14: 417-438.

KOZLOWSKI, T. T. 1949. Light and water relations to growth and competition of Piedmont forest trees. Ecol. Monographs 19: 207-231.

KRAMER, P. J. 1940. Root resistance as a cause of decreased water absorption by plants at low temperatures. Plant Physiol. 15: 63-79.

KRAMER, P. J. 1950. Effect of wilting on the subsequent intake of water by plants. Am. J. Botany 37: 280-284.

LEMON, E. R., and C. L. WIEGAND. 1962. Soil aeration and plant root relations. II. Root respiration. Agron. J. 54: 171-175

LÜTTGE, U. 1962. Über die Zusammensetzung des Nektars und den Mechanismus seiner Sekretion III. Planta 59: 175-194.

LÜTTGE, U., and J. WEIGL. 1962. Mikroradioautographische Untersuchungen der Aufnahme und des Transportes von $^{35}SO_4{}^-$ und $^{45}Ca{}^{++}$ in Keimwurzeln von *Zea mays* L. und *Pisum sativum* L. Planta 58: 113-126.

MCLAREN, A. D., W. A. JENSEN, and L. JACOBSON. 1960. Absorption of enzymes and other proteins. Plant Physiol. 35: 549-556.

MILLER, C. O. 1961. Kinetin and related compounds in plant growth. Ann. Rev. Plant Physiol. 12: 395-408.

MOTHES, K., and A. ROMEKE. 1958. Die Alkaloide. Handb. Pflanzenphysiol. 8: 989-1049.

PARKER, J. 1949. Effects of variations in the root-leaf ratio on transpiration rate. Plant Physiol. 24: 739-743.

PETTERSSON, S. 1961. Ion absorption in young sunflower plants II. The sulphate uptake in apparent free space. Physiol. Plantarum 14: 124-132.

RICHARDSON, S. D. 1957. Studies of root growth in *Acer saccharinum* L. II. Further effects of the shoot system on root growth. Proc. Koninkl. Ned. Akad. Wetenschap. C 62: 624-629.

ROGERS, W. S., and G. A. BOOTH. 1960. The roots of fruit trees. Sci. Hort. 14: 27-34.

RUSSEL, R. S., and D. A. BARBER. 1960. The relationship between salt uptake and the absorption of water by intact plants. Ann. Rev. Plant Physiol. 11: 127-140.

SCHWARZE, P. 1958. Phenole und Chinone und die biogene Bildung von Benzolkernen bei höheren Pflanzen-Krankheits-resistenz. vol. 10, p. 533-536. *In* A. Lang [ed.] Encyclopedia of plant Physiology, Springer Verlag, Berlin.

SIEGEL, S. M., L. A. ROSEN, and G. RENWICK. 1962. Effect of reduced oxygen tension on vascular plants. Growth and composition of red kidney bean plants in 5 per cent O_2. Physiol. Plantarum 15: 304-314.

STÅLFELT, M. G. 1960. Växtekologi. Scandin. Univ. Books, Stockholm. 440 p.

STARKEY, R. L. 1958. Interrelations between microorganisms and plant roots in the rhizosphere Bacteriol. Rev. 22: 154-172.

STENLID, G. 1961. On the effects of some flavanoid pigments upon growth and ion absorption of wheat roots. Physiol. Plantarum 14: 659-670.

STREET, H. E. 1959. Special problems raised by organ and tissue culture. Correlations between organs of higher plants as a consequence of specific metabolic requirements. Handb. Pflanzenphysiol. 11: 153-178.

VOSE, P. B. 1962. Nutritional response and shoot/root ratio as factors in the composition and yield of genotypes of perennial ryegrass, *Lolium perenna* L. Ann. Botany (London) [N.S.] 26: 425-437.

► DISCUSSION OF H. G. BURSTRÖM PAPER

A. S. Sussman:

Inasmuch as viruses are macromolecules, penetration of proteins is of potential interest to the pathologist. Would you care to comment on the uptake of macromolecules?

H. Burström:

As mentioned, antibiotics of molecular weight up to 600 are taken up. Dr. McLaren has reported uptake of protein, but according to private information, only under certain circumstances. The smallest viruses are 10 times as large as this protein. In the plant, viruses pass through plasmodesmata; if Dr. Scott's observations can be generalized, an uptake of viruses should be possible. But it has not been possible to show with certainty an uptake of humus compounds.

A. D. McLaren:

Humic acids probably do not penetrate roots readily since both they and root surfaces are negatively charged, as demonstrated by the speaker and others. Positively charged macromolecules, such as ribonuclease, do penetrate roots with "free space" and cell walls of the cortex and epidermis. This was also demonstrated for pectinases of *Erwinia* by L. R. Jones (Vermont Agr. Exp. Sta. Bull. 147, p. 281-360, 1910). Only when the root hair is mechanically damaged will fluorescein-labeled protein molecules enter it. Since a virus is generally larger than a typical protein molecule of 25-50 Å, it probably will not enter an uninjured root hair.

H. Burström:

May I add this remark: pectinases are able to enter by dissolving the cell wall; it has been said to occur in root hairs. Negatively charged molecules may enter, but we do not know up to what size.

C. Kado:

Supplementing Dr. McLaren and Dr. Sussman's questions regarding uptake of macromolecules, i.e. soilborne viruses, I would like to refer them to the work of Murphy and his co-workers (Virology 6: 612, 623, 1958) in which they were able to recover a mammalian arborvirus from leaves of tomato and potato plants grown in nutrient solutions containing homogenate extracts of infectious mouse-brain tissue. Pea, tomato, potato and lettuce have been tried. Yarwood has shown that roots growing through tobacco-necrosis-infected leaves become infected, and at times the virus has been found in the hypocotyl of bean plants. Although these studies do not negate the fact that the roots may be injured during growth, it may be of interest to the discussion.

H. Katznelson:

You mentioned that vitamin deficiency can occur in roots. Is it your opinion that plants require an exogenous source of vitamins, and do you think this can be made up by microbial synthesis in the rhizosphere or on the root surface?

H. Burström:

Deficiency has been reported to occur in some instances under unfavorable conditions. I doubt that it occurs otherwise, but our experience is certainly lim-ited. As regards the rhizosphere as a source of vitamins, I have no opinion.

L. I. Miller:

Root hairs occur in the peanut plant only under certain poorly defined conditions. Are there any conditions in the physiology of roots which you feel might influence the formation of root hairs?

H. Burström:

Yes. Root-hair growth is definitely promoted by low soil-water content, which might be an oxygen effect, since they develop readily in aerated nutrient solution. They are promoted by calcium, and might—by analogy with solution cultures—be poorly developed at low pH. Effects of soil-microbe metabolites are unknown but possible.

A. D. Rovira:

1. Many soil organisms delay and reduce root-hair growth in our experiments, where we thought we had eliminated oxygen deficiency as a cause of this suppression. Could you suggest the possible mechanisms?

2. This suppression varies with different soil inocula, suggesting that the populations of the various soil types differ. This would suggest that in different soils the extent of root-hair development will vary, which may affect the rate of movement of water at the root surface. To what extent would you predict that these root-hair suppressions affect this rate of water movement?

H. Burström:

1. It is impossible to guess what can suppress root-hair formation in a complicated system containing unknown metabolites. Root hairs are sensitive to all sorts of organic compounds.

2. Reduced root-hair formation in the soil most certainly restricts water uptake and water balance. We know that the resistance to water is great at the surface, but cannot predict how the rate changes—either reduced or unchanged.

A. S. Crafts:

It is important to determine where compounds go after absorption. Some absorbed compounds (i.e. 2,4-D) may be readily absorbed but not readily translocated to the foliage; some readily absorbed compounds (i.e. monuron, simazine) may be rapidly translocated to tops; some compounds (i.e. maleic hydrazide P, K) may be retranslocated from foliage to roots and hence be systemically distributed.

H. Burström:

A very pertinent comment. It has recently been directly demonstrated that the barrier for upward transport is located in the endodermis.

R. R. Baker:

Regarding the necessity of vitamins supplied by microorganisms for growth of higher plants, germ-free beans have been grown through two generations at Colorado State University. There has been no significant difference in dry weight between germ-free and contaminated plants. Thus, beans may be completely autotrophic. Germ-free tomatoes, however, had significantly lower dry weights than contaminated controls. Microorganisms may have an effect on growth and development of higher plants, but reasons for these responses are at present unknown.

J. D. Menzies:

1. If organic substances are not easily absorbed by roots, then they should be screened out at the root surface as water is extracted by transpiration. May this be a supplement to root excretion as a source of the rich substrates in the rhizosphere?

2. Russian workers have claimed that roots can absorb vitamins added to natural soil and that these seem to stimulate the synthesis of amino nitrogen compounds in the roots.

H. Burström:

1. A difficult question, requiring a quantitative evaluation, which is at present impossible. However, a concentration on the root surface would require a mass transport to the root, which can be doubted. It is also necessary to consider that a functioning root is continuously growing and the mature part will eventually lose the absorbing function. As the root grows, the rhizosphere is continuously renewed at the tip, and this presents no static microenvironment.

2. No comment.

J. L. Harley:

In connection with Dr. Rovira's question on the suppression of root hairs by exudates of microorganisms, I would draw his attention to the work of Slankis on the effects of various mycorrhizal fungi of *Boletus* species on the development of pine root hairs in liquid culture. Here considerable effects by various combinations of pure growth substances were matched with those of fungal exudates on the development of roots and their root hairs.

A. S. Sussman:

I would like to ask either Dr. Burström or Dr. McLaren whether the macromolecules that have been worked with have been hydrolyzed first before entrance? Also, if proteins are taken up, does the endodermis act as a barrier?

A. D. McLaren:

Lysozyme which has entered roots can be extracted by homogenizing the root; it is still enzymatically active and has not been hydrolysed by the plant. By means of fluorescent or radioactive tracer moieties of the protein, one can see that penetration is stopped by the Casparian strip or thereabouts.

A. Kerr:

Chemicals such as amino acids and sugars exude from the zone of cell elongation. What are the characteristics of this zone which might explain this exudation? Is it likely to be an active or a passive process?

H. Burström:

1. The zone of elongation and root-hair induction has a higher permeability than the meristem and the mature part. It is also characterized by a high rate of metabolism.

2. Nothing indicates that a passive process does not occur, but it is not clear that the cytological and physiological requirements for an active process are fulfilled.

J. Tammen:

1. Under what conditions might anaerobic respiration be expected to occur in roots?

2. Would you indicate the metabolic pathways in broad outline?

H. Burström:

1. Anaerobic respiration may occur under oxygen deficiency, but the general experience is that the roots do not survive or at least stop growing under such conditions. Anaerobiosis would be physiologically and ecologically of no consequence.

2. I cannot remember that this has been elucidated. Aberrant R.Q.'s have been recorded for the meristematic tip; but no more details, and they may be due to low permeability and poor gas exchange.

N. T. Flentje:

Pathologists frequently find roots of plants stripped of considerable lengths of epidermis and cortex, yet the roots are still actively growing and the plant seems little affected. Can these tissues be lost from roots with little or no effect? How extensive in the root system can the loss be?

H. Burström:

This is an interesting point. Epidermis can be continuously shed artificially, but the roots go on growing. Elongation is obviously located in the border region between cortex and stele. Cortex and epidermis would thus be dispensable for growth, provided that the injuries are restricted. Complete stripping of cortex, however, will kill the roots. It is impossible to predict how extensive injuries may be and still be endured. The decreased surface development must, of course, reduce water uptake.

A. W. Dimock:

Dr. Rovira, in discussing the suppression of root-hair formation by microorganisms, made the statement, ". . . we *thought* we had eliminated oxygen deficiency as a cause of this suppression." Why did you say "we *thought*," and have you had some second thoughts?

A. D. Rovira:

My reason for being cautious when saying that we had adequate aeration in our studies on the effects of microorganisms on root-hair development resulted from Dr. Burström's statement of the marked effect of aeration on root-hair growth. However, in some of our experiments we grew our roots along the surface of agar slopes where aeration could not be questioned and in these conditions microorganisms still reduced root-hair development.

While on this topic of root-hair suppression, I should point out that these effects by microorganisms may be modified by the environmental conditions. The plants do have the ability to counter the root-hair stunting effects under optimum growing conditions.

F. M. Scott:

In relation to exudation in the region of elongation of the root, as Dr. Burström says, the walls in the region of elongation are temporarily thinner and there is a rearrangement of the microfibrils. In the isodiametric cells of the meristematic roots there is a fibrillar network, there are very few intercellular spaces, and the cells are closely packed. In the region of elongation there are cylindrical cells with intercellular spaces. When the cells are stretching, the microfibrils are horizontal to the root axis, and there are a number of pits or pitfields limited to horizontal lines. The region of elongation is an excellent area for research.

B. Zak:

I wish to comment on the point of emergence of lateral roots. Passage of a weak (50 microampere) direct electric current for 3 days through roots of avocado grown in water produced localized killing of tissue in the zone of lateral-root emergence and around lenticels. Root tips were also killed. Low electrical resistance in these areas suggests tissue weakness or leakage of conducting solution and may be related to the attraction of and invasion by pathogens.

Plant Root Exudates and Their Influence upon Soil Microorganisms

A. D. ROVIRA—*Division of Soils, Commonwealth Scientific and Industrial Research Organization, Adelaide, South Australia.*

One of the major factors determining the behaviour of plant pathogens in soil is the availability of nutrients, and it is in this respect that the exudation of organic compounds from plant roots plays an important role in the problem of biological control of root diseases. From the time Hiltner (1904) observed that microorganisms were more abundant in soil near plant roots than in distant soil there has been considerable speculation as to whether soluble organic substances were wholly or partly responsible for this stimulation of the microflora around plant roots.

The two aspects of root-exudate research not dealt with in this review are the interactions between higher plants in relation to root exudates (reviewed by Börner, 1960; Wood, 1960) and the release of nitrogen from nodulated legumes (Wyss and Wilson, 1941; Virtanen, von Hansen, and Laine, 1937; Butler and Bathurst, 1956). This review will deal with the nature of plant root exudates with emphasis on their influence on both the saprophytic and pathogenic soil microflora.

In the field of root-exudate research there are four papers of historic interest reporting the release of nitrogen compounds, sugars, phosphatides and nematode-stimulating factors from roots. The first conclusive evidence of exudation from roots was provided by Knudson (1920), who showed that peas and maize grown under aseptic conditions in sucrose solution produced considerable quantities of reducing sugars. Knudson proposed that the sucrose was absorbed by roots and converted to reducing sugars, which were excreted. Lyon and Wilson (1921) found that organic nitrogen was released from maize roots growing under sterile conditions in large-capacity vessels; they concluded that this material was released by living roots rather than the sloughed-off root cells which accumulated at the bottom of the vessels. Phosphatides were reported by Cranner (1922) as coming from the roots of seedlings and mature plants. The first conclusive evidence of the stimulation of specific organisms by root exudates was that of O'Brien and Prentice (1930). By showing that the cysts of the potato eelworm (*Heterodera schachtii*, now *H. rostochiensis* Woll.) hatched in the presence of root washings of potato but not the washings of beet, rape, lupin, mustard, or oat roots, they demonstrated the biological specificity of the exudates of different plants.

After these early reports little was done in the field until this last decade, during which there has been considerable interest and research into the nature and effects of root exudates. This delay in following up the earlier discoveries was probably due to two major technical problems, namely the growth of plants in sufficient numbers under sterile conditions, and the identification of organic materials at the low concentrations at which they occur in root exudates.

ASEPTIC CULTURE OF PLANTS.—As it is not possible to determine the nature of true root exudates unless plants are grown in the absence of microorganisms, one is faced with the problems of seed sterilization and growth of the plants under aseptic conditions until the exudate is removed for analysis. Seeds can be surface-sterilized without difficulty with mercuric chloride, hypochlorite, and other compounds and germinated on agar (as a sterility check and to remove initial seed exudates), before planting in a suitable apparatus for aseptic culture. Certain plant species, e.g. grasses and cereals, often contain an internal microflora that makes it impossible to conduct exudation studies under the ideal conditions of complete asepsis. In such cases the soaking and heat treatment of seeds may destroy some of these contaminants. If this is not successful, then the presence of contaminants should be noted in any consideration of the nature of the root exudates.

Many methods have been proposed for the aseptic culture of plants. The apparatus used depends to a large extent upon the number of plants required and the age to which the plants will be grown. Several effective types of apparatus have been developed for growing plants with sterile roots. In some of these the tops remain in the open (Nilsson, 1957; Waris, 1958; Szember, 1959; Reuszer, 1949, 1962; Stotzky, Culbreth, and Mish, 1962; Bradfute et al., 1962). The major problems with these methods are the risk of contamination and the fact that it is difficult to grow the large number of plants generally required for root-exudate studies.

The simplest and most effective method of overcoming these problems is to enclose the entire plant. This can be done simply and effectively in large test tubes. The plants are supported by a stainless-steel mesh with the roots in nutrient solution, which can be changed and sampled for analysis when necessary. With seedlings growing under such conditions aeration does not appear to be necessary for healthy root and root-hair development. This technique has the disadvantages that the plants grow in a high-humidity environment and the studies are confined to seedlings.

There is also the possibility of contamination of the root exudate with seed and leaf exudates. Studies on the effects of environment and age of plant on exudation indicate, however, that such contamination is of minor importance.

METHODS OF ANALYSIS.—Although the quantities of organic material exuded from roots are sufficient to support large populations of microorganisms, they are often too low to be determined without the use of sensitive techniques. The advent of paper and column chromatography and biological assay, however, has made it possible to analyse root exudates for many organic compounds, such as sugars, amino acids, organic acids, and nucleic acid derivatives, which might be expected in root exudate.

Microbiological assay methods, developed for the detection of minute quantities of vitamins, can be applied equally successfully to the analysis of root exudates and the detection of biologically significant quantities of growth factors.

Direct observations of exudation from sterile roots, as carried out by Pearson and Parkinson (1961) and by Schroth and Snyder (1961, 1962), have proved useful in determining the sites of major exudation on roots. The exudates from sterile roots can be absorbed onto filter paper and, by using selective sprays, a range of compounds coming from different parts of the root system may be detected. As a further refinement of the technique which may yield more data, these areas may be eluted with sprays prior to development, and the subsequent eluate chromatographed.

Bioassay techniques based on the growth responses of specific organisms (generally plant pathogens) to exudates have often been reported, e.g. spore-germination factors, fungus-attracting factors; but these give little or no information on the composition of the exudates. The precise identification of the compounds involved is often long and tedious and necessitates the services of skilled organic chemists. This has been the case with the potato-eelworm-hatching factor first reported by O'Brien and Prentice (1930) and subsequently partially characterized by a team of organic

chemists headed by Todd (Calum, Raistrick, and Todd, 1949; Calum, Todd, and Waring, 1949; Marrian et al., 1949; Russell, Todd, and Waring, 1949).

The use of *Neurospora* mutants with different nutrient requirements to determine whether different compounds in the exudate originated from different sites along the root has been developed by Frenzel (1960). In this technique direct microscopy is combined with the use of specific *Neurospora* mutants.

In the root-exudate studies little use has been made of radioactive tracer techniques. Their application would help elucidate the mechanisms involved and enable the detection of fluctuations in exudation with changes of environment.

NATURE OF EXUDATES.—*Carbohydrates.*—At least ten sugars, including an oligosaccharide, have been identified in the exudates of a wide range of plants. Although few quantitative estimates of the sugars have been made, glucose and fructose are generally the most abundant. The roots of oats, grown aseptically in nutrient solution, sand, or glass beads, have been found to be covered with a brown mucilaginous material (Rovira, unpublished). This material is insoluble in cold water and soluble in hot water, and is a short-chain oligosaccharide releasing glucose and fructose upon hydrolysis. Under nonsterile conditions this mucilage becomes densely colonized by microorganisms and obviously forms a readily available substrate. Jenny and Grossenbacher (1963) have reported a "mucigel" on the roots of barley seedlings, but this appears to be a pectic acid polymer and is not densely colonized by microorganisms. Dart and Mercer (1964) have also demonstrated the presence of an external gelatinous material on the roots of barrel medic (*Medicago tribuloides*) grown under aseptic conditions (Fig. 1). The nature of this mucilage on medic roots has not yet been characterized.

The range of sugars reported in exudates and the plants from which they were released (Table 1) indicates that exudation of sugars is a general phenomenon playing an important role in the nonspecific stimulation of microorganisms in the rhizosphere.

Amino acids.—Amino acids form the most studied group of compounds in exudates from plant roots. To date 23 have been reported in the exudates of 15 dif-

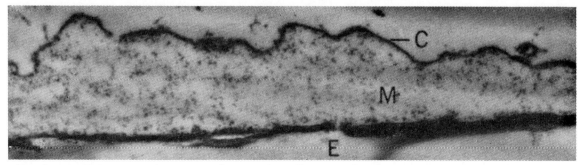

Fig. 1. Mucilaginous material on a sterile root of *Medicago tribuloides* 5 to 15 mm from the tip. ($\times$ 20,000) E = epidermal cell; M = mucilaginous layer; C = "cuticle." (P. J. Dart and F. V. Mercer. Arch. Mikrobiol. 47: 344-378. 1964.)

TABLE 1. Carbohydrates detected in root exudate

Compound	Plant	Reference
Glucose	Peas, wheat	Lundegårdh and Stenlid, 1944
	Peas	Rovira, 1956*a*
	Soybean, barley, wheat	Katznelson, Rouatt, and Payne, 1955
	Wheat	Vrany, Vancura, and Macura, 1962
	Oats, mustard	Bhuvaneswari and Subba-Rao, 1957
	Oats	Rivière, 1960; Rovira, 1956*a*
	White pine	Slankis, 1958
Fructose	Peas, oats	Rovira, 1956*a*
	Sorghum, mustard	Bhuvaneswari and Subba-Rao, 1957
Sucrose	Bean	Schroth and Snyder, 1961
Xylose	Sorghum, mustard	Bhuvaneswari and Subba-Rao, 1957
	Wheat	Vrany, Vancura, and Macura, 1962
Maltose	Mustard	Bhuvaneswari and Subba-Rao, 1957
	Bean	Schroth and Snyder, 1961
Rhamnose	Wheat	Vrany, Vancura, and Macura, 1962
Arabinose Xylose Raffinose	White pine	Slankis, 1958
	Wheat (traces)	Rivière, 1960
Oligosaccharide	Oats	Rovira (unpublished)
	Wheat	Vrany, Vancura, and Macura, 1962
Unidentified	Sugar beet	Geller, 1954

ferent plant species (Table 2). The spectra of amino acids reported for the different plants vary considerably; but such comparisons between plants may be misleading because of the different conditions under which the experiments were conducted by different investigators. Even the exudation patterns for a single plant species such as wheat as found by four different workers vary considerably (Table 2, columns 11, 12, 13, 14). In a direct comparison between the exudates of different plants grown under identical conditions, marked differences were apparent in the amounts and types of amino acids coming from roots (Rovira, 1956*a*, 1959). A list of the principal amino acids exuded from peas and oats during their first 10 days of growth in sterile quartz sand is given in Table 3. It required seven times as much exudate from oats as from peas to yield a suitable chromatogram; this indicates the quantitative differences between the plants. A comparison of the amino acids in pea- and oat-root exudate showed homoserine, threonine, α-alanine, glutamine, asparagine, and serine to be dominant in pea-root exudate; while in oat-root exudate serine, lysine, and glycine were the most abundant. These qualitative and quantitative differences in the amino acid patterns of exudates from different plant species grown under identical conditions will, no doubt, influence the balance of organisms developing in the rhizosphere, and, even without the more complex compounds, may perhaps determine the susceptibility and resistance of plants to root pathogens.

The influence of triiodobenzoic acid and chloramphenicol as foliar sprays on the exudation of amino acids has been studied by Vrany, Vancura, and Macura (1962). They found that chloramphenicol caused a general increase in amino acids in the exudate as well as a relative increase in α- and β-alanine and a decrease in phenylalanine.

Vitamins.—Ten vitamins have been identified in exudates from a wide variety of plants (Table 4) and, although the levels are generally low, these may be sufficient to meet the requirements of some of the vitamin-requiring microorganisms of the rhizosphere.

In an analysis for six vitamins in the exudates from lucerne, field pea, tomato, phalaris, and six clover species, biotin was found to be consistently present at low but biologically active levels (Rovira and Harris, 1961). Pantothenate and niacin generally occurred in the exudate, thiamin was found only occasionally, riboflavine infrequently, and pyridoxine never. The sporadic occurrence of thiamin in legume-root exudate was interesting in view of the statement by Wilson (1940) that "Thiamin can be classed as an essential growth factor for the rhizobia." The exudate findings indicate that the rhizobia must depend upon the synthesis of thiamin by neighbouring organisms rather than upon the host plant. Similarly, it is likely that the high proportion of vitamin-requiring bacteria which occur in the rhizosphere (Wallace and Lochhead, 1949) depends more on vitamin-synthesizing microorganisms than root exudates for growth.

Organic acids.—Although organic acids are involved in the uptake of nutrients by roots and are found inside the root at significant levels, there are few reports of these materials occurring in root exudate (Table 5). The only quantitative data are those of Rivière (1959, 1960), who found that a single wheat plant grown aseptically in nutrient solution to the tillering stage (6 weeks) exuded 13 mg acetic, 3.5 mg propionic, 2 mg butyric, and 1.5 mg valeric acids, which would be significant in the nutrition of the rhizosphere population.

Considering the part played by organic acids in root metabolism and probable fluctuations in levels accord-

TABLE 2. Amino acids detected in root exudate

Amino acid	Sunflower[1]	Oats[2]	Maize[3]	Peas[4]	Peas[5]	Rice[6]	White clover[7]	Perennial rye grass[8]	Wormwood[9]	Tomato[10]	Wheat[11]	Wheat[12]	Wheat[13]	Wheat[14]	Subterranean clover[15]	Phalaris[16]	Monterey Pine[17]	Flax[18]	Cotton[19]
Leucine/isoleucine	+	+	+	+	+	−	+	+	+	−	+	−	+	+	+	+	+	−	+
Valine	+	+	+	+	−	−	+	+	+	−	−	+	+	+	+	+	+	−	−
γ-Aminobutyric acid	Tr*	+	−	+	−	−	−	−	−	−	−	+	+	+	+	+	+	+	−
Glutamine	+	+	+	+	+	−	−	−	−	−	+	+	+	+	+	+	+	−	−
α-Alanine	+	+	+	+	+	−	+	+	+	+	+	+	+	+	+	+	+	+	−
Asparagine	+	+	+	+	+	+	−	−	−	−	+	+	+	+	+	+	+	−	−
Serine	Tr	+	+	+	−	−	Tr	Tr	+	−	−	+	+	+	+	+	+	−	+
Glutamic acid	+	+	+	+	+	+	+	+	Tr	+	−	+	+	+	+	+	+	+	−
Aspartic acid	+	+	+	+	+	+	+	+	+	+	−	−	+	+	+	+	+	+	+
Cystine/cysteine	−	+	−	−	+	+	−	−	−	+	−	+	−	+	+	+	−	−	+
Glycine	−	+	−	−	+	−	−	−	−	+	−	+	+	+	+	+	+	−	+
Phenylalanine	+	+	−	+	−	−	−	−	−	−	−	−	−	+	+	−	Tr	−	+
Threonine	+	+	−	+	+	−	−	−	−	−	−	+	−	+	+	+	+	−	+
Tyrosine	−	+	−	+	−	+	−	−	−	+	−	−	+	−	−	−	−	−	+
Lysine	−	+	−	+	−	+	−	−	−	−	+	−	−	−	−	−	−	−	+
Proline	−	−	−	−	+	−	−	−	−	−	−	+	+	−	−	−	+	+	+
Methionine	−	−	−	+	−	+	−	−	−	−	−	−	+	+	+	+	+	−	−
Tryptophane	−	−	−	+	−	+	−	−	−	−	−	−	−	−	−	−	+	−	−
Homoserine	−	−	−	+	−	−	−	−	−	−	−	−	−	−	−	−	−	−	−
β-Alanine	−	−	−	−	−	−	−	−	−	−	−	−	−	+	−	−	+	−	−
Arginine	−	−	−	−	−	−	−	−	−	−	−	−	−	−	−	−	−	−	+

* Tr = trace; — = absent or not recorded.

References: [1] Frenzel, 1957; [2] Katznelson, Rouatt, and Payne, 1955; Parkinson, 1955; Rovira, 1956a; Martin, 1957; [3] Kandler, 1951; [4] Frank, 1954; [5] Buxton, 1962; [6] Frank, 1954; [7] Andal, Bhuvaneswari, and Subba-Rao, 1956; [8] Linskens and Knapp, 1955; [9] Linskens and Knapp, 1955; [10] Kalyanasundarum, 1958; Rovira, 1959; [11] Katznelson, Rouatt, and Payne, 1955; [12] Rivière, 1960; [13] Tèsar and Kutacek, 1955; [14] Vrany, Vancura, and Macura, 1962; [15] Rovira, 1959; [16] Rovira, 1959; [17] Bowen, 1963; [18] Börner, Martin, and Clauss, 1959; [19] Sulochana, 1962a.

ing to the state of aeration and metabolism of the root, it is not unexpected to find them in the exudate. This group of compounds deserves much more study, not only because they form a source of readily available substrates, but also because of secondary effects, such as the modification of pH in the rhizosphere and the chelation of metals.

Nucleotides, flavonones, and enzymes.—In a study with excised roots of wheat and peas, Lundegårdh and

TABLE 3. Amino acid exudation patterns of peas and oats after 21 days

	Peas (3)*	Oats (20)*
Asparagine	+++	++
Aspartic acid	++	+
Serine	+++	+++
Glutamine	++++	+
Homoserine	++++	−
α-Alanine	++++	+
Leucine	+	++
Lysine	++	+++
Threonine	++++	+/−
Glycine	−	+++

* Number of plants required to provide material for a single chromatogram.

TABLE 4. Growth factors present in root exudate

Compound	Plant	Reference
Biotin Thiamin	Flax; Rice, bean, clover	West, 1939; Bhuvaneswari and Sulochana, 1955
"M" factor	Pine, peas, tomato	Melin and Rama Das, 1954
Biotin Thiamin	Maize, peas	Meshkov, 1959
Biotin Pantothenate Niacin	Clover species (six), lucerne, phalaris, tomato	Rovira and Harris, 1961
Biotin Thiamin Choline Inositol Pyridoxine p-Amino benzoic acid	Cotton	Sulochana, 1962b
n-Methyl nicotinic acid	Radish	Dodman, Kerr, and Atkinson*

* R. Dodman, A. Kerr, and M. R. Atkinson, personal communication.

TABLE 5. Organic acids in root exudate

Compound	Plant	Reference
Tartaric }	{ Sorghum, mustard	Bhuvaneswari and Subba-Rao, 1957
Oxalic }	{ Wheat	Vrany, Vancura, and Macura, 1962
Citric	Mustard	Bhuvaneswari and Subba-Rao, 1957
Malic {	{ Mustard	{ Bhuvaneswari and Subba-Rao, 1957
	{ Wheat	{ Rivière, 1959, 1960
Acetic } Propionic } Butyric } Valeric }	Wheat	Rivière, 1959, 1960
Citric } Succinic } Fumaric } Glycolic }	traces Wheat	Rivière, 1959, 1960 Vrany, Vancura, and Macura, 1962

Stenlid (1944) demonstrated that 3,4 dioxyflavonone, adenine, and guanine were released into the surrounding medium (Table 6). The exudation of these compounds was linked with root respiration, and the authors proposed that leakage took place from the zone of active cell division immediately behind the root cap. It is in this zone that nucleic acids are being synthesized and respiration involving 3,4 dioxyflavonone is greatest. Also reported in Table 6 are the findings of Fries and Forsman (1951) of nucleic acid derivatives coming from roots.

The presence of exoenzymes associated with roots was demonstrated by Rogers, Pearson, and Pierre (1940, 1942). They found that intense phosphatase activity was associated with the gelatinous material surrounding the roots of maize. Although this material contained free nuclei and empty cell walls of sloughed-off root-cap material, they considered that the phosphatases and gel were exuded directly from the root before disintegration of the cell debris. Krasil'nikov (1952) found that the exudates from wheat, maize, and peas contained invertase, amylase, and protease; and Krasil'nikov and Kotelov (1959) also reported phosphatase in the external environment of the roots.

The work of Knudson (1920) reported earlier in this review indicates the caution required in the interpretation of results. His initial conclusions from the observa-

tion that glucose and fructose appeared in a sucrose solution in which plants were growing under sterile conditions was that invertase was being exuded. However, he demonstrated that the sucrose was first absorbed by the plant, hydrolysed to the constituent sugars inside the plant, and these subsequently exuded.

The polygalacturonase reported by Ljunggren and Fåhraeus (1959, 1961) to be released into distilled water by the roots of lucerne and clover occurred as a result of the stimulus of infective rhizobia or polysaccharide extracts of these organisms. This reaction was so specific that no polygalacturonase was produced when noninfective rhizobia colonized the root and demonstrates the effects which different microorganisms have on the composition of exudates.

Miscellaneous compounds.—A wide range of miscellaneous compounds is released from roots, and several of these are toxic to microorganisms (Table 7), e.g. hydrocyanic acid, glycosides, and saponins. This demonstrates that in any study of the effects of root exudates on the soil microflora, consideration must be made of the inhibitory as well as the stimulatory materials.

Elkan (1961) showed that plants with only a single gene difference can vary markedly in their effects upon the rhizosphere population. He found that exudate from nonnodulating strains of soybean altered the morphology of *Rhizobium* in culture solutions and would also prevent nodulation of the normally nodulating strains of soybean.

Factors affecting nematodes.—There is considerable evidence of the ability of roots to attract nematodes in both soil and culture media (Table 8), although the actual materials have seldom been identified. Bird (1959) found that the larvae of *Meloidogyne javanica* and *M. hapla* were attracted by reducing substances and postulated that attraction to the rapidly elongating area of the root was due to the lower oxidation-reduction potential in this area, but later (Bird, 1960) he considered that root exudates could also be significant.

The work of Wallace (1958) on the emergence of eelworm cysts and the subsequent migration of larvae showed conclusively that exudate influenced a considerable zone of sand surrounding the roots. When sand was held at 15 cm suction, the cyst germination factor(s) diffused 3.0 cm from the root and larvae were attracted towards the root from distances of up to

TABLE 6. Nucleotides, flavonones and enzymes detected in root exudate

Compound	Plant	Reference
Flavonone	Peas, wheat	Lundegårdh and Stenlid, 1944
Adenine	Peas, wheat	Lundegårdh and Stenlid, 1944
Guanine }	{ Peas, wheat	Lundegårdh and Stenlid, 1944
Uridine + cytidine }	{ Peas	Fries and Forsman, 1951
U.V.-absorbing compounds	Peas, oats	Rovira, 1956a
Phosphatase	Maize	{ Rogers, Pearson and Pierre, 1942 { Krasil'nikov and Kotelov, 1959
Invertase } Amylase } Protease }	Wheat, maize, peas	Krasil'nikov, 1952
Polygalacturonase	Lucerne, clover	Ljunggren and Fåhraeus, 1959, 1961

TABLE 7. Miscellaneous compounds reported in root exudate

Compound	Plant	Reference
Auxins	Pinto bean	Mitchell, Lindner, and Robinson, 1961
Scopoletin (6 methoxy-7-hydroxycoumarin)	Oats	{ Eberhardt, 1954 { Martin, 1958
Fluorescent substances	{ Oats { Peas { Lucerne { Banana	Eberhardt, 1955 Rovira, 1956*a* Mishustin and Naumova, 1955 Buxton, 1962
Hydrocyanic acid	Flax	Timonin, 1941
Glycosides	{ Asparagus { Oats	Rohde and Jenkins, 1958 Schönbeck, 1958
Saponins (glucosides)	Lucerne	Mishustin and Naumova, 1955
Organic phosphorus compounds	{ Maize { Pumpkin }	Popatov and Molnarne Kerestes, 1956
γ-MnO_2-dissolving compound	Oats, vetch	Bromfield, 1959
Bentonite colouring compound	Red clover	Nutman, 1951
Nodulation inhibitor	Soybean (nonnodulating strain)	Elkan, 1961
Azotobacter growth stimulator	Barley, wheat	Vancura and Macura, 1961

4.5 cm. Diffusion distances were reduced when the water content of the sand was reduced. There are few data on the distance of diffusion of exudates from roots in soil, but this also will be influenced by water content. The adsorption of cationic materials in the exudate by the clay fraction will restrict their effects upon the microflora to a small zone around the root, but neutral or anionic nutrients should diffuse considerable distances. The actual distance involved will also be affected by the rate of decomposition of these compounds during their diffusion through soil.

The specificity of some of these factors was shown by O'Brien and Prentice (1930), who found that potato root exudates stimulated the hatching of potato eelworm cysts, whereas the exudates from beet, rape, lupin, mustard, and oats had no effect. Subsequent work by Calum, Raistrick, and Todd (1949) showed that other members of the Solanaceae also liberated the factor. A large-scale research programme to assess the possibility of controlling potato eelworm with this exudate or a chemical analogue involved growing 150,000 tomato plants in sand culture and leaching on alternate days to obtain 12 g of crude factor per month. The active fraction has been shown to contain a lactone ring, is acidic in nature, and has been named "eclipic acid." Ellanby (1958*b*) and Ellanby and Gilbert (1960) have shown that this factor has certain affinities with cardiac glycosides, probably owing to an unsaturated lactone ring; but precise characterization has not yet been achieved. This factor has been studied by several workers (see Table 8) and considerable information has been obtained on the conditions required for maximum production and its stability to heat and oxidation. Fenwick (1956) found that the activity of the potato-root diffusate was almost completely destroyed 4 days after addition to soil.

Factors affecting fungi.—The many reports of fungi in soil being affected by roots or root exudates are summarized in Table 9. The specificity of root exudate in stimulating plant pathogens was demonstrated by

Kerr (1956), using the cellophane-bag technique. Kerr grew sterile seedlings inside cellophane bags buried in soil inoculated with *Pellicularia filamentosa* and found an intense development of the pathogen on the cellophane opposite the roots of the two susceptible hosts, lettuce and radish, but no stimulation opposite tomato roots, which are not susceptible.

Buxton (1957) also demonstrated a definite specificity with relation to the germination of spores of *Fusarium oxysporum* Fr. f. *pisi* (Linf.) Snyd. and Hans. in the exudates of three pea varieties differing in susceptibility to this pathogen. Exudate from a wilt-resistant variety inhibited spore germination, whereas exudate from a susceptible plant stimulated spore germination. But the exudates showed no differences in their effects on the rate of growth of germ tubes from germinated spores or of the developing mycelium; specificity was restricted to spore germination.

On the other hand, Schroth and Hendrix (1962) found that chlamydospores of *Fusarium solani* f. *phaseoli* germinated in the presence of exudates from many nonsusceptible plants as well as the host plant.

The influence a host plant can have on a pathogenic fungus was demonstrated by Buxton (1958). He found that after several subcultures of *Fusarium oxysporum* f. *pisi* in a medium containing root exudate of a wilt-resistant pea variety, the fungus increased in its pathogenicity towards this wilt-resistant variety. Buxton suggests that this change in pathogenicity may be due to mutagenic substances in the exudate increasing the mutation rate of the fungus or an adaptation by the fungus to either inhibitory materials or previously unavailable nutrients in the root exudate of resistant varieties, but he offers no evidence in support of either hypothesis.

FACTORS AFFECTING EXUDATION.—One of the problems in assessing the significance of analyses of root exudates is that exudation is affected by many factors. Katznelson, Rouatt, and Payne (1954, 1955) demonstrated that temporary wilting of plants increased the

TABLE 8. Nematode-stimulating factors from root exudate

Compound	Plant	Reference
Potato eelworm cyst hatching factor (*Heterodera rostochiensis* Woll.)	Potato and other *Solanaceae*	O'Brien and Prentice, 1930 Calum, Raistrick, and Todd, 1949 Calum, Todd, and Waring, 1949 Marrian et al., 1949 Russell, Todd, and Waring, 1949 Fenwick, 1952, 1956, 1957 Carroll et al., 1958 Widdowson, 1958a,b,c Widdowson and Wiltshire, 1958 Hague, 1958 Ellenby, 1958a,b Ellenby and Gilbert, 1960 Hartwell, Dahlstrom, and Neal, 1960
Beet eelworm cyst hatching factor (*H. schachtii* Schmidt)	Beet	Winslow and Ludwig, 1957 Wallace, 1957 Carroll, 1958
	Rape	Winner, 1958
Cabbage eelworm cyst hatching factor (*H. cruciferae*)	Black mustard	Carroll, 1958
Hop eelworm cyst hatching factor (*H. humili*)	Hop	Carroll, 1958
Heterodera spp. attractors	Potato	Widdowson, Doncaster, and Fenwick, 1958
	Cress	Wallace, 1958
	Tomato	Weischer, 1959 Jones, 1960
Meloidogyne spp. attractors	Tomato	Bird, 1959, 1960 Peacock, 1961

TABLE 9. Factors in root exudates affecting fungi

Factor	Plant	Fungus affected	Reference
Mycelium-growth stimulators	Radish Lettuce	*Pellicularia filamentosa*	1
	Strawberry	*Rhizoctonia* sp.	2
Mycelium-growth inhibitors	Oats	*Byssochlamys nivea*	3
Spore-germination stimulator	Potato *Datura* spp.	*Spongospora subterranea*	4
	Tomato	*Colletotrichum atramentarium*	5
	Turnip	*Pythium mamillatum*	6
	Peas	*Aphanomyces eutiches*	7
	Allium spp.	*Sclerotium cepivorum*	8
	Tomato Radish Lettuce	*Fusarium* spp.	9
	Beans	*Fusarium solani* f. *phaseoli*	10
	Banana (var. Gros Michel)	*Fusarium oxysporum* f. *cubense*	11
Spore-germination inhibitors	Banana (var. Lacatan)	*Fusarium oxysporum* f. *cubense*	11
	Peas	*Fusarium oxysporum* f. *pisi*	12
Zoospore attractors	Strawberry	*Phytophthora fragariae*	13
	Peas	*Phytophthora erythroseptica*	14
	Solonaceae	*Phytophthora parasitica*	15
	Avocado	*Phytophthora cinnamomi*	16
Pathogenicity stimulator	Peas	*Fusarium oxysporum* f. *pisi*	17
Microsclerotia-germination stimulators	Tomato Wheat	*Verticillium albo-atrum*	18

References: [1] Kerr, 1956; [2] Husain and McKeen, 1962; [3] Schönbeck, 1958; [4] White, 1954; [5] Ebben and Williams, 1956; [6] Barton, 1957; [7] Scharen, 1960; [8] Coley-Smith, 1960; [9] Jackson, 1957, 1960; [10] Schroth and Snyder, 1961; [11] Buxton, 1962; [12] Buxton, 1957; [13] Goode, 1956; [14] Bywater and Hickman, 1959; [15] Dukes and Apple, 1961; [16] Zentmyer, 1961; [17] Buxton, 1958; [18] Schreiber and Green, 1962.

release of amino acids from roots in sand or soil. Although this situation of wilting does not arise in most laboratory exudate studies, it could be important in the field, where periods of temporary moisture stress often occur. The rapid release of amino acids from roots of wilted plants upon rewetting will exert a profound effect on the numbers and types of organisms in the rhizosphere.

Exudation is also affected by other environmental conditions. It is increased under high light and temperature conditions and is greatest during the first few weeks of growth (Rovira, 1959). There are no reports available on the influence of transpiration, but it would be surprising if this did not exert some effect. One of the criticisms of using the enclosed-tube technique for the aseptic culture of plants in exudate studies may be that transpiration is limited under these conditions.

Early in this review emphasis was placed on the necessity of growing plants under aseptic conditions in root-exudate studies. This is supported by the work of Martin (1958), who found that the culture filtrates of certain bacteria caused a threefold increase in the exudation of scopoletin without affecting root growth, whereas other culture filtrates had no effect on exudation. The amino acid patterns in exudates from tomato and clover roots were altered by the presence of microorganisms (Rovira, 1959), probably owing to the utilization of certain amino acids and release of others by the microorganisms. The reports of Ljunggren and Fåhraeus, discussed earlier, on polygalacturonase released from roots under the influence of compatible rhizobia are further evidence of the part microorganisms play in the behaviour of plant roots. The observation by Norman (1955) that polymyxin and other polypeptide antibiotics increased the leakage of inorganic and organic materials from roots indicates the effects colonies of antibiotic-producing microorganisms may have upon exudation.

Microorganisms can affect exudate patterns in at least three ways: by altering the permeability of root cells, by modifying the metabolism of roots, and by modifying some of the material released from the roots. In the rhizosphere, where there is an intense development of microorganisms, it would be surprising if exudation were not affected by the presence of organisms or their metabolic products. In this respect, the root should not be considered uniformly populated; it probably has zones of intense microbial colonization and other zones of lower population density. If, in these areas of intense colonization, there develop species of organisms releasing substances which increase the permeability of underlying root cells, then predictions of food supplies to the rhizosphere population on the basis of root-exudate studies carried out under aseptic conditions could be misleading.

In view of these effects of microorganisms on exudation, studies should be conducted under both sterile and nonsterile conditions to assess the potential and actual supply of nutrients in the rhizosphere. The rhizoplane and rhizosphere microflora may be regarded as a selective sieve, absorbing some exudate constituents and, in turn, releasing exudates from their own cells. By studying the materials in the environment around nonsterile roots, information is obtained of the situation existing when plants are growing in the field—this being the environment concerned in the biological control of root pathogens.

The results of Buxton (1960) support the hypothesis that caution is necessary when interpreting actual rhizosphere ecology in terms of the results obtained with root exudates produced under aseptic conditions. He showed that although exudates from peas susceptible to *Fusarium oxysporum* stimulated the fungus in pure culture, they also caused many rhizosphere isolates to antagonize the pathogen; thus there were in fact two opposing systems operating in the rhizosphere of susceptible pea plants. He suggested that "Under natural conditions root exudates are unlikely to be the dominant factors in the rhizosphere environment, for the microflora will rapidly change the chemical nature of the exudates and, in doing so, may acquire metabolic activities not normally detected in the rhizosphere." Although tested with only one host species, its pathogen, and a range of rhizosphere isolates, Buxton's findings and hypothesis could have a general application and should be considered in planning further studies of exudate-pathogen-saprophyte interactions.

MECHANISM OF EXUDATION.—The use of various terms to describe the release of material from plant roots—excretion, exudation, secretion, diffusion, and leakage—indicates that little is known of the mechanisms involved in this process.

Apart from the studies of Lundegårdh and Stenlid (1944), who linked exudation with respiration, no attempts have been made to study the problem at a physiological level. This is because plant physiologists are more interested in the movement of nutrients into plants than in the reverse phenomenon. All the published work other than that of Lundegårdh and Stenlid has been by microbiologists or plant pathologists, who were mainly concerned with exudation as a source of nutrients of microorganisms rather than with the mechanisms. More recently Rivière (1959) has proposed that exudation should be considered a manifestation of the permeability of cells at the particular stage of growth being studied and linked with the metabolism of root cells, but he produced no evidence to prove this statement.

Until more is known of the processes involved in the release of organic material from roots, it is probably best to use the terms exudation or diffusion to describe the process. According to definition these terms mean "oozing out, giving off, sending forth, or shedding abroad." The terms excretion and secretion, on the other hand, imply active physiological mechanisms, while "leakage" implies movement of fluid through perforations.

SIGNIFICANCE OF EXUDATES IN THE RHIZOSPHERE.—In spite of the extensive evidence for exudation of organic material from roots and the specificity of some of these materials in relation to certain soil microorganisms, there is little conclusive evidence of the

relative importance of original exudate, exudate modified by microorganisms, and sloughed-off cell debris in
the establishment and maintenance of the rhizosphere
population during the life of the host plant.

Results with peas and oats indicate that exudation
is more important than cell debris in the young seedling,
but that as the plant develops exudation declines and
decomposition of moribund root hairs, epidermal cells,
and cortex contributes a substantial portion of the
nutrients to the rhizosphere population (Rovira, 1956*a*).
Root exudates no doubt will still be the major factor
for some distance behind each growing tip of the root
system, but they will contribute proportionately less as
the plants develop.

My direct observations support the evidence of
Rogers, Pearson, and Pierre (1942) and others that a
considerable amount of cell material in the form of cast-
off root-cap cells accumulates around the roots during
growth. The quantity and viability of these cells will
depend upon the plant species and the medium through
which the roots are growing. Figures 2 and 3 show two
stages in the decomposition of root hairs of *Phalaris
tuberosa* grown in sand for 6 weeks. In Fig. 2 bacteria
are seen inside what appears to be an intact root hair,
probably at an early stage of decomposition. Fig. 3
shows three portions of a single root hair completely
ensheathed by bacteria, indicating an advanced stage
of decomposition.

DIRECT MICROSCOPY OF ROOT-SURFACE MICRO-
FLORA.—Direct examination of roots stained with
aniline blue (Rovira, 1956*c*) often shows distinct
patterns of development of microorganisms over the
surface of the root. With tomato roots (Fig. 4) bacteria
tend to develop along the root on what appear to be the

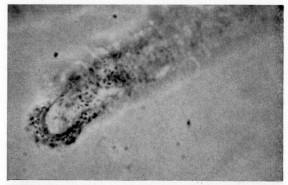

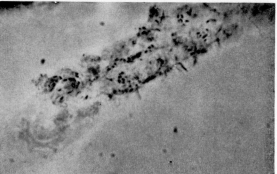

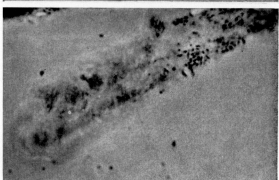

Fig. 3. Moribund root hair of *Phalaris tuberosa* colonized by bacteria. (× 1,000) Three portions of roots
shown by focusing at different levels.

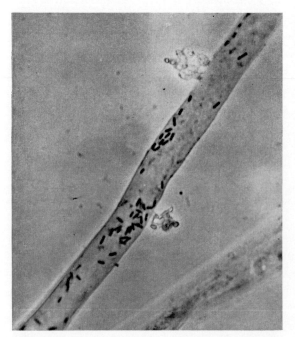

Fig. 2. Root hair of *Phalaris tuberosa* invaded by bacteria. (× 1,000)

junctions of epidermal cells. On *Phalaris* roots (Fig. 5)
the bacteria often develop as distinct colonies, ranging in
size from a few cells to many hundreds of cells per
colony. It is not known whether these patterns are
manifestations of differences in sites of exudation between the two plants or due to differences in the surface
structures of the respective roots.

Although direct observations by the above methods
are useful to indicate the distribution of the microflora
on the root surface, little information can be obtained
on the types and identity of these organisms. By using
the fluorescent-antibody technique, I have been able to
stain specific groups of bacteria in situ and obtain
information on the distribution of serologically different
organisms on the root surface. Further development of
this technique should yield valuable information on the
colonization of roots by different organisms, the relative
proportions of different types, and the degree of com-

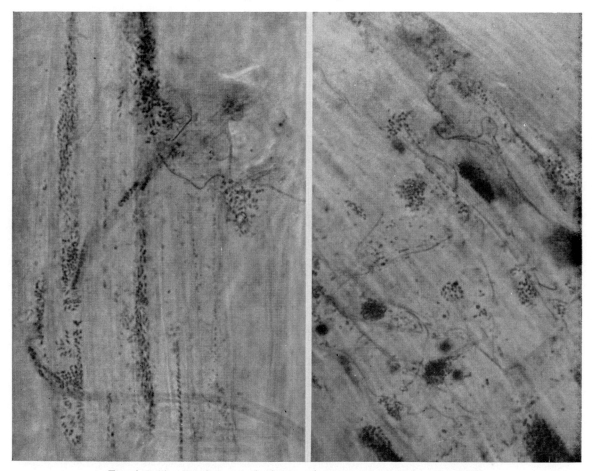

Fig. 4 (left). Development of microorganisms on roots of tomato. ($\times$ 1,000)
Fig. 5 (right). Development of microorganisms on roots of *Phalaris*. ($\times$ 1,000)

petition of root-surface organisms for nutrients from root exudates. That this technique can be used successfully for fungi as well as bacteria has been demonstrated in medical microbiology (Kaufman and Kaplan, 1961) and in the detection of *Aspergillus flavus* in soil by Schmidt and Bankole (1962). The principles and technical details involved in this fluorescent antibody method have been reviewed by Beutner (1961).

Electron microscopy has been used successfully by Dart and Mercer (1964) to study the colonization of the roots of barrel medic (*Medicago tribuloides*) by *Rhizobium meliloti*. There was an intense colonization of the mucilaginous sheath (Fig. 1) by bacteria within two days of inoculation with an effective strain of *R. meliloti* (Figs. 6 and 7). The bacteria colonized between the mucilaginous material and the "cuticle," forcing the latter away from the roots. Some cells are visible within the mucilage but most of these appear to have undergone lysis.

THE USE OF "MODEL SYSTEMS" IN ROOT-EXUDATE STUDIES.—The complexity of the rhizosphere environment in natural soil makes it difficult to resolve such questions as the interactions between organisms, the numbers of viable organisms, and the characteristics

required for an organism to become an inhabitant of the rhizosphere. For these reasons "model" systems which simplify the situation have been developed.

Chan and Katznelson (1961, 1962) have developed "model systems" where cultures, single or mixed, are grown in media with and without root extracts. In root-extract-supplemented medium, they have noted patterns of development in the mixed cultures very similar to those found around plant roots. When cultures of five bacteria were grown together in the presence of oat and soybean root extract, *Azotobacter chroococcum* died, *Bacillus cereus* was a poor competitor, while *Pseudomonas* sp., *Agrobacterium radiobacter,* and *Arthrobacter citreus* all grew well, with *Pseudomonas* giving the highest numbers of cells. This type of experiment with different organisms and concentrations of root exudate could lead to a better understanding of the mechanisms of competition, stimulation, and antagonism which occur in the rhizosphere. The work of Chan and Katznelson has been performed with root extracts rather than root exudates, although there are no data available comparing the contents of these materials. Some information on the behaviour of the five cultures in both root-exudate and root-extract-supplemented media

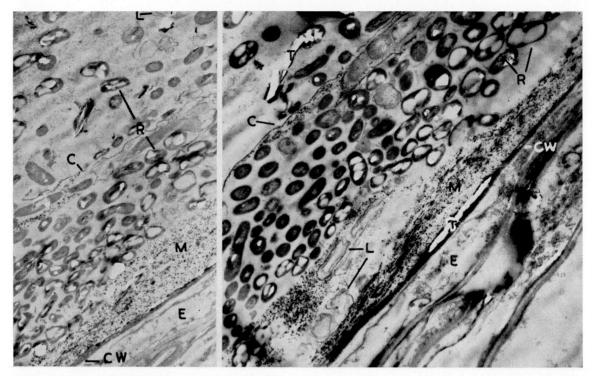

Figs. 6 and 7. Development of *Rhizobium meliloti* beneath the "cuticle" of the mucilage on the root of *Medicago tribuloides* 5 to 15 mm from the tip. (× 8,700) *E,* epidermal cell; *C.W.,* epidermal cell wall; *M,* mucilaginous layer; *C,* "cuticle"; *R, Rhizobium* cells; *L,* possibly lysed rhizobia; *T,* section tear. (P. J. Dart and F. V. Mercer. Arch. Mikrobiol. 47: 344–378. 1964.)

would indicate the value of root extract (which is simpler to prepare) as a substitute for root exudate.

Contrary to the findings of Chan and Katznelson, Meshkov and Khodokova (1954) and Zinov'eva (1958) found that the exudates of peas, maize, oats, and wheat stimulated *Azotobacter chroococcum* more than other soil bacteria, including *Rhizobium* and Gram-positive organisms. These results were obtained with strains of *Azotobacter* "adapted" to the rhizosphere by 7 to 10 passages on the roots of the particular host plant. Possibly the use of adapted strains accounts for the discrepancies between the results of various workers.

Vancura and Macura (1961), in a study of the effects of root exudates on *Azotobacter chroococcum,* also found the exudates of wheat and barley stimulatory provided the organism had previously been "adapted" to growth on roots (Vancura et al., 1959). The organic-acid fraction of root exudate was the most stimulatory fraction to both growth and nitrogen fixation of *Azotobacter.* Of the sugar fraction, galactose and fructose were preferentially utilized by the organisms. In stationary cultures the amino-acid fraction of root exudate was inhibitory, but this was overcome with shaking.

A further extension of the idea of "model systems" is to inoculate seeds with cultures singly or mixed, plant in sterile sand or nutrient solution, and follow the development of the organisms as the plants grow. This method has the advantage that exudate concentrations may be more realistic than when exudates or extracts are added to nutrient media. Also, there is the physical

environment of the root available if surface adhesion, water movement, ion exchange, or carbon dioxide and oxygen levels play significant roles in the rhizosphere phenomenon. With this method, *Azotobacter chroococcum,* even in pure culture, failed to colonize the roots of maize growing for 2 weeks in sterile sand, while *Bacillus polymyxa* and *Clostridium pasteurianum* reached 4 and 8 million per root system, respectively (Rovira, 1963). *Pseudomonas fluorescens* proliferated on the roots and reached 800 million per root system. With tomato, *Azotobacter* reached 40,000 cells per root system, but this was still only 1 per cent of the level reached by *Pseudomonas.*

An alternative technique in the more complex soil environment showed that an "artificial rhizosphere" may be created by continual additions of root exudates to soil (Timonin, 1941; Rovira, 1956b; and Rivière, 1958). The organisms isolated from soil treated in this manner were similar to those in the rhizospheres of the same plants; and although such a system lacks the nutrient depletion, water movement, and surface nature of the root, it could be useful in studying the effects of different root exudates or fractions thereof upon the complex array of microorganisms in natural soil. While it is admitted that there is a considerable difference between the environments of the model systems and the natural situation and that caution is required in reaching any conclusions, it appears that use of model systems of increasing complexity in root-exudate and rhizosphere studies will be necessary to understand the dynamics of the rhizosphere phenomenon.

CONCLUSIONS.—Sufficient chromatographic analyses have been performed on root exudates to indicate the wide spectrum of compounds they contain. More emphasis, however, should be placed on the effects of these exudates, complete and fractionated, on members of the rhizosphere microflora, both pathogens and nonpathogens. In such studies attempts should be made to keep the root-exudate concentration comparable to that which occurs in the rhizosphere. The question of concentration is very difficult to resolve because little is known of the volume of soil around the root into which the exudates diffuse and the extent to which the various constituents are adsorbed by the soil colloids. Possibly the solution lies in using a range of concentrations in the presence or absence of adsorbing materials. Further development of the principle of "model systems" involving plants and mixtures of known microorganisms offers considerable promise in explaining some of the mechanisms operating in the rhizosphere.

Research is also necessary on the effects of various factors such as environmental conditions and microorganisms (pure and mixed cultures) on exudation. A greater understanding of the mechanisms involved in exudation is also required. With more such information it should be possible to predict the behaviour of the rhizosphere microflora of a particular plant species under different soil and climatic conditions.

An interesting development in root-exudate research in relation to controlling the rhizosphere population via the exudate has been proposed by Vrany, Vancura, and Macura (1962). They applied a variety of substances—readily metabolized substances such as urea and inorganic phosphate, growth regulators, and antibiotics—to the foliage of wheat and found that they could modify root exudates and the rhizosphere microflora by such treatments.

The site of exudation in relation to the areas of development of the rhizosphere flora and root pathogens is an important area requiring further investigation. Pearson and Parkinson (1961) and Schroth and Snyder (1961) demonstrated that the root tip is the most important zone of exudation, whereas Frenzel (1960), by using the growth of specific nutrient-requiring mutants of *Neurospora,* found that threonine and asparagine came from the root tip, but leucine, valine, glutamic acid, and phenylalanine were exuded in greater amounts from the root-hair zone. These results indicate the possibility of different organisms developing in different regions of the root—a point which must be clarified if the biological control of root diseases is to be achieved through the rhizosphere population. The use of organisms themselves as indicators of exudation, together with direct microscopic examination under both phase and ultraviolet illumination, should provide useful tools to study this aspect.

In conclusion, it can be said that there is little doubt that root exudates play an important role in the establishment and maintenance of the rhizosphere populations of young plants, often being quite specific in their action. But considerable research is still required along the lines suggested above to assess their true significance in controlling the balance and numbers of organisms in the rhizosphere during the whole life of the plant. Further understanding of the dynamic situation operating in the rhizosphere resulting from root exudate studies will lead to the establishment of basic principles to be used in the biological control of plant root pathogens.

LITERATURE CITED

ANDAL, R., K. BHUVANESWARI, and N. S. SUBBA-RAO. 1956. Root exudates of paddy. Nature (London) 178: 1063.

BARTON, R. 1957. Germination of oospores of *Pythium mammillatum* in response to exudate from living seedlings. Nature (London) 180: 613.

BEUTNER, E. 1961. Immunofluorescent staining: the fluorescent antibody method. Bacteriol. Rev. 25: 49-76.

BHUVANESWARI, K., and C. B. SULOCHANA. 1955. Assay of root exudates. Current Sci. (India) 24: 376-377.

BHUVANESWARI, K., and N. S. SUBBA-RAO. 1957. Root exudates in relation to the rhizosphere effect. Proc. Indian Acad. Sci., Sec. B, 45: 299-301.

BIRD, A. F. 1959. The attractiveness of roots to the plant parasitic nematodes *Meloidogyne javanica* and *M. hapla*. Nematologica 4: 322-335.

BIRD, A. F. 1960. Additional notes on the attractiveness of roots to plant parasitic nematodes. Nematologica 5: 217.

BÖRNER, H. 1960. Liberation of organic substances from higher plants and their role in the soil sickness problem. Botan. Rev. 26: 393-424.

BÖRNER, H., P. MARTIN, and H. CLAUSS. 1959. Experiments using flax and rye in investigating the problem of soil fatigue. Z. Pflanzenkrankh. 66: 691-703.

BOWEN, G. D. 1963. Root exudates of *Pinus radiata* (In preparation).

BRADFUTE, O. E., R. A. LUSE, L. BRAAL, and A. D. McLAREN. 1962. Growth of sterile plant roots in sand or soil in an inexpensive growth chamber. Soil Sci. Soc. Amer. Proc. 26: 406-408.

BROMFIELD, S. M. 1959. The solution of γ-MnO_2 by substances released from soil and from the roots of oats and vetch in relation to manganese availability. Plant Soil 10: 147-160.

BUTLER, G. W., and N. O. BATHURST. 1956. The underground transference of nitrogen from clover to associated grass. Proc. 7th. Intern. Grassland Conf., p. 168-178.

BUXTON, E. W. 1957. Some effects of pea root exudates on physiologic races of *Fusarium oxysporum* Fr. f. *pisi* (Linf.) Snyder and Hansen. Trans. Brit. Mycol. Soc. 40: 145-154.

BUXTON, E. W. 1958. A change of pathogenic race in *Fusarium oxysporum* f. *pisi* induced by root exudate from a resistant host. Nature (London) 181: 1222-1224.

BUXTON, E. W. 1960. Effects of pea root exudate on the antagonism of some rhizosphere microorganisms towards *Fusarium oxysporum* f. *pisi*. J. Gen. Microbiol. 22: 678-689.

BUXTON, E. W. 1962. Root exudates from banana and their relationship to strains of the *Fusarium* causing Panama wilt. Ann. Appl. Biol. 50: 269-282.

BYWATER, J., and C. J. HICKMAN. 1959. A new variety of *Phytophthora erythroseptica*, which causes a soft rot of pea roots. Trans. Brit. Mycol. Soc. 42: 513-524.

CALUM, C. T., H. RAISTRICK, and A. R. TODD. 1949. The potato eelworm hatching factor. 1. The preparation of concentrates of the hatching factor and a method of bioassay. Biochem. J. 45: 513-519.

CALUM, C. T., A. R. TODD, and W. S. WARING. 1949. The potato eelworm hatching factor. 2. Purification of the extract by alkaloid salt fractionation. Anhydrotitronic acid as an artificial hatching agent. Biochem. J. 45: 520-524.

CARROLL, K. K. 1958. Purification and properties of eelworm hatching factors. Hatching factors for the cabbage, hop and beet root eelworms (*Heterodera cruciferae, H. humili* and *H. schachtii* respectively). Nematologica 3: 197-204.

CARROLL, K. K., J. K. HEYES, A. W. JOHNSTON, and A. R. TODD. 1958. The potato eelworm hatching factor. 7. Further methods of concentrating the factor. Nematologica 3: 154-167.

CHAN, E. C. S., and H. KATZNELSON. 1961. Growth interaction of *Arthrobacter globiformis* and *Pseudomonas* sp. in relation to the rhizosphere effect. Can. J. Microbiol. 7: 759-767.

CHAN, E. C. S., and H. KATZNELSON. 1962. Bacterial interactions in relation to the rhizosphere effect. Proc. 8th Intern. Conf. Microbiol., Sec. B, 13.4, p. 53.

COLEY-SMITH, J. R. 1960. Studies of the biology of *Sclerotium cepivorum* Berk. IV. Germination of sclerotia. Ann. Appl. Biol. 48: 8-18.

CRANNER, B. H. 1922. Zur Biochemie und Physiologie der grenzschichten lebender Pflanzenellen. Meldinger Norg. Landbrukhoiskole 5: 1-160.

DART, P. J., and F. V. MERCER. 1964. The legume rhizosphere. Arch. Mikrobiol. 47: 344-378.

DUKES, P. D., and J. L. APPLE. 1961. Chemotaxis of zoospores of *Phytophthora parasitica* var. *nicotianae* by plant roots and certain chemical solutions. Phytopathology 51: 195-197.

EBBEN, N. H., and P. H. WILLIAMS. 1956. Brown root rot of tomatoes. 1. The associated fungal flora. Ann. Appl. Biol. 44: 425-436.

EBERHARDT, F. 1954. Ausscheidung einer organischen Verbindung aus den Wurzeln des Hafers (*Avena sativa* L.) Naturwissenschaften 41: 259.

EBERHARDT, F. 1955. Über fluoreszierende Verbindungen in der Wurzel des Hafers. Ein Beitrag zum Problem der Wurzelausscheidungen. Z. Botan. 43: 405-422.

ELKAN, G. 1961. A nodulation-inhibiting root excretion from a non-nodulating soybean strain. Can. J. Microbiol. 7: 851-856.

ELLENBY, C. 1958*a*. Preliminary observations on the colorimetric assay of the hatching factor of the potato root eelworm, *Heterodera rostochiensis* Wollenweber. J. Helminthol. 32: 219-226.

ELLENBY, C. 1958*b*. Root diffusates of *Solanum tuberosum* and *Digitalis purpurea*. Nature (London) 181: 920-921.

ELLENBY, C., and A. G. GILBERT. 1960. Progress in the study of the physiology of the hatching factor of the potato root eelworm, *Heterodera rostochiensis* Wollenweber. Nematologica, Supp. II, 1960: 106-111.

FENWICK, D. W. 1952. The bioassay of potato root diffusate. Ann. Appl. Biol. 39: 457-467.

FENWICK, D. W. 1956. The breakdown of potato root diffusate in soil. Nematologica 1: 290-302.

FENWICK, D. W. 1957. Some experiments on the vacuum distillation of potato root diffusate. Nematologica 2: 277-284.

FRANK, H. 1954. Über den Stickstoffverlust bei alternden Pflanzen. Planta 44: 319-340.

FRENZEL, B. 1957. Zur Abgabe von Aminosäuren und Amiden an das Nährmedium durch die Wurzeln von *Helianthus annuus* L. Planta 49: 210-234.

FRENZEL, B. 1960. Zur Ätiologie der Anreicherung von Aminosäuren und Amiden im Wurzelraum von *Helianthus annuus* L.: ein Beitrag zur Klärung der Probleme der Rhizosphäre. Planta 55: 169-207.

FRIES, N., and B. FORSMAN. 1951. Quantitative determinations of certain nucleic acid derivatives in pea root exudate. Physiol. Plantarum 4: 410-420.

GELLER, I. A. 1954. [Root excretions of plants.] Dokl. Akad. Nauk. SSSR 95: 1105-1108.

GOODE, P. M. 1956. Infection of strawberry roots by zoospores of *Phytophthora fragariae*. Trans. Brit. Mycol. Soc. 39: 367-377.

HAGUE, H. G. 1958. The concentration of potato root diffusate under reduced pressure. Nematologica 3: 149-153.

HARTWELL, W. V., R. V. DAHLSTROM, and A. L. NEAL. 1960. A crystalline hatching stimulant for the golden nematode. Phytopathology 50: 612-615.

HILTNER, L. 1904. Über neuere Erfahrungen und Probleme auf dem Gebiet der Bodenbakteriologie und unter besonderer Berücksichtigung der Gründüngung und Brache. Arb. Deut. Landwirtsch. Ges. 98: 59-78.

HUSAIN, S. S., and W. E. MCKEEN. 1962. Stimulation of a new Rhizoctonia species by strawberry root exudates (Abstr.) Phytopathology 52: 14.

JACKSON, R. M. 1957. Fungistasis as a factor in the rhizosphere phenomenon. Nature (London) 180: 96-97.

JACKSON, R. M. 1960. Soil fungistasis in the rhizosphere. p. 168-176. *In* D. Parkinson and J. S. Waid [ed.], Ecology of soil fungi. Liverpool University Press, Liverpool.

JENNY, H., and K. GROSSENBACHER. 1963. Root-soil boundary zones as seen in the electron microscope. Soil Sci. Soc. Am. Proc. 27: 273-277.

JONES, F. G. W. 1960. Some observations and reflections on host findings by nematodes. Mededel. Landbouwhogeschool Opzoekingssta. Staat Gent. 25: 1009-1024.

KALYANASUNDARAM, R. 1958. Production of fusaric acid by *Fusarium lycopersici* Sacc. in the rhizosphere of tomato plants. Phytopathol. Z. 32: 25-34.

KANDLER, I. 1951. Papierchromatographischer Nachweiss der Aminosäureabscheidung *in vitro* kultivierter Maizwurzeln. Z. Naturforsch 6 b: 437-445.

KATZNELSON, H., J. V. ROUATT, and T. M. B. PAYNE. 1954. Liberation of amino acids by plant roots in relation to desiccation. Nature (London) 174: 1110-1111.

KATZNELSON, H., J. W. ROUATT, and T. M. B. PAYNE. 1955. The liberation of amino acids and reducing compounds by plant roots. Plant Soil 7: 35-48.

KAUFMAN, L., and W. KAPLAN. 1961. Preparation of a fluorescent antibody specific for the yeast phase of *Histoplasma capsulatum*. J. Bacteriol. 82: 729-735.

KERR, A. 1956. Some interactions between plant roots and pathogenic fungi. Australian J. Biol. Sci. 9: 45-52.

KNUDSON, L. 1920. The secretion of invertase by plant roots. Am. J. Botany 7: 371-379.

KRASIL'NIKOV, N. A. 1952. [The secretion of enzymes by the roots of higher plants.] Dokl. Akad. Nauk SSSR. (Fiziol. Rast.) 87: 309-312.

KRASIL'NIKOV, N. A., and V. V. KOTELOV. 1959. Adsorption of phosphates of soil microorganisms by corn roots. (In Russian with English summary.) Microbiologiya 28: 548-550.

LINSKENS, H. F., and R. KNAPP. 1955. Über die Ausscheidung von Aminosäuren in reinen und gemischten Beständen verschiedener Pflanzenarten. Planta 45: 106-117.

LJUNGGREN, H., and G. FÅHRAEUS. 1959. Effect of *Rhizobium* polysaccharide on the formation of polygalacturonase in lucerne and clover. Nature (London) 184: 1578-1579.

LJUNGGREN, H., and G. FÅHRAEUS. 1961. The role of polygalacturonase in roothair invasion by nodule bacteria. J. Gen. Microbiol. 26: 521-528.

LUNDEGÅRDH, H., and G. STENLID. 1944. On the exudation of nucleotides and flavonones from living roots. Arch. Botan. 31A: 1-27.

LYON, T. L., and J. K. WILSON. 1921. Liberation of organic matter by roots of growing plants. New York Agr. Expt. Sta. (Geneva, N. Y.) Mem. 40: 1-44.

MARRIAN, D. H., P. B. RUSSELL, A. R. TODD, and W. S. WARING. 1949. The potato eelworm hatching factor. 3. Concentration of the factor by chromatography. Observations on the nature of eclipic acid. Biochem. J. 45: 525-528.

MARTIN, P. 1957. Die Abgabe von organischen Verbindungen, insbesondere von Scopoletin, aus den Keimwurzeln des Hafers. Z. Botan. 45: 475-506.

MARTIN, P. 1958. Einfluss der Kulturfiltrate von Mikroorganismen auf die Abgabe von Skopoletin aus den Keimwurzeln des Hafers (*Avena sativa* L.) Arch. Mikrobiol. 29: 154-186.

MELIN, E., and V. S. RAMA DAS. 1954. Influence of root metabolites on the growth of tree mycorrhizal fungi. Physiol. Plantarum 7: 851-858.

MESHKOV, N. V. 1959. The effect of thiamin and biotin

on the development of some soil microbes. (In Russian with English summary.) Mikrobiologiya 28: 894-899.

MESHKOV, N. V., and R. N. KHODOKOVA. 1954. The effect of root excretions of pea and maize on the development of some soil microorganisms when grown in a plant rhizosphere solution. (In Russian with English summary.) Mikrobiologiya 23: 544-550.

MISHUSTIN, E. N., and A. N. NAUMOVA. 1955. Secretion of toxic substances by alfalfa and their effects on cotton and soil microflora. Izvest. Akad. Nauk SSSR, Ser. Biol., 6: 3-9.

MITCHELL, J. W., P. J. LINDNER, and M. B. ROBINSON. 1961. Root exudation of alpha-methoxy phenyl acetic acid. Plant Physiol. 36 (Supplement xxxiv).

NILSSON, P. W. 1957. Aseptic cultivation of higher plants. Arch. Mikrobiol. 26: 285-301.

NORMAN, A. G. 1955. The effect of polymyxin on plant roots. Arch. Biochem. Biophys. 58: 461-477.

NUTMAN, P. S. 1951. Colour reactions between clay minerals and root secretions. Nature (London) 167: 288.

O'BRIEN, D. G., and E. G. PRENTICE. 1930. An eelworm disease of potatoes caused by *Heterodera schachtii*. Scot. J. Agr. 13: 415-432.

PARKINSON, D. 1955. Liberation of amino acids by oat seedlings. Nature (London) 176: 35.

PEACOCK, F. C. 1961. A note on the attractiveness of roots to plant parasitic nematodes. Nematologica 6: 85-86.

PEARSON, R., and D. PARKINSON. 1961. The sites of excretion of ninhydrin positive substances by broad bean seedlings. Plant Soil 13: 391-396.

POPATOV, N. G., and I. MOLNARNE-KERESTES. 1956. [The forms of root exudates of cultivated crops.] (In Hungarian with French and Russian summaries.) Agrokem. Talajtan. 5: 27-36.

REUSZER, H. W. 1949. A method for determining the carbon dioxide production of sterile and non-sterile roots. Soil Sci. Soc. Am. Proc. 14: 175-179.

REUSZER, H. W. 1962. Axenic techniques in the determination of root functions and the interrelationships of microorganisms and plant roots. Soil Sci. 93: 56-61.

RIVIÈRE, J. 1958. Étude microbiologique de la rhizosphère du blé. II. Réalisation et analyse d'une rhizosphère artificielle. Ann. Inst. Pasteur 95: 231-234.

RIVIÈRE, J. 1959. Contribution a l'étude de la rhizosphère du blé. Ann. Agron. 45: 93-337.

RIVIÈRE, J. 1960. Étude de la rhizosphère du blé. Ann. Agron. 11: 397-440.

ROGERS, H. T., R. W. PEARSON, and W. H. PIERRE. 1940. Absorption of organic phosphorus by corn and tomato plants and the mineralizing action of exo-enzyme systems of growing plants. Soil Sci. Soc. Am. Proc. 5: 285-292.

ROGERS, H. T., R. W. PEARSON, and W. H. PIERRE. 1942. The source and phosphatase activity of exo-enzyme systems of corn and tomato roots. Soil Sci. 54: 353-366.

ROHDE, R. A., and W. R. JENKINS. 1958. Basis for resistance of *Asparagus officinalis* var. *altius* L. to the stubby root nematode *Trichodorus christiei*. Maryland Agr. Expt. Sta. Bull. A97, 19 p.

ROVIRA, A. D. 1956a. Plant root excretions in relation to the rhizosphere effect. I. The nature of root exudate from oats and peas. Plant Soil 7: 178-194.

ROVIRA, A. D. 1956b. Plant root excretions in relation to the rhizosphere effect. III. The effect of root exudate on numbers and activity of microorganisms in soil. Plant Soil 7: 209-217.

ROVIRA, A. D. 1956c. A study of the development of the root surface microflora during the initial stages of plant growth. J. Appl. Bacteriol. 19: 72-79.

ROVIRA, A. D. 1959. Root excretions in relation to the rhizosphere effect. IV. Influence of plant species, age of plant, light, temperature and calcium nutrition on exudation. Plant Soil 11: 53-64.

ROVIRA, A. D. 1963. Microbial inoculation of plants. I. Establishment of free living nitrogen fixing bacteria in the rhizosphere and their effects on maize, tomato and wheat. Plant Soil 19: 304-314.

ROVIRA, A. D., and J. R. HARRIS. 1961. Plant root ex-

cretions in relation to the rhizosphere effect. V. The exudation of B-group vitamins. Plant Soil 14: 119-214.

RUSSELL, P. B., A. R. TODD, and W. S. WARING. 1949. The potato eelworm hatching factor. 4. *Solanum nigrum* as a source of the potato eelworm hatching factor. Biochem J. 45: 528-530.

SCHAREN, A. L. 1960. Germination of oospores of *Aphanomyces euteiches* embedded in plant debris. Phytopathology 50: 274-277.

SCHMIDT, L., and R. O. BANKOLE. 1962. Detection of *Aspergillus flavus* in soil by immunofluorescent staining. Science 136: 776-777.

SCHÖNBECK, F. 1958. Untersuchungen über der Einfluss von Wurzelausscheidungen auf die Entwicklung von Bodenpilzen. Naturwissenschaften 45: 63-64.

SCHREIBER, L. R., and R. J. GREEN. 1962. Effect of root exudates in overcoming the soil fungistatic principle. (Abstr.) Phytopathology 52: 751.

SCHROTH, M. N., and W. C. SNYDER. 1961. Effect of host exudates on chlamydospore germination of the bean root rot fungus *Fusarium solani* f. *phaseoli*. Phytopathology 51: 389-393.

SCHROTH, M. N., and F. F. HENDRIX, JR. 1962. Influence of nonsusceptible plants on the survival of *Fusarium solani* f. *phaseoli* in soil. Phytopathology 52: 906-909.

SCHROTH, M. N., and W. C. SNYDER. 1962. Exudation patterns from bean seeds and hypocotyls and their effects on *Fusarium solani* f. *phaseoli*. (Abstr.) Phytopathology 52: 751.

SLANKIS, V. 1958. The role of auxin and other exudates in mycorrhizal symbiosis of forest trees. p. 427-443. *In* Physiology of forest trees, Symposium, Harvard (1957). The Ronald Press Co., New York.

STOTZKY, G., W. CULBRETH, and L. B. MISH. 1962. Apparatus for growing plants with aseptic roots for collection of root exudates and carbon dioxide. Plant Physiol. 37: 332-341.

SULOCHANA, C. B. 1962a. Amino acids in root exudates of cotton. Plant Soil 16: 312-326.

SULOCHANA, C. B. 1962b. B-vitamins in root exudates of cotton. Plant Soil 16: 327-334.

SZEMBER, A. 1959. Providing aseptically cultivated plants with water through bacteria-tight glass filters. Plant Soil 11: 392-394.

TESAR, S., and M. KATACEK. 1955. Root excretions of higher plants. I. Excretion of amino acids by roots of wheat in water culture. (In Czech with English summary.) Sb. Cesk. Akad. Zemedel. Ved. Rostlinná Vyroba 28: 927-940.

TIMONIN, M. I. 1941. The interaction of higher plants and soil micro-organisms. III. The effects of by products of plant growth on activity of fungi and actinomycetes. Soil Sci. 52: 395-413.

VANCURA, V., J. MACURA, O. FISCHER, and J. VONDRACEK. 1959. The relation of *Azotobacter* to the root system of barley. Folia Microbial. 4: 119-129.

VANCURA, V., and J. MACURA. 1961. The effect of root excretions on *Azotobacter*. Folia Microbiol. 6: 250-259.

VIRTANEN, A. I., S. VON HANSEN, and T. LAINE. 1937. Investigations on the root nodule bacteria of leguminous plants. XIX. Influence of various factors on the excretion of nitrogenous compounds from nodules. J. Agr. Sci. 27: 332-348.

VRANY, J., V. VANCURA, and J. MACURA. 1962. The effects of foliar application of some readily metabolized substances, growth regulators and antibiotics on rhizosphere microflora. Folia Microbiol. 7: 61-70.

WALLACE, H. R. 1957. The stimulatory properties of some organic substances on cysts of the beet eelworm, *Heterodera schachtii* Schmidt. Ann. Appl. Biol. 45: 251-255.

WALLACE, H. R. 1958. Observations on the emergence from cysts and the orientation of larvae of three species of the genus *Heterodera* in the presence of host plant roots. Nematologica 3: 236-243.

WALLACE, R. H., and A. G. LOCHHEAD. 1949. Qualitative studies of soil microorganisms. VIII. Influence of various crop plants on the nutritional group of soil bacteria. Soil Sci. 67: 63-69.

WARIS, H. 1958. Simple devices for aseptic culture of seed plants. Physiol. Plantarum 11: 627-630.

WEISCHER, B. 1959. Experimentelle Untersuchungen über die Wanderung von Nematoden. Nematologica 4: 172-186.

WEST, P. M. 1939. Excretion of biotin and thiamin by the roots of higher plants. Nature (London) 144: 1050-1051.

WHITE, N. H. 1954. The use of decoy crops in the eradication of certain soil borne plant diseases. Australian J. Sci. 17: 18-19.

WIDDOWSON, E. 1958a. Potato root diffusate production. Nematologica 3: 6-14.

WIDDOWSON, E. 1958b. The production of root diffusate by potatoes grown in water culture. Nematologica 3: 108-114.

WIDDOWSON, E. 1958c. Observations on the collection and storage of potato root diffusate. Nematologica 3: 173-178.

WIDDOWSON, E., C. C. DONCASTER, and D. W. FENWICK. 1958. Observations on the development of *Heterodera rostochiensis*. Nematologica 3: 308-314.

WIDDOWSON, E., and G. H. WILTSHIRE. 1958. The potato eelworm hatching factor. Ann. Appl. Biol. 46: 95-101.

WILSON, P. W. 1940. The biochemistry of nitrogen fixation. Univ. of Wisconsin Press. Madison, Wisconsin. 302 p.

WINNER, C. 1958. Untersuchungen über die Eigenschaften der auf *Heterodera schachtii* Schmidt aktivierend wirkenden Wurzelexsudate von *Brassica rapa oleifera* D.C. Nematologica 3: 315-326.

WINSLOW, R. D., and R. A. LUDWIG. 1957. Studies on hatching of the beet nematode *Heterodera schachtii* Schmidt. Can. J. Botany 35: 619-634.

WOOD, F. W. 1960. Biological antagonisms due to phytotoxic root exudates. Botan. Rev. 26: 546-569.

WYSS, O., and P. W. WILSON. 1941. Excretion of nitrogen by legumes. Soil Sci. 52: 15-30.

ZENTMYER, G. A. 1961. Chemotaxis of zoospores for root exudates. Science 133: 1595-1596.

ZINOV'EVA, K. G. 1958. Influence of root excretions and root extracts of some agricultural plants on *Azotobacter*. (In Russian with English summary.) Mikrobiologiya 27: 75-81.

► DISCUSSION OF A. D. ROVIRA PAPER

G. H. Hepting:

Do you feel that exudates from foliage and other aerial parts of plants would be likely to influence soil microflora?

A. D. Rovira:

Yes, there is evidence that significant quantities of organic materials are released from leaves and will be washed down into the soil. The amounts and types of materials coming from leaves varies according to plant species, age of plant, and climatic conditions.

There is certainly sufficient nutrient material in leaf exudate to affect the microflora in upper layers of the soil beneath the plant.

L. F. Johnson:

I would like to comment on Dr. Hepting's question about exudation from leaves. At the University of Tennessee we have found that certain plants have a distinct microflora on their leaves. *Streptococcus faecalis* is commonly spread from plant to plant by insects and can be found on the leaves and flowers of many plants. This association is specific, in that when seeds of certain plants are inoculated with this bacterium, it will grow along with the plant and become epiphytic on the leaves. It will not become epiphytic on other species of plants. Therefore, there is an apparent microflora associated with leaves. It is believed that this association is influenced by exudation from leaves. Dr. Rovira, how do you separate or distinguish between root exudates and leaf exudates that might be produced in your test-tube cultures?

A. D. Rovira:

The only precaution one can take when using the test-tube technique is to prevent any wetting of the leaves when changing the nutrient solution.

A. Burges:

1. Referring to Fig. 4: are the rows of bacteria in the longitudinal furrows, and if so, have bacteria which might have been on the ridges been washed off?

2. Regarding the possibility of using bacterial distribution as a means of locating leakage: while this could be used on the macroscale, would not diffusion invalidate the method on the microscale?

A. D. Rovira:

1. In the material used for the illustration, care was taken to avoid washing microorganisms from the roots so we can be confident that the linear orientation on tomato and colony development on *Phalaris* were the natural arrangements at the time of sampling. Briefly, the method consists of carefully removing sand or soil, and staining in Jones and Mollison aniline blue-phenol-acetic acid stain for 3 minutes.

2. Frenzel's experiments using mutants of *Neurospora* with different nutritional requirements show that the development of microorganisms on the root surface can be used to indicate sites of exudation, but there is no doubt that diffusion away from exudation points is a problem to be considered with this technique.

D. Parkinson:

You have stated that studies of root exudates should be made both on plants growing in sterile and in nonsterile culture; however, plant roots in nonsterile soil are surrounded by large populations of microorganisms which are probably more "leaky" than the plant roots. Surely, analyses of such nonsterile systems, from the viewpoint of exuded material, will be extremely difficult to interpret.

A. D. Rovira:

I agree with you, but I consider studies under nonsterile conditions an extension of detailed studies of exudation from roots growing under aseptic conditions.

F. M. Scott:

Grass root epidermis consists of long cells and short piliferous cells. Do bacterial colonies aggregate more densely on short cells?

A. D. Rovira:

I cannot say because I did not observe very closely the patterns of epidermal cells beneath the rhizoplane microflora.

W. D. Thomas:

How prevalent are such acids as chlorogenic and tannic acids in root exudates? Is it likely that all chemical constituents of root cells may show up in tree root exudation?

A. D. Rovira:

To my knowledge there are no analyses for these acids in root exudate. Amino acid analyses do indicate a similarity between the internal and external amino acids but such analyses of extracts of entire root systems may differ from the amino acids in the cells at the sites of exudation.

S. Wilhelm:

Roots of plants growing in nature or under cultivation are commonly and abundantly infected by parasitic fungi, especially those belonging to the genera *Olpidium* and *Endogene* (*Rhizophagus*). Root secretions in nature may thus be largely from parasitized roots and the spectrum of chemicals far greater than envisioned from roots growing under aseptic conditions.

The idea is old that plant roots may secrete complex chemicals involved in stimulation of other organisms. P. A. Mitcheli (Relazione dell' erba detta da' botanici *Orobanche;* Firenze, 1723) suggested it in his discussion of control of *Orobanche* on *Vicia faba*. J. P. Vaucher (Mém. Mus. Hist. Nat. 10: 261-273; 1823) considered it in his detailed studies on germination of seed of *O. ramosa*. R. Wight (Spicilegium Neilgherrense, vol. 2; Madras, 1851), a British physician stationed in India, considered root secretions of tobacco so obviously involved in the question of *Orobanche* seed germination that experimental demonstrations of them were unnecessary. R. M. Barcinsky (Dokl. Akad. Nauk SSSR (N.S.) 1: 343-346, 1934; *ibid.* (N.S.) 2: 311-313, 1935) and B. S. Zakharov (Comptes Rend. [Dokl.] Akad. Nauk. URSS 27: 267-270. 1940) showed that day length may profoundly influence the susceptibility of sunflower to *Orobanche* and implicated root secretions as bringing about the effect.

D. Pramer:

Will you comment on the possibility of controlling soil-borne plant pathogens by treating foliage with compounds that are absorbed by leaves, translocated downward, and exuded by roots?

A. D. Rovira:

Some excellent work on this topic has been done by Vrany, Vancura, and Macura (cited in the paper) in Czechoslovakia, who showed that the application of chloramphenicol to the leaves of wheat not only led to this antibiotic being exuded but also markedly increased the exudation of amino acids and sugars.

R. A. Kilpatrick:

Does the lack of aeration of sterile plants grown in agar affect the rate of release of root exudates?

A. D. Rovira:

Possibly; very little is known about this but the diffusion of oxygen through soft agar differs very little from diffusion through water.

R. A. Kilpatrick:

At the University of New Hampshire, red and white clovers have been grown under sterile conditions (test tubes) under about 400 ft-c fluorescent light. For 4 months, plants appear to grow normally; soon after this period, plants begin to die. Dead plants were removed and the agar was diluted with water, filtered, and then run through several chemical tests. Finally, a white substance was obtained. This was dissolved in water, sterilized, and then used to test the effect on seed germination of white clover. Nontreated seeds germinated 100%. The exudate suspension completely inhibited seed germination. Identification of the compound is unknown at this time.

H. Burström:

Different modes of exudation known from other plant parts will give different types of compounds, and it might thus be of interest to know which are operating in roots. Passive leakage through free space will give any permeable, small-molecular compounds. Active squeezing out of vacuolar sap, occurring in hairs and glands, will give everything stored in the vacuole. This requires pits or ectodesmata. Active exudation from the cytoplasm by the mechanism of phloem and nectaries, according to Lüttge, will give cytoplasmic compounds: sugars, amino acids. Emptying of dying cells will give the whole cell content.

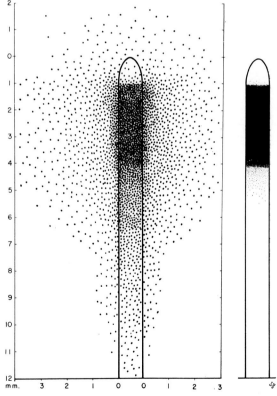

Fig. 8. Within a few minutes of placing excised avocado roottips in a suspension of actively swimming zoospores of *Phytophthora cinnamomi,* the spores are attracted to the root, and particularly to the region of elongation, as indicated in the diagram. In 24 hours the initial root lesion (right) develops at this area of abundant spore attraction and encystment. (See text, p. 186.)

A. D. Rovira:

Thank you, Dr. Burström. I hope that we can encourage plant physiologists to study these mechanisms which you suggest because an understanding of them is essential in any study of the rhizosphere phenomenon.

G. A. Zentmyer:

Zoospores of *Phytophthora cinnamomi* exhibit striking chemotaxy to the region of elongation on avocado roots, which constitutes further indirect evidence of the increased exudation of materials from this area of elongation, as compared with other areas of the root (Fig. 8).

G. Stotzky:

Although we all appreciate the difficulties involved in growing plants with axenic roots, as well as the necessity for growing large numbers of plants, I wonder if oversimplication of the culture apparatus doesn't sometimes defeat the purpose of the experiment. For example, most studies have been restricted to investigating the exudates from young seedlings, and little effort has been made to separate the root zone from the seed. Consequently, is it not possible that a sizable portion of the organic compounds isolated from the culture solution of these seedlings are breakdown products of the endosperm rather than "true" root exudates? The contribution of materials from the endosperm would be especially large with plants like peas, and this source may account for the large quantities of reducing sugars reported to be present, 2 weeks after germination, in culture solutions supporting peas.

A. D. Rovira:

This is a good point, but we consider that by pregerminating the seed on agar before planting in our tubes, we dispose of the bulk of the seed exudate. By having the seeds on stainless steel screen 1 cm above the solution, we consider that most of the material obtained must come from the roots. The fact that we find no differences between the exudates of roots developing from different-sized seeds of one plant species supports our contention that we are analysing root exudates. Further evidence comes from the fact that exudates vary according to the light intensities under which plants are grown. We would not expect light intensity to affect seed exudation.

R. D. Durbin:

Another factor which may influence root exudates is the presence of a disease in the aboveground portion. We have found that rust-infected bean leaves translocate only $\frac{1}{2}$ to $\frac{1}{10}$ the quantity of photosynthates to the root system that healthy plants translocate, and soon after infection the rate of root growth declines. Last in England has found that powdery mildew begins to adversely affect root growth of barley several days after inoculation. Quantitative and perhaps qualitative changes in root exudates possibly could result from this and may in part be responsible for predisposing the plant to root-invading microorganisms.

Nature and Importance of the Rhizosphere[1]

H. KATZNELSON—*Microbiology Research Institute, Research Branch, Canada Department of Agriculture, Ottawa.*

The rhizosphere phenomenon has been reviewed and its salient features described recently (Starkey, 1958; Lochhead, 1959; Katznelson, 1961). An understanding of the extent and nature of the microbial population in the root zone is essential, however, for a critical evaluation of "Factors Determining the Behaviour of Plant Pathogens in Soil" and a discussion of methods of control. Also important is a consideration of the antagonistic and associative biotic events occurring in the rhizosphere and how they may be influenced to create an environment that is unfavorable for a pathogen. It is intended here to reexamine the various features of the rhizosphere with emphasis on current observations. As demonstrated by the methods to be described, the rhizosphere effect is the resultant of two major forces—the plant root and the microorganisms that grow on and around it. This discussion will be confined to microbiological aspects, as the major contributions of the plant have been considered in the preceding paper. Furthermore, the review will be limited to the saprophytic rhizosphere populations of intact roots; the invasion of roots by symbiotic or plant-parasitic organisms will be dealt with elsewhere in this volume.

NATURE OF THE RHIZOSPHERE EFFECT.—The primary biological fact of the rhizosphere or zone of root influence is the greater number and activity of soil microorganisms in this region than in root-free soil. Between these two zones is an area of transition in which the root influence diminishes with distance. It is generally accepted that the term rhizosphere soil refers to the thin layer adhering to a root after the loose soil and clumps have been removed by shaking. The soil coating will vary in thickness with the kind of root and the nature and moisture conditions of the soil; this may influence the magnitude of the rhizosphere effect but will not obscure it nor alter its characteristic features. Clark (1949) has suggested that the root surface itself—the rhizoplane—be used in studying the rhizosphere phenomenon, since it may be a more sensitive index of the specific qualitative effects of roots on soil microorganisms. The rhizoplane offers a distinct advantage in studies of root fungi in that vegetatively active forms rather than rapidly sporing types may be isolated and studied (Warcup, 1960). But freeing roots from soil, usually by washing, removes not only fungus spores but also protozoa and nematodes. Furthermore, certain bacterial types are more abundant in rhizosphere soil than in the rhizoplane (Rouatt and Katznelson, 1961). Quantitatively, also, there are certain drawbacks. Whereas rhizosphere soil counts may be compared directly with those of root-free soil, both calculated on an oven-dry basis, this is not possible with rhizoplane counts, whether dry or moist root weights are used. Nor can an accurate comparison be made of numbers of organisms on fine fibrous roots with those on thick or fleshy ones calculated on a unit-weight basis.

Methods of study.—The rhizosphere effect has been examined by means of cultural, microscopic and manometric techniques. The first includes plating and extinction dilution procedures for over-all quantitative and qualitative information, and pure-culture methods for more detailed morphological, nutritional, physiological, and taxonomic characterization of the rhizosphere population and for investigations on the interactions of its constituent species or groups (Lochhead, 1940; Rouatt and Katznelson, 1961; Chan and Katznelson, 1961).

Rhizosphere soil (as defined above) is obtained by shaking roots in sterile water; decimal dilutions are then prepared and aliquots plated on agar media for bacterial, actinomycete, and fungal counts and transferred to fluid or solid media for enumeration of algae, protozoa, and bacteria capable of specific transformations such as ammonification, nitrification, denitrification, carbohydrate utilization, cellulose decomposition, and nitrogen fixation (Katznelson, 1946; Rouatt, Katznelson, and Payne, 1960). Final counts are based on the dry weight of the rhizosphere soil used. Where plants are grown under identical conditions in the same soil, direct quantitative comparisons of their rhizosphere populations may be made. But when they are grown under any conditions that cause fluctuations in the population of the soil itself, as in the field or as a result of soil treatment, the number of organisms in both rhizosphere and root-free soil should be determined; the extent of, or changes in the rhizosphere effect may then be demonstrated by means of the rhizosphere:soil (R:S) ratio, obtained by dividing the number of organisms in the rhizosphere soil by the number in the soil devoid of roots.

[1] Contribution No. 556.

For an analysis of the rhizoplane population, the practice in our laboratory is to remove the roots from the water blanks used to obtain the rhizosphere soil, wash, dry between paper, and weigh; after several further washings the roots are macerated in a sterile Waring blendor and dilutions prepared; aliquots are also dried and weighed and the counts based on dry and moist weights. For pure-culture studies of rhizoplane or rhizosphere soil populations, all colonies on suitable agar plates used for counting, or on representative portions of these, are picked, and the isolates examined for morphology (Lochhead, 1940), nutritional requirements (Lochhead and Chase, 1943), metabolic activity (Katznelson and Bose, 1959), synthetic abilities (Lochhead and Cook, 1961), and interactions (Chan and Katznelson, 1961). These procedures, with some variation in the choice of plating or selective media, are in general use.

The most important departure during recent years is in the method of studying fungal populations (Clarke and Parkinson, 1960). Instead of plating, which favors the development of rapidly growing and spore-forming types (Warcup, 1960), well-washed root segments are placed on agar plates and isolations made from the developing hyphal tips (Harley and Waid, 1955). This method permits an estimation of the relative proportions of vegetatively active fungi in intimate association with the plant root. Objections may also be raised to plating techniques for counts of actinomycetes that produce conidia, either on aerial hyphae or by their fragmentation, and for counts of bacteria (as the breakup of a single colony on a root may give rise to unusually high numbers). A more cogent drawback to the use of plating procedures for enumerating microorganisms in soil and for isolation purposes is that regardless of the attempts to improve the media used (Bunt and Rovira, 1955; Rovira, 1956a; Louw and Webley, 1959) only 10 to 20 per cent of the bacteria in soil develop. Despite their well-recognized and adequately documented limitations, however, cultural procedures have yielded most of our present information on the distribution, relative proportions, and activity of the bacterial, actinomycete, fungal, algal, and protozoan populations of the root zone.

Because of the above difficulties, which apply equally to studies of soil and root microorganisms, roots have been examined directly by means of the Rossi-Cholodny buried-slide technique (Starkey, 1938), by staining procedures (Linford, 1942; Rovira, 1956), by fluorescence microscopy (Zvyagintsev, 1962), or even by electron microscopy (Jenny and Grossenbacher, 1962). The results support and complement those obtained by cultural means; and although they provide no information on the physiological and metabolic activities or nutritional requirements of the organisms observed, they are of value in studies on the localization of organisms on roots, their relative abundance, morphology, and sequential development (Fig. 1). Direct microscopic counts on suspensions of rhizosphere soil (Louw and Webley, 1959) or root macerates may be useful, especially in conjunction with differential staining procedures (Lehner and Nowak, 1958). The micro-

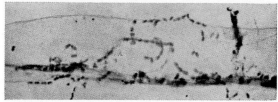

Fig. 1. Bacterial and actinomycete growth on root hairs. (R. L. Starkey. Soil Sci. 45: 207-209. 1938.) Upper, bacterial mantle around tip of a root hair. Lower, short chains of actinomycete conidia, fine filaments, and bacteria.

scope may also be used for protozoan counts (Bunt and Tchan, 1955) and is most important for studying nematode populations. The worms are separated from the soil or root material by means of the Baermann-funnel technique (Oostenbrink, 1960), and total numbers as well as the relative abundance of various types are recorded.

The over-all metabolic activity of the microbial population of rhizosphere soil can be determined manometrically (Katznelson and Rouatt, 1957). Different substrates, labeled or not, may be used under both aerobic and anaerobic conditions to provide information on a variety of inorganic and organic transformations, such as denitrification, nitrification, glycolysis, and oxidation. Specific enzyme activity in the root zone may also be studied (Vlasyuk, Dobrotvorskaya, and Gordienko, 1956; N. V. Peterson, 1961; Estermann and McLaren, 1961). More extensive application of these techniques could yield very interesting data on the predominant chemical processes in the rhizosphere and the adaptability of its population.

Quantitative features.—The rhizosphere effect of an actively growing crop is most pronounced with bacteria, R:S values of 10 to 20 or more and counts in the billions per gram of soil frequently being recorded. Ratios of over 100 have been reported. Smaller, though still significant, increases in numbers of actinomycetes and fungi are obtained in rhizosphere soil. The smallest changes are in numbers of protozoa and algae (Rouatt, Katznelson, and Payne, 1960). Rhizosphere soil also contains distinctly greater numbers of nematodes than root-free soil (Henderson and Katznelson, 1961). The numerical relations of these major groups of organisms do not vary appreciably with plant species, although absolute numbers differ, as in the case of legumes, which appear in general to support larger rhizosphere populations than nonlegumes. It is also of interest that the relative proportions of these large groups in the rhizosphere do not differ significantly from those in the soil itself. Since an inverse relation exists between numbers and size of the organisms considered here

(10^9 bacteria *vs* 10^2 nematodes), it is necessary to interpret counts or numbers with caution. Not only are they far from accurate, as already pointed out, but in addition, one strand of fungus mycelium or one protozoan may be equivalent in weight and metabolic activity to many bacteria. This is especially true for nematodes, whose dimensions range from 500 to 4000 μ in length and from 50 to 240 μ in width (Hirschmann, 1960).

Most of the quantitative work on the rhizosphere effect has been done with bacteria, fungi, and actinomycetes. A wide variety of plants has been studied and positive effects obtained, although their magnitude varies with the plant, nature and treatment of the soil, and environmental factors. As details will be discussed in later sections, only representative contributions from various parts of the world on the over-all effects of plant roots need be noted: Ishizawa et al. (1957), working with barley, timothy and alfalfa; Ramachandra-Reddy (1959), with six types of pteridophytes; Maliszewska and Moreau (1959) with white spruce; Ivarson and Katznelson (1960) with yellow birch; Strzelczyk (1961*a*) with onion, radish, and wheat; Rouatt and Katznelson (1961) with six crop plants including flax, clover, oats, and corn; Zagallo and Bollen (1962) with tall fescue; Rangaswami and Vasantharajan (1962) with citrus; Edward, Shrivastava, and Naim (1960) with a wide variety of crops grown in India; and many others. These examples suffice to show that a positive rhizosphere effect may be expected with most plant species.

Algae, protozoa, and free-living nonparasitic nematodes have received very little attention in rhizosphere investigations. Although no significant effect on algae was reported for wheat and mangels (Katznelson, 1946; Rouatt, Katznelson, and Payne, 1960), Shtina (1954) noted that rye and potatoes stimulated algae, whereas lupins, clover, and timothy did not. Gonzalves and Yalavigi (1959) obtained a positive effect with sorghum, wheat, and cotton; and Hadfield (1960) showed a distinct positive influence in the rhizosphere of cultivated tea plants and a positive effect with other crop plants, both monocotyledons and dicotyledons. Under aseptic conditions, pea roots stimulated good growth of algae, according to Cullimore and Woodbine (1963).

Protozoa appear to be stimulated by wheat roots (Rouatt, Katznelson, and Payne, 1960) and especially by mangels (Katznelson, 1946), in which case an R:S value of 23 was obtained. Shilova and Kondrat'eva (1955) claimed a positive rhizosphere effect with timothy and especially with clover. Varga (1958) found that although total numbers of protozoa were not affected by sugar beets, the number of cysts was much larger in the root-free soil than on the hair roots.

As already mentioned, greater numbers of soil nematodes are found in the rhizosphere than in root-free soil. Shilova and Kondrat'eva (1955) showed nematodes to be particularly abundant on timothy roots in the autumn, and Varga (1958) reported that free-living nematodes were found mainly on the root surface of sugar beets. R:S ratios of 13.5, 27.5, 30.9, 60.1, and 70.8 for oats, barley, soybeans, wheat, and peas, respectively, were recorded by Henderson and Katznelson

(1961); numbers reached 700 per gram of soil from pea roots.

Even less has been done on the influence of plant roots on minute soil animals such as mites and insect larvae. This field is perhaps beyond the scope of the present review, although it should be noted that Shilova and Kondrat'eva (1955) found a greater number of Enchytraeidae in the rhizosphere of timothy and clover than in root-free soil, with an abundance of Collembola feeding on the microflora and microfauna. Müller (1957) observed a high level of mite activity in the rhizosphere of grasses and numerous Collembola in that of legumes; and Führer (1961) reported large numbers of mites in the rhizosphere of *Artemisia campestris* but not in the root zone of *Bromus erectus* or *Dactylis glomerata*.

Qualitative features.—It is generally accepted that actively growing plant roots exert a distinct selective action on soil microorganisms, resulting in the stimulation of certain groups and in the suppression of others. Significant qualitative effects may be demonstrated, even if numerical differences between rhizosphere and root-free soil are slight. It should be emphasized, however, that although this preferential effect occurs in the early stages of plant growth, even from the beginnings of seed germination (Bowen, 1961; Müller, 1962) the microbiological equilibrium in the rhizosphere as usually observed is due to microbial as well as plant activity, with environmental factors influencing both. In most rhizosphere work these two agencies have not been separated; and indeed this is difficult to achieve except by aseptic techniques and possibly by an analysis of the rhizoplane population.

The qualitative features of the rhizosphere are best known and most characteristic for bacteria, less clear results having been recorded with fungi and even less with actinomycetes, algae, and protozoa, nematodes, and other microfauna. There is no evidence that plant species support specific microbial populations, aside from the well-established symbiotic relations between rhizobia and legumes and in mycorrhizal associations.

Bacteria.—As revealed by both pure-culture techniques and microscopic observations, the roots of most plants favor Gram-negative nonsporulating rod-shaped bacteria, whereas Gram-positive nonsporing rods, pleomorphic rods, and cocci are relatively less abundant (Lochhead, 1940; Sperber and Rovira, 1959; Vagnerova, Macura, and Catska, 1960*a,b*; Rouatt and Katznelson, 1961; Rangaswami and Vasantharajan, 1962*b*). Vagnerova, Macura, and Catska (1960*a,b*); Rouatt and Katznelson (1961) and Yoshida and Sakai (1962) have shown that this selective effect is most pronounced in the rhizoplane. Taxonomic studies by these two groups of workers have revealed that *Pseudomonas* species were predominant in the rhizoplane of wheat, whereas pleomorphic forms such as *Arthrobacter,* though numerous, were relatively less abundant. The ability of *Pseudomonas* sp. to outgrow and inhibit *Arthrobacter* in root extract has been demonstrated (Chan and Katznelson, 1961; Chan, Katznelson, and Rouatt, 1963), as

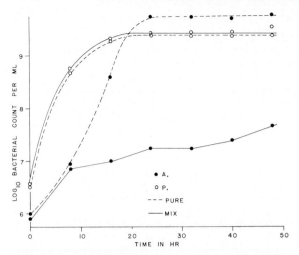

Fig. 2. Growth interaction of *Pseudomonas* sp. (*P*) and *Arthrobacter globiformis* (*A*) in mature soybean root extract, showing inhibition of the latter organism. (E. C. S. Chan and H. Katznelson. Can. J. Microbiol. 7: 759-767. 1961.)

illustrated in Fig. 2. In the rhizosphere soil itself the percentage incidence of these two groups was not appreciably different. Sperber and Rovira (1959) reported 64% and 79% of their isolates from subterranean clover and ryegrass roots, respectively, to be branching forms, chiefly *Arthrobacter* and *Nocardia*. Since the Australian workers used 15-week-old plants whereas the Canadian and Czechoslovakian workers used seedlings, and since different kinds of plants were used, different results might have been anticipated. Numerous other workers using a variety of plants—maize, gooseberry, wheat, rice, soybeans, yellow birch—have also reported that pseudomonads constitute an important fraction of the bacterial population of the root zone (Firsanova, 1956; Vozniakovskaia and Zhil'tsova, 1958; Federov and Savkina, 1960; Rivière, 1961; Katznelson, Peterson, and Rouatt, 1962; Rouatt, Peterson, et al., 1963).

In general *Bacillus* species are not favored in the rhizosphere (Sperber and Rovira, 1959; Vagnerova, Macura, and Catska, 1960*a,b*; Rouatt and Katznelson, 1961) although they may occur in appreciable numbers (Clark, 1940), with the predominance of species such as *B. brevis, B. circulans, B. polymyxa;* the last was more abundant on cereal roots and *B. megaterium* on cotton roots. One of the most characteristic rhizosphere effects is the increase in number of *Agrobacterium radiobacter* on plant roots as observed by Starkey in 1929, and more recently by Rouatt, Katznelson, and Payne (1960). Brown (1961) reported a striking increase in count of streptomycin-resistant bacteria on the roots of leguminous plants; however, the predominant form was identified as a species of *Flavobacterium*. The many studies on *Azotobacter* (Clark, 1949; Katznelson, Lochhead, and Timonin, 1948; Rouatt, Katznelson, and Payne, 1960; Katznelson and Strzelczyk, 1961; Dorosinkii and Krupina, 1960; Brown, Burlingham, and Jackson, 1962) have, in general, failed to show that the roots of most plants favor extensive development of this organism. Exceptions

have been reported by Strzelczyk (1958) in Poland for radish, poppy, lupine, tea, and barley plants which stimulated these bacteria; oats and onions did not. Even in the most favorable instances (radish and poppy) counts did not exceed 43,000 per gram of rhizosphere soil. Gas-producing anaerobes, chiefly species of *Clostridium,* were also numerically higher in the rhizosphere of certain plants such as wheat and mangels (Katznelson, 1946) and in that of lupine, flax, poppy, and radish (Strzelczyk, 1958). Representatives of many other genera of bacteria—*Achromobacter, Flavobacterium, Mycobacterium, Cellulomonas, Micrococcus,* and *Mycoplana*—have been isolated from the rhizosphere of many plants; but so far there is little accurate information regarding their relation, if any, to roots. Rhizobia, too, have been found in the root zone of nonlegumes (Manil, 1958; Rovira, 1961; Tuzimura and Watanabe, 1962), as well as around the roots of legumes (Rovira, 1961; Elkan, 1962).

According to Lochhead (1959), "More important for an understanding of the interrelationships between plant roots and the soil microflora is an appreciation of the physiological activity of the microorganisms at or near the root surface." In the root zone of many plants there is a higher relative incidence of motile, chromogenic, and rapidly growing bacteria (Lochhead, 1940; Rovira, 1956; Rouatt and Katznelson, 1957; Vagnerova, Macura, and Catska, 1960*a,b*); of ammonifying, sugarfermenting, acid-producing, cellulose-decomposing, denitrifying, and methylene-blue or resazurin reducing types (Katznelson, 1946; Katznelson and Rouatt, 1957*a*; Rouatt and Katznelson, 1961; Rangaswami and Vasantharajan, 1962*b*; Rouatt, Peterson, et al., 1963) and of bacteria capable of oxidizing substrates such as glucose, acetate, and alanine (Zagallo and Katznelson, 1957; Katznelson and Bose, 1959; Zagallo and Bollen, 1962). The greater CO_2 evolution by soil adjacent to roots (Starkey, 1931), and the greater oxygen uptake by rhizosphere soil (alone or supplemented with substrates) from various crops (Katznelson and Rouatt, 1957*b*) may be due to greater metabolic activity of the microflora but may also be due to the incorporation and decomposition in the soil of root tissue and substances liberated by roots damaged during sampling.

Another important manifestation of the selective action of plant roots was demonstrated by A. G. Lochhead and his associates in their extensive studies on the nutrition of soil and rhizosphere bacteria. The most significant and consistent features observed were the higher percentage incidence in the root zone of bacteria requiring amino acids for maximum growth and the lower relative proportions of those requiring nutrients contained in soil extract (Lochhead and Rouatt, 1955; Lochhead, 1959). Recent work in India with citrus trees (Rangaswami and Vasantharajan, 1962*b*) demonstrated similar effects. Using six different crops, Rouatt and Katznelson (1961) demonstrated that the amino acid effect was even greater on the immediate root surface (rhizoplane). Bacteria requiring unknown factors in yeast extract or known vitamins occurred in the same proportions in the rhizosphere as in root-free soil (Lochhead, 1959), but those capable of vitamin synthesis were relatively more numerous in the rhizosphere soil and particularly so on the root surface (Lochhead, 1957; Cook and Lochhead, 1959). It should be emphasized that although the relative proportions of the various nutritional groups of organisms studied were as indicated, their actual numbers were always greater in the root zone than in root-free soil.

The preferential stimulation of phosphate-dissolving bacteria by roots has been reported by Nowotny-Mieczynska and Golebiowska (1956) and by Sperber (1958a). Although a selective effect was not observed with wheat (Katznelson and Bose, 1959) or with corn, red clover, and flax (Katznelson, Peterson, and Rouatt, 1962), these organisms were favored in the rhizoplane and rhizosphere soil of barley (29% and 19%, respectively, of the isolates tested, as compared with 10% in root-free soil); oats were somewhat antagonistic to these bacteria. The actual numbers of phosphate-dissolvers, however, were distinctly greater in the root zone than in root-free soil, even with oats.

Fungi.—Despite the objections already raised to the still commonly used dilution-plating method for soil fungi, it is interesting that most counts show a positive rhizosphere effect. Isolations from dilution plates also show qualitative differences between root-free and rhizosphere soil (Parkinson, 1958; E. A. Peterson, 1958; Ebben, 1959; Catska, Macura, and Vagnerova, 1960; Papavizas and Davey, 1961; Goos and Timonin, 1962).

A good deal of the most recent work, however, has been done with washed roots. Peterson (1958) isolated *Fusarium* species most frequently from root segments of wheat and red clover grown in two soils, but *Cylindrocarpon* species were most common on the roots of both plants in a third soil. Stenton (1958) also reported the latter group "as the most vigorous and regular colonizer of the surface of pea roots"; *Fusarium* was well represented. *Cylindrocarpon* spp. were abundant on washed roots of leek seedlings in three different soils (Parkinson and Clarke, 1961) and on roots of yellow-birch seedlings (Katznelson, Rouatt, and Peterson, 1962) with *Fusarium* also occurring in substantial numbers. Goos and Timonin (1962), however, found no striking differences in fungal species on fleshy or fibrous roots of banana. Catska, Macura, and Vagnerova (1960) reported few isolations of *Cylindrocarpon* and not many more of *Fusarium* from wheat roots; however, *Mucor*, *Rhizopus*, and *Penicillium* species were abundant. *Fusarium* species were most frequently isolated from soybeans (Rouatt, Peterson, et al., 1963) with *Cylindrocarpon, Rhizoctonia, Mucor,* and *Rhizopus* also appearing in substantial numbers. *Fusarium, Phoma,* and sterile fungi were the ones most commonly found on wheat roots. It is clear that much remains to be done in this area, although the frequency with which *Fusarium* and *Cylindrocarpon* species appear on roots is suggestive.

The lack of information on the rhizosphere effect on fungi in relation to nutrition and physiology is regrettable. Thrower (1954) found higher percentages of fungi capable of maximum growth in simple and in amino-acid-supplemented media in rhizosphere than in root-free soil, and lower proportions of those requiring more complex substances. The nutritional studies of Atkinson and Robinson (1955) with 1,914 species of fungi from soil on potato tubers and in root-free soil, were somewhat inconclusive. Recently completed work (E. A. Peterson and Katznelson, unpublished) showed a preponderance of amino-acid-requiring fungi in soil devoid of roots and a greater percentage of fungi requiring amino acids plus growth factors on the roots. A high proportion of the isolates from both habitats (40-47%) grew well on a simple medium. To the writer's knowledge, physiological work of the kind done with bacteria has not been attempted with fungi.

Actinomycetes.—Also an important constituent of the soil microflora, the actinomycetes, including so many species with antibotic and other biosynthetic capabilities, have received little attention taxonomically, nutritionally, or physiologically in relation to the rhizosphere phenomenon. Where they have been studied, emphasis has been on their antagonistic potentialities. One of the earliest reports was that of Rouatt, Lechevalier, and Waksman (1951). Using young wheat, oats, soybeans, and potatoes, and more mature oats, soybeans, mangels, and alfalfa, they found higher proportions of antibacterial actinomycetes in the rhizosphere than in root-free soil. Agnihothrudu (1955) isolated *Streptomyces griseus* (the most abundant and inhibitory to *Fusarium udum*), *S. erythrochromogenus,* and species of *Nocardia* and *Micromonospora* from the rhizosphere of pigeon pea resistant to *F. udum*. Certain actinomycete strains inhibited the growth of *Azotobacter* and nodule bacteria in the rhizosphere of lucerne (Ivushkin, 1956). Strzelczykowa and Strzelczyk (1958) found that about 24% of the antagonistic actinomycetes isolated were from soil as compared with 15% in the rhizosphere of 11 crop plants (the antagonisms were for *Rhizobium* species, *Azotobacter, Clostridium,* and other organisms). Actinomycetes from the rhizosphere of wheat, radish, and onion formed a greater proportion of antagonists producing good zones of inhibition against *Azotobacter* than isolates from root-free soil (Strzelczyk, 1961b). Rhem (1961) found that *Streptomyces antibioticus, S. diastaticus, Actinomyces chromogenes* and other species were especially noticeable in direct association with the roots of barley. No rhizosphere effect on any particular taxonomic groups was noted by Rangaswami and Vasantharajan (1962c), but antibacterial forms were more abundant in the root zone of citrus trees. Probably the most extensive study of the actinomycete population in the rhizosphere was done recently with rice by Venkatesan (1962). He reported that late-sporing, aerobic, pigmented and biochemically active types were encouraged in the rhizosphere. The nutritionally simple and soil-extract-requiring types were relatively more abundant in the root-free soil, whereas those requiring amino acids, growth factors, and yeast extract were more numerous in the root zone. On the whole, roots favored antagonistic actinomycetes (both antifungal and antibacterial). *Streptomyces* spp. were the predominant types found (80-90% of the isolates), but a clear-cut difference between soil and rhizosphere was not evident; *S. anti-*

bioticus and *S. fradiae* were more abundant in the latter; *S. lavendulae* and *S. ruber* were more numerous in the rhizosphere at the early stage of growth and *S. griseus* at the later stage. *Micromonospora* spp. were favored in root-free soil but *Nocardia* spp. were selectively stimulated in the rhizosphere.

Algae.—Even less is known of the species distribution of algae than of actinomycetes. In general blue-green algae are more abundant in the mangel rhizosphere than in control soil (Katznelson, 1946); and Shtina (1954) found that green algae predominated in the rhizosphere of lupins and clover, and diatomaceous algae in that of timothy; rye and potatoes were particularly favorable for both types of algae. Different species of algae were associated with different crop plants according to Gonzalves and Yalavigi (1959).

Protozoa, Nematodes, and Other Microfauna.—Ciliates, flagellates, and amoeboid forms were all observed in the rhizosphere of mangels and wheat (Katznelson, 1946), but the methods used were not sufficiently precise to permit recognition of any specific root effects. Varga (1958) identified 16 flagellate, 15 rhizopod, and 7 ciliate species in the root zone of sugar beet. Most of the work with nematodes and roots has been with parasitic types and will not be discussed here. Jones (1959) suggests that the attraction of soil nematodes to roots is not very specific except in the case of hatching and other factors for parasitic forms such as *Heterodera* spp. Deubert (1959) recorded 10 genera and 15 species of free-living forms, with predominance of *Plectus cirratus* and *Rhabditis monhystera* under lucerne, and *Tylenchus filiformis, Tylenchorhynchus dubius,* and *Acrobeles ciliatus* under barley. A broad spectrum of soil nematodes in the rhizosphere of wheat and soybean was reported by Rouatt, Peterson, et al. (1963); species of *Helicotylenchus, Acrobeloides,* and *Cephalobus* were most numerous on both root systems.

FACTORS AFFECTING THE RHIZOSPHERE POPULATION. —Since the primary factor contributing to the rhizosphere phenomenon is the plant, any condition that significantly affects its growth and metabolism will be reflected in quantitative and qualitative changes in the microflora of the root zone. In addition to the obvious effects of stage of plant growth and kind of plant, and the nature, moisture content, reaction, and fertility of the soil, environmental factors such as light and temperature and plant treatment affect the rhizosphere population in varying degree by influencing plant development. They also exert a direct though considerably smaller effect on the microorganisms themselves.

Age and kind of plant.—The rhizosphere effect may be noted within a few days of planting seed, the developing bacterial population being made up of organisms from both seed and soil (Wallace and Lochhead, 1951; Rovira, 1956; Rouatt, 1959; Vagnerova, Macura, and Catska, 1960a). E. A. Peterson (1959), however, found that fungi associated with seed of barley, flax, and wheat, played little part in the colonization of the roots in natural soil. Species of *Aspergillus, Penicillium,*

and *Alternaria,* abundant on the seed, were rarely obtained from root samples. The young roots (2 days after seeding) were relatively free from fungi, but those which were colonized at this time yielded *Pythium* and *Fusarium* spp. predominantly. Ordin (1961) also reported fewest fungi on roots at the time of emergence.

According to most of the relevant literature, the rhizosphere effect increases with the age of a plant and reaches a maximum coincident with its greatest vegetative development. At senescence the root effect diminishes and the microbial picture becomes complicated owing to the decomposition of dead and dying root tissue. Because of the different conditions under which most of this work has been done and because of the different methods of sampling and analysis, it is not possible to make definitive comparisons of the rhizosphere effect of different plants. Several examples from recent investigations, however, may serve to illustrate pertinent features. Rivière (1959) observed that the rhizosphere activity of wheat reached a distinct peak at the stage of tillering; the stimulation of fungi was greater than that of actinomycetes and least with bacteria, a reversal of the usual findings. Also with wheat, Rouatt (1959) noted that by the third day after planting, the bacterial R:S had doubled and continued to increase; fungus counts doubled by the seventh day. The R:S ratios for methylene-blue-reducing bacteria, ammonifiers, denitrifiers, gelatin liquefiers, and starch hydrolyzers increased markedly with time. A distinct increase in the percentage incidence of "amino acid requiring bacteria" and of organisms with rapid growth rates occurred 3 days after the seed was planted, but little change occurred thereafter. In an extensive study with wheat, Vagnerova, Macura, and Catska (1960a,b), noted an increase in bacterial numbers with age; the R:S ratio and the percentage incidence of Gram-negative bacteria were highest at flowering. Bacterial R:S values for onions increased during 100 days of growth according to Strzelczyk (1961a); with radishes maximum counts occurred at 70 days. For both these crops and wheat, specific nutritional groups of bacteria had become established by 21 days and did not change appreciably thereafter, as noted also by Vagnerova, Macura, and Catska (1960a,b). Marked changes in numbers of certain "physiological" groups of bacteria with stage of plant growth were also reported by Strzelczyk (1961a). Onions showed increased R:S values for ammonifiers and methylene-blue reducers for 100 days, but with wheat the ratios declined from 21 days on. The R:S ratio for ammonifiers on radish roots was highest (308) at 70 days. A gradual increase in R:S values for bacteria and actinomycetes occurred with yellow-birch seedlings for 28 weeks after the breaking of dormancy; there was little change in fungal counts (Ivarson and Katznelson, 1960). "Physiological" groups of bacteria also increased, with R:S values for methylene-blue-reducing bacteria rising from 1.3 to 35 at 28 weeks. The pattern of bacterial nutritional groups once established did not change significantly. Working with *Azotobacter*, Strzelczyk (1958) noted that the most favourable period was generally at the flowering stage of the various plants tested. Similar results were obtained with buckwheat (Katznelson and Strzelczyk, 1961); but with field rye, oats, wheat, corn, and peas, the seedling stage appeared to favor this group, although counts were very low in all cases.

Different plants exert rhizosphere effects which vary in magnitude, though generally not in kind. In a study of six crop plants, highest rhizosphere counts were reported with red clover (Rouatt and Katznelson, 1961); flax and oat counts were next, and wheat, barley and corn last. Rhizoplane counts based on dry or moist root weights, however, were highest with corn. Methylene-blue-reducing bacteria were most numerous in both the rhizosphere and the rhizoplane of red clover; glucose fermenters and ammonifiers were more abundant on flax. The percentage incidence of the "amino acid" group was higher in the rhizoplane in every case and especially with flax and barley. Strzelczyk (1958) reported much greater *Azotobacter* counts in poppy and radish rhizospheres than in those of a number of other crops. *Clostridium* counts were highest on poppy roots. In Canadian soil the maximum effect on *Azotobacter* was with buckwheat (Katznelson and Strzelczyk, 1961). Rhizoplane counts of corn were greater than those of barley (Vrany, 1960), the difference not being evident in the rhizosphere; but bacteria capable of utilizing aromatic compounds were always relatively more abundant in soil devoid of roots. The rhizosphere effect of clover on bacteria was three times that of papsalum, according to the R:S ratios calculated from data provided by Rovira (1961). Brown (1961) found that streptomycin-resistant bacteria were preferentially stimulated in the rhizosphere of 11 plant species, most markedly with legumes, and that a distinct increase in R:S ratio occurred with plant age.

Fungal populations also vary considerably with age and kind of plant. E. A. Peterson (1959) showed that *Pythium* spp. predominated on barley, flax, and wheat at the early stages but declined markedly with plant age to be replaced by *Phoma* and *Fusarium* from the fifth to the twentieth day; *Periconia* was more abundant on barley and flax and *Cylindrocarpon* on wheat roots. Few rapidly sporing fungi were found, which indicates the effectiveness of his root-washing procedure; yet Catska, Macura and Vagnerova (1960) obtained appreciable numbers of these fungi on wheat roots, the incidence of Phycomycetes increasing from 26% to 57% at 7 and 21 days, respectively (9% in root-free soil). Fungi Imperfecti decreased from 71% to 42% in this period and were relatively more abundant in the soil (85%). In the period of vegetative growth, the importance of Phycomycetes decreased very much, with *Penicillium* and *Fusarium* spp. dominant. Rouatt, Peterson, et al. (1963) isolated *Phoma*, *Periconia*, and sterile, both light and dark fungi from wheat but not from soybean roots, which harbored more *Mucor, Candida, Fusarium, Cylindrocarpon*, and *Rhizoctonia* species. Roots may also stimulate germination of spores of both root- and soil-inhabiting fungi according to Garrett (1956), Jackson (1957, 1960), Tolle and Rippel-Baldes (1958), Buxton (1957a,b), and Schroth, Toussoun, and Snyder (1963). This effect

varied with the kind of plant and, according to Buxton, with its age.

There are few detailed studies on the influence of age and plant type on the actinomycete population of the rhizosphere. The work of Rouatt, Lechevalier, and Waksman (1951) shows a lower percentage incidence of antibacterial actinomycetes on older roots of oats and soybean and different patterns of antagonism with different plants. Increased R:S values with age of yellow-birch seedlings have been noted (Ivarson and Katznelson, 1960). Rhem (1961) observed a reduction of antifungal streptomycetes in the rhizosphere of barley before heading out, but at the time of ripening numbers had increased considerably. Again reference must be made to the extensive work of Venkatesan (1962) with rice. A gradual increase of R:S ratios from 2 to 7 occurred betwen the 15th and 150th day. Late-sporulating types were more abundant in the rhizosphere for 60 days but were more numerous in root-free soil thereafter. Nonaerial mycelial forms and those producing acid or pigment were more numerous in the root zone in the early stage of growth. Antagonistic types were more abundant among rhizosphere than among soil isolates for 120 days; thereafter there was no difference.

The distribution of protozoa and algae has been referred to earlier, and it is clear that much remains to be done with these organisms and with nonparasitic nematodes. For the latter, highest total numbers have been found in the rhizosphere of peas and lowest in that of oats, the remaining three crops being intermediate in their effect (Henderson and Katznelson, 1961). Total *Tylenchida* and *Paratylenchus* were also highest under peas; cereals seemed to favor *Pratylenchus* species over *Paratylenchus*. Many more *Helicotylenchus, Boleodorus,* and *Cephalobus* forms were counted by Rouatt, Peterson, et al. (1963) in rhizosphere soil suspensions of soybean than of wheat.

Not only are there differences in the root microflora of different plant species but also between varieties of a single species. Early work by Lochhead, Timonin, and West (1940) showed that the rhizosphere of varieties of tobacco and flax susceptible to black root rot and wilt, respectively, had higher bacterial numbers and showed a more pronounced effect on the incidence of certain groups than nonsusceptible varieties. Buxton (1957a,b), reported different effects with three varieties of peas on spore germination of the pea-wilt fungus, *Fusarium oxysporum* f. *pisi*. Numbers of fungi were higher in the rhizosphere of varieties of tomato susceptible to *Verticillium*, with one exception (Subba-Rao and Bailey, 1961). A species of *Fusarium* was dominant on the susceptible varieties and *Trichoderma viride* on the resistant varieties, again with the same exception. Recent studies of Lochhead and Cook (1961) showed that bacteria capable of synthesizing growth factors were proportionally more abundant in the root zone of a flax variety susceptible to *Fusarium oxysporum* f. *lini*.

Microbial differences between sections of roots on one plant have been shown by Rovira (1956b), who observed that root hairs of young tomato plants were free from bacteria but not those of oats. In both plants, root tips were free from organisms, although this is not always so (Starkey, 1938; Linford, 1942). By direct observation Parkinson and Clarke (1961) noted that root hairs of leek roots were rarely colonized by fungal hyphae, although these hyphae grew mainly parallel to the longitudinal axis of the root. Fungal growth down roots is slow, according to Taylor and Parkinson (1961), who concluded that successive lateral colonization from the soil is more important than downward growth. Mycorrhizal roots of yellow-birch seedlings harbor larger numbers of bacteria, including methylene-blue reducers, ammonifiers, and sugar fermenters, and also actinomycetes than nonmycorrhizal rootlets on the same root (Katznelson, Peterson, and Rouatt, 1962).

As mentioned earlier it is difficult to separate plant effects from microbial effects in most rhizosphere work except by aseptic methods or by using the rhizoplane. Root exudates or extracts have also yielded interesting results (Timonin, 1941). Buxton (1957a,b) has demonstrated the specific effect of exudates of pea cultivars on spore germination of *Fusarium oxysporum* f. *pisi*. The root-tip glycoside of *Avena* was found by Schönbeck (1958) to inhibit certain fungi. Metz (1955) reported inhibition of various bacteria by root sap, and extensive suppression of bacterial isolates by oat root extracts have been recorded (Rouatt and Katznelson, 1957). *Agrobacterium radiobacter* was inhibited by root extracts of 8-week-old wheat, oats, and soybean, recovering after 24-48 hours in pure culture, though not in the presence of other bacteria (Chan, Katznelson, and Rouatt, 1963). Extracts of younger plants did not show this effect.

Nature and treatment of the soil.—Although soil type and treatment may be expected to influence the rhizosphere effect, many of the results purporting to demonstrate this must be interpreted with caution. Frequently overlooked, for example, is the fact that the same plant will develop at quite a different rate in soils which differ naturally or as a result of amendment, and at a given time may represent a distinctly advanced or retarded stage of growth. Yet it is the usual practice to analyse these plants at the same time. Another point frequently not considered in studies on the effects of soil treatment is that both soil and plant populations may be altered, and it is therefore desirable to analyse root-free as well as rhizosphere soil to determine whether a significant change has taken place.

Since many studies have been conducted on the rhizosphere effect of various soils, only a few representative examples with distinctly different soils will be discussed. Bacterial counts of 353×10^6 and 180×10^6 were obtained on roots of yellow-birch seedlings in the A (humus) and B (sand) horizons, respectively, of a forest soil (Ivarson and Katznelson, 1960). The corresponding soil counts were 23×10^6 and 3×10^6. It is clear that the absolute increase in numbers of bacteria was greater in the humus layer, but a greater proportional increase occurred in the sandy soil as shown by R:S ratios (A = 15; B = 60). The per-

centage incidence of amino-acid-requiring bacteria was the same on both root systems, but was lower in the sand than in the humus layer. Using a sandy loam and a sand (5% and 1.2% organic matter, respectively) adjusted to pH 7.0, Strzelczyk (1961a) found R:S ratios of radishes and onions to be higher in the latter soil; the values for wheat were higher in the former. With the three crops distinctly higher R:S values for methylene-blue reducers and celulose decomposers were again obtained in the sandy soil at 21 and 70 days. This was also the case with *Azotobacter* on wheat roots, the R:S ratios being 4 and 61 in the loam and sand, respectively (Katznelson and Strzelczyk, 1961). These differences were due primarily to the soil counts since the rhizosphere counts were quite similar. The results provide further evidence of the powerful influence exerted by plant roots on the bacteria surrounding them and the resistance of this population, once established, to change.

A good comparison of the effect of three different soils on the fungal flora of wheat and red-clover roots was made by E. A. Peterson (1958). Whereas the R:S ratios of plate counts did not vary for red clover in the three soils, for wheat a value of 34 was noted in the acid sandy loam and of 10 in the neutral clay loam. With red clover the acid soil favored *Fusarium* species on the root surface whereas the other two soils favored *Cylindrocarpon*. *Gliocladium* was not isolated from roots in acid or alkaline soil but contributed 12% of the isolates from roots in neutral soil. With wheat grown in acid soil *Fusarium* species again predominated, and *Cylindrocarpon* on wheat in the alkaline soil. Rapidly sporing types such as *Penicillium* were most numerous in both acid and neutral rhizosphere and root-free soils for both plants but not in the chalky soil. A dominance of *Fusarium* over *Cylindrocarpon* species on leek roots in acid soil was also shown by Parkinson and Clarke (1961). Species of *Gliocladium* and *Mortierella* were more numerous on roots from acid soil. Soil reaction may therefore have an appreciable influence, as Welte and Trolldenier (1961) have also pointed out, on the microbial population in the rhizosphere.

A survey of the literature (Katznelson, Lochhead, and Timonin, 1948; Lochhead, 1959) reveals that the effects of soil treatment on the root population are often not very striking and usually unpredictable. Voroshilova (1956) reported that complete mineral fertilizers had little effect on the number of organisms in the rhizosphere; whereas Mosolov, Rempe, and Alexandrovskaya (1959) recorded increased counts in both rhizosphere and root-free soil with NPK fertilizer. Gadzhieva (1959) claimed that organo-mineral treatments increased counts in the root zone of winter wheat. Louw and Webley (1959) reported a favorable bacterial response in oat rhizosphere on addition of superphosphate and concluded that this was due to increased plant growth, since no such effect occurred in the uncropped (control) soil. In an extensive report on organic and nitrogen amendments of soil in relation to rhizosphere fungi on bean roots, Davey and Papavizas (1960) obtained a positive effect when the beans were planted 25 days after the amendment was added; the R:S ratio increased from 6.6 in the untreated soil to 9.3 in the amended soil; but the degree of variation was such that this change may not be particularly significant. Similarly the significance of changes in numbers of certain species of fungi as a result of treatment may be open to question if R:S ratios are calculated. With other species (*Penicillium lilacinum*), however, a distinct rhizosphere effect occurred with the organic amendment. The addition of a nitrogen source (NH_4NO_3) increased the fungus R:S from 8 to 20. Again *Penicillium* was favored in all amended soils. In more recent work with fungi of lupine roots, Papavizas and Davey (1961) observed no significant differences in response to corn stover with or without NH_4NO_3. A detailed study of individual fungi of the rhizoplane was claimed to show a preferential effect on species of *Penicillium* and *Mortierella*, yet the counts of penicillia went up from 88 to 584 (a 6.6-fold increase) with corn stover, but soil counts went up from 53 to 334 (a 6.2-fold increase). A clear-cut effect was noted, however, with this material plus NH_4NO_3 on both *P. piscarium* and *Mortierella*. Samtsevich and Borisova (1961) report that in pot experiments, mineral and organic fertilizers had little effect on counts in uncropped soil or in wheat rhizosphere, but in field experiments the effect of the fertilizers depended on the time of year.

Rovira's studies (1961) showed a marked increase in bacterial count due to addition of CaO or CaO plus minerals in both soil and rhizosphere soil, but R:S values actually decreased for clover, and increased (from 7 to 14) with *Paspalum* only with the CaO treatment. For fungi, as for bacteria, treatment increased the counts in both rhizosphere and root-free soil but R:S values on the whole decreased, owing to the fact that numbers increased proportionally more in the soil than near the root. However, the number of clover rhizobia in the rhizosphere was much greater as a result of CaO treatment.

Venkatesan (1962) showed that addition of manures (green leaf, farmyard) lowered the rhizosphere effect of rice for bacteria and fungi for the first 45 days, after which the R:S ratio increased from 4 to 21. Very little effect was observed with actinomycetes. Fertilizer treatment (NPK in various combinations) showed bacterial R:S ratios to be higher with potassium than with other elements, but not higher than in untreated soil; NP and NPK lowered the R:S ratio. Little change due to treatment was recorded for fungi and actinomycetes, the latter being somewhat depressed in the rhizosphere after phosphorus addition. Absalyamova (1963), however, recently reported that the application of organo-mineral mixtures greatly increased the total number of bacteria in the rhizosphere of maize, beet, and winter wheat.

Environmental factors.—With the possible exception of light, these factors—moisture, temperature—may exert both direct and indirect effects. Seasonal effects as reported by various workers (Katznelson, 1946; Miller and Boothroyd, 1962) may be considered to reflect the combined influence of all these environmental conditions. Following the important contribution of

Rovira (1959) on root exudation in relation to light and temperature, detailed microbiological studies were initiated in our laboratory. In the wheat rhizoplane, possibly a more sensitive index of the changes induced by light on a plant, bacterial counts and numbers of glucose fermenters, methylene-blue reducers, ammonifiers, and amino-acid-requiring bacteria were lowered with reduction of light intensity from 1,000 to 300 ft-c (Rouatt and Katznelson, 1960); the decrease of ammonifiers was spectacular and implies a lower quantity of ammonifiable substrate such as amino acids, a view supported by the lowered incidence of the amino-acid group of bacteria. On the other hand, E. A. Peterson (1961) states "that shading of plants had no appreciable effect on vegetatively active fungi colonizing the primary roots of wheat and soybean seedlings." A decrease in total count of nematodes occurred on wheat roots as the light intensity was reduced (Henderson and Katznelson, 1961).

A detailed study on temperature effects has recently been completed in our laboratory (Rouatt, Peterson, et al., 1963) with wheat and soybeans grown at three ranges of temperature: 55-60°, 70-75°, and 85-90° F (12.8-15.6°, 21.1-23.9°, and 29.4-32.2° C). Numbers of bacteria in the rhizosphere and rhizoplane of wheat increased as the temperature decreased, whereas numbers in the root-free soil and on soybean roots increased with increased temperature. The same relations held for methylene-blue-reducing, glucose-fermenting, and ammonifying bacteria and those requiring amino acids for optimal growth. Fungal isolations showed a higher incidence of *Mucor*, *Rhizopus*, *Rhizoctonia*, and *Gliocladium* on soybeans at the high temperature, whereas species of *Fusarium* and *Cylindrocarpon* were prevalent at the low temperature. With wheat the most striking feature was the predominance of nonsporing dark species at the high temperature and of nonsporing hyaline types at the low temperature. The number of soil nematodes decreased in both rhizospheres with higher temperature, especially with soybeans. The results suggest that temperature exerts both direct and indirect effects on the rhizosphere population, the latter being the more important.

Early studies by Clark (1940) and Timonin (1940) showed increased microbial counts in the rhizosphere of wheat and flax, respectively, as the soil moisture content decreased. Similar observations were made later by Clark (1948) with soybeans. Venkatesan obtained highest counts of bacteria, fungi, and actinomycetes in the rhizosphere of rice in soil with 20 and 40% moisture, but the R:S ratio increased with greater moisture content until saturation; the high R:S values under submerged conditions were probably due to the low soil counts. In preliminary studies with wheat and soybean, the highest rhizosphere numbers of bacteria and greatest R:S values were obtained at the lowest moisture level (30% of the moisture holding capacity vs 60 and 90%) (J. W. Rouatt, E. A. Peterson, and H. Katznelson, unpublished data).

Foliar applications.—There is mounting interest in foliar applications because this practice may be a more direct means of influencing the rhizosphere population than soil treatment and may, therefore, be of greater value for purposes of biological control. The increasing use of pesticides and related chemicals and the possibility of their affecting physiological processes in the plant as well as being excreted by the roots and thus exerting direct effects in the root zone, suggest the importance of this line of work. The results of experiments on light intensity (Rovira, 1959; Rouatt and Katznelson, 1960) show the effects of altering plant metabolism on the root population; and Fletcher (1960), and Bollen (1961) have reviewed the effect of herbicide and pesticide chemicals on soil microorganisms. Very recently Kozlova and Dikareva (1963) reported on the toxicity of the octyl ester of 2,4-D to certain types of microorganisms from the rhizosphere of young peas. That some of these substances can be recovered in root exudates after foliar application has already been demonstrated by Preston, Mitchell, and Reeve (1954), Linder et al. (1958), and Davey and Papavizas (1961). Working with fungistatic materials, Hallek and Cochrane (1950) demonstrated that bordeaux mixture, malachite green, and Dithane Z-78 reduced the number of bacteria in the rhizosphere of bean plants, whereas Spergon and related compounds increased counts. A reduction in nodule production on peas as a result of foliar application of sugars and nitrogen was reported by van Schreven (1959). Similar results were obtained by Cartright and Snow (1962) with seven species of legumes. Spraying with urea adversely affected nodulation, presumably by increasing the nitrogen level in the plant and thus lowering the carbon:nitrogen ratio. Foliar treatment with urea (Ramachandra-Reddy, 1959) produced quantitative changes in numbers of bacteria, actinomycetes, and fungi and in the composition of the fungus flora of rice rhizosphere. Venkata Ram (1960) sprayed tea leaves with various inorganic plant nutrients and urea, and caused a decrease in bacterial numbers in the rhizosphere with all these materials. Numbers of fungi, however, were greater with KCl and Na_2HPO_4, although lower with $MgSO_4$ and urea. Spraying also affected the genera and species of fungi in the root zone. Horst and Herr (1962) observed that urea treatment of leaves caused a significant increase in the number of actinomycete antagonists to *Fusarium roseum* f. *cerealis* in the rhizosphere of corn during the first week after application. An extensive study on foliar application of antibiotics, growth regulators, urea, and K_2HPO_4 on wheat growing in nutrient solution inoculated with a soil suspension was made by Vrany, Vancura, and Macura (1962). Not only were there changes in the pattern of root excretions, especially with chloramphenicol, but the rhizosphere microflora also was altered markedly. Both the antibiotic and triiodobenzoic acid reduced the bacterial count, but urea increased it, whereas fungal counts were the reverse. Distinct qualitative differences also were induced by the first two compounds. It would appear from these examples that this type of work holds considerable promise.

Interaction of rhizosphere organisms.—Once the root has begun to exert its influence on the microbial population of the soil, a multiplicity of associative and antagonistic interactions occur which complicate the entire rhizosphere picture. The increased rhizosphere effect during active plant growth and the enhancement of this effect as the root is approached indicate that it exerts a continuing influence. This, however, is modified by microbial interactions, which are intensified by the dense population in this zone. Unfortunately it is difficult to study these interrelations in situ, although this has been done to some extent; and so most of our knowledge is derived from in vitro experiments with pure cultures and in model systems.

Associative activities have been demonstrated in many studies. Amino acids formed by bacteria in a simple medium were found to satisfy the amino nitrogen needs of a large number of amino-acid-requiring bacteria (Lochhead and Thexton, 1947; Vagnerova and Vancura, 1962). Payne, Rouatt, and Lochhead (1957) and Becker and Schmidt (1960) also obtained clear evidence of elaboration of amino acids by rhizosphere and soil bacteria. The synthesis of a variety of vitamins and growth factors by rhizosphere bacteria was shown by Pantos (1961), as well as by Lochhead (1957) and Cook and Lochhead (1959), who also found them to be preferentially stimulated at the root surface. It is not unlikely that organisms requiring vitamins or accessory factors for growth will avail themselves of such microbial products, as well as those produced by the plant itself (Rovira and Harris, 1961). Thus the root zone could be attractive to auxotrophic saprophytes and parasites alike (Fig. 3). Panosyan, Arutyunyan, and Avetisyan (1962) claimed that spore formers, and nonspore formers such as *Pseudomonas* and *Agrobacterium radiobacter*, as well as many actinomycetes, stimulated growth and nitrogen fixation by *Azotobacter*. Associations with predatory overtones have been demonstrated for fungus- and bacterium-feeding nematodes (Jones, 1959; Winslow, 1960; Seinhorst, 1961). The metabolic products of actinomycetes attract certain nematodes very strongly (Katznelson and Henderson, 1962, 1963a,b).

An example of associative and antagonistic interactions that may occur in a relatively simple three-phase system consisting of bacteria, nematodes, and an actinomycete is shown in Fig. 4. Under the conditions of this experiment, bacterial growth was inhibited for about 5 days after the bacteria-feeding nematodes were added to the 7-day actinomycete culture. The nematodes aggregated in large numbers around and under the actinomycete culture. When bacteria began to develop, they were restricted to a zone around the actinomycete colony because of an antibacterial antibiotic it produced. However, the foraging nematodes, finding their food source, began to aggregate in the bacterial mass, leaving very few around the actinomycete colony.

Every conceivable type of microbial antagonism must occur with such a diverse population as is found in the rhizosphere. Although the most obvious antagonistic effect involves the production of inhibitory or antibiotic substances, competition for food and space, lysis, and even parasitism may occur (Weindling, Katznelson, and Beale, 1950; Garrett, 1956; Sanford, 1959). Microbial antagonisms in the rhizosphere have been implicated

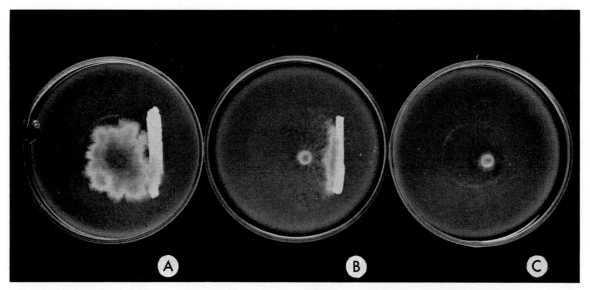

Fig. 3. Effect of thiamine-synthesizing bacterium on mycelial development of *Phytophthora cryptogea,* which requires thiamine for growth. (D. C. Erwin and H. Katznelson. Can. J. Microbiol. 7: 945-950. 1961.) *A,* unrestricted growth of fungus on medium containing excess thiamine. *B,* fungal growth limited to vicinity of bacterial growth on thiamine-deficient medium. *C,* very sparse fungal growth in absence of thiamine.

in the failure of inoculation of subterranean clover by Hely, Bergerson, and Brockwell (1957). Gyurko (1959) working with sugar-beet bacteria, concluded that the rhizosphere organisms may keep certain soil bacteria away from the root zone. A distinct antagonism of a *Pseudomonas* species against *Arthrobacter globiformis* has been noted in a root-extract but much less in a soil-extract medium (Chan and Katznelson, 1961). Later work (Chan, Katznelson, and Rouatt, 1963) with five species of bacteria simultaneously inoculated into root extracts showed the inhibition of *Bacillus* and to some extent of *Azotobacter,* and the dominance of *Pseudomonas* sp.; *Arthrobacter citreus* also grew well but less so than the pseudomonad (Fig. 5). In soil extract, however, *Arthrobacter citreus* grew as well as the *Pseudomonas* sp. Kerr (1961) isolated fifteen organisms antagonistic to *Verticillium albo-atrum* from the surface of tomato roots, with a green fluorescent pseudomonad being the most frequent. Mycolysis by bacteria has been shown to control *Fusarium oxysporum* in soil (Nikitina, 1958; Mitchell and Alexander, 1961); and competition for carbon and nitrogen between *Fusarium* and bacteria has been demonstrated by Finstein and Alexander (1962). Inhibition of bacteria and fungi by actinomycetes from the rhizosphere has been the subject of many studies. Strzelczykowa and Strzelczyk (1958) showed that most of the antagonists isolated from eleven crop plants were actinomycetes, but that the root-free soil contained higher proportions of these (24%) than the rhizospheres (15%). Absolute numbers, however, were greater in the latter. *Azotobacter* was the most susceptible organism, being inhibited by 33% of the isolates, whereas *Rhizobium* reacted very weakly to the antagonists. In a further study with *Azotobacter,* Strzelczyk (1961*b*) reported greater numbers of both bacterial and actinomycete antagonists in rhizosphere soil, the results correlating well with the *Azotobacter*

populations in the rhizosphere of onion, radish, and wheat. Szelenyi and Helmeczi (1960) also reported a definite antagonism between actinomycetes and *Azotobacter*. Antifungal streptomycetes have been isolated from the rhizosphere of pigeon pea (Agnihothrudu, 1955), barley (Rhem, 1961), and rice (Venkatesan, 1962). It is evidently not difficult to demonstrate that antagonistic organisms occur in the root zone; it is much more difficult to assess their importance under the highly competitive conditions existing therein. Not only must they survive but they must also develop and carry on their metabolic activities; they may even inhibit each other (E. A. Peterson, 1953). Thus nutrient, space, and gaseous requirements will undoubtedly exert a powerful influence on these as well as on the other organisms in this zone. Soil and root bacteria limit the growth of the alfalfa root pathogen *Phytophthora cryptogea* by using the thiamine (Fig. 6) and the mineral nutrients it requires (Erwin and Katznelson, 1961). Strong competition by soil bacteria for mineral elements was demonstrated in our laboratory with a large number of fungi from soil and roots. There are many other such examples.

IMPORTANCE OF THE RHIZOSPHERE PHENOMENON.— Various arguments have been advanced contending that the root microflora exerts a beneficial effect on plant growth: increased amount of microbial CO_2 in the root zone; greater number, activity, and turnover of microorganisms therein; increased solubilization of mineral nutrients; greater synthesis of vitamins, amino acids, auxins, and gibberellins, which may stimulate the plant, and of antibiotics, which will protect it; and so on. Despite the evidence marshalled in favor of these positive rhizosphere effects, however, especially in the U.S.S.R., a review of the literature is not reassuring. Soil organisms in general effect transformations of

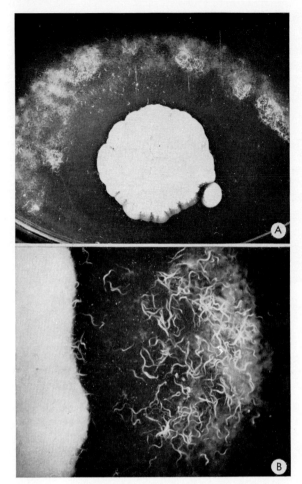

Fig. 4. Interaction of nematodes, bacteria, and an actinomycete (H. Katznelson and V. E. Henderson. Can. J. Microbiol. 8: 875-882. 1962.) *A,* white colony is a 7-day-old culture of a soil actinomycete; clear halo around colony due to antibacterial antibiotic produced by actinomycete; cloudy ring of growth around clear zone due to bacteria and feeding nematodes. *B,* enlargement of section of *A.*

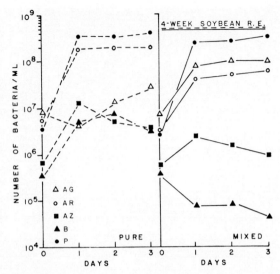

Fig. 5. Growth interrelations of soil bacteria in 4-week-old soybean root extract. (E. C. S. Chan, H. Katznelson, and J. W. Rouatt. Can. J. Microbiol. 9: 187-197. 1963.) *AG = Agrobacterium radiobacter, AR = Arthrobacter citreus, AZ = Azotobacter chroococcum, B = Bacillus cereus, P = Pseudomonas* sp.

organic and inorganic materials with production of CO_2 and liberation of ammonia, minerals, and organic substances on the one hand and with consumption of O_2, denitrification, immobilization of nitrogenous materials and of minerals, etc., on the other. Consequently, it becomes a question of whether the preferentially selected microflora of the root zone exercises a more specific influence in quantity or in kind. Its effect may be due primarily to its proximity to the root, since any biosynthetic product would then be more readily absorbed. On the other hand, this very proximity might be detrimental if the product is toxic. Furthermore, antagonism to favorable bacteria such as the rhizobia, direct competition for plant nutrients, or provision of growth or germination factors or other attractants for plant parasites may be harmful to the plant. Inoculation of soil and seed to increase the numbers of beneficial organisms in the root zone is widely practiced in the U.S.S.R. and although there is some evidence that this

has been of practical value, statistically significant data are few and far between.

Availability of inorganic nutrients and nitrogen.—The availability of inorganic nutrients and nitrogen will be discussed in the following paper; however, a few comments may be desirable in order to complete this account. A major point must be clarified first. If nutrients are made available through microbial action for the plant root, then why not for the organisms surrounding it? This issue may be resolved most readily by the use of labelled compounds, as Krasil'nikov (1958, 1961) has reported. More of this type of work is urgently needed.

Phosphorus and nitrogen availability has been studied most intensively in relation to the rhizosphere phenomenon. Absolute numbers of phosphate-dissolving bacteria are distinctly greater in the root zone. Many seed and root bacteria and fungi are able to dissolve phosphate (Katznelson, Peterson, and Rouatt, 1962). The mechanisms involved are quite well established—CO_2 evolution, acid production, elaboration of metal chelators, and enzymatic action (Sperber, 1958*b*; Sperber and Rovira, 1959; Louw and Webley, 1959; Duff and Webley, 1959; Estermann and McLaren, 1961). The production of 2-ketogluconate by soil pseudomonads and its chelation of calcium, leading to phosphate solubilization, is particularly interesting because of the large numbers of these bacteria in the root zone (over 10^9 per g of dry root, according to recent results of Rouatt and Katznelson, 1961). The enzymatic liberation of phosphate from organic combination as reported by Szember (1960) and Estermann and McLaren (1961) is another means whereby phosphorus can be made available to the plant, assuming that it is not taken up by microorganisms. Unfortu-

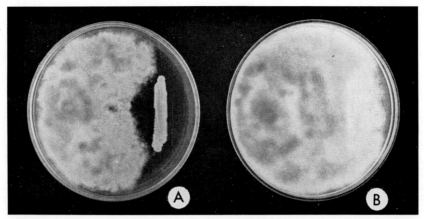

Fig. 6. Effect of thiamine-requiring bacterium on *Phytophthora cryptogea*. (D. C. Erwin and H. Katznelson. Can. J. Microbiol. 7: 945-950. 1961.) *A,* Restricted growth of fungus near bacterium on medium containing a low level of thiamine (10 μg/litre). *B,* Unrestricted growth of fungus on same medium with excess thiamine (200 μg/litre).

nately, there is little satisfactory evidence confirming Gerretsen's (1948) frequently quoted results on the beneficial role of rhizosphere microorganisms on phosphate utilization by plants. Our own tests have been uniformly negative (Katznelson, Peterson, and Rouatt, 1962); in fact, a distinct competition for soluble phosphorus between the bacterial flora and the root was observed (Katznelson, unpublished). Welte and Trolldenier (1962) and Trolldenier and Marckwordt (1962) reported a reduction in ash content of plants and in uptake of Rb^{86} and Ca^{45} in the presence of the rhizosphere microflora; and according to Subba-Rao, Bidwell, and Bailey (1961), uptake of phosphate, sulphate, and bicarbonate is suppressed by rhizoplane fungi. Kulai (1962), however, found that the concentration of available K_2O became greater as the number of silicate-decomposing bacteria in the rhizosphere of pine and birch increased. Earlier work by Timonin (1947) implicated rhizosphere bacteria in the manganese-deficiency symptoms of oats.

Nitrogen transformations in the rhizosphere may also be to the advantage or disadvantage of the plant. The immobilization of this element, even though temporarily, by rhizosphere microorganisms will reduce the amount available to the plant. Starkey (1958) states that "conditions leading to nitrogen immobilization are generally those where the percentage of nitrogen in the organic matter is low." Analyses of the total carbon and nitrogen of root exudates and sloughed-off root tissue are not available; if, however, the C:N ratio is sufficiently high, nitrogen may be immobilized at the expense of the plant (Harmsen and van Schreven, 1955; Legg and Allison, 1960). This would occur with older plants, which slough off cellular debris, high in carbon, rather than with young actively growing plants, which excrete greater amounts of materials high in nitrogen, such as amino acids (Rovira, 1962). Deamination of these compounds by the larger number of rhizosphere bacteria capable of doing this would lead to the liberation of ammonia, which could be taken up as such by the plant (Katznelson, 1961; Kruglov, 1960) or be oxidized to nitrate before absorption. Nitrogen fixation

by nonsymbiotic microorganisms does not appear to be an important function of the normal rhizosphere microflora, although the ever-increasing number of organisms discovered to be capable of fixing small amounts of this element may be of greater significance than suspected at present. N^{15} experiments with wheat seedlings inoculated with *Azotobacter* showed only slight enrichment in the rhizosphere soil after a 5-day incubation period, but not in the whole plant or root-free soil (Nutman, 1963). Moore (1963), however, has very recently recorded a significant increase in soil nitrogen under a tambagrass cover. He attributed this to nonsymbiotic fixation by organisms other than the commonly recognized nitrogen fixers, utilizing root exudates as a source of energy. Nitrogen losses by denitrification were demonstrated with N^{15}-labelled nitrate to be greater with living root systems, owing to decreased oxygen tension in the rhizosphere and to root excretions that functioned as hydrogen donors for the large number of denitrifying bacteria in this zone (Woldendorp, 1962, 1963).

Uptake and influence of microbial products.—Root uptake of organic compounds synthesized by the root microflora—amino acids, vitamins, auxins, gibberellins, and antibiotics—has received more attention in the U.S.S.R. than anywhere else. There is no reason to doubt that organisms in close contact with the plant root liberate organic substances which may diffuse into, or be actively taken up by the root. Absorption of even large molecules such as enzymes and proteins by roots has been reported by McLaren, Jensen, and Jacobson (1960). But since plants are considered to be prototrophic, the importance of amino acid and vitamin absorption may be questioned. These substances may provide some stimulation at the early stages of growth; and their increased content, especially of essential amino acids, in plants may of course be of importance in animal nutrition (Krasil'nikov, 1958, 1961; Gebhardt, 1961).

Andreeva and Marozova (1957), Rishbeth (1957), McManus (1960), and Imsenecki and Ulianova (1962) have all reported increased growth due to production of auxins or unknown substances by soil organisms. With regard to gibberellins, there is less positive evidence of a natural effect, probably because of lack of knowledge regarding microbial synthesis in soil, although Krasil'nikov (1963) has claimed striking results in this connection. Curtis (1957) found that none of the 1,000 fungus cultures and 500 soil actinomycetes tested produced this class of compound. Vancura (1961), however, reported gibberellic acid production by *Azotobacter;* and Katznelson, Sirois, and Cole (1962) reported the synthesis of gibberellinlike substances by *Arthrobacter globiformis.* Experiments in progress in our laboratory show that representatives of eight genera of soil and rhizosphere microorganisms, including *Arthrobacter, Pseudomonas,* and *Agrobacterium,* which occur in large numbers in the rhizosphere, also produce such substances. Increased seed germination and root-hair development and increased rate of mineral nutrient-transport (Audus, 1959; Pecket, 1960; Denisova and Lupinovitch, 1961) are some of the desirable effects of these compounds.

Microbial synthesis of organic substances at the root surface is not an unmixed blessing. Many, if not most, of the rhizosphere organisms are able to synthesize auxins (Brian, 1957; Katznelson and Sirois, 1961), which in very small amounts stimulate growth, but in higher amounts inhibit root elongation (Audus, 1959; McManus, 1960). Toxic by-products of microbial activity have also been reported (Stille, 1957; Krasil'nikov, 1963; Norstadt and McCalla, 1963) and will be considered later in this symposium. Norman (1960) has shown that antibiotics may repress root growth and cause leakage of organic and inorganic materials. Martin (1958) has also reported that a bacterial culture filtrate or one of *Fusarium moniliforme* caused a 3.5-fold increase in release of scopoletin from oats, without affecting root growth, whereas *Penicillium expansum* filtrates curtailed root growth without increasing excretion of this compound. Recently Grineva (1962) observed that under anaerobic conditions young corn and sunflower roots excreted considerable amounts of organic substances including amino acids, organic acids, and monosaccharides. This was increased by microorganisms. Balicka and Kosinkiewicz (1962) noted greater excretion with oats and less with timothy when microorganisms were introduced into the nutrient solution in which the plants were growing. Such phenomena are of obvious importance in that they increase the supply of nutrients for the root microorganisms. The interesting results of Bowen and Rovira (1961), showing a reduction of root growth of five plants and decreased production and growth of root hairs of subterranean clover by soil microorganisms, could conceivably be due to excessive auxin synthesis, although antibiotic and toxic substances could also produce such results.

Interaction of root microorganisms with symbionts and parasites.—Only brief reference will be made to some relations between the rhizosphere population and organisms with known harmful or beneficial effects, since these will be discussed in greater detail by others. In this connection it should again be emphasized that both associative and antagonistic forces may be operative (Lochhead, 1959). Thiamine produced by bacteria increased the growth of an autotrophic root pathogen, *Phytophthora cryptogea,* but competition for mineral nutrients was found to reduce it (Fig. 6) (Erwin and Katznelson, 1961). Mycorrhizal infection by *Endogone* sp. could be achieved aseptically only in the presence of a *Pseudomonas* sp. (Mosse, 1962). The abundance of parasitic and nonparasitic nematodes around roots may be due to "attractants" produced by the root microflora (Katznelson and Henderson, 1962, 1963), as well as to root excretions. The proximity of fungus- and bacterium-feeding worms to the root could also lead to root "nibbling" with undesirable consequences (Seinhorst, 1961). There are many recorded instances of antagonism between soil microbes and root-invading organisms (Garrett, 1956; Sanford, 1959; Krasil'nikov, 1961). Some of these have been mentioned in earlier sections and apply equally to beneficial and to harmful invaders. Hely, Bergerson, and Brockwell (1957), for example, claimed that the rhizosphere population reduced nodulation by rhizobia. *Pseudomonas mycophaga* was found by Nikitina (1958) to be the most active of eighteen mycolytic organisms, isolated from the rhizosphere of lucerne and clover, causing lysis of *Fusarium oxysporum* in soil. Biological control of *Fusarium* in soil by this means has also been advocated by Mitchell and Alexander (1961).

Bacterization for increasing plant growth and for biological control.—Seed inoculation with organisms selected to increase plant growth or reduce disease is extensively practised in the U.S.S.R. Krasil'nikov (1958) has reviewed most of the literature on this subject and papers from other eastern European countries further endorse bacterization both in theory and in practice. Cooper (1959) has presented an excellent summary of the status of this problem, concluding somewhat skeptically "that the value of bacterial fertilizers should not be dismissed as negligible." More recent reports continue to show inconsistent effects from seed inoculation. Vancura and Macura (1959) obtained statistically significant increases in yield of oats (16%-20%) by using selected strains of *Azotobacter;* yet Vancura et al. (1959), working with barley, concluded that "there is no significant difference between the control and bacterized seeds." Adaptation and selection of strains of this organism was reported by Zino'eva (1961) to improve germination and yield of wheat. Although greenhouse pot experiments with six different crops showed a small total increase in yield after inoculation with *Azotobacter,* the results were not significant (Nutman, 1962). Certain treatments such as nitrogen and phosphorus fertilizer and compost, however, showed significant effects of inoculation on the ear weight of wheat and on the weight of green tomatoes, respectively. Positive effects were obtained by Klincare (1961) and Ezubchik and Konashevich (1961) on treating grain and potato with azotobacterin. Panosyan, Arutyunyan, and Avetisyan (1962) claimed that certain bacilli, pseudomonads, and *Bacterium radiobacter,* as well as many species of actinomycetes, increased the stimulatory effect of *Azotobacter* on crop yields; some of these organisms, however, increased yields in the absence of *Azotobacter.* Dorosinskii (1962), in a review of 24 references, states that although yield increases due to bacterial fertilizers do not exceed 10-12%, they are a useful supplement to mineral fertilizers.

A similar body of literature, also discussed by Cooper (1959), has accumulated regarding bacterization with phosphate-solubilizing organisms, such as *Bacillus megaterium* var. *phosphaticum* and silicate bacteria, the latter freeing potassium for plants. Myskow (1961) recorded yield increases of 7-25% by inoculation of phosphorite-treated crops but yields were lower than those in noninoculated soil given superphosphate. In laboratory experiments, Lauzne (1960) obtained good multiplication of phosphorus bacteria on wheat roots and an increase in plant weight, but not in the field. Failure of phosphobacterin with oil crops and maize, presumably as a result of suppression of *B. megaterium* by soil actinomycetes and fungi was reported by Enkina (1962). Mishustin and Naumova (1962), in a realistic and critical review of work on azotobacterin and phosphobacterin, concluded that inoculation did not increase the yield of field crops by more than 10-13% and sometimes was completely ineffective. Vegetables grown in soil rich in organic matter showed yield increases up to 25% either with azotobacterin or with phosphobacterin; but the authors suggested that these beneficial effects were due to suppression of fungi in the root zone and to production of substances that stimulate plant growth. Somewhat similar observations were made at the Rothamsted Experimental Station (Nutman, 1963) in that *Azotobacter* inoculation significantly increased wheat yield by 11-35% in potting compost heavily infested with *Ophiobolus graminis.* After a series of carefully conducted experiments, Smith, Allison, and Soulides (1961, 1962) concluded that phosphobacterin did not benefit vegetable or field crops.

A critical question relating to bacterization is the ability of specific soil organisms, be they *Azotobacter, Bacillus megaterium,* streptomycetes, or fungi to establish themselves in sufficient numbers in competition with the active and versatile microflora which develops around the germinating seed and young root. Presumably this can be achieved by the use of selected, plant-adapted cultures and by creating conditions or using specific substrates that are favorable for their development, as in the case of chitin for mycolytic bacteria (Mitchell and Alexander, 1961). Indeed Brown, Burlingham, and Jackson (1962) have reported successful establishment of *Azotobacter* on roots of cereals and also, though not as successfully, on sugar beets, in the field by seed inoculation; factors influencing growth of *Azotobacter* on the roots were also considered. Another issue which has not been aired adequately concerns the choice of *Azotobacter* as inoculant (Starkey, 1958). It is clear that this organism is not abundant in soil or in the root zone and is easily inhibited by other soil microorganisms (Metz, 1955; Strzelczyk, 1961*b*; Chan, Katznelson, and Rouatt, 1963) and plant extracts

(Metz, 1955; Bukatsch, 1956). Moreover, if its effect is due simply to the production of vitamins, auxins, or other plant growth substances it would seem more reasonable to use other bacteria such as *Arthrobacter, Pseudomonas,* and *Agrobacterium* (Krasil'nikov, 1958) that find the root zone a favorable habitat, produce plant growth substances, and are able to hold their own competitively.

The rapid development of saprophytic organisms on plant roots may also provide a barrier against root pathogens. Inoculating seed with antagonistic organisms may intensify natural control, but this method suffers from the same objections as have been raised against seed inoculants generally (except for rhizobia). The most dramatic antagonistic effect involves the production of antibiotics, which may either be taken up by plants (Starkey, 1958; Krasil'nikov, 1960) or act directly in the rhizosphere. This subject has been adequately reviewed by Weindling, Katznelson, and Beale (1950), Brian (1957), and Sanford (1959). Small amounts of antibiotics may indeed be produced in the root region, but whether in sufficient quantity to inhibit a phytopathogen remains to be established unequivocally. The use of lytic organisms as inoculants may be an effective method of achieving control (Krasil'nikov, 1958) and certainly this avenue requires further exploration. Still another means is by increasing the competition for food, growth factors, mineral elements, and oxygen by intensifying the numbers and activity of or by changing the saprophytic microbial population of the root zone. This may be done, as pointed out earlier, by soil treament, altering environmental conditions, and by foliar application.

CONCLUSIONS.—It is clear that certain aspects of rhizosphere microbiology require much more intensive investigaion. These have been excellently summarized by Starkey:

Whereas there is considerable information about microorganisms in the rhizosphere, what is known is more general than absolute. The rhizosphere effect is definitely established but its significance is obscure. The extent of the absorption of organic materials by plants, particularly the organic compounds of microbial origin, and their effects on plant growth, are practically unknown. There is even limited information on the factors affecting uptake. There are suggestive results on the beneficial and injurious effects of the rhizosphere microorganisms on plants, but the effects have yet to be evaluated. The same applies to the antagonistic and stimulating effects of the rhizosphere microorganisms on one another. The possibilities of controlling the population have been almost completely unexplored (Starkey, 1958).

In the light of the advances in this field during the past five years, this summary may be somewhat pessimistic. Yet there is no doubt that further work along the lines indicated would greatly extend our knowledge of the rhizosphere phenomenon, which might be advanced still more by the use of fewer plants. Clearly there was a need for studies with every kind of plant available; but it would seem that a deeper understanding of plant-microbe relations might now be achieved by work with a few representative plant types.

It seems apparent, too, that a shift in emphasis is developing in rhizosphere investigations. Whereas most of these have been and still are concerned with the influence of plants on soil microorganisms, there is a growing trend towards studies on the influence of these microorganisms, on the plants. This type of work has made greatest progress in the U.S.S.R., as has already been pointed out. Efforts in this direction may be greatly enhanced by the use of labelled organic and inorganic compounds, and it is expected that this sensitive technique will be employed more extensively in the future.

For purposes of biological control of soil-borne plant pathogens, more information is required on simple means of altering the rhizosphere population, quantitatively and qualitatively, so as to render the root zone inimical to the pathogen. Although such changes can be effected by manipulating environmental factors (light, temperature, moisture), this is obviously difficult under field conditions. Soil amendment with organic and inorganic materials is of some value in this connection, although it is frequently not clear whether the suppression of the pathogen is due to effects on the soil population in general, on the rhizosphere population in particular, or both. Foliar treatment with selected substances capable of altering the microbial population and equilibrium in the rhizosphere is another approach to biological control. Studies along these lines, utilizing known root pathogens and susceptible plants, would probably be rewarding. The combined efforts of the soil microbiologist, plant pathologist, and plant physiologist would greatly facilitate the resolution of these problems.

ACKNOWLEDGMENTS.—I am grateful to the Annamali University for permission to use the material from the thesis of R. Venkatesan.

LITERATURE CITED

ABSALYAMOVA, R. A. 1963. [Effect on plant growth of the complex of root microorganisms occurring as a result of application of organo-mineral mixtures.] Agrobiologiya No. 1, 77-81. *Abstr. in* Soils Fertilizers 26: 252, 1963.

AGNIHOTHRUDU, V. 1955. Incidence of fungistatic organisms in the rhizosphere of pigeon pea (*Cajanus cajan*) in relation to resistance and susceptibility to wilt caused by *Fusarium udum* Butler. Naturwissenschaften 42: 373.

ANDREEVA, R. A., and I. B. MOROZOVA. 1957. The influence of indoleacetic acid treatment of the root system upon the growth and metabolism of tomato seedlings. *A transl. of* Doklady, Bot. Sci. Section, Dokl. Akad. Nauk SSSR 125: 90-93. Publ. by American Institute of Biological Science.

ATKINSON, R. G., and J. B. ROBINSON. 1955. The application of a nutritional grouping method to soil fungi. Can. J. Botany 33: 281-288.

AUDUS, L. J. 1959. Plant growth substances. 2d ed. Leonard Hill (Books), London. 533 p.

BALICKA, N., and B. KOSINKIEWICZ. 1962. [The utilization of some nitrogenous compounds by rhizosphere organisms]. Zentbl. Bakteriol. Parasitenk., Abt. II, 115: 737-747.

BECKER, G. E., and E. L. SCHMIDT. 1960. Excretion of amino acids by soil and rhizosphere isolates. Bacteriol. Proc. 3: 29.

BOLLEN, W. B. 1961. Interactions between pesticides and soil microorganisms. Ann. Rev. Microbiol. 15: 69-92.

BOWEN, G. D. 1961. The toxicity of legume seed diffusates toward rhizobia and other bacteria. Plant Soil 15: 155-165.

BOWEN, G. D., and A. D. ROVIRA. 1961. The effects of microorganisms on plant growth. 1. Development of roots and root hairs in sand and agar. Plant Soil 15: 166-188.

BRIAN, P. W. 1957. The effects of some microbial metabolic products on plant growth. *In* The biological action of growth substances, Soc. Exptl. Biol. 11: 166-182.

BROWN, M. E. 1961. Stimulation of streptomycin-resistant bacteria in the rhizosphere of leguminous plants. J. Gen. Microbiol. 24: 369-377.

BROWN, M. E., SUSAN K. BURLINGHAM, and R. M. JACKSON. 1962. Studies on *Azotobacter* species in soil. II. Populations of *Azotobacter* in the rhizosphere and effects of artificial inoculation. Plant Soil 17: 320-332.

BUKATSCH, F. 1956. Zur Analyse der Bakterienhemmstoffe aus der Wurzel vom Schöllkraut und ähnlichen Planzen. Arch. Mikrobiol. 24: 281-296.

BUNT, J. S., and A. D. ROVIRA. 1955. Microbiological studies of some sub-Antarctic soils. J. Soil Sci. 6: 119.

BUNT, J. S., and Y. T. TCHAN. 1955. Estimation of protozoan populations in soils by direct microscopy. Proc. Linnean Soc. N.S. Wales 80: 148-153.

BUXTON, E. W. 1957a. Some effects of pea root exudates on physiologic races of *Fusarium oxysporum* Fr. f. *pisi* (Linf.) Snyder and Hansen. Trans. Brit. Mycol. Soc. 40: 145-154.

BUXTON, E. W. 1957b. Differential rhizosphere effects of three pea cultivars on physiologic races of *Fusarium oxysporum* f. *pisi*. Trans. Brit. Mycol. Soc. 40: 305-316.

CARTWRIGHT, P. M., and D. SNOW. 1962. The influence of foliar applications of urea on the nodulation pattern of certain leguminous species. Ann. Botany (London) [N.S.] 26: 251-259.

CATSKA, V., J. MACURA, and K. VAGNEROVA. 1960. Rhizosphere microflora of wheat. III. Fungal flora of wheat rhizosphere. Folia Microbiol. (Prague) 5: 320-330.

CHAN, E. C. S., and H. KATZNELSON. 1961. Growth interactions of *Arthrobacter globiformis* and *Pseudomonas* sp. in relation to the rhizosphere effect. Can. J. Microbiol. 7: 759-767.

CHAN, E. C. S., H. KATZNELSON, and J. W. ROUATT. 1963. The influence of soil and root extracts on the associative growth of selected soil bacteria. Can. J. Microbiol. 9: 187-197.

CLARK, F. E. 1940. Notes on types of bacteria associated with plant roots. Trans. Kansas Acad. Sci. 43: 75-84.

CLARK, F. E. 1948. Rhizosphere microflora as affected by soil moisture changes. Soil Sci. Soc. Am. Proc. (1947) 12: 239-242.

CLARK, F. E. 1949. Soil micro-organisms and plant growth. Advan. Agron. 1: 241-288.

CLARKE, J. H., and D. PARKINSON. 1960. A comparison of three methods for the assessment of fungal colonization of seedling roots of leek and broad bean. Nature (London) 188: 166-167.

COOK, F. D., and A. G. LOCHHEAD. 1959. Growth factor relationships of soil microorganisms as affected by proximity to the plant root. Can. J. Microbiol. 5: 323-334.

COOPER, R. 1959. Bacterial fertilizers in the Soviet Union. Soils Fertilizers 22: 327-333.

CULLIMORE, D. R., and M. WOODBINE. 1963. A rhizosphere effect of the pea root on soil algae. Nature (London) 198: 304-305.

CURTIS, R. W. 1957. Survey of fungi and actinomycetes for compounds possessing gibberellin-like activity. Science 125: 646.

DAVEY, C. B., and G. C. PAPAVIZAS. 1960. Effect of decomposing organic soil amendments and nitrogen on fungi in soil and bean rhizosphere. Trans. Intern. Congr. Soil Sci., 7th Congr. (Madison, Wisc.) Comm. III, p. 551-557.

DAVEY, C. B., and G. C. PAPAVIZAS. 1961. Translocation of streptomycin from coleus leaves and its effect on rhizosphere bacteria. Science 134: 1368-1369.

DENISOVA, A. Z., and I. L. LUPINOVITCH. 1961. The effect of gibberellic acid on the mineral nutrition of plants. Soviet Plant Physiol. (Fiziologiya Rastenii). *Transl. in* Am. Inst. Biol. Sci. 8: 360-364. 1962.

DEUBERT, K. H. 1959. Über die Bedeutung der Nematodenfauna ackerbaulich genutzter Böden. Zentbl. Bakteriol. Parasitenk., Abt. II, 112: 101-108.

DOROSINSKII, L. M. 1962. Some questions of the use of bacterial fertilizers. Microbiology (U.S.S.R.) (Engl. transl.) 31: 738-744.

DOROSINSKII, L. M., and L. I. KRUPINA. 1960. [The ability of *Azotobacter* to grow in the rhizosphere of various plants.] Byull. Nauchn. Tekh. Inform. po Sel'skokhoz, Mikrobiol. 8: 14-17. *Abstr. in* Biol. Abstr. 39: 3169, 1962.

DUFF, R. B., and D. M. WEBLEY. 1959. 2-Ketogluconic acid as a natural chelator produced by soil bacteria. Chem. Ind. (London) 1959: 1376-1377.

EBBEN, M. H. 1959. Brown root rot of tomatoes. II. The fungal flora of the rhizosphere. Ann. Appl. Biol. 47: 17-27.

EDWARD, J. C., R. N. SHRIVASTAVA, and Z. NAIM. 1962. Microflora of soils and rhizospheres of various field crops of the Allahabad Agricultural Institute farm. Allahabad Farmer 36: 1-14. *Abstr. in* Soils Fertilizers 26: 177, 1963.

ELKAN, G. H. 1962. Comparison of rhizosphere microorganisms of genetically related nodulating and nonnodulating soybean lines. Can. J. Microbiol. 8: 79-87.

ENKINA, O. V. 1962. [Use of phosphobacterin in Ciscaucasian leached chernozem.] Vestn. Sel'skokhoz. Nauki No. 6, p. 101-106. *Translated summary in* Soils Fertilizers 25: 462, 1962.

ERWIN, D. C., and H. KATZNELSON. 1961. Suppression and stimulation of mycelial growth of *Phytophthora cryptogea* by certain thiamine-requiring and thiamine-synthesizing bacteria. Can. J. Microbiol. 7: 945-950.

ESTERMANN, E. F., and A. D. McLAREN. 1961. Contributions of rhizoplane organisms to the total capacity of plants to utilize organic nutrients. Plant Soil 15: 243-260.

EZUBCHIK, A. A., and Z. I. KONASHEVICH. 1961. [Effectiveness of azotobacterin on dernopodzolic soil.] Sb. Nauchn. Tr. Belorussk. Nauchn.-Issled. Inst. Zemled. 8: 150-162. *Translated summary in* Soils Fertilizers 25: 378, 1962.

FEDOROV, M. V., and E. A. SAVKINA. 1960. [Species composition and physiological characteristics of rhizosphere bacteria of maize.] Izv. Timiryazev. Sel'skokhoz. Akad. 4: 7-14.

FINSTEIN, S., and M. ALEXANDER. 1962. Competition for carbon and nitrogen between *Fusarium* and bacteria. Soil Sci. 94: 334-339.

FIRSANOVA, A. N. 1956. [The microflora of the rhizosphere of rice in relation to the stage of its development.] Zap. Leningr. Sel'skokhoz. Inst. 2: 92-99.

FLETCHER, W. W. 1960. The effect of herbicides on soil micro-organisms. p. 20-62. *In* E. K. Woodford and G. R. Sagar [ed.], Herbicides and the soil, Blackwells Scientific Publs., Oxford.

FÜHRER, E. 1961. [The effect of plant roots on the distribution of small arthropods in soil, investigated on *Pseudotritia ardna* (Oribater).] Pedobiologia 1: 99-112. *Abstr. in* Soils Fertilizers 25: 305, 1962.

GADZHIEVA, M. A. 1959. [The importance of organomineral mixtures and their components for the development of the root microflora of winter wheat and grass mixtures.] Agrobiologiya 4: 581-589.

GARRETT, S. D. 1956. Biology of root-infecting fungi. Cambridge University Press, London. 292 p.

GEBHARDT, A. G. 1961. [The role of microorganisms in accumulation of vitamins in soil and their intake by plants.] Trudy Inst. Mikrobiol. Akad. Nauk. SSSR No. 11: 292-300. *Translated summary in* Soils Fertilizers 25: 461, 1962.

GERRETSEN, F. C. 1948. The influence of microorganisms on the phosphate uptake by the plant. Plant Soil 1: 51-81.

GONZALVES, E. A., and V. S. YALAVIGI. 1959. Algae in the rhizosphere of some crop plants. p. 335-342. *In* Proc. Symp. Algology, India Council Agr. Res., New Delhi.

GOOS, R. D., and M. I. TIMONIN. 1962. Fungi from the rhizosphere of banana in Honduras. Can. J. Botany 40: 1371-1377.

GRINEVA, G. M. 1962. Excretion by plants during brief periods of anaerobiosis. Soviet Plant Physiol. (Fiziolo-

giya Rastenii). *Transl. in* Am. Inst. Biol. Sci. 8: 549-552, 1962.

GYURKO, P. 1959. [The antagonistic effect on soil bacteria of rhizosphere bacteria of sugar beet.] Acta Agron. Acad. Sci. Hung. 9: 175-184.

HADFIELD, W. 1960. Rhizosphere effect on soil algae. Nature (London) 185: 179-180.

HALLEK, F. E., and V. W. COCHRANE. 1950. The effect of fungistatic agents on the bacterial flora of the rhizosphere. Phytopathology 40: 715-718.

HARLEY, J. L., and J. S. WAID. 1955. A method of studying active mycelia on living roots and on other surfaces in the soil. Trans. Brit. Mycol. Soc. 38: 104-118.

HARMSEN, G. E., and D. A. van SCHREVEN. 1955. Mineralization of organic nitrogen in soil. Advan. Agron. 7: 299-398.

HELY, F. W., F. J. BERGERSEN, and J. BROCKWELL. 1957. Microbial antagonism in the rhizosphere as a factor in the failure of inoculation of subterranean clover. Australian J. Agr. Res. 8: 24-44.

HENDERSON, V. E., and H. KATZNELSON. 1961. The effect of plant roots on the nematode population of the soil. Can. J. Microbiol. 7: 163-167.

HIRSCHMANN, H. 1960. Gross morphology of nematodes. p. 125-129. *In* J. N. Sasser and W. R. Jenkins [ed.], Nematology, fundamentals and recent advances with emphasis on plant parasitic and soil forms, University of North Carolina Press, Chapel Hill, N. C.

HORST, R. K., and L. J. HERR. 1962. Effects of foliar treatment on numbers of actinomycetes antagonistic to *Fusarium roseum* f. *cerealis* in the rhizosphere of corn. Phytopathology 52: 423-427.

IMSENECKI, A. A., and O. M. ULIANOVA. 1962. On the effect upon higher plants of vital activity products of *Fusarium* mutants. Microbiology (U.S.S.R.) (Engl. transl.) 31: 1029-1037.

ISHIZAWA, S., F. SUZUKI, O. SATO, and H. TOYODA. 1957. Studies on microbial population in the rhizosphere of higher plants with special reference to the method of study. Soil Plant Food (Tokyo) 3: 85-94.

IVARSON, K. C., and H. KATZNELSON. 1960. Studies on the rhizosphere microflora of yellow birch seedlings. Plant Soil 12: 30-40.

IVUSHKIN, I. F. 1956. [Relationship between actinomycetes, nodule bacteria and *Azotobacter* in the rhizosphere of lucerne.] Mikrobiol. Zh. Akad. Nauk Ukr. RSR 18: 14-18. *Translated summary in:* Soils Fertilizers 20: 274, 1957.

JACKSON, R. M. 1957. Fungistasis as a factor in the rhizosphere phenomenon. Nature (London) 180: 96-97.

JACKSON, R. M. 1960. Soil fungistasis and the rhizosphere. p. 168-181. *In* D. Parkinson and J. S. Waid [ed.], The ecology of soil fungi, Liverpool University Press, Liverpool.

JENNY, H., and K. GROSSENBACHER. 1962. Root soil boundary zones. California Agr. 16: 7.

JONES, F. G. W. 1959. Ecological relationships of nematodes. p. 395-411. *In* C. S. Holton et al. [ed.], Plant pathology, problems and progress 1908-1958, University of Wisconsin Press, Madison, Wisc.

KATZNELSON, H. 1946. The rhizosphere effect of mangels on certain groups of soil microorganisms. Soil Sci. 62: 343-354.

KATZNELSON, H. 1961. Microorganisms in the rhizosphere. vol. 1, p. 610-614. *In* Recent advances in botany, (9th Intern. Congr. Botany, Montreal, 1959), University of Toronto Press, Toronto.

KATZNELSON, H., and B. BOSE. 1959. Metabolic activity and phosphate-dissolving capability of bacterial isolates from wheat roots, rhizosphere and non-rhizosphere soil. Can. J. Microbiol. 5: 79-85.

KATZNELSON, H., and V. E. HENDERSON. 1962. Studies on the relationships between nematodes and other soil microorganisms. I. The influence of actinomycetes and fungi on *Rhabditis* (*Cephaloboides*) *oxycerca* de Man. Can. J. Microbiol. 8: 875-882.

KATZNELSON, H., and V. E. HENDERSON. 1963. Ammonium

as an "attractant" for a soil nematode. Nature (London) 198: 907-908.

KATZNELSON, H., A. G. LOCHHEAD, and M. I. TIMONIN. 1948. Soil microorganisms and the rhizosphere. Botan. Rev. 14: 543-587.

KATZNELSON, H., E. A. PETERSON, and J. W. ROUATT. 1962. Phosphate dissolving microorganisms on seed and in the root zone of plants. Can. J. Botany 40: 1181-1186.

KATZNELSON, H., and J. W. ROUATT. 1957a. Studies on the incidence of certain physiological groups of bacteria in the rhizosphere. Can. J. Microbiol. 3: 265-275.

KATZNELSON, H., and J. W. ROUATT. 1957b. Manometric studies with rhizosphere and non-rhizosphere soil. Can. J. Microbiol. 3: 673-678.

KATZNELSON, H., J. W. ROUATT, and E. A. PETERSON. 1962. The rhizosphere effect of mycorrhizal and non-mycorrhizal roots of yellow birch seedlings. Can. J. Botany 40: 377-382.

KATZNELSON, H., and J. C. SIROIS. 1961. Auxin production by species of *Arthrobacter*. Nature (London) 191: 1323-1324.

KATZNELSON, H., J. C. SIROIS, and S. E. COLE. 1962. Production of a gibberellin-like substance by *Arthrobacter globiformis*. Nature (London) 196: 1012-1013.

KATZNELSON, H., and E. STRZELCZYK. 1961. Studies on the interaction of plants and free-living nitrogen-fixing microorganisms. 1. Occurrence of *Azotobacter* in the rhizosphere of crops plants. Can. J. Microbiol. 7: 437-446.

KERR, A. 1961. A study of tomato root surface organisms antagonistic to *Verticillium albo-atrum*. Trans. Brit. Mycol. Soc. 44: 365-371.

KLINCARE, A. 1961. [The effect of mercuran and TMTD preparation on the acclimatization, dynamics and activity of *Azotobacter* in the rhizosphere of spring wheat.] Izv. Akad. Nauk Latv. SSR (Latvijas PSR Zinatnu Akad. Vestis) 1: 109-114. *Translated summary in* Soils Fertilizers 25: 42, 1962.

KOZLOVA, E. I., and T. A. DIKAREVA. 1963. [Effect of herbicides on microflora of rhizosphere of some agricultural plants.] Agrobiologiya 1: 82-87. *Translated summary in* Soils Fertilizers 26: 253, 1963.

KRASIL'NIKOV, N. A. 1958. Soil microorganisms and higher plants. Transl. Y. Halperin. 474 p. Academy of Sciences Press, Moscow, U.S.S.R.

KRASIL'NIKOV, N. A. 1960. The biological role of microbe-antagonists, producers of antibiotic substances. Soil Plant Food (Tokyo) 5: 184-193.

KRASIL'NIKOV, N. A. 1961. On the role of bacteria in plant nutrition. J. Gen. Appl. Bacteriol. 7: 128-144.

KRASIL'NIKOV, N. A. 1963. The role of microorganisms in plant life. p. 282-290. *In* Recent progress in microbiology, Symp. 8th Intern. Congr. Microbiol. (Montreal, 1962), University of Toronto Press, Toronto.

KRUGLOV, Y. V. 1961. Concerning the role of denitrifying bacteria of the genus *Pseudomonas fluorescens* in the root nutrition of plants. Microbiology (U.S.S.R.) (Engl. transl.) 29: 678-679.

KULAI, G. A. 1962. [The dissolving of alumino silicates in the rhizosphere of forest plantations.] Izv. Akad. Nauk Ser. Biol. 6: 915-920. *Transl. summary in* Soils Fertilizers 26: 114, 1963.

LAUZNE, E. 1960. [Interrelations of phosphorus bacteria and some cultivated plants.] Trudy Inst. Mikrobiol. Akad. Nauk Latv. SSR No. 11, p. 153-167. *Translated summary in* Soils Fertilizers 25: 44, 1962.

LEGG, J. O., and F. E. ALLISON. 1960. Role of rhizosphere microorganisms in the uptake of nitrogen by plants. Trans. Intern. Congr. Soil Sci., 7th Congr. (Madison, Wisc.) Comm. III, p. 545-550.

LEHNER, A., and W. NOWAK. 1958. [A rapid method for the practical determination of the soil microflora.] Prakt. Bl. Pflanzenbau Pflanzenschutz 53: 148-152.

LINDER, P. J., J. C. CRAIG, JR., F. E. COOPER, and J. W. MITCHELL. 1958. Movement of 2,3,6-trichlorobenzoic acid from one plant to another through their root systems. J. Agr. Food Chemistry 6: 356-357.

LINFORD, M. B. 1942. Methods of observing soil flora and fauna associated with roots. Soil Sci. 53: 93-103.

LOCHHEAD, A. G. 1940. Qualitative studies of soil microorganisms. III. Influence of plant growth on the character of the bacterial flora. Can. J. Res., Sec. C, 18: 42-53.

LOCHHEAD, A. G. 1957. Qualitative studies of soil microorganisms. XV. Capability of the predominant bacterial flora for synthesis of various growth factors. Soil Sci. 84: 395-403.

LOCHHEAD, A. G. 1959. Rhizosphere microorganisms in relation to root-disease fungi. p. 327-338. *In* C. S. Holton et al. [ed.], Plant pathology, problems and progress 1908-1958. University of Wisconsin Press, Madison, Wisc.

LOCHHEAD, A. G., and F. E. CHASE. 1943. Qualitative studies of soil microorganisms. V. Nutritional requirements of the predominant bacterial flora. Soil Sci. 55: 185-195.

LOCHHEAD, A. G., and F. D. COOK. 1961. Microbial growth factors in relation to resistance of flax varieties to *Fusarium* wilt. Can. J. Botany 39: 7-19.

LOCHHEAD, A. G., and J. W. ROUATT. 1955. The rhizosphere effect on the nutritional groups of soil bacteria. Soil Sci. Soc. Am. Proc. 19: 48-49.

LOCHHEAD, A. G., and R. H. THEXTON. 1947. Qualitative studies of soil microorganisms. VII. The rhizosphere effect in relation to the amino acid nutrition of bacteria. Can. J. Res., Sec. C, 25: 20-26.

LOCHHEAD, A. G., M. I. TIMONIN, and P. M. WEST. 1940. The microflora of the rhizosphere in relation to resistance of plants to soil-borne pathogens. Sci. Agr. 20: 414-418.

LOUW, H. A., and D. M. WEBLEY. 1959. The bacteriology of the root region of the oat plant grown under controlled pot culture conditions. J. Appl. Bacteriol. 22: 216-226.

MALISZEWSKA, W., and R. MOREAU. 1959. [The rhizosphere of white spruce.] Compt. Rend. 249: 303-305.

MANIL, P. 1958. The legume-rhizobia symbiosis. p. 124-133. *In* E. G. Hallsworth [ed.], Nutrition of the legumes, Butterworths Scientific Publications, London.

MARTIN, P. 1958. Einfluss der Kulturfiltrate von Mikroorganismen auf die Abgabe von Scopoletin aus den Keimwurzeln des Hofers (*Avena sativa* L.). Arch. Mikrobiol. 29: 154-168.

McLAREN, A. D., W. JENSEN, and L. JACOBSON. 1960. Adsorption of enzymes and other proteins by barley roots. Plant Physiol. 35: 549-556.

McMANUS, M. A. 1960. Certain mitotic effects of kinetin, G.A., I.A.A. and maleic hydrazide on the root of *Alium cepa*. Nature (London) 185: 44-45.

METZ, H. 1955. Untersuchungen über die Rhizosphäre. Arch. Mikrobiol. 23: 297-326.

MILLER, R. E., and C. W. BOOTHROYD. 1962. Seasonal population of rhizosphere fungi associated with corn roots. Phytopathology 52: 744.

MISHUSTIN, E. N., and A. N. NAUMOVA. 1962. Bacterial fertilizers, their effectiveness and mechanism of action. Microbiology (U.S.S.R.) (Engl. translation) 31: 543-555.

MITCHELL, R., and M. ALEXANDER. 1961. The mycolytic phenomenon and biological control of *Fusarium* in soil. Nature (London) 190: 109-110.

MOORE, A. W. 1963. Nitrogen fixation in latosolic soil under grass. Plant Soil 19: 127-138.

MOSOLOV, I. V., E. KH. REMPE, and V. A. ALEXANDROVSKAYA. 1959. The interactions of the higher plant and micro-organisms. Agrobiology (U.S.S.R.) (Engl. transl.) 3: 425-430.

MOSSE, B. 1962. The establishment of vesicular-arbuscular mycorrhiza under aseptic conditions. J. Gen. Microbiol. 27: 509-520.

MÜLLER, G. 1957. [Soil biological investigations in the near and distant rhizosphere with live and dead roots of fodder crops.] Z. Acker- Pflanzenbau 104: 289-306.

MÜLLER, H. 1962. Untersuchungen zur Frage wechselseitiger Beziehungen zwischen keimenden Samen und Mikroorganismen im Samennähe. Arch. Mikrobiol. 41: 351-382.

Myskow, W. 1961. The influence of bacteria dissolving phosphates on the availability of phosphorus to plants. Acta Microbiol. Polon. 10: 395-401.

Nikitina, Mme. E. T. 1958. [Mycolytic bacteria and the possibility of their use for the control of fusariosis wilt of potatoes.] Inst. Mikrobiol. i. Virusol. Akad. Nauk Kaz. SSR 2: 24-41. *Abstr. in* Rev. Appl. Mycol. 38: 29-30, 1959.

Norman, A. G. 1960. Microbial products affecting root development. Trans. Intern. Congr. Soil Sci., 7th Congr. (Madison, Wisc.) Comm. III, p. 531-536.

Norstadt, F. A., and T. M. McCalla. 1963. Phytotoxic substances from a species of *Penicillium*. Science 140: 410-411.

Nowotny-Mieczynska, A., and J. Golebiowska. 1956. The influence of microbial population on the phosphorus uptake by some crop plants. Acta Microbiol. Polon. 5: 129-132.

Nutman, P. S. 1962. Soil Microbiology Department. Rothamsted Exptl. Sta. Rept. 1961: 73-80.

Nutman, P. S. 1963. Soil Microbiology Department. Rothamsted Exptl. Sta. Rept. 1962: 77-84.

Oostenbrink, M. 1960. Estimating nematode populations by some selected methods. p. 85-102. *In* J. N. Sasser and W. R. Jenkins [ed.], Nematology, fundamentals and recent advances with emphasis on plant parasitic and soil forms, University of North Carolina Press, Chapel Hill, N. C.

Ordin, A. P. 1961. Mycoflora of the rhizosphere and roots of cultivated plants. Microbiology (U.S.S.R.) (Engl. transl.) 30: 679-683.

Panosyan, A. K., R. S. H. Arutyunyan, and N. A. Avetisyan. 1962. [Interrelations of *Azotobacter* and other soil microorganisms.] Izv. Akad. Nauk Arm. SSR Biol. Nauki 15: 12-24. *Translated summary in* Soils Fertilizers 25: 378, 1962.

Pantos, G. 1961. [The vitamin-synthesizing capacity of some dominant strains of bacteria in the rhizosphere of wheat and maize.] Agrokem. Talajt. 10: 511-522.

Papavizas, G. C., and C. B. Davey. 1961. Extent and nature of the rhizosphere of *Lupinus*. Plant Soil 14: 215-236.

Parkinson, D. 1958. New methods for the qualitative and quantitative study of fungi in the rhizosphere. *In* Symp. Meth. E. Microbiol. Sol. Pédologie 7: 146-154.

Parkinson, D., and J. H. Clarke. 1961. Fungi associated with the seedling roots of *Alium porrum* L. Plant Soil 13: 384-390.

Payne, T. M. B., J. W. Rouatt, and A. G. Lochhead. 1957. The relationship between soil bacteria with simple nutritional requirements and those requiring amino acids. Can. J. Microbiol. 3: 73-80.

Pecket, R. C. 1960. Effects of gibberellic acid on excised pea roots. Nature (London) 185: 114-115.

Peterson, E. A. 1954. A study of cross-antagonisms among some actinomycetes active against *Streptomyces scabies* and *Helminthosporium sativum*. Antibiot. Chemotherapy 4: 145-149.

Peterson, E. A. 1958. Observations on fungi associated with plant roots. Can. J. Microbiol. 4: 257-265.

Peterson, E. A. 1959. Seed-borne fungi in relation to colonization of roots. Can. J. Microbiol. 5: 579-582.

Peterson, E. A. 1961. Observations on the influence of plant illumination on the fungal flora of roots. Can. J. Microbiol. 7: 1-6.

Peterson, N. V. 1961. [Sources of enrichment of soil with enzymes.] Mikrobiol. Zh. Akad. Nauk Ukr. RSR 23: 5-11.

Preston, W. H., Jr., J. W. Mitchell, and W. Reeve. 1954. Movement of alphamethoxyphenylacetic acid from one plant to another through their root systems. Science 119: 437-438.

Ramachandra-Reddy, T. K. 1959. Rhizosphere microflora of pteridophytes. Current Sci. (India) 28: 113-114.

Rangaswami, G., and V. N. Vasantharajan. 1962a. Studies on the rhizosphere microflora of citrus trees.

I. Quantitative incidence of microorganisms in relation to root and shoot growth. Can. J. Microbiol. 8: 473-477.

Rangaswami, G., and V. N. Vasantharajan. 1962b. Studies on the rhizosphere microflora of citrus trees. II. Qualitative distribution of the bacterial flora. Can. J. Microbiol. 8: 479-484.

Rangaswami, G., and V. N. Vasantharajan. 1962c. Studies on the rhizosphere microflora of citrus trees. III. Fungal and actinomycete flora of the rhizosphere. Can. J. Microbiol. 8: 485-489.

Rhem, H. J. 1961. Beitrag zur Ökologie der Streptomyceten. 3. Die Streptomycetenarten und ihre antibiotische Aktivität in der Rhizosphäre der Gerste. Zentr. Bakteriol. Parasitenk., Abt. II, 114: 147-155.

Rishbeth, J. 1957. *Fusarium* wilt of bananas in Jamaica. II. Some aspects of host-parasite relationships. Ann. Botany (London) [N.S.] 21: 215-245.

Rivière, J. 1959. Contribution to the study of the wheat rhizosphere. Ann. Agron. 45: 93-337.

Rivière, J. 1961. The effect of rhizosphere micro-organisms on the growth of wheat. I. Distribution of genera and nutritional groups. Ann. Inst. Pasteur 101: 611-618.

Rouatt, J. W. 1959. Initiation of the rhizosphere effect. Can. J. Microbiol. 5: 67-71.

Rouatt, J. W., and H. Katznelson. 1957. The comparative growth of bacterial isolates from rhizosphere and non-rhizosphere soils. Can. J. Microbiol. 3: 271-275.

Rouatt, J. W., and H. Katznelson. 1960. Influence of light on bacterial flora of roots. Nature (London) 186: 659-660.

Rouatt, J. W., and H. Katznelson. 1961. A study of the bacteria on the root surface and in the rhizosphere soil of crop plants. J. Appl. Bacteriol. 24: 164-171.

Rouatt, J. W., H. Katznelson, and T. M. B. Payne. 1960. Statistical evaluation of the rhizosphere effect. Soil Sci. Soc. Am. Proc. 24: 271-273.

Rouatt, J. W., M. Lechevalier, and S. A. Waksman. 1951. Distribution of antagonistic properties among actinomycetes isolated from different soils. Antibiot. Chemotherapy 1: 185-192.

Rouatt, J. W., E. A. Peterson, H. Katznelson, and V. E. Henderson. 1963. Microorganisms in the root zone in relation to temperature. Can. J. Microbiol. 9: 227-236.

Rovira, A. D. 1956a. Plant root excretions in relation to the rhizosphere effect. II. A study of the properties of root exudate and its effect on the growth of microorganisms isolated from the rhizosphere and control soil. Plant Soil 7: 195-208.

Rovira, A. D. 1956b. A study of the development of the root surface microflora during the initial stages of plant growth. J. Appl. Bacteriol. 19: 72-79.

Rovira, A. D. 1959. Root excretions in relation to the rhizosphere effect. IV. Influence of plant species, age of plant, light, temperature and calcium nutrition on exudation. Plant Soil 11: 53-64.

Rovira, A. D. 1961. Rhizobium numbers in the rhizosphere of red clover and papsalum in relation to soil treatment and the numbers of bacteria and fungi. Australian J. Agr. Res. 12: 77-83.

Rovira, A. D. 1962. Plant-root exudates in relation to the rhizosphere microflora. Soils Fertilizers 25: 167-172.

Rovira, A. D., and J. R. Harris. 1961. Plant root excretions in relation to the rhizosphere effect. V. The exudation of B-group vitamins. Plant Soil 14: 199-214.

Samtsevich, S. A., and V. N. Borisova. 1961. Effect of fertilizers on the root microflora of winter wheat. Microbiology (U.S.S.R.) (Engl. transl.) 30: 1033-1041.

Sanford, G. B. 1959. Root-disease fungi as affected by other soil organisms. p. 367-376. *In* C. S. Holton et al. [ed.], Plant pathology, problems and progress 1908-1958, University of Wisconsin Press, Madison, Wisc.

Schonbeck, F. 1958. Untersuchungen über den Einfluss von Wurzelausscheidungen auf die Entwicklung von Bodenpilzen. Naturwissenschaften 45: 63-64.

Schreven, D. A. van. 1959. Effects of added sugars and nitrogen on nodulation of legumes. Plant Soil 11: 93-112.

Schroth, M. N., T. A. Toussoun, and W. C. Snyder.

1963. Effect of certain constituents of bean exudate on germination of chlamydospores of *Fusarium solani* f. *phaseoli* in soil. Phytopathology 53: 809-812.

SEINHORST, J. W. 1961. Plant-nematode inter-relationships. Ann. Rev. Microbiol. 15: 177-196.

SHILOVA, E. I., and K. B. KONDRAT'EVA. 1955. [Certain characteristics of the rhizospheres of clover and timothy.] Vestn. Leningrad Univ. 4: 17-24.

SHTINA, E. A. 1954. [The effect of agricultural plants on the algal flora of soil.] Trudy Kirov. S.-Kh. Inst. 10: 59-69. *Transl. summary in* Soils Fertilizers 19: 850, 1956.

SMALII, V. T. 1962. [Effect of rhizospheric bacteria on the nicotinic and pantothenic acid contents in wheat plants.] Mikrobiol. Zh. Akad. Nauk Ukr. R.S.R. 24: 15-19. *Abstr. in:* Biol. Abstr. 39: 1275, 1962.

SMITH, J. H., F. E. ALLISON, and D. A. SOULIDES. 1961. Evaluation of phosphobacterin as a soil inoculant. Soil Sci. Soc. Am. Proc. 25: 109-111.

SMITH, J. H., F. E. ALLISON, and D. A. SOULIDES. 1962. Phosphobacterin as a soil inoculant. U.S. Dept. Agr. Tech. Bull. 1263, 22 p.

SPERBER, J. I. 1958a. The incidence of apatite-solubilizing organisms in the rhizosphere and soil. Australian J. Agr. Res. 9: 778-781.

SPERBER, J. I. 1958b. Release of phosphate from soil minerals by hydrogen sulphide. Nature (London) 181: 934.

SPERBER, J. I., and A. D. ROVIRA. 1959. A study of the bacteria associated with the roots of subterranean clover and Wimmera rye grass. J. Appl. Bacteriol. 22: 85-95.

STARKEY, R. L. 1929. Some influences of higher plants upon the microorganisms in the soil. II. Influence of the stage of plant growth upon abundance of organisms. Soil Sci. 27: 355-379.

STARKEY, R. L. 1931. Some influences of higher plants upon the microorganisms in the soil. IV. Influence of proximity to roots on abundance and activity of microorganisms. Soil Sci. 32: 367-393.

STARKEY, R. L. 1938. Some influences of the development of higher plants upon the microorganisms in the soil. VI. Microscopic examination of the rhizosphere. Soil Sci. 45: 207-209.

STARKEY, R. L. 1959. Interrelations between microorganisms and plant roots in the rhizosphere. Bacteriol. Rev. 22: 154-172.

STENTON, H. 1958. Colonization of roots of *Pisum sativum* L. by fungi. Trans. Brit. Mycol. Soc. 41: 74-80.

STILLE, B. 1957. Schädigungen an Pflanzenwurzeln durch Kulturfiltrate von Mikroorganismen. Arch. Mikrobiol. 26: 71-82.

STRZELCZYK, E. 1958. The influence of various crop plants on the development of *Azotobacter* and *Clostridium* in their rhizospheres. Acta Microbiol. Polon. 7: 115-123.

STRZELCZYK, E. 1961a. Studies on the incidence of certain "nutritional" and physiological groups of bacteria in rhizosphere and non-rhizosphere soil. Acta Microbiol. Polon. 10: 169-180.

STRZELCZYK, E. 1961b. Studies on the interaction of plants and free-living nitrogen-fixing microorganisms. II. Development of antagonists of *Azotobacter* in the rhizosphere of plants at different stages of growth in two soils. Can. J. Microbiol. 7: 507-513.

STRZELCZYKOWA, A., and E. STRZELCZYK. 1958. The influence of antagonistic actinomycetes on some soil bacteria. Acta Microbiol. Polon. 7: 283-297.

SUBBA-RAO, N. S., and D. L. BAILEY. 1961. Rhizosphere studies in relation to varietal resistance to susceptibility of tomato to *Verticillium* wilt. Can. J. Microbiol. 39: 1747-1758.

SUBBA-RAO, N. S., R. G. S. BIDWELL, and D. L. BAILEY. 1961. The effect of rhizoplane fungi on the uptake and metabolism of nutrients by tomato plants. Can. J. Botany 39: 1759-1764.

SZELENYI, F., and B. HELMECZI. 1960. [Investigation of the problem of antibiosis with *Azotobacter*.] Debr.

Mezog. Akad. Evk. 41-47. *Translated summary in* Soils Fertilizers 25: 299, 1962.

SZEMBER, A. 1960. [The action of soil microorganisms in making phosphorus from organic compounds available to plants. I. The ability of soil microorganisms to mineralize organic-phosphorus compounds.] Ann. Univ. Mariae Curie-Sklodowska, Lublin-Polonia 15E, p. 133-143. *Translated summary in* Soils Fertilizers 25: 461, 1962.

TAYLOR, G. S., and D. PARKINSON. 1961. The growth of saprophytic fungi on root surfaces. Plant Soil 15: 261-267.

THROWER, L. B. 1954. The rhizosphere effect shown by some Victorial heathland plants. Australian J. Botany 2: 246-267.

TIMONIN, M. I. 1940. The interaction of higher plants and soil microorganisms. II. Study of the microbial populations of the rhizosphere in relation to resistance of plants to soil-borne diseases. Can. J. Research, Sec. B, 18: 444-456.

TIMONIN, M. I. 1941. The interaction of higher plants and soil microorganisms. III. Effect of by-products of plant growth on activity of fungi and actinomycetes. Soil Sci. 52: 395-413.

TIMONIN, M. I. 1947. Microflora of the rhizosphere in relation to the manganese-deficiency disease of oats. Soil Sci. Soc. Am. Proc. (1946) 11: 284-292.

TOLLE, R., and A. RIPPEL-BALDES. 1958. Untersuchungen über die Rhizosphäre von Gramineen. Zentr. Bakteriol. Parasitenk., Abt. II, 111: 204-217.

TROLLDENIER, G., and U. MARCKWORDT. 1962. [Investigations on the effect of soil micro-organisms on the rubidium and calcium uptake of plants grown in nutrient solution.] Arch. Mikrobiol. 43: 148-151.

TUZIMURA, K., and WATANABE, I. 1962. The effect of rhizosphere of various plants on the growth of *Rhizobium*. (Part 3). Ecological studies of root nodule bacteria. Soil Sci. and Plant Nutrition. (Univ. Tokyo) 8: 13-17.

VAGNEROVA, K., and V. VANCURA. 1962. Production and utilization of amino acids by various species of rhizosphere bacteria. Folia Microbiol. (Prague) 7: 55-60.

VAGNEROVA, K., J. MACURA, and V. CATSKA. 1960a. Rhizosphere microflora of wheat. I. Composition and properties of bacterial flora during the first stage of growth. Folia Microbiol. (Prague) 5: 298-310.

VAGNEROVA, K., J. MACURA, and V. CATSKA. 1960b. Rhizosphere microflora of wheat. II. Composition and properties of bacterial flora during the vegetation period of wheat. Folia Microbiol. (Prague) 5: 311-319.

VANCURA, V. 1961. Detection of gibberellic acid in *Azotobacter* cultures. Nature (London) 192: 88-89.

VANCURA, V., and J. MACURA. 1959. The development of *Azotobacter* in the oat rhizosphere and its effect on the yield. Folia Microbiol. (Prague) 4: 200-202.

VANCURA, V., J. MACURA, O. FISCHER, and J. VONDRACEK. 1959. The relation of *Azotobacter* to the root system of barley. Folia Microbiol. (Prague) 4: 119-129.

VARGA, L. 1958. [Some data on the protozoa living in the rhizosphere of sugar beet.] Agrokem. Talajtan 7: 393-400.

VENKATA RAM, C. S. 1960. Foliar application of nutrients and rhizosphere microflora of *Camelia sinensis*. Nature (London) 187: 621-622.

VENKATESAN, R. 1962. Studies on the actinomycete population of paddy soil. Ph.D. thesis, Dept. Agr. Annamalai University, Annamalaingor, South India.

VLASYUK, P. A., K. M. DOBROTVORSKAYA, and S. A. GORDIENKO. 1956. [The activity of urease in the rhizosphere of agricultural crops.] Dokl. Akad. S. Kh. Nauk 8: 28-31. *Abstr. in* Soils Fertilizers 19: 495, 1956.

VOROSHILOVA, E. A. 1956. The effect of the apple tree on the number of soil microorganisms. Microbiology (U.S.S.R.) (Engl. transl.) 25: 670-699.

VOZNIAKOVSKAIA, I. M., and G. K. ZHIL'TSOVA. 1958. Species composition of the root microflora of some plants. Microbiology (U.S.S.R.) (Engl. transl.) 27: 611-618.

VRANY, J. 1960. Occurrence of bacteria assimilating benzoic acid and p-hydroxybenzoic acid in cereal rhizosphere and in soil. Folia Microbiol. (Prague) 5: 116-119.

VRANY, J., V. VANCURA, and J. MACURA. 1962. The effect of foliar applications of some readily metabolized substances, growth regulators and antibiotics on rhizosphere microflora. Folia Microbiol. (Prague) 7: 61-70.

WALLACE, R. H., and A. G. LOCHHEAD. 1951. Bacteria associated with seeds of various crop plants. Soil Sci. 71: 159-166.

WARCUP, J. H. 1960. Methods for isolation and estimation of activity of fungi in soil. p. 3-21. *In* D. Parkinson and J. S. Waid [ed.], Ecology of soil fungi, Liverpool University Press, Liverpool.

WEINDLING, R., H. KATZNELSON, and H. P. BEALE. 1950. Antibiosis in relation to plant disease. Ann. Rev. Microbiol. 4: 247-260.

WELTE, E., and G. TROLLDENIER. 1961. [The influence of hydrogen-ion concentration of the soil on the rhizosphere effect.] Naturwissenschaften 48: 509.

WELTE, E., and G. TROLLDENIER. 1962. [Effect of microorganisms on the dry-matter production and ash content of plants grown in nutrient solution.] Arch. Mikrobiol. 43: 138-147.

WINSLOW, R. D. 1960. Some aspects of the ecology of free living and plant parasitic nematodes. p. 341-415. *In* J. N. Sasser and W. R. Jenkins [ed.], Nematology,

fundamentals and recent advances with emphasis on plant parasitic and soil forms, University of North Carolina Press, Chapel Hill, N. C.

WOLDENDORP, J. W. 1962. The quantitative influence of the rhizosphere on denitrification. Plant Soil 17: 267-270.

WOLDENDORP, J. W. 1963. L'influence des plantes vivantes sur la denitrification. Ann. Inst. Pasteur 105: 426-433.

YOSHIDA, T., and H. SAKAI. 1962. Studies on the microbial changes in soil of the rhizosphere during the growth of leguminous plants. Hokkaido Daigaku Nogakubu Enshurin Kenkyu Hokoku 79: 51-57. *Abstr. in* Soils Fertilizers 26: 177, 1963.

ZAGALLO, A. C., and W. B. BOLLEN. 1962. Studies on the rhizosphere of tall fescue. Ecology 43: 54-62.

ZAGALLO, A. C., and H. KATZNELSON. 1957. Metabolic activity of bacterial isolates from wheat rhizosphere and control soil. J. Bacteriol. 73: 760-764.

ZINO'EVA, KH. G. 1961. Interrelationships of azotobacter with higher plants. Microbiology (U.S.S.R.) (Engl. transl.) 29: 680-681.

ZVYAGINTSEV, D. G. 1962. Study of the rhizosphere microflora by means of fluorescence microscopy in reflected light. Microbiology (U.S.S.R.) (Engl. transl.) 31: 111-115.

► DISCUSSION OF HARRY KATZNELSON PAPER

K. H. Garren:

After fertilization in the peanut (*Arachis hypogaea* L.), a specialized meristem at the base of the ovulary grows rapidly and forces the ovulary under the soil surface, where it develops into a fruit. It is amazing, not that so many peanut pods rot, but rather that some of them mature. I would suggest that this fruit which thinks it is a root may be a fertile and convenient means of investigating rhizosphere and soil exudation phenomena. Tying in with Dr. Katznelson's paper: the only thing which has made sense in 2 years of study of peanut-pod rot is that 5 tons CaSO$_4$ per acre consistently reduces it.

S. D. Garrett:

It is of interest to consider what characteristics may enable an organism to obtain and hold a place in the rhizosphere. In this connection, the essential difference between the rhizosphere and other substrates for microorganisms may be that in the rhizosphere, the substrate production is continuous. In the colonization of substrates of fresh plant tissue, the pioneer colonizing fungi are most frequently fast-growing fungi which neither produce antibiotics nor are tolerant of them. This is what one might expect, as neither antibiotic tolerance nor production would have survival value in this situation. But in the rhizosphere, it seems probable that a certain level of tolerance to antibiotics may be essential for survival, because at least some of the rhizosphere organisms are antibiotic producers. One would therefore expect the rhizosphere substrate to select antibiotic producers, and also to enforce a certain level of antibiotic tolerance upon all rhizosphere inhabitants.

H. Katznelson:

A number of reports have appeared suggesting that rhizosphere bacteria are, in general, more resistant to antibiotics than the nonrhizosphere population: our own work with streptomycin-resistant *Agrobacterium radiobacter*, Dr. Margaret Brown's work at Rothamsted

on the streptomycin-resistant bacteria (chiefly *Flavobacterium*) in the rhizosphere of a fairly extensive number of plants, especially legumes, and several papers of European workers. The same applies to acid-tolerant bacteria, which are proportionally more numerous in the root zone.

As to characteristics which may enable an organism to obtain and hold a place in the rhizosphere: rapid growth rate, simple nutritional requirements, antibiotic resistance, and ability to produce antibiotic substances, are some of the more important attributes which, combined with proper time of application (age of plant, environmental conditions), may materially aid in establishing it in the root zone.

B. Zak:

I personally think that it would add greatly to our confusion if the term rhizosphere were redefined to account for every portion of a root studied. Would it not be more desirable to use the current, broad definition but specify the kind, size, and age of the root material with which you are working? There are certainly differences between different portions of a plant root system, as our microbiological analysis of mycorrhizal and nonmycorrhizal rootlets of yellow birch several years ago bears out, and as shown by Parkinson and others, but they are still rhizosphere effects.

M. Alexander:

To what extent can the U.S.S.R.'s reports of beneficial effects resulting from inoculation, where significant, be due to the colonization of roots by microorganisms from the inoculation which ward off, in some way, pathogenic microorganisms?

H. Katznelson:

According to recent reports of Mishustin and to his own remarks at the Eighth International Congress of Microbiology in Montreal in 1962, azotobacterin (the inoculant) may produce its effects by virtue of its antagonism to plant-pathogenic fungi. In experiments with tomatoes growing in a very fertile soil, the higher yields obtained by inoculation were attributed to the antagonistic effects of *Azotobacter* rather than to its nitrogen-fixing ability or its production of auxins or other plant growth substances.

A. D. Rovira:

Inoculation of wheat with *Azotobacter, Clostridium,* and *Bacillus* increased plant growth in nonsterile sand and soil. *Clostridium* gave a 40% increase in growth, *Azotobacter* and *Bacillus* gave a smaller increase. In this work, attention should be drawn to the "training" of *Azotobacter* to growth on roots, which is stressed in Soviet and Czechoslovakian work in this field. Little is known of the changes in the bacteria during this adaptation to the rhizosphere, but it would appear unlikely that even adapted *Azotobacter* could approach the population levels reached by *Pseudomonas* or *Achromobacter*. In reference to this adaptation we should consider the work of Buxton showing that repeated subculturing of *Fusarium* in the rhizosphere of wilt-resistant peas altered the *Fusarium* in that its pathogenicity towards the resistant peas was increased.

Although the mechanisms responsible for crop stimulation by *Azotobacter* and *Clostridium* are still not established, it is probably due to factors other than nitrogen fixation. The characteristics required for organisms to be rhizosphere colonizers have not yet been accurately defined, but the following may be important: growth rate, utilization of exudate, adhesion, mobility, and synthesis of antagonistic substances. [See also Rovira's comment in Discussion of A. Kerr's paper.]

H. Katznelson:

We also have obtained some positive results with *Azotobacter* inoculum, although our yield increases were in the order of 5 to 7%, significant at the 5% level.

W. F. Mai:

Pythium sp. in sand repels *Pratylenchus penetrans.* More individuals of *P. penetrans* were present in tomato roots infected with *Pythium* sp. than in similar noninfected roots. When compared with a high light intensity, significantly more *P. penetrans* developed in roots of pea plants grown at a decreased light intensity which resulted in a moderate reduction in plant weight. On the other hand, there were significantly fewer nematodes in roots of plants grown at a very low light intensity, which resulted in growth considerably less than that at the high light.

H. Katznelson:

Since the metabolism of *Pythium* inside the tomato root may be completely different from that in sand, it is not at all surprising that it no longer repels *Pratylenchus penetrans;* in fact, it could alter the host tissue so as to render it attractive to the nematode. I am pleased to learn that your observations on the influence of light on *P. penetrans* in roots were so similar to ours.

R. Mankau:

Your data relative to the increase in the *Aphelenchus avenae* population at low light intensities are very interesting in that this nematode is probably an obligate fungivore, and therefore one can assume that the low-light condition affects the nematode indirectly through a possible increase in a specific fungus flora upon which this nematode feeds in the rhizosphere.

Would you not agree that the techniques which are normally used to determine numbers of microorganisms in the rhizosphere are not very effective when applied to determining the numbers of nematodes in the rhizosphere? The usual techniques are highly selective for nematodes actually within the roots or feeding on the surface of roots. The nematode species which feed on bacteria and fungi, which are probably very important in the biology of the rhizosphere, are generally not recovered in large numbers, even when the Baermann funnel technique is used. Owing to the relatively large size and motility of nematodes, they are probably very transient in the rhizosphere, although probably spending much of their existence in the vicinity of roots (I refer here to microbivorous and fungivorous species primarily).

H. Katznelson:

The methods normally used in rhizosphere work were not those used to determine numbers of nematodes in the root zone but rather a common nematological technique—the Baermann funnel technique. It is quite possible that nematodes within roots, or feeding on the root surface, might be "extracted" by this method but in direct microscopic observations of stained root segments, these organisms rarely showed up. There was little question that the majority of the nematodes obtained from the rhizosphere were free-living, nonparasitic types.

N. C. Thornton:

Although urea has been found effective in reducing *Fusarium oxysporum* f. *cubense* in laboratory studies, the addition of urea up to 400 pounds actual nitrogen per acre has not been effective in reducing this *Fusarium* in the field when applied either to banana leaves or the ground. Also, the use of potassium nitrite in amounts up to 1,000 pounds per acre has not been effective in eradication of this *Fusarium* from the soil.

H. Katznelson:

It would be interesting to find out if foliar application of urea or even nitrite would reduce the pathogen in the root zone.

J. P. Martin:

Numerous dilution platings of whole soil or citrus rhizosphere soil at the University of California, Riverside, have indicated that growth of citrus causes a marked increase in relative numbers of certain fungus species, and a sharp decrease or almost disappearance of others. In most field soils, sharp increases in the abundance of propagules of *Fusarium* spp., primarily *F. solani* and *F. oxysporum*, *Pyrenochaeta* sp., and *Pullularia pullulans* occur. In the greenhouse *Thielaviopsis basicola* also becomes a dominant species during the second year of cropping. In one greenhouse test, the influence of four common rootstock seedlings and the same seedlings grafted with a navel-orange scion on the fungus population of the soil was observed. All seedlings, namely Troyer citrange, trifoliate orange, Cleopatra mandarin, and sour orange, caused a marked increase in relative numbers of *F. solani, P. pullulans,* and *T. basicola.* The addition of a navel scion to each rootstock doubled the frequency of *F. solani* colonies developing on the soil plates, and increased the growth-retarding effect of a first crop of citrus on a second crop.

S. Wilhelm:

The assumption that nematodes are attracted to colonies of organisms growing on petri dishes, whether they are sources of food or not, is common, and may indeed be true, but another simpler explanation is possible. Nematodes are motile, and if we assume even that their movements are random, some will chance to enter the agar zone modified by the fungus or bacterial organism. These nematodes may sense the altered environment, explore it, and leave the area slowly. The rate of arrival into this area is thus more rapid than the rate of exit, and nematodes accumulate. If the habitat does not offer a food source, the "random" movements of individual nematodes will bring some into the vicinity of the nearby bacterial colony. These, being a food, will be engulfed and also spread around over the surface of the agar by the movements of the nematodes. This greatly enlarges the zone where food occurs. We will not readily observe this spreading around of the bacteria until growth is sufficient to produce colonies (1 or 2 or more days). But the chances of the nematodes finding the food source are greatly increased. Thus, what may in petri-dish tests (Fig. 4 in Dr. Katznelson's paper) appear to be complex, associative, or attractive phenomena, may reflect only the fact that the nematodes are motile.

W. B. Mountain:

I would agree with Dr. Wilhelm that the question of attraction of nematodes is still controversial. It is apparent that any solid substance in agar could act as a barrier to movement, and the resulting accumulation of nematodes may suggest that they have been attracted to the substance. I also suggest that agar is not a good material with which to study movement of nematodes. But studies in which the biological material is separated from the agar by a dialyzable membrane may indicate that nematodes are attracted positively. Of course, we must remember that nematodes are complex organisms, and structures that may be sense organs are readily apparent.

H. Katznelson:

The accumulation of nematodes around certain colonies of microorganisms but not around others cannot be due simply to nematode motility. In addition, as shown in Fig. 4 of this paper, nematodes may move *away* from a solid substance (such as a colony) in agar to an area that they prefer, be it a source of food or a zone that is otherwise favorable to them.

Influence of the Rhizosphere on the Mineral Nutrition of the Plant

D. J. D. NICHOLAS—*Chemical Microbiology Department, Research Station, University of Bristol, Long Ashton, England. (Now: Department of Agricultural Biochemistry and Soil Science, Waite Agricultural Research Institute, University of Adelaide, South Australia.)*

The soil may be regarded not only as a medium for the growth of green plants but also as one that supports an invisible but nevertheless vital crop of microorganisms. Indeed were it not for the soil microflora, green plants and animals would cease to exist. Soil fertility is in great measure controlled by the diverse biochemical activities of the microflora. Besides the well-known carbon, nitrogen, and sulphur cycles, there are also the more complex and less understood interactions between soil microorganisms and plant roots.

A conservative estimate of the numbers of organisms in 1 gram of fertile soil is:

True bacteria	10^6 to 10^9	Algae	10^1 to 10^3
Actinomycetes	10^5 to 10^6	Fungi	10^4 to 10^5
Protozoa	10^4 to 10^5		

It is estimated that the top 6 in of arable land containing 60,000 lb per acre of dry organic matter will contain about 3,500 lb of bacteria live weight (assuming 3×10^9 bacteria per g). Assuming that the cells have 20% dry matter, this represents 700 lb dry organic matter. A rough calculation indicates that another 300 lb dry weight might account for fungi in the same volume of arable soil. These values are, of course, small, amounting to only about 1% of the total organic matter present in the soil. Nevertheless when the diverse and intensive metabolic activities of the soil microflora are considered, their vital role in nature may be appreciated. These metabolic events vary from the fixation of atmospheric nitrogen to the production of an array of complex antibiotics and metabolites.

PRINCIPAL FUNCTIONS OF SOIL MICROORGANISMS.—Before considering the effects of microflora in areas adjacent to plant roots on the growth of plants, it is as well to enumerate briefly some of the main functions performed by the microorganisms.

The desirable processes include the breakdown of complex organic and inorganic substances in the soil. This prevents the accumulation of dead materials and waste products and makes available soluble nutrients and carbon dioxide required for growth of green plants. Organic acids produced by metabolic processes serve as carbon sources for other microorganisms and also react with basic materials in the soil. Soil microflora are concerned in processes that form, or slowly decompose, humus materials and also aid in soil aggregation. Special types of bacteria oxidise simple inorganic compounds and thus produce nutrients that are assimilated by green plants, e.g. nitrification processes.

Undesirable effects include denitrification of nitrates to nitrogenous gases, competition with green plants for mineral nutrients, production of temporary acidity effects, a too rapid decomposition of humus, and in some instances deactivation of pesticides.

RHIZOSPHERE ENVIRONMENT.—As Dr. Rovira mentions in an earlier paper in this symposium, Hiltner (1904) recognised that the region in the immediate vicinity of plant roots, which he termed "rhizosphere," would be markedly different to areas further away. He found greater numbers of microorganisms in this zone which are often qualitatively different from those in the rest of the soil. Since roots absorb oxygen and release carbon dioxide as well as organic and inorganic nutrients, the rhizosphere is under the influence of the growing plant and the microflora in turn affect plant growth. This dynamic metabolic interaction between the rhizosphere microflora and green plants is complex, since the population varies with type of plant or species and even in the same plant at different stages of growth. The rhizosphere is an area of intense microbiological activity, which may extend several millimetres from the roots. It is a zone of influence where saprophytic types of microflora in particular thrive. It is likely that root exudates not only supply organic compounds to support growth of microflora but also compounds that arrest the dormancy of spores which have been in the soil for an appreciable period. Roots are ephemeral structures, since the root cap constantly sloughs off dead cells and cork formation in the older parts of root systems results in the death of the outer tissues. These processes yield cell constituents to the soil. The fact that young seedlings also have a rhizosphere effect indicates that there is a secretion, primarily of organic constituents from living roots, and many workers have considered such exudates to be the main reason for the establishment and maintenance of the rhizosphere.

COMPOSITION OF ROOT EXUDATES.—Although about twenty different amino acids and the amides of glutamine and asparagine have been detected in root exudates, their distribution and type varies greatly with plant and even with plant species (Rovira, 1962; Swaby, 1962). Thus the type and amount of microflora encouraged in the rhizospheres of plants would be expected to vary widely. There is evidence that the root area associated with rapid cell elongation is most active in exuding amino acids, although the mechanism of secretion is not understood. It has been suggested that these and other substances diffuse through intact membranes and that antibiotics produced in the rhizosphere may result in exosmosis effects. Root hairs also guttate fluids and sometimes burst spontaneously, presumably because of abrupt changes in pH, Eh, or nutrient concentration in the rhizosphere.

The amounts of vitamins exuded are usually small. They may include thiamin, niacin, riboflavin, biotin, and pantothenate. This is also true for the carbohydrates, which include glucose, fructose, sucrose, xylose, maltose, arabinose, raffinose, and oligosaccharides. There is usually a preponderance of vitamin-synthesizing bacteria in the rhizosphere. Nucleotides, including adenine, guanine, uridine, and cytidine, are also present in root exudates; their role in metabolism of rhizosphere microorganisms has not been assessed. It is likely that nucleotides are more important than amino acids in influencing the growth of saprophytic types of bacteria by enhancing cell division, which is dependent on RNA and DNA. Organic acids have been found in extracts of cereal crops and mustard, but it is likely that the amounts produced are no greater than those formed by the microflora in the rhizosphere. Greater amounts of amino acids are released than organic acids (Rivière, 1960). More complex materials are known to occur in root secretions. Thus enzymes including invertase, amylase, and protease have been reported to occur in exudates of cereals and legumes (Krasil'nikov, 1952; Krasil'nikov and Kotelev, 1956; Rovira, 1959, 1962). A growth factor "M" identified in root exudates of pine, peas, and tomato, stimulates the growth of *Boletus variegatus* and *B. elegans* in media containing salts, sugars, amino acids, and the B group of vitamins (Melin, 1953, 1963). There is also evidence for a diffusable inhibiting principle produced in association with the "M" factor. Antibiotics and antimetabolites are also present in the rhizosphere (Melin, 1953, 1963; Norman, 1959). It is claimed that some of these inhibit the growth of microorganisms. In the light of recent metabolic studies on the role of antibiotics as inhibitors of protein synthesis and of RNA and DNA functioning in bacteria, antibiotics may have a far more dominant effect in controlling the type of microflora in the rhizosphere than the more nutritional factors, e.g. amino acids, sugars.

Inorganic salts have also been shown to leak from roots. Thus with the aid of a split-root technique and labelled isotopes P^{32} and Ca^{45}, it was shown that between 4 and 25% phosphorus and 10 to 23% calcium were secreted into chernozem and serozem soils. It is of interest that greater amounts of P^{32} were secreted into the chernozem than into the serozem soil and the reverse effect was found with calcium (Fedorovskii, 1958). It is claimed that labelled phosphate applied to

leaves of forest trees appeared in neighbouring trees that were as much as 2 m away. This effect was attributed to root exudation and transfer across the rhizosphere zones of the treated and recipient trees (Rakhteenko, 1958). Although this interpretation has been questioned (Rovira, 1962) it is likely to be correct since roots of forest trees explore large areas of soil and may converge with roots from neighbouring trees.

MICROFLORA IN THE RHIZOSPHERE.—Roots penetrate relatively small areas of the soil; the major part of any soil does not contain rooting material. Thus not only is the rhizosphere a specialised area, but it is also very restricted in dimension in relation to the rest of the soil. Nevertheless it is known that the microbial population is far more active in the rhizosphere than in neighbouring soil. It is claimed that aerobic cellulose-decomposing bacteria and anaerobic gas-producing bacteria, including denitrifiers as well as those producing ammonia, are more abundant in the rhizosphere of cereals and root crops than in that of other plants, whereas anaerobic cellulose-decomposing bacteria are less numerous. The nitrogen-fixing bacteria *Azotobacter* and *Clostridium*, which are present in soils in relatively small numbers, do not appear to show a rhizosphere effect. Despite a good supply of carbon dioxide near the roots, nitrifying bacteria, which derive their carbon from the gas, are no more abundant in the rhizosphere than in other parts of the soil. The limiting factors for nitrification are more likely to be the energy-yielding substrates which they oxidise, viz. ammonia and nitrite; and there is no evidence that these concentrate near root surfaces. The activity of denitrifying bacteria would be encouraged by the semianaerobic conditions set up by the uptake of oxygen and liberation of carbon dioxide by roots, but the rate-limiting factor for their heterotrophic mode of life would be the amount of energy-yielding materials such as sugars and organic and amino acids present in the rhizosphere. Denitrifying bacteria are particularly sensitive to changes in oxygen pressure. Even a small increase in aeration tends to reduce denitrification, since oxygen is a more efficient hydrogen acceptor in these bacteria than is nitrate (Nicholas, 1961).

There is usually a higher percentage of amino-acid-requiring bacteria in the rhizosphere than in neighbouring soil. The rhizospheres of young plants have fewer bacteria requiring yeast-extract supplements for growth than those associated with older plants. Some bacteria in the rhizosphere require methionine and other sulphur-containing amino acids, e.g. cysteine. Bacteria dependent on vitamin B_{12} are more abundant in the root zone, especially of some legumes. Preformed vitamins and amino acids are obtained either from the plant residues or root exudates or from secretions or excretions from microflora. Since the amino acids and vitamins are susceptible to bacterial decomposition, they are likely to be more readily available in those regions of the soil where there is extensive microbial activity, as in the rhizosphere. Autolysis of cells is an important feature of the release of nutrients into the rhizosphere zone.

RHIZOSPHERE EFFECTS ON MINERAL NUTRIENT AVAILABILITY TO PLANTS.—Inorganic nutrients reach the plant roots only after passage through the rhizosphere, where myriads of microflora are at various stages of growth from active metabolism to death and autolysis of the cells. Thus when inorganic nutrients are limiting it is likely that the microflora denude the meagre supply. But there are instances where rhizosphere organisms release nutrients from sources that are unavailable to the plants, e.g. phosphates from apatite or from complex organic compounds. Most microorganisms have the capacity to accumulate luxury amounts of nutrients in particular trace metals.

Nitrogen.—During the breakdown of plant debris from sloughed-off roots, the ammonifying bacteria convert nitrogen-containing materials to ammonia and nitrogen gases. This breakdown is dependent on an energy supply; when the carbon source is limiting, then growth is restricted and the uptake of mineral nutrients by the rhizosphere flora is thereby reduced. Under some types of grass there is an unidentified inhibitor which restricts nitrifying organisms so that there is a tendency for ammonia to predominate over nitrate. Goring and Clark (1949) suggest that less nitrogen is available to plants than would have been transformed to nitrate in soil if it were devoid of plants. Significant amounts of nitrogen are assimilated by microorganisms in the rhizosphere zone and are thus immobilised temporarily so that plants indirectly bring about their own nitrogen deficiency by encouraging rhizosphere microflora. This is particularly the case with some young seedlings which require relatively large amounts of nitrogen for growth. During the first few weeks of seedling growth, when the plant requires appreciable nitrogen, the rhizosphere microorganisms account for a large proportion of fertilizer nitrogen and thus deprive the plants of it. At a later stage of growth, plants recover from this incipient nitrogen deficiency since they now require less nitrogen and the microflora is well established and more nitrogen compounds are released into the rhizosphere, mainly by autolysis of the cells.

The legumes appear to stimulate all groups of rhizosphere organisms and in particular the types of rhizobia that infect them. The stimulation appears to be in the rhizosphere and not on the root surfaces, presumably because young legume seedlings produce antibiotics and bacteriophages of rhizobia are also more prevalent on root surfaces. There is no satisfactory explanation for the predominance of rhizobia in the legume rhizosphere. It is clear that some undetermined factors retard some microorganisms and encourage the specific strain of *Rhizobium* and thus ensure a buildup in its population for root infection and subsequent nodule formation.

Claims put forward by Russian workers that seeds inoculated with *Azotobacter* result in a rhizosphere having increased nitrogen-fixing capacity (Cooper, 1959) have not been fully confirmed by other workers (Swaby, 1962). The beneficial effects from *Azotobacter* inoculation may be explained by phenomena other than nitrogen fixation, such as antagonism to harmful microorganisms or the production of organic growth stimulants (Cooper, 1959; Rovira, 1962). No critical work has been done with the N^{15} stable isotope to confirm that the inoculated plants do in fact contain more nitrogen and that it is derived from the air via *Azotobacter*. A comparison between the nitrogen-fixing capacity of *Azotobacter* in the rhizosphere with that in ordinary soil would be of interest. There is no evidence that the nitrogen-fixing bacteria—*Azotobacter* species, *Clostridium pasteurianum*, or *Bacillus polymyxa*—are more numerous in the root zone.

Phosphorus.—Numerous workers have studied the effect of rhizosphere microorganisms in the solubilization of phosphate from sources unavailable to plants. Thus Gerretsen (1948), Pilkovskaya (1948) and Krasil'nikov and Kotelev (1956) showed an increased uptake of phosphate by plants grown with insoluble sources of phosphate, following addition of rhizosphere organisms to sterile soils. Gerretsen studied solubilization effects of rhizosphere organisms on mono-, di-, and tri-calcium phosphates, bonemeal, rock phosphate and ferrophosphate. The effects of roots on the solubility of phosphate were shown by use of sand cultures. Plants were grown over glass sheets coated with agar films in which insoluble phosphate was dispersed. Clear areas which appeared round the roots were ascribed to microbial activity. It is of interest that microbial development at root surfaces had the opposite effect, i.e. an increase in insoluble material.

Askinazi (1958) concluded that work over the last 12 years with "phosphatic bacterial fertilizers" in the U.S.S.R. has not produced a significant increase in uptake of phosphate by any of a range of crop plants. Louw and Webley (1959) have shown that acid-producing bacteria in the root region of oat dissolve dicalcium phosphate, with resulting increased availability to the plant. The bacteria were preferentially stimulated by exudates from the roots. Sperber (1958) isolated from the rhizospheres of subterranean clover and ryegrass a number of fungi and bacteria that would solubilize apatite. When these were isolated and cultured they lost their capacity to dissolve apatite more slowly than did similar types taken from soil outside the rhizosphere. The principal acids produced by two fungi, an actinomycete, and two bacteria in the root zone were lactic, glycollic, citric, and succinic acids. Bromfield (1953, 1958) showed that hydrogen sulphide produced by several strains of *Bacillus megaterium* in well aerated soils, reduced ferric phosphate to black ferrous sulphide and thus released available phosphate from an insoluble mineral source. Subba-Rao, Bidwell, and Bailey (1961) found that *Fusarium* species in the rhizosphere suppressed the uptake of radioactive phosphate, sulphate, bicarbonate, and glucose by tomato plants. *Trichoderma viride* Pers. also suppressed uptake of the inorganic ions but increased the absorption of glucose by the roots.

Other nutrients.—It is established that the production of carbon dioxide by the microflora supplements the solvent action of roots on calcium carbonate, but it is not known whether this results in increased uptake of calcium by the plants. Larger amounts of bicarbonate are present in the rhizosphere than in neighbouring soil.

Starkey (1958) claims that the solubility of iron and manganese compounds are increased under the influence of microorganisms in the rhizosphere. He suggests that these effects are caused by a marked change in redox potential. Thus iron, manganese, and other metals occur in combination with organic compounds formed by microbes. It is likely that these metal-organo complexes are readily utilized by plants. Thus the rhizosphere seems to perform two functions, complexing or chelating metals so that they are retained in close proximity to roots and also facilitating the entry of trace metals as chelated forms, into roots.

In this connection, work with synthetic iron chelates is of interest. Early workers suggested that only iron is taken up from synthetic chelates, but subsequent results indicate that the whole molecule is absorbed (Wallace, Mueller, et al., 1955; Wallace, 1962). Wallace, Shannon, et al. (1957) found an equivalent uptake of metal and chelate component by plants, but later work from this school suggests a nonequivalent intake. Tiffin, Brown, and Krauss (1960) concluded that iron and the aromatic phenolic polyamino-carboxylic acid (EDDHA) were not absorbed by sunflower plants in equivalent amounts but that iron is released to the roots and most of the chelate remains in the nutrient solution. Hill-Cottingham (1957) analysed nutrient solution containing tomato plants during the growth period and found that Fe^{3+} EDTA decreased without formation of free EDTA. He concluded that the entire molecule was absorbed by roots. The extent to which the iron chelate is absorbed in toto or the iron component only, depends largely on the nutritional status of the plants. Thus when the plant was deficient in iron more of the metal than the chelate entered the root but when the iron status was normal, the iron and chelate were absorbed in equimolecular concentrations. It is clear, however, that many chelating substances such as ascorbic acid, humic acid, citric acid, tartaric acid, and amino acids, that occur in nature have relatively low stability constants for their metal chelates. Under extreme conditions of alkaline soils such chelating agents would be unlikely to prevent iron from precipitating as an insoluble phosphate complex. In the rhizosphere, however, the more acid microenvironment produced by CO_2 and acid production is likely to prolong the life of the chelate sufficiently to render it available for uptake by roots. Weinstein et al. (1954) confirmed that microbial metabolites influenced the uptake of iron by sunflower plants. They suggest that plants take up iron in the form of organomineral substances which are formed in the rhizosphere. It is of interest that Tiffin and Brown (1962) have recently found that iron was transported in stem exudates as the chelate of malate and to a lesser extent of malonate.

Some plants utilize manganese in soil more readily than others. Bromfield (1958) showed that oat roots released substances that dissolve manganese dioxide. These unidentified factors were, however, readily decomposed by microorganisms in the root zone. Timonin (1946) found that manganese was oxidised by rhizosphere microorganisms, resulting in decreased availability to the plants. Partial soil sterilization reduced the manganese-oxidising bacteria in the rhizosphere of a susceptible variety of oat with consequent reduction in symptoms. Timonin (1946) and Gerretsen (1948) found that the addition of antiseptics to soil cured manganese deficiency. They postulated that this was due to the inhibition of bacteria in the rhizosphere that oxidise the manganous ion. The effect is probably more complex since the inhibitors also prevent the decomposition of reducing substances by the microflora.

Little is known about the effect of the rhizosphere microflora on other trace metals. More vitamin B_{12}-producing bacteria are present in the rhizosphere than in adjacent soil and the vitamin accumulates in amounts that are in excess of the plant's requirements. The recent demonstration of a minute requirement for cobalt or vitamin B_{12} (0.1 µg per liter of culture medium) for nodulated plants is of interest (Ahmed and Evans, 1959, 1960). It is also established that vitamin B_{12} is required in similar amounts for nitrogen fixation in *Azotobacter vinelandii* (Nicholas, Kobayashi and Wilson, 1962) and in *Clostridium pasteurianum* (Nicholas et al., 1963). The 5-6 dimethylbenzimidazolylcobamide coenzyme has now been identified in *Azotobacter* (Nicholas, Kobayashi, and Wilson, 1962) and in the nodules of legumes (Kliewer and Evans, 1962).

It has been suggested that boronated sugars are present in the rhizosphere of some plants, and this may facilitate uptake of the micronutrient. The work of Swaby (1962) on the effect of *Aspergillus niger* on the release of trace metals from fifteen rocks and sixty-five mineral types is of interest. The main acids produced by this fungus were citric and gluconic, which released iron and molybdenum followed by manganese and copper from these insoluble materials, but zinc was relatively unaffected.

In considering rhizosphere effects on molybdenum, it is of interest that all microorganisms so far examined require the micronutrient when nitrates are being assimilated or dissimilated (Nicholas, 1961). Since these organisms predominate in the rhizosphere as compared with the neighbouring soil, their activity would be expected to be stimulated by molybdenum provided nitrates and energy-yielding materials were not limiting. Molybdenum is also required for nitrogen fixation by asymbiotic and symbiotic bacteria; the latter concentrate in the rhizosphere of leguminous plants. Recent work has shown that the micronutrient is present in the rhizosphere as a phosphomolybdate complex.

ABSORPTION OF MINERAL IONS BY MICROORGANISMS AND PLANTS.—In considering competition and interactions between the microflora and plant roots for mineral nutrients, it is as well to consider briefly some of the theories proposed for salt uptake. Early workers assumed that mineral salts were absorbed passively with water. After it was established that salt composition of plants differs markedly from that of the environment, this theory was no longer tenable. It has been suggested that increased rates of salt uptake frequently recorded during periods of high transpiration in plants may result from a direct flow of soil solution via "the apparent free space" into xylem cells. This concept, however, seems to overlook the control exercised by the endodermis. The importance of physical processes, such as osmosis and diffusion of substances across membranes in response to concentration gradients, has been stressed: the chemical transformation of particular molecules inside the protoplasm, leading to a continuous absorption, would result in a selective salt uptake. It was soon found that diffusion and osmosis would not account for the observed rates of nutrient uptake. Pfeffer (1895) suggested that living organisms have the capacity to transport substances across membrane structures and suggested that chemical combination with cell constituents may be involved. Thus the idea of "carrier molecules" was born. From 1930 onwards, mainly through the work of Hoagland in the United States, Lundegårdh in Sweden, and Steward in England, it was shown that salt uptake depends largely on aerobic metabolism. Various theories on the relation between salt uptake and respiration and between absorption and exchange mechanisms have been proposed.

Since metabolically mediated ion-accumulation "active transport" was first recognised in plants, it has gained a much wider biological importance, e.g. in muscle contraction and in regulation of ionic composition in erythrocytes and body fluids. Ions combine with "carrier molecules" located in membranes, and these complexes liberate their ions on the inside of the cell. Cell membranes are rich in phosphatides and proteins. It is likely that these carriers function as specific enzyme proteins forming unstable carrier-ion complexes. Cohen and Monod (1957) have proposed the general term permeases for solute carriers of this type in microorganisms. The system is amenable to kinetic analysis similar to the type used in the study of enzyme-substrate complexes. Thus Epstein (1956) and his associates found that ion uptake involves the breakdown of ion-carrier complexes in plant roots. Separate carriers are required for sodium, potassium, calcium, magnesium, and phosphate ions. The mechanism is dependent on an energy supply derived from the formation of adenosine triphosphate during aerobic respiration when oxygen is utilized or when nitrate is the alternative hydrogen acceptor. Since some of the microflora in the rhizosphere have the capacity to generate energy from suitable organic materials under anaerobic conditions during dissimilation and denitrification processes, i.e. nitrate respiration, they can maintain salt uptake when plant roots are relatively ineffective. Under these conditions rhizosphere organisms may compete with plants for mineral salts, especially in soils that are badly aerated and of low fertility.

It has been proposed that roots and microflora absorb basic ions (cations) directly from colloidal particles. Two hypotheses have been suggested to account for this phenomenon. The first takes into account the release of carbon dioxide by roots and microflora resulting in carbonic acid formation, which leads to an exchange of hydrogen for cations on the colloids. The released cations would be absorbed with bicarbonate and other anions. The second idea is that a "contact exchange" of ions occurs whenever the colloidal root surface adheres to the soil colloids. This exchange would proceed without direct mediation of a liquid phase. It is of interest that recent electron micrographs of the rhizosphere zone by Jenny and Grossenbacher (1962) show a jellylike coating on the outer surface of the roots which they term mucigel. They believe that it is produced jointly by the roots and the microbes living in it. The mucigel conforms to the surface contour of both soil particles and roots and thus provides intimate contact for the transfer of soil nutrient ions and water from the soil to the root surfaces. This may well effect not only a gradient contact exchange from the soil via the rhizosphere to the root but also set up microgradients within the rhizosphere zone between the various microflora. Thus a dynamic exchange system is set up between roots and microflora in the rhizosphere.

CONCLUSIONS.—Not only is the rhizosphere a habitat that supports a wide variety of microflora having their own complex interactions but it is also influenced by plant roots, which in turn are affected by microorganisms. This dynamic system is constantly changing since the microflora population varies with the type and age of plant and even with plant species. The growth rate of the microbial population varies from those that grow and autolyse within a few hours to those that persist for a few weeks.

Recent electron micrographs of barley show that outer surfaces of plant roots have a jellylike coating termed mucigel, produced by roots and possibly by the microorganisms living in it, which follows closely the contour of soil particles. This matrix, where rhizosphere organisms thrive, provides intimate contact for transfer of soil nutrient ions, water, and gases from the outer soil to the microflora and plant roots. Within this zone microorganisms are likely to compete effectively with roots for mineral nutrients since their metabolism, geared to a shorter life span, is more intense than for the more gradual root growth. Thus more adenosine triphosphate is generated in microflora per unit weight and time and this provides a continuous supply of energy for the "ion carrier" absorption into the bacterial cells. This advantage would persist even under anaerobic conditions since denitrifying bacteria and other types which also dissimilate nitrates accumulate in the rhizosphere and thereby generate energy by the process of "nitrate respiration." This may be one of the reasons for the accumulation of luxury levels of mineral nutrients, especially trace metals, by some microorganisms. Should the supply of nutrients be limiting, then the microflora are likely to denude the plant of its supply; but beneficial effects of rhizosphere microflora include the release of mineral salts from insoluble materials, which are then made available to plants, especially after autolysis of the cells. Thus trace metals are often released in chelated forms, which would then be taken up directly by the roots since recent evidence, from work with synthetic chelates, indicates that chelate molecules are absorbed directly.

Contributors to this symposium have been asked not only to review their assigned topics but also to pinpoint gaps in knowledge and to suggest lines of work for the future. In regard to the effects of rhizosphere on the availability of mineral nutrients to plants, present-day information is scanty. Work needs to be done on the requirements of the rhizosphere microflora for mineral nutrients using pure-culture techniques. Then interactions and competition between some of these organisms for nutrient supply should be studied. The effects of inoculating known rhizosphere organisms into sterile cultures of excised roots would eliminate the difficulties involved in growing whole plants under aseptic conditions. The recent development of techniques for growing gnotobiotic plants and excised roots may add greatly to our knowledge of the nutrient interrelations between rhizosphere microflora and plant growth. The use of radioactive or stable isotopes has not been exploited to follow the fate of labelled nutrients from soil to the microorganisms and thence to the roots. This might be done in association with the pure-culture techniques discussed previously. Other contributors no doubt will stress that more effective techniques are required for screening, isolating, and identifying the microflora so that physiological and biochemical studies can be made with them.

The results from this type of work will enable a better assessment to be made of the interactions of a mixed microflora in the rhizosphere on the growth of green plants.

LITERATURE CITED

AHMED, S., and H. J. EVANS. 1959. Effect of cobalt on the growth of soybeans in the absence of supplied nitrogen. Biochem. Biophys. Res. Comm. 1: 271.

AHMED, S., and H. J. EVANS. 1960. Cobalt: a micronutrient element for the growth of soybean plants under symbiotic conditions. Soil Sci. 90: 205.

ASKINAZI, D. L. 1958. The possible role of micro-organisms in increasing the effectiveness of ground rock phosphate as a fertilizer. Soviet Soil Science (Engl. transl.) 4: 372.

BROMFIELD, S. M. 1953. Sulphate reduction in partially sterilized soil exposed to air. J. Gen. Microbiol. 8: 378.

BROMFIELD, S. M. 1958. The properties of a biologically formed manganese oxide, its availability to oats and its solution by root washings. Plant Soil 9: 325.

COHEN, G. N., and J. MONOD. 1957. Bacterial permeases. Bacteriol. Rev. 21: 169.

COOPER, R. 1959. Bacterial fertilizers in the Soviet Union. Soils Fertilizers 22: 327-333.

EPSTEIN, E. 1956. Mineral nutrition of plants: mechanisms of uptake and transport. Ann. Rev. Plant Physiol. 7: 1.

FEDOROVSKII, D. V. 1958. O vydelenii mechenogo fosfora i kal'tsiya iz kornei v pochvy pri kornevom pitanii rastenii. [Excretion of labelled phosphorus and calcium from roots into soil during nutrition through the roots.] Pochvovedenie No. 3, p. 17-23.

GERRETSEN, F. C. 1948. The influence of microorganisms on the phosphate intake by the plant. Plant Soil 1:51-81.

GORING, C. A. I., and F. E. CLARK. 1949. Influence of crop growth on mineralization of nitrogen in the soil. Soil Sci. Soc. Am. Proc. (1948) 13: 261-266.

HILL-COTTINGHAM, D. G. 1957. A spectrophotometric method of analysis of chelate solutions and its application to the study of iron chelates in soils and plants. Soil Sci. 84: 43.

HILTNER, L. 1904. Über neuere Erfahrungen und Probleme auf den Gebiet der Bodenbakteriologie und unter besonderer Berücksichtigung der Gründüngung und Brache. Arb. Deut. Landwirtsch. Ges. 98: 59-78.

JENNY, H., and K. I. GROSSENBACHER. 1962. Root soil boundary zones. California Agr. 16: 7.

KLIEWER, M., and H. J. EVANS. 1962. B_{12} coenzyme content of the nodules of alder and of *Rhizobium meliloti*. Nature (London) 194: 108.

KRASIL'NIKOV, N. A. 1952. Vydelenie fermentov kornyami vysshikh rastenii. [Excretion of enzymes by roots of higher plants.] Dokl. Akad. Nauk SSSR (Fiziol. Rast.) 87: 309-312.

KRASIL'NIKOV, N. A., and V. V. KOTELEV. 1956. Vliyarie pochvennykh bakterii na Usvoenie rasteniyami soedinenii fosfora. [Influence of soil bacteria on the assimilation of phosphorus compounds by plants.] Dokl. Akad. Nauk SSSR (Mikrobiologiya) 110: 858-861.

LOUW, H. A., and D. M. WEBLEY. 1959. A study of soil bacteria dissolving certain mineral phosphate fertilizers and related compounds. J. Appl. Bacteriol. 22: 227.

MELIN, E. 1953. Physiology of mycorrhizal relations in plants. Ann. Rev. Plant Physiol. 4: 325.

MELIN, E. 1963. Some effects of forest tree roots on mycorrhizal basidiomycetes. p. 125-145. In: P. S. Nutman and B. Mosse, Symbiotic associations, Cambridge University Press, London.

NICHOLAS, D. J. D. 1961. Minor mineral nutrients. Ann. Rev. Plant Physiol. 12: 63.

NICHOLAS, D. J. D., D. J. FISHER, W. J. REDMOND, and M. OSBORNE. 1963. The cobalt requirement for nitrogen fixation, hydrogenase, nitrite and hydroxylamine reductases in *Clostridium pasteurianum*. Nature (London) 201: 793.

NICHOLAS, D. J. D., M. KOBAYASHI, and P. W. WILSON. 1962. Cobalt requirement for inorganic nitrogen metabolism in micro-organisms. Proc. Natl. Acad. Sci. U. S. 48: 1537.

NORMAN, A. G. 1959. Inhibition of root growth and cation uptake by antibiotics. Soil Sci. Soc. Am. Proc. 23: 368.

PFEFFER, W. 1895. Ueber Election organischer Nährstoffe. Jahrb. Wiss. Botan. 28: 205.

PILKOVSKAYA, R. I. 1948. Mineralization of phosphate in soil in connection with the vital activity of certain microorganisms. Microbiology U.S.S.R. (Engl. transl.) 17: 362.

RAKHTEENKO, I. N. 1958. O sezonnom tsikle, pogloshcheniya i vydeleniya mineral'nykh pitatel'nykh veshchestv kornyami drevesnykh porod. [Seasonal cycle of absorption and excretion of mineral nutrients by roots of woody species.] Fiziol. Rast. 5: 447-450.

RIVIÈRE, J. 1960. Étude de la rhizosphère du blé. Ann. Agron. 11: 397-440.

ROVIRA, A. D. 1959. Root excretions in relation to the rhizosphere effect. IV. Influence of plant species, age of plant, light, temperature and calcium nutrition on exudation. Plant Soil 11: 53-64.

ROVIRA, A. D. 1962. Plant-root exudates in relation to the rhizosphere microflora. Soils Fertilizers 25: 176.

SPERBER, J. I. 1958. Solution of apatite by soil microorganisms producing organic acids. Australian J. Agr. Res. 9: 782-787.

STARKEY, R. L. 1958. Interrelations between microorganisms and plant roots in the rhizosphere. Bacteriol. Rev. 22: 154.

SUBBA-RAO, N. S., R. G. S. BIDWELL, and D. L. BAILEY. 1961. The effect of rhizoplane fungi on the uptake and metabolism of nutrients by tomato plants. Can. J. Botany 39: 1759-1764.

SWABY, R. J. 1962. Effect of micro-organisms on nutrient availability. Intern. Soil Conference, New Zealand. Transactions, Commissions IV and V, p. 154.

TIFFIN, L. O., and J. C. BROWN. 1962. Iron chelates in soybean exudate. Science 135: 311.

TIFFIN, L. O., J. C. BROWN, and R. W. KRAUSS. 1960. Different absorption of metal chelate components by plant roots. Plant Physiol. 35: 362.

TIMONIN, M. I. 1947. Microflora of the rhizosphere in relation to the manganese deficiency disease of oats. Soil Sci. Soc. Am. Proc. (1946) 11: 284-292.

WALLACE, A. 1962. A decade of synthetic chelating agents in inorganic plant nutrition. Lithographed. Edwards Brothers Inc., Ann Arbor, Mich. 195 p.

WALLACE, A., R. T. MUELLER, O. R. LUNT, R. T. ASHCROFT, and L. M. SHANNON. 1955. Comparisons of five chelating agents in soils, in nutrient solutions and in plant responses. Soil Sci. 80: 101.

WALLACE, A., L. M. SHANNON, O. R. LUNT, and R. I. IMPEY. 1957. Some aspects of the use of metal chelates as micronutrient fertilizer sources. Soil Sci. 84: 27.

WEINSTEIN, L., E. PURVIS, A. MEISS, and R. UHLER. 1954. Absorption and translocation of ethylenediamine tetraacetic acid by sunflower plants. J. Agr. Food Chem. 2: 421-425.

► DISCUSSION OF D. J. D. NICHOLAS PAPER

A. D. Rovira:

You predict that simplified units of plants with pure and mixed cultures of microorganisms may provide an answer to their role in the nutrition of plants. I agree that these model systems of increasing complexity offer the best hope of explaining the mechanisms operating in the rhizosphere. The success or failure of these model systems will depend largely on the organisms selected and the degree of complexity achieved.

The point raised about the importance of characterizing rhizosphere microorganisms and studying their biochemistry and physiology will present some very interesting and complex problems, but here again much will depend upon the wisdom with which the types of organisms are selected.

D. J. D. Nicholas:

Since the rhizosphere is a dynamic zone involving complex interactions between a variety of microorganisms and the roots of plants, I suggest that studies with, say, two selected rhizosphere organisms be made in pure culture. Very little work has been done with mixed cultures of microorganisms. The difficulties are formidable but a beginning must be made, using controlled environments in pure cultures. This will enable one to get at the physiology and ultimately the biochemistry of some of the complex interactions between the microflora. In this connection the use of radioactive compounds to study competition for nutrients and substrates should be worthwhile. The selection of organisms can be left to the investigator, who will no doubt choose some of the dominant types of microflora in the rhizosphere under investigation. The next stage would involve the effect of root exudates, already effectively characterized by Dr. Rovira, on these mixed cultures.

B. N. Richards:

I would like to comment on inoculation experiments in general, and in particular those carried out in sterile soil to test for fixation by organisms such as *Azotobacter* and *Clostridium*. While not denying the necessity for conducting experiments in soil systems, it should be remembered that there are soils and soils. Thus the results obtained in a mature soil may be very different from those found with immature soils. For example, available nitrogen is known to inhibit nitrogen fixation by nitrogen-fixing microorganisms, and this may possibly be a contributory factor in the variability of results of inoculation experiments with agricultural soils.

A similar argument might be applied to the mobiliza-

tion of other nutrients such as phosphorus. The point I wish to emphasise is that processes involving nutrient release from primary mineral sources may still be of great significance in pedogenesis even if they are of no agronomic importance.

D. J. D. Nicholas:

Your points confirm my view of the importance of following the fate of nutrients from the soil into microflora and vice versa with labelled isotopes. In this way it will be possible to study the incorporation of labelled nutrients added to a sterile soil into soil microorganisms inoculated into that soil, or the release of labeled nutrients from microorganisms via soil and into plant roots. Numerous experiments along these lines should yield interesting and perhaps unexpected results.

M. I. Timonin:

With reference to manganese-deficiency disease in oats, it was found that soil treated with chloropicrin and cyanogas decreased the gray-speck disease of a susceptible variety of oats, and yield produced was equal to that of the standard variety. The microflora was drastically changed by this treatment. Chloropicrin and cyanogas contain nitrogen in their molecular structures and the plants grown on the fumigated plots appeared dark green. To investigate this phenomenon, plots were treated with various nitrogenous fertilizers. In this case calcium nitrate and ammonium sulphate improved the growth of the susceptible variety and improved the yield to the equivalent of that produced by the standard variety. This treatment completely eliminated gray-speck disease and also changed the microflora of the rhizosphere of the susceptible variety. Application of sodium or potassium nitrates or urea did not decrease the disease or improve the yield to the same degree. Application of boron (15 lb per acre) increased the severity of gray-speck disease and did not improve the yield. Would you comment on the effect of boron on the availability of manganese or the effect on the physiology of the host?

D. J. D. Nicholas:

I wonder whether the addition of borax shifted the pH of the soil to between 6.5 and 7.5 and resulted in the reduced availability of manganese to the plant. This is probably the simplest explanation.

A. D. Rovira:

In connection with your statement that nitrification is inhibited in the rhizosphere, I wish to draw your attention to results recently obtained with corn and alfalfa. We found, in fact, that both *Nitrosomonas* and *Nitrobacter* were stimulated in the rhizosphere of both plants during the first few weeks of growth. As the plants developed, evidence of stimulation disappeared, but there was certainly no inhibition.

Studies with root exudate showed that both inhibitory and stimulatory effects on the autotrophic nitrifiers could be obtained, according to the concentration of exudate in the medium. This raises the important question once again of the problem of using realistic concentrations of exudate in plant-free model systems.

D. J. D. Nicholas:

In my paper I refer to recent work of Russian authors who reported that nitrifying bacteria failed to thrive in the rhizosphere of grass roots because of the presence of inhibitors. I am interested to hear about your experiments in which you found that the growth of *Nitrosomonas* and *Nitrobacter* were stimulated in the rhizosphere of corn and alfalfa during the first few weeks of growth. It is well known that ammonia leaks out of young roots, and I wonder whether the effects noted might result from this phenomenon, since in extensive experiments no organic compounds have been found to stimulate these chemoautotrophic bacteria in pure cultures.

B. N. Richards:

Although much progress has been made in recent years towards an understanding of the nutrient relations of forest stands, most of this knowledge is concerned with ions released from decomposing litter to be reabsorbed and recycled by the trees. Except by inference, little is known about the point of initiation of nutrient cycles, although it is generally acknowledged that primary soil minerals constitute the ultimate source of inorganic nutrient ions. Biological mobilization of these ions is being investigated by Dr. G. K. Voigt of the Yale School of Forestry, with primary emphasis on calcium and potassium. Preliminary release patterns are being established with *Aspergillus niger,* a technique which may give an estimate of the rhizospheric contribution and which provides a rapid means of biological mobilization. The final estimate of nutrient release and uptake is being obtained from chemical analysis of tissues of tree seedlings grown in cultures where potassium is supplied by primary minerals. It has been established that potassium release is related to lattice configuration, particle size, and seasonal variation in seedling metabolism. This latter aspect is possibly related to rhizosphere activity. The total uptake of potassium by seedlings indicates that mobilization of ions from primary nutrient sources can be a significant factor in tree nutrition.

D. J. D. Nicholas:

I am interested to learn of Dr. Voigt's experiments on the release of potassium and calcium from primary minerals by *Aspergillus niger* and the subsequent effect on the growth of tree seedlings. It is well known that *A. niger* produces a mixture of organic acids, including citric and gluconic acids, which effectively degrade and release nutrients from mineral sources.

►

Mycorrhiza

J. L. HARLEY—*Department of Agriculture, University of Oxford, England.*

►

Mycorrhizal associations differ from rhizosphere and root-surface associations of fungi and higher plants in the greater specificity and specialization of their component organisms and in their integrated construction, morphology, and histology. They also contrast with parasitic infections—even from those in which galls and tumours of characteristic structure are formed—by the prolonged period of healthy physiological interaction between fungus and host. In the host there is usually no destructive breakdown of the tissues caused by the fungus even in the infected organs, but there may or may not be a localized control of the fungus by a digestion of hyphae in the host cells. In many cases, too, certain phases of physiological activity of both partners are positively affected by their symbiotic habit so that growth and perhaps reproduction may be more efficient in the associated state. Moreover, a very large number of species of higher plants which form mycorrhizas in their natural ecological habitats are rarely, perhaps never, found in the free condition. The same appears also to be true of some of the mycorrhizal fungi.

Mycorrhizal associations defined loosely in this way are not all of one kind. They are diverse in both structure and physiological function. This arises not only from the wide range of host and fungal species forming associations, but also from their construction. It is therefore rather misleading to attempt very comprehensive generalizations about mycorrhizal phenomena. Nevertheless, mycorrhizal fungi fall into the ecological category of root-inhabiting fungi, as Garrett (1956) has pointed out. They may indeed be regarded as end-terms in the specialization of root inhabitants, that is, of an ecological group that includes many important soil-borne pathogens. Hence their properties in respect of behaviour in the soil, infection of hosts, effect on hosts, and special physiological requirements are relevant to the wider study of soil-borne pathogens.

In this paper a few very different types of mycorrhiza and a few aspects of their study will be described to compare and contrast them with pathogenic infections. A further discussion of mycorrhizal phenomena may be obtained in specialist works (e.g. Harley, 1959), where extensive references are cited.

KINDS OF MYCORRHIZA TO BE CONSIDERED.—The mycorrhiza of forest trees are structurally very different from uninfected roots, as may be seen from Fig. 1. Externally, enclosing the host tissues, is a layer of fungal pseudoparenchyma which may be as much as 40 μ thick and may amount to nearly 40% of the total dry weight of the whole organ. Within the external cortical tissues, intercellular penetration is abundant but relatively rare intracellularly. The outermost few layers of cortical cells are often modified in shape by being elongated in a transverse direction. The meristematic region is reduced in magnitude and mature tissues of stele and cortex are differentiated close behind it (Clowes, 1951). Distal to the meristem, root-cap initials are visible, but mature root-cap tissue is reduced in extent. The infected axes are densely branched so that many fairly compact branched systems, completely clothed by fungus, are borne along the length of main mother-roots. The mother-roots are usually also infected except at their apices. In some hosts a sheath of fungal pseudoparenchyma encloses them as in *Fagus,* but in others the mother-roots are penetrated intercellularly by hyphae but do not have an external fungal sheath, e.g. *Pinus* (Robertson, 1954). Ectotrophic mycorrhizas, like many absorbing organs, are relatively short-lived: their period of activity varies from a few months to about one year.

Mycorrhizas possessing these general characters, but perhaps differing quantitatively, are called ectotrophic and are common in forest trees of temperate regions. They are present in most, if not all, Amentiferae (Fagales), in some angiospermic trees of other families, and in the Pinaceae amongst the conifers. Anatomical and physiological researches have shown that they comprise a kind of mycorrhiza about which generalizations are possible. The fungi concerned have been shown to be most usually Basidiomycetes, especially Agaricaceae and Boletaceae and some Gasteromycetes. A few imperfect fungi, probably of basidiomycetous affinity, and a few Ascomycetes, have also been implicated.

In sharp contrast with the ectotrophic mycorrhizas are those of the Orchidaceae (Fig. 2). In this family the roots, or other absorbing organs which replace the roots, are colonized by hyphae which in most cases form coils within the cells. Each absorbing organ as it develops becomes infected direct from the soil so that new roots are at first fungus-free and later colonized. The tubers or underground storage organs of geophytic orchids are not usually infected.

In the colonized organs the hyphae thrive in the cells for a time and are later disintegrated or digested by host activity. Hence, in the cortex of the infected

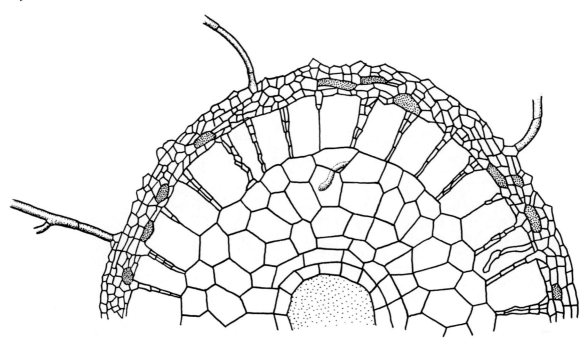

Fig. 1. Transection of ectotrophic mycorrhizal rootlet showing fungal sheath and intercellular penetration.

organs, "host cells" and "digestion cells" are visible. Repeated sequences of infection and digestion may occur within a cell but the details vary so that in some orchid species cells showing colonization and digestion patterns are intermingled, in others there are separate layers of host cells and digestion cells. In certain orchids also, there is a differentiation of roots into long and short roots, analogous to those of forest trees. In the short roots, fungal colonization and digestion are particularly evident. In addition there is a variation in the details of the digestion process (Burgeff, 1932, 1936).

The fungi associated with orchids in mycorrhiza formation are either imperfect fungi of basidiomycetous affinity grouped in the genus *Rhizoctonia* or clamp-bearing or perfect Basidiomycetes. The Orchidaceae, in contrast to the tree hosts of ectotrophic mycorrhiza, are all partial or complete saprophytes for some part of their lives. The structure of their infected organs is not only different from those of the trees but as will be seen, their fungi have wider powers of digestion of carbon compounds than those of the trees. Nevertheless, it will also be seen that variants of ectotrophic mycorrhiza in which considerable intracellular penetration occurs, called ectendotrophic mycorrhiza, may be caused by fungi having some of the properties of those causing orchid mycorrhiza.

The third example of mycorrhiza which will be considered is much more widespread than the last two. It is the endotrophic mycorrhiza caused by phycomycete mycelia and has been called vesicular-arbuscular because of the kinds of organ produced by the endophytic mycelia (Fig. 3). This kind is found in angiosperms of almost all families, in all conifers except the Pinaceae, and in some pteridophytes and bryophytes. It has also been reported in fossils from the Devonian and in later epochs. In the roots of infected plants, as in Orchidaceae, the fungal hyphae penetrate into the cortex. Here they form long branches which usually run between the cells and bear short haustoria which penetrate into the cells. The haustoria are many times dichotomously branched and hence called arbuscules. Digestion of the hyphae within the cells eventually occurs and the exploitation of the tissues seems to be controlled by this means. Large swollen vesicles are also eventually formed outside and inside the host tissues, sometimes even within the cells. Externally to the root a loose weft of mycelium occurs. This may be differentiated into long and short branches and may bear vesicles, spores, or fruit bodies. The hyphae are aseptate except where vesicles or fine lateral branches are cut off. The fungi are clearly of phycomycete affinity. Two types of fungi have been described as causative. Firstly *Endogone* spp. and the somewhat similar aseptate mycelia called *Rhizophagus*, secondly species of *Pythium*. There is, however, a growing body of opinion that the former group of species, which have very specialized cultural characteristics, are the more important and widespread.

In each of these examples of mycorrhiza there is a degree of variability that is important in the present context. Strong evidence has been obtained that certain of the forms of mycorrhizal infection of orchids and forest trees are essential to healthy development in some ecological conditions. Similarly the vesicular-arbuscular infection is at least not harmful to its hosts. In each case, however, there are variants of mycorrhizal structure associated with lack of health in the host. Mycorrhizal infections therefore merge into parasitism. For instance, forest-tree roots are found in which the cells may be extensively penetrated by hyphae, in which

Fig. 2. Transection of orchid mycorrhiza showing fungal penetration and intracellular digestion.

the fungal mantle is deficient or excessively developed, and in which signs of destruction of the host tissue exist. Such rootlets are often unbranched, simple, and have been given the name of "pseudomycorrhiza." They may be produced by special fungi which have some of the properties of mycorrhizal fungi but are incapable of setting up a prolonged healthy steady-state condition. Or they may be the products of special environmental conditions acting upon fungus and host which could elsewhere produce integrated healthy mycorrhizal structures. Many hosts may indeed set up a range of associations from destructive parasitism to loose uncoordinated associated growth with various fungi under various conditions. The remarkable fact is, however, that in their natural ecological ambits, hosts and fungi produce efficient long-lived dual mycorrhizal structures to a dominant degree. Perhaps, since natural selection operates, this is to be expected.

It is the purpose of this paper to consider some of the physiological properties of the kinds of mycorrhizal infection mentioned, to determine their relevance to the activities of the host plant, and to see whether matters arising from their study are relevant to the study of soil-borne pathogens.

ECTOTROPHIC MYCORRHIZA.—*The sequence of infection.*—Seeds of forest trees germinate readily, giving rise to uninfected seedlings. If these grow in their natural soils they remain uninfected until some weeks after germination, when mycorrhizal roots are formed. Infection follows upon the unfolding of the first leaves and upon the onset of photosynthesis (Huberman, 1940; Warren Wilson, 1951). Thereafter infection spreads in the root system so that a large proportion

of sublateral roots become infected in typical fashion. The origin of infection may be from other mycorrhizal roots or from spores present in the soil, for Robertson (1954) has shown that the latter may germinate and produce considerable mycelia in the rooting region. A few species of mycorrhizal fungi of ectotrophic mycorrhiza have been reported to be present as rhizomorphs in soil, e.g. *Boletus bovinus* (Rayner and Levisohn, 1941); but in most cases active mycorrhizas, spores, or resting structures must be the source of infection. As has been mentioned, infection sooner or later spreads to the long mother-roots and thereafter short branches originating from them are infected before they break through the cortex (Clowes, 1951; Robertson, 1954).

The factors affecting the initial susceptibility of the seedlings to infection were first investigated by Hatch (1937) and Björkman (1941, 1942, 1949), and their results have been confirmed in general outline. Hatch showed that the supply of mineral nutrients was particularly important. Seedlings of *Pinus strobus* in his experiments most readily became infected when nitrogen, phosphorus, and perhaps potassium were in moderately deficient supply. Seedlings receiving a high level of mineral nutrition failed to form mycorrhizas or formed them less abundantly. This kind of result has often been obtained with other species of host, and it is commonly observed in forest nurseries that highly fertilized beds produce seedlings with low mycorrhizal infection. Björkman's results, besides being generally in agreement with these, showed that light supply in addition affected mycorrhizal development. In low light intensities seedlings of conifers were relatively unsusceptible to mycorrhizal fungi, whereas in high intensities abundant infection occurred. This kind of result has also

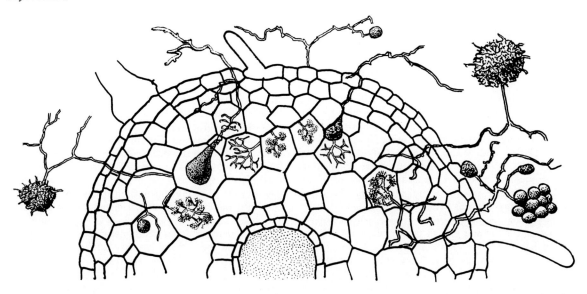

Fig. 3. Transection of vesicular-arbuscular mycorrhizas showing penetrating hyphae, arbuscular haustoria, digestion, and vesicles. Fruit bodies and spores are shown externally on the extramatrical mycelium.

been obtained with pine (Wenger, 1955) and with beech (Harley and Waid, 1955).

It is clear from the results that external conditions, including both nutrient supply and light intensity (hence photosynthesis), so affect the internal status of the roots as to affect their susceptibility. Björkman is of the opinion that the most important internal factor so affected is carbohydrate content. He has shown that a significant quantity of readily soluble reducing substances, assumed to be carbohydrate, is a necessary prerequisite to infection. He regards the carbohydrate status of the root as the primary factor in infection. Others have obtained experimental results of a similar kind, indeed even when methods more specific to carbohydrate were used for analysis. But it does not seem possible that this can be all. Carbohydrates of the common kinds are unspecific in their action on fungi. Even if they were secreted into the soil from the roots, it seems unlikely that carbohydrates would preferentially stimulate mycorrhizal fungi unless they were of a specific nature. For instance, even the stimulant of *Striga* germination, once thought to be D-xyloketose, is now believed to be much more complex (see Tarr, 1962, for references). It may be, on the other hand, that a high carbohydrate status in the root system is a feature correlated with the release or excretion of a substance from the root surface which has a specific stimulatory effect on mycorrhizal fungi; but that has yet to be demonstrated. So far, work on root secretions has yielded interesting but incomplete results. Melin (1954) and Melin and Das (1954) have shown that many of the fungi of ectotrophic mycorrhiza are greatly stimulated in culture by secretions of roots, and some of these, e.g. *Russula xerampelina,* cannot grow without them. There is yet, however, no evidence that the active principles in these root exudates are either specific to mycorrhizal fungi or specifically produced by mycor-

rhizal hosts. So far the evidence is generally to the contrary.

There are in addition complicating features about susceptibility, foreshadowed especially in the work of Warren Wilson (1951). This observer showed that in *Fagus sylvatica* seedlings the short sublateral rootlets of the kind that became mycorrhizic differentiated in a characteristic fashion before infection occurred. Meristematic activity diminished and differentiation of cortical and stelar tissue proceeded to a point close behind the reduced meristem. The root-cap tissue also decreased in extent and the rootlet became apically rounded rather than pointed. It appeared from Warren Wilson's observations that after this sequence of change had occurred infection by mycorrhizal fungi proceeded. Those rootlets which failed to become infected aborted, those which were infected continued to grow and branch into typical mycorrhizal systems. This sequence of change in beech rootlets had been often incompletely described for those of other trees, e.g. *Pinus,* but it had not been explicitly emphasised as a process which precedes infection. Whether or not the process is associated with light intensity, internal carbohydrate supply, or mineral nutrition is not yet known. It is interesting, however, to speculate whether it has anything in common with the ageing of rootlets noted in tissue culture (e.g. Street and Roberts, 1952; Hannay and Butcher, 1961). In the case of groundsel roots investigated by the latter, ageing may occur in both attached and excised roots and the process may be modified both by carbohydrate supply and by growth factors.

The prevention of the abortion of short roots by fungal infection was described by Hatch (1937) in *Pinus.* He showed that, in the final analysis, the effect of infection was an increase of the effective root surface for the absorption of nutrients. The constituent effects were an increase of life of the individual roots, an increase in the degree of branching of them, and an increase of their diameters. The results of McComb (1938) with *Pinus virginiana* illustrate the first of these effects. In them the number of short roots on infected plants was about double that on uninfected plants.

An additional complication is that light intensity is not uniformly important in infection by all ectotrophic mycorrhizal fungi. *Cenococcum graniforme,* for instance, may produce mycorrhizas with appropriate hosts in a lower light intensity than other fungi (Mikola, 1948; Harley and Waid, 1955). Different kinds of mycorrhizas developed at different light intensities; Rhizoctonia-like mycelia colonized the roots of *Fagus* at the lowest light intensities and formed mildly pathogenic pseudomycorrhizas (Harley and Waid, 1955).

The explanation of the effects of mycorrhizal fungi in prolonging the life and growth of host short roots is not yet available. Slankis (1948, 1951) and Ulrich (1960, 1962) have shown, however, that culture filtrates of mycorrhizal fungi, as well as indolyl compounds which may be produced by them, have morphogenic effects on the development of excised pine roots. It is therefore possible that further work with these, as well as possibly with antiageing factors such as 1-naphthoxyacetic acid used by Hannay and Butcher (1961), may lead to a clearer explanation. However, the multiplicity of factors and conditions which have been reported to affect morphogenesis in excised root of trees or in young seedlings (see, for instance, Barnes and Naylor, 1959; Levisohn, 1960), show that the problem is extremely complex.

The effect of infection on the host.—Two effects of infection upon the host are readily observed. The first is that a layer of fungal pseudoparenchyma is interposed between the root surface and the soil. The second is that the total surface offered to the soil by the absorbing organ is increased. Hatch (1937) suggested that the physical increase of absorbing surface might well explain the more rapid growth of mycorrhizal tree seedlings observed in experiments upon deficient soils.

The increased growth might well be a resultant of increased mineral absorption by virtue of the increased root surface area. It is implicit in this suggestion that the uptake of nutrients per unit area of fungal pseudoparenchyma is about the same as or greater than that of the host's own absorbing tissues. There is also the further assumption that the fungal layer must have powers of selective absorption of nutrients and of passage of these to the host.

Melin and his colleagues have shown that in experimental systems the hyphae connecting mycorrhizas of pine with the soil have powers of absorption and translocation to the host (Melin and Nilsson, 1950, 1952, 1955, 1957). This has also been demonstrated by Stone (1950) for pine growing in soil. Excised mycorrhizal roots absorb phosphate more rapidly per unit area than uninfected roots (Kramer and Wilbur, 1949; Harley and McCready, 1950). Wilson (1957) showed this to be true also of alkali metals and that the sheath selects potassium against sodium and rubidium from mixed solutions (Harley and Wilson, 1959).

The hyphal sheath does not, however, operate as a separate organism. The unity of function of the whole mycorrhizal organ has been amply shown by experimental work. The movement of carbohydrates from the host into the fungus has been demonstrated by Melin and Nilsson (1958), who supplied $C^{14}O_2$ to photosynthesising pine seedlings, and more recently by Lewis (1963), who fed C^{14}-sucrose through the host tissue of beech mycorrhizas. In the latter case it was shown by chromatographic means that fungal storage substances, especially trehalose and mannitol, became labelled (Table 1). On the other hand, when carbohydrate was absorbed through the fungal sheath it also moved into the host tissue (Fig. 4).

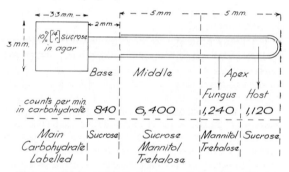

Fig. 4. Feeding C^{14} sucrose to excised ectotrophic mycorrhizas. Above, method. Centre, counts per minute in carbohydrates of various regions after 20 hours. Below, the carbohydrates which are highly labelled after 20 hours.

The study of phosphate absorption by ectotrophic mycorrhiza has also yielded much of interest to the study of the interaction between host and mycorrhizal fungi. In a series of papers (see Harley, 1959) we have demonstrated that phosphate absorption is affected by external factors similar to those which affect absorption by roots. The primary destination of phosphate is into the fungal sheath, where the greater part may be accumulated during periods of rapid absorption whilst a small part only passes to the host. The phosphate accumulated in the fungal layer is however utilized

TABLE 1. Percentage distribution of C^{14}, absorbed as sucrose from an external solution, in the carbohydrate of mycorrhizal and uninfected *Fagus* roots*

Type of root	Insoluble carbohydrate	Soluble carbohydrate				
		Trehalose	Sucrose	Glucose	Mannitol	Fructose
Mycorrhizal	54.0	17.2	2.6	0.9	24.4	0.9
Uninfected	22.5	0	47.5	19.0	0	11.0

* From D. H. Lewis, unpublished data.

when external phosphate is withheld, or presented at very low concentration (Fig. 5). The mobilization of accumulated phosphate depends upon temperature and oxygen supply and hence upon metabolic turnover in

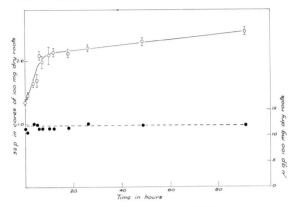

Fig. 5. An experiment in which $KH_2P^{32}O_4$ was fed to mycorrhizas for 1 hour, after which they were kept in phosphate-free buffer. Upper curve shows the movement of phosphate to the host. The lower curve indicates that no loss of phosphate into the external solution occurs.

the mycorrhizal organ. Estimates of the sequence of change in percentage radioactivity in phosphate fractions in the host tissue have indicated that inorganic phosphate passes from fungus to host tissue and is there incorporated into organic compounds.

These results, mainly obtained with excised mycorrhizas, have been upheld by Morrison (1962) and Clode (1956), who have compared the rates of transport of phosphate in pine seedlings when infected and uninfected. Primary phosphate accumulation occurred in the sheath of mycorrhizal roots during absorption. When labelled phosphate had been absorbed and was subsequently withheld, a movement of P^{32} to the shoots and leaves of mycorrhizal seedlings continued for many days. No such continual translocation was observed in uninfected seedlings.

The picture that emerges, therefore, is that infection preserves the life of short roots that might otherwise abort and stimulates them to growth and branching. The explanation of this effect must lie in the field of research on growth substances in which components of fungal origin are probably important either as auxins or perhaps inhibitors of ageing factors produced by the roots themselves. The composite organs are nourished by photosynthesis in the host and have considerable powers of accumulation of ions from the soil, but only the study of phosphate absorption has proceeded far enough for detailed comment. Here the fungal sheath intervenes as an active accumulator of ions that may later become available to both components.

The interchange of materials between fungus and host takes place here without destruction of the cells of either organism; this may also be true of some pathogenic infections, as has been directly demonstrated by Robinson and Lucas (1963 and unpublished). These workers showed that *Helminthosporium sativum* absorbed phosphate from the substrate rapidly and was

capable of translocating it through its mature hyphae to its growing points. Using P^{32} as a label, they showed that when growing upon wheat, this fungus released P^{32}-containing substances into the host which were transported throughout its tissues. *Ophiobolus graminis* by contrast had poor translocating ability and did not release phosphatic substances into the wheat. These points will be recalled later in connection with other forms of mycorrhiza.

The fungi of ectotrophic mycorrhiza.—The fungi of ectotrophic mycorrhiza have been extensively investigated, especially by Melin and his colleagues. The results have allowed certain generalizations about their physiology to be made which have become less firm with increasing knowledge. The majority of these fungi require simple carbohydrates for growth in culture and may so be contrasted with basidiomycetes which directly decompose leaf litter and are capable of utilizing cellulose, lignin, and other complex organic substrates. Nevertheless some proved mycorrhiza formers (see Norkrans, 1949, 1950; Lindeberg, 1948), such as *Boletus subtomentosus*, *Lactarius deliciosus*, *Tricholoma vaccinum* and *T. fumosum*, may attack litter or utilize cellulose or perhaps cellulose and lignin.

Other general characters of mycorrhiza formers include a dependence upon thiamine and often other vitamins. Many, in addition, require or are stimulated in growth by amino acids or organic acids. Many require compounds extractible from roots for growth in culture. As a group they are intolerant of extracts of humus or litter which may contain phenols and of competition in culture from soil saprophytes.

There is nothing in this nutritive selectivity of the mycorrhizal fungi which explains their habit, even though it is attractive to connect demands for simple sugars with the onset of infection when free sugars are present in the root tissues. Not one single item in their requirements, nor the totality of them, is solely theirs. All that is indicated is that they require, in all probability, specialized habitats in the soil, such as root surfaces. Romell (1938) has provided some evidence that many do not fruit unless in association with their hosts; but others, such as *Boletus subtomentosus*, which has been shown to utilize complex carbon sources for growth in culture, seem to break this rule.

There is therefore a range of forms associated with ectotrophic mycorrhiza which varies on the one hand from those highly selective in nutrition to those which may well be able to find a soil habitat away from host trees. Their specificity to host species also varies from *Boletus variegatus*, specific to *Larix*, to *Cenococcum graniforme*, which is mycorrhizal with very many species.

Exploitation of the host.—A limited penetration of host tissues is characteristic of most of the fungi of ectotrophic mycorrhiza. It has been ascribed to a lack of the necessary enzymes for attacking cellulose or other complex compounds in the cell walls. The penetration of the middle lamella by a network of hyphae has, however, been ascribed to their production of pectic enzymes. Again the absence of root-cap tissue in mycorrhizas, although formed in some degree by meristematic activity, has been suggested by Clowes (1954) as possibly due to fungal activity. It has sometimes been suggested that the fungi develop enzyme activities in contact with their hosts which they cannot develop in pure culture. All this implies that ectotrophic mycorrhizas are formed by stimulation of the fungi by the host. The lack of an extensive exploitation of the tissues would, therefore, depend more on the absence of stimulation in the deeper tissues or upon the absence of suitable conditions for growth there, rather than upon a positive host resistance to exploitation. It is of interest in this regard that variations from the usual pattern of exploitation of the tissues are encountered. Ectendotrophic infections, in which there is considerable intracellular as well as intercellular penetration by fungal hyphae, have been described in many hosts in certain localities. These have been ascribed to the presence of mycorrhizal fungi which actively secrete cellulose-splitting enzymes (Norkrans, 1950). Again infections are encountered in which the fungi (e.g. *Rhizoctonia sylvestris* or *Mycelium (radicis) atrovirens*) give rise to structures which depart from the normal in deficient or excessive development of fungal sheath or cortical penetration. Where these have been studied, they have been shown to be parasitic and detrimental to host activities. The fungi concerned may utilize a wider range of carbon substrates than is usual (Schelling, 1950).

We may therefore conclude that there is a fairly wide range of structures grouped under the name of ectotrophic mycorrhizas. Even upon a single host many variants may be found depending upon the conditions or upon the fungal species present. A common central group of these structures are organs of integrated construction which when studied by physiological methods have been found to be efficient absorbing organs with peculiar properties. The extremes of the range depart substantially from the central group in structure and in the degree in which they appear to be integrated functional organs. In many the fungus appears to be parasitic on the host.

To some extent the extreme examples of mycorrhizal fungi of trees which utilize a wide spectrum of carbon sources and produce a greater exploitation of the host, have something in common with the fungi of orchids, and it may be that in time a continuous series may be visualized.

THE FUNGI OF ORCHIDACEAE.—The Orchidaceae all have a saprophytic phase in their life cycle which may be of a few months or a few years' duration or may extend over the whole life of some species. All start as seeds weighing only a few tenths to several micrograms. They contain a relatively undifferentiated embryo and a minimum of food reserves. Hence all but the earliest few cell divisions depend upon absorption of carbon compounds. It is usual in natural conditions for the embryos to become infected in the very early protocorm stage, and it has been shown that in the absence of infection, germination and growth can only

be brought about successfully by supplying sugars and vitamins, e.g. nicotinic acid, as well as mineral nutrients. The evidence strongly suggests that the fungi mediate in carbon absorption, and it is not therefore surprising that the isolated fungi have been found to utilize a range of carbon sources in culture. Most of those investigated can make good growth upon cellulose and lignin also.

The mechanism by which carbon absorption by the host is increased is not unequivocally clear. It seems, however, exceedingly probable that compounds are normally first absorbed by the fungal hyphae and released into the host tissue. Burgeff (1936) has described experiments where mycorrhizal fungi growing upon vegetable fibre released no excess of soluble carbon compounds into the medium under conditions where germination and growth of orchid seedlings would have occurred in the infected state only. Again for many epiphytic orchids the nature of the host plant is important. Epiphytes may be specifically dependent on a certain range of species of supporting plant. This has been explained by Ruinen (1953), who demonstrated direct hyphal connections between endophytic hyphae within the orchid tissues and living hyphae in those of the living or dead supporting plant.

As has already been mentioned, the fungal hyphae undergo digestion or disintegration within the host cells, and this has been accepted as the mechanism of transference of nutrients from fungus to host. Indeed, a considerable release of fungal substance into the digestion cells must occur during the process. It must, however, be borne in mind that there is good evidence in ectotrophic mycorrhiza for an exchange of substances without digestion or even cellular penetration and Robinson and Lucas (1963 and unpublished) have shown that *Corticium solani,* when a pathogen, releases phosphate into its host. Nevertheless, by the digestive process the host appears to control the exploitation of its tissues by the fungus, and the existence of such a process rather sharply defines this orchidaceous mycorrhiza from the ectotrophic kind. Here fungi actively capable of destruction of complex carbon compounds are controlled by the host activity. To underline this, two points are worth noting. During germination in the presence of mycorrhizal fungi, orchid seeds often become completely parasitized in the early stages of seedling growth, for in some circumstances or with particularly virulent fungal strains, control by digestion fails.

The second point relates to the fact that fungi with a considerable parasitic potential on some hosts may form mycorrhizas with species of orchid. Recently Downie (1957) has shown that strains of *Rhizoctonia (Corticium) solani* isolated from wheat, cauliflower, tomato, and other plants, where they are pathogenic, all intervened in seedling development of *Orchis purpurella,* stimulated germination and growth, and infected the young plant as a normal mycorrhizal endophyte. Again it is firmly established that *Armillaria mellea,* widely known as a saprophyte and destructive parasite of woody and herbaceous hosts, forms mycorrhizal associations with many saprophytic orchids in the tropics belonging to the genera *Gastrodia* and *Galeola* (see Burgeff, 1936).

The orchid fungi, all of which appear to be, like most fungi of ectotrophic mycorrhiza, of basidiomycetous affinity, seem to be widely dispersed, to exist as saprophytes, and to have a relatively low specificity to particular orchids. They all possess a well-developed ability for using complex carbon so that at one extreme destructive organisms like *Armillaria* are included, whereas at the other extreme some may resemble the pseudomycorrhizal fungi of forest trees. Kusano in 1911 showed that a single mycelium of *Armillaria* may be concurrently parasitic on one host such as a coniferous tree, and also form a mycorrhizal association with *Gastrodia*. This is a special case, perhaps, of the kind of association described by Ruinen between epiphytes, fungi, and living or dead supporting plants which was mentioned above. It is also comparable with the relation described by Björkman (1960) who showed that C¹⁴-glucose could be injected into a spruce bearing ectotrophic mycorrhiza and radioactivity traced not only into the fungal hyphae but also into the saprophytic *Monotropa hypopithys*, which shared a common mycorrhizal fungus with the spruce.

Control of fungal invasion in Orchidaceae.—The various kinds of digestive process by which orchid hosts appear to control fungal exploitation have been described in fair detail by Burgeff (1932, 1936). In addition he has figured in some species a process of encapsulation of hyphae as they pass from cell to cell in the tissues. The structures enclosing hyphal tips resemble similar structures described in *Monotropa* and also the lignitubers found in parasitic infections such as those of *Ophiobolus graminis*.

A further resistance mechanism restricting fungal exploitation, a chemical one, has been described recently by Gäumann and his colleagues. As long ago as 1911, Bernard first reported a chemical resistance mechanism in orchids. Nobécourt (1923) believed that the resistance of orchid tubers to fungal exploitation depended upon an active production of a substance which destroyed the hyphae. Magrou (1924), on the other hand, described the antifungal substance in orchid tubers as being formed irrespective of any attack by fungi. This was also the view reached by Burges (1939) as the result of microdissection experiments. Gäumann, Braun, and Bazzigher (1950) have, however, reported that the antifungal activity of orchid-tuber tissues was greatly increased when they were acted upon by mycorrhizal fungi. The experiments showed that although fragments of tuber killed by temperatures below —10°C exhibited little antifungal activity against *Rhizoctonia repens*, living fragments developed an intense activity against the mycorrhizal fungus. Gäumann therefore concluded that the defense reaction resulting in the production of an antifungal substance was an active one. In later papers (Gäumann and Kern, 1959*a,b*) it has been described how the antifungal substances have been isolated and examined. Amongst them were p-hydroxybenzaldehyde and a phenolic substance of molecular weight 256, which they called orchinol.

The latter was most strongly antifungal and was found in large quantities in tuber tissues subjected to fungi (e.g. 3 g per kilo in tubers of *Orchis militaris*). Further study of the terrestrial orchids showed that many but not all those tested formed orchinol in their tubers and that those which did not do so produced other substances of similar activity. Although many of the organs and tissues of orchids had slight capacity for producing orchinol in the presence of fungal attack, the tubers were by far the most active in this regard. Gäumann and his colleagues have sought to explain some of the problems of localization of soil-borne infections within the roots of the orchids by the low degree of orchinol production in them as compared with the tubers.

The spectrum of activity of orchinol against soil fungi in general was found not to be specific—numerous of them were inhibited but some were not. Again, although sundry mycorrhizal fungi induced its formation, so also could some saprophytes, potential parasites, and specialized parasites, e.g. *Ophiobolus graminis*.

The interest of these results lies, therefore, not so much in the specificity of orchinol to orchid fungi as in the unspecific chemical resistance to fungal attack of orchid tubers that had been incipiently infected by mycorrhizal fungi. In subsequent papers, Gäumann and Hohl (1960) and Gäumann, Nuesch, and Rimpau (1960) have amplified and expanded these ideas, and further work will no doubt show whether the interpretations put on the results will hold. Gäumann holds the view that the production of orchinol and other substances of similar activity resemble antigen-antibody reactions. Quantitatively, however, the magnitude of production of orchinol seems extremely large and the mechanism of biosynthesis will be of great interest. Also of interest is the fact that a strain of *Rhizoctonia solani* shown by Downie to be capable of mycorrhiza formation could not induce orchinol formation in the orchid tubers tested, although it was orchinol-sensitive.

In orchidaceous mycorrhiza and in the mycorrhizal systems of some other saprophytes, the fungi are potentially aggressive parasites which initially exploit the host tissues and are controlled by various means. The fungi have a considerable saprophytic ability and use a wide range of carbon substrates, some of the products of which are utilized by the hosts. In all these respects they contrast with the majority of the fungi of the ectotrophic mycorrhizal associations.

Vesicular-arbuscular Mycorrhiza.—The mycorrhizas caused by aseptate hyphae form a contrast with those of Orchidaceae and forest trees on many grounds. They are extremely common and widespread in the plant kingdom; indeed they have been described as being almost universally present in seed plants where other kinds of mycorrhiza are absent. This very fact has led to a good deal of skepticism about them and about their possible physiological significance. It was not until very recently that a sure corpus of data was collected about the fungi. Up till 1949 attempts to isolate the fungi met with very limited success. Amongst the mycelia repeatedly obtained were septate fast-growing imperfect mycelia reminiscent of the fungi of orchids and of some of the pseudomycorrhizas of trees. These failed, if back-inoculated, to produce histological patterns present in mycorrhizal roots, and they appeared to be somewhat parasitic. A second group of fungi with aseptate hyphae could be made to grow out onto media but could not be grown in culture in the absence of host tissue. Magrou (1936) and Stahl (1949) were able to encourage such aseptate hyphae to grow across a gap between a mycorrhizal and a non-mycorrhizal plant or root and so cross-inoculation was obtained. In 1947 Barrett isolated and grew in pure culture several strains of an aseptate mycelium to which he gave the old name *Rhizophagus,* and in 1958 he was able to prove by direct inoculation that they were capable of mycorrhiza formation with several species of host. This has recently been confirmed by Mosse. Mosse (1953, 1956) also confirmed the earlier reports that *Endogone* fruit bodies were borne on the same mycelium as formed mycorrhiza with strawberry and other plants. She used sporocarp and spores in inoculation experiments confirming *Endogone* as a mycorrhiza former with many species. Since her work was published, Nicolson (1959, 1960), Dowding (1959), Gerdeman (1955, 1961), and others have all observed or shown by experimental inoculation the association of *Endogone* or similar organisms with the vesicular-arbuscular mycorrhiza of many different plants.

It has become clear that there is a group of generally similar organisms, differing in detail, associated with this kind of mycorrhiza. Mycelia producing *Endogone* fructifications differ in minor detail from those described by Gerdemann as producing large spores in the soil and differ again from Barrett's isolates of *Rhizophagus.* Dowding (1959) has emphasized the widespread occurrence of this group of fungi in organic soils especially but has indicated that there is no evidence that they exist other than in mycorrhizal union. This, of course, falls well in line with the inability of most of them to grow in pure culture (Mosse, 1959). The establishment of mycorrhizal infection from resting spores has proved to be a complicated matter. Penetration of the tissues of a variety of hosts by germ tubes of spores did not readily take place (Mosse, 1962). If the roots were acted upon by mild preparations of pectolytic and cellulolytic enzymes or by a species of *Pseudomonas,* infective penetration was made more probable in a number of hosts. Infection of hosts by mycelium growing out from established mycorrhizas occurred with great readiness in the absence of enzyme treatment or bacteria. This might be taken to indicate that the fungal mycelium was so nourished by its host that it developed the ability to produce enzymes, by which means it penetrated the cells of a new host. This is indeed interesting in view of the observation (Mosse, 1959) that the extramatrical mycelium appears to penetrate soil particles and bring about breakdown of organic matter. Again mycelia of similar nature to these have been reported as the endophytes in saprophytic *Psilotum* prothalli and species of Burmanniaceae.

A further genus of fungi, *Pythium,* has been fre-

quently canvassed as potential mycorrhiza formers. Hawker et al. (1957) and Hepden (1960) have repeatedly isolated a species of this genus, near to *P. ultimum,* from onion roots and occasionally from those of other plants. In inoculation experiments their isolates have been described as forming typical vesicular-arbuscular mycorrhizal infections with certain hosts in a limited range of environmental conditions. The mycelium clearly has a significant parasitic potential, and when tested alongside strains of *Endogone* and *Rhizophagus* by Mosse (1961) gave rise to infections in which considerable exploitation of cortical and even vascular tissue was observed. The most successful inoculation experiments with *Pythium* have been performed with onion as the host, but an approach to the typical histological patterns of infection is obtained only under a limited range of conditions. As Hawker et al. (1957) have suggested, it is no more unlikely that a pathogen like *Pythium* should form mycorrhizal associations than that *Armillaria* or *Rhizoctonia solani* should. Be that as it may, the demonstrated effectiveness of *Endogone* and *Rhizophagus* as a group of mycorrhiza formers and the elaboration of methods for obtaining pure two-membered cultures of host and fungus by Mosse, have opened up the possibility of investigating the physiology of these associations, whereas with *Pythium* we are not yet even sure how prolonged a steady state of interaction can be set up.

Little has yet been ascertained about the effects of vesicular-arbuscular infection on the host plant. A review of the literature shows that it is usually reported that infection is most intense upon poor soils. Infection experiments carried out by Mosse (1957) on apple cuttings have indicated that infected plants grow significantly faster in height and weight and that they look healthier than uninfected plants. Baylis (1959) obtained similar results with *Griselinia littoralis,* a shrub belonging to the Cornaceae. The plants made much better growth on poor soil when infected than when uninfected. Uninfected plants became chlorotic and unhealthy.

Both Mosse and Baylis had analyses made of the plant material produced in their experiments. In Mosse's experiment the absorption of the metals copper, iron, and calcium was increased by infection; in that of Baylis, phosphorus uptake was particularly stimulated.

CONCLUSIONS.—Mycorrhizas have been seen to merge on the one hand into rhizosphere associations and on the other into parasitism involving damage to the host. Our present problem is to attempt to see in what way the study of them, past or future, is relevant to a better understanding of soil-borne pathogens.

In those that have been discussed, the fungi may be viewed as forming a series. The highly specialized *Endogone* endophytes have not only no known vegetative existence away from their hosts but also have not been grown in culture. The related *Rhizophagus* strains which have been cultured resemble in their nutrient demands the basidiomycetes of ectotrophic mycorrhiza. These latter show grades of diminishing nutrient selectivity from those which require highly amended media for growth to those "pseudomycorrhizal" forms which are nutritionally relatively unspecialized. The orchid fungi form a further extension of the series, being free-living, widely distributed forms culminating in omnivorous parasites or saprophytes such as *Armillaria mellea* and *Rhizoctonia solani;* and it is here that we should include the *Pythium* species reported both as vesicular-arbuscular endophytes and virulent parasites.

None of the known properties or characteristics of mycorrhizal fungi in general, nor of those of the particular kinds discussed, is solely theirs. The same kind and degree of nutritional specialization and dependence on particular cultural conditions, can be matched amongst rhizosphere fungi, root-inhabiting organisms, or parasites. Moreover, such end-products of their metabolism as auxinlike substances, which some have been shown to produce, are also formed by nonmycorrhizal fungi. Nevertheless the abundance in nature of mycorrhizal associations and their diversity leads to the conclusion that they include a series of grades of specialization of rhizosphere and parasitic associations of higher plants and fungi. These must possess some selective advantage, or at any rate no selective disadvantage, to the constituent organisms, for they have been preserved in natural selection as a permanent condition.

Much research has been aimed at determining the advantages, if any, of mycorrhizal associations to host plants. But this is not an easily soluble problem unless it is simplified into component problems. The problem is essentially ecological because natural selection has operated in natural surroundings; and only where investigators have borne this in mind, as for instance in tree mycorrhiza, have clear results been achieved. If we consider the results with vesicular-arbuscular mycorrhiza, a very complex situation of doubt and disagreement is apparent. Whereas it is clear that wild plants in large numbers, living and fossil, show this kind of infection naturally, research has often been pursued with crop plants growing in man-made conditions. For instance, if we accept the results of Hawker (1962) and Ham (1962) that a parasitic *Pythium* species can form an innocuous mycorrhizal association or cause disease and death on the same plant according to conditions, the next step must be to mate the results with the known ecological requirements of the host plant. Only in this way can the picture be completed.

There are four problems of great interest other than effects upon the host plant that are directly relevant to the study of soil-borne pathogens. First, there is the mechanism of exchange of materials between host and fungus. In the sense that there is, in mycorrhizal organs, a prolonged steady-state interaction between their components, they provide unique material for the study of host-endophyte relations. In this regard a start has been made in the experimental work on carbohydrate metabolism and phosphate uptake and metabolism in ectotrophic mycorrhiza, in which the whole and the separated host and fungal tissues may

be observed. Similar methods have also been shown to be applicable to the study of pathogens.

Second, there are the problems of the establishment of the association. Here again ectotrophic mycorrhizas are, in some ways, the most readily handled because of their characteristic morphology in the adult state. Already these problems have been seen to be complex. There is the peculiar growth pattern in the roots leading to susceptibility which seems to be correlated with the environmental conditions of photosynthesis and nutrient supply. The internal factors or mechanisms altered by the environment are yet to be guessed. On the other hand, a start has been made on the discovery of the production of morphogenic factors by the fungi.

Third, there are the effects of the host upon the activities of the fungi. The relatively simple question whether the disintegration of carbon substrates by *Endogone* or *Rhizophagus* is enhanced by the host and essentially similar questions for the basidiomycetes of ectotrophic mycorrhiza have not been attacked. These are of fundamental interest, but they have only been touched upon by casual observations made in the course of other study.

Lastly the problems of control of fungal exploitation of the host which have been followed up in Orchidaceae are equally relevant to other cases.

LITERATURE CITED

BARNES, R. L., and A. W. NAYLOR. 1959. Effect of various nitrogen sources on growth of isolated roots of *Pinus serotina*. Physiol. Plantarum 12: 82-89.

BARRETT, J. T. 1947. Observations on the root endophyte Rhizophagus in culture. Phytopathology 37: 359-360.

BARRETT, J. T. 1958. Synthesis of mycorrhiza with pure cultures of Rhizophagus. Phytopathology 48: 391.

BAYLIS, G. T. S. 1959. Effect of vesicular-arbuscular mycorrhiza on the growth of *Griselinia littoralis* (Cornaceae). New Phytologist 58: 274-280.

BERNARD, N. 1911. Sur la function fungicide des bulbes d'Ophrydées. Ann. Sci. Nat. Botan. 14: 225-234.

BJÖRKMAN, E. 1941. Mykorrhizans uitbildning och frekvens hos skogsträd på askgödslade och ogödslade dilar av dikad myr. (With German summary.) Medd. Skogsforsokanst. Stokh. 32: 255-296.

BJÖRKMAN, E. 1942. Über die Bedingungen der Mykorrhizabildung bei Keifer und Fichte. Symbolae Botan. Upsaliensis. 6: 1-191.

BJÖRKMAN, E. 1949. The ecological significance of the ectotrophic mycorrhizal association in forest trees. Svensk Botan. Tidskr. 43: 223-262.

BJÖRKMAN, E. 1960. *Monotropa hypopytis* L.—an epiparasite on tree roots. Physiol. Plantarum 13: 308-327.

BURGEFF, H. 1932. Saprophytismus und Symbiose. G. Fischer, Jena. 249 p.

BURGEFF, H. 1936. Samenkeimung der Orchideen. G. Fischer, Jena. 312 p.

BURGES, N. A. 1939. The defensive mechanism in orchid mycorrhiza. New Phytologist 38: 273-283.

CLODE, J. J. E. 1956. As micorrizas na migração de fósforo. Estudo com o. ^{32}P. Publ. Serv. Flor Aquic. Portugal 23: 167-206.

CLOWES, F. A. L. 1951. The structure of mycorrhizal roots of *Fagus sylvatica*. New Phytologist 50: 1-16.

CLOWES, F. A. L. 1954. The root-cap of ectotrophic mycorrhizas. New Phytologist 53: 525-529.

DOWDING, E. S. 1959. Ecology of Endogone. Trans. Brit. Mycol. Soc. 42: 449-459.

DOWNIE, D. G. 1957. *Corticium solani* as an orchid endophyte. Nature (London) 179: 160.

GARRETT, S. D. 1956. Biology of root-infecting fungi.

Cambridge University Press, London and New York. 292 p.

GÄUMANN, E., R. BRAUN, and G. BAZZIGHER. 1950. Über induzierte Abwehrreaktionen bei Orchideen. Phytopathol. Z. 17: 36-62.

GÄUMANN, E., and H. KERN. 1959a. Über chemische Abwehrreaktionen bei Orchideen. Phytopathol. Z. 36: 1-26.

GÄUMANN, E., and H. KERN. 1959b. Über die Isolierung und den chemischen Nachweis des Orchinols. Phytopathol. Z. 36: 347-356.

GÄUMANN, E., and H. R. HOHL. 1960. Weitere Untersuchungen über die chemischen Abwehrreaktionen der Orchideen. Phytopathol. Z. 38: 93-104.

GÄUMANN, E., J. NUESCH, and R. H. RIMPAU. 1960. Weitere Untersuchungen über die chemischen Abwehrreaktionen der Orchideen. Phytopathol. Z. 38: 274-308.

GERDEMANN, J. W. 1955. Relation of a large soil-borne spore to phycomycetous mycorrhizal infections. Mycologia 47: 619-632.

GERDEMANN, J. W. 1961. A species of *Endogone* from corn causing vesicular-arbuscular mycorrhiza. Mycologia 53: 254-261.

HAM, A. M. 1962. Studies on vesicular-arbuscular endophytes IV. Trans. Brit. Mycol. Soc. 45: 179-189.

HANNAY, J. W., and D. N. BUTCHER. 1961. An ageing process in excised roots of groundsel (*Senecio vulgaris* L.). New Phytologist 60: 9-20.

HARLEY, J. L. 1959. Biology of mycorrhiza. Leonard Hill Books, London. 233 p.

HARLEY, J. L., and C. C. McCREADY. 1950. The uptake of phosphate by excised mycorrhizal roots of the beech. New Phytologist 49: 388-397.

HARLEY, J. L., and J. S. WAID. 1955. The effect of light upon the roots of beech and its surface population. Plant Soil 7: 96-112.

HARLEY, J. L., and J. M. WILSON. 1959. Absorption of potassium by beech mycorrhiza. New Phytologist 58: 281-298.

HATCH, A. B. 1937. The physical basis of mycotrophy in the genus Pinus. Black Rock Forest Bull. 6, 168 p.

HAWKER, L. E. 1962. Studies on vascular-arbuscular endophytes V. A review of the evidence relating to the identity of the causal fungi. Trans. Brit. Mycol. Soc. 45: 190-199.

HAWKER, L. E., R. W. HARRISON, V. O. NICHOLS, and A. M. HAM. 1957. Studies on vesicular-arbuscular endophytes I. Trans. Brit. Mycol. Soc. 40: 375-390.

HEPDEN, P. M. 1960. Studies in vesicular-arbuscular endophytes II. Trans. Brit. Mycol. Soc. 43: 559-570.

HUBERMAN, M. A. 1940. Normal growth and development of southern pine seedlings in the nursery. Ecology 21: 323-334.

KRAMER, P. J., and K. M. WILBUR. 1949. Absorption of radioactive phosphorus by mycorrhizal roots of pine. Science 110: 8-9.

KUSANO, S. 1911. *Gastrodia elata* and its symbiotic association with *Armillaria mellea*. J. Agr. Tokyo 4: 1-66.

LEVISOHN, I. 1960. Physiological and ecological factors influencing the effects of mycorrhizal inoculation. New Phytologist 59: 42-47.

LEWIS, D. H. 1963. Uptake of substances by beech mycorrhiza. D. Phil. thesis, Oxford University, England.

LINDEBERG, G. 1948. On the occurrence of polyphenol oxidases in soil-inhabiting basidiomycetes. Physiol. Plantarum 1: 196-205.

MAGROU, J. 1924. A propos du pouvoir fungicide des tubercles d'Ophrydées. Ann. Sci. Nat. Botan. 10ième ser. 6: 265-270.

MAGROU, J. 1936. Culture et inoculation du champignon symbiotique de l'*Arum maculatum*. Compt. Rend. 203: 887-888.

McCOMB, A. L. 1938. The relation between mycorrhizae and the development and nutrient absorption of pine seedlings in a prairie nursery. J. Forestry 36: 1148-1154.

MELIN, E. 1954. Growth factor requirements of mycorrhizal fungi of forest trees. Svensk Botan. Tidskr. 48: 86-94.

MELIN, E., and V. S. R. DAS. 1954. The influence of root-metabolites on the growth of tree mycorrhizal fungi. Physiol. Plantarum 7: 851-858.

MELIN, E., and H. NILSSON. 1950. Transfer of radioactive phosphorus to pine seedlings by means of mycorrhizal hyphae. Physiol. Plantarum 3: 88-92.

MELIN, E., and H. NILSSON. 1952. Transfer of labelled nitrogen from an ammonium source to pine seedlings through mycorrhizal mycelium. Svensk Botan. Tidskr. 46:281-285.

MELIN, E., and H. NILSSON. 1955. Ca^{45} used as an indicator of transport of cations to pine seedlings by means of mycorrhizal mycelia. Svensk Botan. Tidskr. 49: 119-122.

MELIN, E., and H. NILSSON. 1957. Transport of C^{14} labelled photosynthate to the fungal associate of pine mycorrhiza. Svensk Botan. Tidskr. 51: 166-186.

MELIN, E., and H. NILSSON. 1958. Translocation of nutritive elements through mycorrhizal mycelia to pine seedlings. Botan. Notiser (Lund, Sweden) 111: 251-256.

MIKOLA, P. 1948. On the physiology and ecology of *Cenococcum graniforme*. Commun. Inst. For. Finl. 36: 1-104.

MORRISON, T. M. 1962. Absorption of phosphorus from soil by mycorrhizal plants. New Phytologist 61: 10-20.

MOSSE, B. 1953. Fructifications associated with mycorrhizal strawberry roots. Nature (London) 171: 974.

MOSSE, B. 1956. Fructification of an Endogone species causing endotrophic mycorrhiza in fruit plants. Ann. Botany (London) [N.S.] 20: 349-362.

MOSSE, B. 1957. Growth and chemical composition of mycorrhizal and non-mycorrhizal apples. Nature (London) 179: 922-924.

MOSSE, B. 1959. Observations on the extramatrical mycelium of a vesicular-arbuscular endophyte. Trans. Brit. Mycol. Soc. 42: 439-448.

MOSSE, B. 1961. Experimental techniques for obtaining a pure inoculum of an Endogone sp. and some observations on the vesicular-arbuscular infection caused by it and other fungi. Recent Adv. Botany (Canada) (9th Intern. Botan. Congr., Montreal, University of Toronto Press), Sec. 14, p. 1728-1732.

MOSSE, B. 1962. The establishment of vesicular-arbuscular mycorrhiza under aseptic conditions. J. Gen. Microbiol. 27: 509-520.

NICOLSON, T. M. 1959. Mycorrhiza in Gramineae I. Trans. Brit. Mycol. Soc. 42: 421-438.

NICOLSON, T. M. 1960. Mycorrhiza in Gramineae II. Trans. Brit. Mycol. Soc. 43: 132-145.

NOBÉCOURT, P. 1923. Sur la production d'anticorps par les tubercles des Ophrydées. Compt. Rend. 177: 1055-1057.

NORKRANS, B. 1949. Some mycorrhiza-forming Tricholoma species. Svensk Botan. Tidskr. 43: 485-490.

NORKRANS, B. 1950. Studies in growth and cellulolytic enzymes of Tricholoma. Symbolae Botan. Upsaliensis 11: 1-126.

RAYNER, M. C., and I. LEVISOHN. 1941. The mycorrhizal habit in relation to forestry. IV. Studies on mycorrhizal response in Pinus and other conifers. Forestry 15: 1-36.

ROBERTSON, N. F. 1954. Studies on the mycorrhiza of *Pinus sylvestris* I. New Phytologist 53: 253-283.

ROBINSON, R. K., and R. L. LUCAS. 1963. The use of isotypically labelled mycelia to investigate the host range and rate of spread of *Ophiobolus graminis*. New Phytologist 62: 50-52.

ROMELL, L. G. 1938. A trenching experiment in spruce forest and its bearing on problems of mycotrophy. Svensk Botan. Tidskr. 32: 89-99.

RUINEN, J. 1953. Epiphytosis. A second view on epiphytism. Ann. Bogor. 1: 101-157.

SCHELLING, C. L. 1950. Die Verwertbarkeit verscheidener Kohlenstoffquellen durch *Mycelium radicis atrovirens* Melin. Schweiz. Z. Allgem. Pathol. Bakteriol. 13: 570-574.

SLANKIS, V. 1948. Einfluss von Exudaten von *Boletus*

variegatus auf die dichotomische Verzweigung isolierter Kiefernwurzeln. Physiol. Plantarum 1: 390-400.

SLANKIS, V. 1951. Über den Einfluss von B-Indolylessigsaüre und andere Wirkstoffen auf das Wachstum von Kiefernwurzeln. Symbolae Botan. Upsaliensis 11: 1-63.

STAHL, M. 1949. Die Mykorrhiza der Lebermoose mit besonderer Berucksichtigung der thallosen Formen. Planta 37: 103-148.

STONE, E. L. 1950. Some effects of mycorrhizae on the phosphorus nutrition of Monterey pine seedlings. Soil Sci. Soc. Am. Proc. (1949) 14: 340-345.

STREET, H. E., and E. H. ROBERTS. 1952. Factors controlling meristematic activity in excised roots I. Physiol. Plantarum 5: 498-509.

TARR, S. A. J. 1962. Diseases of sorghum, sudan grass and broom corn. Commonwealth Mycol. Inst., Kew, England. 380 p.

ULRICH, J. M. 1960. Auxin production by mycorrhizal fungi. Physiol. Plantarum 13: 429-443.

ULRICH, J. M. 1962. Cultural requirements for the growth of excised Ponderosa pine roots. Physiol. Plantarum 15: 59-71.

WARREN WILSON, J. 1951. Micro-organisms in the rhizosphere of beech. Thesis, University of Oxford, England.

WENGER, K. F. 1955. Light and mycorrhiza development. Ecology 36: 518-520.

WILSON, J. M. 1957. A study of the factors affecting the uptake of potassium by the mycorrhiza of beech. Thesis, University of Oxford, England.

► DISCUSSION OF J. L. HARLEY PAPER

W. A. Kreutzer:

Would you care to express an opinion as to whether the fungus *Endogone* is a pathogen?

J. L. Harley:

The present evidence on *Endogone* shows that certain definite species are clearly mycorrhizal. A number of other fungi, such as those isolated by Dr. Barrett under the name of *Rhizophagus* and those of Dr. Gerdemann which produce large spores in the soil, seem very likely to belong taxonomically to *Endogone*. Examples of these, as well as *Pythium* from Dr. Hawker, have been tested and shown to form mycorrhiza. The recent work of Mosse has shown the way to the preparation of pure two-membered associations for detailed physiological work. In the meantime, the studies of Baylis in New Zealand, Mosse in England, and Gerdemann in the United States, have all provided some evidence of increased growth of host plants when infected under certain specified conditions. In any event, the widespread occurrence of this type of infection in a large number of species of plants of many taxonomic groups would indicate that it is at least of no selective disadvantage, and, in all likelihood, of selective advantage.

K. F. Baker:

Would you describe the mechanism involved in the transmission of mycorrhizal fungi by seed or other methods, and the subsequent establishment of the fungus on the host? This might shed some light on the mechanisms of establishment of antagonistic microorganisms in the root.

J. L. Harley:

Transmission of mycorrhizal fungi in the seed coat was described in Ericaceae. I doubt whether there is really evidence that this occurs. A similar claim has been made that there is cyclic mycorrhizal infection in certain Cystaceae by Dr. Joan Griffiths Boursnell. Mycorrhizal fungi of Orchidaceae are soil-borne. They invade the young roots as they are formed, and in the case of most tuberous orchids, each root is newly infected from the soil, not from other infected organs of the host.

Infection of root systems of trees by ectotrophic mycorrhizal fungi is a much more permanent matter. The short roots are first infected, but eventually the long pioneer roots become infected. Thereafter, each short root becomes infected as it penetrates the cortex of the plant root.

H. Katznelson:

Although generalized substances such as carbohydrates may not specifically stimulate development and penetration of ectotrophic mycorrhiza, is it not possible that the C:N ratio has an effect? The fact that light favors infection suggests that a change in this ratio may have significance.

J. L. Harley:

The work of Björkman and others clearly indicates a correlation of degree of infection with light intensity and hence photosynthesis. Plants of high carbohydrate status are more susceptible to infection, or rather, become more completely infected than those of low status. I expressed doubt, however, as to whether the contention that the stimulus to fungal invasion of the tissues could be an exuded carbohydrate because this would be unspecific in its action. By the same token, I should have thought that C:N ratio was not sufficiently specific either. I incline to the view that the stimulus, whatever it may be, is likely to be found to be produced by plants of high carbohydrate status, rather than those of low, but is not likely to be one of the common carbohydrates. It is worth noting, also, that in seeking factors which promote mycorrhizal infection, we are looking not only for those which, like Melin's M factor, promote growth, but also for factors which are morphogenic and promote the formation of sheath tissues of ectotrophic mycorrhizas.

A. S. Sussman:

Did I understand you to say that roots do not absorb trehalose?

This is an interesting contradiction in that a plant root doesn't absorb the sugar that is accumulated. Do you know whether the sugars are absorbed as the monosaccharides?

J. L. Harley:

Uninfected roots of *Fagus sylvatica* did not, in the experiments of David Lewis, take up trehalose, nor did they hydrolyse it.

Mycorrhizas of *Fagus* do hydrolyse trehalose by a surface enzyme system and absorb the products. We are reasonably certain that only the monosaccharide products rather than the disaccharide, trehalose, are absorbed. During absorption trehalose is again reformed in the tissue.

J. H. Warcup:

Sclerotia and chlamydospores occur more frequently in Basidiomycetes than has usually been recorded.

J. L. Harley:

I am glad to have your confirmation of the fact that Basidiomycetes, including perhaps mycorrhiza formers, can exist in soil as resting structures. This may well explain some of the problems of spontaneous infection of seedlings.

M. I. Timonin:

It is a well-established fact that the density of microbial populations decreases with the depth; this phenomenon also was observed in the rhizosphere. What is the distribution of mycorrhizae with depth?

Assuming that the mycorrhizae are established at considerable depth, would they still be effective, or parasitic (in view of the oxygen and temperature relation)?

J. L. Harley:

Ectotrophic mycorrhizas are mainly found in the surface horizons of the soil, in the litter and A layers. They are not necessarily absent from the deeper layers but are much less abundant there.

The oxygen supply in the deeper layers of the soil is not necessarily deficient, although carbon dioxide levels may be high. Our own observations have only given evidence of high oxygen availability in the surface and subsurface horizons. Those of others, including Professor Burges, have clearly shown high oxygen levels in lower horizons.

J. T. Barrett:

Pure cultures of the endotrophic mycorrhizal fungus *Endogene* have been established and synthesis has been accomplished on a number of host plants (9th Intern. Botan. Congr. 2: 21, 1959).

K. F. Baker:

Is there any evidence that mycorrhizal roots are more resistant to root-decay organisms than nonmycorrhizal roots of the same host?

J. L. Harley:

This view has been put forward many times. It is certainly true that tree seedlings raised in nurseries or agricultural soils in Britain have been reported by I.

Levisohn (New Phytologist 53: 284-290, 1954) to suffer from infection by weak parasites, often referred to the genus *Rhizoctonia*. These fungi form what have been called pseudomycorrhizas, in which there is some evidence of destruction of root tissues. Where mycorrhizal inoculation is successful, the pseudomycorrhizal infections are rare, or at any rate, far less common.

N. A. Burges:

In E. Gäuman's work, did he find any evidence of a relation between chlorophyll content and orchinol?

J. L. Harley:

As I recall, this relation was not observed. Gäumann was using solely nonchlorophyllous tissues. I agree with Professor Burges that there is good observational evidence that cells containing chlorophyll in the Orchidacae and in Bryophytes and Pteridophytes are not invaded by mycorrhizal fungi.

I. A. M. Cruickshank:

Further to Dr. Baker's question, I should like to indicate that Gäumann, Nüesch, and Rimpau (Phytopathol. Z. 38: 274-308, 1960) have reported that orchinol has a very broad antifungal spectrum. Gäumann and Kern (Phytopathol. Z. 36: 1-26, 1959) have in fact suggested that in the case of orchid tubers, the first infections by mycorrhizal fungi initiate the production of orchinol, which subsequently protects the tissue not only against homologous reinfections but also against a whole series of secondary parasites and saprophytes.

J. L. Harley:

Thank you for this valuable comment. I had assumed that Dr. Baker was only inquiring about ectotrophic mycorrhizas. I certainly agree that orchinol, when produced in orchid tuber tissues, confers resistance against a wide spectrum of potential pathogens. I doubt if it has been shown that the roots produce orchinol in such quantities as to allow mycorrhizal infection, yet prevent pathogenic attack.

G. A. Zentmyer:

Is the proper spelling of the plural of "mycorrhiza" mycorrhizae or mycorrhizas?

J. L. Harley:

This word mycorrhiza is spelled with two r's except by the Encyclopedia Britannica, who told me that I could not spell this word. Its plural in British English is usually *mycorrhizas* and in American English, *mycorrhizae*.

The Relation between Nodule Bacteria and the Legume Host in the Rhizosphere and in the Process of Infection

P. S. NUTMAN—*Soil Microbiology Department, Rothamsted Experimental Station, Harpenden, England.*

The formation of symbiotic root nodules in legumes and nonlegumes follows the invasion of the root by soil microorganisms and would therefore appear to be initially parasitic in character. How such infections are later turned to the benefit of the host and microorganism is outside the scope of this symposium; our discussion will be confined to a consideration of infection and preinfection processes, with particular reference to the ecological relations in the rhizosphere and to the physiology and mechanism of root invasion. It will be necessary, however, to refer to certain aspects of nodule function that influence infection, and to the changes in fine structure that accompany the intracellular establishment of the microsymbiont in the nodule cell. This can be regarded as an extension of the infection process initiated at the root hair, and it is also of general phytopathological interest. Our discussion will further be restricted to the symbiosis as exemplified by the clover plant (*Trifolium* species) and its nodule bacterium (*Rhizobium trifolii*). General accounts of infection in other legumes and nonlegumes are given elsewhere (E. K. Allen and O. N. Allen, 1958, 1961; Bond, 1963; Nutman, 1958; and Raggio and Raggio, 1962).

RHIZOBIUM IN THE RHIZOSPHERE.—Nodule bacteria are facultative symbionts able to live as normal components of the soil microflora in the temporary absence of their hosts, but their continued free existence in soil depends on the presence of the host root, which strongly stimulates their multiplication. The increase in numbers of nodule bacteria in the soil near the legume root differs both qualitatively and quantitatively from the normal "rhizosphere effect" shown by many other soil microorganisms. Nodule bacteria are in general little affected by roots of most nonlegumes—the stimulation of *Rhizobium trifolii* by cotton is an example of an exception (Krasil'nikov, 1958)—and individual strains of nodule bacteria are more strongly stimulated by those hosts they are able to infect than by other legumes (Wilson, 1930, and others); but in water culture or agar media there is no evidence of differential stimulation (Purchase, 1952).

A further feature is that legumes stimulate nodule bacteria much more than they stimulate other rhizosphere microorganisms. The ratio of numbers of *Rhizobium* in the rhizosphere and in soil—the R:S ratio—is rarely smaller than 10^2 and often exceeds 10^6 (except in legume-dominant plant communities, where the whole soil becomes rhizosphere and small ratios are associated with very large numbers). Ratios for other rhizosphere bacteria usually fall within the range of 10-10^2, and even for groups, such as the streptomycin-resistant species of *Flavobacterium*, that are specially stimulated in the legume rhizosphere, the R:S rarely exceeds 10^3 (M. E. Brown, 1961).

The natural geographical distribution of nodule bacteria usually corresponds with that of their legume hosts, and when a leguminous crop is introduced to a new region, also free from its near botanical (or cross-inoculation group) relations, artificial inoculation is usually necessary to ensure successful establishment of a nodulated crop (Thornton, 1931; Fred, Baldwin, and McCoy, 1932; E. K. Allen and O. N. Allen, 1958; Donald, 1960; Vincent, 1962).

There are few studies on the detailed microecology of *Rhizobium* in soil because no selective counting medium is known; estimates are made indirectly using aseptically grown host plants inoculated with diluted samples of soil or rhizosphere (Wilson, 1930; Tsuzimura and Watanabe, 1959; Date and Vincent, 1962). Stimulation has been demonstrated 10-20 mm from the root surface (Rovira, 1961), but the root surface itself appears to be relatively free from nodule bacteria (Rovira and Stern, 1961). The immediate neighbourhood of young seedlings of *Trifolium subterraneum* and *Centrosema pubescens* and other legumes may be unfavourable for nodule bacteria because toxic materials diffuse from the seed coat (Bonnier, 1954; Thompson, 1960; Bowen, 1961). Studies on clover (Hely, Bergersen, and Brockwell, 1957), beans (Nutman, 1963), and trefoil (Radulovic and Nutman, 1963) show that the stimulation is both rapid and progressive so that continued cropping with the same legume leads to further increases each season.

The cause of the large and specific stimulation of *Rhizobium* by the legume root is not known. Presumably it is nutritional and depends in some way on the root exudates, which are more copious and varied from legumes than from other plants (Rovira, 1955, 1962). So far as its growth-factor requirements are concerned, *Rhizobium* is not a typical rhizosphere organism (Bergersen, 1961; Graham, 1963). Dr. Rovira's and Dr. Katznelson's contributions in this symposium deal in greater detail with the chemical and biological factors of rhizosphere stimulation and the possible mechanisms of exudation.

When assessed by ecological criteria, the advantage to the nodule bacteria of the legume association comes largely from the rhizosphere stimulation—which in its turn depends on the vigorous growth of the host and on nitrogen fixation. All the bacteria that enter nodule cells and become changed into "bacteroids" lose their capacity for reproduction (Almon, 1933) and contribute to the host's well-being only by promoting nitrogen fixation. The relatively few bacteria retained within the infection threads remain viable and on the decay of the nodule they multiply and escape into the soil.

Soil populations of nodule bacteria often exceed 10^6 per gram of rhizosphere soil or 10^8 per millilitre of rhizosphere fluid of plants grown in water or agar medium. Such large densities of bacteria are not needed to initiate infection under pure cultural conditions. Using heavy inocula of mixtures of a normal virulent strain and an avirulent mutant, Lim (1963) showed that the number of hairs infected in three species of clover is proportional to the density of bacteria in the rhizosphere. Fewer than 100 bacteria in the whole rhizosphere are enough to start infection. Before nodulation begins, the number of infections and the density of bacteria are simply related, such that doubling bacterial density produces twice as many infections. As soon as the first nodule is formed more bacteria are required for each infection; the additional number of bacteria required is most for those species that are least abundantly infected. In the species studied by Lim, the number of root hairs infected greatly exceeded the number of nodules formed, so that these findings really applied to the infections that were "surplus" to nodule formation. A different relation was found in a study of the influence of bacterial density on nodule formation in *Trifolium pratense,* in which there are few, if any, surplus infections (Purchase and Nutman, 1957). Progressively more bacteria are needed to produce each succeeding nodule, the relation between bacterial numbers in the rhizosphere and the number of nodules formed being Mitscherlich in type. Whereas ca. 10 bacteria per rhizosphere are sufficient to form the first nodule, very large numbers are needed to ensure that later nodulation is not eventually limited by the size of the infecting population. These relations suggest that nodule formation occurs on predetermined sites on the root; only where there are no surplus infections does this also apply to the original infection of the root hair.

These effects of inoculum size on infection and nodule formation in clover were studied under aseptic conditions using special methods, and as yet no comparable work has been done in soil. Lim (1961) showed that, although the "pattern" of infection in agar and unsterilised soil was similar, the rhizosphere stimulation was smaller in soil and both hair infection and nodule formation required more bacteria (per infection or per nodule) in soil than in agar medium. She also showed that certain root-surface fungi (e.g. species of *Verti-*

cillium) consistently decreased infection without effecting the numbers of *Rhizobium* in the rhizosphere; whereas other fungi were either stimulatory (e.g. species of *Paecilomyces*) or had no effect. The causes of these interactions are not known; interactions between nodule bacteria and other soil microorganisms have been very little studied.

The practical limitation of inoculum size to nodule formation comes at densities that are still much smaller than those actually found in soil. These supernumerary bacteria may have some useful function besides forming nodules, such as making mineral phosphate soluble and available to the host, improving soil structure, or merely providing a reserve against unfavourable conditions. Without the host plant, numbers of nodule bacteria in the soil decline rapidly, at a roughly exponential rate (Nutman, 1963). This decline is increased by desiccation, high temperature, and acid conditions (Bonnier, 1955; Vincent, 1958; Bowen and Kennedy, 1959; Jensen, 1961; Vincent, Thompson, and O'Donovan, 1962). Biological factors affecting numbers, such as competition, predacity, antagonism, antibiosis, or phage lysis have been little studied (Demolon and Dunez, 1936; Casas Campillo, 1947, 1951; E. K. Allen and O. N. Allen, 1958; Kecskés and Manninger, 1962).

The soil population of *Rhizobium* is heterogeneous, with different strains competing in the rhizosphere (Nicol and Thornton, 1941; Means, Johnson, and Erdman, 1961; and others) and also in the host for nodule sites (see next section). Little is known about the origin of this heterogeneity, or its persistence. Some of the recognised mechanisms for genetic change or properties associated with genetic change (transformation and lysogeny) have been demonstrated for *Rhizobium* in culture (Balassa, 1954, 1960; Kleczkowska, 1961; Szende et al., 1961; Takahashi and Quadling, 1961); but it is not known whether any operate in soil. Undoubtedly the selective pressures in soil are strong and varied.

In face of all these uncertainties, it is hazardous to extrapolate from the results of experiments in pure culture to conditions in soil. Further work may demonstrate that the phenomenally large rhizosphere populations of nodule bacteria are necessary for efficient and adaptable symbiosis in a way not yet understood.

THE INFECTION OF THE ROOT.—*The curling reaction.* —Very few observations have been made of infection in soil, and the following account is again based on plants grown in water culture or on agar.

Infected hairs are usually, but not invariably, deformed; the growing tip of the hair (or of a lateral branch of the hair) curls in a characteristic "shepherd's-crook" manner (as shown in Fig. 1). Only a small proportion of all hairs are deformed and not all deformed hairs are visibly infected, i.e. contain infection threads (the structure and development of which are considered in a later section).

The curling response in any particular host is induced not only by the limited number of bacterial strains that can form infection threads in its root hairs, but also by bacteria that infect other host species. A

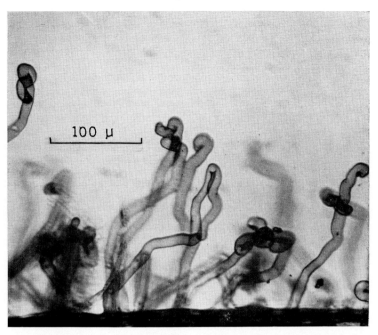

Fig. 1. The root hairs of clover curled by *Rhizobium trifolii*.

curling reaction (though less typical) can also be induced by cell-free filtrates of nodule bacteria (Koster-manns, 1935; Chen, 1938; Thimann, 1939), and also in some roots by plant auxins (3-indoleacetic acid—IAA—and α naphthylacetic acid). Filtrates of nodule bacteria contain auxins that are active in Wents' pea test (Chen, 1938) and have been identified as IAA by chromatographic assay with the *Avena* coleoptile test. *Rhizobium* in culture can oxidise tryptophane to IAA, and when tryptophane is added in amounts more than about 1 ppm to the medium in which legumes are growing, so much IAA is formed that root growth is inhibited (Nutman, Thornton, and Quastel, 1945). Tryptophane is secreted in very small amounts by the growing root (Rovira, 1959), and IAA has been recovered in traces from the rhizosphere fluid of inoculated plants (Kefford, Brockwell, and Zwar, 1960). There is, therefore, much circumstantial evidence to implicate IAA in the curling reaction. IAA affects extension growth, and if produced locally, might be expected to cause curling. Sahlman and Fåhraeus (1962) challenge this simple view, on the grounds that pure IAA is much less active than crude bacterial filtrates in de-forming root hairs and in encouraging hair branching (which in some species is more typically associated with infection than curling). Moreover, filtrates made from bacteria growing in the rhizosphere are more active per cell than those from cells grown in culture, sug-gesting that some cofactor is produced by the root. The root factor is heat-stable and contains a high-molecular-weight component (Fåhraeus, 1963).

The role of pectic enzyme in infection.—Nodule bacteria in culture do not produce any of the pectic or cellulolytic enzymes (McCoy, 1932; Smith, 1955; Clarke and Tracey, 1956), but pectin methyl-esterase (PME) and polygalacturonase (PG) occur in the cul-ture medium where nodulated plants have been grown (Fåhraeus and Ljunggren, 1959). PME also occurs in the medium of uninoculated legumes, but PG is re-stricted to that of plants inoculated with nodule bac-teria able to infect them; for example, clover roots with clover bacteria produce PG, but clover roots with lucerne bacteria do not (Ljunggren and Fåhraeus, 1961). PG is also produced when a cell-free prepara-tion of polysaccharide from a strain of nodule bacteria is added to the root medium of an appropriate host. Enzyme must therefore be formed and secreted by the host root as a result of specific induction by bac-terial polysaccharide or something contained in such a preparation. Ljunggren (1961) showed that an aviru-lent variant of clover bacteria does not induce forma-tion of PG by clover roots, but after treatment with DNA from a virulent strain the capabilities of such a strain to infect the host and to induce PG formation are both restored. Similarly, lupin bacteria were trans-formed to infect lucerne plants (Balassa, 1960) but tests were not made for PG formation. These results suggest that cross-infectability may be controlled, on the one hand, by the constitution of bacterial poly-saccharide, or its determining nucleotides, and, on the other, by the host's capacity to react specifically by producing enzyme. The mere presence of enzyme does not suffice for infection, however; rather it is an indi-cation of some change in host physiology closely connected with infection.

Fig. 2 summarises the present state of our knowl-edge concerning events in the rhizosphere before in-fection, and their possible interrelation. A series of nine stages is distinguished; the first six affect the curling reaction, which is unspecific, and the last three are associated with the specific preliminaries to infection. Other factors probably remain to be discovered. The oxidation of tryptophane may not be the only or most important function of the bacteria in inducing

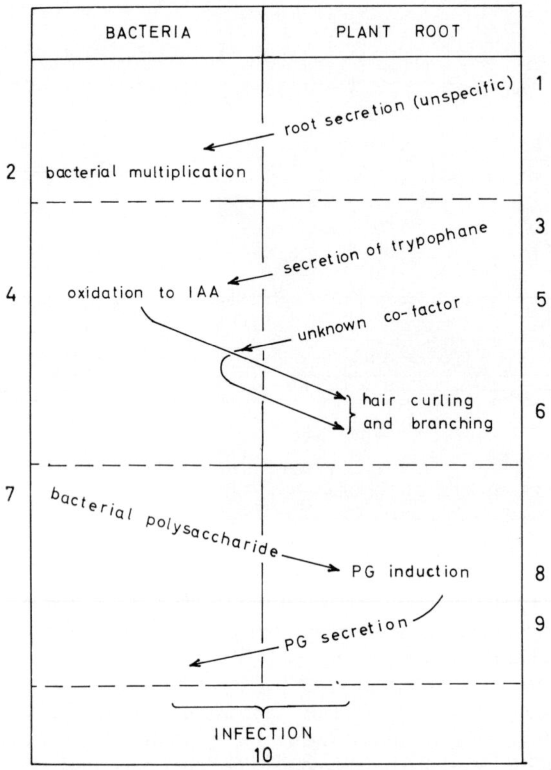

curling, and until the mechanism of infection is known the function of PG remains hypothetical.

The infection thread.—In the group of legumes here considered, the criterion of infection is the formation of the infection thread. This structure is of special interest to the plant pathologist because of its resemblance to an invading fungal hypha—it was so described by some of the earlier investigators (Ward, 1887)—and to other pathological features, such as zoogleal strands and lignotubers. These resemblances are superficial. The infection thread seems to be a unique structure consisting of a cellulose sheath, deposited by the host cell, enclosing a strand of hemicellulosic substance in which the bacteria are embedded (McCoy, 1932; Schaede, 1940). The infection thread grows from the hair into the root cortex and ramifies throughout the central part of the nodule; it is the agent that distributes the bacteria within the tissues of the host. Infection threads within root hairs are shown in Fig. 3.

The way in which the infection thread is initiated remains uncertain. It does not appear to be formed secondarily by the host as a "defence reaction" against invasion by the bacteria. Nodule bacteria occasionally penetrate the hair and have been observed to swim actively in the hair vacuole, but this event is rare (Bürgin-Wolff, 1959). Whenever such undoubted infections were kept under observation, the host cell died and threads were not formed, or the invaded part of the cell was cut off from the rest by a transverse wall (Nutman, 1959).

As an alternative to the hypothesis of infection by actual bacterial entry, I suggested that the infection thread may be formed by a process of invagination of the hair cell wall in the region of curling, this process

Fig. 2. Interactions between bacteria and roots before infection. PG = polygalacturonase. See text for explanation.

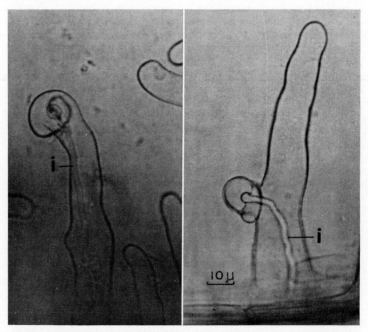

Fig. 3. Infection threads *(i)* within root hairs, arising at apex (left) and in a lateral bud of hair cell (right).

of invagination being repeated at each cell penetrated by the infection thread (Nutman, 1956). Confirmation or otherwise of the hypothesis of the origin of thread growth by invagination must await electron-microscope studies on the initiation of the thread in the root hair.

That thread and hair are homologous in more than the mere possession of a cellulose wall is indicated by similar maximum rates of growth (Fåhraeus, 1957), by the absence of cellulose from their growing tips (McCoy, 1932), and by the circumstance that the growth of both is associated with the very close proximity of the host cell nucleus (Bouet, 1954; Fåhraeus, 1957; Nutman, 1959). Earlier histological studies suggested this association for the nucleus and thread in the cells of cortex and nodule (Thornton, 1930; Schaede, 1932; O. N. Allen and E. K. Allen, 1954).

When the thread is growing, cytoplasm accumulates around the nucleus and protoplasmic streaming is accelerated. Cytoplasmic granules can sometimes be observed moving rapidly to and fro between positions in the region of the thread tip. The tip of the growing root hair is evidently very thin; extrusion of protoplasm is common and not restricted to inoculated roots. Plasmoptysed hairs have not been observed to form infection threads, although they can become invaded by bacteria. Plasmoptysis may be an important mechanism of root exudation.

Movement of the nucleus can readily be observed in the hair of living roots and it appears to have a directing influence in encouraging prompt growth of the thread towards the hair base. Typically, the nucleus can be seen to move towards the root-hair base, closely followed by the growth of the infection thread. Sometimes, however, infection is initiated near the curled apex of a lateral branch of a hair, and the direction the infection thread takes as it grows out of the side branch then depends on the direction of migration of the nucleus. If the nucleus moves towards the hair tip instead of towards its base, the thread grows towards the tip of the hair instead of into the root (Nutman, 1959). Should the nucleus move away from the thread, the thread stops growing and growth is not renewed unless the nucleus soon returns to its original position near the thread tip (Fig. 4).

The separation of thread tip and nucleus may be the cause of thread abortion discussed below. Little seems to be known about the movement of nuclei in normal plant cells, except during fertilization (Miehe, 1901; Buller, 1931; Snider and Raper, 1958; Girbardt, 1962). In some fungal infections the host nucleus is associated with penetration and with haustorial development (Gäumann, 1950). A better understanding of the factors that control the activation of the resting nucleus should do much to elucidate the physiology of infection of the plant cell, particularly in symbioses and in diseases in which pathogens have intracellular phases.

Not all legumes are infected in the manner above described. The most significant divergence in some hosts is the lack of infection threads. How the bacteria

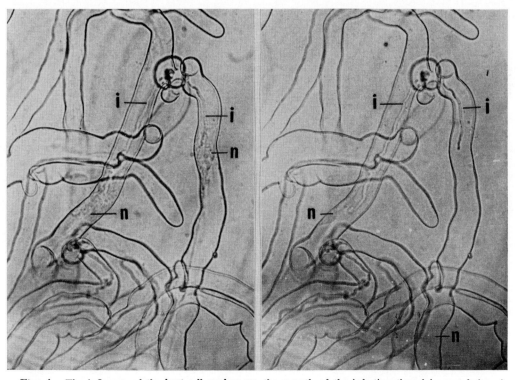

Fig. 4. The influence of the host-cell nucleus on the growth of the infection thread in root hairs of *Trifolium fragiferum;* photo at right 24 hours after photo at left; *i* = infection thread, *n* = nucleus of hair cell. (P. S. Nutman, p. 91, *in* E. G. Hallsworth, Nutrition of the legumes, Butterworths Scientific Publications, London. 1958.)

enter these hosts is not known; but if the crucial mechanism is one of incorporation into primary wall and invagination of plasmalemma, this could occur without thread formation. In hosts without threads bacteria apparently spread from cell to cell in the root and nodule passively by the division of already infected cells (see E. K. Allen and O. N. Allen, 1958).

A corollary of the invagination hypothesis of thread formation is that the bacteria in the thread are strictly intercellular because they have not penetrated the external membrane of the host cytoplast. Even when apparently released from the thread into the nodule cell, the bacteria may not pass through the plasmalemma. Bergersen and Briggs (1958) showed by electron microscopy of thin sections of soybean nodules, that the bacteroids in the nodule cells are aggregated in small groups, each enclosed within folds of host membrane that separates them from the host cytoplasm. Jordan (1962) confirmed these results for soybean, and B. Mosse (private communication) found similar membranes in vetch, broad bean, and clover, each bacteroid being surrounded by three unit membranes, the outer one probably of plant origin (Fig. 5). Recently, Jordan, Gringer, and Coulter (1963) have described the development of the bacteroid-enclosing membrane in alfalfa. It is not yet known how these envelopes arise, but invagination or pinocytosis seems the most likely mechanism. Pinocytosis in plant cells was demonstrated by Weiling (1961) and was earlier proposed by Buvat (1958), Bhide and Brachet (1960), and Jensen and McLaren (1960) as the probable means whereby large molecules such as haemoglobin are taken up by plant cells. Intracellular parasites in many kinds of animal cells have been shown to be surrounded by membranes the function of which may be to separate components that would otherwise be liable to interact immunologically. Boundary membranes of some kind are generally thought to separate host and parasite in some fungal infections (Fraser, 1931; Gäumann, 1950; Moore and McAlear, 1960).

THE DISTRIBUTION AND RATE OF INFECTION.—As with the curling reaction, all root hairs are not equally liable to become infected. The distribution of curling and infection seem to be broadly controlled by the same factors; parts of the root with most curled hairs also tend to have most infections. The ratios of normal to curled or infected hairs depends on the species of host, the strain of bacteria, and the age of the plant (Nutman, 1959).

In the young seedlings of clovers, hairs first become infected on the third or fourth day after germination. These infections are situated high on the root, often close together, and those which arise during the next day or so also tend to occur nearby. It is not until about the seventh day that infected hairs are to be seen on the younger part of the root. Such later infections also usually occur close together, forming a second group of infected hairs well separated from the first. While the second group is appearing, hairs continue to become infected in the region of the first group, which thereby becomes enlarged, particularly distally. After a further 2 or 3 days, a third zone of infected hairs may appear farther down the root, and

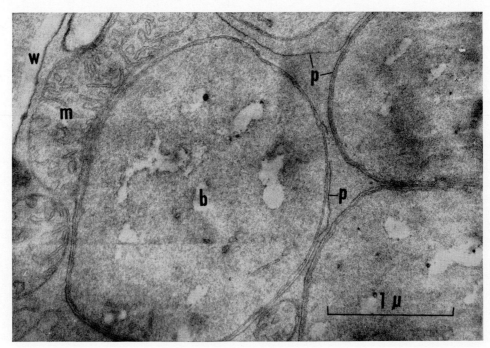

Fig. 5. Electron micrograph of clover-nodule bacteroids (effective strain) surrounded by envelopes of plant origin (*p*); *b* = *bacteroids*; *m* = mitochondria; *w* = host cell wall. Micrograph by B. Mosse. (P. S. Nutman, *in* Monograph on soil nitrogen, American Society of Agronomy, Madison, Wisconsin. 1964.)

like the groups above, it enlarges by having new infections added to its margins, so that by about the fifteenth day the original zones of denser infection may have coalesced, obscuring the initial grouping. These features have been described in detail for *Trifolium fragiferum* (Nutman, 1962); the series of root maps in Fig. 6 show similar distribution patterns for *T. glomeratum* and *Vicia hirsuta*.

Within these zones of denser infection, the individually infected hairs also show a tendency to be in small subgroups. Adjoining hairs are infected more often than can be accounted for on random distribution within zones, and sometimes all the hairs growing within a small part of the root may be infected; these features are shown on the root maps in Figs. 6, 8, 9, and 11.

Infected hairs differ not only in location but in type: whether they contain normal "successful" threads growing into the cortex, or arrested threads or threads arising at the curled apex of the hair or in a lateral branch. Some of these differences depend on the host; for example in *Trifolium scabrum* a high proportion of laterally arising threads are both abortive and grow towards the hair tip. The proportion of lateral infections but not arrested infections increases with seedling age, and the proportion of early arrested threads is highest on plants with most infections (Nutman, 1959).

Positional effects are also shown in the distribution of the different kinds of infection. For example, in Fig. 6*A* all infected hairs, except the two shown near the base of the root, contained single infection threads.

The two marked hairs each contained two infection threads arising laterally. In Fig. 8*A* the four principal types of infection are separately shown on a 13-day old seedling of *Trifolium fragiferum*. Apically arising threads are almost confined to the basal 11 mm of root, threads that enter the root are concentrated in the 5-6 mm section, and lateral unsuccessful infections in the 12-14 mm sections.

In spite of these complexities in spatial distribution, the rate at which infected hairs increase on the young seedling follows a remarkably uniform course, as shown in Fig. 7. During the first 8 or 10 days the number of infected hairs increases exponentially at a relative rate that is similar in different species. At about the tenth day there is a sharp reduction in the rate of infection and this is always associated with the appearance of the first nodules. The new, slower rate of infection is also exponential (Nutman, 1962).

The time at which nodules first appear differs between species and in some species it also differs considerably from plant to plant. Because time of primary nodulation and the change in rate of infection are highly correlated, roots that nodulate late can accumulate very many infections. This relation is illustrated in Fig. 8*B* for early- and late-nodulating plants of *Trifolium fragiferum* and is most simply explained by supposing that the newly formed nodule in some way directly suppresses further infection. That there is a direct connection between nodulation and change in rate was shown by experiments in which nodulation was delayed by adding nitrate or nitrite to the medium.

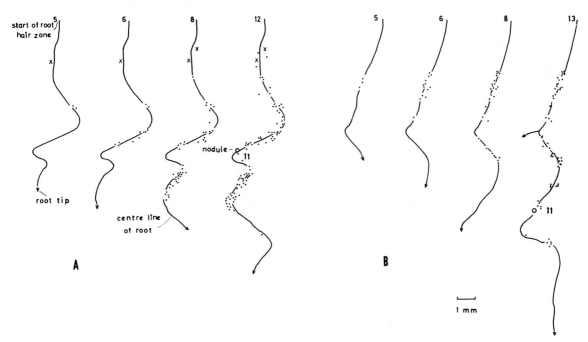

Fig. 6A. A root of *Trifolium glomeratum* (inoculated with *Rhizobium trifolii*, strain C1 F) mapped at 5, 6, 8, and 12 days. Each dot marks the position of a root hair containing a single infection thread. The crosses are for hairs infected laterally, each with two infection threads (only one side of root recorded, representing about 4/5 of total number of infections). A nodule formed on day 11 at the position shown.

Fig. 6B. A root of *Vicia hirsuta* (inoculated with *Rhizobium leguminosarum*, strain 317) mapped at 5, 6, 8, and 13 days, showing the sites of infected hairs, etc.

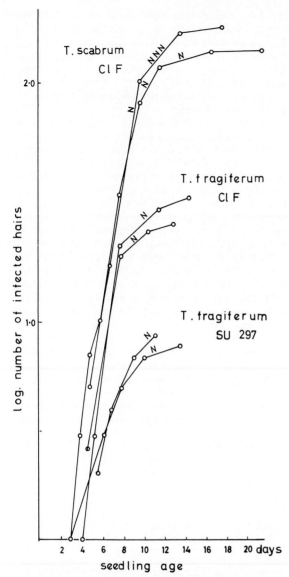

Fig. 7. Rates of infection on typical plants of *Trifolium scabrum* and *T. fragiferum,* inoculated with the strains of *Rhizobium* shown.

Trace amounts (10-25 µg nitrogen per root) of either of these ions delay nodule formation by 2 days (Gibson and Nutman, 1960) and this allows many more infections to take place because the initial rapid phase of infection is correspondingly prolonged. Similar amounts of ammonium nitrogen, urea, or asparagine do not delay nodulation and have no effect on the course of infection. Nitrate added at any time up to 7 days delays nodulation and stimulates infection equally, but added at 9 days or later has no effect (Darbyshire, 1963).

Nodule formation is not alone in inhibiting infection of root hairs; for the formation of a lateral rootlet inhibits about as strongly as does the formation of a nodule. This suggests that the inhibiting influence may originate in the growing meristem, which is very similar in both organs. Studies on the physiology of nodulation show that the nodule and lateral-root meristems also share the ability to inhibit nodule formation (Nutman, 1958). Whether these effects on infection and on nodule inception are expressions of the same basic inhibitory activity is not known. The incidence of infection and nodule formation are certainly not simply related, either in the course of normal seedling development of a single host, as we have seen, or more generally when strains and hosts are compared. Although some strains characteristically produce more infections than others, and some hosts are more susceptible to root-hair infection, neither of these factors controls the number of nodules formed; highly infective strains produce many nodules on some hosts and few on others (Nutman, 1962).

The number of surplus infections formed on a root depends primarily on the duration of the first rapid phase of infection (viz. on when infection and when nodulation starts, which are functions of both host and strain) and on the rate of infection (which may be a strain characteristic—Fig. 7).

Initial infection may be so limited that all or nearly all infections result in nodules, as in *Trifolium pratense* (Purchase, 1958); or some hundreds of hairs are infected for each nodule formed, as in *Trifolium fragiferum.*

The studies on which the above account has been based were all made with an adequate inoculum, and a large population of nodule bacteria, of the order of 10^7 cells per ml of rhizosphere fluid, was soon established in the rhizospheres of the experimental plants, so that it is improbable that the complex features of the distribution of infection correspond to any pattern of bacterial density in the rhizosphere. This conclusion was confirmed by direct observation—bacteria were not concentrated in those parts of the root most infected—and by Dr. Lim's (1963) experiments on the effect of inoculum size, discussed above, which showed that discontinuous patterns of infection occurred at all levels of the bacterial component.

EVIDENCE FOR FACTORS STIMULATING AND INHIBITING INFECTION.—*Effects of pairing and preplanting.*— The way infections spread from a few well-separated centres in the young root suggests that an "infection-stimulating" substance may be produced at these points and that this may then diffuse along the root and stimulate the infection of new hairs. To test the possible diffusion of such a substance into the root medium, infections were counted on plants grown singly and in pairs, and on plants grown in fresh medium and in medium already planted with seedlings—with techniques for culture of plants and observation of infection already described (Nutman, 1959). Six preplanting treatments were used, viz. all combinations of 1, 2, or 4 seedlings per culture, preplanted for 3 or 6 days before the single test seedlings were sown. The results in Table 1 show that the presence of other plants, or preplanting, did not stimulate infection; on the contrary, infections were slightly lower, though significantly only in cultures preplanted for 6 days with 4 seedlings.

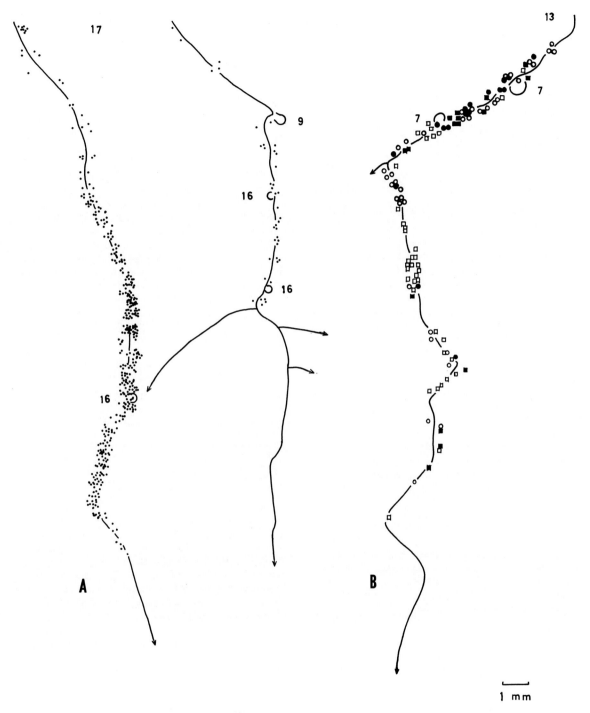

1 mm

Fig. 8A. Root maps of 2 seedlings of *Trifolium fragiferum* (inoculated with *Rhizobium trifolii*, strain C1 F) grown side by side on a Fåhraeus slide in the positions shown. The maps were made from observations 17 days from germination. The right-hand plant first nodulated at 9 days and the left-hand plant at 16 days.

Fig. 8B. Root map of 13-day seedling of *Trifolium fragiferum* (inoculated with *Rhizobium trifolii*, strain C1 F) showing distribution of apical (● = normal and ○ = arrested) and lateral (■ = normal and □ = arrested) infected hairs along the root.

TABLE 1. The effect of pairing and preplanting on number of infected hairs in *Trifolium fragiferum* inoculated with *Rhizobium trifolii*, strain C1 F

	Log.* of number of infected hairs
Expt. 1. (17-day count)	
Seedlings grown singly	2.357 ± 0.061
Seedlings grown in pairs	2.016 ± 0.171
Expt. 2. (14-day count)	
Seedlings grown on fresh media	1.912 ± 0.125
Seedlings grown on preplanted media (all treatments)	1.708 ± 0.127
Ditto (preplanted for 6 days with four seedlings)	1.388 ± 0.142

* Nodule number is not normally distributed; a logarithmic transformation is necessary for statistical treatment.

Infection started at the same time with all the treatments. Because nodule formation itself depresses further infection, the fewer infections found on paired plants may have been an expression of this inhibition. This possibility was examined in experiments with paired plants of white clover in which the primary nodulating time varied widely. As shown on the root maps in Fig. 8A, the depressing effect of nodulation on infection did not spread from one plant to another sharing the same culture vessel, even when one plant of a pair nodulated early and another late. If normal infection is governed by growth-promoting substances these evidently move only within the growing root and do not appear in root exudate.

The formation of root nodules probably requires substances elaborated in and translocated from the top of the plant. This was first suggested by the observation that first leaf opening and nodule initiation are synchronised (Thornton, 1930), and by the fact that nodules very rarely form on fully etiolated plants or on detached roots growing in true root culture (Lewis and McCoy, 1933). Roots freshly excised from 4-day-old seedlings of the black wax bean and soybean will nodulate regularly when they are supplied at the cut end with certain nitrogenous compounds and carbohydrate substrates (Raggio and Raggio, 1956; Raggio, Raggio, and Torrey, 1957). The process of hair infection was not studied in these experiments.

Infection on light- and dark-grown plants and the effect of seedling decapitation.—The influence of the top of the plant and of the products of assimilation on hair infection were examined in experiments made with plants grown in the dark, and with light-grown plants that had their tops removed at different times after germination.

Contrary to expectation, root hairs were fairly readily infected on plants grown in the dark, particularly in some species, although the numbers infected were fewer than on plants grown in the light (Table 2). No nodules were formed. Root maps showed that the spatial, but not the temporal pattern of infection was discontinuous on dark-grown plants. The legume seed therefore seems to contain the "factors" that are neces-

TABLE 2. Numbers of infected root hairs on clovers grown in light and in darkness (inoculated with *Rhizobium trifolii*, strain C1 F)

	Light	Dark
T. parviflorum		
At 5 days	40.0	19.9
At 9 days	107.0	45.0
At 12 days	132.1	60.0
At 15 days	125.0	76.1
T. fragiferum		
At 5 days	4.9	1.4
At 7 days	12.8	9.4
At 11 days	47.9	9.4
At 16 days	72.5	28.9

sary for infection, but these eventually become exhausted and they are maintained only when the whole seedling is assimilating.

The possible translocation of such essential factors from the part of the plant exposed to light was examined by removing the whole top of the plant (plumule and cotyledons) at 5 days, when infection was just beginning. Table 3 shows the number of infected hairs

TABLE 3. Effect of decapitation at 5 days on root-hair infection in *Trifolium* spp. (inoculated with *Rhizobium trifolii*, strain C1 F)

	Numbers of infected hairs at 17 days	
	Decapitated	Control
T. parviflorum	3	90
T. repens (Morso)	50	89
T. repens (S100)	6	31
T. fragiferum	38	74
T. nigrescens	2	40
T. glomeratum	3	26
T. patens	0	4

on the seventeenth day. Like darkness, decapitation depressed but did not prevent infection, and this effect was much greater with some hosts than with others. For example decapitation of *Trifolium parviflorum* almost stopped infection, although intact plants were abundantly infected. Infection on *Trifolium fragiferum* was much less affected by decapitation, and this host was selected for experiments on the effect of time of excision.

Table 4 shows that the effects of decapitation differed according to whether it was performed earlier or later

TABLE 4. Effect of time of decapitation on root-hair infection in *Trifolium fragiferum* (inoculated with *Rhizobium trifolii*, strain C1 F)

Average number of infected hairs at 16 days	
Control	55
Decapitated at	
2 days	2
3 days	83
4 days	61
5 days	38
6 days	25
7 days	22
8 days	31

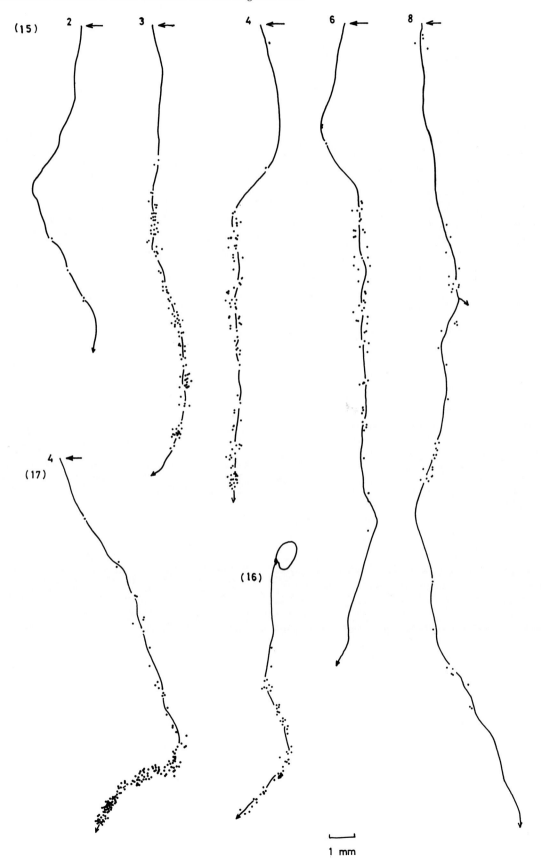

Fig. 9. Maps of 15- or 17-day-old roots of *Trifolium fragiferum* (inoculated with *Rhizobium trifolii*, strain C1 F) after decapitation at 2, 3, 4, 6, and 8 days, and of a 16-day-old seedling of *T. fragiferum* (inoculated with the same strain) the cotyledons of which were retained within the seed coat.

than about 4 days. Decapitation at 2 days almost stopped infection; at 3 days it increased the number of infections. At 4 days it also slightly stimulated infection, but later decapitation again decreased infection.

These results indicate that some factor necessary for infection-thread initiation comes from the cotyledons or plumule and that sufficient moves into the root by about the fourth day to allow the normal amount of infection to take place during the next 2 weeks. It is difficult to understand how decapitation between the fifth and tenth day again decreased the number of infections unless the continued production of stimulant is necessary to offset the inhibitory effects which appear from about the tenth day as a result of nodule and lateral-root formation.

Top excision markedly affects the distribution of infection along the root. This is shown in the root maps of seedlings decapitated at 2, 3, 4, 6, and 8 days from germination (Fig. 9). Decapitation at 3 and 4 days stands out both for the larger numbers of infection and for the way in which infected hairs are concentrated near the root tip; the normal zonation reappears with later excision. Also shown in Fig. 9 is a root of a 16-day-old seedling of *Trifolium fragiferum* which retained its cotyledons unexpanded within the testa. The distribution of infection along this root was similar to that of decapitated seedlings and its growth in length was similarly limited. There was large variation between individual plants in response to decapitation at 4 days, and those with the most infected hairs showed a regular increase in density of infection towards the root tip, especially in the lower half of the root. This is illustrated in Fig. 10, where the logarithms of the mean number of infected hairs on 0.1mm lengths of six decapitated roots of *T. fragiferum* are plotted against distance from the root apex. The points fall along two straight lines, the first extending 1.0 cm from the tip and the second taking in most of the rest of the root. This pattern in decapitated roots is in striking contrast to that of the intact seedling, in which infections occur further from the root tip. Measurements on the control roots in the same experiment showed that the average length of the apical part free from infections was 1.1 cm. Physiological age of the hairs could be invoked to account for the lack of infection near the root tip, although observation shows that very young hairs arising on the older parts of the root can become infected. Alternatively, hairs near the root tip might resist infection because of the inhibiting effect that has already been suggested might originate in the apices of nodules and lateral roots. That removal of the top reverses this supposed meristem inhibition does not necessarily invalidate the theory of meristem inhibition. If it is assumed that the inhibitory activity of the meristem of the root is linked in some way to growth, decapitation will destroy this inhibition because it soon stops the growth of the root apex.

Experiment on root-tip excision.—The possible inhibitory effect of the root apex was examined by cutting off root tips of 4-day and 8-day-old seedlings of *Trifolium repens*. Half of the excisions were made 1 mm

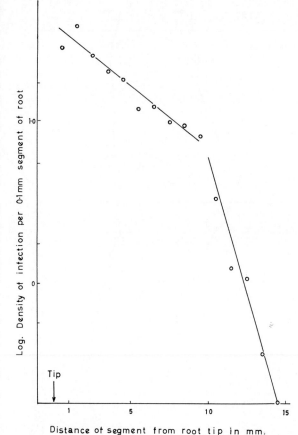

Fig. 10. The mean distribution of infection along the roots of seven plants of *Trifolium fragiferum* (inoculated with *Rhizobium trifolii*, strain C1 F) 17 days after decapitation at 5 days.

from the tips of the root cap and half 3 mm from the tip. The shorter tips were of meristematic tissue only, the longer ones included some extending cells and young root hairs. Table 5 shows the number of infected hairs counted on the seventeenth day.

No effect of excision was found in any treatment. This result, although appearing to argue against the theory of meristem inhibition, was inconclusive because of the rapid regeneration of root growing points—laterals appeared within 4 or 5 days and main apices regenerated within 6 days for the 4-day treatments and within 7 days for the 8-day treatments. This would

TABLE 5. The effect of root-tip excision on root-hair infection of *Trifolium repens* (inoculated with *Rhizobium trifolii*, strain C1 F)

Time of excision	Length of tip excised	Mean number of infections on day 17
Control		26.6
4th day	Short	25.4
4th day	Long	21.9
8th day	Short	23.2
8th day	Long	24.5

tend to counteract any stimulating effect of excision and by encouraging earlier lateral-root formation may also have a direct suppressing effect. The effect of excision on nodule formation differed between treatments: excision at 4 days slightly delayed and decreased nodulation, the 8-day short-tip treatment had no effect on nodulation, and only excision of long tips at 8 days stimulated earlier nodulation. Other experiments have shown that excision of root tips on older plants stimulates nodulation (Nutman, 1952). The distribution of infected hairs on treated and control plants was similar except that rather more infections occurred on the lateral rootlets of plants that had their root tips excised, as shown in Fig. 11.

GENERAL DISCUSSION.—In soil and in water a great diversity of bacteria share with plant roots a common habitat, and yet very few bacteria are pathogenic on roots. The common associations between bacteria and roots appear to be biologically neutral; or perhaps mildly beneficial, as with rhizosphere microorganisms; or definitely symbiotic, as with root-nodulating plants.

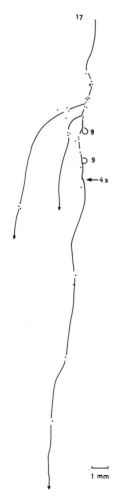

Fig. 11. Root map of *Trifolium repens* (inoculated with *Rhizobium trifolii*, strain C1 F) 17 days after excision of 1 mm of the root tip on the 4th day at the position shown.

Nodule bacteria and their legume hosts have become mutually adapted to increase the advantages each gains from the other; but the more that is learnt about this joint development, the less clear becomes its relation to disease.

As compared with pathogenesis, both bacterial and fungal, the infection process in symbiosis seems to be more complex and although still imperfectly understood, to be more closely integrated with the normal physiology of the host. Thus bacterial IAA may be plausibly implicated as an important factor in hair curling, by promoting local extension growth possibly by stimulating the metabolically linked reactions that are thought to interfere with the establishment of covalent linkages between polysaccharide chains (A. P. Brown, 1963). But nodule bacteria are not the only rhizosphere microorganisms to produce IAA (Katznelson and Sirois, 1961) and hair curling probably depends also on other factors. The mechanism of infection-thread formation remains unexplained. The hypothesis of invagination, which is a host reaction, offers reasonable explanations of many of the facts of infection. PG induction by the host seems to be concerned in this stage of the infection process, and in this respect the roles of nodule bacteria and certain root pathogens seem to be reversed; the fungus pathogen, instead of the host, is induced to form enzyme by the presence of substrate (Husain and Dimond, 1960); Deese and Stahmann, 1960).

The complex and orderly pattern of the location of infection along the root of the young seedlings seems to be controlled entirely by internal host factors, closely concerned with root growth, and it has been shown elsewhere (Nutman, 1958) that initiation and growth of the nodule itself is again coordinated with the processes in the root ordinarily concerned with meristem initiation.

It would be premature to formulate a complete theory of both infection and nodulation in terms of root morphogenesis, but it may be suggested as a working hypothesis that a precursor of an infection-promoting substance may originate in the plant top and be normally translocated towards the growing tip, and that an infection-inhibiting substance may be produced in the root meristems and move in the opposite direction. The primary zones of infection may reflect the localised transformation of precursor into active promoter-substance. This may take place in those parts of the root that are regions of incipient meristematic activity, and so give rise to regions of denser infection. In this way also, the high rate of infection on plants decapitated at about 4 days could be explained because the zones where the precursor is changed to promoting substance have not yet arisen in the normal seedling so the precursor will be translocated unaltered into the main root apex. However, this organ is already, because of decapitation, an "inhibited" meristem so it may become the site of production of promotor substance, and thus cause infection to be concentrated near the root tip.

No close parallel to these processes and patterns of infection can be found in root diseases, so that the study of legume symbiosis may have little to suggest to the phytopathologist in search of biological control. Because of its integration with host physiology, rhizobial symbiosis may be more homologous to highly specialised and obligate fungal parasites, such as rusts, and to mycorrhiza, where intracellular phases are prominent. In each the basic problems of infection may be similar, the parasite or symbiont having to establish, stage by stage, a closer and closer relation with its host: first in the rhizosphere (or rhizoplane), establishing the preconditions for infection, then intercellularly, and culminating in a pseudo-intracellular organisation that may be characteristic of symbiosis or obligate parasitism.

The elucidation of each stage in infection may now require a better understanding of the factors that induce activation and migration in the host nucleus and changes in the host-cell boundary membranes—the primary and secondary walls and the outer cytoplasmic membrane—and particularly those that cause or prevent pinocytosis. This involves fundamental questions of compatibility between unlike cells, embracing the field of immunology in animals and "plasmatic defence reactions" in plants (Gäumann, 1950; Müller, 1959).

LITERATURE CITED

ALLEN, E. K., and O. N. ALLEN. 1958. Biological aspects of symbiotic nitrogen fixation. vol. 8, p. 48-105. *In* A. Lang [ed.], Encyclopedia of plant physiology, Springer Verlag, Berlin.

ALLEN, E. K., and O. N. ALLEN. 1961. Nitrogen fixation. The scope of nodulation in the Leguminosae. p. 585-588. *In* Recent advances in botany (9th Intern. Botan. Congr., Montreal), University of Toronto Press, Toronto.

ALLEN, O. N., and E. K. ALLEN. 1954. Morphogenesis of the leguminous root nodule. p. 209-234. *In* Brookhaven Symposium in Biology, No. 6, Abnormal and pathological plant growth, Lupton, New York.

ALMON, L. 1933. Concerning the reproduction of bacteroids. Zentr. Bakteriol. Parasitenk., Abt. II, 87: 289-297.

BALASSA, R. 1954. Transformationsmechanismen der Rhizobein. Acta Microbiol. Acad. Sci. Hung. 2: 51-78.

BALASSA, R. 1960. Transformation of a strain of *Rhizobium lupini*. Nature (London) 188: 246-247.

BERGERSEN, F. J. 1961. The growth of *Rhizobium* in synthetic media. Australian J. Biol. Sci. 14: 349-360.

BERGERSEN, F. J., and M. J. BRIGGS. 1958. Studies on the bacterial component of soyabean root nodules: cytology and organisation of the host tissue. J. Gen. Microbiol. 19: 482-490.

BHIDE, S. V., and J. BRACHET. 1960. Study of the uptake of ribonuclease by onion root-tip cells. Exptl. Cell Res. 21: 303-315.

BOND, G. 1963. The root nodules of non-leguminous angiosperms. Symp. Soc. Gen. Microbiol. 13: 72-91.

BONNIER, C. 1954. Anti-*Rhizobium* properties of extracts of certain Leguminosae. Compt. Rend. Soc. Biol. 148: 1894-1896.

BONNIER, C. 1955. La conservation du *Rhizobium* en sols steriles (*Rhizobium* spécifique des *Trifolium*). Bull. Inst. Agron. Sta. Rech. Gembloux 23: 359-367.

BOUET, M. 1954. Études cytologique sur la developpment des poils absorbents. Rev. Cytol. Biol. Végétales 15 (4): 261-305.

BOWEN, G. D. 1961. The toxicity of legume seed diffusates towards rhizobia and other bacteria. Plant Soil 15: 155-165.

BOWEN, G. D., and M. M. KENNEDY. 1959. Effect of high soil temperature on *Rhizobium* spp. Queensland J. Agr. Sci. 16: 177-198.

BROWN, A. P. 1963. The chemical and mechanical state of the cell wall of pea root tips. J. Exptl. Botany 14: 114-131.

BROWN, M. E. 1961. Stimulation of streptomycin-resistant bacteria in the rhizosphere of leguminous plants. J. Gen. Microbiol. 24: 369-377.

BULLER, A. H. R. 1931. Researches on fungi. vol. 4, p. 222-223. Longmans, London.

BÜRGIN-WOLFF, A. 1959. Untersuchungen über die Infection von Wurzeln mit Knollchenbakterien. Ber. Schweiz. Botan. Ges. 69: 75-111.

BUVAT, R. 1958. Recherches sur les infrastructures du cytoplasme, dans les allules du mèristéme apical, des èbauches foliares et des feuilles developptes d'*Elodea canadensis*. Ann. Sci. Nat. Botan. Biol. Vegetale 19: 121-161.

CASAS-CAMPILLO, C. 1947. Bacterias aerobias esporuladas con propiedades antagonistas para *Rhizobium*. Ciencia (Méx.) 8: 108.

CASAS-CAMPILLO, C. 1951. Rhizobacidina un antibiotic con particular actividad para las bacterias de los nodulos de las leguminosas. Ciencia (Méx.) 11: 21-28.

CHEN, H. K. 1938. The production of growth substances by clover nodule bacteria. Nature (London) 142: 753-754.

CLARKE, P. H., and M. V. TRACEY. 1956. The occurrence of chitinase in some bacteria. J. Gen. Microbiol. 14: 188-196.

DARBYSHIRE, J. 1963. Clover root hair infection. Rothamsted Exptl. Sta. Rept. 1962: 78.

DATE, R. A., and J. M. VINCENT. 1962. Determination of the number of root-nodule bacteria in the presence of other organisms. Australian J. Exptl. Agr. Animal Husbandry 2: 5-7.

DEESE, D. C., and M. A. STAHMANN. 1960. Role of pectic enzymes to susceptibility and resistance to Fusarium and Verticillium wilts of plants. Phytopathology 50: 633.

DEMOLON, A., and A. DUNEZ. 1936. La fatigue des sols. Causes et remèdes. Compt. Rend. 202: 1704-1706.

DONALD, C. M. 1960. The impact of cheap nitrogen. J. Australian Inst. Agr. Sci. 26: 319-338.

FÅHRAEUS, G. 1957. The infection of clover root hairs by nodule bacteria, studied by a simple glass slide technique. J. Gen. Microbiol. 16: 374-381.

FÅHRAEUS, G. 1963. The deformation of clover root hairs by nodule bacteria and by their culture filtrates. Rothamsted Exptl. Sta. Rept. 1962: 77-78. (In press.)

FÅHRAEUS, G., and H. LJUNGGREN. 1959. The possible significance of pectic enzymes in root-hair infection by nodule bacteria. Physiol. Plantarum 12: 145-154.

FRASER, L. 1931. An investigation of *Lobelia gibbosa* and *L. dentata*. I. Mycorrhiza, latex system and general biology. Proc. Linn. Soc. N.S. Wales 56: 497-525.

FRED, E. B., I. L. BALDWIN, and E. McCOY. 1932. Root nodule bacteria and leguminous plants. Univ. Wisconsin, Madison, Wisconsin. 345 p.

GÄUMANN, E. 1950. Principles of plant infection. (Transl. by W. B. Brierley.) Crosby Lockwood, London. 543 p.

GIBSON, A. H., and P. S. NUTMAN. 1960. Studies on the physiology of nodule formation. VII. A reappraisal of the effects of preplanting. Ann. Botany (London) [N.S.] 24: 420-433.

GIRBARDT, M. 1962. Kernbewegungen. p. 920-939. *In* Handbuch der Pflanzenphysiologie, vol. 17 (2), Physiologie der Bewegungen, Springer Verlag, Berlin.

GRAHAM, P. H. 1963. Vitamin requirements of root nodule bacteria. J. Gen. Microbiol. 30: 245-248.

HELY, F. W., F. J. BERGERSEN, and J. BROCKWELL. 1957. Microbial antagonism in the rhizosphere as a factor in the failure of inoculation of subterranean clover. Australian J. Agr. Res. 8: 24-44.

HUSAIN, A., and A. E. DIMOND. 1960. Role of cellulolytic enzymes in pathogenesis by *Fusarium oxysporum* f. *lycopersici*. Phytopathology 50: 329-331.

JENSEN, H. L. 1961. Survival of *Rhizobium meliloti* in soil culture. Nature (London) 192: 682-683.

JENSEN, W. A., and A. D. McLAREN. 1960. Uptake of

proteins by plant cells—the possible occurrence of pinocytosis in plants. Exptl. Cell Res. 19: 414-417.

JORDAN, D. C. 1962. The bacteroids of the genus *Rhizobium*. Bacteriol. Rev. 26: 119-141.

JORDAN, D. C., I. GRINYER, and W. H. COULTER. 1963. Electron microscopy of infection threads and bacteria in young root nodules of *Medicago sativa*. J. Bacteriol. 86: 125-137.

KATZNELSON, H., and J. C. SIROIS. 1961. Auxin production by species of *Arthrobacter*. Nature (London) 191: 1323-1324.

KECSKÉS, M., and E. MANNINGER. 1962. Effect of antibiotics on the growth of rhizobia. Can. J. Microbiol. 8: 157-159.

KEFFORD, N. P., J. BROCKWELL, and J. A. ZWAR. 1960. The symbiotic synthesis of auxin by legumes and nodule bacteria and its role in nodule development. Biol. Sci. 13: 456-467.

KLECZKOWSKA, J. 1961. Transformation studies on *Rhizobium trifolii*. Rothamsted Exptl. Sta. Rept. 1961: 78.

KOSTERMANS, D. 1935. Over hetero-auxine. Dissertation, University of Utrecht.

KRASIL'NIKOV, N. A. 1958. Soil microorganisms and higher plants. Acad. Sci. U.S.S.R., Moscow. English ed., publ. National Sci. Foundation, Washington. 474 p.

LEWIS, K. H., and E. McCOY. 1933. Root nodule formation on the garden bean, studied by a technique of tissue culture. Botan. Gaz. 95: 316-329.

LIM, G. 1961. Microbial factors influencing infection of clover by nodule bacteria. Doctoral thesis, University of London.

LIM, G. 1963. Studies on the physiology of nodule formation. VIII. The influence of the size of the rhizosphere population of nodule bacteria on root-hair infection in clover. Ann. Botany (London) [N.S.] 27: 55-67.

LJUNGGREN, H. 1961. Transfer of virulence in *Rhizobium trifolii*. Nature (London) 191: 623.

LJUNGGREN, H., and G. FÅHRAEUS. 1961. The role of polygalacturonase in root-hair invasion by nodule bacteria. J. Gen. Microbiol. 26: 521-528.

McCOY, E. 1932. Infection by *Bact. radicicola* in relation to the microchemistry of the host's cell walls. Proc. Roy. Soc. (London), Ser. B, 110: 514-533.

MEANS, U. M., H. W. JOHNSON, and L. W. ERDMAN. 1961. Competition between bacterial strains affecting nodulation in soybeans. Soil Sci. Soc. Am. Proc. 25: 105-106.

MIEHE, H. 1901. Über Wanderungen des pflanzlichen Zellkerns. Flora (Jena) 88: 105-142.

MOORE, R. T., and J. H. McALEAR. 1960. Fine structure of mycota. 2. Demonstration of the haustoria of lichens. Mycologia 52: 805.

MÜLLER, K. O. 1959. Hypersensitivity. vol. 1, p. 469-519. *In* J. G. Horsfall and A. E. Dimond [ed.], Plant pathology, an advanced treatise, Academic Press, New York and London.

NICOL, H., and H. G. THORNTON. 1941. Competition between related strains of nodule bacteria and its influence on the infection of the legume host. Proc. Roy. Soc. (London), Ser. B, 130: 32-59.

NUTMAN, P. S., H. G. THORNTON, and J. H. QUASTEL. 1945. Inhibition of plant growth by 2:4-dichlorophenoxyacetic acid and other plant-growth substances. Nature (London) 155: 497.

NUTMAN, P. S. 1952. Studies on the physiology of nodule formation. III. Experiments on the excision of root-tips and nodules. Ann. Botany (London) [N.S.] 16: 79-101.

NUTMAN, P. S. 1956. The influence of the legume in root-nodule symbiosis. A comparative study of host determinants and functions. Biol. Rev. 31: 109-151.

NUTMAN, P. S. 1958. The physiology of nodule formation. p. 87-107. *In* E. G. Hallsworth [ed.], Nutrition of the legumes, Butterworths Scientific Publications, London.

NUTMAN, P. S. 1959. Some observations on root-hair infection by nodule bacteria. J. Exptl. Botany 10: 250-263.

NUTMAN, P. S. 1962. The relation between root hair infection by *Rhizobium* and nodulation in *Trifolium* and *Vicia*. Proc. Roy. Soc. (London), Ser. B, 156: 122-137.

NUTMAN, P. S. 1963. Factors influencing the balance of mutual advantage in legume symbiosis. Symp. Soc. Gen. Microbiol. 13: 51-71.

PURCHASE, H. F. 1952. Growth of Rhizobium in the root surroundings. Rothamsted Exptl. Sta. Rept. 1951: 60.

PURCHASE, H. F. 1958. Restriction of infection threads in nodulation of clover and lucerne. Australian J. Biol. Sci. 11: 155-161.

PURCHASE, H. F., and P. S. NUTMAN. 1957. Studies on the physiology of nodule formation. VII. The influence of bacterial numbers in the rhizosphere on nodule initiation. Ann. Botany (London) [N.S.] 21: 439-454.

RADULOVIC, V., and P. S. NUTMAN. 1963. Field experiments on legume inoculation. Rothamsted Exptl. Sta. Rept. 1962: 79-81.

RAGGIO, M., and N. RAGGIO. 1956. A new method for the cultivation of isolated roots. Physiol. Plantarum 9: 466-469.

RAGGIO, M., and N. RAGGIO. 1962. Root nodules. Ann. Rev. Plant Physiol. 13: 109-128.

RAGGIO, M., N. RAGGIO, and J. G. TORREY. 1957. The nodulation of isolated leguminous roots. Am. J. Botany 44: 325-334.

ROVIRA, A. D. 1955. Plant root excretions in relation to the rhizosphere effect. I. The nature of the root exudates from oats and peas. Plant Soil 7: 178-194.

ROVIRA, A. D. 1959. Root excretions in relation to the rhizosphere effect. IV. Influence of plant species, age of plant, light, temperature and calcium nutrition on exudation. Plant Soil 11: 53-64.

ROVIRA, A. D. 1961. Rhizobium numbers in the rhizospheres of red clover and paspalum in relation to soil treatment and numbers of bacteria and fungi. Australian J. Agr. Res. 12: 77-83.

ROVIRA, A. D. 1962. Plant root exudates in relation to the rhizosphere microflora. Soils Fertilizers 25: 167-172.

ROVIRA, A. D., and W. R. STERN. 1961. The rhizosphere bacteria in grass-clover associations. Australian J. Agr. Res. 12: 1108-1118.

SAHLMAN, K., and G. FÅHRAEUS. 1962. Microscopic observations on the effect of indole-3-acetic acid upon root hairs of *Trifolium repens*. Kgl. Lantbruks.-Högskol. Ann. 28: 261-268.

SCHAEDE, R. 1932. Das Schicksal der Bakterien in den Knöllchen von *Lupinus albus* nebst cytologischen Untersuchungen. Zentr. Bakteriol. Parasitenk., Abt. II, 85: 416-425.

SCHAEDE, R. 1940. Die Knöllchen der adventiven Wasserwurzeln von *Neptunia oleracea* und ihre Bakteriensymbiose. Planta 31: 1-21.

SMITH, W. K. 1955. The pectic enzymes of bacterial pathogens of plants. J. Gen. Microbiol. 13: xi.

SNIDER, P. J., and J. R. RAPER. 1958. Nuclear migration in the basidiomycete *Schizophyllum commune*. Am. J. Botany 45: 538-546.

SZENDE, K., T. SIK, F. ORDOGH, and B. GYÖRFFY. 1961. Transfer of immunity by nucleic acids of a lysogenic *Rhizobium* strain. Biochim. Biophys. Acta. 47: 215.

TAKAHASHI, I., and C. QUADLING. 1961. Lysogeny in *Rhizobium trifolii*. Can. J. Microbiol. 7: 455-465.

THIMANN, K. V. 1939. The physiology of nodule formation. Trans. Third Comm. Intern. Soc. Soil Sci. (New Brunswick, N.J.), vol. A, p. 24-28.

THOMPSON, J. A. 1960. Inhibition of nodule bacteria by an antibiotic from legume seed coats. Nature (London) 187: 619-620.

THORNTON, H. G. 1930. The early development of the root nodule of lucerne (*Medicago sativa* L.). Ann. Botany (London) 44: 385-392.

THORNTON, H. G. 1931. Lucerne "inoculation" and the factors affecting its success. Imp. Bur. Soil Sci., Tech. Commun. No. 20, 39 p. H. M. Stationery Office, London.

TSUZIMURA, K., and I. WATANABE. 1959. Estimation of numbers of root-nodule bacteria by the nodulation-dilution frequency method and some applications. Nippon Dojo-Hiryogaku Zasshi 30: 292-296.

VINCENT, J. M. 1958. Survival of root nodule bacteria. p. 108-123. *In* E. G. Hallsworth [ed.], Nutrition of the legumes, Butterworths Scientific Publications, London.

VINCENT, J. M. 1962. Presidential address. Australian Studies of the root-nodule bacteria. A review. Proc. Linn. Soc. N. S. Wales 87: 8-38.

VINCENT, J. M., J. A. THOMPSON, and K. O'DONOVAN.

1962. Death of root-nodule bacteria on drying. Australian J. Res. 13: 258-270.

WARD, H. M. 1887. On the tubercular swellings on the roots of *Vicia faba*. Phil. Trans. Roy. Soc. London, Ser. B, 178: 539-562.

WEILING, F. 1961. Pinocytose bei Pflanzen. Naturwissenschaften 48: 411-412.

WILSON, J. K. 1930. Season variation in the numbers of two species of *Rhizobium* in soil. Soil Sci. 30: 289-296.

▶ DISCUSSION OF P. S. NUTMAN PAPER

W. B. Bollen:

For studies of nodule distribution, was the seed or the medium inoculated? If the seed only, how do the *Rhizobium* migrate to distal portions of the root?

P. S. Nutman:

In the experiments described, the whole medium was inoculated, but under ordinary conditions in soil or other media, bacteria introduced on the seed are able to migrate along the root as rapidly as the root grows.

M. Alexander:

In view of your evidence of no stimulatory effect of preplanting and paired seedlings on the number of nodules and your earlier comments on the release of tryptophane, I.A.A., and another plant factor by the symbionts, have you noted a preplanting or paired-seedling influence on curling or infection? Further, is there any evidence suggesting how the large, specific, rhizobial, polysaccharide molecule induces the plant to form polygalacturonase?

P. S. Nutman:

No observations were made in the experiments I described of the effect of preplanting or associated growth on the amount or distribution of curled hairs; but both hair infection and nodule formation are reduced. I have no suggestions as to the mechanism of enzyme induction.

J. Ulrich:

The problem of entry into the cell can be separated into an initial penetration of the cell wall, which may occur by enzymatic dissolution, or possibly through wide spaces between microfibrils and into the region of the endoplasmic reticulum of the host cell. Do you think there is any evidence that pinocytosis (invagination of cell membrane) may function as a mechanism whereby the bacterial cells get into the cytoplasm of the host cells? (Note: should be called phagocytosis, since bacterial cells are solid particles.)

Also, I would appreciate your comments on the work of M. Raggio and N. Raggio with excised bean roots in axenic culture. Do you feel that their work has demonstrated the organic requirements normally provided by the top of the plant so that nodule formation can occur?

P. S. Nutman:

The escape of the bacteria from the vesicles into the nodule cell is envisaged as a process of pinocytosis, since only the plasmalemma seems to be involved. At the root-hair tip, on the other hand, the wall itself has been clearly shown by Sahlman's work to be invaginated

and this process seems more to be in the nature of redirected growth of the primary wall.

Raggio and Raggio's work on excised bean root is in accord with my suggestion that some necessary substance for infection comes from the seed because their excised root systems originated from 4-day-old seedlings, and I understand that it has not yet been possible to obtain nodules on second-transfer root cultures.

G. A. Zentmyer:

Reducing foliage of avocado seedlings results in decreased root rot caused by *Phytophthora cinnamomi*. Plants with intact foliage will average 95% of the roots rotted in the standard 10-day infection period. If half of the leaves are removed, the percentage of roots rotted drops to about 60%, and with all leaves removed, the percentage drops to about 40%. Excised roots from such plants show a correlation between attraction of roots for zoospores and condition of the foliage. Roots from plants with leaves removed showed less attraction for zoospores, per unit area of root, than roots from intact plants.

A. D. Rovira:

During earlier papers in this symposium it has been suggested that exudation may occur from the zone of root elongation behind the root tip. Did you observe any congregation of *Rhizobium* around particular regions of the roots?

P. S. Nutman:

In general, the older parts of the roots were more abundantly populated by bacteria, and no connection was noted between the presence of any local congregations of bacteria and infection-thread formation.

F. M. Scott:

Will future investigation indicate the significance of pits and plasmodesmata for entrance of bacteria?

P. S. Nutman:

This is an interesting suggestion, both with respect to the possible mechanism of infection-thread initiation, and the growth of the thread from cell to cell in the cortex or nodule.

L. I. Miller:

With the peanut, in which root hairs are not obligatory for infection by *Rhizobium*, we have found that there is an apparent competition for infection sites between the *Rhizobium* and the larvae of the northern root-knot nematode, *Meloidogyne hapla*, viz., the more root-knot galls, the fewer nodules formed. To make a critical study of this relation, we lack a quantitative measuring stick of the value to the plant of a certain number of nodules per unit of root. Do you have any suggestions how we might study this problem?

P. S. Nutman:

The sites of nodule formation in *Arachis* seem to be restricted to the axils of lateral roots, and this imposes a restriction on the experiments that can be designed to investigate this problem. The use of different strains of bacteria may be of some help.

L. I. Miller:

It is also of interest that the nematode, *Meloidogyne arenaria,* and the *Rhizobium* live in a commensal relation, that is, a nodule and root-knot gall consortium.

J. Altman:

Regarding the curling of root hairs due to infection, I would like to cite two instances of similar symptoms produced in the absence of a pathogen and one due to a virus.

I have observed for several years (1954-1957) that streptomycin, in the medium of plants grown in culture solutions, has induced the formation of curled and dichotomous root hairs. With onions and sugar beets, bromine in a soil fumigant can produce curled and reduced root hairs.

Curly top of sugar beets will induce the proliferation of short, dichotomous root hairs which, in some instances, will be curled. I have observed this in the field.

P. S. Nutman:

The significance of root-hair curling by secretions of *Rhizobium* is its restriction to legumes, and it would be of interest to determine whether any of the other agents that can deform root hairs have the same specificity.

S. M. Alcorn:

Within recent years attention has been increasingly given to the relative effects of red and far-red light on various physiological processes in plants, ranging from seed germination and internode elongation to coloring in apple fruits. However, I have yet to hear of studies of the relation of such light exposures to plant infections. Have you, by chance, studied such a relation (i.e. exposure of legumes to red or far-red light) in root infection and nodule formation?

P. S. Nutman:

No, our experiments were carried out in a growth cabinet with mixed fluorescent and incandescent lighting.

Summary and Synthesis of Papers on the Soil, the Plant Root, and the Rhizosphere

ALLEN KERR—*Department of Plant Pathology, Waite Agricultural Research Institute, University of Adelaide, South Australia. (Now on secondment to the Tea Research Institute, St. Coombs, Talawakella, Ceylon.)*

I have the unenviable task of "summarising and synthesizing" nine papers dealing with such widely diverse topics as soil physics, soil chemistry, root anatomy, root physiology, and many aspects of soil microbiology. None of these topics deals directly with behaviour of plant pathogens in soil. Instead of summarising each paper, I propose to discuss points which were mentioned by the speakers, or raised in discussion, points which I think have an important bearing on soil-borne plant diseases.

My main theme will be "root exudates" because all papers were relevant to this topic; I shall, however, raise other matters in passing. I consider the greatest advance we have made recently in studying the behaviour of plant pathogens in soil has been through understanding, to some extent at least, the role played by root exudates. As I understand it, fungal propagules are normally dormant in soil and remain so until stimulated to grow by nutrients such as carbohydrates and amino acids or by other more specific materials; and for plant pathogens, the most important source of these materials is the growing root. The more we know, therefore, of root exudates and their effects, the more likely we are to find methods of controlling soil-borne diseases.

Dr. Rovira presented a very comprehensive list of chemicals which have been reported as root exudates. This is very valuable information, but I think we have reached the stage where an extension of this list would be relatively unprofitable unless the specific effects of these materials were determined. Unfortunately the characterisation of chemicals that cause specific effects appears to be exceedingly difficult, the outstanding example being the identification of the cyst-hatching factor of *Heterodera rostochiensis*. Nevertheless these materials are very important and more work should be done on them. Dr. Harley pointed out that infection of tree roots by mycorrhizal fungi is dependent on a specific stimulus that is correlated with a high level of carbohydrate in the root.

We still do not know the mechanism of exudation, whether it is a simple leakage or an active process, but Drs. Scott and Burström have indicated why exudation is greatest in the zone of cell elongation. Here the cell walls are relatively thin, the microfibrils become arranged horizontally allowing pores (0.2 μ in diameter) to develop, so that there is probably high permeability associated with high metabolic activity.

Although not directly relevant to root exudates, I must mention other points of plant-pathological importance which arose from the papers on root anatomy and root physiology. Dr. Scott stated that the younger xylem elements are alive, and this could be very important in the establishment of vascular pathogens. I had always assumed that once wilt fungi entered the vascular tissue, the only factor likely to influence development would be the availability of substrate, but active resistance may also be involved. Great interest was shown in the mucigel which appears to be present on the surface of all roots. Its significance in plant pathology is not apparent, but it was compared with the waxy layer of shoots and it seems not unlikely that it influences infection. The contention that the outer cortex and epidermis of roots are not essential to plants raises the question of the pathogenicity of cortical invaders. It would suggest that the pathogenic effects could be the result of toxins, rather than of tissue damage. Protein uptake by roots was a controversial topic raised by Dr. McLaren in discussion, but the evidence indicates that soil-borne viruses are unlikely to enter roots by this mechanism.

Let us return to root exudates. I have already mentioned that root exudates cause the germination of propagules of plant pathogens. There may be, however, complex interactions between roots and microorganisms or between different microorganisms, such as the attraction of nematodes by fungi and bacteria reported by Dr. Katznelson. In the infection of legumes by *Rhizobium* spp. described by Dr. Nutman, root exudates containing tryptophane stimulate bacteria which produce indoleacetic acid, the substance considered to be responsible for the curling of root hairs which precedes infection. Infection leading to nodulation is dependent on the presence of a specific bacterial polysaccharide, which in turn induces the formation of a polygalacturonase by the roots. The significance of these interactions is not fully understood.

I don't think there is any definite evidence that plants benefit from rhizosphere organisms, except of course, from mycorrhizas and *Rhizobium* and possibly from the inoculation of nonlegumes with certain bacteria, such as *Azotobacter*. Dr. Nicholas reported that soil microorganisms may cause solubilisation or precipitation of nutrients; some may provide the plant with nitrogen, while others compete with it for this or other nutrients. They can antagonise pathogens, but also attract them and stimulate their growth. But we still do not know in any detail what organisms are beneficial, what harmful, how to determine what organisms are beneficial, what harmful, how to encourage one and discourage the other. This, to my mind, is the most important question relevant to biological control that arose from the nine papers.

First of all, how do we determine which organisms are beneficial, which harmful? I am not convinced that the correct approach is by model systems. In root-disease research, what happens in a simple environment may bear little or no relation to what happens in the complex soil environment. Until we started studying the natural environment we made little progress in understanding soil-borne disease. I suspect that the same might apply here. The effect on plant growth or on disease protection of inoculating non-legumes with bacteria can be tested as easily in natural soil as in a model system. It may be difficult to study the development of the inoculated organism in natural soil, but fluorescent microscopy should be a very useful tool. After we have selected certain microorganisms because they affect plant growth or for some other attribute and have determined their fate under natural soil conditions after inoculation, then, and only then in my opinion, should we consider model systems to study the mechanisms involved.

How can we alter the rhizosphere flora? Theoretically there are several ways to approach this problem. First there is direct inoculation of seed or roots, a method which is practised widely in the U.S.S.R. If I had been asked twelve months ago about the prospects of this approach I would have been very pessimistic; but recent results from America, the United Kingdom, and Australia, make me slightly more optimistic. It surprised me that an organism such as *Azotobacter,* which is not normally a successful root coloniser, can become established in the rhizosphere after seed inoculation. In my work with a fast-growing species of *Pseudomonas,* seed and root inoculation of tomatoes did not result in an increased population on the root surface. This method of altering the rhizosphere flora must be fully explored.

Second, we can alter the nature and amount of root exudate. We know that temperature, light, and soil moisture can affect this, but we cannot readily adjust these factors in the field. Much more promising is foliar application of chemicals, many of which have been shown to influence root exudates. I suspect, however, that the effects may be transitory and it is somewhat unrealistic to consider spraying plants every week with substances such as urea. Nevertheless we must learn more about foliar application of chemicals and its influence on exudation from roots and determine if such treatments influence infection of plants by pathogens.

A major advance in the control of soil-borne diseases would be the development of a systematic fungicide which could eliminate pathogens within the plant.

Soil physical and chemical factors which were discussed by Drs. Raney and Chapman respectively and which operate outside the plant can influence root exudates, both quantitatively and qualitatively. It is surprising how little work has been done by plant pathologists on soil physical factors. Before root exudates can affect plant pathogens they must diffuse through soil. I have recently been working on this problem and I have strong evidence that the influence of soil moisture on infection of peas by *Pythium* operates by affecting the amount of sugar lost from seeds. Diffusion of chemicals with a positive charge will be considerably influenced by negatively charged clay and organic colloids. But it is difficult to see how these physical factors can readily be altered to favour the crop and inhibit the pathogen.

One of the most intriguing problems in soil-borne diseases is the marked difference in buildup of a disease in two soils which may appear to be very similar and which have had the same cropping history. In the discussion of Dr. Raney's paper, Dr. Stotsky presented evidence for a strong correlation between rate of development of Panama disease and the presence or absence of a montmorillonoid clay in the soil. The suggested mechanism involving buffering of the soil, which in turn determines the duration of microbial activity, is very interesting and may have much wider implications. Perhaps the application of 5 tons of calcium sulphate to peanuts, also mentioned in the discussion, is effective in controlling disease for a similar reason.

In the citrus-replant problem described by Dr. Chapman, soil fumigation before replanting may give a 0-211% increase in yield. Although yield increase is probably due to control of known or unknown root pathogens, the marked variation in the effectiveness of fumigation would suggest that soil physical and chemical factors are involved, either influencing the distribution of pathogens, or affecting the efficiency of fumigation. Many other soil chemical factors have been shown to influence the incidence of disease. Those mentioned include pH and phosphate interactions, nitrite accumulation, and the contrasting effects of calcium and magnesium versus sodium and potassium on infection of beans by *Rhizoctonia.*

In studying the effects of various factors on soil-borne diseases it is often very difficult to determine whether these factors operate through affecting the host plant, the pathogen, or the soil microflora, or whether a complex interaction between all three is involved. At present it appears that each soil-crop-pathogen combination requires a separate study and generally it is not possible to extrapolate from one set of conditions to another. There should, however, be general principles applicable to the biological control of soil-borne diseases, and the definition of such principles is urgently needed.

► DISCUSSION OF ALLEN KERR PAPER

H. Katznelson:

There are several comments that should be made in connection with your remarks.

1. Granted that it is dangerous to extrapolate from model systems, it is nevertheless essential to isolate organisms to determine their activities, physiological as well as biochemical, and to find out what they are capable of doing under controlled conditions. This need not be done under unusual conditions—in solution or on glass beads; it can be done in gamma-irradiated soil. When you have a few billion organisms in soil, how else are you going to find out which does what?

2. Colonization of roots by organisms such as *Azotobacter* is not as clear-cut as mentioned, as results of work in many laboratories, including our own, attest. Other microorganisms present in large numbers on plant roots might prove much more effective. Even if you establish *Azotobacter* at perhaps the level of 40,000 or so per g of rhizosphere soil, is this so significant when you consider that 10^{12} cells make up 1 g of cells?

3. Considering foliar application in affecting the rhizosphere micropopulation, no one suggests that spraying plants with suitable substances be a weekly affair. But plants could be sprayed at a time when it is considered that they are most susceptible to a particular soil-borne pathogen.

A. Kerr:

1. Model systems can be of great value, but in studying the inoculation of nonlegumes with bacteria, experiments with model systems are likely to give very misleading results. I consider it likely that many organisms will grow on plant roots and influence plant growth in model systems, even a relatively complex system, but not in natural soils. Conversely, organisms that do not develop satisfactorily in model systems, may do so in natural soils. The effect of bacterial inoculation on plant growth can be determined just as easily in natural soil as in a model system. The results of these tests will indicate which organisms to select for more detailed study. With many bacteria, the populations on the root surface or in the rhizosphere can be determined in natural soil, and with those whose identification is difficult, fluorescent microscopy might prove very useful. Model systems may be required to explain the effects of bacterial inoculation on growth of nonlegumes, but to determine if there is an effect, natural soil should be used.

2 and 3. No comment.

S. Wilhelm:

We certainly have insufficient evidence to write off the essentiality of the root cortex for healthy plant growth. To be sure, in cambial roots (the structural system) the cortex is sloughed off and replaced by a bark. Its early destruction, or even invasion, by pathogens is injurious. The noncambial feeder rootlet system is essentially cortex, and its destruction is tantamount to destruction of the absorptive surface, and is manifest in loss of vigor and reduced growth of plants. This is based largely on studies of the strawberry root system.

C. G. Dobbs:

Hinson tried fluorescent microscopy and found that results will depend on the type of soil used. In our forest soils, fluorescent dyes do not show up spores. Even in a sediment, 20% of the particles of which showed by germination that they were spores, scarcely any of them showed up with fluorescent staining before swelling prior to germination, owing to their occlusion by mineral material. On the other hand, I have seen other soils in which the spores do show up.

At Bangor, we have been trying to study effects of sugars formed in soil extracts on spore germination in the presence of inhibitors in soil. In general, of course, they stimulate germination and growth. Occasionally we get an anomalous result, e.g. galactose raised from 0.01 M to 0.05 M suddenly fails to cause any germination in *Penicillium frequentans;* there is no such effect on *Mucor rammanianus.*

It is known that light intensity can influence type of mycorrhizal infection. Is anything else known about the selective effect of the particular sugars exuded by roots or present in the mucigel layer, or the type of fungus which dominates the rhizosphere or rhizoplane?

A. Kerr:

I know of no work on the selective effect of monosaccharides on rhizosphere fungi.

B. N. Richards:

Substantiation of claims for fixation of nitrogen by microorganisms in the rhizosphere must be made by techniques involving N^{15}. In a recent trial, *Pinus radiata* seedlings growing aseptically in nitrogen-free agar were inoculated with a mixed culture containing nitrogenfixing anaerobes. The initial effect was to retard elongation of the primary root, but subsequently this trend was reversed, and when harvested at 21 weeks of age, the taproots of inoculated seedlings were nearly twice as long as those of the controls. Lateral root development was also much enhanced by inoculation, as too was dry-matter production and, to a lesser degree, total nitrogen content. To test whether these responses were due to nitrogen fixation in the rhizosphere, the seedlings were exposed to an atmosphere enriched in N^{15}. While generally greater enrichment occurred in the inoculated seedlings, one of the uninoculated, and apparently uncontaminated, controls also showed enrichment.

Again by means of the N^{15} technique, we have confirmed Stevenson's claim that nitrogen fixation occurs in association with the roots of *Pinus radiata.* Whether this is a rhizosphere effect, or due to incorporation of nitrogen fixed by microorganisms outside the rhizosphere, remains to be seen.

F. E. Clark:

With respect to the occurrence of erratic or puzzling N^{15} data, Arnold Martin has recently noted that mass spectrometer assemblies are capable of showing some quite pronounced "memory effects."

A. D. Rovira:

As I pointed out in the discussion of Dr. Nicholas' paper, the results obtained with model systems must be interpreted with caution, but nevertheless they are an important tool in studying the mechanisms operating in the rhizosphere. I consider that the soil system in its entirety is much too complicated to discover why there is a selective stimulation of microorganisms in the rhizosphere, but this may be overcome by using model systems of increasing complexity.

If I may return to the point of inoculation with *Azotobacter;* I'd like to discuss one reason why *Azotobacter* has certain advantages in these inoculation soils. *Azotobacter* is not found in many soils, so its behaviour can be followed in any inoculation studies in these soils. By using such organisms, which can be easily distinguished from native microflora, we do have an opportunity of studying the behaviour of a particular organism in the complex soil environment.

The fact that it has been possible by seed inoculation to establish *Azotobacter, Clostridium,* and *Bacillus* in the rhizosphere of wheat growing in nonsterile sand does indicate the possibility of controlling the rhizosphere population. In a fertile soil with 6% organic matter, we had no definite evidence of establishment of these organisms in the rhizosphere 7 weeks after planting, although there was an increase in growth. However, there must have been some establishment, and possibly dominance, of these organisms in the rhizosphere in order to affect plant growth. The possible mechanisms responsible for this stimulation in growth were discussed earlier. These results certainly do hold out some hope for the biological control of root diseases by seed inoculation.

PART V

PATHOGENESIS AND RESISTANCE

Pathogenesis by Soil Fungi

N. T. FLENTJE—*Department of Plant Pathology, Waite Agricultural Research Institute, University of Adelaide, South Australia.*

►

Pursuit of knowledge in any field is continually hampered by misunderstandings over terminology. The misunderstandings may arise either improperly, through careless use of the terms, or properly, because the meaning of the term itself must be progressively defined on the basis of investigational work in the field. In plant pathology the terms parasitism, pathogenesis, and virulence are often misunderstood for either or both of the above reasons, despite the regular admonitions in textbooks and review papers covering the field.

Parasitism, a term used more intensively in the early days of plant pathology, has, perhaps unfortunately, become less significant. Superficially we can define parasitism as the process whereby one organism lives at the expense of another; but a more critical analysis brings trouble when we attempt to set limits, either on the host material the parasite uses, as in the case of rhizosphere organisms, or on the contributions the parasite makes to the host, as in the case of symbionts. *Pathogenesis,* as has been ably emphasized by Horsfall and Dimond (1960), is the process or mechanism whereby one organism causes suffering in another. Investigation of pathogenesis, at least for the present, has become a much more important field to the plant pathologist than investigation of parasitism. We should, however, keep clearly in mind that the latter is often an essential part of the former. *Virulence* is a qualification of pathogenesis and should be used to describe the extent, in time or severity, of the pathogenicity of one organism to another.

A change in host range of an organism is then a change in pathogenicity, whereas a change in severity of pathogenesis is a change in virulence. Changes in virulence are much more commonly recorded in the literature than changes in pathogenicity, but there are many instances where it is impossible to determine which type of change has occurred because the conclusions are based only on gross symptomatology and the detailed interaction of host and pathogen has not been studied. Nevertheless, organisms exhibiting changes in virulence or pathogenicity are providing the main tools for investigation of pathogenesis from the genetical or physiological approaches. It is increasingly important to distinguish between differences in pathogenicity and virulence because, as investigations proceed, the possibility of correlating the genetical and physiological information for each host-pathogen interaction becomes more real.

In this paper, rather than add to the existing reviews of pathogenesis by Allen (1959*b*), Braun and Pringle (1959), Dickinson (1960), Wood (1960), Ludwig (1960) and others, I feel it is my task to offer constructive criticism and to attempt some synthesis and stimulation by incorporating ideas and hypotheses which seem feasible, even if at present they have scant experimental support.

METHODS FOR TESTING PATHOGENICITY.—How dull a start for any attempt at stimulation! Yet the methods used to a large extent determine the type of information obtained; this is especially important in studies on soil fungi, where there are so many possibilities for interaction effects between the host, the pathogen, and other organisms. Details of individual methods concern us less in this discussion than the general principles behind the methods. Basically three approaches have been used as follows:

1. Direct addition of the test organism to natural or amended soil in which the host plants are grown, and the natural soil microflora is present.

2. Direct opposition of the test organism to the host in sterile sand or soil or on surfaces such as glass slides in a moisture chamber, where other microorganisms are excluded.

3. Indirect opposition of the test organism to the host by the testing of culture filtrates or extracts of the organism on host tissues.

These different approaches yield quite different types of information, the extent of the information depending largely on the detailed analysis of the interaction.

If the first approach is used, the organism has to grow through the soil in competition with other organisms to be pathogenic. Resulting symptoms in the host indicate the organism was able to grow through the natural soil; in fact this approach is often used specifically to study ability to grow through soil. But it gives no indication how the organism entered the host or how pathogenesis was effected. If no symptoms result, it is difficult, without using other approaches, to determine whether the organism was avirulent, nonpathogenic, or simply unable to grow in the soil.

If the second approach is used, competition from other microorganisms is removed so that little, if any, information on behavior in natural soil is obtained; but the host can be studied directly for information on entry of the organism, type of tissue damaged, and the rate of damage in the absence of other organisms.

If the third approach is used, no information is obtained on growth of the pathogen in soil or mechanism of entry into the host, but the possible mechanisms involved in pathogenesis can be critically studied.

It is obvious that all three approaches are complementary, each yielding information on a different aspect of pathogenesis. If we are to fill in the serious gaps in our knowledge of pathogenesis in almost every host-pathogen reaction, all these approaches must be explored.

Each approach has as many variations, expressed in individual experimental methods, as there are research workers in the field. It is not my purpose to survey the variety of methods. It is sufficient to say that study of some host-pathogen interactions will require special individual methods, whereas in many others more standardized methods are gradually emerging with more critical approaches to the problem. Such standardization, if accepted and objectively followed as it should be, will avoid unnecessary variables in experimentation and will allow a more constructive comparison of the findings of different workers, leading to the development of a more complete picture of pathogen behavior.

A diversion here regarding population studies of pathogens is, I feel, justified, although the subject will be treated more adequately elsewhere in the symposium. Bacteriologists have made significant advances in estimating bacterial populations in soil, but plant pathologists are still frustrated by the inherent difficulties in isolating fungi and estimating populations from spore and hyphal studies. There is now, however, sufficient information regarding some pathogenic fungi to be able, by artificial infestation, to reproduce for pot-culture work soils roughly equivalent to field soils in pathogen population (Kerr, 1963). Further development along these lines, by clarifying the meaning of such terms as inoculum potential (Garrett, 1960) will greatly assist our investigation of pathogenesis.

MECHANISMS OF PATHOGENESIS.—The mechanisms of pathogenesis at present appear to fall into two classes, namely, enzyme activity and "the rest."

The role of enzymic activity postulated by de Bary (1886) was brilliantly developed by Brown (1936, 1955) and his colleagues and there can be little, if any, doubt that enzymes from the pathogen play a large part in tissue rotting, wilting, and other diseases. Enzyme chemistry is of such importance in all biological fields that investigations along these lines in plant pathology have had the advantages of varied and exact techniques, enabling the host-pathogen interactions to be worked out in detail.

"The rest," as it is so often used in a derogatory sense, may be an unfair term. "Toxin" may be more agreeable but there is so little relation physiologically or chemically between the materials presently known, as emphasized by Ludwig (1960), that a grouping under the term toxin may prove a hindrance to thinking and investigation. The growing list of toxic materials cited by Braun and Pringle (1959) and Ludwig (1960) which

have been isolated, identified, and critically but successfully tested on the host, leaves us in no doubt about the importance in pathogenesis of toxic materials other than enzymes.

ACTION OF AN ORGANISM EXTERNAL TO THE HOST.—There is ample evidence that soil fungi are directly pathogenic to plants without entering them. The field has been reviewed recently by Ludwig (1960), who points out that some of these interactions have been known for a long time.

In some instances the known toxic materials, such as aldehydes and HCN (Skinner, 1918; Brauns, 1952; Lebeau and Dickson, 1955) are not produced specifically by the fungus but are by-products from the breakdown of a particular substrate. The occurrence and effect of such materials will be capricious, depending first on the occurrence of the organism and substrate to produce the toxic material in sufficient quantity, and second on soil conditions which slow down the further breakdown or disappearance of the toxic material itself (Graham and Greenberg, 1939).

In other instances, as those cited below, although no clear proof appears to have been furnished, it seems that the toxin is constitutively produced directly by the pathogen rather than indirectly through substrate breakdown. The work of Leukel (1948) and Oswald (1951) on milo disease is an outstanding example where the disease, specific to certain varieties, occurring regularly each year, and building up in severity with continued cropping, is due to a toxic metabolite of the fungus *Periconia circinata,* although the fungus itself does not appear to invade the plant. Other well-recognized diseases, such as tobacco frenching, appear to be caused at least in part (Steinberg, 1952) in a similar manner.

It is surprising in fact that there are still so few documented records of this type of pathogenesis, when we consider the influence of the rhizosphere and the variety of metabolites that are produced in soil, along with the newer varieties of crop plants which have been bred with no conscious selection against such pathogenesis.

It may well be, however, that some of the diseases where no associated pathogen has been found may prove to be of this kind. Our steadily increasing knowledge of the soil microflora will make possible a much more thorough search for such relations.

In addition to direct pathogenesis it seems very probable that materials such as aldehydes produced in soil, while not causing visible injury to plants, nevertheless render the plants more susceptible to pathogens such as *Pythium* and *Helminthosporium* (Rands and Dopp, 1938; Graham and Greenberg, 1939; Ludwig, 1957). The frequency and importance of these effects are not known, but they are unlikely to be confined to one or two diseases caused by *Pythium* and *Helminthosporium.* Furthermore, where so many fungi are known to invade plants only through wounds, I think it probable that the killing of epidermal and cortical cells by metabolites produced in soil would increase substantially the infection by these wound parasites. Wilhelm

(1959) has demonstrated a particular situation of this type in relation to strawberry roots in which the inner dead wood is invaded consistently, probably through wounds, by *Cylindrocarpon radicicola* alone or in association with other organisms. Wilhelm believes *C. radicicola* and the associated organisms, after establishment in the roots, contribute substantially to the death of roots by the liberation of toxic metabolites, and he suggests this type of pathogenesis may be relatively common in perennial plants.

It is interesting that in the work done to date in this field there is little, if any, indication that enzymes produced in soil outside the host plant play any significant part in this pathogenesis. It is perhaps unlikely that enzymes produced at some distance away from roots would affect the roots; but enzymes produced in the rhizosphere, especially on the rhizoplane, might be expected to exert a significant effect unless, as has been strongly suggested, the root is better protected by cuticle than we have previously thought.

Entry into Host.—Work in this field has been reviewed in recent years (Eide, 1955; Flentje, 1959; Dickinson, 1960; and Wood, 1960). Investigations reported since the latest review are discussed later in this section.

Host penetration has been accepted as an accomplished fact for most pathogens by many workers without any detailed examination of the actual process. Yet it would appear from direct or indirect studies, that:

1. The majority of fungi do not penetrate host surfaces on which they grow.

2. Those pathogenic fungi which penetrate usually do so by specialized structures, most commonly an appressorium, which is unique to this situation.

3. There are important behavioral differences between those organisms which enter through intact surfaces and those which enter through wounds.

Apart from the studies of Dickinson (1960) and a few others (Nusbaum and Keitt, 1938; Kerr and Flentje, 1957; and Allen, 1957), little basic work has been carried out on the infection stage of pathogenesis since the early exploratory work, despite the fact that host resistance to many potential pathogens may be determined at this stage and a better understanding of it could lead to new avenues of disease control.

The main task is to obtain an insight into the physiology and biochemistry of appressorium formation.

Most of the investigational work has been carried out by studying infection following germination of air-borne spores and the thorough work of Brown (1936) and his colleagues on the contact-stimulus theory has been accepted as sufficient explanation. Investigation has probably been restricted also by the frequent statement that penetration by a pathogen occurs equally freely on resistant and susceptible varieties of a particular host, suggesting that resistance must be looked for as an internal factor. There is, however, very little information available on the behavior even of germinating air-borne spores on nonhost plants, and such information is necessary to gain a proper perspective.

We have continued our studies on the mechanism of infection of different hosts by *Thanatephorus cucumeris* (= *Pellicularia filamentosa*, *Rhizoctonia solani*). We have been able to obtain infection-cushion formation by *Thanatephorus* on collodion membranes overlying either the host tissue or agar blocks containing exudate from the host, thus demonstrating that the infection structures are formed in response to materials from undamaged hosts (Flentje, Dodman and Kerr, 1963). These structures are illustrated in Fig. 1. Different single-spore isolates from a parent field strain of the fungus show differing responses to exudate material, strongly suggesting that the response is genetically controlled and may be an important aspect of pathogenic specialization. The identification of the responsible host materials has, however, still eluded us because of difficulties in bioassay techniques and in obtaining sufficient amounts of the active materials. Some of the studies, however, have been repeated by other workers (Christou, 1962) with substantial agreement in the results.

Little is known at present of host varieties within one species that differ in susceptibility to *Rhizoctonia* (Kernkamp et al., 1952), but Barker and Walker (1962) have, in agreement with our own results, shown that strains of *Rhizoctonia* which infect some hosts fail to infect plants in other genera.

T. Kommedahl (personal communication), working in Adelaide, investigated the spore germination and subsequent growth and penetration of different races of *Fusarium oxysporum* f. *pisi* in relation to root growth of resistant and susceptible pea varieties. His results differed from those of Buxton (1957) in that he found no significant difference in the effect of root exudates on spore germination and hyphal growth, but there were marked differences in the attachment of hyphae to root surfaces. Hyphae of a race pathogenic to a particular variety attached firmly to the root and penetrated, whereas those of a race not pathogenic to the variety largely failed to attach. Armstrong and Armstrong (1960), however, suggest that some of the wilt fusaria will enter a range of nonhost plants, thus differing from the earlier results of Snyder and Hansen (1940).

Zentmyer (1961) demonstrated clearly that the movement of zoospores of *Phytophthora cinnamomi* towards avocado roots, the directional growth of germ tubes, and the site of infection were largely determined by exudates from the roots. Further, he obtained evidence that the active materials in the exudate were specific in their action and did not influence the zoospores of *P. citrophthora*, whereas exudate from citrus roots did affect the latter.

There is thus accumulating sufficient information on the mechanism of entry into plants by several soil fungi to indicate that host entry is not inevitable, even when potentially pathogenic fungi impinge on the host surface. It has long been obvious that the majority of saprophytic organisms in the rhizosphere make no attempt to enter the host. Presumably our investigations of the rhizosphere-rhizoplane effect will, in the future, move from general growth studies to more

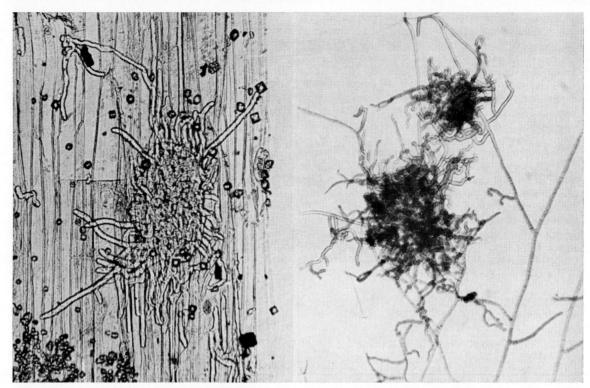

Fig. 1. Infection cushions formed by *Thanatephorus cucumeris* isolate 69: left, on radish stems; right, on collodion over agar blocks containing radish exudate. (N. T. Flentje, R. L. Dodman, and A. Kerr, Austral. J. Biol. Sci. 16: 784-799. 1963.)

specific effects, including that of host penetration. If the materials postulated by various workers mentioned above are as active as they appear, their isolation and identification, followed by the synthesis of analogues, could pave the way for new advances in disease control, just as the analogues of hormones in higher plants have led to effective weed control.

ACTION OF AN ORGANISM INTERNAL TO THE HOST.—
The action of enzymes.—There is little doubt that after host entry, enzymes play an important part in pathogenesis, probably for most diseases other than those characterized by hyperplasia, and the subject has been ably reviewed recently by Wood (1959, 1960) and Husain and Kelman (1959).

The evidence is best documented for pectic enzymes because of the progress made in understanding the chemistry of these enzymes and the substrates which they digest. These enzymes (Brown, 1936) play an important part in the pathogenesis of fungi degrading parenchymatous tissue; there is strong circumstantial evidence that they play a part in the vascular-wilt syndrome (Waggoner and Dimond, 1955) and in the parasitism by rusts (van Sumere, van Sumere-de-Preter, and Ledingham, 1957).

In contrast, there is relatively little direct information on the importance of cellulase enzymes in pathogenesis and still less investigation of the possibility that enzymes other than those attacking carbohydrate substrates may be concerned, as pointed out by Husain and Kelman (1959).

Even our knowledge of the precise role of pectic enzymes in pathogenesis is fragmentary, and most attempts to correlate pectinase-enzyme production with virulence have failed. It would seem that much more information is needed on the actual composition of the middle lamella, not only in different plants but also in different parts of the same plant, as enzyme preparations act quite differently on these different tissues. Also the enzymes formed by one organism on different substrates appear to differ markedly, not only in quantity, but even in actual composition of the enzymes (Bateman, 1963). Also there appear to be substances present in host tissues which can act as inhibitors of pectic-enzyme activity or even of enzyme formation. Finally, although death of cells almost inevitably follows maceration of cell walls and the rates of maceration and killing are closely related, attempts to separate the two effects have failed (Tribe, 1955). It is difficult to find a satisfactory explanation for the cell killing in the presently known activities of the enzymes.

The action of toxic substances.—The circumstantial evidence is overwhelmingly strong that metabolites produced by pathogenic fungi play an important part in pathogenesis, but there are very few instances where such metabolites have been purified and the mechanism of their action worked out (Braun and Pringle, 1959). Claims for the implication of fungal metabolites based on doubtful evidence prompted Dimond and Waggoner (1953) to set out a list of conditions, based on Koch's postulates, which they felt should be fulfilled before a material could be regarded as a toxin. They have made an important contribution in this field at an early stage in the investigation of such toxic materials by emphasizing the need for very critical work, but Braun and Pringle (1959) and Ludwig (1960), in their excellent reviews of this field, have pointed out the strictures that Dimond and Waggoner's conditions would impose and have taken a more liberal though no less critical approach.

As suggested above, the word toxin as applied to pathogenesis of plants has no precise definition at present, and Braun and Pringle's (1959) attempt to group materials by similarity of action appeals to the author as the most productive approach at the present time.

Investigation of the mode of action of toxic materials is beset by exactly the same difficulties as investigation of enzymes, namely, that materials produced in vitro are not necessarily formed in the host tissue, and the cell metabolism of the host itself is as yet so poorly understood that investigation of its interaction with a foreign material is almost beyond our present reach, unless the interaction clearly involves some of the better-known processes of the host cell.

An important advance since the publication of the reviews by Braun and Pringle (1959) and Ludwig (1960) is the further investigation by Cruickshank and Perrin (1961) of the phytoalexin hypothesis developed by Müller (1961), resulting in the isolation of "pisatin," a chromanocoumarane produced by *Pisum sativum* in response to infection by different fungi. This work is dealt with fully elsewhere in this symposium. The host material apparently accumulates through interference, by some material produced by the fungus, with the normal metabolic processes of the host cell. Further investigation of its formation may shed important light on the nature of the fungal products and their mechanisms of action in the host cells.

There has been little attempt so far, aside from the recognition of the part pectic enzymes play in pathogenesis, to separate materials constitutive to the pathogen and largely independent of substrate from those which are produced as the breakdown products from substrates. This stems partly from our inadequate knowledge of fungal physiology, particularly in relation to cell-wall structure and membrane permeability, of the sites of enzyme production and liberation, and of the control of morphogenesis. Attempts to isolate toxic materials from diseased hosts to a certain extent obviate the above distinction, the materials isolated from the host substrate perhaps being less likely to be artifacts; but the possibility that many of the "toxic effects" in pathogenesis may be due to pathogen constitutive materials such as proteinases, lipases, or other enzymes, and hormones should be more searchingly examined. This aspect will be further discussed in the following section.

The work of Thatcher (1942, 1943) and Humphrey and Dufrenoy (1944) was not discussed in the reviews mentioned above. Thatcher, in very careful investigations at the cellular level, demonstrated that a number of pathogens, causing different types of disease, markedly altered the permeability of the plasmatic membranes of the host cells. The permeability showed a decrease where a fungus grew in resistant tissue, but a marked increase in susceptible tissue. Thatcher's work along these lines with the tomato-wilt *Fusarium* has been substantially supported by the more recent investigations on the wilt-producing pathogens. Although he had little supporting experimental evidence, Thatcher suggested that pathogenesis of the rust fungi may be associated with at least two enzymes; one a protease and the other a "lipase" capable of splitting lecithins from the lecithoproteins of the cell membrane. Humphrey and Dufrenoy (1944) extended the investigations beyond those of Thatcher to examine the implications of increased permeability of cell membranes in the reaction of certain pathogen enzymes with phenolic host substrates. They suggested that the derived toxic quinones were a factor in pathogenesis, their importance depending upon their rate of accumulation, which in turn depended upon a number of host and pathogen factors. The question of rate of reaction rather than differences in kind of reaction is an important aspect of pathogenesis that, although frequently mentioned, has been seldom investigated.

Further work may show that enzyme action and toxic metabolites are causally linked together in many instances of pathogenesis, as suggested by Husain and Kelman (1959). There is increasing need for pathologists dealing with soil fungi to study detailed host-cell reactions along with the grosser tissue or whole-plant reactions, as is now being done with air-borne fungi such as the rusts and mildews.

EVOLUTION OF THE PARASITIC HABIT AND ITS RELATION TO PATHOGENESIS.—This section of the paper is largely speculative. But the information on parasitism and pathogenesis is now so bewilderingly diverse I think further serious attempts (McNew, 1960) should be made to find what basic patterns, if any, underlie the host-pathogen interaction. If basic patterns can be found, they will greatly aid our research by giving some aspects a better direction and at the same time offering new leads.

Saville (1955) has suggested that the parasitic habit has been a central core in fungal evolution from the most primitive forms and that the saprophytes have arisen from parasites. He indicates, however, that fungi may reach a common point by diverse pathways through convergent evolution in the achievement of important ends, and that saprophytes may have returned to a parasitic habit. Irrespective of these considerations, even the most primitive fungi must somehow have developed the parasitic habit. Saville also suggests that elaborate sexual mechanisms and self-sterility are, in general, extremely ancient. It seems desirable, in further discussion of the evolution of parasitism and pathogenesis, to continue to separate the fungi that do not enter the host plant from those that do, as this is the major step in parasitism. It requires continuing emphasis, for there are still many people who suggest that if sufficient inoculum is used almost any organism will be pathogenic. The facts do not support this suggestion.

Fungi that fail to enter the host.—Fungi that fail to enter the host derive their nutrients either from the decomposition of dead organic matter or from specialized locations such as the rhizosphere. Their effects on the host through toxic metabolites, even though important, appear to be fortuitous and pose no problem of association development. They are incidental, even if sometimes serious pathogens.

Fungi that enter the plant.—The majority of the fungi that enter the plant appear to do so through the intact surface by means of an appressorium, usually, but not always, distinguished morphologically from the vegetative hyphae. From the appressorium a fine infection peg develops to penetrate the surface mechanically. The process is complex, comprised of several stages and, while it may have evolved in response to selection pressure, this would presumably have involved a number of interdependent but separate genetic changes or mutations in the organism. As an alternative, it seems more conceivable to me that it may have arisen by modification of a process already well developed in the fungi, namely that of sexual fusion.

The analogy between appressorial formation and host infection and antheridial development and oogonial fertilization in *Achlya,* as demonstrated by Raper (1940) is exceedingly close. The antheridium develops in response to a chemical stimulus from the oogonial initials, but it can subsequently attach to an inert membrane surface and produce the fine fertilization tube. A "mistaken" response to a host exudate sufficiently alike, chemically, to the materials released by oogonial initials could readily lead to attempted host infection. In the Ascomycetes and Basidiomycetes, although the anatomical details differ, the basic reactions are similar, particularly in hyphal fusion by anastomoses. It is reported in many instances that hyphae appear to influence the direction of growth of other hyphae by diffusion of materials through agar, so that they grow together and make physical contact; this is followed by changes in the cell walls at the point of contact which allow one to "penetrate" the other. Such instances have been repeatedly observed in our studies of *Thanatephorus.* In many instances the actual fusion appears to take place through a fine tube, which subsequently enlarges. The process is essentially the same in trichogyne fertilization in the Ascomycetes and clamp-connection formation in the Basidiomycetes.

There is still no evidence of a pathogenic fungus being able to chemically attack the cuticle surface of plants, and many investigators have raised the question as to why this has not evolved. If, however, the infection process has developed along the lines suggested above, the presence of cutin would not have played a significant part and the fine fertilization-tube–infection-peg would have obviated the necessity for chemical digestion of cutin.

If such were the development of the infection process what would be the subsequent consequences?

Air-borne fungi may have subsequently developed so that they were independent of a chemical stimulus for the infection process, since the optimum chance of survival is to infect a substrate on which they are deposited (Kerr and Flentje, 1957). Soil fungi, on the other hand, would not be under such a selection pressure and are more likely to have retained the need for such a stimulus.

After infection a number of factors may have influenced further development. First in regard to nutrition, particularly energy sources, most saprophytes would, to survive, have already developed an exoenzyme system capable of attacking those host materials they would have encountered as dead organic matter. Enzyme secretion, particularly pectolytic enzyme secretion, as is frequently measured at the present time on nonspecific substrates, would not be an important criterion for pathogenicity, although it might have an important bearing on virulence. This has in fact been suggested in many investigations where an organism not known to be pathogenic has a well-developed pectolytic enzyme system, and the point has been clearly made in a recent paper by Barker and Walker (1962), with different strains of *Rhizoctonia.* The same argument applies to other enzyme systems involving substrates the fungi would consistently meet as saprophytes.

If, however, as is frequently suggested, the pectic (and other) substrates in different hosts are sufficiently different to require specific pectic (and other) enzymes, then the saprophytic system would be subject to considerable selection for the organisms to develop satisfactorily in the living host. This might alternatively give rise to the situation now suggested for rusts (van Sumere, van Sumere-de-Preter, and Ledingham, 1957) and possibly operating in the case of mycorrhizal fungi, where only a partial cell-wall degradation occurs, sufficient to allow the organism to develop, but not sufficient to kill the cells. There would, however, be many intergrades between the latter condition and the unspecialized system of the saprophyte.

Second, toxic materials, including enzymes produced by the fungus and probably advantageous to its saprophytic existence in soil, may immediately kill the host cells in the vicinity of the penetration. In such cases the infecting fungus would have little advantage as there would be immediate competition from other saprophytes which could invade the dead cells. Thus any selection pressure would tend to be away from such a reaction towards a slower killing of the host cells that allowed the invader to multiply without competition. This would lead to the necrotrophic and biotrophic differences suggested by Gäumann (1950). At this point, however, separation should be made into three possibilities.

1. The toxic materials may be incidental materials to the fungus which could be readily lost through simple genetic change, presumably leading to alternative metabolic pathways. There are many examples in the literature where one particular strain of a fungus produces a material, e.g. penicillin, alcohol, and other closely related strains either produce very little or

none at all. Such a change, involving loss of materials toxic to host cells, could well slow the killing of host cells and confer an advantage on the fungus. Presumably accumulated changes of this kind could easily make the organism a less able saprophytic competitor in the soil in the absence of the host and lead to the differences between soil inhabitor and root invader suggested by Garrett (1956).

2. The toxic materials, while still incidental to the fungus, may not only kill the host cells but may do so in such a way that the fungal cells are also killed, as in the hypersensitive reaction (Müller, 1961). It is more difficult to speculate here because so little is known of the mechanisms involved in this reaction, but again, there are many references in the literature to instances in which, with two closely related fungus strains on one host or one strain on two host varieties, one reaction may be hypersensitive and the other not. Presumably small genetic changes in the fungus can change the hypersensitive reaction to a spreading lesion. These instances in the literature, however, refer almost exclusively to highly specialized parasites, such as the obligate organisms, from which the cruder toxic materials have presumably long been lost. There is little evidence that such a dramatic change can easily occur with the facultative parasites.

3. The toxic materials may be constitutive to the fungus and an essential part of the metabolic system for which there is no easy alternative pathway and hence little or no variability on which selection can take place. In such a case the reaction would remain a hypersensitive one, or, more likely with no selection to preserve it, the infecting form of the fungus would be lost.

In considering these possibilities, recent studies on hyphal anastomosis present an interesting comparison. Garnjobst and Wilson (1956) and Wilson, Garnjobst, and Tatum (1961) analysed heterocaryon formation in *Neurospora crassa* and found that hyphae of the majority of closely related isolates which they tested were able to form cross fusions, but in a percentage of these a "lethal cytoplasmic incompatibility reaction" resulted. They suggested this reaction involved soluble cytoplasmic proteins and was controlled, at least in part, by two genes C D and their alternate alleles, c d. The relation of this to sexual incompatibility, while hinted at, is not known.

We have carried out an extensive survey of anastomoses between different pathogenic strains of *Thanatephorus cucumeris* (Flentje and Stretton, 1964). We have found that single-spore cultures from a homothallic parent readily anastomose with no incompatibility reaction. Single-spore cultures from another isolate that may be heterothallic readily anastomose, but in a percentage of these a lethal incompatibility reaction occurs. Single-spore isolates from different pathogenic strains so far tested all either fail to anastomose or show the lethal incompatibility reaction as illustrated in Figs. 2 and 3.

Extending these comparisons further, although there is relatively little associated cytological information, attempts recorded in the literature to synthesize heterocaryons between widely different pathogenic races of smut fungi, rust fungi, and wilt and other fusaria have largely failed. On the other hand, between races which have a common host but which may differ in virulence, functional heterocaryons can apparently be synthesized.

Along certain lines this situation parallels the parasitism and pathogenesis of higher plants and it is tempting to suggest, as Allen (1959a) has hinted, that it may be more than just a parallel. If the specialized pathogenic strains had a common origin, they may have begun to differ by different mating types responding to different host exudates, leading to infection. This difference would have been widened by further selection in the loss of toxic materials, enabling them to invade the different hosts, and in the specialization of their enzyme systems to attack the substrates peculiar to the different hosts. This specialization affecting so many basic processes in the fungus would then lead to the point where anastomosis would no longer occur, or if it did the interacting cytoplasms would be sufficiently different through altered enzyme systems and other factors that they would be incompatible and the cells would be killed.

I am well aware of the tenuous links in this discussion and the scant supporting evidence I can adduce, but it may stimulate further experimentation along these lines or prompt more plausible theories to guide investigational work in this field.

To summarize, then, it is suggested that the origin of parasitism and evolution of pathogenesis may have been along the following lines:

1. Parasitism originated from existing sexual processes in the fungi, based on chemical stimuli which gave directional stimulus to growth and excited the formation of an infection apparatus.

2. It became diverted to plants by chemical analogues from the host plant or by mutations in the fungi that caused them to respond to different materials.

3. Host invasion after infection was made possible by:

   a) Modifications in the enzyme system of the fungus to meet the different substrates encountered in the host. This led to one aspect of specialized parasitism and influenced virulence.

   b) Modifications in metabolic pathways leading to loss of metabolites that caused immediate killing of the host cells and the penetrating hyphae, thus leading to another aspect of specialized parasitism and again influencing virulence.

4. Major differences already occurred between different saprophytic forms of the same fungus, partly in relation to sexual fusion. These differences allowed successful invasion of different types of hosts. This in time considerably widened the original differences which existed, leading to very specialized pathogenic races or species, as now seen, for example, in the fusaria.

In concluding this section, comment should be made on the gene-for-gene postulate put forward by Flor (1942) and receiving increasing comment in more recent investigations. This hypothesis was put forward in relation to host interaction with obligate fungi, involving a narrow specificity and a highly evolved rela-

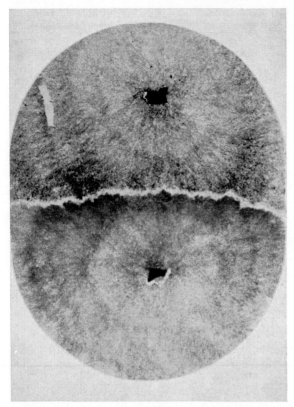

Fig. 2. Zone of dead cells due to incompatibility reaction between different isolates of *Thanatephorus cucumeris* grown on cellophane overlying water agar. (Photo kindly supplied by R. E. Reichle.)

tion in which the cruder enzymic maladjustment and toxic metabolites have presumably been lost from the system. In the broader field of host interaction with facultative pathogens when the cruder maladjustments obscure the interaction, the gene-for-gene hypothesis probably has little meaning so far; and a much broader genetic view must be taken at this stage of our investigations.

PRIMARY AND SECONDARY PATHOGENESIS.—Led by the investigations on air-borne pathogenic fungi and surrounded by the fence of Koch's postulates, investigation of soil-borne pathogens has followed closely the idea of one organism to a disease. Whenever a second organism appeared to be regularly associated with a disease, one of the two was designated a primary invader and the other a secondary. There are also many instances where an organism regularly associated with a particular disease is not "accepted" as a pathogen and is regarded as a secondary organism even where no primary one is known.

The analysis made by Wilhelm (1959) has been extended in the following discussion of ineffective and effective secondary invaders.

Ineffective secondary invaders.—We have learned from long experience that, in general, isolation of a pathogen from a host is easiest in the early stages of

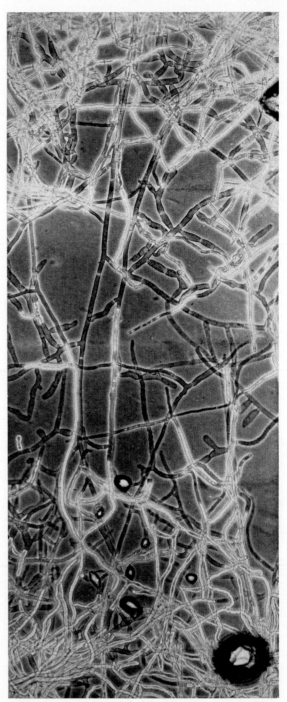

Fig. 3. Death of cells approximately 72 hours after anastomosis between different isolates of *Thanatephorus cucumeris* grown on cellophane overlying water agar. Detail of line of anastomosis in Fig. 2. (Phase-contrast photomicrograph kindly supplied by R. E. Reichle.)

a disease. At later stages a wide range of additional organisms is isolated, often consistently and to the exclusion of the primary pathogen. This is most common with pathogens which invade cortical tissues and cause extensive open lesions. As Wilhelm points out, these other organisms are usually saprophytes, and they are consistently associated with the disease because they have selectively developed in the rhizosphere or can make most rapid use of the breakdown products resulting from the primary pathogenesis or both. In some instances their rapid spread through the original lesion has completely obscured the primary pathogen.

Such organisms when tested against the host in the absence of the primary pathogen have no effect, and when tested in association with the pathogen cause no increase in pathogenesis as compared with the pathogen alone. The literature is replete with references to such investigations.

Effective secondary invaders.—There is accumulating evidence, however, that there is a much more critical relation between some primary and secondary invaders, so much so that we may need other terms to define the relation more accurately.

Snyder and Sciaroni (1953) have shown that if crucifers are grown in soil containing *Plasmodiophora brassicae,* but free of secondary invaders because of fumigation, the plants, although heavily infected with *P. brassica,* show no significant symptoms and the "clubs" do not break down. Breakdown and stunting of plants rapidly occurs, however, where other organisms are present. Similar effects have been suggested in hosts infected with crown gall, but there appears to be no specific investigation of this recorded in the literature.

However, Christie and Perry (1959) and Wilhelm (1959) review a number of instances where interaction between nematodes and other organisms in pathogenesis

have been recorded. In some of these instances the nematode may, as suggested by Lucas, Sasser, and Kelman (1955), act only to open the door for other organisms. In other cases, however, Christie and Perry suggest there is a more interdependent relation between the nematodes and other organisms; but the evidence in most instances, as pointed out by Wilhelm, is insufficient to determine the exact nature of the association.

It is surprising, however, that so few interactions between soil organisms have so far been uncovered. I believe it is partly a preoccupation with single-organism pathogenesis and partly a reflection of our still inadequate techniques for investigation, but the work of the next decade may well uncover important instances.

Two investigations recently carried out in Adelaide provide evidence along these lines, the second investigation being more definitive. In one investigation of the root rot of wheat caused by *Thanatephorus cucumeris,* we attempted to compare the virulence of different single-spore cultures with the parent strain, in the absence of any other organisms, by growing the wheat in sterilized sand inoculated with the different isolates (Flentje and Stretton, 1964). Although each isolate caused lesions on the roots, those caused by the parent isolate spread very slowly and with no obvious affect on the growth of the plants as compared with the controls, whereas in unsterilized soil inoculated with the parent isolate the lesions spread rapidly and the plants were markedly stunted as compared with the controls. The effect of the parent isolate was then

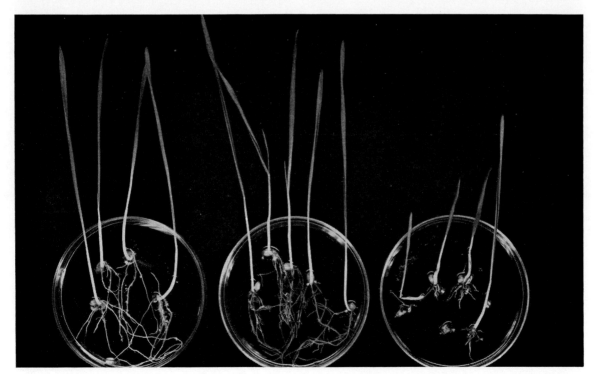

Fig. 4. Severity of root damage to wheat by *Thanatephorus cucumeris* isolate 16 when inoculated into different soils in pot-culture experiments. Left, in autoclaved sand; center, in Urrbrae loam treated at 160°F for 30 min; right, in untreated Urrbrae loam.

studied in natural soil both untreated and heated by aerated steam to 160°F for 30 minutes (Baker, 1962), and in sterilized sand. In the sterilized sand and heated soil *Thanatephorus* entered the roots but caused only small lesions with no apparent effect on seedling growth, whereas in the untreated soil rapidly spreading lesions were formed that completely severed many of the roots and the growth of the seedlings was severely stunted. In root lesions dissected out there were many other organisms present in those from the unsterilized soil, very few from the heated soil, and none from the sand. The work has been repeated several times with the same result, which is illustrated in Fig. 4, but no detailed study of the interaction between *Thanatephorus* and other organisms has yet been made.

In the second investigation Kerr (1963) has demonstrated a more striking interaction between *Pythium* and *Fusarium oxysporium* f. *pisi* in causing pea wilt. By meticulous counting of propagules of these organisms in natural "pea sick" soils, Kerr obtained a workable estimate of the population of these organisms in soil. Then, using soils in which peas had not been grown and where the population of the above organisms was negligible, he studied disease development in peas after infestation of the soil with the two fungi separately and together at population levels corresponding with those in "pea sick" soils. Either fungus alone produced only slight symptoms, but together they produced typical symptoms of *Fusarium* wilt. These direct investigations have been strongly supported by other experiments using Dexon to control *Pythium* in "pea sick" soils and by using pea varieties resistant to *Fusarium* but not *Pythium*. All the evidence suggests that typical wilt symptoms only occur in the presence of the two fungi *Pythium* and *Fusarium*, as illustrated in Fig. 5.

I would suggest then that Wilhelm's host-saprophyte specificity might be developed further. Because of the rhizosphere effect, which has encouraged the buildup of a specific flora in the root zone of different plants, some of these organisms have been further selected by association with root diseases of the host to enable them to utilize the breakdown products from the original pathogenesis and thus closely follow the primary pathogen as secondary invaders. Usually these secondary invaders do not seriously aggravate the host symptoms. In some instances, however, possibly by mutation and selection, the secondary invaders may have reached a point where, though their entry to the host is still dependent on another organism, once established they are, either by themselves or in association with the other organism, serious pathogens.

THE FUTURE.—I may have enough trouble debating the present hypotheses put forward, but in response to the spirit in which contributions were sought for this symposium I feel some comments on possible future developments are necessary.

Fig. 5. Effect of inoculation of Greenfeast peas grown in virgin light soil inoculated with *Fusarium oxysporum* and *Pythium ultimum* singly and in combination. Left to right, in pairs: check; *Fusarium* alone; *Pythium* alone; *Fusarium* and *Pythium*. (A. Kerr. Austral. J. Biol. Sci. 16: 55-69. 1963.)

The hard core of plant pathology is the understanding of pathogenesis and the control of the concomitant diseases. Some outstanding successes have been obtained in control along either ecological lines, e.g. heat therapy, chemotherapy, crop rotation, or disease-resistance breeding. For many important diseases, however, no satisfactory controls are known, and we are forced to investigate the mechanism of pathogenesis for new leads to disease control. Many of these investigations will demand basic genetical and biochemical studies on the pathogens, and, as there seems to be some reluctance among geneticists and biochemists to use plant-pathogenic fungi as their major tools for basic investigations, the plant pathologist must face the tasks involved.

The investigation of root damage by organisms which do not enter the plant, or enter only after damage, is closely linked with our progress in ecology of soil fungi, particularly with better methods of estimating and reproducing populations in soil generally and especially in the rhizosphere.

The mechanism of host entry, so often regarded as automatic, should be investigated with a much wider range of organisms interacting with nonhosts, with the emphasis on the study of appressorial formation. This work may well be carried out in close collaboration with studies on fungal morphogenesis and the possibility of hormonal control analogous to that in the higher plants.

In pathogenesis subsequent to entry, Wood (1960) has ably summarized the immediate work required to clarify the role of pectic enzymes. Braun and Pringle (1959) have given us a start in attempting to group the types of toxic metabolites which may play a part. But there has been a serious neglect of other aspects. The changes in permeability of host cell membranes demonstrated by Thatcher (1943) suggest a more urgent attention to proteolytic and lipolytic enzymes. I believe also that detailed investigation of mating behavior, fungal anastomosis, and the associated incompatibility reaction, as well as parasitism between fungi, may, with the absence of photosynthetic complications, offer new leads.

Basic genetical studies on the soil fungi are long overdue. Increasing emphasis should be given to studies of the factors associated with penetration and subsequent pathogenesis using markers associated with these phenomena in addition to the deficiency markers commonly employed with other fungi. There is a wealth of organisms suitable for this type of study among the soil-borne fungal pathogens. Too often we have made our studies of pathogenesis and virulence on casually obtained isolates with little or no regard to their genetical makeup. The genetics may be complex if heterocaryosis is common; analysis of this may reduce some of the difficult problems of pathogenesis to components more amenable to investigation. Separation into components may in itself hold the key to the repeated failure to obtain host varieties resistant to many soil-borne diseases.

LITERATURE CITED

ALLEN, P. J. 1957. Properties of a volatile fraction from uredospores of *Puccinia graminis* var. *tritici* affecting their germination and development. 1. Biological activity. Plant Physiol. 32: 385-389.

ALLEN, P. J. 1959a. Metabolic considerations of obligate parasitism. p. 119-129. *In* C. S. Holton et al. [ed.], Plant pathology, problems and progress 1908-1958, University of Wisconsin Press, Madison, Wisc.

ALLEN, P. J. 1959b. Physiology and biochemistry of defence. vol. 1, p. 435-467. *In* J. G. Horsfall and A. E. Dimond [ed.], Plant pathology, an advanced treatise, Academic Press, New York.

ARMSTRONG, G. M., and J. K. ARMSTRONG. 1960. American, Egyptian, and Indian cotton-wilt fusaria. Their pathogenicity and relationship to other wilt fusaria. U. S. Dept. Agr. Tech. Bull. 1219, 18 p.

BAKER, K. F. 1962. Thermotherapy of planting material. Phytopathology 52: 1244-1255.

BARKER, K. R., and J. C. WALKER. 1962. Relationship of pectolytic and cellulytic enzyme production by strains of *Pellicularia filamentosa* to their pathogenicity. Phytopathology 52: 1119-1126.

BARY, A. DE. 1886. Uber einige Sclerotinien und Sclerotienkrankheiten. Botan. Ztg. 44: 377-474.

BATEMAN, D. F. 1963. Pectolytic activities of culture filtrates of *Rhizoctonia solani* and extracts of Rhizoctonia-infected tissues of bean. Phytopathology 53: 197-204.

BRAUN, A. C., and R. B. PRINGLE. 1959. Pathogen factors in the physiology of disease—Toxins and other metabolites. p. 88-89. *In* C. S. Holton et al. [ed.], Plant pathology, problems and progress 1908-1958, University of Wisconsin Press, Madison, Wisc.

BRAUNS, F. E. 1952. The chemistry of lignin. Academic Press, New York. 808 p.

BROWN, W. 1936. Physiology of host parasite relations. Botan. Rev. 2: 236-281.

BROWN, W. 1955. On the physiology of parasitism in plants, Ann. Appl. Biol. 43: 325-341.

BUXTON, E. W. 1957. Differential rhizosphere effects of three pea cultivars on physiologic races of *Fusarium oxysporum* f. *pisi*. Trans. Brit. Mycol. Soc. 40: 305-317.

CHRISTIE, J. R., and V. G. PERRY. 1959. Mechanism of nematode injury to plants. p. 419-426. *In* C. S. Holton et al. [ed.], Plant pathology, problems and progress 1908-1958. University of Wisconsin Press, Madison, Wisc.

CHRISTOU, T. 1962. Penetration and host-parasite relationships of *Rhizoctonia solani* in the bean plant. Phytopathology 52: 381-388.

CRUICKSHANK, I. A. M., and D. R. PERRIN. 1961. Studies on phytoalexins. III. The isolation, assay, and general properties of a phytoalexin from *Pisum sativum* L. Australian J. Biol. Sci. 14: 336-348.

DICKINSON, S. 1960. The mechanical ability to breach the host barriers. vol. 2, p. 203-232. *In* J. G. Horsfall and A. E. Dimond [ed.], Plant pathology, an advanced treatise, Academic Press, New York.

DIMOND, A. E., and P. E. WAGGONER. 1953. On the nature and role of vivo toxins in plant disease. Phytopathology 43: 229-235.

EIDE, C. J. 1955. Fungus infection of plants. Ann. Rev. Microbiol. 9: 297-318.

FLENTJE, N. T. 1959. The physiology of penetration and infection. p. 76-87. *In* C. S. Holton et al. [ed.], Plant pathology, problems and progress 1908-1958, University of Wisconsin Press, Madison, Wisc.

FLENTJE, N. T., R. L. DODMAN, and A. KERR. 1963. Mechanism of host penetration by *Thanatephorus cucumeris*. Australian J. Biol. Sci. 16: 784-799.

FLENTJE, N. T., and HELEN M. STRETTON. 1964. Mechanisms of variation in *Thanatephorus cucumeris* and *Thanatephorus praticolus*. Australia J. Biol. Sci. 17. (In press.)

FLOR, H. H. 1942. Inheritance of pathogenicity in *Melampsora lini*. Phytopathology 32: 653-669.

GARNJOBST, L., and J. F. WILSON. 1956. Heterocaryosis

and protoplasmic incompatibility in *Neurospora crassa*. Proc. Natl. Acad. Sci. (U. S.) 42: 613-618.

GARRETT, S. D. 1956. Biology of root-infecting fungi. Cambridge University Press, London and New York. 292 p.

GARRETT, S. D. 1960. Inoculum potential. vol. 3, p. 23-57. *In* J. G. Horsfall and A. E. Dimond [ed.], Plant pathology, an advanced treatise, Academic Press, New York.

GÄUMANN, E. 1950. Principles of plant infection (Transl. W. B. Brierley). Crosby Lockwood & Son, London. 543 p.

GRAHAM, V. E., and L. GREENBERG. 1939. The effect of salicylic aldehyde on the infection of wheat by *Pythium arrhenomenes* Drechsler and the destruction of the aldehyde by *Actinomycetes erythropolis* and *Penicillium* sp. Can. J. Res., Sec. C, 17: 52-56.

HORSFALL, J. G., and A. E. DIMOND. 1960. Prologue—The pathogen: The concept of causality. vol. 2, p. 1-18. *In* J. G. Horsfall and A. E. Dimond [ed.], Plant pathology, an advanced treatise, Academic Press, New York.

HUMPHREY, H. B., and J. DUFRENOY. 1944. Host-parasite relationship between the oat plant (Avena spp.) and crown rust (*Puccinia coronata*). Phytopathology 34: 21-40.

HUSAIN, A., and A. KELMAN. 1959. Tissue is disintegrated. vol. 1, p. 144-188. *In* J. G. Horsfall and A. E. Dimond [ed.], Plant pathology, an advanced treatise, Academic Press, New York.

KERNKAMP, M. F., P. J. deZEEUW, S. M. CHEN, B. C. ORTEGA, C. T. TSIANG, and A. M. KHAN. 1952. Investigations on physiologic specialization and parasitism of *Rhizoctonia solani*. Minnesota Agr. Expt. Sta. Tech. Bull. 200, 36 p.

KERR, A. 1963. The root rot-Fusarium wilt complex of peas. Australian J. Biol. Sci. 16: 55-69.

KERR, A., and N. T. FLENTJE. 1957. Host infection in *Pellicularia filamentosa* controlled by chemical stimuli. Nature (London) 179: 204-205.

LEBEAU, J. B., and J. G. DICKSON. 1955. Physiology and nature of disease development in winter crown rot of alfalfa. Phytopathology 45: 667-673.

LEUKEL, R. W. 1948. *Periconia circinata* and its relation to milo disease. J. Agr. Res. 77: 201-222.

LUCAS, G. B., J. N. SASSER, and A. KELMAN. 1955. The relationship of root-knot nematodes to Granville wilt resistance in tobacco. Phytopathology 45: 537-540.

LUDWIG, R. A. 1957. Toxin production by *Helminthosporium sativum* P K and B and its significance in disease development. Can. J. Botany 35: 291-303.

LUDWIG, R. A. 1960. Toxins. vol. 2, p. 315-358. *In* J. G. Horsfall and A. E. Dimond [ed.], Plant pathology, an advanced treatise, Academic Press, New York.

McNEW, G. L. 1960. The nature, origin and evolution of parasitism. vol. 2, p. 19-70. *In* J. G. Horsfall and A. E. Dimond [ed.], Plant pathology, an advanced treatise, Academic Press, New York.

MÜLLER, K. O. 1961. The phytoalexin concept and its methodological significance. vol. 1, p. 397-400. *In* Recent advances in botany (9th Intern. Botan. Congr., Montreal) University of Toronto Press, Toronto.

NUSBAUM, C. J., and G. W. KEITT. 1938. A cytological study of host-parasite relations of *Venturia inaequalis* on apple leaves. J. Agr. Res. 51: 573-596.

OSWALD, J. W. 1951. The relation of Periconia to milo root rot in California. Phytopathology 41: 28-29.

RANDS, R. D., and E. DOPP. 1938. The influence of certain harmful soil constituents on severity of Pythium root rot of sugar cane. J. Agr. Res. 56: 53-68.

RAPER, J. R. 1940. Sexual hormones in Achlya. II. Distance relations, conclusive evidence for a hormonal coordinating mechanism. Am. J. Botany 27: 162-173.

SAVILLE, D. B. O. 1955. A phylogeny of the Basidiomycetes. Can. J. Botany 33: 60-104.

SKINNER, J. 1918. Soil aldehydes. A scientific study of a new class of soil constituents unfavourable to crops, their occurrence, properties, and elimination in practical agriculture. J. Franklin Inst. 186: 165-186, 449-480, 547-584, 732-741.

SNYDER, W. C., and H. N. HANSEN. 1940. The species concept in Fusarium. Am. J. Botany 27: 64-67.

SNYDER, W. C., and R. H. SCIARONI. 1953. Proc. First Pacific Coast Research Conference on Control of Soil Fungi. (Mimeo.) 4 p.

STEINBERG, R. A. 1952. Frenching symptoms produced in *Nicotiana tabacum* and *Nicotiana rustica* with optical isomers of isoleucine and leucine with *Bacillus cereus* toxin. Plant Physiol. 27: 302-308.

SUMERE, C. F. VAN, C. VAN SUMERE-dePRETER, and G. A. LEDINGHAM. 1957. Cell wall splitting enzymes of *Puccinia graminis* var. *tritici*. Can. J. Microbiol. 3: 761-770.

THATCHER, F. S. 1942. Further studies of osmotic and permeability relations in parasitism. Can. J. Res., Sec. C, 20: 283-311.

THATCHER, F. S. 1943. Cellular changes in relation to rust resistance. Can. J. Res., Sec. C, 21: 151-172.

TRIBE, H. T. 1955. Studies in the physiology of parasitism XIX: On the killing of plant cells by enzymes from *Botrytis cinerea* and *Bacterium aroideae*. Ann. Botany (London) [N. S.] 19: 351-368.

WAGGONER, P. E., and A. E. DIMOND. 1955. Production and role of extracellular pectic enzymes of *Fusarium oxysporum* f. *lycopersici*. Phytopathology 45: 79-87.

WILHELM, S. 1959. Parasitism and pathogenesis of root disease fungi. p. 356-366. *In* C. S. Holton et al. [ed.], Plant pathology, problems and progress 1908-1958. University of Wisconsin Press, Madison, Wisc.

WILSON, J. F., LAURA GARNJOBST, and E. L. TATUM. 1961. Heterocaryon incompatibility in *Hemospora crassa*—micro-injection studies. Am. J. Botany 48: 299-305.

WOOD, R. K. S. 1959. Pathogen factors in the physiology of disease—pectic enzymes. p. 100-109. *In* C. S. Holton et al. [ed.], Plant pathology, problems and progress 1908-1958, University of Wisconsin Press, Madison, Wisc.

WOOD, R. K. S. 1960. Chemical ability to breach host barriers. vol. 2, p. 233-272. *In* J. G. Horsfall and A. E. Dimond [ed.], Plant pathology, an advanced treatise, Academic Press, New York.

ZENTMYER, G. A. 1961. Chemotaxis of zoospores for root exudates. Science 133: 1595-1596.

▶ DISCUSSION OF N. T. FLENTJE PAPER

A. Kelman:

Was it your intent to use the word pathogenicity as equivalent to pathogenesis? We know a great deal about pathogenesis but still know little about the key characteristics of pathogenicity, and it is important to distinguish between these terms.

N. T. Flentje:

No, I do not regard pathogenicity and pathogenesis as equivalent terms.

Pathogenesis concerns the mechanisms by which an organism affects host cells and ultimately causes disease symptoms. These mechanisms include enzyme attack, effect of toxic metabolites, etc.

Pathogenicity includes pathogenesis but it embraces more than this. In the majority of instances known at present it includes the mechanism of host entry—why does the particular organism enter the host plant.

There are many instances in which an organism can affect host tissue presented say as tissue slices; it has well-developed mechanisms of pathogenesis, but it is not pathogenic because it does not attempt to invade that host under natural conditions.

W. C. Schnathorst:

Since no mention of openings at point of emergence of secondary (lateral) roots was made in yesterday's session dealing with root anatomy and physiology, I feel that this question should be brought before the conference. Do openings at these points provide avenues of entrance for pathogenic bacteria, fungi, nematodes, and viruses and of nonpathogenic organisms into the root? I believe comment on this may bring out significant facts that will be helpful to our understanding of entry of plant pathogens into the root.

N. T. Flentje:

We have good evidence that pathogenic fungi at least differ markedly in their sites of entry into plants. Some apparently are unable to enter through a broken surface, others cannot enter through an intact surface but do so readily through a broken surface. The same may well be true for other types of pathogens, particularly bacteria. I believe there are very important differences then in behaviour of "direct penetration" and "wound" pathogens, and these differences should be investigated along with more detailed studies of root surfaces. There have been obvious differences of opinion in this conference on the nature of root surfaces, and further detailed critical work is required to resolve the questions raised.

F. M. Scott:

In healthy roots the epidermis is continuous. Cutinization is frequently heavier around lateral root origin. The mucilaginous layer is apparently uninterrupted.

H. Burström:

A path of entry overlooked is the numerous wounds which arise because root tips regularly die during the vegetative period.

A misunderstanding has developed concerning the dispensability of cortex. The question raised yesterday was: Can a root go on growing even if cortex is infected and destroyed? To this I answered, "Yes, if the injury is local, but we cannot strip the root." This has been misinterpreted.

R. H. Garber:

In a study of the penetration of *Verticillium albo-atrum* into young cotton roots, the rupture created by the emergence of lateral roots was not considered to be an important avenue of entry of the pathogen. By the time the emerging root of cotton reaches the surface of the *primary* root it is well developed in epidermis and cortical tissue (cell layers); therefore, the fungus would have numerous cell layers yet to penetrate before it could reach the vascular tissue.

N. T. Flentje:

Our own work with *Verticillium* infection of apricots supports the view that *Verticillium* can infect undamaged intact root surfaces.

A. D. Rovira:

Although I cannot comment on the penetration of organisms into roots, I should like to draw attention to the work of Schroth and Snyder, and of Parkinson, who found considerable exudation occurring at the points of emergence of the lateral roots.

Another interesting observation has been made by Robert Miller at Cornell University (personal communication) on corn roots stained with aniline blue. These roots became colonized by fungal spores which germinated profusely wherever lateral roots emerged. Although this stimulation of germination and growth may not be a precursor of invasion, these sites may provide a "home base" from which these pathogens may colonize and invade other parts of the root.

N. T. Flentje:

I agree with the comments and they reemphasize the need for integrating the present rhizosphere–root-exudate studies with the growth and infection of roots by pathogenic organisms.

J. G. Horsfall:

I congratulate Dr. Flentje on the brilliant and provocative idea of the genesis of pathogenesis. Someone inevitably had to relate sexuality to pathogenesis. I can foresee a new journal, "Psychiatric Phytopathology."

W. C. Snyder:

Some clones of *Rhizoctonia solani* and of *Fusarium solani* f. *phaseoli* show preference for stem cortex of their hosts rather than for root cortex. Yet you have shown that root exudates bring about a cushion formation by a *Rhizoctonia* specialized to stem tissue. Does this suggest to you a qualitative or quantitative difference between the exudates of stem and root cortex tissues?

N. T. Flentje:

We believe there is probably a qualitative difference, the root exudate containing additional materials which are not in the stem exudate and which affect the formation of the infection structures.

It is also likely that the actual stem and root surfaces are different in nature, and there is evidence that the surface on which the fungus is growing may influence development of infection structures.

J. Altman:

You indicated that one of the difficulties might be due to genetic variation in the fungus. Is it possible to consider the alternative that cortical or parenchyma invaders are confronted with a host of potentially meristematic cells, i.e. parenchyma cells, which have the ability to reproduce and to differentiate readily? These are in essence primitive undifferentiated cells with wide genetic potentialities. This, coupled with the wide genetic base of the fungus, complicates the problem of breeding for resistance. In contrast to this is the success achieved in breeding for resistance in diseases incited by forms of *Fusarium oxysporum* that invade vascular tissue. Could you comment on this, please?

N. T. Flentje:

There is still little information on the exact pathways of infection by root-disease fungi. But root infection does seem to occur commonly through the differentiated epidermal and cortical cells, just as in leaf and stem diseases. These cells do not differ genetically although they may differ greatly in physiology, and this may be of considerable importance in regard to differential susceptibility.

I think these two aspects—susceptibility of root cells in relation to pathway of infection and the genetic makeup of the invading organism—should be studied concomitantly.

J. L. Harley:

The work on electron microscopy of leaf surfaces may be of interest in respect of the experiments in which Flentje, Dodman, and Kerr (1963; cited in the paper) obtained different results with rubbed and unrubbed surfaces. For instance, Dr. B. E. Juniper (Endeavour 18 (69): 20-25, 1959) published some very beautiful photographs showing this complex covering of plates, flakes, granules, etc. of waxes and other material. The effect of rubbing might easily be that it would allow the hypha or spore to make more effective contact with the host.

T. C. Vanterpool:

Dr. Flentje, you made reference to nonhost carriers, and several papers referring to this topic have recently appeared in the literature. In Saskatchewan, Canada, we have a serious seedling blight of flax on the crop following fallow. The causal organism is mainly *Rhizoctonia praticola* rather than *R. solani*. Usually it makes little difference whether the crop preceding fallow was one of the cereals or flax. Further, when the cereals are grown on naturally infested soil, no visible lesion formation by *R. praticola* is found on their roots or coleoptiles. However, if the soil is sterilized and then artificially inoculated with *R. praticola*, moderate infection occurs. The cereals thus appear to be "nonhost" carriers under natural conditions. Would you care to comment on these results, and also, how does a nonhost carry the potential pathogen?

N. T. Flentje:

From some of our own studies with *Rhizoctonia* it is becoming apparent that root infection (but not stem infection) by *Rhizoctonia*, and the subsequent spread of the fungus through the roots, is greatly influenced by soil environment. Results with partially sterilized soil differ markedly from those in the same soil untreated. There is some evidence that this effect is due to associated soil microorganisms.

In regard to "nonhost" carriers, I think it is very likely that pathogenic fungi can be supported in growth in the rhizosphere of plants which are not susceptible to attack. The pathogenic organisms in such relations behave as rhizosphere organisms and the population level is increased. There is much circumstantial evidence to support this idea, but as yet little direct measurement.

J. B. Taylor:

Fusarium and *Verticillium* produce different cortical symptoms when grown on the same host species, and while *Fusarium* produces considerable amounts of pectin methyl esterase, *Verticillium* produces little or none of this enzyme.

The Relation of Plant-pathogenic Bacteria to the Soil

IVAN W. BUDDENHAGEN—*Division of Tropical Research, United Fruit Co., La Lima, Honduras.*

The relation of plant-pathogenic bacteria to the soil is only part of a more general subject—the ecology and biology of the bacterial pathogens and their hosts. This relation cannot be discussed without considering the origin of the diseases and the distribution and dispersal of the pathogens, since the soil relation is profoundly affected by these factors. The subject is one in which very little is known with assurance, and bacterial diseases are so varied that all types of soil-pathogen relations may be expected. This discussion emphasizes differences in origin and general biology of bacterial diseases and is, therefore, somewhat hypothetical. Its purpose is to provide a review of bacterial diseases in the broad sense. A few comments on animal pathogens are included when pertinent, for it appears that their relation to the soil differs little from that of some plant pathogens, and complete separation of these two research fields is not warranted. The actinomycetes are excluded by choice. Details of banana bacterial wilt, the disease with which I am most familiar, are used to illustrate concepts that may be relevant to other bacterial diseases.

What Groups of Soil Bacteria Occur and How May Pathogens Be Grouped in Relation to the Soil?

—Soil bacteria have been divided into various groups by different investigators, bringing some workable order to a diffuse field. The knowledge of cyclic changes of nitrogen, sulfur, and other elements in the soil has been obtained concomitantly with knowledge of soil bacteria that could bring about such changes and, therefore, be grouped by these capabilities (Beijerinck, 1922). Winogradsky (1925) conceived the idea of the constant residents of the soil (autochthonous flora) and the fluctuating opportunists (zymogenous flora). Conn (1948) later redefined these terms and placed specific genera within the groups. Lochhead grouped soil bacteria on the basis of complexity of their nutritional requirements (Lochhead and Chase, 1943; Lochhead, 1952). No one seems to have grouped bacteria found in the soil in relation to their saprophytic or parasitic potential, although Garrett's (1956) grouping of soil fungi into root-inhabiting and soil-inhabiting forms may be considered to have application to bacteria also.

Although the emphasis on grouping by function has been fruitful in clarifying the role of bacteria in the soil, it also has reduced the apparent need for species identification. The difficulty and subjectivity of species identification still plague research on bacteria isolated from the soil. Accurate taxonomic recognition of bacterial pathogens is a prerequisite to investigation of their presence in the soil environment. Recurring controversies on the importance of bacterial pathogens in the soil, and on the importance of saprophytes as progenitors of pathogens are in large part due to difficulties in recognizing and defining the "species." Admitting the inadequacy of bacterial classification (Cowan, 1959; Starr, 1959; Floodgate, 1962), it is still meaningful to know where the pathogens are in at least one taxonomic scheme. Plant-pathogenic bacteria occur in only four families in two orders, and are represented by only five or six genera: *Pseudomonas* (90 species), *Xanthomonas* (60), *Erwinia* (and *Pectobacterium*) (17), *Corynebacterium* (11), and *Agrobacterium* (7). Plant-pathogenic bacteria are aerobic non-spore-forming rods. All except *Corynebacterium* are Gram-negative; most are motile with either polar or peritrichal flagella, but a few are nonmotile. Several species placed within one of the six genera are atypical forms, and current classification is probably neither fixed nor reflective of "natural" relationships. There are as yet no known consistent physiological, morphological, or cytological differences between the plant pathogens and closely related saprophytes.

Animal pathogens occur in at least sixteen families in six orders. Although the animal pathogens appear to have a greater diversity of origin and therefore more flexible and varied pathogenic relations, "the number of undoubtedly phytopathogenic bacteria far exceeds the total number of species pathogenic to man and animals" (Stapp, 1961). One wonders, however, how much this is due to differing propensities to split species. Of the genera of plant pathogens, only *Pseudomonas* and *Corynebacterium* also contain animal pathogens. *P. aeruginosa* appears to be unique in being a pathogen of both plants and animals (Elrod and Braun, 1942). The *Erwinia* plant pathogens have obvious relationships to various coliform bacteria (Elrod, 1942; D. C. Graham and Dowson, 1960). Otherwise the taxonomic relationship between animal and plant pathogens is strikingly distant. With the possible exception of two *Bacillus* species, it has been emphasized that "under natural conditions not one of these numerous and diverse species [the soil-inhabiting spore-formers; some being serious animal pathogens] can be singled out as the causative agent of a plant disease" (Stapp,

1961). This also may be said for the animal pathogens in the families Spirillaceae, Micrococcaceae, Neissariaceae, Brucellaceae, Treponemataceae, the Rickettsiaceae, and Mycoplasmataceae.

In attempting to assess the role of the soil in the biology of bacterial plant pathogens, a division of the pathogens into three groups may be made, based upon the place of origin of their populations and upon their survival ability in the soil. Attention is thereby focused on the nonhost phase of the pathogen, leading to considerations of both the evolution and seasonal regeneration of diseases.

Group A is characterized by pathogens whose populations are developed almost exclusively in the plant host (Fig. 1). The host phase represents the bulk of

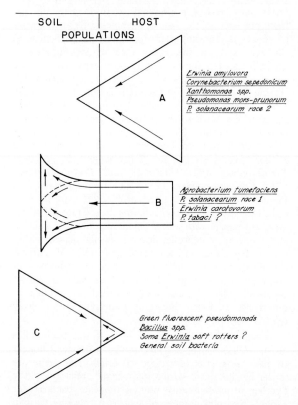

Fig. 1. Plant-pathogenic bacteria grouped schematically according to relative importance of host or soil as site of multiplication and survival of their populations. Arrow tails refer to main site of multiplication; converging arrows to reduction of population; diverging arrows to expansion as population passes from host to soil (or soil to host) environment.

the population and the greatest number of generations. The soil phase is a rapidly declining one, usually not contributing to the propagation of the disease from season to season. Probably most plant-pathogenic bacteria would fit into this group, although data on their nonhost existence are so fragmentary that we cannot place every pathogen. *Erwinia amylovora*, causing fireblight; *Corynebacterium sepedonicum*, causing ring rot, and most *Xanthomonas* species would belong here.

Group B is characterized by pathogens that build up

populations within their hosts, but whose populations only gradually decline in the soil. If the population enters the soil at a sufficiently high rate, there could be a net increase from season to season. According to cropping practices, there could be either a gradual increase of the pathogen population in the soil, a gradual decrease, or eventual extinction. These bacteria would, in reality, not be soil bacteria, since their long-term presence in the soil is host-dependent. They could appear, however, to be soil saprophytes under certain cropping practices if consideration were not given to their site of origin. Pathogens such as *Agrobacterium tumefaciens*, the cause of crown gall; *Pseudomonas solanacearum* race 1, the cause of bacterial wilt of Solanaceae; *E. carotovora*, the cause of soft rots; the *P. tabaci* group, the cause of wildfire and angular leaf spot of tobacco; and *Bacillus anthracis* (Van Ness and Stein, 1956), the cause of anthrax, probably fit into this group. For spore-forming animal pathogens the meaning of the soil phase is complicated by the surviving spore which contributes no new generations to the soil population. For plant-pathogenic bacteria, in contrast to both spore-forming animal pathogens and the fungi, the soil phase has to be one of either survival of quiescent vegetative cells, or of cells growing and dividing in the soil. The groups A and B for bacteria are similar to but not exactly equatable with Garrett's groups of "root inhabiting" and "soil inhabiting" fungi. Plant-pathogenic bacteria might better be considered as "transient visitors" and "resident visitors" of the soil.

Group C is characterized by those bacteria whose populations are largely produced in the soil, including the rhizoplane, and whose relation to plant disease is erratic and transitory. This group would include the true soil saprophytes, the rhizoplane bacteria, the green-fluorescent *Pseudomonas* soft rotters, and the *Bacillus* forms pathogenic to plants. Research on soil bacteria that has produced concepts of element cycles, rhizosphere effects, the zymogenous and autochthonous flora, etc., has been exclusively concerned with bacteria that fit into this group.

Emphasis in these groupings is upon the location of the population at any given time and upon the site of its production. For instance, where is the bulk of the population of the species *Agrobacterium tumefaciens*, or of *Erwinia amylovora* at this moment? Is it within plants, in the soil, or in association with another narrower ecological niche? The answers to such questions have obvious implications upon the direction of evolution of the pathogenic species, and upon periodic disease reappearance.

WHAT TYPES OF HOST-PARASITE RELATIONS HAVE EVOLVED AND ARE THEY RELATED TO A SOIL-BASE ORIGIN?—Phytopathogenic bacteria upset normal plant processes in about as many ways as the larger group of pathogenic fungi (McNew, 1960). They cause overgrowths (*Agrobacterium, Corynebacterium, Pseudomonas, Xanthomonas*); wilts (*Pseudomonas, Erwinia, Corynebacterium, Xanthomonas*); fruit, root, and storage-organ rots (*Pectobacterium, Pseudomonas, Coryne-*

bacterium); leaf spots and blights (*Xanthomonas, Pseudomonas, Erwinia*). Any given type of disease can be caused by bacterial pathogens in several rather unrelated genera, indicating that each disease class has had diverse origins. In contrast to the fungi, none of the pathogens is an obligate parasite. The number of bacterial vascular wilts is large in comparison with fungal vascular wilts, and the relative number of root-rot diseases is small.

The relation of the soil to bacterial diseases may be considered in two different ways: (1) Have bacterial pathogens evolved from forms originally present as saprophytes in the soil? and (2) In the seasonal cycle of established bacterial diseases, what is the role of the soil?

Since bacteria have no direct way of launching themselves from the soil, it would seem logical that diseases most likely to be caused by bacteria derived from the soil would be those resulting from root invasion. Root invasion could result in root-rots, galls, vascular wilts, or systemic diseases. When one considers the numbers of bacteria that are at plant root surfaces, the countless root wounds that occur, the minuteness of the bacteria, and the ease of entrance into plant roots and the vascular system, one would expect innumerable diseases from this source. But, as Stapp (1961) says, "This argument is not only precipitate but unfounded." It appears that roots of evolving plants have been immersed in a "bacterial suspension" so long that the present-day survivors are resistant to the bulk of the soil-inhabiting bacteria, and they become diseased only when exposed to stress or a rare organism never before encountered.

Regardless of the type of disease they cause, the bacterial pathogens more likely to be evolutionarily derived from saprophytic soil bacteria would be those most similar to common soil or rhizoplane bacteria. Here we should consider pathogens in *Corynebacterium, Agrobacterium, Pectobacterium,* and *Pseudomonas.* Although coryneform bacteria are often common soil inhabitants (Jensen, 1952), the pathogenic species have not retained the ability to live long in soil lacking host tissue. The more important plant diseases caused by corynebacteria—tomato canker, potato ring rot, bean and alfalfa wilt—are usually controlled by short rotations with nonsusceptible crops. Diseases caused by *Agrobacterium, Pectobacterium,* and certain *Pseudomonas* species appear to be more closely related to the soil. Whether this is due to a retention of an original saprophytic ability or to the particular seasonal disease cycle is debatable.

The idea that highly evolved parasitism is correlated with poor saprophytic ability and vice versa is widely held (Garrett, 1956; McNew, 1960) but also questioned (Bawden, 1957). There seems to be no a priori reason why saprophytic ability and specialized parasitism should be mutually exclusive. It has been pointed out for several vascular-wilt fusaria that their saprophytic abilities may be quite different even though their parasitic specialization is the same (Sadasivan and Subramanian, 1960). A consideration of several types of bacterial diseases and their possible evolution will illustrate how saprophytic ability of a pathogen may or may not be important to the perpetuation of the disease. Three hypothethical disease categories will be discussed, starting from the most soil-bound and advancing to the least soil-involved type. (It will be seen that these three categories are the same as those shown in Fig. 1, taking the lowest group first).

The first group is characterized by diseases closely bound to the soil. If a soil saprophyte such as a *Pseudomonas* or a coliform-type organism is able to invade roots or storage organs and cause disease, its population is thus increased somewhat but is returned to the soil. While in the plant, mutation away from "saprophytic ability" will not be selected out. But *if a means of transmission is not available or does not evolve,* mutants that cannot compete saprophytically will soon be lost when the population returns to the soil. Thus, one might envision alternating selection pressures shaping the bacterial population. While in the host poor saprophytes would not be removed, but they would be quickly eliminated as the population returns to the soil. Mutations toward greater aggressiveness would have no advantage in this soil environment and would not be favored. A balance in this simple state might result which would not progress further. If the host phase is very discontinuous, the saprophytic phase will be necessary for the survival of the species. The types of bacterial parasites we consider "less advanced" parasitically are those which have a discontinuous host phase. It follows automatically that these primitive parasites are good saprophytes since no survival stage involving spores or sclerotia occurs. Diseases that could be placed in this category would be those caused by *Bacillus* sp., usually on plants under stress (Volcani, 1956; Volcani and Dowson, 1948), or some leaf spots and soft rots caused by green-fluorescent pseudomonads (Dowson, 1958). Some of the *Erwinia* (*Pectobacterium*) soft rotters also might be included here.

The second disease category, comparable to group B in Fig. 1, may be considered an evolutionary advance in host-parasite relations. It is characterized by diseases caused by pathogens that can be transmitted fairly readily during the growing season but that are not associated in a pathogenic phase with the host during part of the annual season. Two pathogens differing in their mode of transmission will be discussed for this disease group. *Pseudomonas solanacearum,* race 1, the cause of wilt of Solanaceae, spreads from plant to plant because it can ooze from diseased roots and infect adjacent plants. Since many individual plants are infected from an original focus, there will be a large population of the pathogen subjected to selection for transmissibility and aggressiveness. Mutants that grow faster within the host, ooze more readily from it, and infect adjacent roots more readily will become established initially, whether or not they have a lessened saprophytic ability. But between each plant the population will often be subjected to a short period in the soil where poorly competing mutants will be removed. At the end of the growing season mutants with reduced survival ability will be selected out, leaving for the following crop only aggressive forms that are also good soil saprophytes. The need for root spread tends to tie the pathogen more closely to the soil; and root spread does not provide unlimited spread over great distances. Selection operates to favor *population increase* in hosts and *transmission* between them alternately with saprophytic ability. The host population also is influenced by pathogen-induced selection over long periods, complicating the simple picture of selective forces acting on the pathogen alone (Person, Samborski, and Rohringer, 1962). In addition, with time, there are increasing chances that further mutations to aggressiveness will decrease the gene balance for saprophytism. The selection, then, is not towards "advanced parasitism" but rather towards greater aggressiveness and transmissibility coupled with saprophytic ability, three characteristics that contribute to greater populations of the pathogen. Provided that transmission does not become so efficient that it eliminates the need for a soil phase, selection will continue to remove poor saprophytes and the pathogen may thus become a rather advanced parasite, such as the solanaceous-wilt pathogen, which still retains saprophytic ability.

Pseudomonas tabaci, causing wildfire of tobacco, differs in being a leafspot pathogen, spread from plant to plant via rain splash. During a seasonal epiphytotic the pathogen population is increased greatly in the absence of any selection pressure against mutants poorly adapted as soil saprophytes. At the end of the growing season, however, the part of the pathogen population that may have lost its saprophytic capabilities will be reduced or eliminated. This pathogen in the soil phase appears to be associated with living roots of nonhost plants (Valleau, Johnson, and Diachun, 1944). Thus, with this leaf pathogen, as with a few others, the absence of a continuous association with the host has imposed a soil phase, even though it may be only in association with the rhizoplane of nonhosts. Further research may show that the *Erwinia* soft rotters have a similar association with plant roots.

The third category, comparable to group A in Fig. 1, is characterized by diseases caused by pathogens that have evolved further away from the requirement of a soil-saprophytic existence. They developed even more sustained plant-to-plant infection cycles, often via insect transmission. In addition, owing either to the perennial nature of the host or to an association with the vegetative host or its seed, they have lost the more complex requirements of survival in the soil. *Erwinia amylovora* is a classical example. It is insect-transmitted on an epiphytotic scale, it is aggressive, and it associates with the perennial host in the dormant phase of its biological cycle. It cannot survive long in the soil. But selection which occurs during winter survival in an essentially saprophytic state on the host is probably quite unrelated to the type of selection manifested during the pathogenic phase. *Pseudomonas solanacearum*, race 2, causing banana wilt, is another example. Since it occurs in the tropics where the vegetative and flowering host is constantly present, there is no climatic check on selection for greater aggressiveness, greater invasiveness, and greater transmissibility via insects. At the present time the disease is spreading

rapidly in parts of Central America, where a more invasive clone has become established. The banana-wilt pathogen also does not survive long in the soil, as measured by replanting trials.

The point is thus made that *when the pathogen is first readily transmitted to nearby plants and is associated continually with the host without going through a soil phase, it is free to evolve in any direction, and saprophytism in soil becomes irrelevant to its further evolution. The long developing phase of gene interaction with the host towards increasingly complex parasitism is now possible.* In addition to fireblight and bacterial wilt of bananas, many other bacterial diseases are caused by pathogens which have been essentially liberated from the requirement of a soil phase by insects (*Erwinia tracheiphila* cucumber wilt, *Xanthomonas stewartii* wilt of corn, *Pseudomonas savastanoi* knot of olive), by vegetative propagation of the host (*Corynebacterium sepedonicum* ring rot of potatoes, *X. vasculorum* gumming disease of sugar cane, *P. marginata* neck rot of gladiolus), or by association with the perennial host (*P. mors-prunorum* bacterial canker, *P. syringae* blights, *X. juglandis* walnut blight), or with the seed (*X. malvacearum* blight of cotton, *X. campestris* black rot of crucifers, *P. medicaginis* halo blight of beans, *P. glycinea* blight of soybeans, *P. pisi* blight of peas, and many others).

In seasonally cold climates there must be selection for survival in an essentially saprophytic state associated with host tissue or soil. This selective check, in effect for half or more of each year, and not related to pathogenic capability, must limit the pathogens. In the moist lowland tropics, where seasonal changes are minor and biological activity is high at all times, the requirements for survival in the soil between hosts must be quite different. Temperature is always favorable for growth of both the pathogen and soil inhabitants and the soil phase is never one of a winter-time quiescence. One would expect a greater attrition of phytopathogens in the soil due to biological activity. On the other hand, the continued presence of the vegetative host and the rapid succession of crops would appear to provide pathogenic bacteria with ample opportunity for development exclusively in the host phase.

This consideration of the evolution and biology of bacterial diseases, plus an examination of bacterial-disease distribution maps and of what is known of the history of some diseases (Jenkins and Fawcett, 1933; Knight, 1948; Burkholder, 1948; Patel and Kulkarni, 1953; Crosse, Bennett, and Garrett, 1960; Schnathorst, Haliski, and Martin, 1960; Buddenhagen, 1961) leads one to the conclusion that bacterial diseases originate only rarely and in a localized area at some point in time and must evolve and be *distributed* from those foci. Exceptions may be some of the simple bacterial diseases that do not spread readily and "spontaneously" reappear from quasi parasites present in the soil. Consideration of the localized origin of bacterial diseases is usually obscured by our pragmatic approach to diseases and their control. Likewise, the past millennia during which migrations of people and their crop plants occurred tend to obscure the perspective of the present-day observer of the "natural order." Such considerations of origins are not just idle curiosity; a different approach is necessary for a disease investigation if the pathogen is in reality a recent invader of most soils where it occurs.

It has been suggested that the tobacco-wildfire group of bacteria is regenerated out of the saprophytic species *Pseudomonas fluorescens* (Reid et al., 1942). As inviting as it is to believe that such bacterial plant pathogens often reappear out of the vast and diverse population of soil saprophytes (Starr, 1959; McNew, 1960), the onus of proof still lies with those who would like us to believe it. Stapp concluded that common soil fluorescent bacteria were not pathogenic and they could not be held responsible for sudden outbreaks of diseases among cultivated plants (Stapp, 1955). But a detailed study on *P. fluorescens* and 150 phytopathogens has appeared recently with opposite conclusions (Stolp, 1961). Different species of phytopathogenic pseudomonads were considered to have similar pathogenic potentials. Fluorescent isolates from soil that were similar to phytopathogens in phage sensitivity behaved like typical saprophytes. But, from a "statistically avirulent" population virulent mutants could be selected. The conclusion was made that the connection between these saprophytic and parasitic bacteria represents a problem in population genetics. It was concluded also that the systematics of the phytopathogenic pseudomonads at the species level is wrong, and that a close relationship exists between parasitic and saprophytic bacteria of the fluorescent pseudomonads. Reports of similar "creations" of pathogens of insects from saprophytic relatives have appeared (Le Corroller, 1958) and although unconfirmed, should not be ignored (Steinhaus, 1960). Phenomena such as the conversion of avirulent throat commensals of *Corynebacterium diphtheriae* into virulent pathogens by lysogenization (Anderson, 1957) are not yet known for phytopathogens.

WHAT IS KNOWN ABOUT THE LIFE OF BACTERIAL PATHOGENS OUTSIDE THE HOST?—We know of the existence of bacterial pathogens only because they cause disease. Although this is pointing out the obvious, it emphasizes the fact that any bacterium isolated from nonhost material by a microbiologist not also a pathologist would not be identified as a pathogen. It also emphasizes the orientation of research in bacterial phytopathology, which has been directed at the disease and its control.

It seems strange that we still have these divergent viewpoints from eminent bacteriologists and phytopathologists: "Bacterial plant pathogens are not soil-inhabiting organisms and are apparently unable to stand the competition in nature" (Burkholder, 1959); "The tobacco leaf spot phase of the life cycle of these two parasitic organisms [*Pseudomonas tabaci; P. angulata*] is more or less accidental . . ." (Valleau, Johnson, and Diachun, 1944); ". . . It is not known from which of these countries it [*Agrobacterium tumefaciens*] originated . . . it may yet prove possible to trace the origin of this world-wide bacteriosis to the

Asiatic countries" (Stapp, 1961). The implication in this last statement is that originally *A. tumefaciens* was not generally present as a soil inhabitant. Few phytopathogenic bacteria appear to be soil inhabitants, but many do have a soil phase, even if only one of a rapidly decreasing population.

Some of the early disease investigations were thorough enough to obtain general information on disease epiphytology and pathogen biology, including the role of the soil (E. F. Smith, 1911, 1914; Skoric, 1927; Bryan, 1930; Ivanoff, 1933). Many other studies include pertinent observations on survival of the non-pathogenic phase, often based on inferences from rotation studies. Thus, *Corynebacterium michiganense*, the tomato canker pathogen, was considered to survive poorly from one season to the next in New York and Washington, D. C., based on replanting trials; but in Georgia it survived composting until the following season (Bryan, 1930). In California, field carryover of this pathogen was not considered important (Grogan and Kendrick, 1953), but in Italy the disease reappeared four years after the previous tomato crop, presumably due to survival in the soil (Ciccarone and Carilli, 1948). *C. sepedonicum* is considered not to overwinter in field soil (Snieszko and Bonde, 1943). *C. flaccumfaciens* is considered to survive poorly in soil but was shown to be viable after 24 years on stored bean seed (Burkholder, 1945). The role of the soil in the biology of *C. fascians* is uncertain.

The *Xanthomonas* pathogens are generally considered not to survive well in the soil, although the soil relation has not been investigated for many of them. *X. citri* was shown to die rapidly in field soil but not in sterile soil (Lee, 1920; Fulton, 1920). *X. phaseoli* var. *sojense* survived for a longer period, but field tests did not recover the pathogen in the succeeding crop (J. H. Graham, 1953). *X. pelargoni* survived less than one year in moist soil (Munnecke, 1956). *X. malvacearum* overwintered on cottonseed but not in soil in Arizona (Hare and King, 1940), and existed during only part of the year in association with roots of nonhost plants (T. E. Smith, 1962). *X. campestris* was considered to overwinter on seed (Walker and Tisdale, 1920) and not invade from the soil (Clayton, 1924). *X. translucens* did not overwinter in soil, but did so in association with winter wheat and quack grass (Boosalis, 1952). *X. vesicatoria* overwintered until March on roots of wheat plants in field soils in Kentucky (Diachun and Valleau, 1946). *X. stewarti* was shown to overwinter in corn stubble, not freely in the soil (Ivanoff, 1933).

Different pathogens in the genus *Pseudomonas* appear to vary greatly in their ability to survive in the soil. As mentioned earlier, some of the pathogenic green-fluorescent forms appear to be soil organisms (D. C. Graham, 1958; Holding, 1960; Paton, 1960). But *P. medicaginis* var. *phaseolicola*, the cause of halo blight of beans, apparently does not survive in soils from season to season (Wilson, 1946) and like so many legume pathogens is perpetuated in seed. *P. marginata*, the cause of gladiolus scab, can apparently overwinter in soil (Patel, 1929), but this is not the major source of reinfection. *P. pisi* was shown to overwinter on seed, not in soil (Skoric, 1927). *P. savastanoi,* the cause of olive knot, was found to survive for 8 months in the most favorable soil (Beltra, 1957), although considering the insect-spread etiology of the disease it is questionable if soil survival has any relation to the disease. *P. tabaci* and *P. angulata* apparently live as rhizoplane bacteria on the roots of many plants (Valleau, Johnson, and Diachun, 1944). Soil is not considered to be important in the diseases caused by *P. syringae, P. mors-prunorum,* and *P. lachrymans.*

Pseudomonas solanacearum must be discussed apart from other *Pseudomonas* pathogens since it has received more attention with respect to the soil than all other species combined. It is one of only a few vascular-wilt-inducing pseudomonads, is not a fluorescent form, and is quite distinct from many other species placed in the same genus (Colwell and Liston, 1961). The literature on this pathogen before 1953 has been comprehensively reviewed (Kelman, 1953). Although the comments in this review on the soil in relation to the banana strain are known now to be invalid, the majority of the discussion on soil aspects for other strains remains intact. The wilt disease caused by various strains of this pathogen in the East Indies, in southeastern United States, and in many other tropical or subtropical parts of the world occurs on soils of every imaginable type and pH. All of the studies on survival of the pathogen in soils have been indirect, based on disease incidence. Thus, the extreme diversity of results of rotations, of studies on disease spread, of the effect of soil temperatures and soil treatments, is difficult to interpret in terms of effects upon the pathogen itself. The absence of consistent correlations of soil type, moisture, pH, and previous cropping histories with disease incidence indicates that unsuspected or undetermined means of dissemination and reintroduction were occurring. Or that undetermined rates of spread from foci, strain differences, or past localized buildup in native flora may have been important, confounding efforts to implicate soil factors. It is certain, however, that continued cropping with a susceptible host such as tobacco increases the inoculum in the soil from season to season for that particular host but not for all other hosts (Schwarz, 1926; T. E. Smith, 1944). Different resistant plants grown in rotation affect the pathogen population to different degrees, presumably owing to biological effects of the crop on the soil-microbial flora (Palm, 1924; van der Poel, 1940; T. E. Smith, 1944). Disease after inoculation is more severely expressed in moist and warm soils, at least on tomatoes (Vaughan, 1944; Gallegly and Walker, 1949). It also appears certain that the tobacco strain can remain in soil in the absence of any plants or in the absence of hosts for many years (Schwarz, 1926; T. E. Smith, 1944). The banana race, however, is reduced to levels where only a low disease incidence recurs after 18-24 months in host-free soil (Sequeira, 1962). In Java the tobacco strain was reduced to levels where it could not be recovered by a baiting technique in land flooded for 3 months for rice rotation (van Schreven, 1954). In one recent preliminary study various soil factors have been tested on the actual growth of the pathogen (Gondo and Arimura, 1960).

Agrobacterium tumefaciens survives for a year or two in field soils but is not usually found where infected stock has not been grown (Patel, 1928; Hildebrand, 1934, 1941). It is spread on nursery stock to new areas and passes into the soil from the surfaces of developing galls (Banfield, 1934). One of few studies on direct measurement of the pathogen population under different soil conditions has recently appeared (Dickey, 1961). The pathogen only gradually decreased in soils and was favored by lower temperatures, higher pH's, and moist soil conditions. An improved biological technique for recovery of the hairy-root *Agrobacterium,* which should aid studies of its biology in the soil, has recently appeared (Ark and Thompson, 1961). The related genus *Rhizobium* is believed to survive saprophytically in nonhost soils, decreasing gradually, but it was able to multiply in the presence of competition when the soil was remoistened (Tuzimura and Watanabe, 1960).

Erwinia amylovora, the fireblight organism, cannot survive long in soil although it was recovered after 7 months in one instance (Ark, 1932). This pathogen has received attention for persistence in insects (Ark and Thomas, 1936) and regarding the effects of such factors as temperature, moisture, and reducing substances on longevity in bacterial ooze (Rosen, 1938; Hildebrand, 1939; Ark, 1940). Such studies have shown that the natural bacterial ooze is protective, especially in the dry state, and that studies on survival of culture-raised bacteria may be misleading. Bacterial ooze was examined thoroughly for other pathogens and found to be protective against various adverse factors (Hedrick, 1956; Leach et al., 1957). The cucumber-wilt pathogen, *E. tracheiphila,* does not survive well in the soil (Rand and Enlows, 1916). The soil probably plays a major role, however, in the biology of the soft-rot erwinias (*Pectobacterium*), although there is still controversy on whether or not they are natural soil inhabitants (D. C. Graham, 1958). Whether soil is the natural habitat for other coliform bacteria is also uncertain, although evidence is accumulating that some forms are part of the normal soil microflora (Taylor, 1951; Medrek and Litsky, 1960).

The effect of soil microflora in inhibiting disease expression or reducing the bacterial pathogen population is often mentioned but usually only as an inference. Patrick (1954) showed that many soil microorganisms are antagonistic to various bacterial pathogens in culture. Brian (1957) considered antibiotic production in soil to be important in microbial ecology. In mixed inoculation studies, antagonistic bacteria reduced infection by several pathogens (Jacobs and Mohanty, 1951; Teliz-Ortiz and Burkholder, 1960). On the other hand, nematodes increased disease incidence with several bacterial pathogens, usually by providing wounds for entry (Crosse and Pitcher, 1952; Lucas, Sasser, and Kelman, 1955; Stewart and Schindler, 1956). Their relation to bacterial diseases has been reviewed recently (Pitcher, 1963).

Bacteriophages were considered to be important in

reducing bacterial pathogens in the soil (Coons and Kotila, 1925). Although this thesis appears to have been only slightly pursued, phages have been found commonly in soil under diseased hosts (Stolp, 1956; Crosse and Hingorani, 1958; Crosse, 1959). It has been contended, based on work with *Corynebacterium diphtheriae,* that infection of bacteria by temperate phages plays a decisive role in controlling bacterial behavior and evolution (Hewitt, 1954). The relation of bacteriophages to the ecology of bacteria of medical and industrial importance has been more recently reviewed with the conclusion that phages are not usually important in bacterial ecology because of the rarity with which conditions necessary for phage action occur in nature (Anderson, 1957). The recent discovery of a new group of obligately parasitic "microbacteria" that lyse bacteria in the soil, including plant pathogens, is an interesting one (Stolp and Petzold, 1962).

The fate of nonpathogenic mutants of the bacterial population is little known. During the later stages of disease development, mutation to avirulence is well known. Sometimes the avirulent mutants represent a shift from the smooth- to rough-colony type, involving loss of capsular or polysaccharide material. Such mutants occurring in nature are still part of the biological species, but they are not studied by the pathologist because they do not induce disease. Their fate in the soil is unknown. If they had enhanced saprophytic ability, they could increase in the soil since they would be introduced into it each growing season. The question of whether disease reinitiation could be due to back-mutation from these avirulent forms has rarely been considered. Such a possibility has been provisionally examined for avirulent colony types of *Erwinia amylovora* isolated from healthy plant tissue (Goodman, Shafter, and Baldwin, 1962).

Another seldom-considered aspect of the relation of bacteria to plants is that of bacteria present in plants infected with fungi or other pathogens. In order to satisfy Koch's postulates, special media are used to exclude bacteria from isolations if a fungus is suspected as the primary cause of the disease. Inoculation and reisolation of the suspected fungal pathogen may be successfully done, thereby satisfying the postulates, but bacteria invariably present in the diseased inoculated plants are again excluded by choice from isolations. This argument can be overstated, but there should be no doubt that the bacteria invariably present along with the fungus pathogen, especially in root diseases or systemic diseases, affects the pathogen and the disease syndrome in some way (Gorlenko, Voronkevitch, and Chumaevskala, 1953). The Koch's postulate approach is a considerable oversimplification of what really obtains in nature (Dubos, 1959), especially when applied to plant diseases.

Recent evidence indicates that different organs of plants and different plant species support a normal characteristic epiphytic bacterial flora (Wallace and Lochhead, 1951; Stout, 1958; Rouatt and Katznelson, 1961; Ruinen, 1961). Even the coli-aerogenes bacteria appear to be normal flora on some grasses (Thomas and McQuillin, 1952). Further, it appears that some animal commensals have a phase as plant epiphytes with transmission cycles from plant to plant via insects (Eaves and Mundt, 1960; Mundt, Coggin, and Johnson, 1962). An appreciation that such associations, at present largely unknown, have been occurring for countless years, emphasizes the difficulty in distinguishing a soil bacterium from a plant epiphyte or an animal commensal, or from a weak plant parasite capable of causing disease only under plant stress.

It may be unrealistic to expect pathogens to have a large soil-saprophytic population. Direct studies of pathogen decline in soil may be unrealistic; why should we expect a stable high population among many other already established saprophytes? There may be only a small niche available for a particular pathogen and after its decline to a low level comparable to other zymogenous bacteria it may be undetectable even by baiting or host-replanting tests. Early information indicated that the more important factors in disease reappearance were reintroduction and survival in host material. As a result, few basic studies on soil survival have been carried out. Research on the soil aspect has been emphasized only for diseases such as crown gall or bacterial wilt, where there may be a net increase of inoculum in certain soils from year to year. The extremely interesting fundamental question of why many bacterial pathogens are poor survivors in the soil has thus been neglected completely.

WHY ARE THERE NOT MORE BACTERIAL EPIPHYTOTIC DISEASES?—When one considers that there are some 300,000 or more species of higher plants, and that we know of bacterial diseases in only a few hundred species, it is obvious that only a fraction of possible bacteria-plant relations have been examined. Only a small proportion of plant species are of economic importance and in the tropics some of these have not received careful observation by the bacterial phytopathologist. Diseases of wild plants growing in natural environments are virtually uninvestigated. Thus, our view of bacterial diseases is narrow and biased by our crop-oriented understanding of plant ecology.

Although certain bacterial diseases are among the most destructive known (fireblight of pear, bacterial wilt of Solanaceae and *Musa*), causing recurring epiphytotics, most bacterial diseases do not reach epiphytotic levels. When compared with fungi, bacteria as a group are not very successful plant pathogens, much less successful as plant than as animal pathogens. Crosse has admirably summarized the difficulties of dispersal and the poor nonhost survival of bacterial plant pathogens (Crosse, 1957). Several questions, however, are left unanswered. (1) Why do not bacterial plant parasites survive better saprophytically, like many of their closely related saprophytic counterparts? If they did, they would be much more successful pathogens. (2) Since some bacterial pathogens are readily transmitted, rapidly causing epiphytotic levels of disease, why are not more? Although there is a need for rain and high humidity in order to obtain bacterial ooze for transmission, many locations satisfy these requirements. The limitations that a bacterium must overcome to be a successful pathogen will be discussed, starting with its presence at a host surface.

The pathogenic bacterium must first enter the plant. It is generally accepted that the cuticle prevents entry of bacteria, which must, therefore, enter stomata, other natural openings, or wounds. Although this limits them, some fungi also must enter through stomata and are likewise handicapped. Probably the microenvironmental conditions required are more stringent at this point for bacteria, watersoaking often being necessary. Entrance through uninjured trichomes of tomatoes may be possible (Kontaxis, 1962). Entrance into uninjured plant roots has only been proved for *Rhizobium* (Ljunggren and Fåhraeus, 1961). Openings provided by secondary roots as they emerge from parent roots apparently provide avenues of infection for some bacteria (Kelman and Sequeira, 1962), although their importance is not yet clear.

Once inside, the bacterium must be able to overcome "physiological host defenses" and multiply. This is an area of research that has hardly been touched for bacterial diseases although the importance of exploring early host-parasite interactions in order to understand the nature of pathogenic specificity was carefully detailed by Kern (1956). Two interesting papers have recently appeared proposing hypotheses to explain the differing trends of populations of pathogens, nonpathogens, and saprophytes occurring after inoculation of sterile bean pods (Klement and Lovrekovich, 1961, 1962). Interesting approaches to host-parasite enzyme interactions occurring in later stages of pathogenesis with several pathogenic and "nonpathogenic" bacteria have been reviewed by Brown (1955).

In order to induce vascular disease, bacteria must multiply and move readily within the xylem. It is probable that the fungus-stimulated defense reactions within the xylem of roots (Beckman and Halmos, 1962)

also preclude the growth and movement of the innumerable bacteria that normally reach the xylem of roots. We know that roots of banana plants in plantations, for instance, are constantly being wounded by many agents and that bacteria of many kinds enter the xylem vessels. Yet only one race of one species is able to grow well and become established therein. Certainly this is remarkable and not explainable on a nutritional basis. Not only this pathogen but most Gram-negative bacterial pathogens have simple nutritive requirements (Starr, 1945, 1946; Starr and Mandel, 1950), as do many saprophytes also.

The tomato race of *Pseudomonas solanacearum* is present in soils of banana plantations and contacts and invades roots of bananas. But normal defense reactions preclude establishment and systemic movement in the xylem. When inoculated directly into the fruit, however, the tomato race is more virulent than the clones of the banana race, and results in a typical fruit rot which is the most destructive aspect of bacterial wilt (Fig. 2). The tomato-wilt pathogen is never found as a banana-fruit pathogen in nature because it is unable to reach the fruit. This inability to reach the fruit by becoming distributed systemically within the xylem vessels is not due to its inability to produce pectic and cellulolytic enzymes, host-stimulating indoleacetic acid, or wilt-inducing polysaccharides, all of which it readily does (Husain and Kelman, 1958a,b; Sequeira and Kelman, 1962).

It has been shown with mixed inocula of *Pseudomonas solanacearum* in tomato plants that nonpathogenic strains reduce the expression of virulence of the virulent strain (Averre and Kelman, 1960). Similarly, we have shown that if the pathogen is introduced into banana roots with a nonpathogenic race at levels still obviating dilution effects, pathogenicity is precluded. We attribute this to a normal host response to the

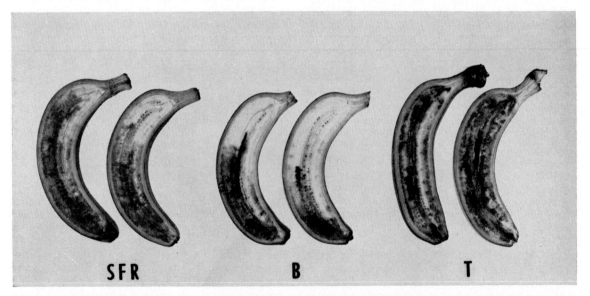

Fig. 2. Banana fruits inoculated with *Pseudomonas solanacearum* strains. *SFR* and *B* are pathogens of bananas in nature; *T* is race 1, the pathogen of solanaceous hosts, never affecting banana fruits in plantations because it is unable to reach the fruit after root invasion from the soil.

nonpathogenic race, since no interaction occurs when the two races are mixed in culture. Further research is needed to elucidate the mechanisms of these specific host-nonparasite interactions. It is surprising that for bacterial diseases, where the complex interactions imposed by the presence of appressoria, sporulation, and mycelial growth are not involved, more studies have not been done on the nature of the physiology and biochemistry of the early host-parasite reactions influencing establishment and growth. More often it has been the later pathological conditions following multiplication of the parasite that have been investigated. Hypotheses on the nature of pathogen specificity or host resistance drawn from these studies have seldom been meaningful.

After the bacteria have multiplied within their host they must exit from it or they will have no future bearing on disease of the host population. This appears to be a major obstacle for many bacterial pathogens. Some escape may occur through roots but with poor soil survival this results only in localized spread. Bacteria exude from leaf spots and blighted tissues during rains or periods of high humidity. Insects or other agents cause wounds that allow escape in some diseases. Escape to the plant surface is not necessary for perpetuation, however, only for spread. Thus, many bacterial diseases avoid extinction by the intimate association of the pathogen with the resting host, e.g., on buds, branches, the seed or propagule.

The fourth major difficulty for bacteria is their dispersal to other plants during the growing season. Although bacterial diseases may be perpetuated by association with seed, their ultimate success in causing epiphytotics depends upon their ability to spread, a limitation very real for these sporeless and conidiophoreless forms. The susceptibility of the pathogenic bacterial cell to desiccation, light, and other rigors of the external environment, and its short life expectancy in competition with other microorganisms emphasize the need for rapid and direct dispersal. But for the help of man and insects, bacterial pathogens would be quite unsuccessful.

How Have the Limitations Been Bypassed for Specific Diseases?—We have seen that entrance, growth, exit, and transmission are the requirements for success as a bacterial pathogen. Survival ability and a wide host range may compensate for an inadequacy in one of the primary requirements. *Agrobacterium tumefaciens* would be a less successful pathogen if it could affect only one host species or was unable to have a net survival in the soil from season to season. Its growth, exit, and transmission are often limited. A narrow-host-range bacterium such as *Pseudomonas medicaginis* is limited by poor nonhost survival, but is nevertheless successful due to its oozing and subsequent local transmission, and seed-association for survival and long-range dispersal.

Bacterial wilt of bananas will be discussed to illustrate how, within one pathogenic species, a diverging biology has occurred, profoundly affecting the relation of the pathogen to the soil. The differences in the biology of the banana race from that of the tomato race of *Pseudomonas solanacearum* are no less great than the differences in the biologies of many unrelated pathogenic species. They provide an example of how diseases may have evolved irrespective of an original dependence on the soil. Bacterial wilt or Moko disease of bananas is an example of synthesis and evolution of a disease within a short historical period from an originally limited host-pathogen relation (Fig. 3). Unlike most diseases, we can reconstruct its evolution and our insight into the disease is not confounded by years of adjustment to an agriculturally modified environment.

Bananas are planted in unplowed land of felled virgin jungle comprised of hundreds of species of trees and understory vegetation, among which are various species of *Heliconia*, an ornamental relative of the banana. Some of the *Heliconia* plants are infected with a strain of *Pseudomonas solanacearum* known as D. There are numerous clones of D, which have probably been evolving in the lowlands of southwestern Costa Rica with its extremely varied vegetation since early Pleistocene times from a more generalized biological species of *P. solanacearum* that was not pathogenic to monocot hosts. Bananas planted in these soils at first wilted following root infection only when they were planted near diseased heliconias. But two curious things happened: (1) many bananas did not wilt even though they were planted beside diseased heliconias; and (2) many areas where young bananas wilted remained static, with no spread to adjacent plants as normally occurs in old plantations. The disease spread from only a few sites. The explanation was that the D strain, the normal pathogen of *Heliconia*, was not sufficiently aggressive to bananas to wilt them unless they were small, vigorously growing, and exposed to sufficient inoculum. Some members of the D strain could not cause bananas to wilt under any condition, remaining only as pathogens of the heliconias. Thus, the D strain was not able to establish itself as a continuing pathogen in the banana plantation (Fig. 4). A few original disease cases did result in spread, however, and from these "advancing disease holes" a clone designated as B was always isolated. This clone was more aggressive to bananas and under experimental field trials was shown to maintain itself as a continuing spreading pathogen from plant to plant, via root infection. That the B clone can be selected out of the original D strain population by serial passage through the banana has been shown (Sequeira and Averre, 1961). We now know, however, that the change to B is not simple, and the establishment of a B clone in the plantation out of a D population is a rare event. When a B mutant from a diseased *Heliconia* would infect a banana root without its D counterpart, a spreading disease would be established directly. At first, the B clone was moderately successful on banana, having the ability to enter (through root wounds), multiply systemically, exit (through roots), and transmit (to adjacent roots of healthy plants). But these characteristics could only create slowly expanding "holes" in the plantation from a few original foci. A greater opportunity was con-

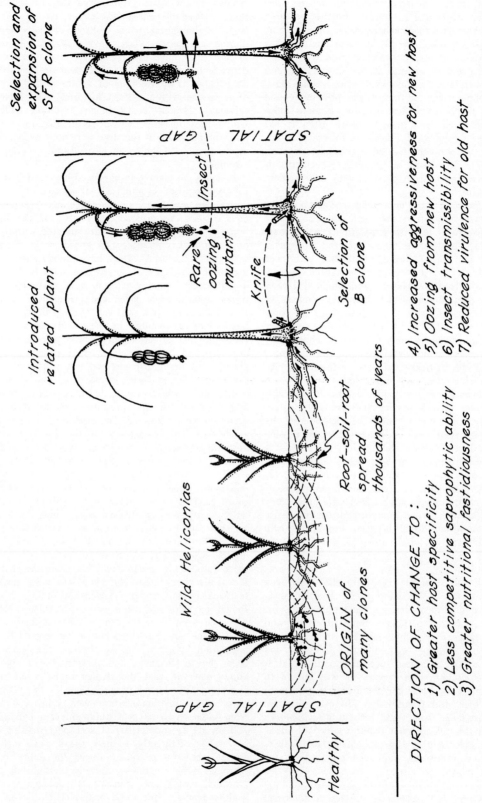

Fig. 3. Evolution of epiphytotic capability of a *Pseudomonas solanacearum* clone on bananas from an originally limited root-infecting pathogen of other hosts.

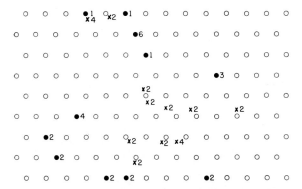

Fig. 4. Disease incidence of bananas and heliconias during first 26 months after planting bananas in virgin land. Limited root invasion of individual young plants occurred but the strain involved (*D*) failed to become established as a spreading pathogen in the plantation. Numbers refer to cycle month when diseased plants were found, 1 being April 1960, shortly after plants emerged.

tributed by the pruning knife, providing simultaneously an aerial exit for bacteria at the cut surface and the means of transmission and inoculation. Moreover, insects could now mechanically transmit the bacteria from cut surface to cut surface, and over long distances. A much greater opportunity was provided, however, by the appearance of a clone of still greater aggressiveness, designated as SFR. (We are uncertain of the exact origin of this SFR clone; it may not be derived directly from B). This clone oozes readily from parts of the inflorescence and is more invasive through fresh bract and flower-trace surfaces. The intercourse normally occurring between banana inflorescences of up to a thousand insects per day was immediately exploitable, although passively, by this SFR clone (Buddenhagen and Elsasser, 1962).

From a localized area in Honduras where the SFR clone was present in early 1961, the disease has spread into Guatemala and now can be found wherever its host occurs in an area of over 5,000 km². Thus the spatial gap between hosts, uncrossable by D and partially overcome on a limited scale by B, was fully spanned by the oozing and invasive characteristics of SFR. The direction of evolution of this disease, originally caused by a limited soil-borne, root-infecting strain, has been toward one caused by a more aggressive, more transmissible, and more aerially oriented parasite. The other less aggressive strains were left behind, unable to utilize an opportunity that has been before them for several hundred years. This opportunity, inflorescence invasion, was exploitable because a series of limitations was overcome step by step, each suceeding clone surviving sufficiently to maintain a population within reach of the next level. That this evolution of a disease to an epiphytotic level was a complicated stepwise process, impossible without the intermediate evolutionary host, *Heliconia,* is shown by the fact that bananas evolved in southeast Asia, where the parent biological species of *Pseudomonas solanacearum* is also present, but where the disease has never evolved. Likewise, the parent *P. solanacearum* species

is present on solanaceous weed hosts in banana plantations throughout Central America, yet the banana clones have not evolved directly from this complex. In Central America, banana bacterial wilt occurred originally only in a location where *Heliconia* wilt was already present.

SUGGESTIONS FOR FUTURE WORK.—By dwelling at length on the example of banana bacterial wilt I have emphasized the origin and evolutionary changes of a disease, and have shown that the pathogen's relation to the soil is not static. This relation changes with time, as limitations to completion of disease cycles are overcome by ecological changes or by mutations and strain selection. Limitations which prevent the development of widespread bacterial diseases can be due to many factors. Insight into one aspect—the mechanisms of pathogenic specificity and host resistance—may come from studies on the biochemical nature of limitations to aggressiveness expressed on *nonpathogenic* bacteria after they contact the host. That there are few widely applicable concepts of pathogenesis is probably due to the varied nature of pathogens and the diseases they cause. Both specific diseases and disease types must be considered as units and the disease as a whole occurring in nature must be constantly kept in mind when studies are undertaken to add to our understanding and aid in control.

The role of the soil in bacterial diseases is varied, ranging from one of significance to one of insignificance. The information we have on soil aspects is almost wholly indirect. We need better techniques for isolating and detecting pathogens in the soil. We need to know more about threshold levels for infection in natural soils and the relation between soil saprophytes and pathogens, both regarding competition and genetic relations. We need to know more about pathogen population shifts as reasonable selective forces are applied under experimental conditions. We should know what effect plant roots have on pathogens adjacent in the soil. We need to formulate questions clearly and not give complete trust to indirect evidence. We cannot even state today that a pathogen will survive at a different rate from a saprophyte if both are introduced into a given soil. We need to work with many isolates and know that these represent the variability of the pathogenic population and are not avirulent mutants. We need to consider how many of our conclusions are based upon laboratory artifacts; there are many more than is realized. And finally, considering the great amount of fundamental work recently compiled on bacteria in general (Gunsalus and Stanier, 1960-1963; Jacob and Wolman, 1961) we can see how far we must travel to understand more fully the behavior of bacterial plant pathogens.

LITERATURE CITED

ANDERSON, E. S. 1957. The relations of bacteriophages to bacterial ecology. Symp. Soc. Gen. Microbiol. 7 (Microbial ecology): 189-217.
ARK, P. A. 1932. The behavior of *Bacillus amylovorus* in the soil. Phytopathology 22: 657-660.
ARK, P. A. 1940. Relation of reducing substances to

longevity and virulence of phytopathogenic bacteria. (Abstr.) Phytopathology 30: 1.

ARK, P. A., and H. F. THOMAS. 1936. Persistence of *Erwinia amylovora* in certain insects. Phytopathology 26: 375-381.

ARK, P. A., and J. P. THOMPSON. 1961. Detection of hairy root pathogen, *Agrobacterium rhizogenes,* by the use of fleshy roots. Phytopathology 51: 69-71.

AVERRE, C. W., III, and A. KELMAN. 1960. Virulence of *Pseudomonas solanacearum* as influenced by proportion of virulent to avirulent cells. (Abstr.) Phytopathology 50: 627-628.

BANFIELD, W. M. 1934. Life history of the crown-gall organism in relation to its pathogenesis on the red raspberry. J. Agr. Res. 48: 761-787.

BAWDEN, F. C. 1957. The role of plant hosts in microbial ecology. Symp. Soc. Gen. Microbiol. 7 (Microbial ecology): 299-314.

BECKMAN, C. H., and S. HALMOS. 1962. Relation of vascular occluding reactions in banana roots to pathogenicity of root-invading fungi. Phytopathology 52: 893-897.

BEIJERINCK, M. W. 1922. Verzamelde Geschriften. 5 vols. Nijhoff, Delft, The Netherlands.

BELTRA, R. 1957. El agente etiologico de la tuberculosis del olivo en relacion con el suelo. Anales Edafol. Fisiol. Vegetal 16: 557-577.

BOOSALIS, M. G. 1952. The epidemiology of *Xanthomonas translucens* (J. J. and R.) Dowson on cereals and grasses. Phytopathology 42: 387-395.

BRIAN, P. W. 1957. The ecological significance of antibiotic production. Symp. Soc. Gen. Microbiol. 7 (Microbial ecology): 168-188.

BROWN, W. 1955. On the physiology of parasitism in plants. Ann. Appl. Biol. 43: 325-341.

BRYAN, M. K. 1930. Studies on bacterial canker of tomato. J. Agr. Res. 41: 825-851.

BUDDENHAGEN, I. W. 1961. Bacterial wilt of bananas: History and known distribution. Trop. Agr. (London) 38: 107-121.

BUDDENHAGEN, I. W., and T. A. ELSASSER. 1962. An insect-spread bacterial wilt epiphytotic of Bluggoe banana. Nature (London) 194: 164-165.

BURKHOLDER, W. H. 1945. The longevity of the pathogen causing the wilt of the common bean. Phytopathology 35: 743-744.

BURKHOLDER, W. H. 1948. Bacteria as plant pathogens. Ann. Rev. Microbiol. 2: 389-412.

BURKHOLDER, W. H. 1959. Present-day problems pertaining to the nomenclature and taxonomy of the phytopathogenic bacteria. p. 120-127. *In* Omagiu lui Traian Săvulescu. Editura Academiei Republicii Populare Romîne, Bucharest.

CICCARONE, A., and A. CARILLI. 1948. Feldbeobachtungen an *Corynebacterium michiganense* (Smith) Jensen und Betrachtungen über die Möglichkeit seines Überlebens im Boden. Staz. Pat. Veg. Roma. Boll., Ser. 3, 6: 177-179.

CLAYTON, E. E. 1924. A progress report on black-rot investigations, with special reference to cauliflower on Long Island. (Abstr.) Phytopathology 14: 24.

COLWELL, R. R., and J. LISTON. 1961. Taxonomic analysis with the electronic computer of some Xanthomonas and Pseudomonas species. J. Bacteriol. 82: 913-919.

CONN, H. J. 1948. The most abundant groups of bacteria in soil. Bacteriol. Rev. 12: 257-273.

COONS, G. H., and J. E. KOTILA. 1925. The transmissible lytic principle (bacteriophage) in relation to plant pathogens. Phytopathology 15: 357-370.

COWAN, S. T. 1959. Bacterial classification—problems and developments. p. 54-79. *In* Vernon Bryson [ed.], Microbiology, yesterday and today, Rutgers University, New Brunswick, N. J.

CROSSE, J. E. 1957. The dispersal of bacterial plant pathogens. p. 7-12. *In* C. Horton-Smith [ed.], Biological aspects of the transmission of disease, Oliver and Boyd Ltd., Edinburgh.

CROSSE, J. E. 1959. Plant pathogenic bacteria and their phages. Com. Phytopathol. News 5: 17-19.

CROSSE, J. E., M. BENNETT, and C. M. E. GARRETT. 1960. Investigation of fireblight of pear in England. Ann. Appl. Biol. 48: 541-558.

CROSSE, J. E., and M. K. HINGORANI. 1958. A method of isolating *P. mors-prunorum* phages from the soil. Nature (London) 181: 60-61.

CROSSE, J. E., and R. S. PITCHER. 1952. Studies in the relationship of eelworms and bacteria to certain plant diseases. I. The etiology of strawberry cauliflower disease. Ann. Appl. Biol. 38: 475-486.

DIACHUN, S., and W. D. VALLEAU. 1946. Growth and overwintering of *X. vesicatoria* in association with wheat roots. Phytopathology 36: 277-280.

DICKEY, R. S. 1961. Relation of some edaphic factors to *Agrobacterium tumefaciens*. Phytopathology 51: 607-614.

DOWSON, W. J. 1958. The present position of bacterial plant diseases, and subjects for future research. Com. Phytopathol. News 4: 33-35.

DUBOS, R. 1959. Mirage of health-utopias, progress and biological change. Harper and Brothers, New York. 236 p.

EAVES, G. N., and J. O. MUNDT. 1960. Distribution and characterization of streptococci from insects. J. Insect Pathol. 2: 289-298.

ELROD, R. P. 1942. The Erwinia-coliform relationship. J. Bacteriol. 44: 433.

ELROD, R. P., and A. C. BRAUN. 1942. *Pseudomonas aeruginosa;* its role as a plant pathogen. J. Bacteriol. 44: 633-646.

FLOODGATE, G. D. 1962. Some remarks on the theoretical aspects of bacterial taxonomy. Bacteriol. Rev. 26: 277-291.

FULTON, H. R. 1920. Decline of *Pseudomonas citri* in the soil. J. Agr. Res. 19: 207-223.

GALLEGLEY, M. E., and J. C. WALKER. 1949. Relation of environmental factors to bacterial wilt of tomato. Phytopathology 39: 936-946.

GARRETT, S. D. 1956. Biology of root-infecting fungi. Cambridge University Press, London and New York. 292 p.

GONDO, M., and M. ARIMURA. 1960. Soil ecological studies on soil pathogens. III. Effect of various soil factors on the growth of *Pseudomonas solanacearum*. Kagoshima Daigaku Nogakubu Gakujutsu Hokuku 9: 96-100.

GOODMAN, R. N., W. H. SHAFFER, JR., and C. H. BALDWIN, JR. 1962. Reversions of *Erwinia amylovora* from the avirulent rough to the virulent smooth form on exposure to aphid extracts. (Abstr.) Phytopathology 52: 734.

GORLENKO, M. V., I. V. VORONKEVITCH, and M. A. CHUMAEVSKALA. 1953. [Bacteria-saprophytes as stimulators of plant disease.] Agrobiologiya 3: 55-63.

GRAHAM, D. C. 1958. Occurrence of soft rot bacteria in Scottish soils. Nature (London) 181: 61.

GRAHAM, D. C., and W. J. DOWSON. 1960. The coliform bacteria associated with potato black leg and other soft rots. I. Their pathogenicity in relation to temperature. Ann. Appl. Biol. 48: 51-57.

GRAHAM, J. H. 1953. Overwintering of three bacterial pathogens of soybean. Phytopathology 43: 189-192.

GROGAN, R. G., and J. B. KENDRICK. 1953. Seed transmission, mode of overwintering and spread of bacterial canker of tomato caused by *C. michiganense*. (Abstr.) Phytopathology 43: 473.

GUNSALUS, I. C., and R. Y. STANIER. 1960-1963. The bacteria. vol. 1: Structure. vol. 2: Metabolism. vol. 3: Biosynthesis. vol. 4: Growth. vol. 5: Heredity. Academic Press, New York.

HARE, J. F., and C. J. KING. 1940. The winter carry over of angular leaf spot infection in Arizona cotton fields. Phytopathology 20: 679-684.

HEDRICK, H. G. 1956. Exudates produced by phytopathogenic bacteria. (Abstr.) Phytopathology 46: 14-15.

HEWITT, L. F. 1954. Autoadaptation of bacterial viruses and its effect on bacterial variation and evolution. J. Gen. Microbiol. 11: 261-271.

HILDEBRAND, E. M. 1934. Life history of the hairy root organism in relation to its pathogenesis on nursery apple trees. J. Agr. Res. 48: 857-885.

HILDEBRAND, E. M. 1939. Studies on fire-blight ooze. Phytopathology 29: 142-156.

HILDEBRAND, E. M. 1941. On the longevity of the crown gall organism in soil. Plant Disease Reptr. 25: 200-202.

HOLDING, A. J. 1960. The properties and classification of the predominant gram negative bacteria occurring in soil. J. Appl. Bacteriol. 23: 515-525.

HUSAIN, A., and A. KELMAN. 1958a. Relation of slime production to mechanism of wilting and pathogenicity of *Pseudomonas solanacearum.* Phytopathology 48: 155-165.

HUSAIN, A., and A. KELMAN. 1958b. The role of pectic and cellulolytic enzymes in pathogenesis by *Pseudomonas solanacearum.* Phytopathology 48: 377-386.

IVANOFF, S. S. 1933. Stewart's wilt disease of corn, with emphasis on the life history of *Phytomonas stewarti* in relation to pathogenesis. J. Agr. Res. 47: 749-770.

JACOB, F., and E. L. WOLLMAN. 1961. Sexuality and the genetics of bacteria. Academic Press, New York. 374 p.

JACOBS, S. E., and U. MOHANTY. 1951. Studies in bacteriosis. XXVII. Factors influencing infection by *Corynebacterium fasciens* (Tilford) Dowson. Ann. Appl. Biol. 38: 237-245.

JENKINS, A. E., and H. S. FAWCETT. 1933. Records of citrus scab mainly from herbarium specimens of the genus *Citrus* in England and the United States. Phytopathology 23: 475-482.

JENSEN, H. L. 1952. The coryneform bacteria. Ann. Rev. Microbiol. 6: 77-90.

KELMAN, A. 1953. The bacterial wilt caused by *Pseudomonas solanacearum.* North Carolina Agr. Expt. Sta. Tech. Bull. 99, 194 p.

KELMAN, A., and L. SEQUEIRA. 1962. Root infection in relation to spread of *Pseudomonas solanacearum.* (Abstr.) Phytopathology 52: 16.

KERN, H. 1956. Problems of incubation in plant diseases. Ann. Rev. Microbiol. 10: 351-368.

KLEMENT, Z., and L. LOVREKOVICH. 1961. Defense reactions induced by phytopathogenic bacteria in bean pods. Phytopathol. Z. 41: 217-227.

KLEMENT, Z., and L. LOVREKOVICH. 1962. Studies on host-parasite relations in bean pods infected with bacteria. Phytopathol. Z. 45: 81-88.

KNIGHT, R. L. 1948. The genetics of blackarm resistance. VII. *Gossypium arboreum* L. J. Genet. 49: 109-116.

KONTAXIS, D. G. 1962. Leaf trichomes as avenues for infection by *Corynebacterium michiganense.* Phytopathology 52: 1306-1307.

LEACH, J. G., V. G. LILLY, H. A. WILSON, and M. R. PURVIS JR. 1957. Bacterial polysaccharides: the nature and function of the exudate produced by *Xanthomonas phaseoli.* Phytopathology 47: 113-120.

LE CORROLLER, Y. 1958. À propos de la transformation de souches banales de *Bacillus cereus* Frank. et Frank. en souches crystallophores pathogenes pour les insectes. Ann. Inst. Pasteur 94: 670-673.

LEE, H. A. 1920. Behavior of the citrus canker organism in the soil. J. Agr. Res. 19: 189-205.

LJUNGGREN, H., and G. FÅHRAEUS. 1961. The role of polygalacturonase in root-hair invasion by nodule bacteria. J. Gen. Microbiol. 26: 521-528.

LOCHHEAD, A. G. 1952. The nutritional classification of soil bacteria. Proc. Soc. Appl. Bacteriol. 15: 15-20.

LOCHHEAD, A. G., and F. E. CHASE. 1943. Qualitative studies of soil microorganisms: V. Nutritional requirements of predominant bacterial flora. Soil Sci. 55: 185-195.

LUCAS, G. B., J. N. SASSER, and A. KELMAN. 1955. The relationship of root-knot nematodes to Granville wilt resistance in tobacco. Phytopathology 45: 537-540.

McNEW, G. 1960. The nature, origin, and evolution of parasitism. vol. 2, p. 19-69. *In* J. G. Horsfall and A. E. Dimond [ed.], Plant pathology, an advanced treatise, Academic Press, New York.

MEDREK, T. F., and W. LITSKY. 1960. Comparative incidence of coliform bacteria and enterococci in undisturbed soil. Appl. Microbiol. 8: 60-63.

MUNDT, O. J., J. H. COGGIN, JR., and L. F. JOHNSON. 1962. Growth of *Streptococcus faecalis* var. *liquefaciens* on plants. Appl. Microbiol. 10: 552-555.

MUNNECKE, D. E. 1956. Survival of *Xanthomonas pelargonii* in soil. Phytopathology 46: 297-298.

PALM, B. T. 1924. De stand van het slijmziekte-vraagstuk in de Deli-tabak. Mededeel. Deli Proefsta. Medan-Sumatra, 2nd ser., No. 32, 20 p.

PATEL, M. K. 1928. A study of pathogenic and non-pathogenic strains of *Pseudomonas tumefaciens* Sm. and Town. Phytopathology 18: 331-343.

PATEL, M. K. 1929. Viability of certain plant pathogens in soils. Phytopathology 19: 295-300.

PATEL, M. K., and Y. S. KULKARNI. 1953. A review of bacterial plant disease investigation in India. Indian Phytopathol. 6: 131-140.

PATON, A. M. 1960. The role of Pseudomonas in plant disease. J. Appl. Bacteriol. 23: 526-532.

PATRICK, Z. A. 1954. The antibiotic activity of soil microorganisms as related to bacterial plant pathogens. Can. J. Botany 32: 705-735.

PERSON, C., D. J. SAMBORSKI, and R. ROHRINGER. 1962. The gene-for-gene concept. Nature (London) 194: 561-562.

PITCHER, R. S. 1963. Role of plant-parasitic nematodes in bacterial diseases. Phytopathology 53: 35-39.

POEL, J. VAN DER. 1940. Verdere gegevens over beinvloeding van de tabak door de voorafgaande begroeiing der grond. Mededeel. Deli Proefsta. Medan-Sumatra, 3rd ser., no. 9, 35 p.

RAND, F. V., and E. M. A. ENLOWS. 1916. Transmission and control of bacterial wilt of cucurbits. J. Agr. Res. 6: 416-434.

REID, J. J., J. NAGHSKI, M. A. FARRELL, and D. E. HALEY. 1942. Bacterial leaf spots of Pennsylvania tobacco. I. Occurrence in nature of the microorganisms associated with wildfire. Pennsylvania Agr. Expt. Sta. Bull. 422, 36 p.

ROSEN, H. R. 1938. Life span and morphology of fire blight bacteria as influenced by relative humidity, temperature, and nutrition. J. Agr. Res. 56: 239-258.

ROUATT, J. W., and H. KATZNELSON. 1961. A study of the bacteria on the root surface and in the rhizosphere soil of crop plants. J. Appl. Bacteriol. 24: 164-171.

RUINEN, J. 1961. The phyllosphere I. An ecologically neglected milieu. Plant Soil 15: 81-109.

SADASIVAN, T. S., and C. V. SUBRAMANIAN. 1960. Interaction of pathogen, soil, other microorganisms in the soil, and host. vol. 2, p. 273-313. *In* J. G. Horsfall and A. E. Dimond [ed.], Plant pathology, an advanced treatise, Academic Press, New York.

SCHNATHORST, W. C., P. M. HALISKY, and R. D. MARTIN. 1960. History, distribution, races, and disease cycle of *Xanthomonas malvacearum* in California. Plant Disease Reptr. 44: 603-608.

SCHREVEN, D. A. VAN. 1954. The influence of a wet rice culture on the survival of tobacco virus 1, *Phytophthora parasitica* var. *nicotianae* and *Pseudomonas solanacearum* in tropical soil. Trans. Intern. Congr. Soil Sci., 5th (Leopoldville) 3: 88-92.

SCHWARZ, B. M. 1926. De invloed van de voorvrucht op het optreden van slijmziekte (*Bacterium solanacearum*) in *Arachis hypogea* en eenige andere gewassen. Mededeel. Inst. Plantenziekten 71, 37 p.

SEQUEIRA, L. 1962. Control of bacterial wilt of bananas by crop rotation and fallowing. Trop. Agr. (London) 39: 211-217.

SEQUEIRA, L., and C. W. AVERRE, III. 1961. Distribution and pathogenicity of strains of *Pseudomonas solanacearum* from virgin soils in Costa Rica. Plant Disease Reptr. 45: 435-440.

SEQUEIRA, L., and A. KELMAN. 1962. The accumulation of growth substances in plants infected by *Pseudomonas solanacearum.* Phytopathology 52: 439-448.

SKORIC, V. 1927. Bacterial blight of pea: overwintering, dissemination and pathological histology. Phytopathology 17: 611-628.

SMITH, E. F. 1911. Bacteria in relation to plant disease. vol. 2. Carnegie Institute of Washington, Washington, D. C. 368 p.

SMITH, E. F. 1914. Bacteria in relation to plant disease. vol. 3. Carnegie Institute of Washington, Washington, D. C. 309 p.

SMITH, T. E. 1944. Control of bacterial wilt (*Bacterium solanacearum*) of tobacco as influenced by crop rotation and chemical treatment of the soil. U. S. Dept. Agr. Cir. 692, 16 p.

SMITH, T. E. 1962. A variant culture of *Xanthomonas malvacearum* obtained from weed roots. Phytopathology 52: 1313-1314.

SNIESZKO, S. F., and R. BONDE. 1943. Studies on the morphology, physiology, serology, longevity and pathogenicity of *Corynebacterium sepedonicum*. Phytopathology 33: 1032-1044.

STAPP, C. 1955. Zur Pathogenität fluorescierender Bakterien. Beitr. Biol. Pflanzen 31: 515-524.

STAPP, C. 1961. Bacterial plant pathogens. Oxford University Press, London. 292 p.

STARR, M. P. 1945. The nutrition of phytopathogenic bacteria. I. Minimal nutritive requirements of the genus Xanthomonas. J. Bacteriol. 51: 131-143.

STARR, M. P. 1946. The nutrition of phytopathogenic bacteria. II. The genus *Agrobacterium*. J. Bacteriol. 52: 187-194.

STARR, M. P. 1959. Bacteria as plant pathogens. Ann. Rev. Microbiol. 13: 211-238.

STARR, M. P., and M. MANDEL. 1950. The nutrition of phytopathogenic bacteria. IV. Minimal nutritive requirements of the genus Erwinia. J. Bacterial. 50: 668-672.

STEINHAUS, E. A. 1960. Symposium: Selected topics in microbial ecology. II. The importance of environmental factors in the insect-microbe ecosystem. Bacteriol. Rev. 24: 365-371.

STEWART, R. N., and A. F. SCHINDLER. 1956. The effect of some ectoparasitic and endoparasitic nematodes on the expression of bacterial wilt in carnation. Phytopathology 46: 219-222.

STOLP, H. 1956. Bacteriophagenforschung und Phytopathologie (ein Sammelreferat). Phytopathol. Z. 26: 171-218.

STOLP, H. 1961. Neue Erkenntnisse über phytopathogene Bakterien und die von ihnen verursachten Krankheiten. I. Verwandtschaftsbeziehungen zwischen phytopathogenen Pseudomonas—"Arten" und saprophytischen Fluoreszenten auf der Grundlage von Phagenreaktionen. Phytopathol. Z. 42: 197-262.

STOLP, H., and H. PETZOLD. 1962. Untersuchung über einen obligat Parasitischen Mikro-Organismus mit lytischer Aktivität für *Pseudomonas* Bakterien. Phytopathol. Z. 45: 364-390.

STOUT, J. D. 1958. Biological studies of some tussock-grassland soils. IV. Bacteria. New Zealand J. Agr. Res. 1: 943-957.

TAYLOR, C. B. 1951. Coli-aerogenes bacteria in soil. J. Hyg. 49: 162-168.

TELIZ-ORTIZ, M., and W. H. BURKHOLDER. 1960. A strain of *Pseudomonas fluorescens* antagonistic to *Pseudomonas phaseolicola* and other bacterial plant pathogens. Phytopathology 50: 119-123.

THOMAS, S. B., and J. McQUILLIN. 1952. Coli-aerogenes bacteria isolated from grass. Proc. Soc. Appl. Bacteriol. 15: 41-52.

TUZIMURA, K., and I. WATANABE. 1960. [The saprophytic life of *Rhizobium* in soils free from the host plants. Ecological studies of *Rhizobium* in soils. Part 2] Nippon Dojo-Hiryogaku Zasshi 31: 506-510.

VALLEAU, W. D., E. M. JOHNSON, and S. DIACHUN. 1944. Root infection of crop plants and weeds by tobacco leafspot bacteria. Phytopathology 34: 163-174.

VAN NESS, G., and C. D. STEIN. 1956. Soils of the United States favorable for anthrax. J. Am. Vet. Med. Assoc. 128: 7-9.

VAUGHAN, E. K. 1944. Bacterial wilt of tomato caused by *Phytomonas solanacearum*. Phytopathology 34: 443-458.

VOLCANI, Z. 1956. Two bacterial diseases of *Capsicum annuum* and *Solanum melongena* fruits. Ktavim (Rec. Agr. Res. Sta. [Rehovot] Israel) 4: 5-14.

VOLCANI, Z., and W. J. DOWSON. 1948. A plant disease caused by a spore forming bacterium under natural conditions. Nature (London) 161: 980.

WALKER, J. C., and W. B. TISDALE. 1920. Observations on seed transmission of the cabbage black rot organism. Phytopathology 10: 175-177.

WALLACE, R. H., and A. G. LOCHHEAD. 1951. Bacteria associated with seeds of various crop plants. Soil Sci. 71: 159-166.

WILSON, R. D. 1946. Soil carry-over of the bean halo blight disease. J. Australian Inst. Agr. Sci. 12: 103-107.

WINOGRADSKY, S. 1925. Études sur la microbiologie du sol. I. Sur la méthode. Ann. Inst. Pasteur 39: 299-354.

▶ DISCUSSION OF I. W. BUDDENHAGEN PAPER

A. Kelman:

About 50 years ago, Erwin F. Smith stated erroneously that insects were the major means of transmission of bacterial wilt of potatoes. Although it was shown conclusively that solanaceous species are mainly attacked via the roots, E. F. Smith's idea of the potential significance of insect transmission has been confirmed on the basis of the work on Moko disease of bananas in an entirely new concept.

In view of the suggestion that populations gradually increase in pathogenicity, what explanation can you offer for the absence of new, more virulent races or strains of *Pseudomonas solanacearum* in North Carolina on tobacco, and in Indonesia on peanut? In North Carolina, varieties with resistance have been planted (often in the same fields in successive years) for 17 years. In Indonesia, a peanut variety, developed for resistance in the late twenties, has been planted since then over a wide acreage without evidence that it is any less resistant at present than when first released.

I. W. Buddenhagen:

Why are most plants resistant to most bacteria? Why do triploid bananas, growing on soil containing the tomato race of *Pseudomonas solanacearum*, never become diseased by it? In a broader sense, these questions are the same as yours. It must be that resistance is conditioned by multiple genes, or rather, in any plant a pathogen must overcome defenses at many different levels. Successful pathogenicity must indeed be a difficult attainment, more complex than we would like to believe. If there is no conserving mechanism in the bacterial pathogen to save mutant genes that are only one step toward a ten-step need for pathogenicity, eventual attainment of a multigenic requirement is extremely remote. Once attained in an individual cell in an individual plant, the obstacles to widespread distribution to thousands of other plants remain before we would be aware of its existence. These obstacles are also very great. To have a documented case of population shifts to increased virulence and expansion does not mean that it is an event that is general or commonplace. It does indicate, however, that once rarely accomplished it can result in the "birth" of the epiphytotic diseases that we have with us today.

G. Stotzky:

What evidence have you that there is, in fact, a decrease in competitive and saprophytic capacity of a pathogenic bacterial population that is concomitant with its increased virulence (specificity)? For example, is the wild type → B → SFR progression characterized by a decrease in competitive, saprophytic, and survival ability, and an increase in, for example, nutritional specificity of *Pseudomonas solanacearum* in soil? What is this evidence?

I. W. Buddenhagen:

Virulence has meaning only in relation to a given host. Thus the population shift from D to B to SFR is one of increasing virulence to bananas but not to heliconias (for which it is the reverse), and these differences have been measured by various means. All of the banana strains are less able than the tomato race to survive in soil as measured by direct plating of introduced populations. SFR is less able to survive in soil than the other banana strains when similarly measured. SFR is more fastidious nutritionally than the other banana strains, being unable to utilize several sugars that are utilized by the other strains. The host range of all the banana strains is very narrow, unlike that of the more saprophytically capable tomato race.

R. G. Grogan:

Would Dr. Kelman comment on his evidence that bacterial plant pathogens can enter through uninjured roots?

A. Kelman:

It has been possible to demonstrate that *Pseudomonas solanacearum* enters through the points at which secondary roots emerge on tomato and tobacco. The bacteria also can emerge at these same points from infected plant roots before the plants die. Whether or not the points at which secondary roots emerge can be considered as wounded areas is a matter of debate.

F. M. Scott:

As a lateral root emerges, cortical cells are crushed. The epidermal surface, however, is continuous—cuticle and mucilage. This area, however, may be permeable to exudates and allow accumulation of organisms.

I. W. Buddenhagen:

There is no proof that plant-pathogenic bacteria (*Rhizobium* excepted) enter or penetrate intact root-cell surfaces. This does not mean that a *root system* cannot be entered through minute wounds or through breaks that may occur where secondary roots emerge. We need to know more about these root-emergence areas on a microscopical level for different plants.

W. F. Mai:

I would like to hear your comments concerning the importance of bacteria as secondary or copathogens of roots. This was not emphasized in your talk.

I. W. Buddenhagen:

I consider that bacteria as copathogens are much more important than has been believed. Rigidly follow-ing Koch's postulates, combined with use of techniques to exclude bacteria from isolations, tends to narrow our appreciation of the role of bacteria in fungus and nematode diseases.

L. I. Miller:

I would appreciate your comments on the chances of survival in a soil environment of the pathogenic strains of nodule-forming *Rhizobium* which are associated with chlorotic disorders of soybeans.

I. W. Buddenhagen:

It appears that *Rhizobium* is often better adapted as a soil inhabitant than most plant-pathogenic bacteria. It is possible that some rather well-adapted soil forms can also cause over-all host injury. I have excluded *Rhizobium* from this review and therefore am unable to reply to your specific question.

L. W. Nielsen:

In the evolution of saprophytes to pathogens, is there any evidence of an increased host specificity by the evolved pathogens? The corynebacteria seem to indicate such specialization.

I. W. Buddenhagen:

In many cases it seems that the more highly specialized pathogens have more limited host ranges than nonspecialized pathogens. However, the example of *Agrobacterium tumefaciens* would appear to indicate that this may be only an apparent correlation, rather than a required one.

C. G. Dobbs:

The mycostasis problem has drawn some attention to the role of soil bacteria in the inhibition of fungal growth in soil. This effect may be differential as between pathogens and saprophytes, which may be of importance in the ecology of disease. Unfortunately, all this work is being done by mycologists. Please, will the soil bacteriologists look into it!

P. A. Ark:

What is the mechanism of mutation in *Pseudomonas solanacearum,* or other plant pathogens, indigenous to soil? How common is mutation in phytopathogenic bacteria inhabiting the soil?

I. W. Buddenhagen:

We only assume that mutational phenomena described for other bacteria occur with phytopathogenic ones.

Since the pathogen's greatest population is in the host, it is there that the environment can exert its greatest selective effects to perpetuate the more pathogenic mutants. But for diseases of host populations to continue through time, many other requirements are selected for—thus, the population that continues is a balanced one around three main foci: pathogenicity, transmissibility, and nonhost survival.

With *Pseudomonas solanacearum* there is a continued tendency to mutate to nonvirulent, butyrous forms that lack the wilt-inducing polysaccharide. However, as long as one obtains the pathogen from recently diseased plants, this mutant form is rare, indicating a continual selection against this form within the plant. But we know nothing about the survival of this butyrous form in the soil since we cannot distinguish it from similar forms of other bacteria in the soil.

S. D. Garrett:

1. For plant-infecting fungi, as for bacteria, there are two criteria of parasitic specialization: (*a*) in the host-parasite relation and (*b*) in the breadth of host range. At present, the correlation between these two criteria seems rather poor and this remains a problem.

2. I should like to congratulate Dr. Buddenhagen on his courage in tackling this very difficult problem of the nonhost phase in the life of plant-infecting bacteria; to me, his paper has been one of the most encouraging events in this symposium. Only those of us who have endeavored to elucidate the nonhost phase in the life of root-infecting fungi can appreciate the difficulties of this problem, which is much easier for mycologists than for bacteriologists because fungi are easier to recognize or identify than are species of bacteria. I need only point to the great volume of work done on the nonhost phase of *Fusarium oxysporum* f. *cubense* to show that even after much effort by many workers, it may still prove impossible to say which is the most important amongst several possible modes of survival for a root pathogen in the nonhost phase.

In tackling a problem of this kind, the first barrier is often lack of interest. During the past 20 years, I have endeavored to arouse the interest of workers with *Rhizobium* spp. in the survival of these organisms apart from their hosts, but with little success. This is why Dr. Buddenhagen's paper has been so encouraging a sign of some real progress at last.

W. D. Thomas:

Does a successful soil-borne bacterial pathogen require saprophytism, or can it remain for extended periods in a quiescent stage? Examples: *Corynebacterium sepedonicum* and *Pseudomonas caryophylli* are very successful pathogens which can survive on either organic or mineral matter for extended periods of time. We have shown what appears to be direct invasion of carnation roots in liquid culture by *P. caryophylli*. If Dr. Scott's premise that lateral roots rupture the cortex of primary roots is correct, or if root caps provide natural openings, we must reorient our thinking concerning uninjured roots to assume that there are no such things.

I. W. Buddenhagen:

Survival as quiescent cells definitely occurs for some pathogens in a dried state on seeds or in the case of *Corynebacterium sepedonicum,* on sack material. Survival in that way in soil that is periodically moistened appears to be quite another situation. Bacterial ring rot of potato is not to be considered as being caused by a successful soil-borne pathogen, since seasonal recurrence rarely follows if clean seed is used and vegetable matter is not allowed to remain in the field. As a practical criterion, it seems reasonable to consider pathogens controlled by short rotations and use of clean seed to be poor soil saprophytes. Undoubtedly, however, survival and even growth may occur for some

time, especially if previously colonized host material is present, or if the bacteria remain in a dried state in protective colloidal material.

A. D. Rovira:

The survival of *Rhizobium* in soil varies according to the species of *Rhizobium* and the soil conditions. In red-brown earths of approximately neutral reaction, *R. trifolii* appears to survive indefinitely in the absence of its host. This is probably because it may be regarded as an inhabitant of the rhizosphere of many non-legumes. We have evidence, for example, that it will establish to significant levels in the rhizosphere of the grass *Paspalum*, although the levels do not approach those reached in clover rhizosphere. On the other hand, *R. meliloti* appeared to be less suited to live in soil as a saprophyte, and its numbers rapidly fall off in the absence of the host. Survival of both of these organisms depends greatly upon the physical and chemical nature of the soil. In sandy soils, survival is low but may be increased by the addition of small amounts of clay. In acid soils, survival is again much reduced.

J. Altman:

Your discussion and your presentation implied a study of an evolution of a microorganism toward parasitism. Is it not just as relevant to consider the possibility of evolution toward saprophytism; for example, the loss in pathogenicity, i.e. in virulence, would imply that such a trend exists. Would not such a study be fruitful?

Evolution toward parasitism $\longrightarrow$ specificity $\longrightarrow$ host dependence.

Evolution toward saprophytism $\longleftarrow$ less specificity $\longleftarrow$ less host dependence.

Would not such a study aid in ascertaining evolution toward parasitism?

I. W. Buddenhagen:

This is an interesting concept deserving study. We have in the past approached this problem from the viewpoint of a parasite in search of greater host populations to conquer. There is a limit to evolution toward virulence; when it becomes so great that transmissibility is interfered with, it is selected against. When mutation occurs to avirulence, we, as plant pathologists, lose sight of these new individuals, even if they are good saprophytes. It seems to me that various pathogens have reached balances at very different levels in the triumviral requirements of virulence, transmissibility, and nonhost survival. A wide latitude exists in each of these criteria, and the stages reached by a *Rhizobium*, for instance, are quite different than for *Pseudomonas solanacearum*. A new host offers an already adapted parasite a new environment, and, in this exploitation, a new level may be reached within each category, changing our idea of its specificity, virulence, and saprophytic nature.

Pathogenesis by Soil Nematodes

W. B. MOUNTAIN—*Research Station, Canada Department of Agriculture, Harrow, Ontario.*
(*Now: Research Station, Canada Department of Agriculture, St. Catherines, Ontario.*)

The development of relatively inexpensive and effective soil fumigants in the late 1940's demonstrated that spectacular increases in crop production could be associated with the control of plant-infesting nematodes. With this, the efforts and teachings of early nematologists relating to the importance of these pests in agriculture were justified. But the introduction of these soil fumigants turned out to be a mixed blessing to plant nematology, for while it focused great attention on nematodes and led to a rapid growth in the discipline, it also led to an erroneous principle that tended to stultify real progress in the field of plant-nematode relations for some years. This principle might be stated somewhat as follows: A plant response that follows the application of a fumigant to soil infested with plant-parasitic nematodes results from the control of these organisms. The corollary of this principle was more damaging: The role of a soil nematode in plant disease can be established by the use of a soil fumigant. The naivety of this concept is apparent to present-day biologists.

It is obvious that the precise definition of the plant-nematode relation is a most important component of plant nematology because it will determine to a large extent whether this discipline is of mere academic interest to biologists or of fundamental importance to mankind in the production of food. An oversimplified and false image of the plant-nematode relation will result if one is not aware of the microbiological complexity of the soil environment (Steiner, 1953; Mountain, 1954). Lack of appreciation of this has led many nematologists to equate pathogenicity with association; the results of such studies have not been accepted by critical plant pathologists. To determine the plant-nematode relation one must define precisely how the nematode interacts with the host plant in the development of disease, in both the absence and the presence of other soil microorganisms. Such a definition must be based on principles acceptable to biologists, and the only principles that appear to be valid and applicable are Koch's postulates (Mountain, 1957, 1960a).

Indeed, Koch's postulates may be even more valid and applicable in plant nematology than with soil-borne fungi. Because present knowledge suggests that all plant-pathogenic nematodes are plant parasites, the "despotism of Koch's postulates" (Garrett, 1959) may never restrict one's concept of the plant-nematode relation per se. Under field conditions, however, the host-parasite relations are much more complex, for nematodes interact with fungi and perhaps bacteria within the host, and such relations may be most complex.

The nematologist has one important advantage in that all known plant-pathogenic nematodes are highly adapted morphologically for plant parasitism. They all possess a more or less prominent stylet for at least part of their life cycle. This identifying feature eliminates one of the major problems facing the soil microbiologist. But not all stylet-bearing nematodes are plant parasites. Another important advantage in plant nematology is that quantitative methods can give a level of precision in the use of Koch's postulates that is not easily attained with the soil fungi. For example, controlled experiments can duplicate closely the inoculum levels that occur in the field, and the host reaction can be studied in relation to a precisely measured level of nematode infestation.

There are, however, serious difficulties in applying Koch's postulates to plant nematology. In many cases it is extremely difficult to obtain sufficient numbers of a particular species of nematode to provide suitable inoculum for experiments. Plant-parasitic nematodes have only been reared on living tissues of higher plants (or fungi in a very few cases). The difficulties of obtaining aseptic monospecific nematode inoculum have been largely overcome by one of two methods. A single species may first be surface-sterilized and then propagated aseptically on roots in culture (Tiner, 1960) or on callus tissue in culture (Krusberg, 1961). The great advantage of this method is that aseptic monospecific inoculum is always available for experiments and one can maintain stock cultures in the laboratory of a wide range of plant-parasitic nematodes. The system must be maintained under sterile conditions, however, and it is sometimes difficult to obtain sufficient inoculum by this technique because, in some cases, the nematode does not reproduce well in this rather artificial environment. A second method is to raise single species of nematodes on host plants growing in open pots in the greenhouse. When inoculum is required, the nematodes are removed and then surface-sterilized (Mountain and Patrick, 1959). The advantage of this method is that the nematodes propagate under more natural conditions and large numbers are readily obtained with very little effort. On the other hand, it is extremely difficult to surface-sterilize large masses of nematodes in this manner, and this technique will not guarantee sterility in every case. Fortunately, the digestive tract of plant-parasitic nematodes is free of microorganisms that can be cultured (Feder and Feldmesser, 1957; Hawn, 1963), and surface sterilization will ensure that the inoculum is axenic.

EVOLUTION OF PLANT PARASITISM.—The evolution of nematodes toward plant parasitism is basic to the development of any plant-nematode relation. Even with our present fragmentary knowledge, it is possible to discern stages in the evolution of plant parasitism among groups of nematodes. There appear to be two main trends in the development of plant parasitism among nematodes. First, there is a trend from ectoparasitism to migratory endoparasitism to sedentary endoparasitism. With the development of sedentary endoparasitism, which is restricted to the female, there is also morphological adaptation leading to a high rate of reproduction. Second, there is a trend from indiscriminate feeding on the epidermis and cortex with accompanying cell necrosis and tissue damage to discrete feeding areas with specific plant responses and a suppression of cell necrosis. Although most genera of plant-parasitic nematodes can be fitted to these various stages, there are distinct exceptions. The genera *Ditylenchus* and *Aphelenchoides* are unique in that there is the full range from ectoparasitism to endoparasitism accompanied by an increased complexity of the host-parasite relations at each stage (Winslow, 1960). Some ectoparasitic and semiendoparasitic nematodes become sedentary but the host response remains primitive, that is, necrosis occurs. A number of nematodes that are normally ectoparasitic may become semiendoparasitic or completely endoparasitic, but again the host response remains primitive. The feeding position assumed by these forms apparently depends on the thickness and fleshiness of the root. Finally, certain ectoparasitic nematodes produce discrete and highly evolved host-parasite interactions. An excellent review by Seinhorst (1961a) discusses plant parasitism by nematodes in greater detail.

It is apparent that endoparasitism does not necessarily indicate a highly evolved level of plant parasitism, neither is evolution toward plant parasitism necessarily accompanied by evolution toward endoparasitism. Nevertheless, the trend from ectoparasitism to sedentary endoparasitism is normally associated with an evolution toward a precise and balanced host-parasite relation. Myuge (1960) suggests that the evolution of host-parasite relations can be characterized by an increasing complexity in the enzymes released by the nematode during feeding. He states that in the most highly evolved forms, the release of specific proteolytic enzymes by the nematode evokes the production by the host plant of specific enzyme inhibitors, resulting in a highly balanced and specific plant-nematode interaction.

HOST-PARASITE RELATIONS OF PLANT-PARASITIC NEMATODES.—Several recent reviews on host-parasite relations of plant-parasitic nematodes cover the available literature in greater detail than could be included in this paper (Fielding, 1959; Dropkin, 1955; Mountain, 1960b; Seinhorst, 1961a). My object is to attempt to synthesize concepts on the pathogenicity of a few genera that have received critical and intensive study in recent years. I propose to discuss the host-parasite relations of these forms arranged in descending order of their evolution toward plant parasitism.

Sedentary endoparasitic nematodes.—Four genera, *Heterodera*, *Meloidogyne*, and *Meloidodera* of the family Heteroderidae and *Nacobbus* of the family Tylenchidae will be considered, although little information is available on the host-parasite relations of the latter two genera.

Infection.—Second-stage larvae of *Heterodera* and *Meloidogyne* normally enter the root at or just behind the root tip. Occasionally, larvae of *Meloidogyne* will enter ruptures made by emerging roots, cracks on the surface of roots (Krusberg and Nielsen, 1958), nodular tissue of legumes (Robinson, 1961), and leaves, stems, and cotyledons (Steiner, 1940; Linford, 1941; Miller and DiEdwardo, 1962). The larvae move through the cortex both intracellularly and intercellularly (Christie, 1936; Dropkin and Nelson, 1960) aided, perhaps, by pectin-dissociating enzymes (Goffart and Heiling, 1962; Morgan and McAllan, 1962). As larvae of *Heterodera* move through the cortex toward the vascular elements, they may cause extensive necrosis (Fassuliotis and Willey, 1954; Mankau and Linford, 1960; Endo, 1962), whereas larvae of *Meloidogyne* usually cause little visible damage (Christie, 1936; Dropkin and Nelson, 1960). Larvae take up a position in or near the vascular tissue or in the meristematic cells of the root tip. The head may be embedded in the endodermis or pericycle and the body may extend into the cortex (Christie, 1936; Mankau and Linford, 1960). Occasionally, the larvae may be completely embedded in the stele (Davis and Jenkins, 1960b). Little is known of the feeding of these larvae.

Bird (1959) suggests that nematodes do not feed during penetration and the energy required for movement into the host root must come from body reserves. Loewenberg, Sullivan, and Schuster (1960), however, observed larvae of *Meloidogyne* feeding on the root surface for periods up to 4 days before entering the root. The second-stage larva of *Meloidogyne* feeds in the host, but apparently the third and fourth stages do not (Bird, 1959). Therefore, food required during these latter stages of development must come from reserves stored by the second stage. C. F. Marks (unpublished) found that the rate of development of all larval stages of *M. incognita* in the roots of cucumber increased with increasing levels of potassium supplied to the host. Potassium must therefore affect development of the nematode not only during the feeding stage but also during those stages in the life cycle that do not feed. Marks was unable to detect any effect of potassium level in cucumber roots on the rate of development of *M. javanica* or *M. hapla*, and Oteifa (1953) was unable to find any effect of potassium on the rate of development of larvae of *M. incognita* in the roots of lima beans; these observations suggest that the influence of this mineral element depends upon the nematode species and the host plant.

Larvae of *Meloidodera floridensis* will enter lateral roots and mycorrhiza of pine, apparently at or near the root tip, in fissures of the outer bark layers or wounds in the root. Destruction of cells is slight (Ruehle, 1962). Larvae of *Nacobbus* may feed on the surface of the root, but normally they penetrate the root and migrate through the cortex to the vascular tissue. They cause necrosis of the cortex (Schuster and Sullivan, 1960).

Giant Cells.—The establishment of a successful host-parasite relation by *Heterodera, Meloidogyne,* and *Meloidodera* depends upon the formation of giant cells or, more properly, syncytia. The syncytium usually develops from vascular parenchyma cells (Davis, 1959) but may occasionally arise in the cortex (Cole and Howard, 1958). Apparently, this latter condition is not normal because the nematode will not thrive unless a cortical syncytium extends into the stele to intercept translocated nutrients (Mankau and Linford, 1960). The number of syncytia that may develop around the head of a single female varies from 2 to 12 (Davis and Jenkins, 1960b). The cells adjacent to the head of the nematode first enlarge, then nuclei swell and the cell walls disintegrate (Christie, 1936). Cell-wall dissolution proceeds outwards from the hypertrophied cell, resulting in large, multinucleate units, sometimes containing fragments of the old cell walls (Endo, 1962). The cytoplasm becomes increasingly granular (Cole and Howard, 1958). The syncytium continues to expand by a combination of increased turgor pressure and cell-wall digestion (Owens and Novotny, 1960), perhaps as a result of secretions from the stylet (Linford, 1937) containing cellulase (Krusberg, 1960; Morgan and McAllan, 1962). A young syncytium may contain 30 to 40 nuclei, pooled from the cells that coalesced (Owens and Novotny, 1960), whereas older syncytia contain fewer nuclei (Davis and Jenkins, 1960b). Apparently nuclear division rarely occurs in the syncytium (Dropkin and Nelson, 1960; Owens and Novotny, 1960). The development and reproduction of *Meloidogyne* and *Heterodera* depend on the formation of well-developed syncytia (Dropkin, 1959; Mankau and Linford, 1960). Maximum reproduction of the nematode occurred with syncytia consisting of large, thick-walled, multinucleate units with dense cytoplasm and few cell inclusions (Dropkin and Nelson, 1960).

Both the development and maintenance of syncytia depend on a continuous stimulus from the nematode. If this stimulus is removed, the cytoplasm becomes vacuolated and breaks down, and the syncytium is gradually encroached upon by the surrounding cells of the host (Bird, 1962). Amino acids accumulate in syncytia (Owens and Novotny, 1960). The presence of the tobacco-ringspot virus in soybean causes the syncytia to show a greater clumping of nuclei, a greater number of nuclei in the vicinity of the head of the nematode, and a greater amount of protoplasm than in the roots of soybeans that are free of the virus

(Ryder and Crittenden, 1962). The application of maleic hydrazide to the foliage of tobacco plants leads to the development of small, poorly developed syncytia (Nusbaum, 1958). Syncytia may also arise in fully formed nodules on roots of cowpea after invasion by *Meloidogyne* (Robinson, 1961), as well as in leaf or stem tissue if invasion occurs in these areas (Linford, 1941; Miller and DiEdwardo, 1962).

Giant cells arise in the cortex of lateral roots or in undifferentiated tissue in meristematic regions in tips of mycorrhiza of pine infested with *Meloidodera*. They appear to be identical in structure to the syncytia described above (Ruehle, 1962). True syncytia do not develop as a result of infection by *Nacobbus* (Schuster and Thorne, 1956). But a spindle- or egg-shaped area that arises in the vascular tissue near the head of a nematode may be analogous to the syncytium. This structure is composed of amorphous tissue with atypical cell walls that commonly collapse, and enlarged cells result from the coalescence of adjacent cells. The cells are multinucleate with granular cytoplasm.

Root Galls.—One of the basic differences between the host-parasite relations of *Meloidogyne* and *Heterodera* is the development of galls on roots invaded by the former. Occasionally, *Heterodera* will produce galls, for example, *H. rostochiensis* on tomato (Fassuliotis and Willey, 1954); but these are usually small and are not a characteristic feature of the host-parasite relation. Although the formation of a syncytium is essential for reproduction of *Meloidogyne*, the development of the gall apparently is not. Larvae of *Meloidogyne* may invade the roots of nonhost plants and cause extensive galling, but reproduction of the nematode will not occur (Gaskin, 1959). Also, galling can be induced by surface-feeding of larvae of *Meloidogyne*, even though they may not enter this area (Loewenberg, Sullivan, and Schuster, 1960). Most species of *Meloidogyne* produce large, massive galls without proliferation of lateral roots. *M. hapla* however, causes very little hypertrophy of the host tissue so that the galls are small, but extensive lateral roots and root primordia are developed from the cortex and pericycle (Davis and Jenkins, 1960b). When root tips of soybeans are invaded by larvae of *M. hapla*, growth of the apical meristem ceases and two to ten lateral roots arise (Schilke and Crittenden, 1959).

Hypertrophy usually begins in the cortical cells (Christie, 1936), although proliferation and hypertrophy of stelar parenchyma also occur (Schilke and Crittenden, 1959; Davis and Jenkins, 1960b). The response of cortical cells to invasion by larvae of *Meloidogyne* is rapid; considerable hypertrophy may occur within 24 hours after invasion (Christie, 1936). The size of the gall can be correlated with the number of larvae in the galled area; the response of the root to the presence of the nematode appears to be a local one, related to the amount of stimulation provided by each nematode (Dropkin, 1954). Schuster and Sullivan (1960) compared gall formation on the roots of tomato seedlings caused by *M. incognita* and *M. hapla*. The former "prevented" root-hair formation, especially if the roots were growing on the agar surface, whereas the latter species stimulated root-hair formation in the galled area.

The relation between *Meloidogyne* and nodules on the roots of legumes appears interesting. Larvae of *M. javanica* have a distinct affinity for the nodules of cowpea; on certain plants, the nodules only may be attacked (Robinson, 1961). In the presence of legume bacteria, the amount of root galling on roots of varieties of soybean susceptible to *M. incognita acrita* and the rate of entry of the larvae into the roots of resistant varieties are increased (Shands and Crittenden, 1957). *M. incognita acrita* causes excessive root galling on the roots of nodulating strains of soybeans, but only slight galling on roots of nonnodulating strains (Crittenden, 1962).

There are indications that metabolic activity is higher in galled tissue than in adjacent ungalled areas. The respiration rate was higher in young galls on the roots of cucumber and lettuce than in healthy rootlets (Turlygina, 1957). Owens and Novotny (1960) reported an increase of total free amino acids, amides, protein, nucleic acids, phosphorus, nitrogen, and general enzyme activity within galls. Phosphorus, especially, accumulates in galled tissue in amounts significantly higher than in ungalled root tissues of the same plants (Maung and Jenkins, 1959; Oteifa and Elgindi, 1962a,b; Shafiee, 1962).

As noted earlier, *Meloidogyne* will sometimes invade the leaves and stems of plants, in which case galled tissues develop. Invasion of *Siderasis* (*Tradescantia*) *fuscata* by larvae of *M. incognita* gives rise to galls along the leaf veins and midrib. As these galls become older, the epidermal cells adjacent to the nematode become necrotic or slough away, leaving holes in the gall tips (Miller and DiEdwardo, 1962).

Hyperplasia of cortical and vascular parenchyma cells surrounding the syncytium is common in the roots of pine infected by *Meloidodera floridensis*, but extensive root galling does not occur (Ruehle, 1962).

Nacobbus has an interesting life cycle in that there are two periods of parasitism, the first by larvae in small roots, followed by migration of the preadult form back into the soil, where the final molt occurs. The immature females then invade larger roots. Galls develop in both cases and root proliferation from these galls may be extensive (Thorne and Schuster, 1956).

Mechanism of Gall Formation.—There is little doubt that gall formation by *Meloidogyne* is associated with plant-growth regulators of some type. Sayre (see Mountain, 1960b) has postulated that gall formation is due to the release of auxin or auxinlike substances in the affected area. For example, the antiauxin maleic hydrazide suppressed the formation of hyperplastic tissue on the roots of tobacco when the material was applied to the leaves (Nusbaum, 1958). The reduction in galling following treatment of the plant with maleic hydrazide is not due to any nematicidal activity (Peacock, 1960). Peacock also found that sprays of maleic hydrazide applied 2 days before inoculation with the nematode were more effective in reducing galling than sprays applied 2 days after inoculation.

There are several possible mechanisms by which root galls could develop in the presence of *Meloidogyne*:

1. The nematode could release growth-promoting substances in its salivary secretions.

2. The nematode could release proteolytic enzymes in its salivary secretions. These could either release indolacetic acid (IAA) bound to cytoplasmic proteins or could split the peptide bonds of the structural protein chain and release a number of amino acids. These amino acids could stimulate growth directly (Sanders and Burkholder, 1948), or the tryptophane could be metabolized by the host to IAA.

3. The nematode could release enzymes in its salivary secretions that are capable of destroying or inhibiting the indolacetic acid oxidase system of the plant, allowing the concentration of IAA to increase (Lipetz, 1959).

It is possible that *Meloidogyne* could release IAA or some other growth-promoting substance in the saliva, but these have not been detected to date (Lefkowitz, 1961). However, *Meloidogyne* does release proteolytic enzymes (Zinoviev, 1957), so that it is possible that the second mechanism listed above could operate. This should lead to an accumulation of IAA in the galled areas. Bird (1962) was able to detect a growth-promoting substance in the galls that was absent in adjacent roots. Although it did not appear to be IAA, it may be closely related to that substance. Lefkowitz (1961) was unable to detect IAA in extracts of galled and healthy tomato roots.

Recent studies by Myuge (1960) might explain why *Meloidogyne* causes galls in host tissue and *Heterodera* does not, assuming that gall formation is essentially the effect of proteolytic enzymes on plant proteins. Myuge found that each species of the genus *Heterodera* may release highly specific enzymes in its host. In response to this release of enzymes, the plant releases specific enzyme inhibitors. Thus, an extract of potato root infested with *H. rostochiensis* inhibited only the proteolytic enzymes released by that species. An extract of sugarbeet root infested with *H. schachtii* produced an enzyme inhibitor specific for the proteolytic enzymes released by that species; the same for an extract of cactus root infested with *H. cacti*. However, *Meloidogyne* appears to release a wider range of proteolytic enzymes and enzyme inhibition does not occur as readily. This leads to an accumulation of free amino acids in root areas affected by *Meloidogyne,* but not in root areas affected by *Heterodera* (Owens and Novotny, 1960; Myuge, 1960).

A hypothesis for the formation of galls by *Meloidogyne* is as follows: Both *Heterodera* and *Meloidogyne* release proteolytic enzymes within the host tissue. The enzymes released by the former are highly specific and are rapidly inhibited by specific substances released by the host, so that accumulation of free amino acids, including tryptophane, does not occur and growth-promoting substances are not released (or only in very small quantities as perhaps in the case of the small galls produced by *H. rostochiensis* on tomato roots). In contrast, the enzymes released by *Meloidogyne* are less specific (which may help explain the broad host range of some species). Therefore, enzyme inhibitors released by the host are unable to inactivate all the proteolytic enzymes released by the nematode. Hence amino acids are released and the tryptophane is ultimately metabolized to IAA (perhaps only intracellularly and in quantities too minute to be detected by methods used to date). This excess IAA is then able to stimulate overgrowths in the area of root elongation, a plant tissue that is capable of responding to plant-growth substances.

One could postulate that suppression of gall formation represents the more highly evolved type of plant parasitism. Therefore, large, massive, galls such as those produced by *Meloidogyne incognita* and *M. javanica* might indicate that these species are not as highly evolved for plant parasitism as is *M. hapla,* which produces small galls and lateral roots. These responses are indicative of lower concentrations of IAA in plant tissues (Leopold, 1960). *Heterodera avenae,* which may produce a slight swelling of the root and numerous lateral roots, could represent one of the less highly specialized species of that genus and could be close to *Meloidogyne hapla* in its host-parasite relations. Finally, the very highly evolved species, such as *H. rostochiensis,* give little indication in their host-parasite relations of any profound disturbance to the growth-regulating mechanisms of their hosts.

Migratory endoparasitic nematodes.—These nematodes usually colonize cortical tissues; the adult female remains wormlike in shape and motile. The host-parasite relations are not as highly developed as with the sedentary endoparasites. In the more highly developed forms, necrosis does not occur, but secondary organisms will frequently cause extensive necrosis under field conditions, and it is most important, therefore, that the host-parasite relations be defined under sterile conditions.

Ditylenchus.—As mentioned earlier, *Ditylenchus* is most interesting in that there is a range from ectoparasitism to endoparasitism, with increasing complexity of the host-parasite relation at each stage. I propose to discuss the host-parasite relations of three species in descending order of their evolution toward plant parasitism.

Ditylenchus radicicolus is a root parasite mainly of the Graminae. Invasion by second-stage larvae occurs at the root tip or along the root surface. Cortical cells are stimulated by the nematode and hypertrophy and hyperplasia of these cells result in a gall. The nematode is contained in a cavity in the center of this gall. Root hairs are generally absent from the surface of these galls. The lateral walls of the endodermis tend to break down and the central vascular cylinder becomes much enlarged through hypertrophy and hyperplasia. There are no definite feeding areas such as syncytia, and the nematodes do not seem to puncture the enlarged cortical cells (Goodey, 1932). The structure of these galls has been compared to those formed by cynipid wasps (Seinhorst, 1961a).

Ditylenchus dipsaci is an endoparasite of stems and leaves. Larvae may enter the roots of some hosts and cause cavities in the cortex (Krusberg, 1961). The typical response of host tissues to invasion by larvae of *D. dipsaci* is a swelling of the affected area, and necrosis may not occur. Mesophyll cells around the nematode enlarge and begin to separate (Blake, 1962). Cavities may form in the cortical parenchyma within 12 hours after invasion (Krusberg, 1961). Histogenesis is greatest around the nematode but effects were evident four cells away. Cells, especially the smaller ones, became more spherical as they enlarged (Blake, 1962). Free tryptophane was found in affected areas, but not in healthy tissues (Krusberg, 1961), indicating protease activity. This host response is undoubtedly brought about by enzymes secreted by the nematode. A number of enzymes have been identified, including chitinase, amylase, invertase, cellulase, pectinase, and proteolytic enzymes (Myuge, 1957b; Zinoviev, 1957; Tracey, 1958; Krusberg, 1960; Goffart and Heiling, 1962). Myuge states that the nematode releases protopectinase, which breaks down the intercellular protopectin, and this results in maceration of the tissue. A lowered pH in the affected area suggests pectic acid formation. Goffart and Heiling also found pectin-dissociating enzymes in *D. dipsaci,* but Krusberg was unable to detect such an enzyme. He suggested that the breakdown of cohesion between the cells might result from the nematode's interfering with the metabolism of the host in such a manner that polygalacturonase is released. Also, the tryptophane could be converted to IAA, which could cause hypertrophy of parenchyma cells (Krusberg, 1961).

Ditylenchus destructor is more primitive in that it may feed and reproduce on a wide range of fungi as well as on plant tissue. The species has a wide host range and usually causes necrosis. On potato tubers, the nematode penetrates the periderm, travels through the outer 4 to 5 cortical cells, and begins to feed. The starch content of the cells immediately adjacent to the feeding area is greatly reduced. The host reaction often extends several cells beyond the point of feeding. The cells collapse, giving rise to cavities (Faulkner and Darling, 1961). This species also produces a wide range of enzymes including amylase, proteolytic enzymes, cellulase, chitinase, invertase, and pectinase (Myuge, 1957a; Zinoviev, 1957; Tracey, 1958; Goffart and Heiling, 1962). The role of fungi in the host-parasite relations of this species is not clear, but reproduction appears to be much more rapid if fungi are present in the lesioned area (Faulkner and Darling, 1961), and the nematodes may actually feed on the fungi in the lesioned area in preference to the host tissue (Baker, Brown, and James, 1954).

Radopholus.—The burrowing nematode, *Radopholus similis,* is a root endoparasite with a broad host range. Under sterile conditions, the nematode causes extensive disruption of citrus root tissue without necrosis. The nematode enters roots in the region of cell elongation, and the only evidence of penetration may be a slight discoloration and splitting of the epidermis. Root tissues are penetrated by lysis of successive cells, and discrete tunnels and cavities, containing many nematodes, are formed in this tissue. The nematode may penetrate the endodermis through passage cells and feed in the phloem-cambium ring, destroying these tissues and forming a large cavity girdling the stele. Tumors may be produced in the pericycle if the nematode penetrates the endodermis. There is hypertrophy of pericycle cells, followed by hyperplasia in other cells, resulting in tumors. Individual tumors eventually coalesce and the stele becomes girdled by this much-enlarged pericycle. As the tumors increase in thickness, the endodermis is pushed outward and ruptured. The nematodes feed on and burrow into these tumors. If a root tip is invaded by *R. similis*, it becomes swollen by hyperplasia of meristematic cells. Although the mechanisms involved have not been studied, it has been postulated that growth-promoting substances are elaborated and released by the nematode and result in hypertrophy, and that enzymes released by the nematode give rise to lysis and hydrolysis (DuCharme, 1959). The roots of grapefruit seedlings infested with *R. similis* eventually show swellings of the tips and large swellings along the entire lengths of some roots, giving them a beaded appearance (Feder and Feldmesser, 1956).

Under nonsterile conditions, *Radopholus similis* produced necrotic lesions in the cortex of banana roots (Blake, 1961). Most of the nematodes occurred in advance of the region of cortical necrosis. In this area, cells were enlarged, abnormal tangential division had occurred, and the intercellular movement of the nematodes and their feeding on cell protoplasm had ruptured cell walls and disorganized the tissue. In a third zone, which formed the boundary to the lesion, mild hypertrophy was evident, but no nematodes were found. Unlike citrus, the stele of banana was not invaded by *R. similis*.

Pratylenchus.—*Pratylenchus* species invariably colonize cortical root tissue and cause extensive necrosis in this area. All active stages move freely and rapidly through the cortex (DiEdwardo, 1960) and can move out into the cortex of developing lateral roots (Mountain, 1954). The nematode therefore is able to move away from the area of necrosis, feeding on intact cells and maintaining a high rate of reproduction until the cortex is completely destroyed. *P. penetrans* is the most pathogenic species and causes severe and extensive root necrosis in a wide range of crops (Pitcher, Patrick, and Mountain, 1960; Mountain and Patrick, 1959; Seinhorst, 1961b; Chen and Rich, 1962; Townshend, 1962a,b; Osborne and Jenkins, 1962; Shafiee, 1962).

The pathogenicity of this genus was reviewed recently (Mountain, 1961). The conclusion was that necrosis results from interactions between plant glycosides and enzymes released by the nematode in feeding. The host-parasite relations depend on the concentration and location within the root tissue of specific glycosides, as well as on the concentration and complexity of the enzymes released by the nematode during feeding. Necrosis results when hydrolysis of these plant glycosides releases phytotoxic products. Recent studies have strengthened this thesis. In one of these (Pitcher, Patrick, and Mountain, 1960) the pathogenicity of *Pratylenchus penetrans* was compared on the roots of apple

and peach. Apple feeder roots reacted to nematode invasion by rapid discoloration of the outermost (i.e. epidermis and hypodermis) and the innermost (i.e. inner cortex and endodermis) cortical tissues, but showed little or no reaction in the intervening cortical parenchyma. In contrast, all cortical tissues in the roots of peach were readily discolored by the nematode. Histochemical tests indicated that the sensitivity to *P. penetrans* is correlated with the presence and concentration of phenolic substances in the various tissues of the two hosts. The extent of necrosis caused by *P. penetrans* under sterile conditions in various root tissues of strawberry and celery could be correlated with the concentration of phenolic substances in these areas (Townshend, 1963a,b). Hydrolytic enzymes have been demonstrated in *P. zeae* (Krusberg, 1960) and, in extremely large quantities, in *P. penetrans* (Morgan and McAllan, 1962).

Aphelenchoides.—The host-parasite relations of this genus are similar to those of *Ditylenchus* in that there is a range from ectoparasitism to endoparasitism and the complexity of the host-parasite interaction varies. Only the pathogenicity of *Aphelenchoides ritzemabosi* will be considered here. This species feeds ectoparasitically within leaf buds of strawberry. Under sterile conditions, the nematode inhibits expansion of the leaf lamina, which gives rise to "alaminate" leaves (Pitcher and Crosse, 1958). It is suggested that the nematode causes some fundamental disturbance of the growth-regulatory mechanism of the apical meristem, but the biochemical mechanism has never been investigated (see Mountain, 1960b).

On alfalfa, *Aphelenchoides ritzemabosi* fed as an ectoparasite on epidermal cells of embryonic leaves and the shoot apex. Feeding killed the outer two to three layers of cells and caused the formation of a thick, red-stained layer which inhibited growth and division of the underlying intact cells. These cells became large, vacuolate, and contained a large, granular nucleus. Growth of the entire shoot was inhibited. A few nematodes penetrated the stoma and caused cavities in the spongy mesophyll around the vascular bundle. Necrosis also occurred. Free tyrosine, but no tryptophane was recovered from plants infested with *A. ritzemabosi*. The nematode also fed on alfalfa roots (Krusberg, 1961).

Aphelenchoides ritzemabosi is an endoparasite of chrysanthemum leaves. The nematode enters the stoma and migrates into the airspaces of the mesophyll. Infection causes an increase in the permeability of the epidermis (Wallace, 1959). Adults, especially, are very active in the mesophyll of moist leaves (Wallace, 1960). The first external sign of infection is a small brown-green area on the leaf. This discoloration rapidly spreads until the entire sector between the leaf veins becomes brown. There is no doubt that the nematode is the primary cause of this browning reaction. Leaf cells of chrysanthemum contain polyphenols, especially chlorogenic acid and isochlorogenic acid, and polyphenol oxidase. These are separated in healthy cells, but mechanical damage to the cell by means of a needle results in oxidation and polymerization leading to the formation of brown pigments. It is postulated (Wallace, 1961a) that the feeding of the nematode on the cell causes sufficient mechanical damage to result in the browning reaction.

Sedentary ectoparasitic nematodes.—In several genera of plant-parasitic nematodes, the female becomes sedentary and saccate. The anterior portion of the swollen female becomes embedded in the root tissues to varying degrees. Although the pathogenicity of these forms has not been studied critically, it appears that root necrosis is the only consistent host response to parasitism, and therefore the host-parasite relations are primitive.

Migratory ectoparasitic nematodes.—Many soil nematodes feed as ectoparasites on the roots of plants and may become partially or, at times, completely embedded in root tissues. They may feed at the root tip or along the root surface, and the only host reaction for most of the migratory ectoparasites is necrosis. In a few cases, the host-parasite relations are more highly evolved and examples of these will be considered here.

Trichodorus.—The host-parasite relations of *Trichodorus christiei* have been studied more intensively than those of any other species. The nematode is an ectoparasite and its head rarely becomes embedded in or attached to the root (Christie and Perry, 1951). Apparently the cells of the host are punctured by a rasping motion of the stylet rather than by direct thrust (Rohde and Jenkins, 1957). The nematode feeds at the root tip and mechanical damage appears to be slight (Rohde and Jenkins, 1957; Standifer and Perry, 1960; Zuckerman, 1962). The nematode does, however, have a pronounced effect on root tissues. There may be a stimulation of cell division in the pericycle (Standifer and Perry, 1960) resulting in flattened and abnormally enlarged rootlets (Christie and Perry, 1951; Zuckerman, 1962). There is sometimes an indication in the swollen root tips that one or more adventitious root laterals had been stimulated into a temporary period of growth (Zuckerman, 1961).

Hemicycliophora.—*Hemicycliophora* has a large spear which can be inserted deep enough to penetrate a vessel seated well within the root (Zuckerman, 1961). *H. arenaria* exerts a marked physiological effect on the host tissues. Feeding by the nematode results in a distinctive galling of the terminal and lateral root tips. There is an almost immediate inhibition of cell elongation at some distance from the feeding site, but cell division continues and may even be accelerated. Nuclei are prominent and somewhat hypertrophied. The process continues only so long as the nematode feeds and its removal allows the return of normal root growth. On roots of citrus, tomato, beans, peppers, and squash, the nematode produces numerous small galls, whereas on roots of celery the galls consist of large, multibranched growths. In contrast to *Meloidogyne*, where gall formation is not essential for reproduction of the nematode, *H. arenaria* only produces galls on plants that support reproduction (Van Gundy and Rackham, 1961).

Hemicycliophora similis feeds at or near the tips of cranberry roots. Two distinct forms of injury occur. First, root cells contiguous to the stylet appear to stop elongating, whereas normal growth continues on the opposite side of the root, resulting in a distinct curvature. Second, there is a galling of the root tissue (Zuckerman, 1961).

Xiphinema.—*Xiphinema americanum* is one of the most common nematodes associated with agricultural crops in North America, but its host-parasite relations are not highly developed; necrosis appears to be the only host response (Perry, 1958; White, 1960).

Xiphinema index feeds on the root tips of grape, fig, and rose. Cellular hypertrophy and a multinucleate condition of undifferentiated cortical cells develop near the feeding sites. Necrosis and hypertrophy are most severe on root tips exposed to large populations of *X. index* for long periods of time (Radewald and Raski, 1962).

Xiphinema diversicaudatum causes gall formation due to the hyperplastic response of cortical cells. The galls occur at the root tips and are associated with a curling of the end of the root (Schindler, 1957), which results from proliferation of cortical cells on the one side of the root (Davis and Jenkins, 1960). Giant cells, approximately twice as large as other surrounding cortical cells, are formed in association with the feeding sites (Davis, 1959). These giant cells are similar in appearance to those caused by *Meloidogyne*, except that the nuclei exhibit only slight hypertrophy and only 2 to 3 occur in each cell (Davis and Jenkins, 1960a). Gall formation also occurred on the roots of peanuts and figs as a result of parasitism by *X. diversicaudatum*. The supernatant water that had originally contained the nematode, caused a growth response This suggested that some growth-promoting agent had diffused into the water from the nematodes (Schindler, 1957), but nothing is known of the biochemistry of the host-parasite relations.

INTERACTIONS WITH SOIL FUNGI AND BACTERIA.—It is possible that the pathogenicity of soil nematodes per se may prove to be less important in the etiology of plant disease than interactions between nematodes and the soil microflora. Recent critical studies prove that complex synergistic relations between nematodes and the parasitic microflora exist in plant diseases, although studies of such associations have only begun (Powell, 1963; Pitcher, 1963). Factors affecting biological control of such diseases must involve the nematode. I propose to survey some of the better illustrated instances of interactions between nematodes and other organisms as a basis for discussing possible mechanisms of such interactions.

Sedentary endoparasitic nematodes.—Heterodera.— One might postulate that interactions between the soil microflora and nematodes in plant disease should be most evident with those nematodes that are highly developed for plant parasitism. Therefore, it is surprising to find no evidence of any clear-cut interrelation between species of *Heterodera* and plant-parasitic fungi. There are several references, all prior to 1949, describing associations between *Heterodera* and species of *Fusarium, Thielaviopsis, Colletotrichum,* and *Aphanomyces* in plant disease. In no case was there any evidence of any interrelation between the nematode and these fungi. On the other hand, there doesn't appear to have been any serious attempt to look for such relations, certainly in modern times, and this should be a very promising area for future study.

Meloidogyne.—There are many references describing interrelations between this genus and soil microorganisms. The most common of these appears to be with the genus *Fusarium,* especially with varieties of plants that are resistant to this fungus.

The association of root-knot nematodes with cotton wilt has been observed in the field for at least 70 years. As early as 1928, Rosen postulated that the action of root-knot nematodes on roots is largely that of producing localized hyperplastic overgrowths consisting mostly of soft parenchymatous tissue and a reduced amount of cork and wood; this type of tissue offers an excellent opportunity for the growth of the cotton-wilt organism. The incidence of wilt in susceptible and resistant varieties of cotton by *Fusarium oxysporum* f. *vasinfectum* was significantly increased in the presence of *Meloidogyne incognita* and *M. incognita acrita* (Martin, Newsom, and Jones, 1956).

Critical work has been carried out on the interaction between root-knot nematodes and fusarium wilt of tomato. Jenkins and Coursen (1957) found that *Fusarium oxysporum* f. *lycopersici* alone, or with root wounding, did not cause wilt in the tomato variety Chesapeake. But when *Meloidogyne hapla* was also present, 60% of the plants wilted; and when *M. incognita acrita* was present 100% of the plants wilted. Similar studies by Cohn and Minz (1960) show conclusively that root-knot nematodes can interact with *Fusarium* in tomato wilt. Interactions between *Meloidogyne* and *Fusarium* have also been demonstrated on alfalfa (McGuire, Walters, and Slack, 1958), blackeye beans (Thomason, 1958), cowpea (Thomason, Erwin, and Garber, 1959), mimosa (Gill, 1958), and carnation (Schindler, Stewart, and Semenick, 1961). It is apparent that the mechanism is not one of simple wounding and may be quite complex, because certain species of *Meloidogyne* are frequently more effective than others in these interactions.

The interrelation between *Meloidogyne incognita* and *Phytophthora parasitica* var. *nicotianae* in black shank of tobacco is most interesting. The resistant variety Dixie Bright 101 is much more susceptible to the fungus in the presence of the root-knot nematode (Sasser, Lucas, and Powers, 1955). It was demonstrated that the fungus has a distinct affinity for hypertrophied and hyperplastic areas of galled root tissue. In such regions, the mycelium is more extensive and vigorous than in the nongalled areas. The hyphae progressed rapidly and directly into hyperplastic tissue and syncytia. After invasion, a compatible relation apparently exists between the fungus and the host cells undergoing hyperplasia. The syncytia, however, are highly sensitive to infection, degenerate rapidly, and within 72 hours after invasion appear to be completely devoid of protoplasm. It appears that the root-knot nematode provides a highly suitable substrate for the development of the fungus (Powell and Nusbaum, 1960).

Interactions between *Meloidogyne* and *Rhizoctonia* have been reported on cotton (Reynolds and Hanson, 1957), soybeans (Taylor and Wyllie, 1959), and peas (Sayed, 1961). *M. hapla* had a much greater effect than *M. javanica* on incidence of damping-off of soybeans (Taylor and Wyllie, 1959).

Root-knot nematodes have also been implicated in bacterial wilt of tobacco (Lucas, Sasser, and Kelman, 1955) and carnations (Stewart and Schindler, 1956). Although the rate of wilting of both hosts was increased by the nematode, it was never higher than that induced when the bacterial suspension was poured over freshly cut roots. In both cases, the bacteria are endophytic vascular pathogens capable of entering the host through mechanical wounds, and this probably is the main role of the nematode.

It is interesting to note that there is no evidence of any interrelation between root-knot nematode and *Verticillium.* Indeed, Parker (1959) states that damage to plants by root-knot nematodes and *Verticillium* species may be additive but there is no evidence of any synergism. In our laboratory, we have not found any synergism between *Meloidogyne hapla* and *Verticillium dahliae* in eggplant wilt (Mountain and McKeen, unpublished).

Migratory endoparasitic nematodes.—Ditylenchus.—There may be a very interesting relation between *Ditylenchus dipsaci* and *Botrytis allii* in collar rot of onion. When water into which the nematode had excreted enzymes was injected into onion plants in the presence of *B. allii,* 100% of the plants became infected with collar rot, in contrast to a disease incidence of 30% when pure water was used under similar circumstances (Myuge, 1959).

The incidence of bacterial wilt in a resistant variety of alfalfa was increased from approximately 4% to 27% in the presence of *Ditylenchus dipsaci.* The nematode carried the bacterium on its body into the crown buds. The nematode did not affect the incidence of wilt on plants that were first wounded. Apparently the nematode acts as a simple vector (Hawn, 1963). There is no evidence of any interactions between *D. dipsaci* and fungi. This species, however, does not normally attack the roots of plants, so that interactions are not likely to develop between this nematode and root-attacking soil fungi.

Radopholus.—*Radopholus similis* is the causal agent of citrus decline, but species of *Fusarium* may be associated with the nematode in the etiology. Lesions produced on citrus roots by *R. similis* appear to be different from those produced under field conditions; *Fusarium,* together with *Sclerotium* and *Thielaviopsis,* appear to be important in the "decay phase" of the disease (DuCharme and Hanks, 1957). The incidence of infection of citrus crown pieces by *Fusarium* was increased four-fold in the presence of *R. similis* (Feder and Feldmesser, 1961). There may be somewhat complex interrelations between these two organisms in citrus because varieties that are tolerant to the nematode appear also to be tolerant to the fungus (Feder and Ford, 1961).

Although *Radopholus similis* is not a prerequisite to Panama wilt in the Gros Michel variety of banana, caused by *Fusarium oxysporum* f. *cubense,* the disease expression was aggravated and the period between inoculation and appearance of marked disease symptoms was considerably shortened when the nematode was also present (Loos, 1959).

The root-rot disease of the banana varieties Dwarf Cavandish and Williams in Australia appears to be entirely due to *Radopholus similis,* and the fungi *Fusarium oxysporum* and *Rhizoctonia solani* act only as secondary organisms (Blake, 1961).

Pratylenchus.—Root-lesion nematodes have been associated with fusarium wilt of cotton (Smith, 1940; Holdeman, 1954), but the relation has never been examined critically. *Rhizoctonia solani* and *Pratylenchus neglectus* are closely associated in a root rot of winter wheat (Benedict and Mountain, 1956). The combined effect of the fungus and the nematode in reducing growth of wheat was approximately twice that produced by either pathogen alone. The incidence of fungal infection of the roots may be correlated with the nematode population, but the effect of the two parasites appears to be additive rather than synergistic.

The classical studies on the interrelation of *Pratylenchus penetrans* and *Cylindrocarpon radicicola* (Hastings and Bosher, 1938) showed that the fungus alone reduced growth of a number of plants, including potato, carrot, red clover, and violet, by 6% to 11%, whereas the fungus and the nematode reduced growth by 50% to 75%. More recently, Slootweg (1956) reported that *C. radicicola* alone produced no lesions on the roots of narcissus, whereas the fungus and *P. penetrans* produced extensive lesions.

True synergism between *Verticillium dahliae* and *Pratylenchus penetrans* has been demonstrated in the etiology of eggplant wilt (McKeen and Mountain, 1960) and to a lesser extent in tomato wilt (Mountain and McKeen, 1962*b*). The incidence of wilt is strikingly increased by the nematode if the level of the fungus in the soil is low. In recent experiments (Mountain and McKeen, unpublished), the fungus inoculum in the soil was reduced to extremely low levels, while the nematode inoculum was maintained at levels comparable to those in field soil. Symptoms of wilt in eggplant appeared 20 days earlier and incidence of wilt at the end of 8 weeks was 65% higher in plants growing in soil containing both organisms, than in soil containing only the fungus. The mechanism of this interaction is not known. The nematode causes extensive cortical necrosis within 24 hours on the roots of eggplant and the fungus may utilize this necrotic pathway to the vascular tissues. The root population of the nematode is usually much higher when the fungus is also present, and there are indications that complex interrelations exist between the host plant, the fungus, and the nematode (Mountain and McKeen, 1962*a*).

The presence of *Pratylenchus penetrans* resulted in earlier and more severe symptoms of verticillium wilt in a susceptible variety of strawberry. However, varieties of strawberry resistant to wilt were not affected by *Verticillium albo-atrum* when the nematode was also present, although the latter reproduced readily and caused many root lesions (Abu-Gharbieh, Varney, and Jenkins, 1962).

In the etiology of charcoal rot of sorghum, the nematode *Pratylenchus hexincisus* and the fungus *Macrophomina phaseoli* caused a significantly higher disease rating under dry soil conditions than did the fungus alone (Norton, 1958).

Aphelenchoides.—The bud and leaf nematode, *Aphelenchoides ritzemabosi,* interacts with *Corynebacterium fascians* in cauliflower disease of strawberry and the full disease syndrome appears only when a pathogenic strain of the bacterium and the nematode are present (Crosse and Pitcher, 1952; Pitcher and Crosse, 1958). The nematode alone, or associated with nonpathogenic strains of the bacterium, produces localized feeding areas on the crown bud, followed by the formation of "alaminate" leaves. These structures appear as a rosette of 3 to 5 leaf initials whose expansion has been checked. If the pathogenic strain of *C. fascians* is inoculated mechanically into the bud, the second symptom, "leafy gall" results. Under these conditions, the bacterium stimulates the apical and axillary meristems. In the presence of both the nematode and a pathogenic strain of the bacterium, the full disease syndrome of strawberry cauliflower develops. Apparently there are two opposing forces in the development of cauliflower disease, a checking of growth by the nematode and a stimulation of growth by the bacterium. The nematode acts as a vector by carrying the bacterium into the meristem of a crown bud, where they could not otherwise enter. But the interaction between the nematode and the bacterium may be more complex than a simple pathogen-vector relation (Pitcher, 1963).

Sedentary ectoparasitic nematodes.—Tylenchulus.— Rough-lemon feeder roots and crowns infected for the longer time with *Tylenchulus semipenetrans* had the highest incidence of infection with *Fusarium solani* and *F. oxysporum.* Roots from areas newly invaded or not yet invaded by the nematode had much lower percentages of *Fusarium* infection. There was no apparent relation between this nematode and infection by *Pythium, Phytophthora,* or *Thielaviopsis* (Feldmesser, Feder, and Rebois, 1962).

Migratory ectoparasitic nematodes.—Hoplolaimus.— *Hoplolaimus uniformis* is associated with *Fusarium oxysporum* f. *pisi* in early yellowing of peas (Labruyère, den Ouden, and Seinhorst, 1959). Inoculation with the nematode alone caused a slight grey discoloration of portions of the root and cracks in the cortex within which the nematode occurred. Inoculation with the fungus alone produced a superficial discoloration of the cortex when the inoculum was placed in direct contact with the root and no visible damage when the inoculum was placed a short distance from the root. Inoculation with both organisms resulted in extensive dark-brown discolorations along the roots and complete decay at the point of inoculation. In the absence of the nematode, the fungus colonized only the outer layers of the cortex, whereas in the presence of the nematode, the fungus penetrated into the vascular bundle.

Tylenchorhynchus.—*Tylenchorhynchus claytoni* will cause a slight to moderate increase in incidence of black shank of tobacco on the resistant variety Dixie Bright 101, in association with *Phytophthora parasitica* var. *nicotianae*, but the effect is not nearly as marked as with *Meloidogyne* (Graham, 1958).

Tylenchorhynchus claytoni increased the incidence of wilt caused by *Fusarium oxysporum* f. *nicotianae* in a susceptible variety of tobacco (Holdeman, 1956).

The severity of a root rot of peas caused by *Aphanomyces euteiches* was increased by *Tylenchorhynchus martini*, and this increase was directly related to the population of the nematode (Haglund and King, 1961).

Paratylenchus.—The pin nematode, *Paratylenchus hamatus*, has been associated with a species of *Rhizoctonia* in a root rot of celery (Lownsbery and Lownsbery, 1952), and with *Rhizoctonia, Pythium,* and *Fusarium* in a root rot of mint (Horner and Jensen, 1954), but these interrelations have not been studied critically.

Belonolaimus.—*Belonolaimus gracilis* greatly facilitated the development of fusarium wilt in susceptible and resistant varieties of cotton (Holdeman and Graham, 1952).

Helicotylenchus.—The incidence of southern bacterial wilt of tomato, caused by *Pseudomonas solanacearum*, was increased from 17% to 42% when the ectoparasitic nematode *Helicotylenchus nannus* was also present (Libman and Leach, 1962).

Mechanisms of the interaction between nematodes and the microflora.—Several facts are apparent from the examples of interrelations between nematodes and the plant-parasitic microflora described above. Relatively little work has been done in this area and, with a few outstanding exceptions, studies have not been carried out critically. In many experiments, for example, there is no indication of the level of the inoculum used and how this might relate to field conditions. Frequently, there was no attempt to control other potential pathogens. The data often have no statistical support.

In many cases, the fungus involved is one of the vascular-wilt organisms. The relation between root-knot nematodes and species of *Fusarium* and *Phytophthora* appears to be highly developed, but more critical studies similar to those of Powell and Nusbaum (1960) are required. There is evidence that fusarium wilt may be much more severe if infection by *Meloidogyne* precedes the addition of *Fusarium* (Powell, 1963); it is important to establish whether *Fusarium* has an affinity for the galled tissue similar to that of *Phytophthora*.

The association between fungi and nematode appears to be more common among the highly evolved parasitic nematodes and suggests that nematodes such as *Meloidogyne* have had a long association with plants and the root-disease fungi. Because synergism between fungi and certain species of *Meloidogyne* is more marked than with other species of this nematode, there may be fundamental differences in the host-parasite relations among the different species of root-knot nematode. The association between the plant-parasitic microflora and ectoparasitic nematodes may be less well developed, and frequently the effects of the two organisms are merely additive.

The interaction between *Verticillium* and nematodes may depend on root necrosis rather than the more highly developed host responses caused by *Meloidogyne*. Therefore, there may be important differences in the colonization of cortical tissue between *Verticillium* and *Fusarium*.

Interactions between nematodes and bacteria may be simpler than with fungi: with a few possible exceptions, the nematodes appear to act as vectors or wounding agents.

Despite the paucity of critical information available on interactions between nematodes and other plant pathogens, it is possible to speculate on possible mechanisms by which such interactions do occur.

The Rhizosphere.—It is established that the characteristics of the rhizosphere microflora can influence the pathogenicity of soil microorganisms. In some cases, resistance may be associated with a higher incidence of organisms in the rhizosphere that are antagonistic to the pathogen in question. Severity of root rot can be correlated in some instances with a decrease in the number of bacteria in the rhizosphere that require amino acids (Lochhead, 1959). The effect of the rhizosphere on root parasitism by nematodes has never been investigated. It is interesting to recall that synergism between fungi and *Meloidogyne* is frequently most pronounced in host varieties that are resistant to the fungus. Infection of roots by nematodes could alter the physiology of the host in such a manner that the composition of root exudates is changed. This, in turn, could change the rhizosphere microflora and increase the infectiveness of pathogenic soil fungi. The relation of plant-parasitic nematodes to the rhizosphere is a most promising area for future research.

The Epidermis.—It has been stated on many occasions that nematodes may create openings in the root epidermis to allow entry of other organisms. It is possible that, in cases where root wounding gives a response similar to that of the nematode, or where synergism disappears after root wounding, nematodes do create openings for the other pathogen. It must be remembered however, that root wounding involves far more tissue than the epidermis. Damage to the epidermis by some ectoparasitic nematodes is much greater than that caused by entry of larvae of *Meloidogyne*, for example, and one might expect to find far more evidence of associations involving ectoparasitic nematodes than is the case, if fungi were utilizing breaks in the epidermis. Then too, certain species of *Meloidogyne* interact more effectively than other species with fungi; one would expect the extent of epidermal wounding to be similar for all species. It is likely therefore, that where complex interactions occur between nematodes and other pathogens, the mechanism involved is more fundamental than simple wounding of the epidermis.

The Cortex.—Many fungi have difficulty in colonizing the cortex of healthy roots and certainly the wound parasites might require a necrotic lesion for initial colonization prior to pathogenesis. Most fungi and bacteria present in necrotic lesions with the nematode do not cause specific plant disease, but may contribute to the development of the lesion.

The Endodermis.—Van Fleet (1961) suggests that it is quite likely that resistance to colonization of the vascular elements by wilt pathogens lies in the endodermis. A common observation is that many fungi do not penetrate or even approach this tissue. The endodermis contains large quantities of phenols, naphthols, and anthrols and, in later stages of development, the corresponding benzoquinones, naphthoquinones, and anthroquinones. Naphthoquinones, especially, are inhibitors of the growth of bacteria and fungi. Parasitic nematodes have a profound effect on the endodermis. The syncytia and galls caused by *Meloidogyne* are mainly pericyclic in origin, and the endodermis is not differentiated in affected areas. *Radopholus similis* causes pericyclic tumors in the roots of citrus, which displace the endodermis and prevent suberization. *Pratylenchus penetrans* causes marked necrosis of the endodermis. In every instance, where there is marked synergism between nematodes and wilt-producing fungi, the endodermis is prevented from forming, or disrupted, or killed.

Production of Fungus Toxins.—The theory that pathogens of wilt disease injure their hosts, at least partly, by the production of toxic substances appears to be well established. Experiments have shown that toxins produced by pathogens in vitro may be very damaging to susceptible varieties, but do not damage resistant varieties. Gäumann (1957) suggests that certain varieties of tomato resistant to wilt do not provide conditions under which *Fusarium lycopersici* can form adequate toxin, but if the physiology of the host is altered, the resistant plants become diseased. It is apparent from earlier discussions in this paper that *Meloidogyne* has a profound effect on the physiology of the root in the galled area. Because synergism between this nematode and *Fusarium* occurs most frequently in the resistant varieties of tomato, Gäumann's thesis might explain the mechanism of this interaction.

Effect of Biological Factors on Reproduction of Nematodes.—To a large extent, the rate of reproduction of a nematode is an inherent characteristic of the organism, upon which may be superimposed a wide range of factors affecting metabolic rate. With plant-parasitic nematodes, it may be very difficult to determine whether the effect of such factors is on the nematode itself or on the interaction between the nematode and the host. I wish to discuss some of the biological factors that might influence the rate of reproduction of plant-parasitic nematodes.

Population density.—The relation between initial and final populations of many plant-parasitic nematodes is linear over a certain range of the population. It is obvious, however, that the initial population can be increased to the point where factors, such as competition within the host, may limit the rate of increase. The slope of the equation for linearity then becomes smaller, or the population reaches a "ceiling" beyond which the relation is no longer linear. Jones (1959) and Seinhorst (1961a) discuss this subject in greater detail than is possible in this paper. Then too, with increasing initial population, the sex ratio may change toward an increase in the proportion of males (Tyler, 1933; Ellenby, 1954; Triantaphyllou and Hirschmann, 1959; Lindhardt, 1960), which would tend to reduce the final population.

Physiology of the host.—The nutrition of the host plant affects the rate at which nematodes develop (Oteifa, 1953; Bird, 1960; C. F. Marks, unpublished). Bird (1960) found that *Meloidogyne javanica* grows more rapidly on tomato plants that are deficient in nitrogen, while Oteifa (1955) showed that both the number of mature females and the number of egg masses of *M. incognita* were greater in the roots of lima beans that had received nitrate nitrogen than in plants receiving ammonia nitrogen. In general, the rate of reproduction of nematodes tends to be highest in plants that receive their full nutritional requirements. Little work has been done however, on the effects of host nutrition on nematode reproduction.

The amount of light received by the plant may affect the rate of reproduction of nematodes. An increase in the photoperiod significantly increased the total number of females and egg masses, per plant, of *Meloidogyne incognita* on tomato (Tarjan and Hopper, 1953). Tomato plants grown under red light, either completely or as supplementary illumination, had a higher population of female *M. arenaria* in the roots than plants grown under natural light, or green, blue, or white light. But it is not certain that the total effect was on reproduction of the nematode (Gillard and Van den Brande, 1956). Under short-day conditions, the potato variety Majestic bore more cysts of *Heterodera rostochiensis* than did the varieties Redskin and Doon Star, but fewer than these varieties under long-day conditions (Ellenby, 1958).

Reduced concentration of oxygen in the soil lowered the rate of reproduction of *Meloidogyne javanica* and *Tylenchulus semipenetrans* (Van Gundy and Stolzy, 1961; Stolzy et al., 1962).

The rate of reproduction of *Meloidogyne incognita* in tobacco was reduced by foliar applications of maleic hydrazide (Nusbaum, 1958).

Populations of *Pratylenchus penetrans* in the soil and in roots of peas were higher after treatments that reduced growth of the host plant to a moderate extent. These treatments included unfavorable light and temperature, excision of plant parts, and limitation of nutrient supply. Treatments to the plants that had a more severe effect on growth reduced the reproduction of the nematode. It was assumed that reproduction was related to the physiological status of the plant and, under conditions of moderate stress, the host might provide a more suitable substrate for this nematode (Dolliver, 1961).

Effect of other parasites.—It is inconceivable that, under field conditions, a single species of a nematode will infect a plant in the absence of any other parasitic organism. The reproduction of a nematode could be affected by the presence in the host of other pathogens. One might expect, for example, that a nematode which causes extensive root necrosis such as *Pratylenchus*, could have a detrimental effect on reproduction of a nematode with a more highly developed host-parasite relation such as *Meloidogyne*. Very little work has been done in this area, however, which is most surprising, since such effects may be very important in the study of population dynamics.

There is an interaction between the root-knot nematode *Meloidogyne incognita* and the cyst nematode *Heterodera glycines* in the roots of soybean. At the end of 53 days, the population of the latter was lower in the presence than in the absence of the former. But this trend later reversed and by the end of 110 days, there were over twice as many larvae of the cyst nematode in the presence of the root-knot nematode. On the other hand, *Meloidogyne* was suppressed by *H. glycines* and the population fell to about one third of that in the control (Ross, 1959).

Pratylenchus penetrans reproduced equally well in the presence and absence of *Tylenchorhynchus martini*, whereas reproduction of the latter was reduced by 75% to 90% when *P. penetrans* was also present (Chapman, 1959).

Populations of *Pratylenchus penetrans* in roots of tomato (Mountain and McKeen, 1962*b*) and eggplant (McKeen and Mountain, 1960) and of *Tylenchorhynchus capitatus* on roots of tomato (Mountain and McKeen, 1962*a*) are significantly higher when the fungus *Verticillium dahliae* is also present. More recent studies (Mountain and McKeen, unpublished) show that *P. penetrans* penetrates the roots of eggplant much more quickly when the fungus is also present. It appears that the fungus-infected roots may be more attractive to the nematode or enable it to penetrate more quickly. It is not yet known whether the nematode actually reproduces at a faster rate in the fungus-infected roots, or whether the increase in numbers merely reflects the more rapid rate of invasion by the nematode. There is, however, a direct association between the incidence of verticillium wilt and the suitability of the plant as a host for *P. penetrans*, also some relation between incidence of wilt and the increase in the numbers of nematodes, so that complex interactions probably occur between the plant, the fungus, and the nematode (Mountain and McKeen, 1962*a*).

Root populations of *Pratylenchus zeae* were higher in sugarcane when a species of *Phytophthora* was also present than when it was absent (Khan, 1959).

OUTLOOK.—The ability of a parasitic organism to evoke disease in a host depends on two factors, the qualitative effect of the host-parasite interaction and the quantitative effect of the number of parasites that attack the host. Regrettably, this latter phase could not be fully assessed in this paper, although biological control could have wide application here.

The "descriptive phase" of the host-parasite relations of many nematodes is now largely complete, and future work will emphasize the much more difficult study of the mechanisms involved in such relations. Clearly, the biochemical interaction of the parasite and the host must now receive major emphasis. The most important objective for such studies is the culturing of plant-parasitic nematodes on a chemically defined medium. Only then can one determine the nutritional requirements of these organisms (Wallace, 1961*b*) and the significance of enzyme-substrate activities in the host-parasite relation. At that time, biological control might be effected through manipulation of the host physiology, perhaps by host resistance, cultural amendments, or systemic chemicals.

The interaction of nematodes and the soil fungi should be of great interest both to the nematologist and the plant pathologist. Synergism between plant-parasitic nematodes and the soil microflora may occur frequently in plant disease; its effect on etiology, epidemiology, population dynamics, and general ecology of both organisms may be profound. There is now no valid reason for not considering nematodes as an essential component in all aspects of soil microbiology. The microfauna and microflora do interact in common hosts, and these interactions cannot be delimited by any artificial boundaries demanded by separate disciplines.

Plant nematology stands between botany and zoology; nematologists must be prepared to adapt principles from both disciplines to their own studies. The degree to which they succeed in this endeavor will determine, to a large extent, whether or not plant nematology will exist as a valid and recognized discipline.

LITERATURE CITED

ABU-GHARBIEH, W., E. H. VARNEY, and W. R. JENKINS. 1962. Relationship of meadow nematodes to Verticillium wilt of strawberries. (Abstr.) Phytopathology 52: 921.

BAKER, A. D., G. L. BROWN, and A. B. JAMES. 1954. Relationships of fungi, mites, and the potato-rot nematode. Science 119: 92-93.

BENEDICT, W. G., and W. B. MOUNTAIN. 1956. Studies on the etiology of a root rot of winter wheat in southwestern Ontario. Can. J. Botany 34: 159-174.

BIRD, A. F. 1959. Development of the root-knot nematodes *Meloidogyne javanica* (Treub) and *Meloidogyne hapla* Chitwood in the tomato. Nematologica 4: 31-42.

BIRD, A. F. 1960. The effect of some single element deficiencies on the growth of *Meloidogyne javanica*. Nematologica 5: 78-85.

BIRD, A. F. 1962. The inducement of giant cells by *Meloidogyne javanica*. Nematologica 8: 1-10.

BLAKE, C. D. 1961. Root rot of bananas caused by *Radopholus similis* (Cobb) and its control in New South Wales. Nematologica 6: 295-310.

BLAKE, C. D. 1962. The etiology of tulip-root disease in susceptible and in resistant varieties of oats infested by the stem nematode, *Ditylenchus dipsaci* (Kühn) Filipjev. II. Histopathology of tulip-root and development of the nematode. Ann. Appl. Biol. 50: 713-722.

CHAPMAN, R. A. 1959. Development of *Pratylenchus penetrans* and *Tylenchorhynchus martini* on red clover and alfalfa. Phytopathology 49: 357-359.

CHEN, TSEH-AN, and A. E. RICH. 1962. The role of

Pratylenchus penetrans in the development of strawberry black root rot. Plant Disease Reptr. 46: 839-843.

CHRISTIE, J. R. 1936. The development of root-knot nematode galls. Phytopathology 26: 1-22.

CHRISTIE, J. R., and V. G. PERRY. 1951. A root disease of plants caused by a nematode of the genus *Trichodorus*. Science 113: 491-493.

COHN, E., and G. MINZ. 1960. Nematodes and resistance to Fusarium wilt in tomatoes. Hassadeh 40: 1347-1349.

COLE, C. S., and H. W. HOWARD. 1958. Observations on giant cells in potato roots infected with *Heterodera rostochiensis*. J. Helminthol. 32: 135-144.

CRITTENDEN, H. W. 1962. Effect of *Meloidogyne incognita acrita* in nodulating and non-nodulating strains of soybeans. (Abstr.) Phytopathology 52: 163.

CROSSE, J. E., and R. S. PITCHER. 1952. Studies in the relationship of eelworms and bacteria to certain plant diseases. I. The etiology of strawberry cauliflower disease. Ann. Appl. Biol. 39: 475-484.

DAVIS, R. A. 1959. Cytological and histological effects of *Xiphinema diversicaudatum* and *Meloidogyne hapla* on rose roots. (Abstr.) Phytopathology 49: 523.

DAVIS, R. A., and W. R. JENKINS. 1960*a*. Nematodes associated with roses and the root injury caused by *Meloidogyne hapla* Chitwood, 1959, *Xiphinema diversicaudatum* (Micoletzky, 1927) Thorne, 1939, and *Helicotylenchus nannus* Steiner, 1945. Maryland Agr. Expt. Sta. Bull. A-106, 16 p.

DAVIS, R. A., and W. R. JENKINS. 1960*b*. Histopathology of gardenia (*Gardenia jasminoides veitchi*), infected with three species of *Meloidogyne*. Nematologica 5: 228-230.

DIEDWARDO, A. A. 1960. Time-lapse studies of movement, feeding and hatching of *Pratylenchus penetrans*. (Abstr.) Phytopathology 50: 570-571.

DOLLIVER, J. S. 1961. Population levels of *Pratylenchus penetrans* as influenced by treatments affecting dry weight of Wando pea plants. Phytopathology 51: 364-367.

DROPKIN, V. H. 1954. Infectivity and gall size in tomato and cucumber seedlings infected with *Meloidogyne incognita* var. *acrita* (root-knot nematode). Phytopathology 44: 43-49.

DROPKIN, V. H. 1955. The relations between nematodes and plants. Exptl. Parasitol. 4: 282-322.

DROPKIN, V. H. 1959. Varietal response of soybeans to *Meloidogyne*—a bioassay system for separating races of root-knot nematodes. Phytopathology 49: 18-23.

DROPKIN, V. H., and P. E. NELSON. 1960. The histopathology of root-knot nematode infections in soybeans. Phytopathology 50: 442-447.

DUCHARME, E. P. 1959. Morphogenesis and histopathology of lesions induced on citrus roots by *Radopholus similis*. Phytopathology 49: 388-395.

DUCHARME, E. P., and R. W. HANKS. 1957. Pathogenic complex of citrus spreading decline. Florida Agr. Expt. Sta. Ann. Rept. 1956-57: 190-191.

ELLENBY, C. 1954. Environmental determination of the sex ratio of a plant parasitic nematode. Nature (London) 174: 1016-1017.

ELLENBY, C. 1958. Day length and cyst formation in the potato root eelworm, *Heterodera rostochiensis* Wollenweber. Nematologica 3: 81-90.

ENDO, B. Y. 1962. Anatomical studies of soybean roots artificially inoculated with *Heterodera glycines*. (Abstr.) Phytopathology 52: 731.

FASSULIOTIS, G., and C. H. WILLEY. 1954. The histological effects of the golden nematode, *Heterodera rostochiensis* on potato root. Anat. Record 120: 226.

FAULKNER, L. R., and H. M. DARLING. 1961. Pathological histology, hosts, and culturing of the potato rot nematode. Phytopathology 51: 778-786.

FEDER, W. A., and J. FELDMESSER. 1956. Root abnormalities caused by burrowing nematode infections. (Abstr.) Phytopathology 46: 11.

FEDER, W. A., and J. FELDMESSER. 1957. Observations on the absence of an internal microflora of surface-sterilized *Radopholus similis*. (Abstr.) Phytopathology 47: 11.

FEDER, W. A., and J. FELDMESSER. 1961. The spreading decline complex: the separate and combined effects of *Fusarium* spp., and *Radopholus similis* on the growth of Duncan grapefruit seedlings in the greenhouse. Phytopathology 51: 724-726.

FEDER, W. A., and H. W. FORD. 1961. Effect of *Fusarium* upon the growth of seedlings of several burrowing nematode-tolerant citrus rootstocks. Proc. Florida State Hort. Soc. 74: 43-45.

FELDMESSER, J., W. A. FEDER, and R. V. REBOIS. 1962. Movement of *Tylenchulus semi-penetrans* into Rough lemon roots and in soil and its relation to *Fusarium* in the roots. (Abstr.) Phytopathology 52: 9.

FIELDING, M. J. 1959. Nematodes in plant disease. Ann. Rev. Microbiol. 13: 239-254.

GARRETT, S. D. 1959. Biology and ecology of root-disease fungi. p. 309-316. *In* C. S. Holton, et al. [ed.], Plant pathology, problems and progress 1908-1958, Univ. Wisconsin Press, Madison, Wisc.

GASKIN, T. A. 1959. Abnormalities of grass roots and their relationship to root-knot nematodes. Plant Disease Reptr. 43: 25-26.

GÄUMANN, E. 1957. Fusaric acid as a wilt toxin. Phytopathology 47: 342-357.

GILL, D. L. 1958. Effect of root-knot nematodes on Fusarium wilt of mimosa. Plant Disease Reptr. 42: 587-590.

GILLARD, A., and J. VAN DEN BRANDE. 1956. Influence de la lumière sur le developpement du nematode des racines, *Meloidogyne* sp. Nematologica 1: 184-188.

GOFFART, H., and A. HEILING. 1962. Beobachtungen über die enzymatische Wirkung von speicheldrüsensekreten pflanzenparasitärer Nematoden. Nematologica 7: 173-176.

GOODEY, T. 1932. Some observations on the biology of the root-gall nematode, *Anguillulina radicicola* (Greeff, 1872). J. Helminthol. 10: 33-44.

GRAHAM, T. W. 1958. Root-knot and other nematodes in relation to the development of black shank. (Abstr.) Phytopathology 48: 343.

HAGLUND, W. A., and T. H. KING. 1961. Effect of parasitic nematodes on the severity of common root rot of canning peas. Nematologica 6: 311-314.

HASTINGS, R. J., and J. E. BOSHER. 1938. A study of the pathogenicity of the meadow nematode and the associated fungus *Cylindrocarpon radicicola* Wr. Can. J. Research, Sec. C, 16: 225-229.

HAWN, E. J. 1963. Transmission of bacterial wilt of alfalfa by *Ditylenchus dipsaci* (Kühn). Nematologica. 9: 65-68.

HOLDEMAN, Q. L. 1954. Nematodes as possible members of disease complexes involving other plant pathogens. Plant Disease Reptr. Suppl. 227: 77-79.

HOLDEMAN, Q. L. 1956. The effect of the tobacco stunt nematode on the incidence of Fusarium wilt in flue-cured tobacco. Phytopathology 46: 129.

HOLDEMAN, Q. L., and T. W. GRAHAM. 1952. The association of the sting nematode with some persistent cotton wilt spots in northeastern South Carolina. (Abstr.) Phytopathology 42: 283-284.

HORNER, C. E., and H. J. JENSEN. 1954. Nematodes associated with mints in Oregon. Plant Disease Reptr. 38: 39-41.

JENKINS, W. R., and B. W. COURSEN. 1957. The effect of root-knot nematodes, *Meloidogyne incognita acrita* and *M. hapla* on Fusarium wilt of tomato. Plant Disease Reptr. 41: 182-186.

JONES, F. G. W. 1959. Ecological relationships of nematodes. p. 395-411. *In* C. S. Holton, et al. [ed.], Plant pathology, problems and progress 1908-1958, Univ. Wisconsin Press, Madison, Wisc.

KHAN, A. 1959. Pathogenic effects of *Pratylenchus zeae* on sugarcane. (Abstr.) Phytopathology 49: 543.

KRUSBERG, L. R. 1960. Hydrolytic and respiratory enzymes of species of *Ditylenchus* and *Pratylenchus*. Phytopathology 50: 9-22.

KRUSBERG, L. R. 1961. Studies on the culturing and parasitism of plant-parasitic nematodes, in particular

Ditylenchus dipsaci and *Aphelenchoides ritzemabosi* on alfalfa tissues. Nematologica 6: 181-200.

KRUSBERG, L. R., and L. W. NIELSEN. 1958. Pathogenesis of root-knot nematodes to the Porto Rico variety of sweetpotato. Phytopathology 48: 30-39.

LABRUYÈRE, R. E., H. DEN OUDEN, and J. W. SEINHORST. 1959. Experiments on the interaction of *Hoplolaimus uniformis* and *Fusarium oxysporum* f. *pisi* race 3 and its importance in "early yellowing" of peas. Nematologica 4: 336-343.

LEFKOWITZ, S. S. 1961. Plant growth substances in root galls induced by *Meloidogyne incognita acrita* Chit. Dissertation Absts. 22: 1788.

LEOPOLD, A. C. 1960. Auxins and plant growth. University of California Press, Berkeley and Los Angeles. 354 p.

LIBMAN, G., and J. G. LEACH. 1962. A study of the role of some nematodes in the incidence and severity of southern bacterial wilt of tomato. (Abstr.) Phytopathology 52: 1219.

LINDHARDT, J. 1960. Nogle undersogelser over infektionsgradens indflydelse pa havrealens kon *Heterodera major*. Tidsskr. Planteavl. 64: 889-896.

LINFORD, M. B. 1937. The feeding of root-knot nematode in root tissue and nutrient solution. Phytopathology 27: 824-835.

LINFORD, M. B. 1941. Parasitism of the root-knot nematode in leaves and stems. Phytopathology 31: 634-648.

LIPETZ, J. 1959. A possible role of indolacetic acid oxidase in crown gall tumour induction. Nature (London) 184: 1076-1077.

LOCHHEAD, A. G. 1959. Rhizosphere microorganisms in relation to root-disease fungi. p. 327-338. *In* C. S. Holton et al. [ed.], Plant pathology, problems and progress 1908-1958, Univ. Wisconsin Press, Madison, Wisc.

LOEWENBERG, J. R., T. SULLIVAN, and M. L. SCHUSTER. 1960. Gall induction by *Meloidogyne incognita incognita* by surface feeding and factors affecting the behaviour pattern of the second-stage larvae. Phytopathology 50: 322-323.

LOOS, C. A. 1959. Symptom expression of Fusarium wilt disease of the Gros Michel banana in the presence of *Radopholus similis* (Cobb, 1893) Thorne, 1949, and *Meloidogyne incognita acrita* Chitwood, 1949. Proc. Helminthol. Soc. Wash., D. C. 26: 103-111.

LOWNSBERY, B. F., and J. W. LOWNSBERY. 1952. *Paratylenchus hamatus* Thorne & Allen associated with celery disease in Connecticut. (Abstr.) Phytopathology 42: 13.

LUCAS, G. B., J. N. SASSER, and A. KELMAN. 1955. The relationship of root-knot nematodes to Granville wilt resistance in tobacco. Phytopathology 45: 537-540.

MANKAU, R., and M. B. LINFORD. 1960. Host-parasite relations of the clover cyst nematode, *Heterodera trifolii* Goffart. Illinois Agr. Expt. Sta. Bull. 667, 50 p.

MARTIN, W. J., L. D. NEWSOM, and J. E. JONES. 1956. Relationship of nematodes to the development of Fusarium wilt in cotton. Phytopathology 46: 285-289.

MAUNG, M. O., and W. R. JENKINS. 1959. Effects of a root-knot nematode *Meloidogyne incognita acrita* Chitwood, 1949, and a stubby-root nematode *Trichodorus christiei* Allen, 1957, on the nutrient status of tomato, *Lycopersicon esculentum* hort. var. Chesapeake. Plant Disease Reptr., 43: 791-796.

MCGUIRE, J. M., H. J. WALTERS, and D. A. SLACK. 1958. The relationship of root-knot nematodes to the development of Fusarium wilt in alfalfa. (Abstr.) Phytopathology 48: 344.

MCKEEN, C. D., and W. B. MOUNTAIN. 1960. Synergism between *Pratylenchus penetrans* (Cobb) and *Verticillium albo-atrum* R. & B. in eggplant wilt. Can. J. Botany 38: 789-794.

MILLER, H. N., and A. A. DiEDWARDO. 1962. Leaf galls on *Siderasis fucata* caused by the root-knot nematode, *Meloidogyne incognita incognita*. Phytopathology 52: 1070-1073.

MORGAN, G. T., and J. W. MCALLAN. 1962. Hydrolytic enzymes in plant-parasitic nematodes. Nematologica 8: 209-215.

MOUNTAIN, W. B. 1954. Studies of nematodes in relation to brown root rot of tobacco in Ontario. Can. J. Botany 32: 737-759.

MOUNTAIN, W. B. 1957. Pathogenicity of nematodes in relation to Koch's Postulates. p. Path. 1-8. *In* E. J. Cairns [ed.], Proceedings of the S-19 Workshop in Phytonematology. (Processed.)

MOUNTAIN, W. B. 1960a. Theoretical considerations of plant-nematode relationships. p. 419-421. *In* J. N. Sasser and W. R. Jenkins [ed.], Nematology, fundamentals and recent advances with emphasis on plant parasitic and soil forms, University of North Carolina Press, Chapel Hill, N. C.

MOUNTAIN, W. B. 1960b. Mechanisms involved in plant nematode relationships. p. 426-431. *In* J. N. Sasser and W. R. Jenkins [ed.], Nematology, fundamentals and recent advances with emphasis on plant parasitic and soil forms, University of North Carolina Press, Chapel Hill, N. C.

MOUNTAIN, W. B. 1961. Studies on the pathogenicity of *Pratylenchus*. p. 414-417. *In* Recent advances in botany (Canada) (9th Intern. Botan. Congr., Montreal) Univ. Toronto Press, Toronto.

MOUNTAIN, W. B., and C. D. MCKEEN. 1962a. Effect of *Verticillium dahliae* on the population of *Pratylenchus penetrans*. Nematologica 7: 261-266.

MOUNTAIN, W. B., and C. D. MCKEEN. 1962b. Interaction of *Verticillium dahliae* and *Pratylenchus penetrans* in tomato wilt. (Abst.) Phytopathology 52: 744.

MOUNTAIN, W. B., and Z. A. PATRICK. 1959. The peach replant problem in Ontario. VII. The pathogenicity of *Pratylenchus penetrans* (Cobb, 1917) Filip. & Stek. 1941. Can. J. Botany 37: 459-470.

MYUGE, S. G. 1957a. On the trophic characteristics of the potato stem nematode. (In Russian, with English summary). Izv. Akad. Nauk Uz. SSR, Ser. Biol. 3: 357-359.

MYUGE, S. G. 1957b. On the physiological specificity of the bulb nematode, *Ditylenchus allii*. (In Russian, with English summary). Zool. Zh. 36: 620-622.

MYUGE, S. G. 1959. [The reciprocal action between nematodes and lower fungi in plants.] Zashchita Rast. Moscow 1: 34-35.

MYUGE, S. G. 1960. On the interrelations of some phytonematodes with its plant-host. p. 333-338. Conf. Sci. Probl. Plant Protect., Budapest.

NORTON, D. C. 1958. The association of *Pratylenchus hexincisus* with charcoal rot of sorghum. Phytopathology 48: 355-358.

NUSBAUM, C. J. 1958. The response of root-knot infected tobacco plants to foliar applications of maleic hydrazide. (Abstr.) Phytopathology 48: 344.

OSBORNE, W. W., and W. R. JENKINS. 1962. Effect of *Pratylenchus penetrans*, *Meloidogyne incognita acrita* and *Meloidogyne* sp. on *Forsythia intermedia*. (Abstr.) Phytopathology 52: 926.

OTEIFA, B. A. 1953. Development of the root-knot nematode, *Meloidogyne incognita*, as affected by potassium nutrition of the host. Phytopathology 43: 171-174.

OTEIFA, B. A. 1955. Nitrogen source of the host nutrition in relation to infection by a root-knot nematode, *Meloidogyne incognita*. Plant Disease Reptr. 39: 902-903.

OTEIFA, B. A., and D. M. ELGINDI. 1962a. Influence of subsequent infections with root-knot nematode *Meloidogyne javanica*, on P^{32} absorption and translocation in tomato plants. (Abstr.) Nematologica 7: 8-9.

OTEIFA, B. A., and D. M. ELGINDI. 1962b. Influence of parasitic duration of *Meloidogyne javanica* (Treub) on host nutrient uptake. Nematologica 8: 216-220.

OWENS, R. G., and H. M. NOVOTNY. 1960. Physiological and biochemical studies on nematode galls. (Abstr.) Phytopathology 50: 650.

PARKER, K. G. 1959. Verticillium hadromycosis of deciduous fruit trees. Plant Disease Reptr. Suppl. 255.

PEACOCK, F. C. 1960. Inhibition of root-knot development on tomato by systemic compounds. Nematologica 5: 219-227.

PERRY, V. G. 1958. Parasitism of two species of dagger nematode (*Xiphinema americanum* and *X. chambersi*) to strawberry. Phytopathology 48: 420-423.

PITCHER, R. S. 1963. The role of plant-parasitic nematodes in bacterial diseases. Phytopathology 53: 35-39.

PITCHER, R. S., and J. E. CROSSE. 1958. Studies in the relationship of eelworms to certain plant diseases. II. Further analysis of the strawberry cauliflower disease complex. Nematologica 3: 244-256.

PITCHER, R. S., Z. A. PATRICK, and W. B. MOUNTAIN. 1960. Studies on the host-parasite relations of *Pratylenchus penetrans* (Cobb) to apple seedlings. I. Pathogenicity under sterile conditions. Nematologica 5: 309-314.

POWELL, N. T. 1963. The role of plant-parasitic nematodes in fungus diseases. Phytopathology 53: 28-35.

POWELL, N. T., and C. J. NUSBAUM. 1960. The black shank-root-knot complex in flue-cured tobacco. Phytopathology 50: 899-906.

RADEWALD, J. D., and D. J. RASKI. 1962. Studies on the host range and pathogenicity of *Xiphinema index*. (Abstr.) Phytopathology 52: 748-749.

REYNOLDS, H. W., and R. G. HANSON. 1957. Rhizoctonia disease of cotton in presence or absence of the cotton root-knot nematode. Phytopathology 47: 256-261.

ROBINSON, P. E. 1961. Root-knot nematodes and legume nodules. Nature (London) 189: 506-507.

ROHDE, R. A., and W. R. JENKINS. 1957. Host range of a species of *Trichodorus* and its host-parasite relationships on tomato. Phytopathology 47: 295-298.

ROSEN, H. R. 1928. A consideration of the pathogenicity of the cotton-wilt fungus *Fusarium vasinfectum*. Phytopathology 18: 419-438.

ROSS, J. P. 1959. Interaction of *Meloidogyne incognita incognita* and *Heterodera glycines* on soybeans. (Abstr.) Phytopathology 49: 549.

RUEHLE, J. L. 1962. Histopathological studies of pine roots infected with lance and pine cystoid nematodes. Phytopathology 52: 68-71.

RYDER, H. W., and H. W. CRITTENDEN. 1962. Interrelationships of tobacco ringspot virus and *Meloidogyne incognita acrita* in roots of soybean. (Abstr.) Phytopathology 52: 165-166.

SANDERS, M. E., and P. R. BURKHOLDER. 1948. Influence of amino acids on growth of Datura embryos in culture. Proc. Natl. Acad. Sci. U.S. 34: 516-526.

SASSER, J. N., C. B. LUCAS, and H. R. POWERS, JR. 1955. The relationship of root-knot nematodes to black-shank resistance in tobacco. Phytopathology 45: 459-461.

SAYED, M. Q. 1961. The effect of nutrition, pH and nematodes on damping off disease of pea, tomato, and cucumber. Dissertation Abst. 21: 1701-1702.

SCHILKE, P. J., and H. W. CRITTENDEN. 1959. Host-parasite relationships of soybean and a root-knot nematode *Meloidogyne hapla*. (Abstr.) Phytopathology 49: 525.

SCHINDLER, A. F. 1957. Parasitism and pathogenicity of *Xiphinema diversicaudatum*, an ectoparasitic nematode. Nematologica 2: 25-31.

SCHINDLER, A. F., R. N. STEWART, and P. SEMENIUK. 1961. A synergistic Fusarium-nematode interaction in carnations. Phytopathology 51: 143-146.

SCHUSTER, M. L., and T. SULLIVAN. 1960. Species differentiation of nematodes through host reactions in tissue culture. I. Comparisons of *Meloidogyne hapla*, *Meloidogyne incognita incognita* and *Nacobbus batatiformis*. Phytopathology 50: 874-876.

SCHUSTER, M. L., and G. THORNE. 1956. Distribution, relation to weeds, and histology of sugar beet root galls caused by *Nacobbus batatiformis* Thorne & Schuster. J. Am. Soc. Sugar Beet Technologists 9: 193-197.

SEINHORST, J. W. 1961a. Plant-nematode inter-relationships. Ann. Rev. Microbiol. 15: 177-196.

SEINHORST, J. W. 1961b. Annual Report. Instuut voor Plantenziektenkundig Onderzoek. 188 p. (See specifically English summary, p. 174.)

SHAFIEE, M. F. 1962. Pathogenicity of a root-knot nematode (*Meloidogyne incognita acrita*) and a root-lesion nematode (*Pratylenchus penetrans*) on pepper (*Capsicum frutescens*). (Abstr.) Phytopathology 52: 927.

SHANDS, W. A., JR., and H. W. CRITTENDEN. 1957. The influence of nitrogen and potassium on the relationship of *Meloidogyne incognita acrita* and soybeans. (Abstr.) Phytopathology 47: 454.

SLOOTWEG, A. F. G. 1956. Rootrot of bulbs caused by *Pratylenchus* and *Hoplolaimus* spp. Nematologica 1: 192-201.

SMITH, A. L. 1940. Distribution and relation of meadow nematode, *Pratylenchus pratensis*, to Fusarium wilt of cotton in Georgia. (Abstr.) Phytopathology 30: 710.

STANDIFER, M. S., and V. G. PERRY. 1960. Some effects of sting and stubby root nematodes on grapefruit roots. Phytopathology 50: 152-156.

STEINER, G. 1940. The root-knot nematode attacking stems and leaves of plants. (Abstr.) Phytopathology 30: 710.

STEINER, G. 1953. Changes in basic concepts in plant nematology. Plant Disease Reptr. 37: 203-205.

STEWART, R. N., and A. F. SCHINDLER. 1956. The effect of some ectoparasitic and endoparasitic nematodes on the expression of bacterial wilt in carnations. Phytopathology 46: 219-222.

STOLZY, L. H., S. D. VAN GUNDY, C. K. LABANAUSKAS, and T. E. SZUSZKIEWICZ. 1962. Influence of soil-oxygen diffusion rates and temperature on the citrus nematode and sweet orange seedlings. (Abstr.) Phytopathology 52: 754.

TARJAN, A. C., and B. E. HOPPER. 1953. Effect of increased photoperiod on egg mass production by the root-knot nematode, *Meloidogyne incognita* (Kofoid & White) Chitwood. Plant Disease Reptr. 37: 313-314.

TAYLOR, D. P., and T. D. WYLLIE. 1959. Interrelationship of root-knot nematodes and *Rhizoctonia solani* on soybean emergence. (Abstr.) Phytopathology 49: 552.

THOMASON, I. J. 1958. The effect of the root-knot nematode, *Meloidogyne javanica*, on blackeye bean wilt. (Abstr.) Phytopathology 48: 398.

THOMASON, I. J., D. C. ERWIN, and M. J. GARBER. 1959. The relationship of the root-knot nematode, *Meloidogyne javanica*, to Fusarium wilt of cowpea. Phytopathology 49: 602-606.

THORNE, G., and M. L. SCHUSTER. 1956. *Nacobbus batatiformis*, n.sp. (Nematoda: Tylenchidae), producing galls on the roots of sugar beets and other plants. Proc. Helminthol. Soc. Wash., D. C. 23: 128-134.

TINER, J. D. 1960. Cultures of the plant parasitic nematode genus *Pratylenchus* on sterile excised roots. I. Their establishment and maintenance. Exptl. Parasitol. 9: 121-126.

TOWNSHEND, J. L. 1962a. The root-lesion nematode, *Pratylenchus penetrans* (Cobb, 1917) Filip. & Stek. 1941, in celery. Can. J. Plant Sci. 42: 314-322.

TOWNSHEND, J. L. 1962b. The root-lesion nematode *Pratylenchus penetrans* (Cobb, 1917) Filip & Stek., 1941, in strawberry in the Niagara Peninsula and Norfolk County in Ontario. Can. J. Plant Sci. 42: 728-736.

TOWNSHEND, J. L. 1963a. The pathogenicity of *Pratylenchus penetrans* to celery. Can. J. Plant Sci. 43: 70-74.

TOWNSHEND, J. L. 1963b. The pathogenicity of *Pratylenchus penetrans* to strawberry. Can. J. Plant Sci. 43: 75-78.

TRACEY, M. V. 1958. Cellulase and chitinase in plant nematodes. Nematologica 3: 179-183.

TRIANTAPHYLLOU, A. C., and H. HIRSCHMANN. 1959. Development and sex determination in *Meloidogyne incognita* and intersexuality in *M. javanica*. (Abstr.) Phytopathology 49: 552-553.

TURLYGINA, S. 1957. [Changes in the respiratory process in plants affected by gallic nematodosis.] Dokl. Akad. Nauk SSR 115: 1227-1228.

TYLER, J. 1933. Reproduction without males in aseptic root cultures of the root-knot nematode. Hilgardia 7: 373-388.

VAN FLEET, D. S. 1961. Histochemistry and function of the endodermis. Botan. Rev. 27: 165-220.

VAN GUNDY, S. D., and R. L. RACKHAM. 1961. Studies

on the biology and pathogenicity of *Hemicycliophora arenaria*. Phytopathology 51: 393-397.

VAN GUNDY, S. D., and L. H. STOLZY. 1961. Influence of soil oxygen concentrations on the development of *Meloidogyne javanica*. Science 134: 665-666.

WALLACE, H. R. 1959. Movement of eelworms. V. Observations on *Aphelenchoides ritzema-bosi* (Schwartz, 1912) Steiner, 1932 on florists' chrysanthemums. Ann. Appl. Biol. 47: 350-360.

WALLACE, H. R. 1960. Observations on the behaviour of *Aphelenchoides ritzemabosi* in chrysanthemum leaves. Nematologica 5: 315-321.

WALLACE, H. R. 1961a. Browning of chrysanthemum leaves infested with *Aphelenchoides ritzemabosi*. Nematologica 6: 7-16.

WALLACE, H. R. 1961b. The nature of resistance in chrysanthemum varieties to *Aphelenchoides ritzemabosi*. Nematologica 6: 49-58.

WHITE, L. V. 1960. Host-parasite relationship of *Xiphinema americanum* Cobb, 1913, on apple, corn and strawberry. Dissertation Abst. 20: 3919.

WINSLOW, R. D. 1960. Some aspects of the ecology of free-living and plant-parasitic nematodes. p. 341-415. *In* J. N. Sasser and W. R. Jenkins [ed.], Nematology, fundamentals and recent advances with emphasis on plant parasitic and soil forms, University of North Carolina Press, Chapel Hill, N. C.

ZINOVIEV, V. G. 1957. [Enzymatic activity of the nematodes parasitizing plants.] Zool. Zh. 36: 617-620.

ZUCKERMAN, B. M. 1961. Parasitism and pathogenesis of the cultivated cranberry by some nematodes. Nematologica 6: 135-143.

ZUCKERMAN, B. M. 1962. Parasitism and pathogenesis of the cultivated highbush blueberry by the stubby root nematode. Phytopathology 52: 1017-1019.

▶ DISCUSSION OF W. B. MOUNTAIN PAPER

G. H. Hepting:

Do you feel that fungus-feeding nematodes might play a role in the annual or ephemeral nature of ectotrophic mycorrhizae?

W. B. Mountain:

Theoretically, there is no reason to believe that fungus-feeding nematodes could not play an important role in the activities of ectotrophic mycorrhizae. It is well known that some nematodes are very destructive to fungus colonies in agar medium as well as in mushroom compost, and occasionally in plant lesions. There is no doubt that nematodes must play an important role in the microbiological activity at the root surface, but almost no work has been carried out to date in this area.

R. Mankau:

The rupture of the cortex caused by secondary rootlets is a very important site of penetration for nematodes such as *Heterodera* spp. and *Meloidogyne* spp. I have observed this especially among several species of *Heterodera*.

I have also observed that the penetration of a single larva of *Heterodera trifolii* into a single epidermal cell creates a wound which attracts other larvae of this species as well as other organisms, undoubtedly among them fungi which can attack roots. The host-parasite relation is probably delicately balanced between an amount of wounding that does not upset this relation, and a more extensive wounding that causes an excessive tissue damage, by fungi and bacteria, to the detriment of the nematode.

W. B. Mountain:

Dr. Mankau's observations are very pertinent to the subject of the mechanisms involved in nematode-fungus interrelations. While it is known that infective larvae of *Heterodera* do damage root tissue, there is some controversy as to the amount of root damage caused by the infective larvae of *Meloidogyne*. We require comparative studies of the host-parasite relations of the second-stage larvae of the various species of *Heterodera* and *Meloidogyne,* carried out under controlled conditions and, if possible, on common hosts.

L. W. Nielsen:

In roots undergoing secondary radial growth, as the sweet potato, the root surface is covered with periderm. This periderm ruptures as the lateral root emerges from the cortex. *Meloidogyne* spp. larvae enter this rupture in large numbers.

W. B. Mountain:

There is little doubt that plant-parasitic nematodes are attracted to areas along the root where lateral roots subsequently emerge and that some nematodes will enter the root adjacent to emerging lateral roots in large numbers. As Dr. Nielsen points out, this mechanism may be of great importance in secondary roots in which periderm formation has occurred.

M. G. Boosalis:

Would you please give us your views regarding the use of tissue cultures for studying the interaction of nematodes, fungi, and bacteria?

W. B. Mountain:

The main objection to the use of tissue cultures for studying such interactions is that the substrate upon which the plant tissue grows is also an excellent medium for the growth of fungi and bacteria. Consequently, the activities of these organisms in such a system will be much different than in soil. It is possible, of course, that such a system might be used with obligately parasitic fungi that could not utilize the nutrient medium per se.

W. D. Thomas, Jr.:

As reported, *Meloidogyne* synergizes *Fusarium*. Is there any proved evidence to support circumstantial evidence that *Fusarium*-infected plants attract *Meloidogyne?*

W. B. Mountain:

Not to my knowledge. However, I don't think anyone has ever considered this possibility in their studies.

D. Pramer:

We have recently learned that nematodes excrete a great variety of organic compounds, many of which are common substrates for microorganisms. Although this information comes from laboratories where the primary interest is in immunity to animal parasites, it can be expected to hold for plant parasites. Excretions from a heavy infestation of nematodes may influence the abundance and types of microorganisms in the root zone, and be responsible for the association of certain fungus diseases with nematode infections. If this area appears worthy of investigation, it may be termed the *analsphere!*

W. B. Mountain:

Dr. Pramer's concept of the analsphere must surely represent the end point in soil microbiological interactions. Unfortunately, the term would not be accept-

able in the case of nematodes because excretory products are released through a separate opening far anterior to the anus. Nevertheless, Dr. Pramer's idea is sound, because all animals do release organic substances. In earlier publications, I have considered the possible role of such excretory products in the etiology of root disease, and in the textbook *Nematology* (Mountain, 1960a, p. 420, cited in the paper), I defined the term aggravator as "any nematode which, while present in a necrotic area formed by a pathogen or incitant, releases metabolic by-products capable of killing host-cells directly and/or predisposing unaffected host cells to invasion by microorganisms and/or stimulating the growth of harmful microorganisms." Dr. Pramer's concept extends this activity to the rhizosphere and is therefore certainly worthy of investigation.

Pathogenesis by Soil-borne Viruses

C. H. CADMAN—*Scottish Horticultural Research Institute, Invergowrie, Dundee.*

The title of this contribution is misleading and calls for some words of explanation. There are probably many viruses in soils other than those which infect plants, but as this symposium is devoted to the study of plant pathogens, the term soil-borne denotes viruses which are pathogens of higher plants and which have some natural underground mode of spread. But if "pathogenesis" means the production of pathological effects, then there is nothing about pathogenesis by soil-borne as distinct from other kinds of plant viruses that need detain us. Indeed the main reason why many soil-transmitted viruses have for so long escaped detection is that they cause diseases virtually indistinguishable from those caused by viruses which spread in other ways.

The unique feature of soil-borne viruses which distinguishes them from any other kind of plant pathogen likely to be considered in this symposium is that they have no existence in soils independent of the organisms that transmit them and the plants they infect. The idea that some kinds of plant viruses survive in soils solely by adsorption to colloidal particles and that they gain entry to plant roots by some semimechanical means still has its supporters, but the bulk of the evidence is against this view. It seems now much more likely that the transmission of viruses through soils is a biological process in which soil-living organisms function as virus vectors, and that the relations between viruses and the organisms that transmit them are every bit as specific in soil as aboveground. The survival and spread of soil-borne viruses must therefore depend on a tripartite relation between viruses, vectors, and their host plants. The nature of this relation is a topic quite distinct from pathogenesis but one so apposite to this symposium as to justify discussion here and abandonment of an inappropriate title.

Much of the information on soil-borne viruses and their transmission is new enough to make it difficult to avoid some repetition of what has already been written about them elsewhere. Two recent review articles (Harrison, 1960; Cadman, 1963) serve as a background to this contribution, which aims to summarize information on the relations between soil-borne viruses and their vectors and the factors affecting the persistence of the viruses in soils, and to appraise the possibilities of biological control.

RELATIONS BETWEEN SOIL-BORNE VIRUSES AND THEIR VECTORS.—The fact that bacteriophages occur in soil has long been known, but the possibility that soil organisms might harbour other kinds of viruses and that some of these might infect plants has, until quite recently, never been very seriously considered. Many kinds of soil inhabitants seem well fitted to act as virus vectors, but so far ectoparasitic nematodes and chytrid fungi (represented by *Olpidium brassicae*) are the only groups implicated (Table 1).

Nematodes and viruses.—Grapevine fanleaf was the first soil-borne plant virus shown to have a nematode, *Xiphinema index*, as a vector (Hewitt, Raski, and Goheen, 1958). Since 1958, nematode vectors have been discovered for a number of other such viruses that cause important diseases in a great variety of crops in the United States, Britain, and Europe (Fig. 1). The

Fig. 1. Outbreak of raspberry ringspot virus in a field of strawberry var. Talisman.

species concerned are all ectoparasites, that is, they feed superficially on plant roots but live freely in soils. All are equipped with long mouth spears, which are used to puncture cell walls to gain access to the cell contents (Rohde and Jenkins, 1957a; Zuckerman, 1961) (Fig. 2). Root-tip regions are favoured feeding sites, and the activities of the nematodes sometimes cause characteristic root malformations. Stubby roots are typical of many plants attacked by *Trichodorus christei* (Christie and Perry, 1951), and *Xiphinema diversicaudatum*, as Dr. Mountain mentioned in the preceding paper, causes galls on the roots of many of its hosts (Schindler, 1945b). When plants are exposed to large populations of such nematodes, their growth

TABLE 1. Vectors of soil-borne viruses

Vector	Virus	Reference
Nematoda		
Dorylaimoidea		
Xiphinema index	Arabis mosaic (grapevine strain)	Hewitt, Raski, and Goheen, 1958; Hewitt, Goheen et al., 1962
X. diversicaudatum	Arabis mosaic (type strain)	Jha and Posnette, 1959
X. americanum	Tobacco ringspot	Fulton, 1961
	Tomato ringspot	Breece and Hart, 1959
Longidorus elongatus	Tomato black ring (Scottish strain)	Harrison, Mowat, and Taylor, 1961
	Raspberry ringspot (type strain)	Taylor, 1962
L. attenuatus	Tomato black ring (English strain)	Harrison, Mowat, and Taylor, 1961
L. macrosoma	Raspberry ringspot (English strain)	Harrison, 1961
Diptherophoroidea		
Trichodorus pachydermus	Tobacco rattle (Dutch isolate)	Sol, van Heuven, and Seinhorst, 1960
	Pea early browning	van Hoof, 1963
T. primitivus	Tobacco rattle (English isolate)	Harrison, 1961
T. christei	Tobacco rattle (N. American isolate)	Walkinshaw, Griffin, and Larson, 1961
T. teres	Pea early browning	van Hoof, 1963
Chytridiales		
Olpidium brassicae	Lettuce big vein	Campbell, Grogan, and Purcifull, 1962; Tomlinson and Garrett, 1962
	Tobacco necrosis	Teakle, 1960, 1962a
	Tobacco stunt	Z. Hidaka, unpublished

is impaired, often seriously, and such effects were noticed in the United States long before any connection between ectoparasitic nematodes and soil-borne viruses was suspected. Much of the work in the United States has been concerned with establishing the pathogenicity of particular species of ectoparasites, but despite the economic importance of the diseases, there is still a great lack of information on life histories and ecology that would shed light on the activities of the nematodes as virus vectors. Studies such as those of Radewald and Raski (1962a, 1962b) on *X. index* and Harrison and Winslow (1961) on *X. diversicaudatum* are examples of work much in need of extension.

As Table 1 shows, the species so far implicated as virus vectors belong to the genera *Xiphinema, Longidorus,* and *Trichodorus.* All belong in the order Dorylamina but the first two are closely related genera of the superfamily Dorylaimoidea, whilst *Trichodorus* is the sole representative of the superfamily Diphtherophoroidea. Studies on soil-borne viruses have already led to the discovery of several new species of *Longidorus* and *Trichodorus* (Hooper, 1961, 1962), and it is a safe prediction that the list of species and genera concerned in virus transmission will be extended. The three genera *Xiphinema, Longidorus,* and *Trichodorus,* as well as some of their species, are extremely widely distributed. Cobb (1913) identified *X. americanum* in soil samples from many parts of the United States,

and *T. christei* seems equally widespread. Both *X. diversicaudatum* and *L. elongatus* have been reported from tropical countries as well as from Britain, Europe, and North America (Luc, 1958; Siddiqi, 1959; Goodey, Peacock, and Pitcher, 1960; Schindler, 1954a).

Only partly apparent in Table 1 is the specific nature of the association between particular species of nematodes and the viruses they transmit. Species of *Xiphinema* and *Longidorus* are vectors of viruses all of which have polyhedral particles of the order of 25 mμ diameter and possess broadly similar physical and biological properties, whereas species of *Trichodorus* transmit tobacco rattle and pea early browning, viruses which have rodshaped particles and rather similar physical properties (Cadman, 1963; Bos and van der Want, 1963). Within each group there is evidence of further degrees of specificity. Whilst populations of one and the same species of nematode have been found to transmit serologically unrelated viruses, antigenically related strains of the same virus may have different nematode species as vectors. Tomato- and tobaccoringspot viruses, for example, each have *X. americanum* as a vector (Breece and Hart, 1959; Fulton, 1961); but antigenically related strains of arabis-mosaic virus have different species of *Xiphinema* as vectors: *X. index* transmits the grapevine strain whereas *X. diversicaudatum* is a vector of the type strain of this virus (Hewitt, Raski, and Goheen, 1958; Hewitt, Goheen,

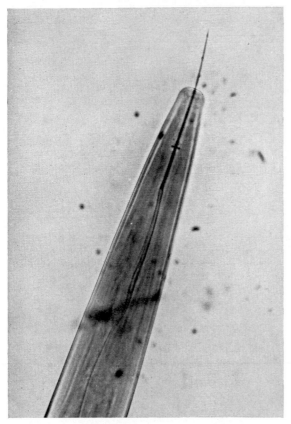

Fig. 2. Head of larval *Longidorus elongatus* with stylet protruded.

et al., 1962; Jha and Posnette, 1959; Harrison and Cadman, 1959). Table 1 lists other examples. Whether this specificity is real or apparent is still uncertain. With *X. diversicaudatum* and strains of arabis-mosaic virus, there is good evidence that it is real (Dias and Harrison, 1963). If this is also true of raspberry-ringspot and tomato-black-ring viruses and their vectors, the distribution of antigenically distinct strains of these viruses will reflect the distribution of specific nematodes and not, as had been suggested previously (Harrison, 1958; Cadman, 1960*a*), geographical variation in the viruses.

There is no evidence incompatible with the assumption that nematodes act as vectors in the commonly accepted sense, and much to suggest that the nature of the association between nematodes and viruses is analogous to that between arthropods and the viruses they transmit. Although virus is detectable in extracts made from infective *Trichodorus christei* and *Xiphinema index* (Sänger, Allen, and Gold, 1962; Raski and Hewitt, 1963), it is extremely unlikely that the viruses are carried in any way externally by their vectors.

Few of the associations between viruses and nematodes have yet been investigated in any detail and I can only generalise here, even at the risk of oversimplification. Both field and experimental populations of nematodes vary widely in infectivity depending, among

other things, on their access to and the abundance of sources of infection. With grapevine-fanleaf, arabis-mosaic, strawberry-latent-ringspot, and tobacco-rattle viruses, there is evidence that single nematodes transmit (Raski and Hewitt, 1960; Jha and Posnette, 1961; R. M. Lister, unpublished; Sol and Seinhorst, 1961). Adults and larvae of *Xiphinema index* and *X. diversicaudatum* transmit with equal facility, but larvae of *Longidorus elongatus* seem much more efficient vectors of tomato-black-ring virus than are adults (Raski and Hewitt, 1960; Harrison, Mowat, and Taylor, 1961). The *Xiphinema* species acquire viruses and infective individuals are able to transmit within a 24-hr period; but with *L. elongatus* and tomato-black-ring and raspberry-ringspot viruses, populations become infective only when allowed some weeks' access to infected plants (Raski and Hewitt, 1960; Jha and Posnette, 1961; Harrison, Mowat, and Taylor, 1961; Taylor, 1962). Experiments with grapevine-fanleaf, arabis-mosaic, raspberry-ringspot, and tobacco-rattle viruses suggest that, once acquired, the nematodes retain the viruses for long periods when denied access to plants. Raski and Hewitt (1963) found that *X. index* remained infective for 4 months when kept in moist soil, and Harrison and Winslow (1961) found populations of *X. diversicaudatum* still infective after 8 months when kept in soil with raspberry plants immune from infection by arabis-mosaic virus. These periods are much longer than those for which the viruses retain infectivity in sap at 20°C, suggesting that in the bodies of their vectors the viruses are protected from inactivation even if they do not multiply there. Whether or not multiplication does occur, *X. index* and *X. diversicaudatum* lose infectivity when they moult (Taylor, unpublished; Harrison and Winslow, 1961), and there is no evidence yet that any of the nematode-borne viruses pass into the eggs of their vectors.

For reasons mostly ill understood, many details of experimental technique, such as the method used for extracting nematodes from soils, the kind of bait plants used, and the potting medium and temperature in which these are grown, all vitally affect the results of transmission experiments with nematodes, for different species are affected in different ways. Considering the technical difficulties involved, the progress made since 1958, when Hewitt, Raski, and Goheen published their original discovery, is quite remarkable.

Chytrid fungi and viruses.—The association between viruslike symptoms in lettuce plants (Fig. 3) and the presence of *Olpidium brassicae* in their roots has puzzled many investigators since it was first noticed by Jagger in 1940 (Fig. 4). Evidence that *O. brassicae* is a vector of big vein and tobacco necrosis, viruses which commonly occur together in lettuce, is of very recent origin. Grogan et al. (1958) established the consistent nature of the association between *O. brassicae* and lettuce big-vein disease, but after carefully reviewing the evidence, rejected the idea that the symptoms were caused by a virus transmitted by *O. brassicae* because they failed to detect any infectious entity transmissible by mechanical inoculation of sap from diseased lettuce

Fig. 3. Outbreak of big-vein disease in lettuce var. Trocadero. The four plants at bottom right are symptom-free.

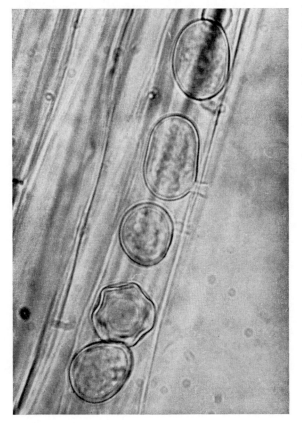

Fig. 4. Epidermal cell of turnip root containing resting sporangium and zoosporangia of *Olpidium brassicae*.

leaves. Hidaka (Cadman, 1961a) was the first to suggest that *O. brassicae* might act as a vector of a plant virus, a suggestion which he has since confirmed (Z. Hidaka, personal communication), as a result of work with tobacco-stunt virus in Japan. Relationship between tobacco-stunt virus and either lettuce-big-vein or tobacco-necrosis viruses has not been established, and the virus will not be considered further here because no details of transmission experiments are available.

A reexamination of the association between *O. brassicae* and lettuce-big-vein and tobacco-necrosis viruses has yielded a crop of fascinating results. There is no convincing evidence that these viruses are related, but studies on their transmission have been complementary in a useful way. Lettuce big vein has so far been transmitted only by grafting (Campbell, Grogan, and Purcifull, 1961; Tomlinson, Smith, and Garrett, 1962), and this is virtually the only evidence that the disease is caused by a virus. But the evidence is no worse than that on which the virus nature of many diseases of fruit trees, for example, is accepted. By contrast, tobacco-necrosis viruses are readily sap-transmitted, retain infectivity for long periods in vitro, and have thermal inactivation points in the range 75°-90°C. Indeed, the facts that these viruses are sometimes detectable in soil extracts (Cadman and Harrison, 1960; Gold, 1960) and that plants become infected when grown in soil watered with infective sap (Smith, 1937) have been misleading in suggesting that no agent was needed for their transmission.

The experiments of Campbell and co-workers (Campbell, Grogan, and Purcifull, 1962; Campbell, 1962) and Tomlinson and Garrett (1962) have shown that lettuce plants become infected with big-vein virus when their roots become parasitized by zoospores of *Olpidium brassicae* released from the roots of infected lettuce plants. Though other explanations are possible, the simplest is that the zoospores act in a vectorlike manner and that they carry the virus internally in some way. Further evidence of this intimate relation between virus and vector is the fact that lettuce plants developed big-vein symptoms when infected by zoospores released from resting sporangia that had been kept dry for 5 months before treatment with hydrochloric acid or trisodium phosphate (Campbell, 1962). That the virus survives within the resting sporangia therefore seems probable, and this would explain Pryor's (1946) observation that big-vein-infested soils were still infective after 8 years' storage in a dry state. Thus, lettuce big vein seems entirely dependent on *O. brassicae* for its survival and transmission in soils.

Teakle (1960, 1962a) has shown that a similar kind of relation exists between *Olpidium brassicae* and tobacco-necrosis viruses. His initial results (Teakle, 1960) were unconvincing evidence of this because they showed merely that sap from roots of lettuce plants which had been watered with virus suspension plus *Olpidium* zoospores was more infective than that from plants which had received virus but no *Olpidium*. This could have meant that invasion of roots by the fungus in some way provided more entry points for the large number of virus particles present in the soil. His subsequent work (Teakle, 1962a), however, suggests that, as with lettuce-big-vein virus, *Olpidium* zoospores act in a vectorlike manner. Treatments which destroy or immobilise the zoospores or prevent their association with the virus also prevent infection. Infection cannot be prevented once the zoospores have encysted on plant roots, and the time needed for encystment coincides with that needed for infection to occur. Further evidence for the specific nature of the association between virus and fungus are the facts that isolates of *O. brassicae* which infect lettuce transmit whereas those which infect crucifers apparently do not; and that the roots of mung bean (*Phaseolus mungo*) plants often develop characteristic virus lesions when colonised by zoospores released from roots of plants in which little or no virus is detectable by mechanical inoculation of sap (Teakle and Yarwood, 1962). Teakle's results suggest that when tobacco-necrosis-virus particles come in contact with *Olpidium* zoospores, the two unite in some way which protects the virus from inactivation by antiserum (Teakle, 1962*b*). If the particles actually enter the zoospores the phenomenon is extremely interesting and unusual among plant viruses in implying that tobacco-necrosis viruses are able to enter uninjured cells. No attempt seems to have been made to find if tobacco-necrosis viruses persist in the resting sporangia of *O. brassicae* but, by analogy with lettuce-big-vein virus, it would be surprising if they did not.

Chance and the widespread distribution of *Olpidium brassicae* presumably account for the almost coincidental discoveries of its association with different soil-borne viruses because other members of the Chytridiales would, a priori, seem just as well fitted to act as virus vectors. That there are other soil-borne viruses transmitted by chytrid fungi seems almost certain. Many features of the North American and Japanese soil-borne cereal viruses match those of lettuce-big-vein virus, and a reinvestigation of these long-standing problems is bound to yield interesting results.

FACTORS AFFECTING THE SURVIVAL OF VECTORS AND VIRUSES IN SOILS.—Persistence within their vectors is obviously one means by which viruses may survive in soils. The vectors, however, are vehicles rather than hosts for the viruses. Consequently survival and spread of the viruses depends on complex environmental factors which affect the survival and movement of their vectors, and the multiplication of each depends on the presence of susceptible host plants. These topics are essentially the province of other contributors to this volume. All that remains here is to point to the need for more detailed study of the ecological factors which affect specifically the organisms concerned in virus transmission.

There is, for example, a wealth of general information on ecological factors which affect the behaviour of nematodes in soils, but little of this relates to the particular species of ectoparasitic nematodes found to transmit viruses. Such information as there is on the distribution of nematode-borne viruses reinforces the knowledge that the moisture content and physical structure of soils affect the distribution and movement of their vectors, but individual species clearly differ in their requirements and tolerances. Moisture is vital because the infectivity of soils containing nematode-borne viruses is abolished and their vectors are killed when soils are allowed to dry in air (Harrison and Cadman, 1959; Cadman and Harrison, 1960; Cadman, 1960*b*; McGlohen, Sasser, and Sherwood, 1962; Sol, van Heuven, and Seinhorst, 1960). Arabis-mosaic virus

occurs in many parts of southern and western Britain and in a wide variety of soils, but all are of a moisture-retentive type (Lister, 1960*a*; Harrison and Winslow, 1961). The virus has never been found in the free-draining sedimentary soils of eastern Scotland, which commonly contain both raspberry-ringspot and tomato-black-ring viruses. Both in Europe and Britain, tobacco-rattle and pea-early-browning viruses seem confined to sandy soils (Sol and Seinhorst, 1961; Cadman and Harrison, 1959; Bos and van der Want, 1963). These observations may indicate real differences in distribution of the vectors of these viruses; exact knowledge is fragmentary.

The effects of soil moisture and structure on the movement of nematodes have been studied with some endoparasitic species such as *Heterodera schachtii* (Wallace, 1958) but apparently not with ectoparasitic ones. Observations on the spread of raspberry-ringspot virus in raspberry plantations in Scotland (Cadman, 1956) and of grapevine-fanleaf and yellow-mosaic viruses in Portugal (Harrison, 1960) and California (Hewitt, Goheen, et al., 1962) suggest that the vectors of these viruses move little more than 1 ft per year even in cultivated soils, a rate close to that estimated by Harrison and Winslow (1961) for the movement of *Xiphinema diversicaudatum* through uncultivated soil at Rothamsted. Factors affecting the distribution of nematodes in depth of soil are largely unstudied. *X. diversicaudatum* has been found at depths of 3 ft in soils in Britain, *X. index* up to 8 ft in California soils, and *Trichodorus teres* at 2 ft in soils in Holland (van Hoof, 1963), but there is no published information on other nematode vectors.

Chytrid fungi have been the province of a few specialists and, so far as I am aware, there is little detailed knowledge of the factors which affect their distribution and behavior in soils. Moisture obviously must be important, and the oft-noticed association of outbreaks of tobacco-necrosis and lettuce-big-vein viruses with moist soil conditions is simply explained in the light of what is now known about their transmission. The North American soil-borne wheat- and oat-mosaic viruses and sugar-cane-chlorotic-streak virus also spread more rapidly in moist than in dry soils (Webb, 1927; Antoine, 1957; Sturgess, 1962), and this lends colour to the idea that these viruses too may have chytrid fungi as vectors.

In the form of resting sporangia, *Olpidium brassicae* evidently survives for years despite adverse physical conditions in soils and the absence of suitable host plants. Whether the eggs of ectoparasitic nematodes survive desiccation seems unknown, but the adults and larvae of several species are able to survive for long periods in soils without access to living plants and are doubtless able to migrate to levels in soils unaffected by rapid changes in temperature and moisture content. Ultimately, however, the survival and spread of vectors and the viruses they transmit depends on the presence of host plants acceptable to the vectors and susceptible to infection by the viruses.

Most of the nematode-borne viruses have extremely wide natural host ranges, suggesting that their vectors are polyphagous. Tobacco-rattle virus, for example, has been found naturally infecting more than 100 different species, including woody and herbaceous plants (Uschdraweit and Valentin, 1956). Arabis-mosaic, raspberry-ringspot, tobacco-ringspot, and tomato-ringspot viruses have each been isolated from both woody and herbaceous species in many different families of plants (Cadman, 1960a; Lister, Raniere, and Varney, 1963; Milbrath and Reynolds, 1961). There are exceptions, however, and these extend the results of such experimental studies as have been made in showing that different species of nematodes have different host preferences. Experimentally, tomato-black-ring virus infects many species of common weeds including *Chenopodium album* and *C. bonus-henricus*, yet these last are rarely or never found infected in the field. The grapevine strains of arabis-mosaic virus infect herbaceous plants, yet weeds in vineyards are never found infected with them. This fits with Radewald and Raski's (1962b) evidence that herbaceous plants are poor hosts for *Xiphinema index* whilst grapevine, fig, and rose are good ones. By comparison, *X. diversicaudatum* is highly polyphagous, yet both Harrison and Winslow (1961) and Pitcher and Jha (1961) found that the highest populations were associated with the roots of woody perennial plants. Rohde and Jenkins (1957b) tested 42 plant species for suitability as hosts for *Trichodorus christei* and classified them into excellent, good, poor, and nonhosts. Among the excellent hosts were tomato, lettuce, turnip, cabbage, and maize. Yet maize is an unsuitable host for other species of *Trichodorus* (M. W. Allen, unpublished). Rohde and Jenkins (1958) also reported the interesting fact that *T. christei* multiplied rapidly on tomato alone but failed to multiply on tomatoes grown in association with asparagus (*Asparagus officinalis*). The nematode did not feed on asparagus roots and these were shown to produce a nematicidal carbohydrate, which diffused through soil and killed the nematodes.

The biological peculiarities of *Olpidium brassicae* have provided a forum for controversy which it would be rash to enter. Jacobsen (1943) has aptly summed up the position and the evidence that different isolates of *O. brassicae* differ in host range. Whether these differences are sufficiently consistent and are coupled with morphological differences that merit taxonomic recognition is another matter. Grogan et al. (1958) found that big-vein symptoms developed in lettuce that had been exposed to *Olpidium*-infected roots from celery, radish, onion, broccoli, or *Lactuca serriola*, but not in plants exposed to infected roots of other species. These included *Chenopodium murale*, *Brassica campestris*, *Senecio vulgaris*, *Polygonum aviculare*, *Poa annua*, and also sugar beet, a host which will at least maintain both virus and fungus for a period (Campbell, 1962). There is no indication yet of whether the ability to transmit lettuce-big-vein virus is a property of particular strains of *O. brassicae*, but if, as present evidence suggests, this is true of *O. brassicae* and tobacco-necrosis viruses, then possibly virologists may rescue the systematists from their dilemma.

Information on the ecology of the vectors of soil-borne viruses is all too scarce and there is much need for more detailed studies. Even from the few examples quoted it must be evident that these could shed much light on the interrelations between viruses, vectors, and plants in soils, and thus make a major contribution to knowledge of the epidemiology of the viruses.

SURVIVAL OF VIRUSES IN PLANTS.—Once infected by viruses, plants remain so. Thus the roots of perennial hosts of soil-borne viruses are permanent reservoirs of infection for populations of vector organisms. More than this, the vegetative propagation and distribution of infected plants are means by which the viruses become disseminated and established in soils which did not previously contain them. There is ample evidence to show that this commonly occurs in practice with such crops as potato and strawberry (Cadman and Harrison, 1960; Lister, 1960b). It is virtually certain that the presence of grapevine-fanleaf and yellow-mosaic viruses in plants and soils of all the major vine-growing countries of the world is the result of propagation and distribution of infected scions and rootstocks. One of the major problems of ridding Californian vineyards of these viruses is the fact that the roots of infected grapevines survive and act as sources of infection for several years after their tops have been destroyed (Hewitt, Goheen, et al., 1962).

The distribution and host ranges of soil-borne plant viruses suggest, however, that essentially they are pathogens of wild plants and hence must have evolved means of survival and dissemination independent of human activities. Transmission through the seeds of infected plants is one means by which this could occur (Lister, 1960c), and here there is a striking difference in behaviour between the chytrid-borne and nematode-borne viruses. Lettuce-big-vein, tobacco-stunt, and tobacco-necrosis viruses are not seed-borne in any of their hosts, and this is true also of the North American soil-borne cereal viruses (Pryor, 1946; Hidaka, 1956; Smith, 1957; Koehler, Bever, and Bonnett, 1952). By contrast, nematode-borne viruses usually pass into the seeds of many of the plants they infect. Viruses which are intrinsically seed-borne usually invade pollen cells as well as ovules (Bennett, 1956) and the nematode-borne viruses are no exception. Water extracts of pollen from sugar-beet plants containing tomato-black-ring virus or from raspberry or strawberry plants containing raspberry-ringspot virus produce some hundreds of lesions when rubbed on leaves of *Chenopodium amaranticolor*. When the flowers on healthy raspberry or strawberry plants are pollinated with virus-containing pollen, a proportion of the seeds set give rise to infected seedlings. The mother plants do not, however, become infected, and there is no evidence that dissemination by pollen plays any part in plant-to-plant spread of these viruses such as Das, Milbrath, and Swenson (1961) demonstrated with fruit-tree-necrotic-ringspot virus in squash plants.

Tobacco-rattle virus is detectable in the pollen of systemically infected *Petunia* plants (Cadman, 1962) and is transmitted through a small proportion of seeds produced by infected plants of *Capsella bursa-pastoris*

TABLE 2. Percentage transmission of soil-borne viruses through seed of various hosts*

Host species	Percentage transmission†		
	Arabis-mosaic virus	Raspberry-ringspot virus	Tomato-black-ring virus
Soybean (*Glycine soja*)	5	4-8	83
Strawberry (*Fragaria chiloensis* var. *ananassa*)	17	40	34
Raspberry (*Rubus idaeus*)	—	10	1
Sugar beet (*Beta vulgaris*)	—	—	36
Shepherd's purse (*Capsella bursa-pastoris*)	34	2-3	71
Groundsel (*Senecio vulgaris*)	2	0	17
Chickweed (*Stellaria media*)	55	34	58

* Unpublished data of R. M. Lister and A. F. Murant.
† Figures are percentage of infected seedlings in progenies from naturally or artificially infected plants.

and *Myosotis arvensis* (Lister and Murant, 1962). Pea-early-browning virus is likewise seed-borne in some of its hosts (Bos and van der Want, 1963).

Two of the most interesting points about seed transmission of nematode-borne viruses are illustrated by Table 2 and Fig. 5. Table 2 shows that the viruses are efficiently transmitted through the seeds of several common weed species as well as through those of cultivated plants. But the efficiency of transmission differs with different viruses and hosts and depends also on the stage of growth at which plants first become infected. Both Crowley (1959) and Athow and Bancroft (1959) have shown that fewer infected seeds are set by soybean plants when inoculation with tobacco-ringspot virus is delayed until the plants are in flower. When plants become naturally infected through their roots, a delay of some weeks or even months may ensue before the viruses invade plants systemically. Fig. 5 illustrates the striking fact that plants which develop from infected seeds contain virus but may be indistinguishable from healthy plants in appearance. They are protected from infection by the viruses they contain and never at any time display the symptoms characteristic of newly infected plants. Such plants transmit the viruses to their progeny, and in some, such as soybean, where the transmission rate is unusually high, the viruses are transmitted through successive generations and virtually become part of the genetic complement of their hosts.

Unpublished work by Lister and Murant shows that seed transmission is no mere laboratory phenomenon, for samples of seeds collected from naturally infected plants in the field behave like those harvested from

Fig. 5. Progeny from groundsel (*Senecio vulgaris*) plant naturally infected with tomato-black-ring virus. Seedlings containing virus are labeled.

artificially infected plants. When samples of soil from outbreaks of nematode-borne viruses are allowed to dry out, in order to kill the nematodes, and are then remoistened, a proportion of the seedlings which grow are found to contain the viruses. The proportions of infected weed seedlings vary widely in soils from outbreaks of different viruses, and even in soils from different outbreaks of the same viruses. For example, infected seedlings are usually much commoner in soils from outbreaks of raspberry-ringspot and tomato-black-ring viruses than in those from outbreaks of arabis-mosaic virus, yet all three are transmitted efficiently through the seeds of susceptible hosts (Table 2). Even with raspberry-ringspot and tomato-black-ring viruses, some soils contain many more infected weed seeds than others. Whatever the reasons for these differences, the dispersal of infected weed seeds is a possible way in which the viruses spread over a distance—an interesting alternative to spread by infective vectors.

The importance of seed transmission as a means of perpetuation and spread possibly differs with different viruses. For instance, seed transmission of fanleaf or yellow-mosaic viruses in grapevine has not yet been reported although the viruses have been detected in grapevine pollen (Williams, Trayler, and Wagnon, 1962) and both are seed-borne in *Chenopodium* spp. (Brückbauer and Rudel, 1961; Dias, 1963). With raspberry-ringspot and tomato-black-ring viruses, however, there is now much evidence to show that weed seeds are important reservoirs of infection in soils. Lister and Murant (1962) have found that soils kept free from weeds rapidly lost infectivity but regain it when cropped with infected weeds. In their experiments these treatments had little or no effect on the numbers of *Longidorus elongatus* present, but the level of infectivity depended on the species of weed allowed to grow. Thus soil previously uninfective remained so when cropped with infected spurrey (*Spergula arvensis*) but became highly infective when cropped with infected chickweed (*Stellaria media*), which suggests that the two species differ in acceptability as hosts for the nematode.

Towards Biological Control.—Biological control is not, for fairly obvious reasons, a weapon which has found much favour in the fight against viruses that have aerial vectors, but there are various ways in which natural agencies could be used to combat soil-borne viruses successfully. With what degree of success clearly depends on the nature of the virus–vector–host-plant relation and the ease with which the links in this relation can be broken. The prerequisites for spread of a soil-borne virus are plants susceptible both to infection by the virus and attack by its vector, and the presence of sources of infection along with the presence of the specific vector organism. Preventing fulfilment of one or more of these must therefore be the objective of biological control.

Already the production of varieties of crop plants immune from infection by soil-borne viruses has received attention and achieved some notable success. Indeed, one reason why search for the vector of soil-

borne wheat-mosaic virus in the United States has not been more actively pursued is the success with which wheat varieties immune from the virus have been selected (McKinney, 1953; Sill, 1958). In Japan also, varieties of wheat and barley immune from soil-borne viruses are known (Miyamoto, 1958), and some varieties and species of tobacco resistant to infection by tobacco-stunt virus have been found (Hidaka, Uozumi, and Hiruki, 1956). In Britain, the raspberry variety Lloyd George is immune from infection by arabis-mosaic, raspberry-ringspot and tomato-black-ring viruses (Cadman, 1961b). Other commercial raspberry varieties possess immunity from one or other of these viruses, and there is evidence that this immunity is genetic (Jennings, 1960). On the other hand, no varieties of oat immune from North American soil-borne oat-mosaic virus are known (Coffman et al., 1962). Likewise no species or variety of *Vitis* immune from grapevine-fanleaf or yellow-mosaic viruses has been found (Vuittenez, 1959), and all strawberry varieties of commercial importance in Britain are susceptible to arabis-mosaic virus (Lister, 1960a). Because soil-borne viruses are essentially pathogens of wild plants, the likelihood that genetic immunities or resistances to them exist among the wild relatives of cultivated plants seems strong and worth searching for. There can be little doubt of the value of immune varieties and rootstocks to the culture of long-lived plants, such as cherry and grapevine, where the prospects of other means of controlling the soil-borne viruses that infect them seem unpromising.

So far there has been little call deliberately to produce varieties of plants immune from or resistant to attack by vectors of soil-borne viruses. McKinney (1948) found that some varieties of wheat, immune from wheat mosaic when grown in the field, were susceptible when inoculated mechanically with infected sap, a result which could mean that these varieties escaped infection because immune from the vector.

In a more general way, crop rotation offers means of modifying the soil environment in directions disadvantageous to both viruses and vectors by depriving either or both of suitable host plants. Ectoparasitic nematodes seem able to survive for long periods in soils in the absence of plants, but sufficient examples have been quoted to show that populations increase only when suitable host plants are present. Strains of *Olpidium brassicae* and probably those of other chytrid fungi seem to have restricted host ranges and it is perhaps relevant that crop rotation is an efficient means of ridding soils of wheat-mosaic virus (Koehler, Bever, and Bonnett, 1952).

With crops that are propagated vegetatively, the use of virus-free planting material is a desirable precaution against the introduction of viruses to soils where the vectors but not the viruses already occur. Plant-health schemes operated in some countries now take account of this.

Elimination of sources of infection from soils in which the viruses are already established may be practicable with some kinds of soil-borne viruses but not with others. Fallowing decreases the infectivity of soils containing raspberry-ringspot and tomato-black-ring viruses, and efficient control of weeds by means of herbicides may, by preventing the regain of infectivity which follows the germination of fresh populations of weed seeds, be an efficient means of ridding soils of these viruses. The incidence of fanleaf virus in replanted vineyards in France (Vuittenez, 1957) and California (Hewitt, Goheen, et al., 1962) decreased after fallowing, and control might be achieved if some means of hastening the destruction of grapevine roots could be found. Viruses like lettuce big vein are at the other extreme. If those transmitted by *Olpidium brassicae* behave alike and persist more or less indefinitely in the resting sporangia of their vector, elimination of infected plants would have little or no effect on the incidence of the viruses.

So far, most effort to control soil-borne viruses has been expended on testing various chemicals as means of eliminating the vectors of viruses from soils. This is hardly within the scope of biological control as defined earlier in this volume; but the effects of mixing plant residues with soils, or those of growing crops the root exudates of which are toxic to vector organisms may be considered so. Populations of *Longidorus elongatus* decline and infectivity is decreased or abolished when soils containing raspberry-ringspot and tomato-black-ring viruses are watered with dilute solutions of tannins or simpler polyphenols such as resorcinol and benzoic acid (Cadman and Harrison, 1960; A. F. Murant and C. E. Taylor, unpublished). Similar effects result when pulverised raspberry canes, which contain tannin (Cadman, 1959), are mixed with infective soils (Murant and Taylor, unpublished). Whether the effect is specific to polyphenols or results from a decrease in the pH level is uncertain. The toxic effects of the root exudate from asparagus on *Trichodorus christei* has been noted, and possibly other examples of such interaction between the roots of higher plants and vector organisms will be found if looked for.

Attempts to upset virus-transmitting systems in soils by more subtle means have failed; but these have, for the most part, been made in ignorance of the nature of the systems involved. Better knowledge of these may, in the light of the information contributed to this symposium, make biological control an attractive solution to some of the problems posed by soil-borne viruses.

LITERATURE CITED

ANTOINE, R. 1957. Cane diseases. I. Chlorotic streak. Rept. Mauritius Sugar Ind. Res. Inst. 1957: 53-57.

ATHOW, K. L., and J. B. BANCROFT. 1959. Development and transmission of tobacco ringspot virus in soybean. Phytopathology 49: 697-701.

BENNETT, C. W. 1956. Biological relations of plant viruses. Ann. Rev. Plant Physiol. 7: 143-170.

BOS, L., and J. P. H. VAN DER WANT. 1963. Early browning of pea, a disease caused by a soil- and seed-borne virus. Tijdschr. Plantenziekten 68: 368-390.

BREECE, J. R., and W. H. HART. 1959. A possible association of nematodes with the spread of peach yellow bud mosaic virus. Plant Disease Reptr. 43: 989-990.

BRÜCKBAUER, H., and M. RUDEL. 1961. Untersuchungen über die Viruskrankheiten der Rebe. III. Samenübertragbarkeit der Reisigkrankheit des Silvaners bei einer Testpflanze sowie Untersuchungen über das evtl. Vorkommen des Virus in Weinbergsunkrautern. Wein-Wiss. Beil. Fachz. Deut. Weinbau 16: 187-189.

CADMAN, C. H. 1956. Studies on the etiology and mode of spread of Scottish raspberry leaf curl disease. J. Hort. Sci. 31: 111-118.

CADMAN, C. H. 1959. Some properties of an inhibitor of virus infection from leaves of raspberry. J. Gen. Microbiol. 20: 113-128.

CADMAN, C. H. 1960a. Studies on the relationship between soil-borne viruses of the ringspot type occurring in Britain and continental Europe. Virology 11: 653-664.

CADMAN, C. H. 1960b. Virology. Rept. Scot. Hort. Res. Inst. 7: 50.

CADMAN, C. H. 1961a. Symposium on soil-borne viruses. Rept. Scot. Hort. Res. Inst. 8: 74-79.

CADMAN, C. H. 1961b. Raspberry viruses and virus diseases in Britain. Hort. Res. 1: 47-61.

CADMAN, C. H. 1962. Evidence for association of tobacco rattle virus nucleic acid with a cell component. Nature (London) 193: 49-52.

CADMAN, C. H. 1963. Biology of soil-borne viruses. Ann. Rev. Phytopathol. 1: 143-172.

CADMAN, C. H., and B. D. HARRISON. 1959. Studies on the properties of soil-borne viruses of the tobacco-rattle type occurring in Scotland. Ann. Appl. Biol. 47: 542-556.

CADMAN, C. H., and B. D. HARRISON. 1960. Studies on the behavior in soils of tomato black ring, raspberry ringspot and arabis mosaic viruses. Virology 10: 1-20.

CAMPBELL, R. N. 1962. Relationship between the lettuce big-vein virus and its vector *Olpidium brassicae*. Nature (London) 195: 675-677.

CAMPBELL, R. N., R. G. GROGAN, and D. E. PURCIFULL. 1961. Graft transmission of big vein of lettuce. Virology 15: 82-85.

CAMPBELL, R. N., R. G. GROGAN, and D. E. PURCIFULL. 1962. Studies on the transmission of the virus causing big vein of lettuce. Phytopathology 52: 5.

CHRISTIE, J. R., and V. G. PERRY. 1951. A root disease of plants caused by a nematode of the genus *Trichodorus*. Science 113: 491-493.

COBB, N. A. 1913. New nematode genera found inhabiting fresh water and brackish soils. J. Wash. Acad. Sci. 3: 432-444.

COFFMAN, F. A., T. T. HEBERT, U. R. GORE, and W. P. BYRD. 1962. Reactions of winter oats to soil-borne mosaic. Plant Disease Reptr. 46: 438-440.

CROWLEY, N. C. 1959. Studies on the time of embryo infection by seed-transmitted viruses. Virology 8: 116-123.

DAS, C. R., J. A. MILBRATH, and K. G. SWENSON. 1961. Seed and pollen transmission of Prunus ringspot virus in buttercup squash. Phytopathology 51: 64.

DIAS, H. F. 1963. Host range and properties of grapevine fanleaf and grapevine yellow mosaic viruses. Ann. Appl. Biol. 51: 85-95.

DIAS, H. F., and B. D. HARRISON. 1963. The relationship between grapevine fanleaf, grapevine yellow mosaic and arabis mosaic viruses. Ann. Appl. Biol. 51: 97-105.

FULTON, J. P. 1961. Transmission of tobacco ringspot virus by *Xiphinema americanum*. Phytopathology 52: 375.

GOODEY, J. B., F. C. PEACOCK, and R. S. PITCHER. 1960. A redescription of *Xiphinema diversicaudatum* (Micoletsky 1923 and 1927) Thorne 1939 and observations on its larval stages. Nematologica 5: 127-135.

GOLD, A. H. 1960. A tobacco-necrosis-like virus isolated from potato-tuber lesions and California soils. Phytopathology 50: 84.

GROGAN, R. G., F. W. ZINK, W. B. HEWITT, and K. A. KIMBLE. 1958. The association of *Olpidium* with the big-vein disease of lettuce. Phytopathology 48: 292-297.

HARRISON, B. D. 1958. Relationship between beet ringspot, potato bouquet and tomato black ring viruses. J. Gen. Microbiol. 18: 450-460.

HARRISON, B. D. 1960. The biology of soil-borne viruses. Advan. Virus Res. 7: 131-161.

HARRISON, B. D. 1961. Soil-borne viruses. Plant Pathology Department. Rothamsted Expt. Sta. Rept. 1960: 118.

HARRISON, B. D., and C. H. CADMAN. 1959. Role of a dagger nematode (*Xiphinema* sp.) in outbreaks of plant diseases caused by arabis mosaic virus. Nature (London) 184: 1624-1626.

HARRISON, B. D., W. P. MOWAT, and C. E. TAYLOR. 1961. Transmission of a strain of tomato black ring virus by *Longidorus elongatus* (Nematoda). Virology 14: 480-485.

HARRISON, B. D., and R. D. WINSLOW. 1961. Laboratory and field studies on the relation of arabis mosaic virus to its nematode vector *Xiphinema diversicaudatum* (Micoletsky). Ann. Appl. Biol. 49: 621-633.

HEWITT, W. B., D. J. RASKI, and A. C. GOHEEN. 1958. Nematode vector of soil-borne fanleaf virus of grapevines. Phytopathology 48: 586-595.

HEWITT, W. B., A. C. GOHEEN, D. J. RASKI, and G. V. GOODING. 1962. Studies on virus diseases of the grapevine in California. Vitis 3: 57-83.

HIDAKA, Z. 1956. Studies on the tobacco stunt disease III. On symptoms and causal agent of the tobacco stunt disease. Hatano Tobacco Expt. Sta. Bull. 40: 19-23.

HIDAKA, Z., T. UOZUMI, and C. HIRUKI. 1956. Studies on the tobacco stunt disease. VII. Relations of species and varieties of *Nicotiana* and stages of tobacco plant to development of the tobacco stunt disease. Hatano Tobacco Expt. Sta. Bull. 40, p. 47-52.

HOOF, H. VAN. 1963. *Trichodorus pachydermus* and *T. teres,* vectors of the early browning virus of peas. Tijdschr. Plantenziekten 68: 391-396.

HOOPER, D. J. 1961. A redescription of *Longidorus elongatus* (de Man 1876) Thorne and Swanger 1956 (Nematoda: Dorylaimoidea) and descriptions of five new species of *Longidorus* from Great Britain. Nematologica 6: 237-257.

HOOPER, D. J. 1962. Three new species of *Trichodorus* (Nematoda, Dorylaimoidea) and observations on *T. minor* Colbran 1956. Nematologica 7: 273-280.

JACOBSEN, B. 1943. Studies on *Olpidium brassicae* (Wor.) Dang. Medd. Plantepatol. Afdeling Kgl. Vet. Landbohøjskole, Copenhagen, No. 24, p. 1-53.

JAGGER, I. C. 1940. Brown blight of lettuce. Phytopathology 30: 53-64.

JENNINGS, D. L. 1960. Genetics of resistance to raspberry viruses; Pomology. Rept. Scot. Hort. Res. Inst. 7: 13.

JHA, A., and A. F. POSNETTE. 1959. Transmission of a virus to strawberry plants by a nematode. Nature (London) 184: 962-963.

JHA, A., and A. F. POSNETTE. 1961. Transmission of arabis mosaic virus by the nematode. *Xiphinema diversicaudatum* (Micol.). Virology 13: 119-123.

KOEHLER, B., W. M. BEVER, and O. T. BONNETT. 1952. Soil-borne wheat mosaic. Illinois Agr. Expt. Sta. Bull. 556: 567-599.

LISTER, R. M. 1960a. Occurrence of soil-borne virus diseases of strawberry in Britain. Plant Pathol. 9: 102-105.

LISTER, R. M. 1960b. Strawberries and soil-borne virus diseases. Agriculture (London) 67: 25-29.

LISTER, R. M. 1960c. Transmission of soil-borne viruses through seed. Virology 10: 547-549.

LISTER, R. M., and A. F. MURANT. 1962. Virology. Rept. Scot. Hort. Res. Inst. 9: 68.

LISTER, R. M., L. C. RANIERE, and E. H. VARNEY. 1963. Relationships of viruses associated with ringspot diseases of blueberry. Phytopathology. (In press.)

LUC, M. 1958. *Xiphinema* de l'Ouest Africain: description de cinq nouvelles espèces (Nematoda: Dorylaimoidea). Nematologica 3: 57-72.

McGLOHEN, N. E., J. N. SASSER, and R. T. SHERWOOD. 1962. Effects of fallowing, desiccation and soil temperature on certain plant-parasitic nematodes. Phytopathology 52: 20.

McKINNEY, H. H. 1948. Wheats immune from soil-borne mosaic viruses in the field, susceptible when inoculated manually. Phytopathology 48: 1003-1013.

McKINNEY, H. H. 1953. Virus diseases of cereal crops. Yearbook of Agr. (U.S. Dept. Agr.) 1953: 350-360.

MILBRATH, J. A., and J. E. REYNOLDS. 1961. Tomato ringspot virus isolated from Eola rasp leaf of cherry in Oregon. Plant Disease Reptr. 45: 520-521.

MIYAMOTO, Y. 1958. Studies on soil-borne cereal mosaics IV. On the barley yellow-mosaic virus. Ann. Phytopathol. Soc. Japan 23: 199-206.

PITCHER, R. S., and A. JHA. 1961. On the distribution and infectivity with arabis mosaic virus of a dagger nematode. Plant Pathol. 10: 67-71.

PRYOR, D. E. 1946. Exploratory experiments with the big vein disease of lettuce. Phytopathology 36: 264-272.

RADEWALD, J. D., and D. J. RASKI. 1962a. A study of the life cycle of *Xiphinema index*. Phytopathology 52: 748.

RADEWALD, J. D., and D. J. RASKI. 1962b. Studies on the host range and pathogenicity of *Xiphinema index*. Phytopathology 52: 748.

RASKI, D. J., and W. B. HEWITT. 1960. Experiments with *Xiphinema index* as a vector of fanleaf of grapevines. Nematologica 5: 166-170.

RASKI, D. J., and W. B. HEWITT. 1963. Plant-parasitic nematodes as vectors of plant viruses. Phytopathology 53: 39-47.

ROHDE, R. A., and W. R. JENKINS. 1957a. Effect of temperature on the life cycle of stubby-root nematodes. Phytopathology 47: 29.

ROHDE, R. A., and W. R. JENKINS. 1957b. Host range of a species of *Trichodorus* and its host-parasite relationships on tomato. Phytopathology 47: 295-298.

ROHDE, R. A., and W. R. JENKINS. 1958. Basis for resistance of *Asparagus officinalis* var. *altiles* L. to the stubby-root nematode *Trichodorus christei* Allen, 1957. Maryland Agr. Expt. Sta. Bull. A-97, 19 p.

SÄNGER, H., M. W. ALLEN, and A. H. GOLD. 1962. Direct recovery of tobacco rattle virus from its nematode vector. Phytopathology 52: 750.

SCHINDLER, A. F. 1954a. Nematodes associated with roses in a survey of commercial greenhouses. Plant Disease Reptr. 40: 277-278.

SCHINDLER, A. F. 1954b. Root galling associated with dagger nematode *Xiphinema diversicaudatum* (Micol. 1927) Thorne 1939. Phytopathology 44: 389.

SIDDIQI, M. R. 1959. Studies on *Xiphinema* spp. (Nematoda: Dorylaimoidea) from Aligarh (North India) with comments on the genus *Longidorus* Micoletsky 1922. Proc. Helminthol. Soc. Wash. D.C. 26: 151-163.

SILL, W. H. 1958. A comparison of some characteristics of soil-borne wheat mosaic viruses in the Great Plains and elsewhere. Plant Disease Reptr. 42: 912-924.

SMITH, K. M. 1937. Studies on a virus found in the roots of certain normal-looking plants. Parasitology 29: 70-85.

SMITH, K. M. 1957. A textbook of plant virus diseases. Churchill, London. 652 p. (See specifically p. 38.)

SOL, H. H., and J. W. SEINHORST. 1961. The transmission of rattle virus by *Trichodorus pachydermus*. Tijdschr. Plantenziekten 67: 307-309.

SOL, H. H., J. C. VAN HEUVEN, and J. W. SEINHORST. 1960. Transmission of rattle virus and *Atropa belladonna* mosaic virus by nematodes. Tijdschr. Plantenziekten 66: 228-231.

STURGESS, O. W. 1962. Studies with chlorotic streak disease of sugar cane V. Factors affecting soil transmission. Bur. Sugar Expt. Sta. (Brisbane) Tech. Commun. No. 1, 10 p.

TAYLOR, C. E. 1962. Transmission of raspberry ringspot virus by *Longidorus elongatus* (de Man) (Nematoda: Dorylaimoidea). Virology 17: 493-494.

TEAKLE, D. S. 1960. Association of *Olpidium brassicae* and tobacco necrosis virus. Nature (London) 188: 431-432.

TEAKLE, D. S. 1962a. Transmission of tobacco necrosis virus by a fungus, *Olpidium brassicae*. Virology 18: 224-231.

TEAKLE, D. S. 1962b. Serological evidence that *Olpidium*

zoospores carry tobacco necrosis virus. Phytopathology 52: 754.

TEAKLE, D. S., and C. E. YARWOOD. 1962. Improved recovery of tobacco necrosis virus from roots by means of *Olpidium brassicae*. Phytopathology 52: 366.

TOMLINSON, J. A., and R. G. GARRETT. 1962. Role of *Olpidium* in the transmission of big vein disease of lettuce. Nature (London) 194: 249-250.

TOMLINSON, J. A., B. R. SMITH, and R. G. GARRETT. 1962. Graft transmission of lettuce big vein. Nature (London) 193: 599-600.

USCHDRAWEIT, H. A., and H. VALENTIN. 1956. Das Tabak-mauchevirus an Zierpflanzen. Nachrbl. Deut. Pflanzen-schutzdienst (Braunschweig). 8: 132-133.

VUITTENEZ, A. 1957. Lutte préventive contre le court-noué de la vigne par la disinfection chimique du sol avant plantation. Compt. Rend. 43: 185-192.

VUITTENEZ, A. 1959. Inoculation de différéntes espèces de *Vitis* par les virus du groupe de la dégénérescence infecti-ieuse. Application au diagnostic de la maladie. Proc.

Intern. Cong. Plant Protection, IV, Hamburg, 1957, 1: 361-366.

WALKINSHAW, C. H., G. D. GRIFFIN, and R. H. LARSON. 1961. *Trichodorus christei* as a vector of potato corky ringspot (tobacco rattle) virus. Phytopathology 51: 806-808.

WALLACE, H. R. 1958. Movement of eelworms. I. The influence of pore size and moisture content of the soil on the migration of larvae of the beet eelworm, *Hetero-dera schactii* Schmidt. Ann. Appl. Biol. 46: 74-85.

WEBB, R. W. 1927. Soil factors influencing the develop-ment of the mosaic disease in winter wheat. Jour. Agr. Res. 35: 587-614.

WILLIAMS, H. E., J. A. TRAYLER, and H. K. WAGNON. 1962. Recovery of virus from refrigerated fruit tree and grapevine pollen collections. Phytopathology 52: 367.

ZUCKERMAN, B. M. 1961. Parasitism and pathogenesis of the cultivated cranberry by some nematodes. Nemato-logica 6: 135-143.

► DISCUSSION OF C. H. CADMAN PAPER

G. Stotzky:

There have been several reports in the literature that some viruses *persist* in soil for long periods of time, in the absence of a host, by adsorption on inorganic soil colloids. Would you please comment on this mech-anism of persistence? If one group of viruses persists after soil drying, would this not indicate survival by mechanisms other than the vector, assuming that drying kills the vector?

C. H. Cadman:

There is evidence that viruses, both soil-borne and insect-borne, retain infectivity longer when absorbed on soil colloids, such as clay particles, than when kept in plant sap. But there is no evidence of any conse-quence to show that absorption on soil colloids plays any role in the persistence and transmission of viruses in soils. The fact that soils containing some kinds of viruses retain infectivity when dried points to survival of these viruses within some drought-resistant form of their vector(s).

D. Park:

At Wellesbourne, Tomlinson has shown that by in-fecting *Plantago* with virus-carrying *Olpidium* the virus infection may be eliminated from the fungus. Can a mechanism of this sort have any significance for bio-logical control of diseases caused by soil-borne viruses?

C. H. Cadman:

Yes; R. N. Campbell has also shown that *Olpidium* can be freed from lettuce-big-vein virus by passage through sugarbeet roots. These results suggest that crop rotation might be a possible means of freeing soils from infection by this virus.

K. W. Kreitlow:

In soil-borne cereal viruses where no vector has yet been found, and in view of Dr. Scott's observation that plasmodesmata may occur at the surface of root-hair cells, is it possible this may be a means of entrance for soil-borne cereal virus? Perhaps this can be checked by fumigation.

C. H. Cadman:

I doubt if this has any relevance to this problem. There is much evidence to suggest that the soil-borne cereal viruses have chytrid fungi as vectors, and the results of extensive experiments with soil fumigants are best interpreted as demonstrating effects on the vectors and not on the viruses themselves.

R. N. Campbell:

First, I would like to emphasize that the big-vein virus (BVV) survives within the resting sporangium of *Olpidium*. This accounts for survival of the virus in air-dry soil and provides an easy method of reinfect-ing lettuce when the resting sporangium germinates.

Second, you have placed tobacco-necrosis virus (TNV) in the group surviving air-drying in the soil. Harrison's review contains no reference to this effect, and I know of none. What is the evidence upon which you made this distinction?

C. H. Cadman:

I hope I made it clear that my table included some speculations: this is one of them. So far as I know, no air-drying experiments have been made with TNV-containing soils. TNV is transmitted by *Olpidium bras-sicae*, however, and, if someone is prepared to make this experiment, I shall be surprised if this virus is not found to persist within the resting sporangium of *O. brassicae*.

A. S. Sussman:

Can *Olpidium* acquire the virus from clay? How does the virus enter the fungus? Is it possible that the pres-ence of phagocytic stages in these primitive fungi ex-plains why Phycomycetes are the vectors?

R. N. Campbell:

J. A. Tomlinson has presented evidence that BVV-free *Olpidium* can acquire BVV from lettuce. Our evi-dence also indicates that this occurs, and, furthermore, that this occurs during one vegetative generation of *Olpidium*. How the virus gets into the *Olpidium* is unknown.

M. G. Boosalis:

Dr. Myron Brakke of the University of Nebraska is currently attempting to delineate factors conducive to infection by soil-borne virus of wheat. He feels that such information may yield valuable clues about the specific vector. One of the most important factors is concerned with time of inoculation. Briefly, it is important to inoculate very young seedlings if symptoms are to develop early, and to use a large source of root inoculum.

M. I. Timonin:

Forest nursery seedlings are susceptible to nematodes. Are there any reports that such seedlings are also susceptible to viruses?

C. H. Cadman:

It is widely believed that Gymnosperms are not susceptible to viruses which infect Angiosperms. But Yarwood reported infection of the roots of pine seedlings with tobacco necrosis, a soil-borne virus, and a virus infecting spruce has been described from Czechoslovakia by Blattny and Čech. Deciduous trees are susceptible to infection by some of the nematode-borne ringspot viruses and, if the attempt were made, it might well be found that coniferous trees are also susceptible to infection by these viruses.

R. G. Grogan:

Why did you include TMV in the group in the table containing lettuce-big-vein, tobacco-stunt virus, etc. (Cadman, Ann. Rev. Phytopathol. *32*: 143-172, 1963)? Are you suggesting a similar vector relation?

C. H. Cadman:

This also is speculation. There are many features of TMV which suggest to me that it may belong in the group of viruses which have chytrid fungi as vectors. Like TNV, it is stable, is widespread in wild plants, and is not seed-borne. Outbreaks seem confined to particular soils and localities. This is all evidence of a circumstantial and flimsy kind, but I think it more likely that TMV belongs in the group containing lettuce-big-vein and tobacco-necrosis virus than in the group of nematode-borne viruses.

A. H. Gold:

Transmissibility of tobacco-necrosis virus in field soil is rapidly lost on drying; in this respect it differs from the reported behavior of lettuce-big-vein virus. I would also like to mention the morphological variability of the tobacco-rattle group. Recently we have encountered a virus in lettuce which appears to be very close to tobacco-rattle virus with respect to vector relations and its symptom expression on various hosts, but the size and the ratio between the long and the short particles are different. The sizes are precisely the same that van der Want found with respect to the early-browning virus of peas. This is the first instance I know of where there is rather strong evidence of variability in morphology.

C. H. Cadman:

What was the kind of variability and how great were these differences?

A. H. Gold:

European workers have reported length ratios in the order of 1:3 between the long and the short particles. We have found a 1:2 ratio and I am certain that this is not a matter of statistics or calibration. The early-browning virus of peas has a 1:2 ratio, and moreover, the length of the long particle varies somewhat from the classical tobacco-rattle picture.

Host Resistance as It Relates to Root Pathogens and Soil Microorganisms

J. C. WALKER—*Department of Plant Pathology, University of Wisconsin, Madison.*

▶

RESISTANCE TO VASCULAR INVADERS.—It is most convenient to approach this subject by considering first some of the pathogens which are primarily vascular invaders, and then discussing some of those which are concerned chiefly with subterranean nonvascular tissue. The wilts which are incited by various forms and pathogenic races of *Fusarium oxysporum* Schlecht. have received the greatest attention. This is probably because beginning early in this century several of them were brought under control by selection and breeding. The early successes of Orton (1909) with cotton, cowpea, and watermelon, and of Bolley (1907) with flax, were followed promptly by those of Essary (1912) with tomato and Jones and Gilman (1915) with cabbage.

Of the root invaders, *Fusarium oxysporum* is probably the most highly specialized as to pathogenicity. Although it is capable of growing well on an inorganic mineral substrate containing a simple carbohydrate, it exhibits the high degree of selectivity in its host plants which we commonly associate with obligate parasites. This provides the systematist with the bases for defining pathogenic forms and races. When rather clear-cut differences in susceptibility provide a means for such differentiation, it is to be expected that resistance is controlled by relatively few genes. When genetics of resistance has been studied critically, as in cabbage, pea, and tomato, single dominant genes controlling high degrees of resistance have been described (Walker, 1930; Wade, 1929; Bohn and Tucker, 1940). Resistances in these cases are highly stable over a fairly wide range of environmental conditions. It so happens, however, in the cases of cabbage and tomato, that the first few resistant varieties developed were of the multigenic type.

It is important to emphasize here in light of what I shall say later that multiple-gene resistance, while very satisfactory under some conditions, is more likely to be suppressed in its expression under extremes of environment, especially in temperature and sometimes in host nutrition. It is common experience with some other cases of resistance where both types exist in the same plant that monogenic resistance breaks down more often, not because of variation in environmental factors, but because of the appearance of "new" pathogenic races of the parasite. In the rusts, for instance, this situation provides the uredinologist's paradise and the breeder's nightmare. In the light of current-day rapidly unfolding revelations of molecular biology, this is just what we would anticipate. It is reasonable to expect that a single gene is more likely to control a much simpler metabolic process in the host than that which depends upon a large number of genes. By the same token, it may be expected that the organism is much more likely to change from nonpathogen to pathogen by mutation or recombination when there is a single-gene mechanism in the host to overcome than when the mechanism is multigenic.

Since *Fusarium oxysporum* is much like the rusts in its pathogenic specificity, it would not be surprising if resistant varieties succumbed to new races within a relatively short time, as in the case of rust diseases. This has not always proved to be the case. Varieties of cabbage dependent upon one gene for their resistance to yellows have been in use for nearly 40 years in many parts of the world without any valid report of breakdown of resistance. Likewise, the first multigenic-resistant variety introduced 43 years ago is still equally successful and widely used. This is in spite of the fact that four distinct pathogenic races of *F. oxysporum* f. *conglutinans* have been described which vary in their pathogenicity on other crucifers; but they are not effective in breaking down either type of resistance in cabbage. In tomato, most resistant varieties now depend on one gene for resistance to *F. oxysporum* f. *lycopersici* race 1. Alexander and Tucker (1945) reported a second race from Ohio and Missouri which threatened to decimate these varieties. This, however, did not take place. In fact, for most of the time since this report the geographic distribution of race 2 has been the test tubes in which it resides in the laboratories at Wooster and Columbia. Only recently what may be the same race has been reported from Florida (Stall, 1961).

When processing varieties of canning peas were rapidly converted in the 1930's and 1940's to monogenic resistance to *Fusarium oxysporum* f. *pisi* race 1, the common wilt disease in this country was practically eliminated. But a second race was soon delineated to which all such varieties were susceptible. This new race, unlike race 2 of *lycopersici,* was widespread and still is. It is much less destructive than race 1, however, largely because of its much higher temperature requirement for active pathogenicity.

While mutation or recombination of genes for pathogenicity has not been a serious problem as yet in these three wilts, it is so in diseases incited by some other forms of *Fusarium oxysporum,* notably f. *lini.* Even though multigenic resistances in cabbage and tomato are not as stable as monogenic resistances, they should be retained and improved by selection because if and when new races appear multigenic resistance may save these crops where monogenic resistance breaks down. In some crops, such as watermelon and radish, monogenic resistance to wilt has not been described, and it would appear from published reports that resistance is largely multigenic in currently used resistant varieties. In muskmelon wilt, resistance is controlled by a single dominant gene, which may be supported by two complementary dominant genes (Mortensen, 1959; Messiaen, Risser, and Pecaut, 1962). In resistant Upland cotton, wilt resistance is controlled by a single dominant gene; in Sea Island cotton, two dominant genes, additive in effect, control resistance (Smith and Dick, 1960). Three genes in flax contributing resistance to certain clones of the *F. oxysporum* f. *lini* have been described (Knowles, Houston, and McOnie, 1956).

Verticillium wilt was discovered on hops in southeastern England in 1924. Since 1940 or earlier, breeding for resistance to *Verticillium albo-atrum* has been under way. In this program, it has been necessary to consider also resistance to mosaic and downy mildew, as well as the exceedingly exacting requirements of industry for acceptable cultivars of this crop. Much progress has been made in controlling this disease through resistance. By 1947, several promising lines were reported (Keyworth, 1947), all derived from either a wild Canadian or a New Mexican male plant. Two strains of *V. albo-atrum,* fluctuating (mild) and progressive (virulent), are reported as prevalent in the area concerned, but there appears to be no striking selective pathogenicity of these on the numerous breeding lines which have been developed.

The development of varieties of tomato resistant to *Verticillium dahliae* has progressed rapidly since the description by Schaible, Cannon, and Waddoups (1951) of a dominant monogenic resistance derived from an accession from South America. These newer varieties have been used chiefly in areas where *V. dahliae* rather than *V. albo-atrum* is predominant. Alexander (1962) has recently reported an isolate from Ohio which attacks newer varieties, but it is not clear whether this is *V. albo-atrum* or *V. dahliae.*

RESISTANCE TO NONVASCULAR INVADERS.—Let us now consider the situation as to resistance to some "root rot" pathogens. At the same time that Jones and Gilman (1915) began selection of cabbage for yellows resistance in Wisconsin, tobacco growers in the same state were confronted with increasing losses from black root rot (*Thielaviopsis basicola* [Berk.] Ferr.). At that time, James Johnson began selection for resistance to this disease. He succeeded in developing varieties in which resistance was comparable to that in multigenic-resistant cabbage. Black-root-rot resistance varied from year to year with variation in climate. It was least effective in cool growing seasons, while multigenic-yellows resistance in cabbage was least effective in hot seasons. This black-root-rot resistance has since been incorporated into many varieties of the several commercial types of tobacco grown in this country and elsewhere. The multiple-gene character of black-root-rot resistance was indicated by an intermediate degree of resistance in F_1 progeny from a resistant-susceptible cross, while in the F_2 there was evidence of transgressive segregation (Johnson, 1930). Stover (1950) has shown considerable variability of the pathogen in cultural characters and virulence, but there seems to be little evidence of clear-cut differences in specialization of pathogenicity on tobacco.

Soon after the program was initiated on black-root-rot resistance, W. B. Tisdale, who had worked with Jones on cabbage yellows, went to the Experiment Station at Quincy in north Florida. He was called there because black shank (*Phytophthora parasitica* var. *nicotianae* Tucker) was raising havoc with shade-grown tobacco in that area. He followed the same approach as had Jones and Johnson. By repeated selection of the most resistant individuals he succeeded in saving this industry by building up moderately to highly resistant lines (W. B. Tisdale, 1931). Much later, Clayton and Smith (1942) developed tobacco varieties resistant to Granville wilt (*Pseudomonas solanacearum* E. F. Sm.) which saved the flue-cured cigarette-tobacco industry in certain areas in the Southeast.

The cases of tobacco root rot, black shank, and bacterial wilt are outstanding successes in the use of disease resistance as a means of control where up to now every attempt by other means has failed. In each case, resistance is not complete, it is multigenic in its inheritance, and it is influenced to some extent in its expression by environment. The root-rot and black-shank resistances have been successfully combined in commercial varieties for use in northern areas where wilt does not occur, and they have been combined with wilt resistance in varieties adapted to the requirements of southern tobacco-growing areas. Although there are variations in virulence and to some extent in selective pathogenicity in the three pathogens concerned, these factors seem not to have seriously interfered with the progress of breeders nor with the stability of resistances as they are transferred from variety to variety or as resistant varieties are transferred from one region to another. This leads one to speculate that the multigenic-resistant characters have such a complex metabolic basis that they enable the host to "outwit" the pathogenic versatility of the organisms.

From the experiences of tobacco breeders with root rot, black shank, and bacterial wilt, one would expect that many other root-rot diseases would be controlled by this means. It appears, however, that tobacco is one of the exceptions to the rule. Diseases incited by various forms of *Fusarium solani,* e.g. root rots of pea and bean, and by *Aphanomyces,* e.g. *Aphanomyces* root rot of pea, still remain uncontrolled, as do, by and large, the various *Rhizoctonia* root diseases. In some of these at least there has been no lack of persistent search for resistance germ plasm, but as yet good basic material for the breeder, with the possible exception of bean root rot, has not been forthcoming.

Pythium diseases are apparently in the same class.

One apparent exception of long standing is the milo disease of sorghum, which was formerly destructive throughout the Southwest. The disease was attributed by Elliot et al. (1937) to *Pythium arrhenomanes* Drechs. as early as 1936. Here was a case where breeders quickly found monogenic resistance (Bowman et al., 1937) in certain varieties, and by crossing and backcrossing developed resistant cultivars so rapidly that they practically eliminated the disease before pathologists got around to studying it critically. Melchers and Lowe (1943) suspected that it was not a simple pythium root rot and Leukel (1948) published irrefutable evidence that *Pythium* had nothing to do with it, while the real McCoy was *Periconia circinata* (Mang.) Sacc., a common "soil saprophyte" described as long ago as 1899. I will refer to this disease again a little later. Suffice it to say here that no beginning student of plant pathology should escape the story and moral of milo disease, and all root-rot investigators might well be reminded that a new look from a different angle from time to time is a good investment.

NATURE OF RESISTANCE TO ROOT PATHOGENS.—While some outstanding successes in the control of diseases incited by pathogens which invade roots from the soil have been accomplished, our understanding of the nature of such resistances is far from satisfying. About all I can do in this paper is to record a few successes and failures in this area.

Assuming that the soil-residing pathogens in the main attack the host through fibrous roots, they must first encounter the rhizosphere. Having adapted themselves to this environment and having overcome competition and resistance within the complex flora, they usually penetrate either resistant or susceptible hosts. Lockhead (1959) cites several reports that varieties susceptible to soil-borne fungi exert a greater (and presumably a more favorable) rhizosphere effect than resistant varieties. Buxton (1957) reports differential rhizosphere effects of resistant and susceptible peas on races of *Fusarium oxysporum* f. *pisi*. He has reported a similar relation between resistant and susceptible banana and *F. oxysporum* f. *cubense* (Buxton, 1962). Even though the antagonisms in this zone may be at a high level, they are not always great enough to prevent penetration. Kerr (1961) has emphasized this recently in the case of *Verticillium*. It would be enticing if we could demonstrate that the resistant host secretes something into the rhizosphere that reduces the invasion potentiality of the pathogen. Timonin (1941) claimed such a situation in flax wilt. The deterrent was HCN, which was supposed to be given off in sufficiently higher amount by resistant roots to ward off *F. oxysporum* f. *lini*. Recent studies by Trione (1960) failed to confirm this. We are still looking for a valid example to substantiate this theory.

The case of milo disease of sorghum is of interest in this connection. The inciting organism is apparently not a parasite at all but brings about a serious disease on susceptible varieties through its exotoxin, which has recently been shown by Scheffer and Pringle (1961) to be heat-stable and probably a polypeptide. The

disease can be produced on soil containing the toxin but from which the organism has been removed by proper treatment. Incidentally some isolates produce the toxin, others do not. We have here apparently a differential effect of the toxin on the host. When absorbed by a susceptible host, the latter succumbs to the disease. There is no reason to believe that it is not also absorbed by the resistant host, but it is obvious that if such is the case, the latter metabolizes the toxin so that it immediately becomes harmless. This case has much similarity to that of Victoria blight of oats (*Cochliobolus* [*Helminthosporium*] *victoriae* Nelson), where the exotoxin, another polypeptide, has a profound effect on the metabolism of susceptible tissue, but little or no effect on the metabolism of resistant tissue (Krupka, 1959). One may speculate here also that the exotoxin is metabolized by the resistant host cells. Paddock (1953) showed that penetration of epidermal cells of resistant leaves took place, but while the invaded cells gradually deteriorated, no further progress of the organism occurred.

Let us now look at some diseases where the pathogen invades resistant and susceptible varieties in like manner, and where the resistance mechanism is expressed after penetration. One of the first such cases was flax wilt, studied by W. H. Tisdale (1917). He believed that the resistance mechanism was expressed in the greater production of suberized cork-cambium layers in resistant roots, which provided a mechanical barrier to invasion of the vascular elements. He held out the possibility, however, that an inhibitor in the cortical cells slowed down fungus activity to permit time for cork-cambium activity to become effective. Boyle (1934), on the other hand, after an extensive study of the same disease, failed to establish a valid connection between resistance and suberization. Nair (1957) reported that in a resistant flax variety, the wilt pathogen was restricted to the cortex, but he did not indicate any suberized barriers.

Talboys (1958*a,b*), who has made a critical histological study of *Verticillium albo-atrum* in relation to resistant and susceptible hop roots, emphasizes suberization of the endodermis as an important factor in the expression of resistance. In a study of black root rot of tobacco, Conant (1927) concluded that resistance is correlated with ability of the host to develop a cork layer beneath points of infection. In the more susceptible varieties, this activity was increased at higher soil temperatures where disease development was slowest. Jewett (1938), in a later study of the same subject, did not confirm Conant's findings and interpretations and concluded that resistance was due to chemical factors rather than to anatomical modifications.

Smith and I (1930) and Anderson and I (1935) studied by histological techniques the relation of *Fusarium oxysporum* f. *conglutinans* to susceptible and to monogenic- and multigenic-resistant cabbage. The chief locus of penetration is in the undifferentiated or only partially differentiated portion of the root and sometimes of the hypocotyl. Penetration was similar in all cases. The amount of penetration was sometimes but not always lower in the monogenic-resistant root. The chief difference between the latter and the susceptible root was that the pathogen remained almost entirely in the cortex in the resistant root while it progressed to the vascular system with little injury to the cortex in the susceptible root. Pathogenesis is dependent upon subsequent activity in the xylem. Thus, the striking difference between monogenic-resistant and susceptible roots is not the matter of penetration but a restriction of the parasite in the former to the cortex. There is no evidence of a hypersensitive reaction by invaded cortical cells. Winstead and I (1954) described a thermostable low-molecular material from culture filtrates which when applied to sand in which resistant and susceptible cabbage was growing was more toxic to the latter than the former. This material has not been characterized further. When applied to loam soil it had no effect, indicating that it was adsorbed or destroyed. If such material is produced in the root cortex, it would be expected to be more injurious to susceptible plants. Although fusaric acid is produced in culture, it is apparently readily metabolized in the host (Heitefuss, Stahmann, and Walker, 1960). The cabbage race is a sparse producer of pectolytic enzymes, and these apparently have little to do with disease production in cabbage.

In the cabbage yellows disease, resistance of multigenic lines differs from that of monogenic lines in degree rather than in kind. While invasion of the stele in the latter is exceedingly rare, it does occur in the former, although to a lesser degree than in the susceptible root. The seat of resistance, therefore, appears again to be in the cell contents rather than in cell membranes. Peterson and Pound (1960), in a study of multigenic resistance to *Fusarium oxysporum* f. *conglutinans* race 2 in radish, found the situation to be quite similar to that in multigenic-resistant cabbage.

If monogenic-resistant cabbage plants are grown in infested soil or in sand culture, where the soil-rhizosphere factor is eliminated, and the substrate temperature is maintained at 28°C (optimum for growth of the fungus on agar and well above optimum for host root development), plants are eventually killed (Walker and Smith, 1930). In this abnormal environment, however, the fungus becomes a cortical parasite, and the plants die from root rot but not from yellows. When multigenic-resistant plants are thus exposed, they succumb to yellows rather than to root rot. These two resistances are quite similar phenotypically under field conditions, but by controlled manipulation of soil temperature they are shown to be quite different physiologically.

Beckman, Halmos, and Mace (1962) studied the relation of *Fusarium oxysporum* f. *cubense* in roots of susceptible Gros Michel and resistant Lacatan bananas. Since growth and sporulation in the xylem were similar in both types, they ruled out biochemical inhibition as a primary resistance factor. On the other hand, rapid vascular occlusion of the fungus by gel in the xylem followed by tyloses in the resistant variety served to restrict distribution of spores in roots held at 21°, 27°, and 34°C. This occurred only at 34° in the susceptible variety, while at 27° the gel disappeared rapidly and tylosis formation was delayed. Resistance, therefore, appears to depend on trapping of spores at perforation plates or vessel endings and on host responses which seal off the vascular system and prevent the distribution of subsequently produced spores.

Keyworth (1953) and Talboys (1958a,b) have both emphasized that resistance in hops to *Verticillium albo-atrum* is a character of the root rather than of the stem. We have found monogenic resistance to *Fusarium oxysporum* in cabbage to be expressed in both root and stem. Heitefuss, Stahmann, and I (1960) introduced spores into the vascular systems of resistant and susceptible cuttings, rooted them, and grew them at temperatures favorable to yellows. There was a rapid rise in oxidative-enzyme activity in resistant tissue followed by an abrupt drop, while in the susceptible there was a steady increase. No symptoms developed in the former, while the typical disease syndrome occurred in the latter. The same test with tomato and *F. oxysporum* f. *lycopersici* resulted in no development of permanent wilt in monogenic resistant as compared to the usual syndrome in the susceptible plant (Scheffer and Walker, 1954).

Another obvious possibility in explaining resistance is that the susceptible host may contain a unique entity which stimulates the potential pathogen and which is lacking in the resistant host. Such a case has been documented by Flentje and Kerr (Flentje, 1957; Kerr, 1956; Kerr and Flentje, 1957). The pathogen is *Pellicularia filamentosa* (Pat.) Rogers (*Rhizoctonia solani* Kühn), which we have long known to have distinct pathogenic races, although it is also a ubiquitous soil saprophyte. These investigators have shown that the fungus approaching the hypocotyl of a nonhost fails to form the characteristic appressorial contact which precedes penetration of the cuticle. The appressorium will form, however (as Dr. Flentje mentioned in his paper in this symposium), on an artificial (or natural epidermal) membrane through which an extract properly prepared from the root of the susceptible host is allowed to diffuse. It should be emphasized here that penetration in the cases studied is through hypocotyl cuticle and not into the root, but root-invading strains do occur. Although the susceptible-host-root extract is stimulatory, it does not encourage root penetration. Even the hypocotyl is not invaded through artificial wounds. Apparently the fungus requires not only the proper host stimulus but also the proper stage of host cuticle development for the penetration mechanism to function. As the host cuticle thickens or matures penetration is precluded. The results of this research comprise an outstanding breakthrough, first because they demonstrate for the first time since the contention by de Bary (1886) that host materials diffusing through the cuticular membrane can influence the parasitic ability of an organism which has not yet penetrated, and secondly because it points up the fact that resistance may depend fundamentally upon a lack of stimulus rather than upon the presence of a chemical deterrent, preformed or incited by the pathogen during the act of penetration and invasion.

I have been discussing possible antibiotic and stimulatory substances produced by or inherent in the host and those of the rhizosphere flora which may influence or account for host resistance. It has been shown that the expression of resistance may be enhanced or suppressed by shifts in environmental factors such as soil temperature and host nutrition. The possible symbiotic effect of two or more organisms in relation to host resistance has been studied in relatively few cases. In concluding my remarks, I should like to dwell briefly on this subject in relation to plant-parasitic nematodes. What I have to say is drawn chiefly from the recent review by Powell (1963). Workers at the North Carolina Agricultural Experiment Station have shown that the presence of *Meloidogyne incognita acrita* Chitwood increases the severity of black shank. The level of resistance is reduced in resistant varieties. When root-knot-resistant lines and root-knot-susceptible breeding lines from the same parentage were compared on soil infested with both black-shank fungus and the root-knot nematode, there was less black shank in the root-knot-resistant lines, but no difference was noted when they were exposed only to the black-shank fungus. The latter colonized most profusely in the hyperplastic and hypertrophied tissue resulting from invasion by the root-knot nematode. It was concluded that through this host-nematode interaction the host became more favorably predisposed to pathogenesis of the fungus.

There have long been noticed and recorded cases of association between the root-knot nematode and infection by and resistance to the cotton-wilt fungus, *Fusarium oxysporum* f. *vasinfectum*. This has been studied most extensively by Smith and Dick (1960), who emphasized that the inherent resistance to wilt was not fully expressed unless the nematode population was reduced by a nematocide. Thomason, Erwin, and Garber (1959) showed that the symptoms of wilt (*F. oxysporum* f. *tracheiphilum*) were increased in resistant varieties of cowpea when root-knot nematodes were concomitant parasites.

SUMMARY.—*F. oxysporum* is the most highly specialized in selective pathogenicity among root pathogens, and with it control of the diseases through the development of resistant cultivars has been most successful. Distinct progress in this direction is also recorded in hop wilt incited by *Verticillium albo-atrum,* tomato wilt incited by *V. dahliae,* and bacterial wilt of tobacco incited by *Pseudomonas solanacearum.* While use of host resistance as a means of control has been less common among nonvascular invaders, outstanding successes have been had in the cases of tobacco black root rot and tobacco black shank. Dominant monogenic host resistance is common among the fusarium wilts and in verticillium wilt of tomato. Multigenic resistance, however, may occur along with monogenic resistance, as shown in the cases of cabbage yellows, fusarium wilt of pea, and fusarium wilt of tomato. Resistances to nonvascular root pathogens recorded so far are multigenic. Two points of difference between monogenic and multigenic resistance are emphasized. First, the expression of multigenic resistance is usually influenced more by environmental factors than is that of monogenic resistance. Secondly, monogenic resistance is often effective against only a single or a limited number of pathogenic races of the causal organism, while multigenic resistance usually has a broader spectrum in this regard. Theoretical explanations for these phenomena are offered.

As to the nature of the various resistances, definite information is still meager. While the effect of root excretions directly or through their effect on the rhizosphere have been suggested, there is as yet little substantial evidence that this is an important basis of host resistance. Milo disease of sorghum is cited as a unique case in which the exotoxin of the soil saprophyte involved is apparently absorbed and inactivated by the metabolism of the resistant host. In hop wilt, resistance appears to be a property confined largely to the subterranean parts of the host while in fusarium wilt of tomato and in cabbage yellows aboveground and subterranean host tissues appear to be equally resistant. In hop wilt, suberization of the endodermis appears to be an important basis of resistance. In monogenic resistance to cabbage yellows, the fungus concerned is restricted to the cortex after penetration, without any discernible anatomical reaction in the host. In fusarium wilt of banana, resistance is expressed in the form of rapid vascular occlusion of the pathogen by gel in the xylem, followed by prompt formation of tyloses. The work with pellicularia foot rot is the first to give conclusive evidence of an entity in the hypocotyl of the susceptible host which diffuses through the cuticle to stimulate production of the appressorium in a pathogenic race but not in a nonpathogenic race. While the importance of symbiosis in pathogenicity of root invaders is largely unexplored, the interaction of the tobacco-black-shank fungus and the root-knot nematode in relation to resistance, and a somewhat similar relation between the cotton-wilt fungus and the same nematode are recently documented cases. It is obvious that there are various factors which underlie the resistant character in any one disease and no single pattern for all cases can be expected.

LITERATURE CITED

ALEXANDER, L. J. 1962. Susceptibility of certain Verticillium-resistant tomato varieties to an Ohio isolate of the pathogen. Phytopathology 52: 998-1000.

ALEXANDER, L. J., and C. M. TUCKER. 1945. Physiologic specialization in the tomato wilt fungus *Fusarium oxysporum* f. *lycopersici.* J. Agr. Res. 70: 303-313.

ANDERSON, M. E., and J. C. WALKER. 1935. Histological studies of Wisconsin Hollander and Wisconsin Ballhead cabbage in relation to resistance to yellows. J. Agr. Res. 50: 823-836.

BARY, A. DE 1886. Ueber einige Sclerotinien und Sclerotienkrankheiten. Botan. Ztg. 44: 377-387, 393-404, 409-426, 433-441, 449-461, 465-474.

BECKMAN, C. H., S. HALMOS, and M. E. MACE. 1962. The interaction of host, pathogen, and soil temperature in relation to susceptibility to Fusarium wilt of bananas. Phytopathology 52: 134-140.

BOHN, G. W., and C. M. TUCKER. 1940. Studies on Fusarium wilt of the tomato. I. Immunity in *Lycopersicon pimpinellifolium* Mill. and its inheritance in hybrids. Missouri Agr. Expt. Sta. Res. Bull. 311, 82 p.

BOLLEY, H. L. 1907. Plans for procuring disease resistant crops. Proc. Soc. Promoting. Agr. Sci. 28: 107-114.

BOWMAN, D. H., J. H. MARTIN, L. E. MELCHERS, and J. H. PARKER. 1937. Inheritance of resistance to Pythium root rot in sorghum. J. Agr. Res. 55: 105-115.

BOYLE, L. W. 1934. Histological characters of flax roots in relation to resistance to wilt and root rot. U. S. Dept. Agr. Tech. Bull. 458, 18 p.

BUXTON, E. W. 1957. Differential rhizosphere effects of three pea cultivars on physiologic races of *Fusarium oxysporum* f. *pisi*. Trans. Brit. Mycol. Soc. 40: 305-316.

BUXTON, E. W. 1962. Root exudates from banana and their relationship to strains of the *Fusarium* causing Panama wilt. Ann. Appl. Biol. 50: 269-282.

CLAYTON, E. E., and T. E. SMITH. 1942. Resistance of tobacco to bacterial wilt (*Bacterium solanacearum*). J. Agr. Res. 65: 547-554.

CONANT, G. H. 1927. Histological studies of resistance in tobacco to *Thielavia basicola*. Am. J. Botany 14: 457-480.

ELLIOTT, C., L. E. MELCHERS, C. L. LEFEBVRE, and F. A. WAGNER. 1937. Pythium root rot of milo. J. Agr. Res. 54: 797-834.

ESSARY, S. H. 1912. Notes on tomato diseases with results of selection for resistance. Tennessee Agr. Expt. Sta. Bull. 95, 12 p.

FLENTJE, N. T. 1957. Studies on *Pellicularia filamentosa* (Pat.) Rogers. III. Host penetration and resistance, and strain specialization. Trans. Brit. Mycol. Soc. 40: 322-336.

HEITEFUSS, R., M. A. STAHMANN, and J. C. WALKER. 1960. Production of pectolytic enzymes and fusaric acid by *Fusarium oxysporum* f. *conglutinans* in relation to cabbage yellows. Phytopathology 50: 367-370.

JEWETT, F. L. 1938. Relation of soil temperature and nutrition to the resistance of tobacco to *Thielavia basicola*. Botan. Gaz. 100: 276-297.

JOHNSON, J. 1930. Breeding tobacco for resistance to *Thielavia* root rot. U. S. Dept. Agr. Tech. Bull. 175, 20 p.

JONES, L. R., and J. C. GILMAN. 1915. The control of cabbage yellows through disease resistance. Wisconsin Agr. Expt. Sta. Res. Bull. 38, 70 p.

KERR, A. 1956. Some interactions between plant roots and pathogenic soil fungi. Australian J. Biol. Sci. 9: 45-52.

KERR, A. 1961. A study of tomato root surface organisms antagonistic to *Verticillium albo-atrum*. Trans. Brit. Mycol. Soc. 44: 365-371.

KERR, A., and N. T. FLENTJE. 1957. Host infection in *Pellicularia filamentosa* controlled by chemical stimuli. Nature (London) 179: 204-205.

KEYWORTH, W. G. 1947. Verticillium wilt of the hop (*Humulus lupulus*). II. The selection of wilt resistant varieties. J. Pomol. Hort. Sci. 23: 99-108.

KEYWORTH, W. G. 1953. Verticillium wilt of the hop. VI. The relative roles of root and stem in the determination of wilt severity. Ann. Appl. Biol. 40: 344-361.

KNOWLES, P. F., B. R. HOUSTON, and J. B. McONIE. 1956. Inheritance of resistance to Fusarium wilt of flax in Punjab 53. Agron. J. 48: 135-137.

KRUPKA, L. R. 1959. Metabolism of oats susceptible to *Helminthosporium victoriae* and victorin. Phytopathology 49: 587-594.

LEUKEL, R. W. 1948. *Periconia circinata* and its relation to milo disease. J. Agr. Res. 77: 201-222.

LOCKHEAD, A. G. 1959. Rhizosphere microorganisms in relation to root-disease fungi. p. 327-328. In C. S. Holton, et al. [ed.], Plant pathology, problems and progress 1908-1958. Univ. Wisconsin Press, Madison.

MELCHERS, L. E., and A. E. LOWE. 1943. The development of sorghums resistant to milo disease. Kansas Agr. Expt. Sta. Tech. Bull. 55, 24 p.

MESSIAEN, C. M., G. RISSER, and P. PECAUT. 1962. Study of plants resistant to *Fusarium oxysporum* f. sp. *melonis* in the Charentais cantaloupe melon var. Ann. Amelioration Plantes 12: 157-164.

MORTENSEN, J. A. 1959. The inheritance of Fusarium resistance in muskmelons. Dissertation Abstr. 19: 2209.

NAIR, P. N. 1957. Factors affecting resistance of flax to *Fusarium lini* Bolley. Dissertation Abstr. 17: 942.

ORTON, W. A. 1909. The development of farm crops resistant to disease. U. S. Dept. Agr. Yearbook 1908: 453-464.

PADDOCK, W. C. 1953. Histological study of suscept-pathogen relationships between *Helminthosporium victoriae* M. and M. and seedling oat leaves. New York Agr. Expt. Sta. (Geneva, N. Y.) Memoir 315, 63 p.

PETERSON, J. L., and G. S. POUND. 1960. Studies on resistance in radish to *Fusarium oxysporum* f. *conglutinans*. Phytopathology 50: 807-816.

POWELL, N. T. 1963. The role of plant-parasitic nematodes in fungus diseases. Phytopathology 53: 28-35.

SCHAIBLE, L., O. S. CANNON, and V. WADDOUPS. 1951. Inheritance of resistance to Verticillium wilt in a tomato cross. Phytopathology 41: 986-990.

SCHEFFER, R. P., and R. B. PRINGLE. 1961. A selective toxin produced by *Periconia circinata*. Nature (London) 191: 912-913.

SCHEFFER, R. P., and J. C. WALKER. 1954. Distribution and nature of Fusarium resistance in the tomato plant. Phytopathology 44: 94-101.

SMITH, A. L., and J. B. DICK. 1960. Inheritance of resistance to Fusarium wilt in Upland and Sea Island cottons as complicated by nematodes under field conditions. Phytopathology 50: 44-48.

SMITH, R., and J. C. WALKER. 1930. A cytological study of cabbage plants in strains susceptible or resistant to yellows. J. Agr. Research 41: 17-35.

STALL, R. E. 1961. Development of Fusarium wilt on resistant varieties of tomato caused by a strain different from race 1 isolates of *Fusarium oxysporum* f. *lycopersici*. Plant Disease Reptr. 45: 12-15.

STOVER, R. H. 1950. The black rootrot disease of tobacco. II. Physiologic specialization of *Thielaviopsis basicola* on *Nicotiana tabacum*. Can. J. Res., Sec. C, 28: 726-738.

TALBOYS, P. W. 1958a. Some mechanisms contributing to Verticillium-resistance in the hop root. Trans. Brit. Mycol. Soc. 41: 227-241.

TALBOYS, P. W. 1958b. Association of tylosis and hyperplasia of the xylem with vascular invasion of the hop by *Verticillium albo-atrum*. Trans. Brit. Mycol. Soc. 41: 249-260.

THOMASON, I. J., D. C. ERWIN, and M. J. GARBER. 1959. The relationship of the root-knot nematode, *Meloidogyne javanica*, to Fusarium wilt of cowpea. Phytopathology 49: 602-606.

TIMONIN, M. I. 1941. The interaction of higher plants and soil microorganisms: III. Effects of by-products of plant growth on activity of fungi and actinomycetes. Soil Science 52: 395-413.

TISDALE, W. B. 1931. Development of strains of cigar wrapper tobacco resistant to blackshank (*Phytophthora nicotianae* Breda de Haan). Florida Agr. Expt. Sta. Bull. 226, 45 p.

TISDALE, W. H. 1917. Flaxwilt: a study of the nature and inheritance of wilt resistance. J. Agr. Res. 11: 573-606.

TRIONE, E. J. 1960. The HCN content of flax in relation to flax wilt resistance. Phytopathology 50: 482-486.

WADE, B. L. 1929. Inheritance of Fusarium wilt resistance in canning peas. Wisconsin Agr. Expt. Sta. Res. Bull. 97, 32 p.

WALKER, J. C. 1930. Inheritance of Fusarium resistance in cabbage. J. Agr. Res. 40: 721-745.

WALKER, J. C., and R. SMITH. 1930. Effect of environmental factors upon the resistance of cabbage to yellows. J. Agr. Res. 41: 1-15.

WINSTEAD, N. N., and J. C. WALKER. 1954. Toxic metabolites of the pathogen in relation to Fusarium resistance. Phytopathology 44: 159-166.

► DISCUSSION OF J. C. WALKER PAPER

N. T. Flentje:

We are beginning to get information that some root-rot organisms have a multinucleate system carrying forward a range of nuclei in hyphal tips.

Is it possible that our failure to get resistance to many of these fungi (including Phycomycetes) is because the multinucleate condition is the equivalent of more than one pathogenic race? If so, perhaps we may get success by splitting the parent into homocaryon components representing single races.

J. C. Walker:

In view of the fact that it has been amply demonstrated in *Venturia,* which has a uninucleate thallus, that there are a large number of distinct genes which control, independently, phenotypically similar types of selective pathogenicity, it may be reasonably expected that in multinucleate fungi, the possibility of even greater numbers of pathogenic races might be found. However, this does not necessarily follow. Witness the highly mutable pathogenicity of *Cladosporium fulvum* versus the apparently stable pathogenicity of *Cladosporium cucumerinum.* Your idea of accumulating homocaryons is the best approach to analyzing the genotypic nature of selective pathogenicity in *Pellicularia* and other fungi, e.g. Phycomycetes. This has been done with *Phytophthora infestans.* It is essential, however, to select hosts for disease reaction that are also as homozygous as possible.

L. F. Johnson:

It was mentioned that the mechanism of resistance to root diseases might be due to root exudations and their effect on the rhizosphere microflora. It has been found at the University of Tennessee that tobacco varieties resistant to fusarium wilt have a higher population of antagonistic actinomycetes (antagonistic to *Fusarium* in agar culture) present in the rhizosphere than do varieties susceptible to the disease. These plants were all grown in the absence of the parasite. No such relation, however, was found with varieties resistant and susceptible to black shank and microbial antagonism to *Phytophthora.*

J. C. Walker:

This is an important observation and is in line with evidence cited in the paper presented by Buxton with reference to fusarium wilts of pea and banana.

G. W. F. Sewell:

You commented that all root-infecting fungi must first encounter the rhizosphere. I would like to suggest that *Verticillium albo-atrum* (dark mycelial form), may, to some extent, evade this competitive region by the production of infection processes directly from the conidium. Thus infection may be achieved without the prior establishment of a root-surface mycelium.

J. C. Walker:

This would be in line with the observation by Kerr, with reference to rhizosphere effects on *Verticillium* cited in this paper.

R. J. Green:

The question of the geographic distribution of these two different morphological forms of *Verticillium* (dark mycelial and microsclerotial) has not been clearly defined. Is there evidence of distinct ranges of these forms?

J. C. Walker:

Our experience at the University of Wisconsin has been that when we ask for *Verticillium* cultures from workers to the south of us, and generally to the west, we get *V. dahliae.* The only area where we get *V. albo-atrum* consistently is northern Wisconsin and Prince Edward Isle. I understand that *V. albo-atrum* is predominant in Kent. Note that *V. dahliae* was first distinguished from *V. albo-atrum* by Klebahn at Hamburg, Germany.

A. E. Dimond:

The *Verticillium dahliae* type occurs regularly in Connecticut, but the *V. albo-atrum* type, common in Maine, may also occur in Connecticut in cool summers.

A. Kerr:

In work with peas and *Fusarium oxysporum* f. *pisi* race 2, I have demonstrated an interaction between *Fusarium* and *Pythium.* *Pythium* causes early root damage which apparently enables *Fusarium* to reach the vascular tissue of resistant varieties. In soil containing both pathogens, control of *Pythium* by Dexon controls *Fusarium* wilt.

G. A. Zentmyer:

Roots of avocado varieties with some resistance to *Phytophthora cinnamomi* generally attract fewer zoospores per unit area of root than do roots of highly susceptible varieties. There are indications, however, that this difference may be related to the less vigorous type of root usually produced by the resistant varieties, rather than actual difference in type of exudate attracting the zoospores.

Summary and Synthesis of Papers on Pathogenesis and Resistance

J. E. DeVAY—Department of Plant Pathology, University of California, Davis.

It is my task to summarize briefly the noteworthy papers of Drs. Cadman, Flentje, Buddenhagen, Mountain, and Walker, and to attempt a synthesis of these papers as well as the discussions that followed.

Dr. Cadman surveyed the relations between soil-borne viruses and their vectors, the factors affecting the persistence of viruses in soils, and finally the possibilities of biological control of soil-borne viruses. Before mentioning some of the highlights of his talk, the research involved deserves some special mention. Of the many experiments that are made, few are distinguished by being what we might call "breakthrough" experiments—experiments that yield results that change the course of our thought, that suddenly unravel years of confusion and thus give rise to a flood of new work. Such experiments are those that revealed the role of ectoparasitic nematodes and *Olpidium brassicae* as vectors of soil-borne viruses.

The specialization of nematodes in the transmission of viruses is of great interest. Some nematodes, like *Xiphinema* and *Longidorus*, transmit polyhedral particles, whereas others, like *Trichodorus*, transmit rod-shaped particles. Moreover, while the same species of nematode may transmit serologically unrelated viruses (*X. americanum:* tomato and tobacco ringspot), antigenically related viruses may have different nematode species as vectors (*X. index*, grape fanleaf; *X. diversicaudatum*, the type strain of arabis mosaic). Other lines of evidence reviewed by Dr. Cadman indicate that these viruses are carried internally by the nematodes; they are retained for long periods when the nematodes are denied access to infected plants, and the viruses can be extracted from the nematodes. At present, however, there is no evidence that any of the 14 known nematode-borne viruses pass into the eggs of their vectors.

In reviewing the work on the transmission of viruses by *Olpidium* zoospores, it was pointed out that after serial culture on virus-resistant plants, *Olpidium* will lose these viruses but that the big-vein virus will survive long periods (8 years) in dry soils in the resting sporangium. This point adds greatly to the significance of the discovery of the relation between big vein and its fungus vector; it suggests that other viruses that can persist in dry soil, such as soil-borne wheat- and oat-mosaic and sugarcane-chlorotic-streak viruses, may also be transmitted by a chytrid fungus. The question was raised as to how *Olpidium* acquires the big-vein virus and it was answered that it was acquired only from infected plants but the mechanism was not known. Some interesting contrasts were drawn by Dr. Cadman between viruses transmitted by nematodes and those transmitted by *Olpidium*, based on characteristics of their vectors. For nematode-transmitted viruses, infectivity is destroyed by drying the soil, whereas for those transmitted by *Olpidium*, infectivity survives drying. Second, nematode-borne viruses are usually seed-transmitted whereas the viruses carried by *Olpidium* are not.

In regard to control, Dr. Cadman emphasized that transmission of viruses in soils is a biological process, and that effective control depends on a knowledge of the virus, its vector, and host plants. Specific viruses have specific vectors and conditions that limit the vectors limit the viruses. Thus control of vectors and the selection and breeding of plant varieties resistant to these vectors and viruses offer the best means of control.

Continuing with the role of nematodes in the development of plant diseases, Dr. Mountain reviewed and clearly illustrated the host-parasite relations between nematodes and plants. He discussed the pathogenicity of individual species of nematodes and the pathogenicity of nematodes as partners with soil fungi and bacteria. Of particular interest in this regard was the role that nematodes play by inducing the formation of gall-type tissues and root wounds that are readily infected by other soil-borne plant pathogens. Of significance also is the role of nematodes such as *Ditylenchus dipsaci* as a vehicle for the transportation of plant-pathogenic bacteria such as *Corynebacterium insidiosum* to susceptible plant tissues (crown buds of alfalfa).

Dr. Buddenhagen described other means for the entry of soil-borne bacteria into plants and expanded on their biology. He surveyed the various kinds of plant-pathogenic bacteria, their changing populations in soil and plant environments, and their pathologic effects on host plants. He stressed the means and importance of their exit from diseased plants for continued invasion of other susceptible hosts. Of particular interest, as evidenced by later discussion, was the means of survival of these bacteria in the soil during the intermission of their role as parasites and the evolution of new pathogenic clones.

Dr. Buddenhagen made the point that highly specialized and virulent clones were less able to survive their sojourn in the soil environment than less specialized and less virulent strains. The conditions causing their decline in the soil were not clear but one could visualize the effects of antibiosis, lack of suitable nutrient balances, and predatory organisms. Not mentioned was the lethal effect of a new group of filterable bacteria, much smaller than any of the plant pathogens we recognize, that were recently discovered by Dr. Heinz Stolp of Berlin (Stolp and Petzold, 1962). These ultra-microscopic bacteria, visible with a phase or electron microscope, resemble the stalk bacteria or vibrio forms and are widely distributed in the soil environments in different parts of the world. They attack and are obligately parasitic on most *Pseudomonas* and *Xanthomonas* species. Their role in the decline of populations of plant-pathogenic bacteria in the soil has not as yet been reported. The possibility that these newly discovered bacteria may be a means of biological control of bacterial plant pathogens suggests an exciting field for future research.

In regard to the evolution of new pathogens from nonpathogenic populations, Dr. Buddenhagen predicted possible mutations of bacteria that could give rise to new pathogenic clones. The difficulties likely to be encountered by these new clones in microbial communities, however, especially if their egress from host plants and spread occurred in the soil environment, greatly lessens the possibility of their establishment and survival. There is much literature dealing with changes in virulence of plant pathogens after passage through their respective hosts (Christensen and DeVay, 1955) but the mechanisms of these changes are unknown. However, the possible occurrence of heterocaryosis or other changes in the nuclear condition among weakly virulent clones as mechanisms to yield highly virulent pathogens seems apparent. Another speculation concerning the evolution of new pathogens is the transformation of potential pathogens in host tissues by cytoplasmic substances of that host. That common antigens between host cells and pathogenic bacterial cells are prerequisite for the increase of these pathogens and the development of disease has been suggested by the studies of Doubly, Flor, and Clagett (1960) on *Melampsora lini* and flax, of Flangas and Dickson (1961) on *Puccinia sorghi* and corn, and of Schnathorst and myself (1963) on *Xanthomonas malvacearum* and cotton. Another mechanism of evolution of bacterial plant pathogens that has received only token attention is the possible role of lysogenic conversions of potential pathogens to highly virulent forms. Well, to get back to earth, Dr. Buddenhagen cited the necessity of wounds or other plant openings for the entry of root-invading bacteria. Of particular interest as avenues of entry were the ruptures in cortex tissues caused by the emergence of lateral roots. However, the absence of these openings on primary roots was emphasized by Dr. Flora Scott. The discussion of these possible root openings and their significance as avenues of entry for fungal pathogens carried over into Dr. Flentje's paper. He pointed out that while such openings may exist, fungi such as *Rhizoctonia* prefer to make their own way into roots and probably avoid such openings.

Thielaviopsis basicola, however, takes full advantage of these openings where lateral roots emerge (Conant, 1927).

To briefly summarize the thought-provoking paper of Dr. Flentje, the mechanisms of plant pathogenesis by soil fungi were divided into two categories: those involving enzymic action and those involving a multiple of other interactions that he called "the rest." After citing a number of examples to illustrate these various mechanisms, he discussed some of the recent studies conducted in his laboratory on mechanisms of pathogenesis by *Rhizoctonia solani.* Most of us have followed with great interest the ingenious experiments of Drs. Flentje and Kerr that demonstrate the exudation of one or more substances by roots of susceptible hosts such as bean that attract and stimulate the colonization of hypocotyl tissues by *Rhizoctonia* and, further, the apparent absence of this attractant in root exudates of resistant plants. Their more recent work demonstrated also the diffusion of such an attractant through the cuticular membrane of hypocotyls of susceptible plants and the capture of the attractant in agar blocks. As yet the identity of this attractant is unknown. An important adjunct to the work done by Drs. Flentje and Kerr on the mechanism of pathogenesis by *Rhizoctonia* is the contribution by Dr. Bateman on mechanisms of host susceptibility that are evident after infection cushions have formed. Dr. Bateman described his findings following the talk of Dr. Chapman and pointed out that the salt forms of pectate in bean hypocotyls influence the virulence of *Rhizoctonia.* Fungal polygalacturonase is most active on sodium pectate and least active on calcium pectate. It is interesting to note that Kernkamp et al. (1952) reported that soybeans were most susceptible to *Rhizoctonia* when grown in a medium deficient in calcium.

Another highlight of Dr. Flentje's paper was the unique relation envisioned by him between the evolution of parasitism in *Rhizoctonia* and the sexual tendencies of this fungus. He compared the infection peg of the appressorium to fusion hyphae in the Basidiomycetes or to the fertilization of a trichogyne in the Ascomycetes. The idea was expressed that host emanations might be mistaken by the infecting hyphae for possible hormonal secretions of a composition similar to that from the usual hyphal prospect, thus causing the development of the appressorial mechanism. While trying to put this into words, I couldn't help but wonder how Dr. E. E. Butler might relate the parasitic tendencies of *Rhizoctonia* on other fungi with its sexual behavior, especially when filaments of glass wool cause the same excitation of *Rhizoctonia* that occurs when this fungus contacts a hypha of *Mucor recurvis* (Butler, 1957).

Dr. Flentje concluded his paper with a discussion of primary and secondary pathogenesis. The result of this discussion and those that followed, including Dr. Kerr's report on his studies with isolates of *Pythium* and *Fusarium* pathogenic on peas, will probably be a better recognition of the fact that a multiplicity of organisms is frequently involved as the cause of a plant disease and that the damage caused by so-called secondary invaders is often more important than that caused by the primary invader.

I should like to summarize several of the points Dr. Walker made concerning host resistance as it relates to root pathogens. Of particular interest was his comparison of multiple gene and monogene resistance. While monogenic resistance in plants may be more easily overcome by new races of a pathogen, multigenic resistance is usually more subject to change due to changes in environmental conditions. Considering cabbage yellows caused by *Fusarium oxysporum* f. *conglutinans*, the difference between monogenic-resistant roots and susceptible roots is not in a resistance to the penetration by the fungus but in a restriction of the fungus to the cortical tissues in resistant roots. In susceptible roots, the fungus progresses to the vascular system with little or no injury to the cortex.

In view of the variability we usually associate with *Fusarium oxysporum*, it was of interest to hear that two varieties of cabbage that have been grown for many years, one with multigenic resistance and the other with monogenic resistance, are still being grown and are still resistant to cabbage yellows.

In conclusion, I should like to comment on several problems to be faced in our search for specific substances of plant origin that affect the plant's resistance or susceptibility to disease. It will be a difficult task to identify the specific chemical substances that exude from plant roots and appear to attract pathogenic organisms to the plants or to act as inhibitors. Root exudations are apparently a complex mixture of all the substances in root cells, and the exudates may be interpreted as inhibitors as they pertain to disease resistance or as attractants as they pertain to disease susceptibility. An answer to this dilemma may be found in the fact that quantitative chemical differences in the composition of the root exudations form favorable or unfavorable nutrient balances for various soil-borne pathogens and may thus appear as specific attractants or inhibitors. It is interesting to note that E. M. Freeman wrote a paper years ago (Freeman, 1937) entitled "In Praise of Parasitism." The main theme of this paper was that the quest for food was the basis for parasitism. Yet with the many growth-factor deficiencies that exist naturally among plant pathogens, only one case has been reported where the need for such growth factors is apparently related to a parasitic tendency or host specificity by a biochemically deficient pathogen (Lukezic and DeVay, 1964).

LITERATURE CITED

BUTLER, E. E. 1957. *Rhizoctonia solani* as a parasite of fungi. Mycologia 49: 354-373.

CHRISTENSEN, J. J., and J. E. DEVAY. 1955. Adaptation of plant pathogen to host. Ann. Rev. Plant Physiol. 6: 367-392.

CONANT, G. H. 1927. Histological studies of resistance in tobacco to *Thielavia basicola*. Am. J. Botany 14: 457-480.

DOUBLY, J. A., H. H. FLOR, and C. O. CLAGETT. 1960. Relation of antigens of *Melampsora lini* and *Linum usitatissimum* to resistance and susceptibility. Science 131: 229.

FLANGAS, A. L., and J. G. DICKSON. 1961. The genetic control of pathogenicity, serotypes, and variability in *Puccinia sorghi*. Am. J. Botany 48: 275-285.

FREEMAN, E. M. 1937. In praise of parasitism. Sci. Monthly 44: 67-76.

KERNKAMP, M. F., D. J. DE ZEEUW, S. M. CHEN, B. C. ORTEGA, C. T. TSIANG, and A. M. KHAN. 1952. Investigations on physiologic specialization and parasitism of *Rhizoctonia solani*. Minnesota Agr. Expt. Sta. Tech. Bull. 200, 36 p.

LUKEZIC, F. L., and J. E. DEVAY. 1964. Effect of myoinositol in host tissues on the parasitism of *Prunus domestica* var. President by *Rhodosticta quercina*. Phytopathology 54: 697-700.

SCHNATHORST, W. C., and J. E. DEVAY. 1963. Common antigens in *Xanthomonas malvacearum* and *Gossipium hirsutum* and their possible relationship to host specificity and disease resistance. Phytopathology 53: 1142.

STOLP, H., and H. PETZOLD. 1962. Untersuchungen über einen obligat parasitischen Mikroorganismus mit lytischer Aktivität für Pseudomonas-Bakterien. Phytopathol. Z. 45: 364-390.

▶ DISCUSSION OF J. E. DEVAY PAPER

D. Teakle:

It should not be assumed that the only possible site and method of survival of soil-borne viruses transmitted by *Olpidium* are inside the resting sporangium of *Olpidium*. K. M. Smith in 1937 reported that tobacco-necrosis virus survived in soil for 2½ months, the longest time for which tests were run, and longer than even tobacco-mosaic virus.

J. E. DeVay:

Clearly, tobacco-necrosis virus is relatively stable in soil, and can last for long periods of time. Until more is known about the physical properties of other viruses transmitted by *Olpidium*, the assumption that they survive in soil only in the resting sporangium is unwarranted.

N. T. Flentje:

I should like to clarify comments I made yesterday in relation to the multinucleate condition of *Rhizoctonia* hyphae. We know from single-basidiospore studies that there must be at least 2 different nuclear types present in the total of 7 or 8 nuclei. We do not know that there are more than 2 types of nuclei. We have no evidence that the behavior of the fungus in relation to pathogenicity or virulence can be altered by environmental conditions. This is a tremendously important area of work, and I believe the preliminary and controversial results of Buxton in this field need confirmation and extension before their significance can be evaluated, and before we can begin to theorize along these lines.

L. W. Boyle:

Resistance to flax wilt by a vascular-invading fusaria was mentioned by Dr. Walker in his discussion of the nature of tolerance to invasion. The resistance to cortical-invading fusaria is due to deposits of suberin and ligninlike materials. These materials are not deposited in sufficient amounts to alter resistance under greenhouse conditions of reduced light in winter. The gradient in the cortex may be mistaken for incomplete genetic resistance to wilt.

J. E. DeVay:

Another example which bears on this is the finding by Conant, cited in my paper, that in selections of tobacco that are resistant to *Thielaviopsis basicola*, the opening caused in the root cortex by emerging lateral roots is rapidly sealed by suberinlike materials preventing invasion by this fungus. In susceptible selections of tobacco, the openings caused by ruptured cortex tissues around emerging lateral roots did not seal, and the fungus invaded the roots via these openings.

Pisatin Studies: The Relation of Phytoalexins to Disease Reaction in Plants

I. A. M. CRUICKSHANK—*Division of Plant Industry, Commonwealth Scientific and Industrial Research Organization, Canberra, Australia.*

Müller and associates (Müller and Börger, 1940; Müller, Klinkowsky, and Meyer, 1939; Meyer, 1940) proposed a theory to explain the difference in disease reaction they observed, in the course of studies of the symptom responses of cut tuber surfaces of potato varieties to inoculation with virulent and avirulent strains of *Phytophthora infestans*. This theory, which has since been called the phytoalexin theory, stated that resistance was due to the formation of an antifungal compound in the host cell as a response to fungal infection, and that such a newly formed chemical substance, designated as "phytoalexin," was responsible for the inhibition of further fungal growth in such tissue. Phytoalexin was considered to be nonspecific in its toxicity towards fungi. The basic response which occurred in resistant and susceptible host varieties was considered to be qualitatively similar. The basis of differentiation between resistant and susceptible host varieties was postulated to be the speed of formation of phytoalexin.

The term phytoalexin is derived from *phyton*, Greek, a plant, and *alexin*, Greek, a warding-off compound. Phytoalexins have been defined (Müller, 1956) as antibiotics that are produced as a result of the interaction of two metabolic systems, host and parasite, and that inhibit the growth of microorganisms pathogenic to plants. The phytoalexin theory has been restated by Müller (1956, 1958, 1961) in the light of subsequent experiments, but no major changes of theoretical importance have been made.

At about the same time as Müller and associates were working in Germany, Offord (1940) in California also advanced a theory to explain disease resistance in plants. Offord postulated that the toxic action of tannin to the fungus in plant cells is initiated and conditioned by enzymes or hormones secreted by the infecting fungus. The ultimate toxicity of the tannin was considered to depend partially on the type of phenolics and other potentially toxic constituents formed by the reaction of host and parasite, and partially on the quantity and manner of distribution of the "tannin mass."

These two theories are complementary. They both emphasize the dynamic nature of the interaction resulting from host-parasite associations. Offord's theory, if interpreted broadly, suggests a possible biochemical mechanism which may be involved in the formation or release of phytoalexins. The concept of a response or interaction between host and parasite with the formation or release of new antifungal compounds has been investigated by Gäumann, Braun, and Bazzigher (1950), Mizukami (1953), Uritani, Azakawa, and Uritani (1954), Kuć (1955), Müller (1956, 1958), Uehara (1958a,b,c), Condon and Kuć (1960), and the present Canberra group. This discussion will be limited primarily to the results of the latter group. For a more detailed discussion of this general field the reader is referred to the recent reviews (Farkas and Király, 1962; Cruickshank and Perrin, 1964b; and Cruickshank, 1963).

EXPERIMENTAL DEMONSTRATIONS OF ANTIFUNGAL COMPOUNDS FORMED FOLLOWING INFECTION.—*Sources of antifungal activity.*—The presence of an antifungal "principle" (or "principles") produced by pods of peas (*Pisum sativum*) in response to inoculation with *Monilinia fructicola* and *Ascochyta pisi* was originally demonstrated by Müller (1958) and Uehara (1958c). For the purpose of isolating the compound primarily responsible for the antifungal activity reported, and in order to obtain a sufficient quantity of it for chemical identification, a large-scale inoculation of pea pods with *M. fructicola* was carried out in our laboratory (Cruickshank and Perrin, 1961) with the drop-diffusate technique described by Müller (1956).

While detached pods were most convenient for the bulk extraction of the antifungal compound formed after inoculation, toxin formation was not limited to detached pod tissues. Pods attached to plants, growing both in the glasshouse and field, were inoculated by injection of a spore-suspension directly into the cavity of the pods with a hypodermic syringe. Leaves and stems were inoculated after first removing the waxy bloom from their epidermal tissues; nodular tissues on the roots were also studied. In all instances where plant tissues were inoculated, and in the case of nodular tissues, where these tissues were discoloured, a single toxic compound, identified as pisatin (Cruickshank and Perrin, 1960), was isolated. The isolation of pisatin from pea leaf, stem, pods, and root nodules indicated the wide distribution of the capacity to form this compound within pea-plant tissues, and suggested that the results obtained in terms of pod tissues may be of pathological significance in relation to the whole pea plant.

Bioassay of pisatin.—For the purpose of guiding the chemical extraction and purification of the antifungal component from the diffusate, a quantitative bioassay was developed (Cruickshank and Perrin, 1961) on the basis of the technique described by Müller (1958). *Monilinia fructicola* was used as the test organism. Percentage germination was determined by classifying the first 100 spores in each agar block into germinated and nongerminated using the convention, spore tube length greater than spore diameter equals germination. The mean percentage of germinated spores, corrected for control germination, was plotted against log concentration of extract and the data was empirically transformed to achieve a linear relation. From the regression line obtained, the ED_{50} value of the test solution was read off. The fungitoxicity of a solution in phytoalexin germination units (PAG units) was given by ($100/ED_{50}$).

Isolation and chemical assay of pisatin.—The diffusate collected from the endocarp of inoculated pods after centrifuging was chemically fractionated by extraction with light petroleum (b.p. 55°-60°C) and paper chromatography (solvent n-propanol; water; 20:80 v/v) followed by strip elution by aqueous ethanol. No antifungal activity remained in the residue after four extractions with light petroleum. On paper, the fungus-inhibiting component corresponded to the strip fraction with an Rf value of 0.6-0.7. The antifungal compound corresponding to this fraction was subsequently isolated by repeated recrystallisation from light petroleum and then from aqueous ethanol.

Once a purified extract of the antifungal compound was available, its ultraviolet absorption spectrum was used for its identification and estimation. The concentration of pisatin in extracts of diffusates was calculated from the optical density (OD) in 309 mμ, taking an OD value of 1.00 for a 5 ml solution as equivalent to 43.8 μg/ml of the original solution. When pisatin was the only light-absorbing compound, the ratio OD 309 mμ to OD 286 mμ was 1.47. The level of correlation between the biological and physical assays was tested by plotting the PAG values of samples in a series of experiments against their OD 309 mμ values in ethanol. The results are presented in Fig. 1. The high level of correlation was confirmed by the subsequent isolation of pure samples of pisatin.

STRUCTURE OF PISATIN.—Pisatin contains carbon, hydrogen, and oxygen only, is optically active, and has the molecular formula $C_{17}H_{14}O_6$ (Dawn R. Perrin and Bottomley, 1961). It has a characteristic ultraviolet absorption spectrum, λmax. 286 mμ (log ε 3.68) and 309 mμ (log ε 3.86) in ethanol. The solubility of pisatin at 23°C is 0.03 mg per ml in water, 0.5 mg per ml in light petroleum, 6 mg per ml in oleyl alcohol, and >42 mg per ml in ethanol. Pisatin is stable in neutral or alkaline solutions but is very acid-labile. In acid solution in the cold it loses a molecule of water and is converted to an optically inactive molecule, anhydropisatin ($C_{17}H_{12}O_5$). The loss of a molecule of water is accompanied by a marked bathochromic shift and

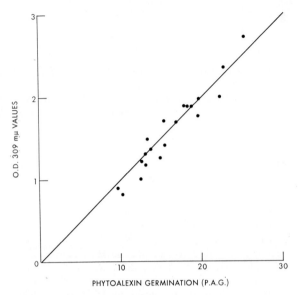

Fig. 1. Biophysical correlation diagram. $O.D.$ = optical density; $P.A.G.$ = phytoalexin germination units. (I. A. M. Cruickshank and D. R. Perrin. Austral. J. Biol. Sci. 14: 336-348. 1961.)

intensification of the ultraviolet absorption spectrum with maxima at 339 mμ (log ε 4.58) and 358 mμ (log ε 4.60). The quantitative formation of anhydropisatin from pisatin as measured at these maxima, has been used to confirm the identity of pisatin and the presence of low levels (1-5 μg/ml) of this substance.

Exposure of an ethanolic solution of anhydropisatin to diffuse daylight or mercury 365 mμ light produced a phenol with a molecular formula corresponding to the addition of one molecule of ethanol to the anhydropisatin molecule. On the other hand, if an alcoholic or aqueous solution of pisatin was irradiated for 45 minutes with mercury 253.7 mμ light, a substance was formed whose ultraviolet spectrum differed from that of pisatin only by the absence of an inflexion at 280 mμ and by a shift of the 309 mμ maximum to 312 mμ. This substance had no antifungal activity and did not dehydrate under the same conditions as pisatin. On further irradiation a yellow material having two visible absorption maxima, 425 mμ (log ε 4.0) and 550 mμ (log ε 4.2) was produced. In strongly acid solutions the colour changed to a bright cherry red. The solution became yellow on dilution or neutralization. The photodegradation product was identified as an isoflavylium pseudobase. Further chemical and spectroscopic evidence established that pisatin contains one alcoholic hydroxyl, one methoxyl and one methylenedioxy group. Detailed examination of pisatin and some of its degradation products by physicochemical methods, including ultraviolet, infrared, and nuclear magnetic resonance spectra (Dawn R. Perrin and Bottomley, 1962; D. D. Perrin and Dawn R. Perrin, 1962) have established that pisatin has the structure 3-hydroxy-7-methoxy-4′5′ methylenedioxychromanocoumarane (Fig. 2).

Pisatin appears to be the first naturally occurring chromanocoumarane to be characterized with a hy-

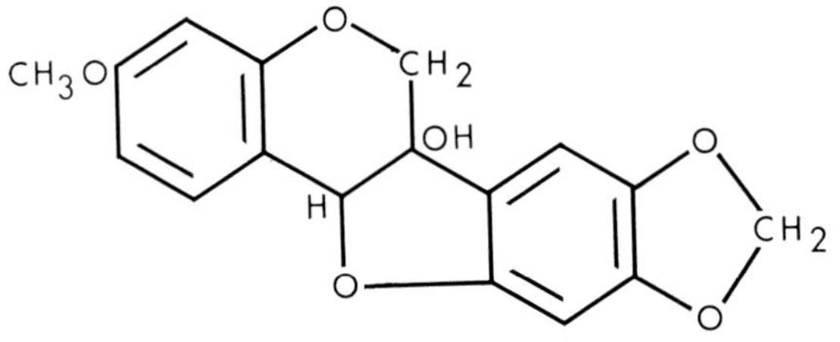

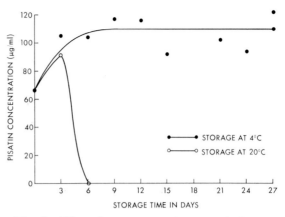

Fig. 2. Structure of pisatin.

droxyl group in the nonaromatic portion of the molecule; however, the ring skeleton of pisatin occurs in nine other known natural products (Dawn R. Perrin and Bottomley, 1962; Bredenberg and Hietala, 1961a).

SOME FACTORS AFFECTING THE QUANTITATIVE FORMATION OF PISATIN.—Pathogenesis axiomatically implies the presence of a host and parasite. Toxic compounds are widely distributed in the plant kingdom as normal constituents of many plant species; they are also common products of fungal metabolism. Toxins of both origins have been claimed to be involved in pathogenesis. With the exception of toxins involved in symptom formation in susceptible varieties (Braun and Pringle, 1959), the role of toxins in pathogenesis remains to be proved.

The physiological condition of the host tissues or the fungus spores has been shown to affect the concentration of pisatin formed after inoculation, and this has been correlated directly with the disease reaction of the host tissues. An inverse relation has been shown between pea-pod maturity and pisatin concentration (Table 1). For stored pea pods the conditions of storage

TABLE 1. Relation between maturity of pea-pod tissues and their capacity to form pisatin after inoculation with *Monilinia fructicola**

Maturity class	Description of pea pods	Pisatin concentration, µg/ml	
		Spore suspension	Water
1	Green, flat, seeds < 2 mm diam	110	9.6
2	Green, slightly rounded, seeds 2-4 mm dia.	72.7	9.1
3	Green, developed to full size, seed 8-10 mm dia.	28.9	< 3
4	Pale green, slightly wrinkled, seeds mature	14.6	< 3

* From: I. A. M. Cruickshank and Dawn R. Perrin. Australian J. Biol. Sci. 16: 111-128. 1963.

were important. Storage temperature (Fig. 3) and aeration (Fig. 4) prior to inoculation very significantly affected the length of time endocarp tissues of pea pods retained their capacity to form pisatin.

The effects of temperature after inoculation are nonspecific; they influence simultaneously processes in the parasite and the host tissues. The over-all effect of temperature for the pathogen and nonpathogen host-parasite combinations studied (Fig. 5) suggest that

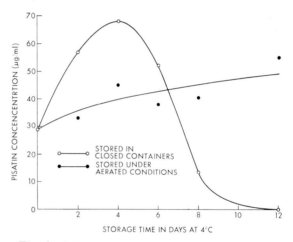

Fig. 3. Effect of temperature of storage of whole pea pods on their subsequent capacity to form pisatin after inoculation with *Monilinia fructicola*. (I. A. M. Cruickshank and D. R. Perrin. Austral. J. Biol. Sci. 16: 111-128. 1963.)

Fig. 4. Effect of aeration of storage of whole pea pods on their subsequent capacity to form pisatin after inoculation with *Monilinia fructicola*. (I. A. M. Cruickshank and D. R. Perrin. Austral. J. Biol. Sci. 16: 111-128. 1963.)

within the normal range of environmental temperatures occurring in nature, temperature normally would not be a limiting factor in pisatin formation.

Aeration affects the general metabolic processes within both the host and parasite. To this extent its effect is nonspecific. Pisatin was not formed under anaerobic conditions (Cruickshank and Perrin, 1963). Partial oxygen tensions have not been studied, but as some microorganisms are known to be able to grow at lower oxygen tensions than higher plants, critical oxygen-tension values may exist where the metabolism and growth of fungi and higher plants may be affected differentially. This aspect will be discussed in a subsequent section of this paper.

A direct relation between inoculum concentration and pisatin concentration for a pathogen and a nonpathogen of peas has been reported (Fig. 6). An apparent anomaly existed where inoculum of low spore density was used. Endocarp tissues of pea pods inoculated with low concentrations of spores of *Monilinia*

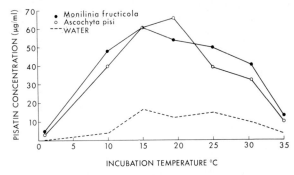

Fig. 5. Relation between incubation temperature and pisatin concentration. (I. A. M. Cruickshank and D. R. Perrin. Austral. J. Biol. Sci. 16: 111-128. 1963.)

fructicola produced low concentrations of pisatin; the inoculated tissues were not susceptible. Analyses of inoculated endocarp tissue for total pisatin in this laboratory have shown that the concentrations of this compound per unit of host tissue are several fold those of the corresponding diffusate solutions. The concentration of free pisatin in the infected host cells is not known; it may be intermediate between that of the diffusate and the infected tissue. A two- or threefold increase in the case of even the lowest concentrations measured would be sufficient to explain the resistance of pea tissues to *M. fructicola*.

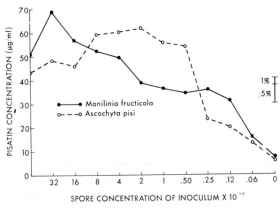

Fig. 6. Relation between concentration of inoculum and concentration of pisatin formed. (I. A. M. Cruickshank and D. R. Perrin. Austral. J. Biol. Sci. 16: 111-128. 1963.)

Low concentrations of pisatin have been detected in sterile water applied to endocarp tissues and incubated for 40 hours (Figs. 5 and 8). These values may be explained as probably due to the physicochemical changes in the endocarp cells associated with the experimental technique. Formation of pisatin has been induced in concentrations comparable with those resulting from fungal inoculation, by placing dilute chemical solutions on pea pods. The results (Table 2) showed first that pisatin formation may be initiated in the complete absence of microorganisms, and secondly that heavy metal ions such as copper and mercury were effective in this regard. The concentration of chemical solution determined the concentration of pisatin; the

optimum concentration depended on the particular ion used. The optimum concentration range of mercuric chloride was relatively wide (3×10^{-5} to 10^{-4} M), on the other hand, cupric chloride was effective over a much narrower concentration range (ca. 3×10^{-3} M). Symptoms of phytotoxicity were macroscopically visible only at concentrations of the applied chemical solutions exceeding those required for maximum pisatin formation. In fact, as visible phytotoxicity increased, pisatin concentration rapidly decreased.

TABLE 2. Pisatin formation after application of chloride solutions*

Concentration of chemical solution	Pisatin concentration, µg/ml			
	$CuCl_2$	$CaCl_2$	$HgCl_2$	NaCl
3×10^{-6} M	< 5	< 5	< 5	< 5
3×10^{-5}	< 5	< 5	> 100	< 5
1×10^{-4}	11	—	> 100	—
3×10^{-4}	11	< 5	> 100	< 5
1×10^{-3}	26	—	80	—
3×10^{-3}	94	< 5	20	< 5
3×10^{-2}	< 5	< 5	< 5	< 5
3×10^{-1}	Nil	< 5	Nil	< 5

* From: I. A. M. Cruickshank and Dawn R. Perrin. Australian J. Sci. 16: 111-128. 1963.

PATHOGENS AND NONPATHOGENS OF PEAS.—The results discussed above represent important and necessary investigations if the phytoalexin theory is to rest on a sound chemical basis. They do not, however, represent anything basically new, for toxic compounds associated with infected or healthy plant tissues are not uncommon. A reasonable question for you to ask might be: How does pisatin differ from other toxins previously isolated?

Toxicity of pisatin.—The sensitivity of a range of filamentous fungi to pisatin has been reported (Table 3). The most significant result demonstrated was the characteristic toxicity of pisatin. A comparison of the ED_{50} values of pisatin towards the fungi tested showed that the organisms fell into two groups, namely those that were relatively insensitive to pisatin (known pea pathogens) and those that were sensitive to pisatin (all other fungi tested). In the first group of six known pathogens of peas, the ED_{50} value for five of them was greater than 100 µg/ml; for the exception (*Septoria pisi*), the ED_{50} value fell within the range 75-100 µg/ml. In the second group of fungi, which represented many important plant pathogens of hosts other than *P. sativum*, taken from the three main fungal classes and the Fungi Imperfecti, the individual ED_{50} values varied with the fungus. The ED_{50} values for 38 out of 44 of this group were less than 50 µg/ml and only one of them, *Fusarium graminearum*, had an ED_{50} value in excess of 75 µg/ml. A comparison of the degree of inhibition of growth of each fungus at 100 µg/ml (Table 3) showed that if this parameter of toxicity is used, in five out of the six pea pathogens inhibition was less than 50%, while in 37 of the 44 fungi in the non-pathogenic group inhibition was more than 90%.

Results of a more detailed comparison of the sensi-

TABLE 3. Antifungal spectrum of pisatin*

Microorganism	ED$_{50}$ range, μg/ml of agar	Per cent inhibition at 100 μg/ml
A. Assays in vitro, 96 hr (20°C)		
Phycomycetes		
Phytophthora cactorum (Leb. & Cohn) Schroet.	25–50	>90
Pythium de baryanum Hesse	25–50	>90
Pythium ultimum Trow.	25–50	>90
Thamnidium sp.	25–50	>90
Mucor mucedo (L.) Fres.	25–50	>90
Ascomycetes		
Glomerella cingulata (Stonemn.) Spauld and V. Schr.	25–50	>90
Leptosphaeria maculans (Desm.) Ces. de Not.	<25	>90
Monilinia fructicola (Wint.) Honey	<25	>90
†*Mycosphaerella pinodes* (Berk. & Blox.) Vestergr.	>100	<50
Sclerotinia libertiana (Lib.) Fekl.	25–50	>90
Basidiomycetes		
Corticium fusiforme (Berk.) Wakef.	<25	>90
Pellicularia filamentosa (Pat.) Rogers Str. 1	50–75	50–90
Pellicularia filamentosa (Pat.) Rogers Str. 2	50–75	50–90
†*Pellicularia filamentosa* Str. 3 ex *Pisum sativum* L.	>100	<50
Stereum purpureum Pers.	<25	>90
Ustilago bullata Berk.	<25	>90
Ustilago avenae (Pers.) Rostr.	<25	>90
Fungi Imperfecti		
Alternaria solani (Ellis & Martin) Sorauer	25–50	>90
Aspergillus nidulans (Eidam) Wint.	25–50	50–90
†*Ascochyta pisi* Lib.	>100	<50
Ascochyta pisi (Lib.) var. *fabae* Speg.	25–50	>90
†*Ascochyta pinodella* L.K. Jones	>100	<50
Botrytis cinerea Pers.	25–50	>90
Botrytis allii Munn.	25–50	>90
Colletotrichum lindemuthianum (Sacc. & Magn.) Bri. & Cav.	<25	>90
Colletotrichum graminicolum (Ces.) G.W. Wils.	25–50	>90
Colletotrichum linicolum Pethybr. & Laff.	25–50	>90
Fusarium graminearum Schw.	75–100	50–90
Fusarium oxysporum f. *melonis* Snyder & Hansen	50–75	50–90
Fusarium oxysporum f. *gladioli* Snyder & Hansen	50–75	50–90
Fusarium oxysporum f. *lycopersici* (Sacc.) Snyder & Hansen	25–50	50–90
†*Fusarium solani* f. *martii* Appel & Wollenw.	>100	<50
Helminthosporium cynodontis Marig.	25–50	>90
Kabatiella caulivora (Kirch.) Karak.	25–50	>90
Penicillium gladioli McCull. & Thom	25–50	>90
Penicillium digitatum (Fr.) Sacc.	25–50	>90
Phoma foveata Foister	25–50	>90
Phomopsis viticola (Sacc.) Sacc.	<25	>90
Polyspora lini Laff.	25–50	>90
Sphaerella linorum Wollenw.	25–50	>90
Thielaviopsis basicola (Berk. & Br.) Ferraris	25–50	>90
Trichoderma lignorum (Tode.) Harz.	<25	>90
Verticillium albo-atrum Reinke & Berth.	25–50	>90
B. Assays in vitro 10-15 days (20°C)		
Ascomycete		
Venturia inaequalis (Cke) Wint. emend. Aderh.	<25	>90
Basidiomycetes		
Armillaria mellea (Fr.) Quel.	50–75	>90
Fomes australis (Fr.) Che	<25	>90
Fungi Imperfecti		
Fusicladium carpophilum Thun.	25–50	>90
Septoria apii Chester	25–50	>90
Septoria lycopersici Speg.	25–50	>90
†*Septoria pisi* Westend.	75–100	>90

* From I. A. M. Cruickshank. Australian J. Biol. Sci. 15: 147-159. 1962.
† Known pea pathogens.

tivity of six selected fungi from the groups pathogenic and nonpathogenic towards peas were also reported (Fig. 7). These results emphasized the differential sensitivity between the fungi in the two groups. With the two taxonomically related pea pathogens (*Ascochyta pisi* and *Mycosphaerella pinodes*), the curves were of similar shape. Essentially there was an initial growth inhibition in each case, and then very little further effect with increase in pisatin concentration. In the case of the third pea pathogen, the root and stem-infecting fungus *Fusarium solani* var. *martii* f. *pisi,* there was increasing inhibition with increase in dosage. K. Uehara (private communication) has shown a similar dosage-response relation between *F. oxysporum* var. *pisi*—a wilt-inducing species—and pisatin concentration. The three fungi nonpathogenic to peas in Fig. 7 formed another quite distinct group. The slope of their dosage-response curves varied according to the fungus, but in each case the slopes were highly significantly different from those of the pea-pathogen group and in all cases inhibition was greater than 95% at the pisatin concentration of 100 µg/ml.

Two new compounds have recently been isolated in this laboratory from inoculated pods of broad bean (*Vicia faba*) and French bean (*Phaseolus vulgaris*) under conditions similar to those used to isolate pisatin. These compounds, tentatively designated viciatin and

phaseollin, have shown the same type of differential selectivity towards pathogens and nonpathogens of the hosts from which they were isolated as pisatin showed towards the pathogens and nonpathogens of peas. The report of Kuć (1961) in relation to toxins isolated from infected root tissues of a range of host species indicates a wider occurrence of toxic compounds with selective toxicity patterns basically similar to pisatin.

Bioassays in culture of the toxicity of any one toxin, such as pisatin, can never give a complete explanation of the role of such toxins in vivo. They can, however, present a broad picture of the primary pattern of activity of a toxin. The pattern of selective toxicity shown by pisatin, viciatin, and phaseollin is that which would be expected if these three compounds play a primary role in the disease resistance of the tissues in which they are formed.

Formation of pisatin.—Studies on the formation of pisatin following inoculation of endocarp of pea pods with a range of fungi have shown that the capacity to stimulate pisatin formation was not limited to any particular class of fungi (Table 4). It has, in fact, been formed following inoculation of endocarp tissue with all the plant-parasitic fungi that have been tested (Cruickshank and Perrin, 1963). It appeared that the qualitative nature of the response of endocarp of pea pods to inoculation was independent of the fungus used as inoculum. Different fungus species did not,

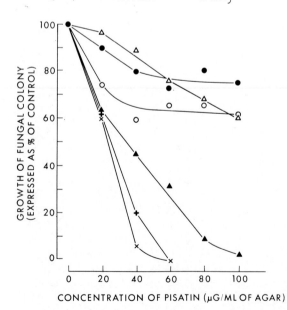

● Ascochyta pisi	20 mm	Radii of Control Colonies
○ Mycosphaerella pinodes	21 mm	
△ Fusarium solani var. martii	32 mm	
▲ Botrytis allii	66 mm	
+ Colletotrichum lindemuthianum	16 mm	
× Leptosphaeria maculans	12 mm	

Fig. 7. Comparison of dosage-response curves of three pathogens (*Ascochyta, Mycosphaerella,* and *Fusarium*) and three nonpathogens (*Botrytis, Colletotrichum,* and *Leptosphaeria*) of pea to pisatin. (I. A. M. Cruickshank. Austral. J. Biol. Sci. 15: 147-159. 1962.)

TABLE 4. Concentrations of pisatin formed after inoculation of the endocarp of pea pods with a range of fungal phytopathogens*

Fungal species	Plastin concentration µg/ml after 72 hours
A. Facultative pathogens	
†*Ascochyta pisi* Lib.	116
†*Ascochyta pinodella* L.K. Jones	53
Botrytis allii Munn	65
Botrytis cinerea Pers.	85
Colletotrichum lindemuthianum (Sacc. Magn.) Bri. & Cav.	110
†*Fusarium solani* var. *martii* f. *pisi* Appel & Wollenw.	90
Kabatiella caulivora (Kirch.) *Karak.*	62
Leptosphaeria maculans (Desm.) Ces. de Not.	109
Monilinia fructicola (Wint.) Honey	81
Penicillium digitatum (Fr.) Sacc.	59
Penicillium gladioli McCull. & Thom	51
Septoria apii Chester	88
†*Septoria pisi* West.	10
B. Obligate pathogens	
Erysiphe sp. ex. Marrow	54
Puccinia coronata Cda	17
Peronospora tabacina Adam.	26
Uromyces fabae Pers.	14
Uromyces phaseoli var. *typica* Arth.	27
Ustilago bullata Berk.	45
C. Controls	
Water	<3
Tween 20 (1:10,000)	<3

* From I. A. M. Cruickshank and Dawn R. Perrin. Australian J. Sci. 16: 111-128. 1963.
† Known pea pathogens.

however, induce equal concentrations of pisatin; there was a quantitative difference in the host response associated with the fungus in the host-parasite combinations studied.

Time-course studies on the change of pisatin concentration in diffusate solutions have shown that there was an initial lag phase of 6 to 8 hours after inoculation before pisatin could be detected. Pisatin concentration then rose almost linearly with time for a period of 12 to 30 hours. A second cycle of increase commenced between 48 and 60 hours after inoculation. This multi-inflexional pattern of progressive change in pisatin concentration was characteristic of most fungi studied. For individual species, however, the details of the curves varied (Fig. 8).

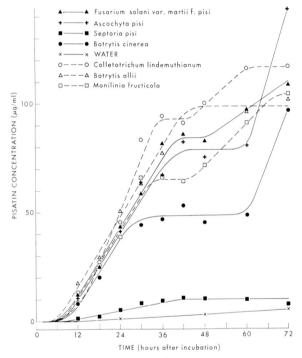

Fig. 8. Comparison of time-course curves for rate of increase of pisatin concentration in diffusate solutions following inoculation of pea-pod endocarp with three pathogens (*Fusarium, Ascochyta,* and *Septoria*), a wound pathogen (*Botrytis cinerea*), and three nonpathogens (*Colletotrichum, Botrytis allii,* and *Monilinia*) of *Pisum sativum.* (I. A. M. Cruickshank and D. R. Perrin. Austral. J. Biol. Sci. 16: 111-128. 1963.)

Comparison of the concentrations of pisatin after 72 hours (Table 4) and the time course of change in pisatin concentration (Fig. 8) in relation to pathogens and nonpathogens of peas has shown that *Ascochyta pisi* and *Fusarium solani* var. *martii* f. *pisi,* two pathogens of peas, induced the formation of high concentrations of pisatin and that the rate of formation compared favourably with that of any of the nonpathogens studied. *Septoria pisi,* a third pea pathogen, on the other hand, induced the formation of only very low concentrations of pisatin. *Botrytis cinerea,* a wound pathogen of peas, occupied an intermediate position in

terms of rate of formation; however, the final concentration of pisatin produced by this fungus after 72 hours compared favourably with the first two pea pathogens. The fungi nonpathogenic to peas, without exception, induced the formation of pisatin at moderate to high concentrations.

Disease reactions of the host-parasite combinations discussed above cannot be explained by either the selective toxicity of pisatin alone or the quantitative aspects of pisatin formation in the tissues of the pea pod alone. But when both aspects are considered together it is seen that nonpathogens of peas induce the formation of pisatin in concentrations in excess of the ED_{50} values of pisatin towards them. On the other hand, when pea pathogens induce the formation of pisatin, they induce it at concentrations less than that of the ED_{50} values of pisatin towards them. If pisatin is a typical phytoalexin, and if it is assumed that phytoalexins occur generally in plants, then the situation required for a resistant reaction is a host in which infection stimulates the production of a phytoalexin to a concentration above the threshold which inhibits the fungus. Susceptibility, on the other hand, may be due to the inability of the infecting fungus to stimulate the formation of the phytoalexin characteristic of the host, or to the capacity of the fungal pathogen to be tolerant of the phytoalexin produced.

AN EXTENSION OF THE PHYTOALEXIN THEORY AND SOME INTERESTING SPECULATIONS.—*Varietal resistance.*—Chester (1933), in an extensive review of the early literature on the problem of acquired physiological immunity in plants, stated that most plants are resistant to most fungi, or put in a more orthodox way, the host range of most plant-pathogenic fungi is very narrow. Disease-resistance mechanisms are, in fact, present in all plants. Varietal resistance to a specific disease is only one aspect of the much broader phenomenon of immunity.

The phytoalexin theory was put forward by Müller and Börger (1940) as a basis for an explanation of varietal resistance. Up to the present the experimental results obtained with this theory as a working hypothesis have contributed chiefly to our knowledge of the pea plant's capacity to ward off nonpathogens of peas, that is, the phenomenon of immunity. At the varietal level, a given variety of plant may be highly resistant to strain α, but highly susceptible to strain β of the same pathogenic fungal species. On a second variety of the same host species the virulence of the two fungal strains may be reversed. When several strains of a pathogenic fungal species and several host varieties are involved, there is virtually an unlimited array of possible reaction types (Brown, 1948).

Uehara (1958a) reported a correlation between the toxicity of a compound induced in rice leaves inoculated with *Piricularia oryzae* and varietal resistance to this fungus. Similar correlations have been reported between the concentration of ipomeamarone, a compound induced in sweet potato by *Ceratocystis fimbriata,* and varietal resistance of sweet potatoes to this pathogen (Akazawa and Wada, 1961). Concentrations of pisatin formed following inoculation of peas with *Aschochyta pisi* have been shown in this laboratory to vary with variety. Although the data are only fragmentary, it appears worth while to attempt to synthesize from the results available an extension of the phytoalexin theory that may serve as a guide for further investigations in this field.

The proposed scheme is shown in its simplest form in Fig. 9. The histogram section represents the phytoalexin concentration formed in response to fungal infection in several varieties of a given host species. The dosage-response curves represent the sensitivity of the pathogen Y to a range of concentrations of phytoalexin in vitro. The curve $Y\beta$ (solid line) is based on the dosage-response curve for *Septoria pisi* to pisatin (Cruickshank, 1962). The dotted curves represent the responses of two hypothetical strains of the pathogen Y. The ED_{50} value is used in the following discussion because it is the most accurate parameter of toxicity. Mycelial growth is used because it is more realistic than germination when toxicity is considered in relation to disease resistance as a postinfectional phenomenon.

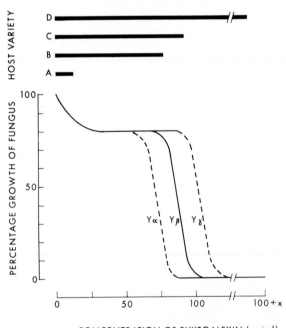

Fig. 9. Varietal reaction: hypothetical relations between dosage-response curves of three strains of a pathogenic fungus to phytoalexin in vitro and the concentration of phytoalexin they induce in vivo (histograms). For explanation see text. (I. A. M. Cruickshank. Ann. Rev. Phytopath. 1: 351-374. 1963.)

In variety and strain interactions, the phytoalexin does not vary qualitatively. Quantitative differences in concentration may occur, however, according to the variety and strain combination. Similarly the relative sensitivity of a fungus species to the phytoalexin of the host species involved may vary from strain to strain. Some simple situations are represented in Fig. 9. If the fungus strain α is first considered, then the reaction

types of the varieties would be A susceptible, B, C, and D resistant. If the fungal strain β is considered, varieties A and B would be susceptible and C and D resistant. Finally if the fungal strain γ is used to inoculate the four host varieties, the reaction types would be A, B, and C susceptible and D resistant. For the purpose of simplicity the phytoalexin concentrations are represented as being constant. This is not necessarily so. The varietal designations assigned within the histogram in Fig. 9, may be rearranged according to the fungus strain used to inoculate them. Thus if strain β is considered, the concentrations of phytoalexin induced in varieties B and C may be reversed. Then variety B would be resistant and variety C susceptible. Obviously a multiplicity of host-parasite combinations and disease-reaction types is possible. The simplest situation where a single phytoalexin is characteristic of a host species (e.g. pisatin, *Pisum sativum*) is envisaged in the above discussion. If more than one phytoalexin is involved within a single host species, the complexities of such a system would be infinite.

Chemotherapy.—The mode of action of chemotherapeutants has been discussed recently by Dimond and Horsfall (1959) and Oort and van Andel (1960). While a few compounds have been shown to be translocated within plants and to act in the form in which they are applied, in other cases they act indirectly through the formation of a derivative of the compound applied, or through some modification of the host-plant metabolism. Into the third group fall compounds which increase in the host the content of polyphenols or other compounds believed to determine resistance to disease. It is of interest in relation to this idea to discuss some results reporting the effect of metal ions on disease reaction.

Forsyth (1957) stated that the uptake of iron salts (40-200 ppm of ferric sulphate in the nutrient solution) by roots of wheat caused a resistant reaction to rust (*Puccinia graminis* var. *tritici*), in a normally susceptible plant. It was suggested that the metabolism of iron may have a role in the defensive mechanism of the wheat plant. Wang, Isaac, and Waygood (1958) have studied the effects of various metal ions on rust development in detached leaves. Nickel at 4 ppm was very effective in preventing rust development in susceptible varieties of wheat. The mechanism involved in the inhibition of rust by metal ions is not understood. It has been postulated, however (Forsyth, 1962), that the effect of nickel when applied on the fourth day after inoculation of plants is to favour the oxidation of phenols either by direct action or by reducing the activity of a quinone reductase.

Heavy metal ions, especially mercury, silver, and copper, when applied in dilute solution (10^{-5} to 10^{-3} M) to endocarp tissues of the pea pod (Cruickshank and Perrin, 1963, and unpublished data), induced pisatin formation at concentrations comparable with those induced by fungal spore suspensions. It is interesting to speculate whether phytoalexin formation occurs in the wheat example discussed above and is responsible for the change in type of disease reaction. The stimulation of pisatin formation by chemical treatments may also suggest that some heavy-metal-containing fungicides may act, in part, through the formation of phytoalexins within the host tissues to which they are applied, in addition to their normally accepted protectant action.

It has been suggested (Cruickshank, 1962) that phytoalexins may provide a new source of biologically active molecules for use in plant chemotherapy. The relatively weak antibiotic activity of pisatin when considered along with some of its physical properties do not make pisatin attractive for direct application to plant surfaces. In the light of the effect of metal ions, it is suggested that compounds may be designed, which on application to plant surfaces are taken up by the plant cell and act as pro-drugs by inducing the formation of phytoalexin in the tissues involved. Treatment of this type would be expected to be effective against pathogens which normally induce only low concentrations of phytoalexin (for example, *Septoria pisi,* Cruickshank and Perrin, 1963) and are sensitive to high concentrations.

Biological control.—The roots of plants living in a normal field soil are constantly exposed to infection by bacteria and fungi. In spite of the apparently favourable conditions that exist in soil environments for infection of roots, relatively few species of fungi are capable of successfully infecting the roots of any given host species. Flentje (1957) reported in relation to studies on *Pellicularia filamentosa* that host-parasite combinations could occur where resistance was due to failure of fungal hyphae to attach themselves to the host surface, to their failure to form appressoria, or to the thickening of the host cell wall. Where penetration occurred, however, breakdown of the infection process was considered to be due to a hypersensitive reaction resulting in small necrotic flecks. Flentje stressed that penetration of the host tissues must occur before hypersensitive reactions occur. Infection is not necessary for the stimulation of phytoalexin formation provided physiologic contact occurs between host and parasite (Müller, 1958).

As discussed earlier in this paper, pisatin formation in inoculated pea-plant tissues is not confined to the aboveground portions of the plant, neither is there any a priori reason for believing that the same defensive mechanism does not occur in the pods, leaves, stems, and roots. Examination of Table 3 indicates that among pathogens and nonpathogens of peas the root-infecting species show the same differential sensitivity pattern as leaf- and stem-infecting species. In many cases the capacity of these species to induce pisatin formation is not known. In the cases that have been studied (Table 4), however, the results indicate that a similar situation is true for root-infecting as for leaf- and stem-infecting species.

Trifolirhizin, a new antifungal compound chemically related to pisatin, has been isolated (Hietala, 1960) and identified (Bredenberg and Hietala, 1961*a,b*). The occurrence of this compound was reported to be confined to the root tissues of red clover (*Trifolium pratense*). Studies in Canberra, however, have established that a compound which may be identical with

trifolirhizin develops in red-clover leaflets after inoculation with *Monilinia fructicola.* The clover roots examined by Hietala (1960) were not artificially inoculated. They were not, however, grown under aseptic conditions. It is suggested that trifolirhizin and pisatin may occur in roots of red clover and peas respectively owing to hypersensitive reactions initiated by naturally occurring soil fungi in their unsuccessful attempts to infect them.

Disease reaction, although primarily controlled by the gene-for-gene relation in host-parasite systems (Flor, 1956) may be affected by environmental factors (Yarwood, 1959). While no direct evidence is available, the inability of the endocarp tissue to form pisatin under anaerobic conditions may be relevant to certain problems of root diseases and their control. Plant roots in heavy waterlogged soils generally show greater susceptibility to certain groups of soil-inhabiting fungi (Garrett, 1956) as compared with their resistance to these same fungi in light, well drained and aerated soils. This difference in disease reaction may well be related to the root's incapacity to form its characteristic phytoalexin under the former conditions.

CONCLUSION.—The phytoalexin theory was postulated in 1940; it is only in the last five to ten years, however, that attempts have been made to obtain experimental evidence to support or refute this hypothesis. In one example, namely, the garden pea, the evidence is becoming more complete. The basic postulates of the phytoalexin theory have been confirmed and there appear good grounds for considering that pisatin plays a primary role in the disease reaction not only of the pod tissues, which have been most extensively used in these studies, but also of the leaves, stems, and roots of *Pisum sativum.*

At first glance the occurrence of phytoalexins, exemplified by pisatin, may appear to have little relevance as a factor determining the behaviour of plant pathogens in soil. If, however, the phenomenon of immunity, in which pisatin appears to be involved, is considered, then compounds of this type are extremely important, and may, in fact, be primary factors in biological control. The isolation, characterization, mode of action, and biosynthesis of phytoalexins in a large group of plants represents a major challenge and one of the most exciting fields in plant pathology.

ACKNOWLEDGMENTS.—The unpublished experiments referred to here were all done in collaboration with Mrs. Dawn R. Perrin. Figures 1, 3, 4, 5, 6, 7, and 8, and Tables 1, 2, and 4 are reproduced with permission of the Australian Journal of Biological Science.

LITERATURE CITED

AKAZAWA, T., and K. WADA. 1961. Analytical study of ipomeamarone and chlorogenic acid alterations in sweet potato roots infected by *Ceratocystis fimbriata.* Plant Physiol. 36: 139-144.

BRAUN, A. C., and R. B. PRINGLE. 1959. Pathogen factors in the physiology of disease—toxins and other metabolites. p. 88-89. *In* C. S. Holton [ed.], Plant pathology, problems and progress 1908-1958, University of Wisconsin Press, Madison, Wisc.

BREDENBERG, J. B., and P. K. HIETALA. 1961*a*. Investigation of the structure of trifolirhizin, an antifungal compound from *Trifolium pratense* L. Acta Chem. Scand. 15: 696-699.

BREDENBERG, J. B., and P. K. HIETALA. 1961*b*. Confirmation of the structure of trifolirhizin. Acta Chem. Scand. 15: 936-937.

BROWN, W. 1948. Physiology of the facultative type of parasite. Proc. Roy. Soc. (London), Ser. B, 135: 171-179.

CHESTER, K. S. 1933. The problem of acquired physiological immunity in plants. Quart. Rev. Biol. 8: 129-154, 275-324.

CONDON, P. and J. KUĆ. 1960. Isolation of a fungitoxic compound from carrot root tissue inoculated with *Ceratocystis fimbriata*. Phytopathology 50: 267-270.

CRUICKSHANK, I. A. M. 1962. Studies on phytoalexins. IV. The antimicrobial spectrum of pisatin. Australian J. Biol. Sci. 15: 147-159.

CRUICKSHANK, I. A. M. 1963. Phytoalexins. Ann. Rev. Phytopathol. 1: 351-374.

CRUICKSHANK, I. A. M., and DAWN R. PERRIN. 1960. Isolation of a phytoalexin from *Pisum sativum* L. Nature (London) 187: 799-800.

CRUICKSHANK, I. A. M., and DAWN R. PERRIN. 1961. Studies on phytoalexins. III. The isolation, assay and general properties of a phytoalexin from *Pisum sativum* L. Australian J. Biol. Sci. 14: 336-348.

CRUICKSHANK, I. A. M., and DAWN R. PERRIN. 1963. Studies on phytoalexins. VI. Pisatin: the effect of some factors on its formation in *Pisum sativum* L., and the significance of pisatin in disease resistance. Australian J. Biol. Sci. 16: 111-128.

CRUICKSHANK, I. A. M., and DAWN R. PERRIN. 1964. Pathological function of phenolic compounds in plants. p. 511-544. *In* J. B. Harborne, [ed.], Biochemistry of phenolic compounds, Academic Press, Inc., London.

DIMOND, A. E., and J. G. HORSFALL. 1959. Plant chemotherapy. Ann. Rev. Plant Physiol. 10: 257-276.

FARKAS, G. L. and Z. KIRÁLY. 1962. Role of phenolic compounds in the physiology of plant diseases and disease reaction. Phytopathol. Z. 44: 105-150.

FLENTJE, N. T. 1957. Studies on *Pellicularia filamentosa* (Pat.) Rogers. III. Host penetration and resistance and strain specialization. Trans. Brit. Mycol. Soc. 40: 322-336.

FLOR, H. H. 1956. The complementary genic systems in flax and flax rust. Advan. Genet. 8: 29-54.

FORSYTH, F. R. 1957. Effect of ions of certain metals on the development of stem rust in the wheat plant. Nature (London) 179: 217-218.

FORSYTH, F. R. 1962. Inhibition by nickel of the respiration and development of established infections on Thatcher wheat caused by *Puccinia recondita* Rob ex. Desm. Can. J. Botany 40: 415-423.

GARRETT, S. D. 1956. Biology of root-infecting fungi. Cambridge University Press, London and New York. 292 p. (See specifically p. 28-33.)

GÄUMANN, E., R. BRAUN, and G. BAZZIGHER. 1950. Über induzierte Abwehrreaktionen bei Orchideen. Phytopathol. Z. 17: 36-62.

HIETALA, P. K. 1960. A countercurrent distribution method for separation of chemical compounds. Ann. Acad. Sci. Fennicae, Ser. A II, 100: 1-69.

KUĆ, J. 1955. A biochemical study of the nature of disease resistance in plants. Ph.D. Thesis, Purdue University, Lafayette, Indiana.

KUĆ, J. 1961. The plant fights back. Meded. Landbouwhogeschool Opzoekingssta. Staat Gent 26: 997-1004.

MEYER, G. 1940. Zellphysiologische und anatomische Untersuchungen über die Reaktion der Kartoffelknolle auf den Angriff der *Phytophthora infestans* bei Sorten verschiedener Resistenz. Arb. Biol. Reichsanst. Land-Forstwirtsch. Berlin 23: 97-132.

MIZUKAMI, T. 1953. Observations on the reactions of plant to the infection of some pathogens. I. On the difference of the influence of the barley juice on the germination of *Fusarium nivale* and *Fusarium solani*. Ann. Phytopathol. Soc. Japan 17: 57-60.

MÜLLER, K. O. 1956. Einige einfache Versuche zum Nachweis von Phytoalexinen. Phytopathol. Z. 27: 237-254.

MÜLLER, K. O. 1958. Studies on phytoalexins. I. The formation and immunological significance of phytoalexin produced by *Phaseolus vulgaris* in response to infections with *Sclerotinia fructicola* and *Phytophthora infestans*. Australian J. Biol. Sci. 11: 275-300.

MÜLLER, K. O. 1961. The phytoalexin concept and its methodological significance. p. 396-400. *In* Recent Advan. Botany (Canada) (9th Intern. Botan. Congr. Montreal), University of Toronto Press, Toronto.

MÜLLER, K. O., and H. BÖRGER. 1940. Experimentelle Untersuchungen über die Phytophthora Resistenz der Kartoffel. Arb. Biol. Reichsanstalt. Land- Forstwirtsch. Berlin 23: 189-231.

MÜLLER, K. O., M. KLINKOWSKI, and G. MEYER. 1939. Physiologisch-genetische Untersuchungen über die Resistenz der Kartoffel gegenüber *Phytophthora infestans*. Naturwissenschaften 27: 765-768.

OFFORD, H. R. 1940. The function of tannin in host-parasite relationships with special reference to *Ribes* and *Cronartium ribicola*. U.S. Dept. Agr. Bureau of Entomology and Plant Quarantine E-518, 27 p.

OORT, A. J. P., and O. M. VAN ANDEL. 1960. Aspects of chemotherapy. Meded. Landbouwhogeschool, Opzoekingssta. Staat Gent 25: 981-992.

PERRIN, DAWN R., and W. BOTTOMLEY. 1961. Pisatin; an antifungal substance from *Pisum sativum* L. Nature (London) 191: 76-77.

PERRIN, DAWN R., and W. BOTTOMLEY. 1962. Studies on phytoalexins. V. The structure of pisatin from *Pisum sativum* L. J. Am. Chem. Soc. 84: 1919-1922.

PERRIN, D. D., and DAWN R. PERRIN. 1962. The N.m.r. spectrum of pisatin. J. Am. Chem. Soc. 84: 1922-1925.

UEHARA, K. 1958*a*. On the production of phytoalexin by the host plant as a result of interaction between the rice plant and the blast fungus *Piricularia oryzae* Cav. Ann. Phytopathol. Soc. Japan 23: 127-130.

UEHARA, K. 1958*b*. On the phytoalexin production of the soybean pod in reaction to *Fusarium* sp., the causal fungus of pod blight. I. Some experiments on the phytoalexin production as affected by host plant conditions and the nature of the phytoalexin produced. Ann. Phytopathol. Soc. Japan 23: 225-229.

UEHARA, K. 1958*c*. On some properties of phytoalexin produced as a result of the interaction between pea (*Pisum sativum* L.) and *Ascochyta pisi* Lib. I. On the activity as affected by ultra-violet irradiation and some physico-chemical properties of phytoalexin. Ann. Phytopathol. Soc. Japan 23: 230-234.

URITANI, I., T. AKAZAWA, and M. URITANI. 1954. Increase in respiratory rate in sweet potato tissue infected with black rot. Nature (London) 174: 1060.

WANG, D., P. K. ISAAC, and E. R. WAYGOOD. 1958. Effect of metal ions on the development of wheat stem rust. Nature (London) 182: 268-269.

YARWOOD, C. E. 1959. Predisposition. p. 521-562. *In* J. G. Horsfall and A. E. Dimond [ed.], Plant pathology, an advanced treatise, Academic Press, Inc., New York.

► DISCUSSION OF I. A. M. CRUICKSHANK PAPER

J. L. Harley:

The quantities of pisatin reported as formed after infection, like those of orchinol given by Professor Gäumann in his work on orchidaceous reaction to infection, are very large. Would you like to comment on this? Is it possible that the process of biosynthesis is simply a hydrolysis of a glycoside yielding the pisatin which might be the aglycone moiety of the molecules?

I. A .M. Cruickshank:

It is quite true that the concentrations of orchinol and pisatin in plant tissues resulting from infection is high in comparison with the concentrations of auxins required for responses in plant tissues. They are, however, quite realistic in relation to the concentrations of these compounds required to provide a satisfactory explanation for the inhibition of growth of the fungal species involved.

The biosynthesis of pisatin is at present being studied in Canberra. Experimental results at the moment suggest that pisatin is not a hydrolysis product of a glycoside. It appears to be much more complex than this.

J. G. Horsfall:

1. Can pisatin be introduced into susceptible varieties, or other species, and induce resistance?
2. If mixed inoculation of *Septoria pisi* and *Colletotrichum lindemuthianum* is used, will the latter act to inhibit infection by the former?

In general, researchers on phytoalexins have not fulfilled Koch's postulates. They associate the compound with resistance. They have seldom induced resistance experimentally. They have, therefore, not yet distinguished concomitance from causality.

I. A. M. Cruickshank:

To your first two questions I cannot give you an answer in terms of our material, as the points have not been tested. It is, however, relevant to point out that it is not difficult by several methods (heat, chemicals, and anaerobic storage) to change the reaction of pea pods to *Monilinia fructicola* from resistance to susceptibility. By choice of treatment these changes can be induced permanently, or they may be only transitory in character. In all instances, the concentration of pisatin, resulting from inoculation of the treated pods, corresponded to that expected in relation to the resulting reaction type and the conclusions drawn in the experimental section of this paper.

In relation to your third comment, the problem of disease resistance is, in my opinion, a delicate problem of plant physiology. I consider it unrealistic to expect that the introduction of the toxic end product of a complex biochemical process into plant tissues should be expected to reproduce the reaction to that compound produced naturally.

Indirectly, this induction was, however, demonstrated in the classical paper of Müller and Börger (1940, cited in the paper) in their studies using virulent and avirulent strains of *Phytophthora infestans* on potato tubers.

S. Wilhelm:

Will fungi that are recognized as obligate saprophytes induce the formation of phytoalexins? Could you, for instance, take an array of *Fusarium oxysporum* individuals and determine which among them were parasites and which saprophytes?

I. A. M. Cruickshank:

Trichoderma viride and *Aspergillus* sp. are two saprophytes which have been tested. Both have induced pisatin formation. The studies have, however, largely dealt with pathogenic fungi. By studies on induction of pisatin and their sensitivity to pisatin, I consider it should be possible to identify parasitic from saprophytic *Fusarium oxysporum* individuals.

D. Pramer:

You find no pisatin in diffusates from control pods, but do these diffusates contain any coumarinlike compounds? If so, pisatin may be produced, not by the plant, but by the fungus acting metabolically on coumarinlike substances in the plant tissue.

I. A. M. Cruickshank:

The diffusates contain a range of compounds in addition to pisatin. These may be readily demonstrated chromatographically, and some of them may be coumarins. The residues after pisatin extraction are, however, nontoxic and have not been studied in detail. Pisatin may be induced in the complete absence of microorganisms by chemical methods (see Table 2). These data leave little doubt as to the host origin of the compound.

N. A. Burges:

How local is the reaction? In orchid mycorrhiza, histological evidence suggests that the response is on an individual-cell basis.

I. A. M. Cruickshank:

Studies on diffusion and translocation of pisatin in plant tissues have been carried out. The results confirm the histological evidence that the responses involved are on an individual-cell basis, even though at a maximum only 2 to 3 cells are involved in a single infection.

J. B. Taylor:

Some factor in wood of *Prunus* spp. prevents the isolation of *Verticillium albo-atrum* (microsclerotial form) at certain times of the year. This factor could be a phytoalexin if a phytoalexin were produced only at certain times of the year. Have you observed a seasonal fluctuation in the production of phytoalexins?

I. A. M. Cruickshank:

Seasonal fluctuation of pisatin has not been studied. Physiological conditions of many kinds do, however, influence the quantitative aspects of pisatin formation.

M. N. Schroth:

You indicated that pisatin is not an aglycone. Would you consider the aglycone of a glucoside a phytoalexin if it is released as a result of the action of a pathogen and is toxic to it? Pear, for example, contains the glucoside arbutin. When hydrolyzed by β-glucosidase, the aglycone hydroquinone is released and is toxic to *Erwinia amylovora*. Certain tissues of the plant contain β-glucosidase and some strains of the organism produce it.

I. A. M. Cruickshank:

Phytoalexins have been defined by Müller (1956, cited in the paper). This definition would not exclude your example. As a rider to this, I would add that unless the reaction on a particular host is an all-or-none reaction, in relation to induction of the compound and the host reaction, I would include in my definition the property of pathogen-nonpathogen differential selectivity as exemplified by pisatin before I would accept a compound into the phytoalexin class.

D. F. Bateman:

Do virus infections of tissue induce the formation of pisatin?

I. A. M. Cruickshank:

Such studies have not been made.

D. F. Bateman:

In the work of Dr. A. F. Ross and Dr. C. E. Yarwood, the area surrounding virus-induced lesions became resistant to further virus infections. Also, in recent work of Eva Poinar, at Cornell, it was demonstrated that lesions induced in tobacco leaves by *Thielaviopsis basicola* develop a zone around them which becomes resistant to virus infection. The virus-virus-induced resistance, as well as the *Thielaviopsis*-virus-induced resistance may also be expressed in a systemic manner. Since your work indicates that pisatin is localized in tissue, it would appear that induced resistance of tissue to virus infection by prior virus or fungus infections is mediated through some other mechanism.

C. E. Yarwood:

How would you detect the production of a phytoalexin produced by a virus and active against a virus?

I. A. M. Cruickshank:

Pisatin may be readily detected in plant tissue by chemical extraction and assay (Cruickshank and Perrin, 1961). I cannot suggest how it would be tested for anti-viral activity in vivo.

E. W. Hanson:

What is the relation of age of plant to pisatin production? Are very young seedlings able to produce this substance? It has been observed that certain small-seeded forage legumes (*Trifolium, Medicago,* and *Melilotus*) are very susceptible to attack by some *Pythium* spp. when the fungus is added to soil at time of sowing, or 1 or 2 days later, but are nearly immune when inoculum is added 1 to 2 weeks after sowing. Would you care to speculate as to the nature of the development of this type of resistance?

I. A. M. Cruickshank:

This aspect of the problem has been studied only in relation to maturity of pod tissues (see Table 1). My only comment is that there is no a priori reason to believe that changes in disease reaction of host tissues that occur are not associated directly with the host's capacity to respond to infection with phytoalexin formation. Other modifying factors, which I consider secondary, may, however, also be involved.

K. H. Garren:

In some of your concluding remarks you indicated a desire to find some more convenient means of connecting your pisatin studies with the edaphic habitat. I would once again draw attention to the peanut fruit which "thinks it is a root" and develops in the legume pod, which is closely related to the pea pod with which you have worked. I suggest that studies similar to your pisatin studies should be conducted with the peanut fruit as the inoculated substrate.

D. J. Hagedorn:

Do you have any evidence that pisatin is more or less fungitoxic to nonpathogens of the host involved than materials produced in pods of *Phaseolus vulgaris* or *Vicia faba* following inoculation?

I. A. M. Cruickshank:

The order of toxicity of phaseollin and viciatin is similar to that of pisatin.

PART VI

◄

THE MECHANISMS OF ANTAGONISM

The Concept of Competition in Microbial Ecology

FRANCIS E. CLARK—*Agricultural Research Service, United States Department of Agriculture, Fort Collins, Colorado, and Plant Chemistry Division, Department of Scientific and Industrial Research, Palmerston North, New Zealand.*

▶

Many microbiologists believe that in the microbial struggle for occupancy of any given environment, the decisive factor is antibiosis and that the factor of competition is hardly worthy of mention. Others accord competition distinct and perhaps equal status, while still others believe competition to be the larger and more inclusive term, under which antibiosis is considered as one of the mechanisms by which success in competition is achieved. In undertaking to discuss competition, then, one finds himself confronted first of all with the necessity of deciding just how much of the microbial struggle for existence should be included in his assignment.

If one turns to textbooks of microbiology for guidance, he is struck first by the number of authors who fail to mention competition at all, and secondly by the regularity with which those who do mention it so neatly limit their discussion to the proposition that "in nature microorganisms may compete for food, water, air, and space." This uniformity of opinion among textbook writers concerning the items for which organisms compete is at least for the moment reassuring, even though later in this discussion I will find it necessary to scrutinize more closely the validity of several of these items as objects of microbial competition.

If one turns from the textbook literature to the more specialized journals reporting individual researches, or to reviews of this literature, he is confronted by the several extremes of opinion mentioned in the opening paragraph. Finally, if he turns to the much more extensive literature concerning the competitive interrelations among higher plants or animals, he quickly finds that differences of opinion concerning the meaning of competition are not unique to the microbiologists.

Milne (1961) has reviewed eleven definitions given within the last quarter century concerning competition among animals. He concluded that although the term ought to have but one meaning, clear, precise, and unambiguous, unfortunately this was not so, and the result was confusion, with competition meaning different things to different people. Harper (1961), in considering approaches to the study of plant competition, has likewise noted the many different senses in which the term competition currently is used. He concluded that it might be best to drop the word altogether and to substitute some blanket word, such as interference, with its very wide meanings and few special acquired meanings. Apparently, the microbiologists can turn neither to the botanists nor to the zoologists for any model solution of their own difficulties.

I ask your indulgence in accepting, in lieu of a more formal review, these few fragmentary references to the textbook, technical, and review literature concerning competition. In the aggregate, such literature is interesting, extensive, and well deserving of more detailed attention, if only time would permit. Proceeding still more summarily, I am now going to state not one but two definitions of competition.

Broadly, competition means not merely direct antagonism and struggle for space, etc., but rather it is an objective description of the interplay of longevity and fatality factors of all kinds favoring one species at the expense of another. In this sense, competition may involve common space, food or nutrients, light, waste-material action, mutual predation, susceptibility to carnivores or to disease, and many other types of mutual interaction—in short, it is any interaction between two or more species populations which affects their growth and survival (Elton, 1946; Odum, 1959).

In a narrower sense, competition is a more or less active demand in excess of the immediate supply of material or condition (space, etc.) on the part of two or more organisms; it is the endeavor of two or more organisms to gain the same particular thing, or to gain the measure each wants from the supply of a thing when that supply is not sufficient for both (Clements and Shelford, 1939; Milne, 1961).

Obviously, these two concepts differ. To most microbial ecologists, at least to those concerned with the microorganisms in soil, some parallelism between the broader concept of competition as stated above and Garrett's (1950, 1956) concept of competitive saprophytic ability is immediately apparent. So too is the parallelism between the secondly stated concept and that implied by many writers when listing the things for which microorganisms compete. As noted earlier, these commonly are listed as food, water, air or oxygen, and space. I have an uneasy feeling that this listing has been borrowed quite superficially from the botanists and that as microbiologists we have not been sufficiently critical of it. Accordingly, let us make it our next concern to inquire more closely into the background and validity of certain concepts associated with the narrow definition of competition.

The botanists became concerned with competition much earlier than did the microbiologists. Clements, an exceptionally able spokesman among the plant ecologists for many years (Clements, 1907, 1916; Clements, Weaver, and Hanson, 1929; Clements and Shelford, 1939—to cite but a few of his many publications), regularly emphasized light and water as the principal physical factors for which plants compete. Space was mentioned with considerable reservation—"plants are sometimes said to compete for space, but this hardly occurs, but in wet soils, there may be competition for air." He also recognized the competition of plants for nutrients—"for water and the nutrients dissolved therein."

With only minor variations or additions, these several items are those very commonly listed by plant or crop-production ecologists. Donald (1956), for example, lists light, water, nutrients, heat, and rarely space; and Jackman (1960), light, water, air, space, and nutrients. The standard microbiological listing duplicates these and similar lists, except the factor of light is deleted. This deletion in the course of borrowing the botanical listing certainly required no monumental intellectual effort on the part of the microbiologists.

Perhaps it is time for some further mental gymnastics by the microbiologists. I have long believed that the soil organisms occupy only a negligible fraction of the total physical space available to them in soil (Clark, 1949). Recently, Park (1960) has stated quite effectively the case against the proposition that microbes compete for space. Although his immediate argument was that competition for space was not an adequate explanation of fungal antagonism in soil, his discussion appears equally convincing that in soil generally, space must exist in amounts sufficient to accommodate the bodies of microorganisms. He noted that microscopic examination of soil or of decomposing organic materials in soil showed that fungal structures are normally not sufficiently numerous to be able physically to prevent further fungal development there.

Although physical space is not fully occupied, there remains the possibility that a certain amount of biological space or living room is required by microorganisms. Several decades ago this proposition was quite widely endorsed in the microbiological literature, largely because of the work of Bail (1929). It was Bail's contention that for any given species of bacteria, there was a typical constant number of cells capable of living in a given space. With attainment of this maximum population level, multiplication came to a standstill, independently of exhaustion of available foodstuffs or formation of toxic factors. In brief, the biological space requirement became limiting long before full occupancy of the available physical space was obtained.

This sort of biological space requirement possibly may exist intraspecifically among animal populations, presumably because of factors of "sociopsychological" stress and concomitant effects upon the hormonal and reproductive functions of the animals involved (Christian, 1950, 1956; Chitty, 1957). In this connection,

however, it should be pointed out that according to Munday (1961) there is no really convincing evidence concerning the existence of psychological factors operating as checks and balances on either mammalian or avian populations. It would appear desirable to await the outcome of studies on the "sociopsychological stresses" of the soil bacteria before subscribing to the existence of a similar requirement for them.

Within recent years, various authors (Monod, 1949; Ecker and Lockhart, 1961; Stotzky and Norman, 1961) have shown that bacterial populations can be increased well beyond the maxima initially obtained, provided all the bacterial nutrient requirements are properly satisfied. I personally have no hesitancy in removing space, physical or biological, from the listing of items for which microorganisms compete nor in remaining of the opinion that seldom if ever is lack of space, in and of itself, responsible for curtailment of microbial growth.

Do microorganisms compete for water? Although competition for water undoubtedly occurs among higher plants, one must seriously question the occurrence of any such competition among microscopic organisms. Available water is essential for microbial activity, but any unavailability of water to microbes is primarily a question of the physical forces with which water is held in the environment. In the strict sense competition implies a struggle between two or more organisms for some item that is in short supply. It does not imply the struggle of one organism with an adverse physical environment. Clements (1916) recognized that the initial crustose lichens which colonize bare rock compete with each other little or not at all. Their struggle for existence is with their physical environment and not with one another for very limited and very transitory supplies of water.

Microbial activity is more likely to produce water than to consume it. In many instances in which dryness is inhibitory to microbial activity, such as in stored hay or grain that is not sufficiently dry for safe storage, microorganisms more correctly can be viewed as commensalistic in their water relations rather than as competitive. The shortage of water at first inhibits microbial activity, but if only a few microsites exist or develop in which a few organisms can initiate decomposition, then the process becomes autocatalytic in that metabolic water is produced. Spoilage thereafter becomes more rapid and more cosmopolitan.

In the presence of an initially favorable water supply in the soil, depletion of that supply is not caused by microbial activity, but by such factors as evaporation or salt accumulation or by the evapotranspiration carried out by plants. Contrariwise, plants growing in a soil quite often are the agents mainly responsible for removal of the favorable water supply initially stored therein. As with the factor of space, I personally see little justification for listing water as one of the items for which soil microorganisms compete. Any statement that bacteria do not compete for water should not be interpreted to imply that bacteria do not have a water requirement or that they are not influenced by the quantity and quality of the water available to them.

The question of whether microorganisms compete for

oxygen can be answered in the affirmative, but even here some comment appears to be in order. Admittedly, most soil microorganisms consume oxygen, many are limited in their activity by oxygen deficiency, and the supply of oxygen in soil at times is exhaustible. Perhaps one point on which some documentary reassurance is needed is the rapidity of oxygen depletion in soil into which the inflow of air is interrupted. Obviously, if this exhaustion takes place very rapidly, within a very few minutes for example, then the period of competition must be correspondingly short, and the importance of such competition should be negligible. Once the supply of oxygen is exhausted, the question of real significance is whether one or both organisms can function as facultative anaerobes.

If some given volume of a furrow slice of field soil having an oxygen consumption rate of 2 pounds per acre per hour becomes sealed off by a water or other barrier, then the contained air, assuming that the air-filled pores constitute 30 per cent of the soil volume, should supply the microbial oxygen demand in that soil for about 108 hours. If one further assumes that the contained microflora is represented by two species equally responsible for the oxygen consumption and both obligately aerobic, then the competition for oxygen, assuming no other complications or interactions, simply reduces the growth of each by a factor of 50% of that which either would attain if present as the sole occupant of the environment. If, however, one species utilizes oxygen at a higher rate, then it has a correspondingly higher competitive advantage over the associated species, and it would gain the greater measure of oxygen from the supply which was not sufficient for both.

Into this example concerning 108 hours of oxygen supply one could build all sorts of variations. The soil could be made waterlogged and thus the quantity of contained oxygen would be far smaller. Or consideration could be given to the unequal or spotty distribution of organisms in soil and to the occurrence of foci or microsites of greater oxygen demand. Such modifications would alter the duration but not the occurrence of competition, provided only obligate aerobes were involved. One cannot help feeling, however, that this sort of simplicity, or this sort of a concept of competition for oxygen, is misleading. For the soil organisms taken collectively, there is no limiting aeration point that is analogous to the permanent wilting point of the higher plants. Insofar as soil microorganisms and soil oxygen are concerned, there are two sides to the coin. One is that oxygen can be an item in short supply and for which the soil organisms can compete for a longer or shorter interval. The other is that the presence or absence of oxygen can be considered as a substrate condition, or if you wish, as making a single substrate such as glucose into two dissimilar substrates biochemically.

Presenting glucose anaerobically to a facultative anaerobe and to an obligate aerobe, both glycolytic, is somewhat analogous to presenting cellulose to a cellulolytic and a noncellulolytic species. Admittedly it would be quite easy to call one side of the coin as heads and the other as tails, and to let it go at that, but this I am not going to do. First, because I think we have essentially the same problem with numerous other elements as well as with oxygen. In this connection one could mention nitrogen, phosphorus, sulfur, various micronutrients, and even accessory growth factors. Second, so far as microbial ecology is concerned, should we differentiate between glucose presented aerobically and anaerobically or between nitrogen presented in the ammonium and in the nitrate form in some dissimilar fashion than we differentiate between glucose presented at one or another pH or at one or another ambient temperature? We are interested in the total condition of the substrate, hydrogen-ion content as well as oxygen content. Microorganisms are of course never said to compete for pH or for temperature but on the other hand they are almost always said to compete for oxygen and water. I have already pointed out that competition for water is of questionable occurrence, simply because water, like temperature, is more strictly an environmental than a consumptive factor. Oxygen and several mineral nutrients, however, while consumptives, in another sense function no differently than do some of the obviously environmental factors. In brief, this leads us to the proposition that basically competition among microorganisms is for a substrate, in the specific form and under the specific conditions in which that substrate is presented.

Such a conclusion pushes one toward the broader rather than toward the narrower definition of competition, and admittedly I lay myself open to verbal barrages from all those who insist on the latter type of definition. Other than to say that so far as soil microorganisms are concerned, any concept of competition as simply for water, space, oxygen, and food appears largely impractical, I shall not belabor this controversy any further. There appear several other questions more deserving of our immediate attention.

Is antibiosis to be considered as subsidiary to or as entirely distinct from competition? This is a question with which microbial ecologists have been particularly concerned. Of the considerable number of soil microbiologists who have preferred to treat antibiosis and competition as separate phenomena, I will mention, again under the excuse of brevity, only two. Waksman (1952) listed five factors as being of importance in determining microbial activity. These were (1) competition, as for nutrients; (2) the production of unfavorable environmental conditions, as alcohols or acidity; (3) the production of specific antibiotics; (4) parasitism; and (5) predation. Park (1960) subscribed to the use of the term antagonism for all those species interactions in which at least one of the interacting species is harmed. The mechanisms of antagonism are three—antibiosis, exploitation, and competition. This list does not differ significantly from that of Waksman as given immediately above, inasmuch as parasitism and predation can readily be equated to exploitation, and antibiosis in its very broad sense as employed by Park can be equated to factors (2) and (3) of Waksman. In brief, both Park and Waksman would restrict the term competition to the indirect rivalry of two species for some feature of the environment that is in short supply. Neither of them considered antibiosis as a mechanism of competition.

Many ecologists, however, do consider antibiotics and metabolites to be specific mechanisms of competition. Salisbury (1944) pointed out nearly two decades ago that "it may well be that water-soluble antibiotics are of widespread occurrence as one of the factors concerned in the competition of both lower and higher organisms occupying the same substratum."

Of the many soil microbiologists who have been concerned with the role that antibiotics play in species interactions, Garrett (1950, 1956) in particular has made antibiosis subsidiary to competition. Possibly in order to avoid using any narrow definition of competition, Garrett has employed the expression of competitive saprophytic ability. This is defined as the summation of physiological characteristics that make for success in the competitive colonization of dead organic substrates. The four characteristics that favor a high competitive saprophytic ability were listed as (1) high growth rate and rapid germinability of spores, (2) good enzyme-producing equipment, (3) production of antibiotic toxins, and (4) tolerance of antibiotics produced by other organisms. Competitive saprophytic ability, then, is inherently the sum of the physiological traits of an organism, and is one of the three factors that determine the competitive saprophytic colonization of any substrate. The other two named by Garrett were the inoculum potential of the microorganism and the environment under which the substrate was presented, including its population of competing microorganisms.

I see no objection to placing antibiosis as one of the mechanisms of competition. In this light it serves very nicely to bridge the gap between the statement a few paragraphs above that microbes in the soil could be viewed as competing for a substrate in the specific form and under the specific conditions in which that substrate is presented and Park's (1960) closing words that "the organisms in a habitat produce substances that are added to the abiotic environment, from which they subsequently affect the other organisms under the influence of that modified environment. Soil antagonism in this sense is a non-specific background effect, cumulative and common in its production by all the organisms present, and acting on all those organisms."

Another helpful concept concerning the role played by specific antibiotics in the broader phenomenon of competition is that presented by Philip (1955). Competition was viewed as existing at three levels of intensity—the imperfect, the perfect, and the hyperperfect. At the first level, interspecific competition is a limiting factor, but neither species succeeds in eliminating the other; at the second, one species eventually eliminates the other; and at the third, one organism very rapidly represses or eliminates the other, inasmuch as the depressing effects immediately become effective because of antibiotic production.

If it is to be admitted that such physiological characteristics as high growth rate or good enzyme equipment are functional in enabling one organism to eat faster than his competitor at the table and thereby to gain a greater measure of the food supply that is available, then is it not equally logical to consider as still more efficient in competition that microbe who by antibiotic production can elbow his competitor completely away from the table?

How extensively do microbes compete for substrates in the soil? Are they more involved in competitive interactions in their microenvironments than are the higher plants and animals in their respective environments? As prelude to answering this question, brief presentation should be made of a concept that is quite commonly encountered in the ecological literature. This concept, generally known as Gause's principle, is that as a general rule only one species occupies any one specific niche in a habitat (Gause, 1934). For the most part, therefore, interspecific competition does not occur within the life spans of the individual organisms secure in their niches. Competition can only occur when niches overlap.

The ecological literature abounds with examples of situations wherein two species among higher plants or animals occupy the same habitat but occupy dissimilar niches within that habitat. As one example, two fish-eating species of aquatic birds occupying the same area were shown by Lack (1945) to be feeding upon different species of fish and therefore even though jointly present in a particular habitat were not in the same niche nor in actual competition for food. Another example can be found in the work of Crombie (1947). In the course of studies on competition among flour beetles, he noted that when two species were placed in an ordinary jar of flour, one species eventually eliminated the other, primarily because it was more active in destroying immature stages of the other species. If, however, early in the course of the competition, small glass tubes were introduced into the jar of flour, both species populations did survive. In this case, a one-niche habitat was changed sufficiently by the introduction of small glass tubes to become a two-niche habitat.

The first reaction of many soil microbiologists to Gause's principle might well be that his principle, even though quite applicable to the problem of competition among higher plants and animals, is hardly applicable to microbial ecology in the soil. Discussions of the soil life almost invariably emphasize that the soil literally swarms with microbes. There are indeed millions or even billions of unicellular organisms per gram of soil. It is also well known that the soil flora and fauna are very complex, consisting of hundreds of species. So far as Gause's principle is concerned, however, we may reasonably presume that many of the species present at a given time in a given soil are resting or dormant and that their ecological significance must be quite analogous to ungerminated but viable seeds in a plant community.

That considerable microbial dormancy must exist in the soil became impressed on me recently when I undertook to reconcile the known output of respiratory carbon dioxide from soil with the numbers of microorganisms in soil as estimated by generally accepted laboratory procedures. The respiratory output from soil is subject to quite precise measurement. Using some standard estimates of microbial numbers in soil and some standard estimates for rate of carbon dioxide production per bacterial cell as measured for resting cells in laboratory culture, the calculable output of respiratory carbon dioxide was found to be many times the output of carbon dioxide as actually measured for soil. The only plausible conclusion was that a goodly part of the soil microflora must be, for all intents and purposes, in a dormant condition.

Why should a sizable number of the soil organisms be dormant at any given time? The primary reason, even though by no means the sole reason, is undoubtedly the lack of suitable and available energy material. In some of the recent literature dealing with the phenomenon of soil fungistasis and with the mechanisms involved therein, there appear statements to the effect that there is no shortage of available food materials in the soil or in the soil solution. Any such concept appears unreconcilable with a mountainous microbiological literature concerning the numbers and the distribution of organisms in the soil. Wherever the available energy material is abundant in soil, microorganisms are also usually abundant. However efficient or inefficient the laboratory technician, he usually will find more microorganisms in the presence of plant or animal residues than in their absence. He can expect a higher microbial population in the rhizoplane than in root-free soil, as well as a higher population in the upper layers of the soil profile than in the deeper layers.

This emphasis on the perennial shortage of available nutrients or energy material in soil is not to affirm that microbial activity in a soil faithfully mirrors the quantity of organic material in soil nor to deny that many other factors may also be influential. The current emphasis on food shortage and microbial dormancy is primarily to point out that ecological niches need not be postulated for every one of the many microorganisms that can be seen in or cultured from soil.

Among the active microbial species in soil, food specialization makes possible the existence of a large number of ecological niches within any given habitat. Even in such a specialized and restricted habitat as the rhizoplane of an individual plant, it is probable that most of the microbial species that are present therein are not competitive. A wide assortment of materials are known to be exuded or sloughed from root surfaces. The composition of the organic residues that reach the soil is similarly complex. The microbial specialization that occurs in what is glibly termed the mineralization process must be enormous. Many of the microbial species that are involved must be in separate ecological niches and therefore are not in actual competition. Indeed, many times their relations are more likely commensalistic.

One of the simplest examples that comes quickly to mind is that involving the nitrifying bacteria. Ammonia commonly is one product of the mineralization cycle. But even its oxidation is stepwise. For the most part its oxidation to nitrite is carried out by the genus *Nitrosomonas,* and the oxidation of the nitrite to nitrate, by the genus *Nitrobacter.* The two genera are not in competition for energy-yielding substrate material. Inasmuch as both are obligate aerobes, perhaps someone will raise the point that the two genera are in competition for oxygen. This may well be true. However, it ill avails *Nitrobacter* to compete successfully for and use up the available oxygen supply, because in so doing it would be blocking the formation of nitrite, its energy-yielding substrate. Nor does *Nitrosomonas* suffer materially by the extent to which *Nitrobacter* consumes available oxygen. Ammonia is reasonably stable in soil, as well as a very specialized substrate, and so it really makes little difference whether the oxidation is accomplished on Tuesday or on Wednesday.

Even when one considers a substrate that is utilizable by a number of organisms, as for example cellulose, any number of biotic and abiotic factors may come into play and serve to make what is potentially a joint substratum into a single-niche substratum.

An example is the recent work of Keynan, Henis, and Keller (1961). They determined the soil organisms emerging as dominant when soil crumbs were seeded on cellulose presented as strips of filter paper and as strips of cellophane. On the filter paper, *Cellvibrio* and *Cytophaga* became dominant, and on the cellophane, *Stachybotrys.* Further studies revealed that cellophane was not a suitable substrate for *Cellvibrio* even when presented to this bacterium free from competing microorganisms. Apparently some unrecognized abiotic factor served to make cellulose in the form of cellophane unacceptable to *Cellvibrio.* The emergence of *Stachybotrys* as dominant following use of a mixed soil inoculant can therefore hardly be considered as an example of successful competition by *Stachybotrys* over *Cellvibrio.*

On the other hand, cellulose filter paper strips presented to *Stachybotrys* either in monoculture or in mixed culture in the presence of a commercially produced antibiotic antibacterial to *Cellvibrio* did serve as an entirely suitable substrate for *Stachybotrys.* Therefore it appears reasonable that in mixed culture on filter paper the two genera are in competition and that *Cellvibrio* is the successful competitor. Keynan and co-workers noted further that in mixed culture the propagules of *Stachybotrys* started to grow, but very quickly became arrested in their development. No filtrable or diffusable substances that could be held responsible for the antagonism were detected.

For the moment at least, this observed colonization of filter paper by *Cellvibrio* in the presence of *Stachybotrys* can be construed as an example of competition, and even as one wherein diffusible antibiotics are not operative. The qualification of "for the moment at least" appears desirable. Eventually, some explanation of the effective mechanism involved will almost certainly be published—perhaps it is already published but unseen by me. Once the precise explanation is known, then very probably the successful dominance of the one organism over the other will be called something other than competition.

At this point let me summarize very briefly the discussion that has been offered thus far. Doubt has been cast on both the originality and the judgment of the microbiologists in their listing of certain items as objects of microbial competition. Doubt has been cast on the concept that the soil contains a teeming mass of active microorganisms that are fiercely competitive for common substrates. Rather, the soil organisms have been viewed, in the words of Hutner (1961), as a "consortium of chemical specialists," within which, as befits a consortium, the members are more apt to be cooperative than competitive. Finally, a question has been raised as to whether specific interrelations now termed as competition will continue to be so designated once it becomes known precisely how the competitive dominance is achieved. It is against this backdrop of pessimism that I wish to raise a final question. What are the future prospects for the study of competition and how can the concept of competition be applied in the control of soil-borne diseases?

Opportunities in the study of competition appear almost limitless. What needs to be known can almost be equated to all that is still unknown about microbial ecology in the soil. Herein lies the real challenge. When I undertook to prepare this assignment, I was convinced that the *sine qua non* was a precise definition of competition. My thinking has since changed to the extent that I am now willing to agree with Beament (1961) that competition is neither a limited nor a precisely definable phenomenon, nor should it be. The concept of competition might well be considered simply as a challenge to find out why one or another species is to be found where it is found in the soil. As rapidly as that information is obtained, the answers most probably will be given in terms of specific or nonspecific antibiotics, or growth rates, or specific enzyme equipment. One might even go so far as to say that the objective in studying competition is the same as the objective of the actual phenomenon itself—namely, to eliminate competition. Certainly this provides no limited or precisely definable assignment.

Once it becomes known just why one or another species is to be found in a particular niche at a particular time as well as just what other species if any are able to overlap into this niche, then there arises opportunity for disturbing the one-niche environment of an undesirable species; or, in the case of an overlapping occupancy of a single microenvironment by a desirable and an undesirable species, of tipping the balance in favor of the former. In a sense this is being done currently or at least being attempted, mostly on a trial and error basis, with organic-matter amendments, chemical or fertilizer additions, microclimate modifications, or tillage practices. Such ecological information as is currently being obtained by direct or plate counts on treated soils or by testing the antagonisms of selected isolates against the pathogen in vitro in the laboratory barely scratches the surface of what needs to be known. In many instances all that is being determined is whether some measure of disease control is achieved. Frequently our results are so strikingly successful that neither we ourselves nor our colleagues can duplicate them. At other times they are so near the borderline of failure that one must ask the statistician whether or not they are significant. More extensive

knowledge concerning the interactions and interferences of microorganisms within their habitats in soil undoubtedly will lead to improvement in management practices and in turn to more successful disease control.

It matters little whether the concept of competition is ever accorded any credit for these improvements. As successful applications are achieved, almost certainly the solution will be viewed simply as a physical or chemical or tillage treatment, and not as an application of the concept of competition. Perhaps this is as it should be. A concept that deals with a phenomenon that is neither limited nor precisely definable should not expect precise and definitive credit for the fruits of its application in the control of soil-borne diseases.

LITERATURE CITED

BAIL, O. 1929. Ergebnisse experimenteller Populationsforschung. Z. Immunitätsforsch. 60: 1-22.

BEAMENT, W. L. 1961. The role of physiology in adaptation and competition between animals. p. 62-71. *In* F. L. Milthorpe [ed.], Mechanisms in biological competition, Symp. Soc. Exptl. Biol. 15: 62-71. Cambridge University Press, London.

CHITTY, D. 1957. Self-regulation of numbers through changes in viability. Cold Spr. Harbor Symp. Quant. Biol. 22: 277-280.

CHRISTIAN, J. J. 1950. The adreno-pituitary system and population cycles in mammals. J. Mammal. 31: 247-259.

CHRISTIAN, J. J. 1956. Adrenal and reproductive responses to population size in mice from freely growing populations. Ecology 37: 258-273.

CLARK, F. E. 1949. Soil microorganisms and plant roots. Advan. Agron. 1: 241-288.

CLEMENTS, F. E. 1907. Plant physiology and ecology. A. Constable and Co., London. 315 p.

CLEMENTS, F. E. 1916. Plant succession: an analysis of the development of vegetation. Carnegie Inst. Wash. Publ. 242, 512 p.

CLEMENTS, F. E., J. E. WEAVER, and H. C. HANSON. 1929. Plant competition: an analysis of community functions. Carnegie Inst. Wash. Publ. 398, 340 p.

CLEMENTS, F. E., and V. E. SHELFORD. 1939. Bio-ecology. John Wiley and Sons, New York. 425 p.

CROMBIE, A. C. 1947. Interspecific competition. J. Animal Ecol. 16: 44-73.

DONALD, C. M. 1956. Competition among pasture plants. Proc. 7th Intern. Grasslands Conf., Palmerston North, N. Z., p. 80-90.

ECKER, R. E., and W. R. LOCKHART. 1961. Relationships between nutrient concentration and total growth. J. Bacteriol. 82: 80-84.

ELTON, C. 1946. Competition and the structure of ecological communities. J. Animal Ecol. 15: 54-68.

GARRETT, S. D. 1950. Ecology of the root-infecting fungi. Biol. Rev. 25: 220-254.

GARRETT, S. D. 1956. Biology of root-infecting fungi. Cambridge University Press, London and New York. 292 p.

GAUSE, G. F. 1934. The struggle for existence. Williams & Wilkins, Baltimore, Md. 163 p.

HARPER, J. L. 1961. Approaches to the study of plant competition. *In* F. L. Milthorpe [ed.], Mechanisms in biological competition, Symp. Soc. Exptl. Biol. 15: 1-39. Cambridge University Press, London.

HUTNER, S. H. 1961. The environment and growth: protozoan origins of metazoan responsitivities. p. 1-18. *In* G. G. Meynell and H. Gooder [ed.], Microbial reaction to environment, Cambridge University Press, London.

JACKMAN, R. H. 1960. Competition between pasture species for nutrients from the soil. p. 75-83. *In* Sheepfarming Annual for 1960, Massey Agr. College, Palmerston North, N. Z.

KEYNAN, A., Y. HENIS, and P. KELLER. 1961. Factors

influencing the competition of the cellulose-decomposing microflora on soil crumb plates. Nature (London) 191: 307.

LACK, D. 1945. Ecology of closely related species with special reference to cormorant (*Phalocrocorax carbo*) and shag (*P. aristotelis*). J. Animal Ecol. 14: 12-16.

MILNE, A. 1961. Definition of competition among animals. *In* F. L. Milthorpe [ed.], Mechanisms in biological competition, Symp. Soc. Exptl. Biol. 15: 40-61. Cambridge University Press, London.

MONOD, J. 1949. The growth of bacterial cultures. Ann. Rev. Microbiol. 3: 371-394.

MUNDAY, K. A. 1961. Aspects of stress phenomena. *In* F. L. Milthorpe [ed.] Mechanisms in biological competition, Symp. Soc. Exptl. Biol. 15: 168-189. Cambridge University Press, London.

ODUM, E. P. 1959. Fundamentals of ecology. W. B. Saunders Co., Philadelphia and London. 546 p.

PARK, D. 1960. Antagonism—the background of soil fungi. p. 148-159. *In* D. Parkinson and J. S. Waid [ed.], The ecology of soil fungi, Liverpool University Press, Liverpool.

PHILIP, J. P. 1955. Note on the mathematical theory of animal population dynamics and a recent fallacy. Australian J. Zool. 3: 287-294.

SALISBURY, S. D. 1944. Antibiotics and competition. Nature (London) 153: 170.

STOTZKY, G., and A. G. NORMAN. 1961. Factors limiting microbial activities in soil. Arch. Mikrobiol. 40: 341-382.

WAKSMAN, S. A. 1952. Soil microbiology. John Wiley and Sons, New York. 356 p.

► DISCUSSION OF F. E. CLARK PAPER

M. Alexander:

I wish to avoid any overt signs of semantic sensitivity. Defining competition for the purposes of my question as a rivalry for limited supplies of essential nutrient elements, would you speculate on the relative significance in soil of competition in this sense and toxin production? Further, would you care to comment on the relative importance of saprophytic bacteria and saprophytic fungi as competitors of pathogenic fungi?

F. E. Clark:

I believe that shortages of substrate materials, or the conditions of almost chronic starvation confronting the soil microorganisms, are more important in limiting soil microbial activity than are soil toxins. Admitting that it is dangerous to generalize about the relative importance of the saprophytic bacteria and the saprophytic fungi as competitors of the pathogenic fungi, I would suspect that at least under some soil conditions the saprophytic fungi are the more likely to be in competition with the pathogenic fungi, inasmuch as these two groups should be the more likely to attempt to occupy the same ecological niche and hence to be in competition.

R. R. Baker:

Lignin and chitin added together to soil reduce severity of *Fusarium* root rot of bean. The more nitrogen added to the system, the better the control. One of the possible explanations for this may be competition for simple carbon substrate. Addition of lignin-chitin may stimulate populations of microorganisms able to utilize complex substrates. Simple carbohydrates become limiting since the organisms are also capable of utilizing them. It is known that *Fusarium solani* f. *phaseoli* requires simple carbon compounds (and nitrogen) not only for penetration and infection but also for germination. Thus, control might be explained by postulating that simple carbon compounds were not available to the pathogen. Addition of small amounts of glucose to the lignin-chitin system nullifies control, thus contributing evidence for competition.

F. E. Clark:

The type of work that you summarized provides a good example of the way that I think we need to study competition. We need to sort out the precise mechanisms that are involved so that we can speak specifically of them and not simply use the term competition as a sort of a vague umbrella.

A. Kerr:

I agree with you that microorganisms are unlikely to compete for water. On the other hand, water is important in competition in at least two ways. Firstly, it has a marked influence on the diffusion of soluble materials, and secondly, as soil dries, water becomes discontinuous. This inhibits bacterial activity much more than fungal activity. Perhaps the difference between plant diseases favoured by dry soil versus wet soil could be explained in these terms.

F. E. Clark:

I see no real disagreement in our thinking. Certainly water has a marked influence on the diffusion of soluble materials and, also, as soil dries, water becomes discontinuous. Referring specifically to your statement "as soil dries," I am of the opinion that environmental factors (evaporation, evapotranspiration) are responsible, and not that competition is causing the utilization or removal of the water, or that microbes are consuming water to the extent that they are playing a key role in the soil drying. Using the narrow or "rivalry for" definition of competition, I am questioning the competition of microorganisms for water, and not the importance of water to microorganisms.

J. E. DeVay:

I am interested in your reasons for omitting temperature as a factor contributing to the competition for survival among soil microorganisms. I ask this question because some years ago doubt was raised in Minnesota and New York as to the relative importance of *Diplodia zeae* and *Gibberella zeae* as causal agents of root and stalk rots of corn. In northern areas *G. zeae* was considered more important whereas in southern states such as Missouri and Oklahoma, *D. zeae* was considered more important. Dr. Koehler resolved this apparent contradiction by a survey of these organisms as causal agents of root and stalk rot of corn in Illinois. He found that *D. zeae* was of greater importance in the southern areas of Illinois but that *G. zeae* became more important in the more northerly and cooler areas of Illinois.

F. E. Clark:

I don't omit temperature and numerous other soil factors as being of biological significance. I simply did not list temperature as a factor for which microorganisms compete, nor is it hardly ever so listed in the ecological literature. Factors usually listed as objects of microbial competition are food, water, space, and oxygen. My discussion has been focused on the validity of these items. An organism can presumably use up food, water, or oxygen, or occupy space. In my discussion I did emphasize, among other factors, both temperature and acidity as being of great environmental importance—so great indeed that I stated that I preferred to think of competition for a food supply or substrate as being for that substrate "in the specific form and under the specific conditions in which that substrate is presented." I have not attempted to discuss in any detail the many environmental influences, nor the several types of biological interaction other than competition, that may affect microbial dominance in soil.

W. A. Kreutzer:

Would you agree that competition, or competitive utilization of substrates in soil by heterotrophic microorganisms, can be defined only in terms of *specific* substrate?

F. E. Clark:

I would go even further than saying that competition is for a specific substrate by saying that competition should be viewed both in terms of a given substrate and the specific conditions under which that substrate is presented.

H. Katznelson:

Granted that there may be a considerable amount of space in soil, we have to consider the available space on particular substrates, or, if you like, biological space which may even include oxygen and water. It is not at all inconceivable that a fragment of organic matter might be completely colonized by a few types of organisms to the physical exclusion of others; bacteria with short generation time may easily inundate such a substrate whereas more slowly growing types are left out. Root hairs may be so completely covered with bacteria that other organisms such as fungi and possibly nematodes can't get through, so they have to wait; hence competition.

Competition for vitamins and accessory growth factors seems to me also to be an important element in microbial interactions and one which cannot be overlooked. A number of fungus pathogens have specific vitamin requirements, as do some saprophytic fungi and quite a few bacteria.

F. E. Clark:

In the specific sense that you have chosen to discuss space, namely, encirclement of food particles or root hairs to the exclusion of other microbes, and hence unavailability of the substrate to the excluded organisms, my reply is simply that organisms cannot compete for food which is unavailable to them, either spatially or enzymatically. If an organism does not have access to the substrate, whether the reason be a dry soil zone, a barrier of living cells, or by reason of lack of oxygen

(as in the case of a glycolytic obligate aerobe presented with glucose in a fully anaerobic environment), then that organism cannot compete for the given substrate, any more than a noncellulolytic organism can compete for cellulose. In the instance you have cited, I would prefer to consider that lack of high growth rate, or intolerance to antibiotics, or inability to produce antibiotics, or lack of oxygen, or at least some factor other than space, more properly should be implicated. Likewise, in my plea for specificity in the use of the concept of competition, I would not want to define space as inclusive at times even of oxygen and water. I fully agree with you that vitamins and growth factors can be important factors in microbial interactions. The paper mentions briefly their role, as well as that of nitrogen and other mineral nutrients, in the general problem of substrate availability.

A. G. Norman:

Although in general agreement with Dr. Clark's conclusion that competition for substrate is the predominant situation in soils, had there been time I would have liked the opportunity of debating some other aspects of the topic of competition. The soil population is one which lives up to its income or available capital in terms of food supply but one has to remember that soil in general does not have substrate uniformity, and that one is, in fact, dealing with innumerable microhabitats that differ in substrate nature and supply.

I would associate myself with the previous two speakers in questioning whether Dr. Clark adequately treated the situation with respect to water. The water film constitutes the ecological niche to which some organisms are limited, and is the only space which they can colonize. Small changes in percent water content may alter quite disproportionately the volume of micropools, contact rings, etc. Changes in water content also are accompanied by diverse physicochemical consequences that in turn may have effects on competitive abilities.

F. E. Clark:

Apparently I have failed to make sufficiently clear my position concerning the lack of microbial competition for water. I do readily admit that soil organisms are profoundly influenced by the quantity and quality of the water available to them, that they need water, that small changes in the water content may alter soil microhabitats, or change microbial physicochemical abilities. What I have been attempting to emphasize is that physical removal or consumption of water by microorganisms is negligible, that they are possibly more likely to add metabolic water to their environment than to decrease its water content. In short, changes in the amount of soil water are brought about by factors which do not involve the consumptive use of the water supply by one microbe and thus leave an insufficient supply for a competing microorganism. I believe that we can remove the concept of competition for water and still admit that water is an extremely important environmental factor—just as pH or temperature or other factors can also determine microbial growth, survival, or dominance.

D. Barbe:

Could you comment on mechanisms of competition by means of antibiotic production? How does the antibiotic work to hinder the competing organisms? I am thinking particularly of the preemption of food particles by being impregnated with the preempting organism's own "brand of poison," as it were.

F. E. Clark:

Your question indicates that you prefer to consider antibiotic production as a mechanism of competition—in short, that you define competition in a broad rather than in a narrow sense. In my paper I have attempted to point out several different points of view concerning the role of antibiotics in the phenomenon of competition. Personally, I prefer to think of an antibiotic as acting as a definitive factor, just as temperature or acidity or water. I have stated that the concept of competition might well be considered as a challenge to find out why one or another species is to be found where it is found in the soil. As rapidly as that information is obtained, the answers should be given in terms of specific antibiotics, or growth rates, or enzymes, or temperature, or whatever other specificity that can be delineated.

►

The Role of Biological Eradication in Root-Disease Control in Replantings of Hevea brasiliensis

R. A. FOX—*Pathological Division, The Rubber Research Institute of Malaya, Kuala Lumpur.*

►

This paper reports the practical utilization of biological competition, antagonism, and eradication in the control of root diseases of a perennial crop where one possible solution—crop rotation with nonsusceptible plants—cannot be used. The concept of biological control is not limited to effects produced by microorganisms but is extended, as has been done by Dr. Garrett in his paper in this symposium, to effects of the roots of higher plants including, in this case, those of the host. The principles involved may briefly be summarised as follows.

Chemicals are used, before the new stand of rubber trees is planted, to mediate competition between parasites and saprophytes for woody substrates, and thereby inhibit the extension of existing sites of infection and reduce the exploitation of potential new ones. A planted ground cover of creeping legumes, which protects the soil against insolation, erosion, and leaching, also provides conditions favouring rapid decay of timber and thus hastens the process of biological eradication by the succession of saprophytes in infected wood. The cover plants also improve the physical structure and nutrient status of the soil and, concomitant with the general stimulus to microbial activity which results from those improvements, there is an increase in antagonistic activity. Cover plants also act as a decoy or bait crop, breaking down large and potentially dangerous inocula into smaller and shorter-lived units. Further, they encourage the development of the host's feeding roots, which also help in the breakdown of infected wood.

Control procedures after planting make the maximum use of the foregoing biological phenomena and of the host's resistance and include a method of detecting infected trees which automatically discriminates between effective and ineffective sources of infection.

In a recent discussion on cultural practices in disease control, Stevens (1960) has commented that the process of disease control by cultural measures is often obscure as well as indirect. He further notes that "No association is more inextricably close than that between cultural measures and biological control. In many instances we are not yet even certain whether the ultimate effectiveness of a given practice is the one or the other, particularly when available evidence suggests that the immediate result is so to alter the environment that the growth of non-pathogenic organisms is accelerated at the expense of pathogenic forms."

The survey of experiments given below and the discussion which follows is an attempt to show that whilst on the one hand we alter an environment to favour saprophytes at the expense of pathogens, paradoxically, by another operation, we encourage growth of the pathogens—to the ultimate detriment, however, of their inoculum potential (sensu Garrett, 1956*b*, p. 79).

Details of postwar field experiments are given in Annual Reports of the Rubber Research Institute of Malaya; the results of many of these have been summarised by Hutchison (1961). Direct comparisons between experiments are not always admissible, especially because of changes in control procedures and costs of labour. Unless otherwise stated the term "creeping leguminous covers" refers to a mixture of *Pueraria phaseoloides* Benth., *Centrosema pubescens* Benth., and *Calopogonium mucunoides* Desv.

THE PROBLEM AND THE PATHOGENS.—Malaya has over one third of the estimated 12 million acres of rubber planted in the Far East. As the commercial life of a rubber tree is 40 years or less, there is, on the average, a very large acreage to replant each year. The rubber grower in Malaya is fortunate in that the only killing diseases he usually has to combat are those of the root system, but these diseases can decimate plantations and yet, being underground, are hard to detect, so that their capacity for causing damage cannot easily be forecast at the time of preparing a new planting or replanting. Infection of the young rubber tree usually occurs by direct contact between its roots and infected roots or boles of trees or, sometimes, from surface timber which may be infected after felling.

Losses in the early years of most new rubber plantings on jungle land are usually low, a reflection of the uneven distribution of susceptible hosts in the jungle. In a recent tree-poisoning experiment in 20 acres of jungle, it was found that, after all commercial timber had been removed, 2,711 trees of more than 12 inches girth remained, comprising 361 species representing 144 genera in 45 families. The "compound interest" (Garrett, 1956*b*) of disease which can accrue when the root systems of so heterogeneous a flora are replaced with those of a uniformly susceptible species is evident. If the planter neglects disease control on his older and relatively unprofitable rubber, the position may be further aggravated by the time he comes to replant.

The aerial photograph in Fig. 1, taken in mid 1962,

shows an example of the havoc which root disease of rubber may cause. It illustrates a new planting where, as a consequence of neglect during the war years, the estate was forced to abandon an attempt to control white-root disease, caused by *Fomes lignosus* (Klotzsch) Bres. In some places there are gaps in an otherwise continuous stand; in others only scattered groups of trees remain in a continuous stand of weeds. Red-root disease, caused by *Ganoderma pseudoferreum* (Wakef.) van Over. et Steinm., may also be very serious, extending, if uncontrolled, to produce large confluent vacant patches. The common names of these diseases derive from the characteristic colour of their epiphytic growth on the root surface. Of far less importance is *Fomes noxius* Corner, causing brown-root disease, and *Ustulina zonata* (Lev.) Sacc., which, lacking epiphytic growth and distinguishing external features, is called simply ustulina root rot. The last-named fungus also differs from the others in that in one situation which has been studied observations have led to the conclusion that it is not a root-inhabiting fungus (sensu Garrett, 1950). Full descriptions of these diseases are given in Planters' Bulletin 10 (Rubber Research Institute of Malaya, 1954) and illustrated in Hilton (1959).

In the early years after rubber is replanted, most losses are caused by *Fomes lignosus. Ganoderma pseu-*

doferreum and *F. noxius* appear later and make slower progress; their epiphytic growth ahead of the penetrated part of the root is usually to be measured in inches, whereas feet are more appropriate units for *F. lignosus. Ustulina zonata* progresses slowly within roots and rarely kills a group of trees because it can be detected by death or obvious symptoms in an infected tree before much tree-to-tree spread by root contact can occur. Lacking epiphytic growth, it is less influenced by soil conditions than are the other three pathogens, and usually enters the base of a tree as a wound parasite. As it differs so markedly from the other pathogens, it will not be discussed further.

THE OBJECTIVES.—Rubber trees are planted at a high initial stand per acre to allow for casual failures and root-disease losses. Their numbers are later reduced to about 120 per acre by thinning out the less vigorous or lower-yielding trees. Unselected seed at one time was planted at densities as high as 500 per acre. Now seeds from proved seed gardens are rarely planted at densities greater than 250 per acre, and seedlings for budding with selected clones at not more than 180 per acre. One object of root-disease control is to ensure an adequate and uniform stand from which to thin. Large gaps in the planting rows represent inefficient use

Fig. 1. Aerial photograph illustrating the results of abandoning root-disease control measures; the dominant pathogen causing nearly all the losses in this area is *Fomes lignosus.*

of the land and, as the trees grow older, these may become centres of progressive wind damage.

The aim of our current recommendations, briefly summarised below, is to eradicate all disease before the final stand is selected. Foliage symptoms in the young trees indicate where disease is active, but usually too late for the infection to be treatable; thus we sacrifice a proportion of the stand for the benefit of the field as a whole. This is neither a sacrifice of crop nor a loss of capital; until a tree comes into tapping it has only a hypothetical value, for it may at an early age be thinned as a runt. Even after tapping commences it has only a potential value, though it is bringing in some revenue, for it may later be thinned on the basis of yield. Only when the final stand is selected does the individual tree represent a direct proportion of the capital expended and, of course, an equivalent proportion of future revenue.

CURRENT RECOMMENDATIONS.—*Preplanting.*—

A. All trees of the old planting, diseased or otherwise, are treated alike: namely, the tree is either poisoned while still standing or, if it is felled, the stump is poisoned and the cut surface immediately treated with creosote. The poisons used are either sodium arsenite or *n*-butyl, 2,4,5-T.

B. A mixed cover of creeping legumes is established as soon as possible between the new planting rows. The cover plants are not allowed to grow across the planting rows, and a clean-weeded strip, some 6 ft wide, is maintained.

Postplanting.—

C. Quarterly rounds of foliage inspection begin when the young stand is about a year old. Where foliage symptoms are found the diseased tree is removed and the "collars" of its neighbours inspected. The inspection is continued along the row in either direction until a disease-free tree is found. Diseased trees detected by collar inspection are treated if possible and, together with all trees which have been collar-inspected, given a distinctive mark with the date of inspection and treatment. The marked trees have their collars reinspected in the course of later routine rounds of foliage inspection.

D. Disease sources within the clean-weeded planting row are eradicated and burnt, together with any diseased roots of the young trees. If the sources of infection are outside the planting row they are left alone, diseased roots being traced only as far as the edge of the row.

E. If a stump outside the planting row persistently causes new infections, it is isolated by a trench, all lateral roots are severed and infected ones removed, the bole of the stump being left perched on its tap-root.

F. A collar inspection is made of a part of each field before final thinning commences, primarily to detect centres of the slower-moving pathogens *Ganoderma pseudoferreum* and *Fomes noxius,* also because the larger trees are proportionately slower in developing foliage symptoms of root disease. The area sampled

is extended only if much disease is found in parts of a field where foliage inspection had previously failed to disclose it.

Trees are usually planted some 6 to 12 ft apart within the rows and the distance between rows varies from 18 to 30 ft. *Hevea brasiliensis* (Muell.) Arg. is a vigorous tree and by the age of 3 to 4 years the roots have spread between the planting rows and begun to intermingle. Recommendations A, part of D, and even E would seem, therefore, to be somewhat hazardous; yet field experiments have shown that they are entirely practicable. Over the last decade we have recommended carrying out fewer and fewer physical operations. Leguminous creeping covers shift the microbial balance and physical conditions in our favour and the less we disturb the soil (by digging) the better.

EXPERIMENTS AND OBSERVATIONS.—Experiments are referred to by the code numbers used in the Annual Reports of the Rubber Research Institute of Malaya.

Disposal of the old stand.—Tree poisoning and stump poisoning are both established clearing procedures which are satisfactory from the point of view of root-disease incidence. We regard the employment of one or the other as an essential operation.

Possible reasons for the observed superiority of tree poisoning over stump poisoning have been given (Hutchison, 1961; Fox, 1961a); colonisation by wind-borne spores of the cut surfaces of stumps and of trunks left lying on the ground and of the latter by vegetative growth of the pathogens from infected roots in the ground below them are known to occur. Colonisation of timber on the ground has been discussed and illustrated (Rubber Research Institute of Malaya, 1957), and the less satisfactory results of stump poisoning in experiment CI-51 as compared with experiment G-50 (Hutchison, 1961) have been in part explained by the fact that in the former experiment the felled trees were left on the ground whereas in the latter they were removed.

Evidence has been presented by Hutchison (1961) from experiments G-50, CI-51, and CI-56 that a wood preservative applied to the cut surface of stumps after felling inhibits spore colonisation. In the first two experiments, where a proprietary wood preservative was used, there were some indications of a beneficial effect. Creosote was used in experiment CI-56 and in another concurrent experiment at the Rubber Research Institute of Malaya Experiment Station, with results that were significant.

Tree poisoning is not only more efficient than stump poisoning in reducing losses of young trees but is also cheaper. These savings, however, must be offset against three important factors; there is danger of personal injury and of damage to young trees by falling trees or branches, and the cost of clearing up the fallen litter is accompanied by increased weeding costs. For 2 months, and often longer, poisoned trees can be left standing without presenting any danger to the labourers. The greater the time interval between poisoning and felling the more the trunks and branches will be invaded by saprophytes. The maximum period that can be allowed is limited by the amount of loss of production which can be accepted.

Sodium arsenite poisoning is a satisfactory procedure for disposing of the old stand (Napper, 1939), which has the added benefit, as compared with leaving stumps of felled trees unpoisoned, of greatly reducing disease incidence in the young stand. Unfortunately sodium arsenite is largely denied to small-holders (who produce over 40% of Malayan rubber), and to some estates, by restrictions on its use imposed by a poisons ordinance (Rubber Research Institute of Malaya, 1953). In testing possible alternative arboricides, pilot experiments indicated that 2,4,5-T could give as quick a kill as sodium arsenite (Rubber Research Institute of Malaya, 1955). In a preliminary report on a series of studies designed to further our understanding of factors affecting decay of rubber wood, Newsam, John, and Rao (1961) have also shown that 2,4,5-T, whether used as a tree or stump poison, induces markedly faster decay than sodium arsenite. This had been anticipated because the presence of arsenic must result in some degree of preservation. Altson (reported by Newsam, 1953) found concentrations of arsenic in poisoned stumps too low to inhibit the growth of *Fomes lignosus* or *Ganoderma pseudoferreum*, though it might locally reach levels inhibitory to *F. noxius*. It is reasonable to assume that some other wood-decaying organisms might also be inhibited.

Some aspects of the foregoing interrelated problems were investigated in experiments CI-56, J-57, and SR-57. In experiment CI-56, trees were poisoned with either sodium arsenite or 2,4,5-T and then felled immediately, 1 month, or 2 months after poisoning. Using postplanting control procedures closely similar to those given under "Current Recommendations," delayed felling showed the expected advantage of lower losses. As a stump poison, 2,4,5-T was superior to sodium arsenite whether or not the cut surface was treated with creosote; where felling was delayed it was not consistently superior to sodium arsenite but the results were satisfactory.

Although 2,4,5-T is more costly than sodium arsenite, it can be unreservedly recommended for use by small-holders and for water-catchment areas on estates, where, of course, sodium arsenite cannot be used.

Experiment J-57 was sited in an area where nearly all the disease in the old stand was caused by *Ganoderma pseudoferreum*, whereas *Fomes lignosus* was the dominant pathogen in SR-57. Largely as a result of improved methods of postplanting control which have been followed (basically as described in "Current Recommendations" above), losses to date have been too low for preplanting treatment effects to be established with confidence. Experiment SR-57 has again shown tree poisoning and delayed felling to be superior to stump poisoning. The removal of surface timber has resulted in lower losses than nonremoval, but the cost is so great, in relation to the potential value of the very small number of additional young trees saved, that the operation is quite uneconomic.

Apart from the general problem of disposing of the old stand, there is the special problem of what to do with trees known to be diseased. Before the last war planters were advised to inspect the boles of trees of the old stand prior to replanting a field, to remove all trees found to be diseased, and to dig over disease patches to remove all infected roots. Although these procedures were sometimes effective in reducing subsequent losses (Altson, 1950a) they had not been adequately evaluated. Postwar increases in wages made such measures almost prohibitively expensive. Experiment CI-51 was in part designed to determine the value of partial or complete eradication of diseased trees of the old stand. Unfortunately accidents of randomisation gave anomalous results (Fox, 1961a). The design of experiments SR-57 and J-57 accommodated this problem. The cost of saving a given number of young trees must be evaluated against the fact, already stated, that the number of trees initially planted is considerably in excess of the number ultimately needed for tapping. The results to date for SR-57 are in the order expected but there is no possibility that the costs of preplanting expenditure for eradication will be recovered. Likewise, in experiment J-57 the total losses to date average 2 and 3 per acre respectively for the eradicated and noneradicated plots, a gain of but 1 young tree per acre in return for the preplanting cost of M$132 for eradicating an average of 28 diseased trees per acre from the old stand. We therefore recommend that all the old trees be treated the same way, by poisoning, as indicated under "Current Recommendations."

Detection of disease.—The notion of using the root system of the young tree to indicate the presence of root disease, in this case *Fomes lignosus*, was first advanced in 1914 by R. M. Richards in Malaya, and shortly afterwards in 1915 by H. Collanbrander working independently in Indonesia; reference to both their schemes was made by Brooks (1916). Napper (1932a) realised that the epiphytic habit of *F. lignosus*, *Ganoderma pseudoferreum*, and *F. noxius*, where superficial growth precedes penetration, could be utilised in a unified scheme of control (Napper, 1932b). In the light of experience, the method was subsequently modified (Napper, 1938) and his scheme of periodic rounds of tree-to-tree collar inspection as a method of detecting root disease was standard practice in Malaya until 1954 (Rubber Research Institute of Malaya, 1954) and was not radically changed until 1958 (Rubber Research Institute of Malaya, 1958).

Napper, possibly in search of economy (Fox, 1961a), laid down an experiment in 1941 to compare his standard recommendations with schemes based on detecting disease by foliage symptoms, but this was lost owing to unavoidable neglect in the war years. Altson (1950c) initiated an experiment in 1948 (P-48) to compare Napper's collar-inspection scheme with one based on detecting disease by foliage symptoms. For comparison there were plots receiving no treatment, where dead trees were recorded during routine rounds of inspection in the other schemes. The three procedures were designated by colour codes.

Green: Collar inspection; removal or treatment of infected trees; tracing and removal of sources of infection.

Red: Foliage inspection; treatment as in Green.

Yellow: No treatment.

This experiment had to be abandoned after 4 years, all the plots first being collar-inspected and the trees classified as to whether or not they were treatable. Surprisingly, the sums of the past and potential losses were about one third lower in the untreated plots than in the Green and Red plots, where they were equal. The same three systems were superimposed on experiment CI-51, and after 5½ years the recorded tree losses and tree treatments were as shown in Table 1.

TABLE 1. Experiment CI-51. Number of casualties per acre, after 5½ years, with three methods of controlling root disease

Control system	Number of trees	
	Lost	Treated
Green*	24	10
Red*	21	1
Yellow*	11	0

* For details see text.

The disastrous long-term results of not controlling root diseases were too well known for the results of a no-treatment policy to be taken at face value, but it appeared that the Red treatment might be modified by further curtailment of physical operations. In experiment G-50 it had been found that isolating sources of infection as opposed to eradicating them was not only cheaper but resulted in lower losses (Hutchison, 1961). In CI-56 we therefore retreated from physical operations still further and compared a modified Green treatment with a compromise between treatments Red and Yellow, appropriately designated Orange.

Recently it has been found that the losses in CI-51 must have been more nearly equal than was supposed at the time. Had the true position then been known it is doubtful if we would have introduced the Orange treatment of CI-56, described below, on which our current recommendations are based, and the savings in trees and capital expenditure which have resulted would have been greatly delayed.

Disposal of infected material.—The modified Green treatment in experiment CI-56 was essentially the control procedure recommended by Napper, except that disease sources and infected material were eradicated only if they were within the planting row; where they lay in the interrows they were isolated as has been described under E in "Current Recommendations." The Orange treatment consisted of regular rounds of foliage inspection accompanied by eradication as in the Green treatment, but where the sources of disease were outside the planting row they were left untouched, no digging being done in the cover plants in the interrows. A final assessment was made in August 1962 by collar-inspecting all trees to a depth of 2 ft and outwards along the lateral roots for 2 ft from the bole. The

excess cost of this final inspection has been omitted from the calculations, which, however, include a figure which would have applied to a normal inspection; the results are presented in Table 2.

TABLE 2. Experiment CI-56. Number of casualties and labour costs per acre, after 6 years, with two methods of controlling root disease

Control system	Number of trees		Labour costs, man-days
	Lost	Treated	
Green*	9.5	9.3	16.1
Orange*	8.0	3.6	4.6

* For details see text.

Cover plants and root disease.—In the past the main beneficial effect of cover plants in reducing disease losses has been considered to result from the physical conditions which they provide for encouraging decay and hastening the succession of saprophytes in infected wood. A good ground cover of creeping legumes creates ideal conditions for wood-rotting fungi (Newsam, John, and Rao, 1961). Their over-all effect has been described as biological eradication (Fox, 1961b). Altson (1953b) thought it likely that ground covers maintain the soil in a condition which favours the development of microorganisms antagonistic to the root parasites. Later it was shown that direct microbial antagonism by actinomycetes parasitic on *Fomes lignosus* is enhanced in the soil beneath cover plants (Fox, 1961a).

Nowadays rubber trees are not grown under conditions of clean-weeding so it would be pointless to establish large-scale experiments comparing bare soil with any potential new cover plant. Physical conditions most nearly approaching those obtaining with bare soil are now encountered in places where grasses have been allowed to grow. The grasses are mostly *Axonopus compressus* (Sw.) Beauv. and *Paspalum conjugatum* Berg. The data presented in Table 3 have been averaged

TABLE 3. Number of casualties per acre averaged from four comparable field experiments with different cover plants

Cover plants	Number of trees	
	Lost	Treated
Creeping legumes	15	29
Grasses	32	78

from four comparable cover-plant trials conducted by the Botanical and Soils Divisions of the Rubber Research Institute of Malaya at the Experiment Station and on cooperating estates.

Napper (1932a) reported that the over-all incidence of *Fomes lignosus* with three different leguminous cover plants was half that where the ground was clean-weeded. Experiment H-2, put down by Napper in 1938 and summarised by Altson (1950a), showed a reduction in incidence from 239 under clean-weeded conditions to 120 under creeping legumes. Cronshey and Barclay (1939), in a replanting experiment covering some 240 acres planted at a density of 300 trees per acre, compared the leguminous creeper *Pueraria phaseoloides* with clean-weeding. In a period of 18 months, beginning 6 months after planting, they recorded root-disease losses (mainly caused by *F. lignosus*) totalling 5,082 under clean-weeding and 2,212 for the legume plots.

Factors affecting the decay of rubber wood reported by Newsam, John, and Rao (1961) are being intensively studied in additional small-plot experiments. Losses of 17% in the presence of creeping legumes and 34% with bare soil 18 months after planting, were incurred at a time when no difference in the rate of rotting of stumps was discernible. On the other hand, at 24 months, when the amount of rotting was markedly higher with 2,4,5-T poisoning than where sodium arsenite had been used, there was no appreciable difference in the losses, which were 27% and 29% respectively. More interesting still are the early results from another experiment, replanted in November 1961, comparing the presence and absence of covers combined with inoculation or no inoculation of the stumps of the old stand with either *Fomes lignosus* or *Ganoderma pseudoferreum*. The first round of inspection was made in November 1962. No difference in the rates of rotting were evident, but 79 trees have died in the plots inoculated with *F. lignosus* where there is no cover, yet none has died in the *F. lignosus* plots under a legume cover. It is quite clear that other factors operate in the early years, before the beneficial effects of rotting per se are evident.

Host-parasite relations.—Garrett (1959) has recently paid tribute to contributions by mycologists working on tropical plantation crops in developing the notion of inoculum potential, particularly Petch (1921, 1928) and de Jonge (1933). A significant contribution to this subject was made earlier by Bancroft (1912). This paper is not readily available and brief quotations are therefore given. Bancroft had observed that under very damp conditions the mycelium of *Fomes lignosus* could spread out freely into heavy soils for nearly a foot from infected roots. He buried infected roots in soil which was kept damp and observed that "the mycelium will frequently spread through it, permeating it with white silky strands," and, "if the infected root be removed, the hyphae soon die, there being no evidence of mycelium in the soil at the end of four or five days after the root has been removed. Similarly, if the mycelium does not come into contact with any material from which it can derive nutriment it soon dies out. The growing mycelium does not appear to have any appreciable capacity for retaining its vitality when it is separated from its source of nutriment." As a sequel to those observations he placed infected roots in boxes of soil into which he allowed the mycelium to grow, removed the infected roots and then transplanted pairs of young rubber seedlings into the boxes. He commented that "I have made many attempts to infect young plants . . . but I have never obtained any positive results." Following this he used pieces of infected roots to inoculate 3-month-old seedlings and killed 13 of 18 plants so treated.

Bancroft clearly showed that infection was not a necessary sequel to the presence of the parasite. Petch (1921) established by observation the need for a food base, which de Jonge (1933) confirmed experimentally. That death was not a necessary sequel to infection was observed in East Java and the East Coast of Sumatra by Reydon (1931), who recorded 50-75% spontaneous recovery of trees infected by *Fomes lignosus* and 20% in the case of *Ganoderma pseudoferreum*, which might rise to 50% if drainage was improved. Spontaneous recovery was confirmed by de Jonge (1933) in his inoculation experiments with *F. lignosus* and by field observation. This led him to conclude that the fungus is but a feeble parasite.

Despite these early observations, there has been continued misunderstanding of their applicability to pre- and postplanting control measures, in relation to which we have coined the terms "fear factor" and "despair factor" (Fox, 1961*a*) and in the use—or abuse—of fungicides (Fox, 1961*b*).

Observations in experiments SY-60 and B-60 (Newsam, 1962) have shown (in a flat area of heavy alluvial clay, a situation where *Fomes lignosus* frequently causes severe losses) that up to 13% of trees with *more than half* the collar penetrated may heal spontaneously (B-60). In SY-60, sited on steeply sloping lateritic soil, the corresponding figure is 36%.

In experiment CI-51, the Yellow (no treatment) plots were collar-inspected during April 1957 to assess the extent of concealed disease. In one plot disease cases were either treated or eradicated. In the remaining seven plots 180 cases of *Fomes lignosus* were recorded but they were not treated. Five years later, in March 1962, 90 of these trees had either died or were dying. Only 4 of the remaining 90 required treatment, 86 showing no signs of infection other than irregular cavities or areas of callus tissue to indicate where they had once been penetrated. In the same experiment a comparison of the over-all figures for the Green (collar inspection) and Red (foliage inspection) detection schemes suggests that spontaneous healing occurred in about 50% of the cases of both *Ganoderma pseudoferreum* and *F. noxius*, and there are indications of similar effects from the uncompleted experiment P-48.

Apart from the expected phenomenon of wound-barrier formation, one of the most intriguing defence mechanisms is the reduction and destruction of infected wood by the feeding roots of the tree. Excellent illustrations of this have been given by John (1958, Figs. 6-9) for *Fomes lignosus*, but it commonly occurs also with wood invaded by *Ganoderma pseudoferreum*, *F. noxius*, and *Ustulina zonata*. It is, indeed, one of the common causes of failure in our inoculation experiments.

There is another defence mechanism which is peculiar to trees infected by *Ganoderma pseudoferreum*. At a distance of up to 2 or 3 ft ahead of the limit of penetration by the fungus, a lateral root will often produce, usually fairly close to the bole, a bushy mass of slender adventitious roots, as has been illustrated by Sharples (1936). These compensate to a considerable extent for the loss of absorbing rootlets cut off by the advance of the fungus. When successful wound-barrier formation occurs, halting the progress of the pathogen, it commonly takes place in the region where these adventitious roots have their origin. The mechanism has not been investigated. It may be that the pathogen liberates a root-inducing hormone or that one is induced in the tree as a response to some compound, possibly a toxin, produced by the fungus. The ability to produce a toxin certainly exists in *Fomes lignosus*. Several years ago it was found that immersion of leaf petioles in cell-free culture filtrates of this fungus caused a distortion of mature leaflets and prevented the expansion of young ones. Infiltration of young branches with the same filtrates induced the fall of mature leaves, and flushes of new leaves were pale and reduced in size, as occurs with trees naturally infected in the field. Seedlings grown in culture filtrates eventually wilted, the leaf distortion being usually, but not always, different from that induced by drought. Later Peries (1959) in Ceylon demonstrated toxin production using tomato seedlings as test plants.

Growth of the pathogens.—The difference in the rates of spread of the three parasites with epiphytic growth habits is, perhaps, more related to their mode of growth than to their intrinsic speed of growth. *Ganoderma pseudoferreum* is slow to grow in culture; on the other hand *Fomes noxius*, which in nature progresses at a rate comparable to that of *G. pseudoferreum*, grows faster in vitro when newly isolated than does *F. lignosus*. The last-named pathogen forms characteristic rhizomorphs but *G. pseudoferreum* and *F. noxius* develop a mycelial investment round the root. The hyphae of *G. pseudoferreum* aggregate into a tough skin, the outer layer of which is like that of a sclerotium; likewise the investing mycelium of *F. noxius* exudes a mucus which firmly binds particles of soil to it. Both these fungi might be said to consolidate their advance by protecting their lines of communication.

Consider a root of radius r with a completely encircling investment of fungus of thickness t: then the ratio of food (root) volume over fungus volume per unit length is $\dfrac{r^2}{t(2r+t)}$. On the other hand, with a fungus such as *Fomes lignosus* if there are, say, four strands of thickness t, the breadth of which would subtend an angle of $9°$, then the corresponding ratio is

$$\frac{10r^2}{t(2r+t)}$$

Assuming that in both examples the food reserves of the wood are equally mobilised, the strands have a potential for growth ten times greater than the investment, provided they can translocate adequately. Although the rhizomorph of *Fomes lignosus* is not highly organised, there is morphological differentiation into what it would be tempting to describe as "protective" and "vascular" hyphae were it not for the results obtained by Schütte (1956), who observed that the main paths of dye translocation in agaric fruit bodies did not coincide with areas of "vascular" hyphae. Whatever correlation there may or may not be between morphol-

ogy and function, the extent of epiphytic growth which occurs in the field indicates highly effective translocation. It might be argued that the ability to grow epiphytically for up to 15 ft is in part the result of feeding en route. Minute points of penetration beneath epiphytic growth have, indeed, been observed; but these are too small and too few to explain many observations of extensive penetration at the collar of a tree at the end of as much as 5 ft of epiphytic growth. In such cases inoculum potential (sensu Garrett, 1956b) sufficient to overcome the host's resistance is mobilised at the infection court by translocation.

In contrast to the other two parasites, *Fomes lignosus* might be described as adopting the principle of attack in force on a limited front employing its rapid rate of advance to outflank the host's defence (Fox, 1961b). It does not stop to consolidate and its lines of communication are open to attack.

The military analogies used above are convenient and as there is also an authoritative precedent (Garrett, 1956a) for similar use, they will be extended. My dictionary defines "strategy" as the "art of war," the object being "to impose upon the enemy the place, time and conditions of fighting preferred by oneself." The art in the control of rubber root diseases as advocated by us has as its aim the usual desideratum of obtaining the maximum favourable balance between expenditure and acceptable losses. The general strategy employed is that of preventing the pathogen from exploiting immediately available resources or from developing new ones, and then leading it to expend its energy in a hostile environment. Tactical procedures, in which direct contact is made with the enemy, are limited to the preferred place of the planting row and are employed only where the pathogen has broken through in force and the host's defences have failed.

DYNAMICS OF THE METHOD.—*Chemical mediation.*—The stump and roots of an unpoisoned rubber tree die very slowly. In experiment CI-51, 77% of 645 roots sampled in the unpoisoned control plots were still alive one year after felling. It is evident that a parasite already present in the roots has a competitive advantage and its inoculum will increase at an increasing rate as the host's resistance decreases and will be checked only when the roots become so moribund that saprophytes can enter. Tree or stump poisoning prevents this exploitation, most of the bole of a tree being dead within one year from poisoning, the rapid kill permitting early colonisation by saprophytes.

The application of a wood preservative to the cut surface of stumps immediately after felling inhibits spore colonisation by the pathogens, and thereby denies their extension into hitherto uninfected boles. It may be assumed that this procedure also delays entry to desirable saprophytes, but it appears that the soil provides an adequate reservoir of these, which may enter through the roots. Further, the data presented by Newsam, John, and Rao (1961) on the effects of insecticides on the decay of rubber wood, whilst not being significant for both tree and stump poisoning, support the expectation that organisms of decay are transmitted by insects. There is no evidence to show that rubber root pathogens are transmitted in this manner.

The notion of altering the specialised environment of the roots, to confer competitive advantage on saprophytes as a means of biological control, originated with Leach (1937, 1939), working with *Armillaria mellea* (Vahl.) Quél. in Africa. It was closely paralleled in Malaya by Napper (1939). A similar parallel in time has occurred between work in Malaya on the protection of the cut surfaces of stumps, and that initiated somewhat earlier in the United Kingdom by Rishbeth (1948, 1950, 1951) in relation to *Fomes annosus* Fr. A suggestion that chemicals might find application in the control of plant pathogens by stimulating antagonistic organisms was made by Altson (1950b) as a result of his observation that D-D, which was being investigated as a possible direct chemical control of root disease, stimulated the growth of *Trichoderma viride* (Pers.) Fries. Later he showed that culture filtrates of *T. viride* inhibited the growth of *F. lignosus* in culture (Altson, 1953b). This approach was, in turn, independently paralleled by the investigations of Bliss (1951) on the control of *A. mellea* in citrus soils by stimulating the growth of *T. viride* with carbon disulphide.

Decay effects.—The use of cover plants, both as an agricultural practice and in relation to root diseases, has been the subject of many articles in the Far East. To discuss these disputes would be out of place here. Their cultural value has been reviewed by Watson (1957a), and the undesirability of using shrubby plants as indicators of potential sources of infection has already been discussed (Fox, 1961a). A single example of the common misinterpretation of observations will suffice. Birkinshaw (1923), referring to an area planted with a creeping legume, observed that the mycelium of *Fomes lignosus* was present in large quantities in the litter of the cover and on its living stems and stated that "it was clear that the fungus was spreading more rapidly than it would have done had the area been clean weeded." This raises the paradox referred to in the introduction. Cover plants encourage the spread of the pathogen but not necessarily of the disease. If, contrary to our advice, the cover plants are allowed to grow over the planting rows and round the base of the trees, then the epiphytic growth in and on the litter and on the runners of the cover plants will readily reach the collar, and, unhindered mechanically or biotically by the soil, will encircle it aboveground and quickly kill the tree.

The cover plants provide a favourable milieu for the decay of timber, as has already been noted; the root-disease pathogens are primary decay organisms which are likewise encouraged to grow, but to the detriment of their ultimate survival. There are many facets to this process and to disentangle the interrelations and evaluate them quantitatively is a formidable task. The breakdown of large and potentially dangerous inocula into small and ineffective ones when the small cover-plant roots are infected has been referred to before (Fox, 1961a).

Prolific growth of the pathogens may occur in and on the litter layer as soon as the cover plants are sufficiently well established to provide a favourable environment, and this growth begins before there are many rubber roots to infect. Such roots as may be infected in the first year or two are usually small and, from the arithmetical relations given above, it may be seen that small infected roots will not support the progress of infection as well as will large ones because the ratio of food volume to fungus volume is a function of the root radius.

The general stimulus to vegetative growth by physical conditions also encourages, especially in the case of *Fomes lignosus*, the production of fruit bodies. Infected stumps in bare soil or where grass is grown rarely produce fructifications. They do so only after prolonged spells of heavy rain and high humidity and even then the sporophores are small and transient. Under cover plants, however, masses of imbricate fruit bodies of *F. lignosus* develop, sometimes completely encircling the base of a stump and extending outwards for as much as a foot. Their fresh weight is to be measured in pounds, and their growth unquestionably represents a great drain on the food reserve available to the pathogen. *Ganoderma pseudoferreum* is not so prolific, though its sporophores are proportionately heavier than those of *F. lignosus*, whilst *F. noxius* fructifies more rarely.

The extensive vegetative and reproductive growth may also be stimulated by an over-all effect that hastens the decay of timber. In general the inherent limiting factor in the rate of decay of wood is its high carbon:nitrogen ratio; data relating to this and to increased rates of decay promoted by additional nitrogen have been given by Cartwright and Findlay (1958). Pot-culture experiments by Watson (1957b) have shown that *Centrosema pubescens*, in the absence of added nitrogenous fertiliser, may mobilise the equivalent of 210 lb of nitrogen per acre in 5 months from sowing, and that this excess over other treatments was most probably the result of nitrogen fixation. In a number of field experiments, differences in the total nitrogen content held in leguminous creeping covers and in grasses ranged from 150 to 240 lb per acre, and these differences were maintained for several years (Watson, Wong, and Narayanan, 1964b). These experiments also showed much higher levels of nitrate nitrogen, and incubation tests from other experiments demonstrated far higher rates of nitrification in soil under creeping legumes than under other cover plants (Watson, Wong, and Narayanan, 1964a,c).

Antagonistic effects.—The vegetative growth in and on the litter layer represents a twofold loss to the pathogen. It fails in what should be its primary function of finding and exploiting new food sources and it occurs in an environment which generally encourages microbial activity. Thus the mycelium is subject to vigorous attack and destruction by antagonists of the microflora and by mycophagous members of the fauna, whose importance in this role is often underrated. Furthermore, nearly all the roots which the pathogens encounter in this situation are feeding roots, which not only are virtually immune to attack but whose ability to break down potential inocula is increased because they too are provided with a favourable environment and they also ramify and feed in the litter layer. Being susceptible to desiccation, the feeding roots do not occur on timber in exposed situations, but under cover plants they extend into and over stumps, fallen logs, and branches aboveground. Their relative immunity to infection and their ability to feed on and destroy in-

fected wood may be related to rhizosphere effects or mycostatic or mycotoxic root exudates.

The production of fruit bodies is also largely a waste of the pathogen's food resources; most of the spores produced probably fail to escape through the dense canopy of the cover plants and the sporophores are soon heavily attacked by mycophagous members of the fauna.

Mycostatic and mycolytic effects of the soil beneath the litter layer can be demonstrated by the simple technique illustrated in Figs. 2 and 3. Samples of soil are transferred directly to petri dishes, the soil surface

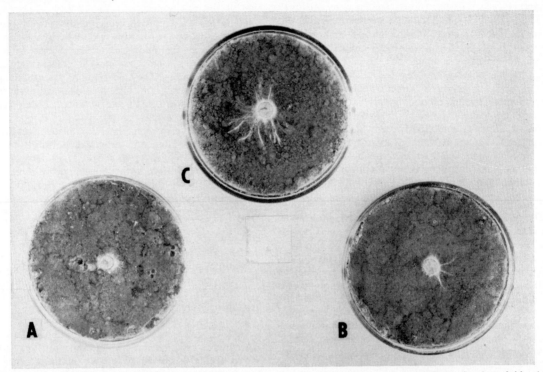

Fig. 2. Mycostatic effect of soil on the growth of *Fomes lignosus*. Soil taken from beneath *Pueraria phaseoloides* (*A*); *Centrosema pubescens* (*B*); and clean-weeded area (*C*).

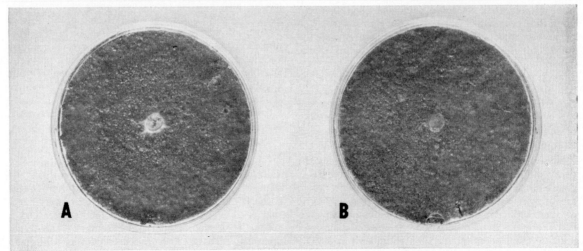

Fig. 3. Mycolytic effects on *Fomes lignosus;* soil taken from beneath *Centrosema pubescens* (*B*) and a clean-weeded area (*A*).

is smoothed, and onto it is poured a thin layer of cooled sterile tapwater agar. The plates are inoculated within 24 hours, and inhibition of growth is evident before microscopic examination reveals any growth of soil organisms through the agar. This can be interpreted as a diffusion through agar of a mycostatic factor(s). Fig. 3 shows almost complete lysis, after a lapse of 16 days, of an inoculum placed on soil taken from beneath a legume cover; lysis is also becoming evident, but more slowly, above the "bare" soil. At this stage attack by other microorganisms, including nematodes, can be seen under the microscope. This technique supports earlier work in which the buried-slide method was used in the field.

The extensive epiphytic growth of *Fomes lignosus* enables it to outflank the host's defences, and John (1958) has shown that physically preventing this growth halts the infection. It is clear that such extended lines of communication are vulnerable to physical or biological severance or interference which would reduce the inoculum potential at any point beyond it.

The rhizomorph of *Fomes lignosus* terminates in a

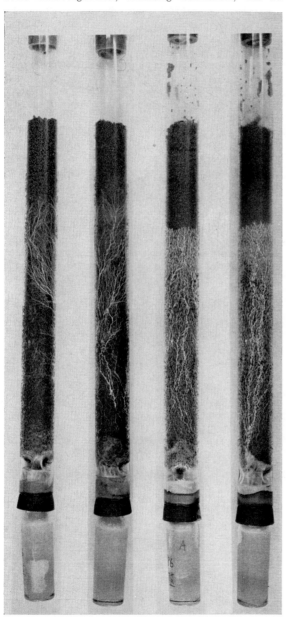

Fig. 4. Soil tubes (3 cm diameter) in which the soil is supported on glass wool held in position by indentations near the base. The food base is a bottle containing 26 cc of 2% malt-extract agar. The left and right pairs are front and back views of tubes containing nonsterile and sterile soil, respectively.

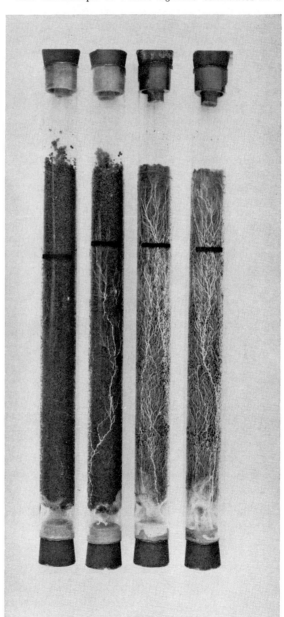

Fig. 5. Pairs of tubes similar to those in Fig. 4. The black bars show the approximate limit of growth when the food base was removed and replaced with a rubber bung.

diffuse fan of fine strands between which individual hyphae ramify. Some strands assume dominance by, presumably, an accident of growth and continue to increase in thickness by progressive parallel branching, the rhizomorph obtaining its coherence by the interweaving and anastomoses of its constituent hyphae. The remaining strands and hyphae are deleted by antagonistic processes which perhaps are accelerated by a withdrawal from them of nutrients by the strands which have assumed dominance. This withdrawal mechanism is postulated because dominance is indicated by the deletion of the smaller strands under sterile conditions, as may be seen by comparing the older and younger areas in Figs. 4 and 5. Physiological apical dominance is indicated by the continued apical growth that occurs after the food base has been removed (Fig. 5).

That there is some degree of interference with translocation in the rhizomorphs may be inferred by treating them as infected roots from which it is desired to isolate pathogens. Sections of rhizomorphs are vigorously washed on a wrist-action shaker, briefly immersed in alcoholic mercuric chloride, rinsed, and then dissected and plated out. Bacteria, actinomycetes, Phycomycetes, Ascomycetes, and Fungi Imperfecti have been isolated in this way. Undoubtedly from the nature of the development of the rhizomorph, some of the isolates obtained by this technique would be "accidental" contaminants of no significance. It is of interest to record, however, that two thirds of a random selection of actinomycetes so isolated inhibited the in-vitro growth of *Fomes lignosus*.

A more direct effect is illustrated in Fig. 6. Such

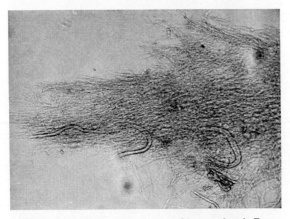

Fig. 6. A section of a young rhizomorph of *Fomes lignosus* partly dissected; three nematodes are visible.

nematode infestations occur more frequently beneath cover plants than where the soil is bare, and preliminary investigations in these two situations have shown that there are marked qualitative differences in the nematode populations. The comprehensive review by Drechsler (1941) gave a great impetus to the study of the influence of fungi on nematode diseases. A casual perusal of a recent book by Thorne (1961) will reveal many references to nematodes which are mycophagous, or presumed to be so, yet but few studies have been made of the influence of nematodes on fungus diseases.

In view of the foregoing observations it was interesting to read, during the preparation of this paper, the abstract by Mankau and Mankau (1962) describing the preferred feeding by *Aphelenchus avenae* Bastian on several phytopathogenic fungi, including *Armillaria mellea*. With the same species Rhoades and Linford (1959) obtained control, in pot culture, of root rot of corn caused by *Pythium arrhenomanes* Drechsler.

It is pertinent to draw analogies between roots and rhizomorphs. Roots induce quantitative and qualitative changes—defined within the concepts of rhizoplane and rhizosphere—in the soil population close to them. An increase in the population of a root pathogen, requiring implementation of control measures, is an adverse change falling within the framework of these concepts.

Most mycophagous organisms are not obligately so. ("Mycophagous" is used here, and later, in a broad sense, to include any organism of the flora or fauna that uses fungi as a source of food.) Fungi in the soil provide only intermittent substrates as alternatives to a few or many other sources of food, depending on the organism concerned. Concentrations of such organisms in the soil, by multiplication or migration, are likely to be transient and to arise only locally when preferred species of fungi develop on particular substrates. Mycelial aggregates—as rhizomorphs—may, however, be expected to influence the soil population in a manner analogous to roots.

A rhizomorph offers a relatively large, persistent, and static bulk of food and dynamic replenishment of it at a given site by translocation. Translocated food might be in a form suitable for direct uptake by mycophagous organisms, or it might be used to replace hyphae damaged or destroyed by them, the new mycelium, in turn, being available as further food. The rhizomorphs of *Fomes lignosus* and the mycelial investments of *Ganoderma pseudoferreum* and *F. noxius* may thus be visualized as having rhizoplane or rhizosphere effects detrimental to their survival in that they encourage growth of their own antagonists. This phenomenon is viewed as an integral part of the process of ecological succession.

After a few months a root which has been infected by *Fomes lignosus* rarely shows active surface growth of the pathogen and, indeed, epiphytic rhizomorphs may be almost absent, having been mostly destroyed by antagonists. Ecological succession may then slow down until it reaches a stage of near equilibrium; on the one hand the pathogen appears to be moribund within the infected root and shows no signs of epiphytic growth, but on the other hand its antagonists may not succeed in displacing it for several years. This state of near equilibrium can, however, readily be upset. If such a root is exposed by digging and the soil then replaced, reexposure a few days later will reveal fresh mycelial growth on its surface. Such roots, in which the pathogen appears to be inactive, may be dug up and used successfully in inoculation experiments, as may roots infected by *Ganoderma pseudoferreum* and *F. noxius* in which the pathogens also appear moribund. Field observations on *G. pseudoferreum* have also shown that a young root may be in contact with a potential source of infection for up to a year before the pathogen begins to attack it. The young root appears to activate the pathogen either by physical pressure which breaks its pseudosclerotial skin or, perhaps, by biological changes induced by its rhizosphere, altering the balance between the pathogen and its containing antagonists. Another explanation is that there may be gradual physiological changes in the pathogen accompanying the progressive decay (and concomitant nutrient changes) of the infected wood which require enzymic adaptation by the fungus before it can again attack a living root.

The implementation of Napper's scheme of control required extensive digging between the planting rows and within them when tracing and eradicating sources of infection. Where the soil is dug over, and in the immediate vicinity of such areas, changes in aeration and water relations, with concomitant changes of microbial equilibrium, are bound to occur. If these changes adversely influence the equilibrium between the pathogen and the antagonists which contain it within infected wood, then overlooked, moribund potential sources of infection may become active.

The adverse effects of soil disturbance in increasing disease incidence have been discussed (Fox, 1961a; Hutchison, 1961), and increased growth rates for *Fomes lignosus* have been recorded in soil which had been dug over (Fox, 1961a). In parenthesis, it should be noted that the extensive digging in the interrows required in Napper's scheme results in the wholesale destruction of many square yards of the cover plants.

In experiments designed to study factors affecting the initiation and growth of rhizomorphs of *Fomes lignosus*, "soil tubes," as illustrated in Figs. 4 and 5, have been employed. In such tubes an oxygen gradient is likely to develop. In acid-washed sand at 60% water-holding capacity the effect of aeration, which accompanies soil disturbances, was demonstrated by *increasing* growth rate with increasing distance from the inoculum. In dry sand, oxygen was not a limiting factor, yet little or no growth was obtained, which indicates that effective water translocation does not occur. This implies that the rhizomorph is largely dependent on water uptake from the soil.

Reference must also be made to an extreme but beneficial example of soil disturbance when mechanical replanting methods are employed. Trees are uprooted by bulldozers, stacked in windrows, and burnt. The ground is then cross rooted with deep tines, the roots thus brought to the surface are collected and burnt, and the operation completed by ploughing. Inevitably some infected roots are left in the soil because they fracture more readily than those that are sound. The results, after 4 years, of a pilot experiment on 24 acres of our Experiment Station, comparing mechanical clearing with stump poisoning where surface timber was removed, are given in Table 4.

The low incidence of *Fomes lignosus* following mechanical clearing was expected, for the infected root fragments left in the soil are relatively ineffective, being small and decaying quickly. John (1960) has demonstrated the relations between size, time, and viability of the three major pathogens in pieces of infected roots

TABLE 4. Number of casualties, after 4 years, from two pathogens following two methods of clearing the old stand

Pathogen	Method of clearing	Number of trees	
		Lost	Treated
Fomes lignosus	S. p.*	100	71
	Mech.†	35	35
Ganoderma pseudoferreum	S. p.	33	5
	Mech.	2	1

* S. p. = Stump poisoning; † Mech. = Mechanical clearing.

buried in soil. The reduced incidence of *Ganoderma pseudoferreum* is proportionately far higher than that of *F. lignosus*. It is suspected that this greater reduction relates to the readiness with which *G. pseudoferreum* can be displaced by other fungi once its pseudosclerotial skin is broken. *Trichoderma viride* is evident within 48 hours on the surface of infected wood after the skin is broken. Invasion of wood infected by *G. pseudoferreum* by either this fungus or *Botryodiplodia theobromae* Pat. is considered to be a common cause of failure of inocula of *G. pseudoferreum* in inoculation experiments.

Detection and host resistance.—Garrett (1956b), in discussing Napper's scheme of control based on collar inspection, suggested that it uncovered only those sources of disease which were actually dangerous. It is clear from the experimental results which have been quoted that many sources detected by it were not actually dangerous, unnecessary tree treatment was carried out, and the "despair factor" must have operated and resulted in needless eradication of trees which might well have recovered. In addition, rhizomorphs similar to those of *Fomes lignosus* but belonging to a harmless saprophyte may be discovered (Altson, 1953a) and lead to needless expenditure (Fox, 1961c). We now employ the tactical strike only where the pathogens have broken out in sufficient force to overcome the host's defences and kill the young trees. Frequent rounds of foliage inspection, the cost of which is trifling, ensure that no buildup of inoculum occurs in the planting row. Repeated collar inspections at infected sites as described in C under "Current Recommendations," further aim at diminishing this hazard as well as minimising losses.

Leaving the sources of infection to be biologically neutralized is a calculated risk. As an additional insurance against this risk, however, we have developed a collar fungicide to be applied to those trees opened for inspection as described in C. The loss, by excision, of an infected lateral root has little effect on the growth of a young tree, and it is usually the extent of penetration at the collar which decides whether or not a tree can be treated. Wound-barrier formation by the host prevents invasion by *Fomes lignosus* if the pathogen's epiphytic growth is physically halted (John, 1958), and we have found that the same result may be achieved chemically—an integration of biological and chemical control. Formulations of pentachloronitrobenzene in thick carriers, which inhibit leaching and degradation of the fungicide, have protected the collars of experimentally infected trees against *F. lignosus* for up to a year. Extended field trials will show whether the cost of this protection can be offset by reducing the frequency of reexamining the collars of trees at known sites of infection, and, if losses are reduced, by giving a more uniform stand from which to thin.

CONCLUSIONS.—An attempt has been made to synthesize the results of field observations and field and invitro experiments to show that biological competition, antagonism, and eradication play major roles in the control of root diseases of *Hevea brasiliensis*. The current recommendations of the Rubber Research Institute of Malaya, relying heavily on biological control, are simpler, more effective, and cheaper than earlier, more intensive schemes.

White-root disease causes more losses in young rubber in Malaya than all other pests and diseases combined, and the emphasis on *Fomes lignosus* in this paper reflects this position. The early wastage of potential sources of infection by the decoy effects of the cover plants is, of course, but one facet of the process of ecological succession in the woody substrates. It has, however, been somewhat arbitrarily separated in the discussion because it is considered that it plays a more important role in the biological control of *F. lignosus* than it does for *Ganoderma pseudoferreum* and *F. noxius*—a consequence of their differing growth habits. The last two pathogens suffer less early wastage not only because they produce less epiphytic growth but also because they are less stimulated by exterior physical conditions. They are, to some extent, contained (and protected) within their mycelial investments. Further, both these pathogens may also form pseudosclerotia consisting of pieces of wood permeated by their hyphae and surrounded by a pseudosclerotial skin which is not always entirely of their own making: it may in part be zone plates in the wood formed by other fungi. Thus, on balance, the beneficial effect of cover plants in reducing losses caused by these two pathogens is more by encouraging antagonists that contain them within infected roots, where they slowly waste away, and by encouraging saprophytes that deny potential food sources to them, rather than by early dissipation of their food reserves by enhanced vegetative or reproductive growth.

The capacity to hasten the wastage effect, the speeding of succession of saprophytes, and the enhancement of microbial antagonism in the soil are not, of course, a prerogative of creeping leguminous covers. From observations made to date, such cover plants are superior to others as far as the first two factors are concerned. Antagonistic effects in the soil are enhanced by all cover plants so far investigated, but no evaluation of the relative merits of different species or mixtures of species has yet been made.

The need to replant rubber on the same land is a consequence of land-utilisation policies which rightly restrict excessive exploitation of virgin jungle. Crop rotation, as stated in the first sentence of this paper, would afford a possible solution to the root-disease replant problem but is precluded on economic grounds.

It is only proper, however, that I should draw attention to a fact which may be evident from what has been written, that this preclusion accords more with common usage of the term "crop rotation" than with the realities of the situation. For economic reasons the new stand of rubber trees is planted within a few weeks of the old stand's being destroyed and, at about the same time, the creeping leguminous covers are sown in drills between the rows of the young rubber trees. Within a few months the cover plants spread to occupy all the ground except for the 6-ft-wide clean-weeded planting row. Thus where the distance between the rows of trees is 22 ft—a spacing often used—the cover plants occupy some 70% of a field. Although the young rubber roots rapidly extend in all directions, the roots of the cover plants initially occupy a far greater proportion of the soil than do those of the young trees. This proportion decreases with time, the cover plants being progressively shaded out by the trees until, after 4 to 6 years, they are largely replaced by a sparse ground cover of shade-tolerant indigenous species, mainly grasses and herbs. The complex role played by the cover plants in reducing disease incidence includes, therefore, a considerable element of "crop rotation."

Since problems of biological control of root diseases are so intricate, it is inevitable in our present state of knowledge that chance or accidental observations may still lead to solutions where reasoned and methodical approaches fail. It is evident from this paper that chance and empiricism have played their role in the development of our current recommendations and may continue to do so in the future.

Future fields of study are largely indicated by the qualifications and speculative comments that I have had to make. Many problems are already in hand in the field and in laboratory experiments, as may be seen in the Annual Reports of the Pathological Division, Rubber Research Institute of Malaya. These include various aspects of mechanised replanting, the testing of new arboricides and stump protectants, and studies on factors affecting the decay of rubber wood. An interesting lead, already followed up by Morris and Knox (1962), has been given by Rishbeth (1959) in using chemicals for stump-surface treatment which favour the development of some saprophytes and lack the undesirable general inhibitory effect of creosote. Fields of work which may lead to further practical benefits lie in studies on interactions between cover-plant mixtures and the soil microflora and microfauna, and on factors influencing the growth of rhizomorphs and mycelial investments. Of the more fundamental approaches, that which perhaps needs most attention is a study of the mycophagous fauna.

Many contributors to this symposium have reviewed the extensive investigations which have been made on the interactions between plant roots and soil microorganisms. Root structure and physiology, root exudates, rhizosphere and rhizoplane effects have been debated and assessed in relation to their influence on soil-borne pathogens. Analogies between roots and rhizomorphs, root hairs and hypha are self-evident. Substrate colonisation by fungi usually requires translocation, be it in a rhizomorph, a mycelial aggregate, a single hyphal strand, or a germ tube. The effects of hyphal exudates on the immediate spatial development of the soil microflora and microfauna are technically more difficult to study than parallel investigations with roots. Nevertheless, since such effects have been observed, attention to their influence directly on growth of and, less directly, on substrate colonisation by soil-borne pathogens merits further study.

In conclusion, there is the obvious question of the value of our findings in other root-disease problems. Of immediate importance to us, and currently being investigated, is the applicability of our recommendations to new plantings from jungle, where potential disease sources may persist longer in timber more resistant to decay than the relatively rapidly rotting wood of *Hevea*. Of interest and, I hope, stimulus to other investigators are our findings that an integrated programme of chemical, physical, and biological control, with special emphasis on the last named, may be successfully employed in a situation where on a priori grounds it might be thought to have little chance of success.

ACKNOWLEDGMENTS.—The studies reported here are the cooperative work of past and present members of the Pathological Division, Rubber Research Institute of Malaya; the late Mr. R. A. Altson, Head of Division from 1946 to 1952, Dr. A. Newsam, present Head of Division, Mr. F. W. Hutchison, Mr. R. N. Hilton, Dr. R. L. Wastie, Mr. K. P. John, and Mr. B. Sripathi Rao. I would also like to express appreciation to Mr. P. B. Menon and Mr. T. K. Nayar, Field Assistants, and to Mr. Foong Kum Mun, Laboratory Assistant.

LITERATURE CITED

ALTSON, R. A. 1950a. Pathological Division, Report for the period Jan. 1941-Aug. 1945. Rubber Res. Inst. Malaya Rept. 1941-1945, p. 41-68.

ALTSON, R. A. 1950b. Pathological Division, Report for the year 1947. Rubber Res. Inst. Malaya Repts. 1945-1948, p. 111-135.

ALTSON, R. A. 1950c. Pathological Division, Report for the year 1948. Rubber Res. Inst. Malaya Repts. 1945-1948, p. 135-190.

ALTSON, R. A. 1953a. Pathological Division, Report for the year 1950. Rubber Res. Inst. Malaya Repts. 1949-1951, 34 p.

ALTSON, R. A. 1953b. Pathological Division, Report for the year 1951. Rubber Res. Inst. Malaya Repts. 1949-1951, 34 p.

BANCROFT, K. 1912. A root disease of the Para rubber tree (*Fomes semitostus* Berk.) Dept. Agr. Federated Malay States, Bull. 13, 30 p.

BIRKINSHAW, F. 1923. Cover crops and the spread of *Fomes lignosus*. Malayan Agr. J. 11: 216.

BLISS, D. E. 1951. The destruction of *Armillaria mellea* in citrus soils. Phytopathology 41: 665-683.

BROOKS, F. T. 1916. Observations on some diseases of plantation rubber in Malaya. Ann. Appl. Biol. 2: 209-227.

CARTWRIGHT, K. ST. G., and W. P. K. FINDLAY. 1958. Decay of timber and its prevention. 2nd ed. H.M. Stationery Office, London. 332 p.

CRONSHEY, J. F. H., and C. BARCLAY. 1939. Replanting in areas infested with root disease. Arch. Rubbercult. Ned.-Ind. 23: 163-169.

DRECHSLER, C. 1941. Some hyphomycetes parasitic on free living terricolous nematodes. Phytopathology 31: 773-801.

FOX, R. A. 1961a. White root disease of *Hevea brasiliensis*: recent developments in control techniques. Commonwealth Mycol. Conf., 6th (1960) Rept., p. 41-48. Commonwealth Mycol. Inst.

FOX, R. A. 1961b. White root disease of *Hevea brasiliensis*: the role of fungicides in control techniques. Commonwealth Mycol. Conf., 6th (1960) Rept., p. 97-100. Commonwealth Mycol. Inst.

FOX, R. A. 1961c. White root disease of *Hevea brasiliensis*: the identity of the pathogen. Proc. Nat. Rubber Res. Conf., Kuala Lumpur, 1960, p. 473-482. Rubber Res. Inst. Malaya.

GARRETT, S. D. 1950. Ecology of the root-inhabiting fungi. Biol. Rev. Cambridge Phil. Soc. 25: 220-254.

GARRETT, S. D. 1956a. Rhizomorph behaviour in *Armillaria mellea* (Vahl.) Quél. II Logistics of infection. Ann. Botany (London) [N.S.] 20: 193-209.

GARRETT, S. D. 1956b. Biology of root-infecting fungi. Cambridge University Press, London and New York. 292 p.

GARRETT, S. D. 1959. Biology and ecology of root-disease fungi. p. 309-316. *In* C. S. Holton, et al. [ed.], Plant pathology, problems and progress 1908-1958, Univ. Wisconsin Press, Madison, Wisc.

HILTON, R. N. 1959. Maladies of Hevea in Malaya. Rubber Res. Inst. Malaya. 101 p.

HUTCHISON, F. W. 1961. Factors affecting root disease incidence and control in replantings. Proc. Nat. Rubber Res. Conf., Kuala Lumpur, 1960, p. 483-495. Rubber Res. Inst. Malaya.

JONGE, W. H. DE 1933. Het parasitisme van *Rigidoporus microporus* (Swartz) van Overeem, Syn: *Fomes lignosus* Klotzsch, bij *Hevea brasiliensis*. Arch. Rubbercult. Ned.-Ind. 17: 83-100.

JOHN, K. P. 1958. Inoculation experiments with *Fomes lignosus* Klotzsch. J. Rubber Res. Inst. Malaya 15: 223-230.

JOHN, K. P. 1960. Loss of viability of three root parasites in infected root sections buried in the soil. J. Rubber Res. Inst. Malaya 16: 173-177.

LEACH, R. 1937. Observations on the parasitism and control of *Armillaria mellea*. Proc. Roy. Soc. London, Sec. B, 121: 561-573.

LEACH, R. 1939. Biological control and ecology of *Armillaria mellea* (Vahl.) Fr. Trans. Brit. Mycol. Soc. 23: 320-329.

MANKAU, SAROJAM K., and R. MANKAU. 1962. Multiplication of *Aphelenchus avenae* on phytopathogenic soil fungi. (Abstr.) Phytopathology 52: 722.

MORRIS, C. L., and K. A. KNOX. 1962. *Fomes annosus*: a report on the production of conidia in nature and other studies in Virginia. Plant Dis. Reptr. 46: 340-341.

NAPPER, R. P. N. 1932a. Observations on the root disease of rubber trees caused by *Fomes lignosus*. J. Rubber Res. Inst. Malaya 4: 5-33.

NAPPER, R. P. N. 1932b. A scheme of treatment for the control of *Fomes lignosus* in young rubber areas. J. Rubber Res. Inst. Malaya 4: 34-38.

NAPPER, R. P. N. 1938. Root disease and underground pests in new plantings. Planter (Kuala Lumpur) 19: 453-455.

NAPPER, R. P. N. 1939. Root disease investigations. Pathological Division, Report for the year 1938. Rubber Res. Inst. Malaya Rept. 1938, p. 116-123.

NEWSAM, A. 1953. Pathological Division, Report for the year 1949. Rubber Res. Inst. Malaya Repts. 1949-51. 50 p.

NEWSAM, A. 1962. Pathological Division, Report for the year 1961. Rubber Res. Inst. Malaya Rept. 1961, p. 77-89.

NEWSAM, A., K. P. JOHN, and B. SRIPATHI RAO. 1961. Decay of rubber wood. Proc. Nat. Rubber Res. Conf., Kuala Lumpur, 1960, p. 503-509. Rubber Res. Inst. Malaya.

PERIES, O. S. 1959. Studies on the production of toxins by *Fomes lignosus*. I. Preliminary investigations. Rubber Res. Inst. Ceylon, Quart. J. 35: 38-40.

PETCH, T. 1921. The diseases and pests of the rubber tree. Macmillan and Co., London. 278 p.

PETCH, T. 1928. The parasitism of tea root disease fungi. Tea Quart. 1: 10-15.

REYDON, G. A. 1931. Over de meest in Bosoeki voorkomende Wortelschimmels bij Rubber en Koffie. Bergcultures 5: 892-909.

RHOADES, H. L., and M. B. LINFORD. 1959. Control of *Pythium* root rot by the nematode *Aphelenchus avenae*. Plant Dis. Reptr. 43: 323-328.

RISHBETH, J. 1948. *Fomes annosus* Fr. on pines in East Anglia. Forestry 22: 174-183.

RISHBETH, J. 1950. Observations on the biology of *Fomes annosus*, with particular reference to East Anglian pine plantations. I. The outbreaks of disease and ecological status of the fungus. Ann. Botany (London) [N.S.] 14: 365-383.

RISHBETH, J. 1951. Observations on the biology of *Fomes annosus*, with particular reference to East Anglian pine plantations. II. Spore production, stump infection and saprophytic activity in stumps. Ann. Botany (London) [N.S.] 15: 1-21.

RISHBETH, J. 1959. Stump protection against *Fomes annosus*. II. Treatment with substances other than creosote. Ann. Appl. Biol. 47: 529-541.

RUBBER RESEARCH INSTITUTE OF MALAYA. 1953. Uses of 2,4,5-T on *Hevea*, preliminary note. J. Rubber Res. Inst. Malaya 14: 179-182.

RUBBER RESEARCH INSTITUTE OF MALAYA. 1954. Root disease. Rubber Res. Inst. Malaya Planters' Bull. 10, p. 14-19.

RUBBER RESEARCH INSTITUTE OF MALAYA. 1955. Poisoning *Hevea* with 2,4,5-T. Rubber Res. Inst. Malaya Planters' Bull. 17, p. 41.

RUBBER RESEARCH INSTITUTE OF MALAYA. 1957. Decaying timber spreads root disease. Rubber Res. Inst. Malaya Planters' Bull. 29, p. 31-35.

RUBBER RESEARCH INSTITUTE OF MALAYA. 1958. Root disease and replanting. Rubber Res. Inst. Malaya Planters' Bull. 35, p. 35-41.

SCHÜTTE, K. H. 1956. Translocation in fungi. New Phytologist 55: 164-182.

SHARPLES, A. 1936. Diseases and pests of the rubber tree. Macmillan and Co. London. 480 p.

STEVENS, R. B. 1960. Cultural practices in disease control. vol. 3, p. 357-429. *In* J. G. Horsfall and A. E. Dimond [ed.], Plant pathology, an advanced treatise. Academic Press, New York and London.

THORNE, G. 1961. Principles of nematology. McGraw-Hill Book Co. Inc., New York. 553 p.

WATSON, G. A. 1957a. Cover plants in rubber cultivation. J. Rubber Res. Inst. Malaya 15: 2-18.

WATSON, G. A. 1957b. Nitrogen fixation by *Centrosema pubescens*. J. Rubber Res. Inst. Malaya 15: 168-174.

WATSON, G. A., P. W. WONG, and R. NARAYANAN. 1964a. Effect of cover plants on the growth of *Hevea*. III. A comparison of leguminous creepers with grasses and *Mikania cordata*. J. Rubber Res. Inst. Malaya 18: 18-95.

WATSON, G. A., P. W. WONG, and R. NARAYANAN. 1964b. Effect of cover plants on the growth of *Hevea*. IV. Leguminous creepers compared with grasses, *Mikania cordata* and mixed indigenous covers on four soil types. J. Rubber Res. Inst. Malaya 18: 123-145.

WATSON, G. A., P. W. WONG, and R. NARAYANAN. 1964c. Effect of cover plants on the growth of *Hevea*. V. Soil nitrogen and cation status: a progress report on results from a small scale trial. J. Rubber Res. Inst. Malaya 18: 161-174.

▶ DISCUSSION OF R. A. FOX PAPER

G. H. Hepting:

Is infection at the root collar from a long root rhizomorph due so much, as you say, to a mobilization of energy needed for infection, or is it due to openings or better infection courts at the root collar?

R. A. Fox:

It is correct to say that often infection courts at the collar are more readily invaded than lateral roots in the immediate vicinity; this has been previously discussed (Fox, 1961b, cited in the paper.). But a rhizomorph detached from its food base is unable to penetrate these infection courts, and it may therefore be assumed that mobilisation of energy is necessary for infection to occur.

S. D. Garrett:

Mr. Fox has presented substantial evidence to show that in the root-disease phase of a young rubber plantation in Malaya, losses of young trees (and cost of treatment) are much lower if the plantation is planted with a covercrop and is left undisturbed by digging than if Napper's inspection and treatment routine is followed.

This evidence I think we can accept, but I do want to say that under Napper's method, planters were assured of bringing a young rubber plantation through its root-disease phase and of achieving a satisfactory stand of mature rubber—despite the high cost of treatment. The question I want to ask is this: what is the precise nature of the modified treatment that Mr. Fox is likely to recommend as a result of these experiments, and will it provide the same assurance of a satisfactory stand of mature rubber as did Napper's admittedly more expensive treatment?

R. A. Fox:

All the evidence available indicates that the planter will be assured of a satisfactory stand of mature rubber. The exact treatment recommended is given in the text.

Antibiosis and Fungistasis of Soil Microorganisms

R. M. JACKSON—*Soil Bureau, Taita Experimental Station, Department of Scientific and Industrial Research, Lower Nutt, New Zealand* (*On secondment from Soil Microbiology Department, Rothamsted Experimental Station, Harpenden, England.*)

A logical approach to the successful control of root diseases requires as deep an understanding as possible of the complex ecosystems existing in the soil horizons occupied by roots, where a large variety of organisms interact in such a way that a relatively stable community develops, provided there is no major change in the environment. In fact it is usually found that changes in environmental factors are constantly taking place, creating a dynamic system. Particularly well marked are seasonal changes reflected directly by changes in temperature and moisture status of the soil, and indirectly by plant growth and nutrient supply. In soil, probably more than in any other habitat, growth and development of individual species is dependent upon others, not only for supplies of nutrients, but also because of the growth-regulatory activities of a wide range of metabolites that are excreted into the environment and have been aptly termed environmental hormones or ectotrines by Lucas (1947). These metabolites may have beneficial stimulatory or growth-regulatory activity, as nutrients, growth substances, or vitamins, or they may have inhibitory effects and then be described as antibiotics. Often the same substance acts in more than one role, the expression of its effects depending upon the species affected, concentration, and perhaps our interpretation of the situation. We can now define antibiosis as the condition in which one or more metabolites excreted by an organism have a harmful effect on one or more other organisms. It may be considered as a facet of the more general condition of antagonism. Antagonism embraces competition, antibiosis, predation, and parasitism. While these phenomena may be defined so as to avoid confusion, the comparative rarity in nature of one unaccompanied, to a greater or lesser degree, by at least one of the others, leads inevitably to difficulties as soon as we attempt to analyse a natural situation. These difficulties are further aggravated by the fact that in soil we can hardly ever afford the luxury of restricting our vision to two species.

TYPES OF ANTIBIOTIC INTERRELATIONS.—In the simplest model situation, species *a* produces a substance which is in some way detrimental to species *b*, and as a consequence the growth or reproduction (or both) of *b* is retarded or stopped. Since the species pairs will almost certainly be competing for at least some factors of the environment, usually nutrients, a secondary effect of antibiosis will be to reduce the competitive ability of species *b* relative to species *a*.

In our consideration of the biological control of root diseases, we will be thinking most often in terms of antibiosis between different microorganisms. But substances secreted by microorganisms are also known to have a directly harmful effect on plants without any invasion of their tissues. Reduction in root elongation, as may be caused in wheat and other plants, for example, by *Azotobacter chroococcum* (Krasilnikov, 1939), or the modifications in root growth and morphology resulting from ectotrophic mycorrhizal infection, are probably the direct effect of growth substances produced by the microorganisms and, unless demonstrably harmful, are excluded from this discussion. That some modification of root morphology may be a normal concomitant of growth in an environment inhabited by microorganisms has been shown by the experiments of Bowen and Rovira (1961); it need not be assumed that such changes are necessarily deleterious to plant growth. Numerous reports of damage to seedlings due to toxic metabolites of microorganisms have been made, particularly by Russian authors (Mirchink and Greshnykh, 1962; Stepanova and Fish, 1958), who have emphasized the effect of manurial practices on the activity of these organisms. A specific case of damage caused by toxin production was brought to light by Steinberg (1950) in his classic investigation of frenching of tobacco. It would seem probable that more or less severe damage to seedlings not infrequently results from the production of toxins by soil microorganisms. In many instances a precondition of this form of antibiosis may be selective stimulation of the toxin producers by plant root exudates. Such a stimulation was shown by Kerr (1956) to be related to the degree of damage produced. Kerr's experiments, using cellophane bags to prevent direct contact between seedlings and the fungi studied, *Pellicularia filamentosa* and *Sclerotinia homoeocarpa*, gave a clear demonstration of the ability of these fungi to cause severe stunting and necrosis to roots with which they were not in contact. It is worth remembering, also, that several purified antibiotics, including some of fungal origin, are known to have phytotoxic properties (Wright, 1951).

The reverse situation to that considered above, where the plant exercises an antibiotic effect on the microorganism, is probably of no less importance. Reference has been made by other contributors to the presence of specific inhibitory substances in root exudates, and their possible role in resistance to root infection. There is clear evidence that the seed itself may exude antibiotics which have a significant effect on the establishment of organisms within the rhizosphere. Of particular practical significance is the toxicity of legume seeds towards *Rhizobium* species (Bowen, 1961). Antagonism in the rhizosphere between *Rhizobium* and other organisms was originally suggested as the reason for obtaining unsatisfactory nodulation of subterranean clover in certain Australian soils (Hely, Bergerson, and Brockwell, 1957); but more recent work (Thompson, 1961) indicates that toxic seed exudates are at least partly responsible and that pelleting is effective in improving nodulation because it separates the *Rhizobium* to some extent from the seed coat.

The next order of complexity to that in which two organisms are involved in an antibiotic relation is that between three or more species, as for example, where we have an antibiotic producer *a,* a pathogenic organism *b* susceptible to the antibiotic, and a plant *c* acting as a host for the pathogen. Such a system is still relatively simple and does not involve the kind of interactions which have been postulated by Park (1960) and which must give a truer picture of the likely complexity of soil interrelations. The equilibria between soil organisms are so complex and finely balanced that we should not be too optimistic about our ability to analyse accurately any antibiotic system involving more than three interrelated members.

Certain varieties of crop plants resistant to root pathogens may owe their resistance to peculiarities in their root exudates, favouring the establishment of rhizosphere organisms antibiotic towards pathogenic fungi. Timonin's study (1940, 1941) of the resistance of the flax variety Bison to fusarium wilt showed that differences in the rhizosphere fungi of susceptible and resistant varieties were correlated with differences in susceptibility to hydrocyanic acid, which was secreted in appreciable quantities by roots of resistant varieties, but only in traces by susceptible plants. *Trichoderma viride* was shown to be actually stimulated by the presence of hydrocyanic acid. Subba-Rao and Bailey (1961) found an association between the high incidence of *T. viride* in the rhizoplane and resistance to verticillium wilt in two resistant varieties of tomatoes, but not in a third, from the rhizoplane of which *Trichoderma* was absent. Although no antibiosis was shown between their isolates of *Trichoderma* and *Verticillium* in vitro on a medium not containing root exudate, the fact that some protection was afforded to susceptible varieties inoculated with *Trichoderma* suggested that in some instances there may be a causal relation between predominance of this fungus in the rhizoplane and resistance.

Another example of the association of organisms inhibitory to a pathogen, with a resistant variety, has been provided by work on varieties of pigeon-pea resistant and susceptible to wilt caused by *Fusarium udum* (Agnihothrudu, 1955). In seven different soils from 13 to 33% of rhizosphere isolates from the resistant variety strongly inhibited *F. udum,* whereas organisms isolated from the rhizosphere of the susceptible variety were inhibitory from one soil only, and these constituted only 6% of the isolates. The active organisms were all species of *Streptomyces,* and it is of interest that they were much more effective in vitro in media containing root extracts from the resistant variety than with extracts from the susceptible variety.

The probable importance of root exudates in determining antibiotic relations is also shown by Buxton's (1960) studies with pea wilt. It is perhaps worth emphasizing here the dangers of assuming that high counts of organisms capable of producing antibiotics in vitro gives proof of significant antibiotic activity in the rhizosphere. Such counts only indicate the potentialities of the population and may bear no causal relation to the occurrence of a pathogen.

THE OCCURRENCE AND SIGNIFICANCE OF ANTIBIOTICS IN SOIL.—In my discussion of antibiotic relations in soil, I have been assuming that antibiotics are produced in soil and that they have a significant and even determining influence on the ecosystems therein. This assumption is not one which has received universal acceptance, so it is necessary to examine some of the evidence upon which it is based. I think it is important to remind ourselves that natural soils, far from being homogeneous, are composed of a complex of discontinuous microhabitats. These microhabitats may differ widely one from another in any of the factors which determine microbial behaviour within them. Experiments designed to determine the fate of antibiotics added to rather large masses of soil or to evaluate the antibiotic-producing potentialities of specific organisms in variously treated soil masses have an undoubted value, but are largely irrelevant to the conditions within microhabitats which determine the success of individual organisms.

It has been unequivocally demonstrated by Wright (1956*a,b*) and others that antibiotic production will take place in organic substrates, such as pieces of straw or seedcoats, buried in soil. It cannot be doubted in these instances, where the quantities of antibiotic involved are large enough for extraction and characterization, that concentrations sufficient to influence the pattern of microbial colonization of these substrates must occur. Similar concentrations are also likely to occur in smaller pieces of organic matter in which the quantities of antibiotics produced are too small for detection by conventional means. Perhaps the development of microtechniques, such as used by Stevenson (1956) and Rangaswami and Ethiraj (1962), will enable us to extend our knowledge of antibiosis in microhabitats.

The focal points of our interest in root diseases are the rhizosphere and rhizoplane, where antibiosis, if it occurs, may be expected to be crucial in the establishment or failure of infection. Direct evidence for the presence of specific antibiotics in the rhizosphere has not been easily forthcoming (Kalyanasundaram, 1958). This is hardly surprising considering the difficulties attendant even upon the detection of individual constituents of root exudates in soil, which must be produced in quantities large relative to those of any one antibiotic. Indirect evidence is, however, accumulating that antibiotic production in the rhizosphere may have a determining influence on root infection. Reference has already been made to instances where the occurrence of antibiotically active organisms in the rhizosphere may explain the resistance of certain varieties of crop plants to root disease. The differences in the occurrence of a disease in contrasting types of soil may also be explained by antibiosis. Rishbeth's work (1950, 1951a,b) on a root disease of pines caused by *Fomes annosus*, provides a well-documented example. The spread of this disease was much more rapid in alkaline soils in East Anglia than on more acid heath and woodland soils. Superficial growth of *Fomes annosus* was abundant on roots in the alkaline soils but absent or feeble in the more acid soils. Roots in the latter soils were found to be colonized by *Trichoderma viride*, which was demonstrated to have a marked in-vitro antibiotic effect on *Fomes annosus*. A substantially similar situation has been found by Moreau and Schaeffer (1959) in the Jura region of France. The difficulties of interpretation of observations and experimental results are well illustrated by the examples given involving *T. viride*. This fungus, in addition to producing antibiotics, is known to have a high growth rate and competitive ability and also to possess potentialities for parasitism upon other fungi.

WIDESPREAD SOIL FUNGISTASIS.—Consideration of the possibility that antibiotics may accumulate in soil sufficiently to give the soil as a whole antibiotic properties, brings us to the difficult question of a widespread soil fungistasis. It is to the work of Dobbs and Hinson (1953), just 10 years ago, that the general recognition by mycologists of the problem of soil fungistasis is due, although isolated observations, which may now be explained by the phenomenon, had been made earlier. They found complete inhibition of germination of spores of *Penicillium frequentans*, buried in soil in folds of cellophane. This inhibition, which occurred in all 13 soils tested in the original work, could be overcome by the addition of glucose to the soil. Their original findings have now been confirmed and extended (Hinson, 1954; Dobbs, Hinson, and Bywater, 1960; Dobbs and Griffiths, 1961, 1962; Jackson, 1958a,b). The results make it certain that the spores of most fungi do not readily germinate in natural soil unless stimulatory substances, usually associated with plant residues or living plant roots, are present in sufficient concentration. Failure to germinate in soil is not usually due directly to a deficiency of nutrients.

Lingappa and Lockwood (1961) have criticised the interpretation of some of the experimental work on soil fungistasis in which cellulose film or agar has been used on the grounds that these substances may provide a substrate for the growth of antagonistic organisms. Their criticism cannot detract from the validity of the many related observations which confirm the existence of soil fungistasis. Their discovery that bacteria and actinomycetes growing from a mixed soil population on an agar surface for a short period could influence fungal spore germination at a distance of at least 2 mm in the absence of high concentrations of nutrients, must strengthen the case for accepting the significance of antibiosis in soil. The same workers showed that rather high concentrations of alcohol extracts of fresh spores of *Ustilago zeae* had an inhibitory effect on the soil microflora, but strongly stimulated growth at lower concentrations. Lingappa and Lockwood (1962b) later reported the observation of areas of stimulation of bacteria in the vicinity of fungal spores added to soil. These observations led them to the hypothesis that individual spores might release nutrients into the soil, stimulating the growth of antagonistic organisms in their vicinity, which then inhibit spore germination. This hypothesis might be valid for a short period after the spore first makes contact with the soil, but nutrient leak could not be expected to be sustained at a rate sufficient to maintain an active episporic flora for more than a few hours or perhaps days. Bacteria and actinomycetes, which can often be observed on the surface of growing hyphae, might easily affect hyphal growth by producing antibiotics.

EXPRESSION OF SOIL FUNGISTASIS.—The most easily recognisable expression of fungistasis is inhibition of spore germination. Once germination has occurred, the germ tube is less susceptible to soil fungistasis, but subsequent development may be strongly influenced. In particular it has been observed that in unsterile soil, macroconidia of *Fusarium* spp. may germinate, but that after a short period of growth the germ tube is terminated by a chlamydospore (Jackson, 1960; Nash, Christou, and Snyder, 1961; Toussoun and Snyder, 1961). Sometimes the conidia themselves are converted into chlamydospores. In sterile soil, or in the absence of soil, chlamydospore formation is usually considerably delayed. Venkat Ram (1952) discovered that the production of chlamydospores in cultures of *F. solani* was much enhanced when the medium was inoculated with a soil isolate of *Bacillus licheniformis* or another, unidentified, bacterial isolate. Development of chlamydospores, as well as other morphological changes, in cultures of *F. oxysporum* have been attributed by Park (1961) to the accumulation of unidentified staling substances. It seems highly probable that many phases of fungal development in soil, particularly germination, vegetative growth, and onset and intensity of sporulation (Boosalis, 1962), are subject to some degree of influence by a variety of microbial metabolites acting as environmental hormones.

Death and lysis of hyphae, and less readily of spores, often follows contact with unsterile soil. What relation, if any, such lysis bears to soil fungistasis is not clear. It is known that a number of substances induce lysis (Carter and Lockwood, 1957) and that lysis may be common in cultures (Park, 1961). Reinoculation of autoclaved soil with isolates of *Streptomyces* spp.

known to be lytic in culture also induces lytic and fungistatic properties in the soil (Lockwood, 1958).

THE SOURCE OF SOIL FUNGISTASIS.—There is, as yet, no clear evidence of the origin or nature of soil fungistasis. When Brian (1960) discussed the possible role of antibiotics in soil, he concluded that although antibiotic accumulation was unlikely to occur in many of the soils in which fungistasis had been detected, antibiotic production nevertheless seemed the most likely explanation of fungistasis. He also pointed out that no detailed studies had yet been made of production in soil of the polypeptide antibiotics of bacteria, or of the antifungal polyenic antibiotics of actinomycetes, the chemical properties of which were in many ways rather distinct from those of the antibiotics which had so far received most attention.

It is true that the accumulation and activity of antibiotics in soil away from microhabitats of active metabolism has not generally been regarded as plausible, because of adsorption by clays and rapid degradation by the soil flora. But in recent studies of the adsorption of antibiotics in soil (Pinck, Holton, and Allison, 1961; Pinck, Soulides and Allison, 1961; Soulides, Pinck, and Allison, 1961, 1962) it has been shown that, for example, adsorption of streptomycin by the kaolinitic fraction of an unsterilized clay loam soil could result in the persistence of the antibiotic, in the adsorbed condition, up to 28 days after its introduction into the soil. A slow release during this period was apparent from the reaction of the bacterial flora. It would thus seem possible that an antibiotic adsorbed by the clay colloids might subsequently be released, perhaps after a pH change produced by local microbiological activity. While in the adsorbed state, an antibiotic would be protected from microbial degradation, but might still undergo physical or chemical breakdown (Soulides, Pinck, and Allison, 1962). Similar protection from the action of microorganisms through adsorption or inaccesibility has also been shown for humus and other organic molecules in soil (Ensminger and Gieseking, 1942; Rovira and Graecen, 1957; Esterman, Peterson, and McClaren, 1959).

Release of aromatic compounds resulting from the degradation of lignin by macrofungi (Henderson, 1960) may give rise to fungitoxicity, similar in some respects to soil fungistasis (Lingappa and Lockwood, 1962a). The action of these compounds seems to differ somewhat from normal fungistasis in that even at concentrations permitting germination, a strong inhibition of germ-tube growth was noted. Lignin monomers may be important in soils rich in organic matter, and their formation may also sometimes explain the action of soil amendments in disease control.

The similarities between fungal behaviour in staled cultures and in natural soil have suggested that soil fungistasis may be a form of general staling between both like and unlike organisms (Park, 1960). Recent support for this concept has been given by Griffin's (1962) experiments, which showed that autoclaved soil reinfected with several of a variety of microorganisms developed fungistatic properties, but that there was no correlation between ability to produce a fungistatic effect in soil and production of an antibiotic effect in culture. Griffin postulated that normal soil fungistasis may be partly a result of the general saprophytic activities of the soil microflora and partly that of toxic metabolites, other than specific antibiotic substances. It seems to me that description of the fungistatic situation in soil as a type of staling phenomenon is quite acceptable and not incompatible with the theories discussed. The situation will not, however, be materially advanced until we are able to isolate and identify with certainty at least some of the substances implicated. Whether we then choose to designate them antibiotics or staling substances is probably of no great importance and will depend only on precise definition of these terms. Perhaps Winter's (1961) conclusion, that widespread inhibiting conditions in soil must be ascribed to a complex of different inhibitory factors, including the synergistic effect of amounts which separately are below threshold levels of toxicity, may prove justified and help to explain some of the difficulties familiar to workers in this field.

THE SIGNIFICANCE OF SOIL FUNGISTASIS.—The ecological significance of the sensitivity of fungi to soil fungistasis, and the amelioration of inhibition by sufficient concentrations of nutrients would be difficult to overestimate. Sensitivity to a general and widespread soil fungistasis is of great survival value, particularly to the more ephemeral saprophytes and those fungi associated primarily with roots. Spores sensitive to fungistasis normally lie dormant in soil until stimulated by contact with soluble nutrients, when germination, followed by more or less extensive vegetative growth and often sporulation, can be achieved. The evolution of this mechanism can be regarded as an adaptation to a heterotrophic existence in a medium providing substrates which are discontinuous in space or time. This adaptation finds some parallel in the necessity for stimulation by a host, shown by parasitic angiosperms such as *Striga* spp. and by root-parasitic nematodes. These parasitic plants and nematodes, in common with some specialized fungal resting bodies, exhibit constitutive dormancy, in contrast to the fungal spores subjected to fungistasis, which may be regarded as exogenously induced dormancy.

ANTIBIOSIS AND FUNGISTASIS IN DISEASE CONTROL.— Most attempts to achieve disease control through antibiosis depend for their success on changing the equilibrium between the pathogen and its natural antagonists in favour of the antagonists. We have already seen how this may be the indirect outcome of the plant breeder's efforts, by selecting varieties whose rhizosphere offers a favourable environment to antagonists; and there is evidence that a difference in one gene may have a strong effect on the rhizosphere population (Elkan, 1962). Changes in the rhizosphere population can also be induced by foliar application of nutrients or other substances (Venkata Ram, 1960). Horst and Herr (1962) were able to detect a temporary increase in actinomycetes antagonistic to *Fusarium roseum* f.

cerealis in the rhizosphere of corn seedlings after the foliar application of urea.

The effects of adding organic amendments to the soil to change the microbial equilibrium so as to favour antagonistic organisms are well known and have been discussed by Dr. Garrett and others. Recent examples of the successful application of this method are the addition of chitin to the soil to control fusarium root diseases of radishes, beans, and peas (Mitchell and Alexander, 1961, 1962; Buxton, 1962). The control achieved in these cases appears to be associated with an increase in the numbers of bacteria and actinomycetes, which possess chitinolytic activity, and also inhibit or lyse fusaria. The value of chitin in selective media for the isolation of actinomycetes from soil was already known (Lingappa and Lockwood, 1960).

Attempts to introduce antagonistic organisms into an environment which is relatively permanent and stable and where they are not already present are unlikely to succeed. If, however, at least one factor of the environment is changed, the chances of successful introduction may be improved. Total sterilization of soil produces drastic changes, and the introduction of antagonists after such treatment may not be successful because of the unstable conditions created. More emphasis is now being placed on the use of less drastic methods such as treatment with low-temperature air and steam mixtures (Baker and Olsen, 1960; Baker, 1962) with the object of killing the more heat-sensitive pathogens but causing the least possible disturbance to the saprophytic flora. Inoculation of soil treated in this way with antibiotic-producing organisms may give useful results. The developing rhizosphere of a seedling plant does provide a new and changing environment which is normally colonized more or less fortuitously by seed surface and soil organisms. Suitable organisms may be introduced artificially into this environment. If their numbers are large relative to those of the normal colonizers, they may become established and sometimes remain in considerable numbers throughout the life of the plant (Brown, Burlingham, and Jackson, 1962). Such organisms are obviously well placed to influence the behaviour of root pathogens, and it is significant that the effectiveness of seed inoculation with *Azotobacter* and other bacteria is now being ascribed, in part at least, to the control of pathogenic fungi, perhaps by antibiosis (Mishustin and Naumova, 1962).

Inoculation of seed with organisms of known antibiotic potential has been successful in the control of certain diseases, for example fusarium blight of oat seedlings (Tveit and Wood, 1955), which has been controlled as effectively by inoculation of the seed with isolates of *Chaetomium,* as by mercurial seed dressings. The lack of clear correlation between in vitro and in vivo activity of different *Chaetomium* isolates may have been due, as suggested by Tveit and Wood, to the binding of antibiotic to the hyphae, or perhaps to a failure to include root exudates in the test media.

In exploring the possibilities of disease control by introducing antagonists into the rhizosphere, the potentialities of strains of fungi known to be normal col-onizers of the root surface have not yet received sufficient attention. As an example, *Fusarium oxysporum* and *Cylindrocarpon radicicola* are two of the most abundant rhizoplane inhabitants of grasses and cereals as well as other crops in many soils. Strains of both of these species show antifungal activity (Buxton, 1960; White, Chilvers, and Evans, 1962), which may contribute to their status as successful root colonizers. Selection of active antifungal strains of either of these organisms, followed by seed inoculation, could form a useful basis for work on biological control. Ectotrophic mycorrhizal fungi may constitute a defensive barrier against pathogenic fungi, for there is evidence both of the production of antibiotics by these fungi (Santoro and Casida, 1959) and of a marked modification of the microflora in the vicinity of mycorrhizal roots (Robertson, 1954). Inoculation with specific mycorrhizal fungi could perhaps be a factor in decreasing disease susceptibility.

Alteration of the normal fungistatic equilibrium in soil offers a possible approach to the control of some soil pathogens. Chinn and his colleagues (1953) found that helminthosporium root rot of wheat seedlings could be controlled by adding to the soil organic amendments such as soybean meal. The effect of these additions was to induce germination in fungistatically inhibited conidia of the root-rot fungus. After germination, lysis of germ tubes occurred, resulting in a reduction in the population of the fungus. In later studies Chinn and Ledingham (1957, 1961) found that the most effective substances in promoting germination of *Helminthosporium sativum* conidia in soil were natural products, such as wheat germ, bran, molasses. They suggested that some of the effects of green manuring might be explained by stimulation of germination, which is then followed by lysis. Various crop residues can stimulate, to differing degrees, the germination of inactive chlamydospores of *Fusarium solani* f. *phaseoli* (Toussoun, Patrick, and Snyder, 1963), the germ tubes formed sometimes then undergoing lysis. The situation is, however, complicated by the fact that substances from decomposing plant residues may increase the susceptibility of host tissues to invasion by fungal pathogens (Toussoun and Patrick, 1963).

Since the proximity of roots may also provide a stimulus to the germination of inhibited spores or other resting bodies in soil (Jackson, 1960; Schroth and Snyder, 1961; Shreiber and Green, 1963), trap-cropping with stimulatory but nonhost species to reduce soil infestations of a pathogenic fungus offers another possible avenue of control. Success depends upon three conditions: stimulation of germination in the rhizosphere of the "bait" plant, noninfection of this plant, and inability to reproduce in its rhizosphere. Unfortunately, there is evidence, as Schroth and Snyder have shown, that even when the first two conditions are satisfied, saprophytic growth and reproduction can lead to an actual increase in the infestation.

A consideration of all the evidence we now have must convince us that antibiosis, in one form or another, plays a key role in the ecology of soil microorganisms, being perhaps second in importance only to competition for nutrients. Increasing knowledge of the interrelations and dynamics of the rhizosphere population will lead to increasing possibilities for the biological control of root diseases through antibiosis.

LITERATURE CITED

AGNIHOTHRUDU, B. 1955. Incidence of fungistatic organisms in the rhizosphere of pigeon-pea (*Cajanus cajan*) in relation to resistance and susceptibility to wilt caused by *Fusarium udum* Butler. Naturwissenschaften 42: 373.

BAKER, K. F. 1962. Principles of heat treatment of soil and planting material. J. Australian Inst. Agr. Sci. 28: 118-126.

BAKER, K. F., and C. M. OLSEN. 1960. Aerated steam for soil treatment. Phytopathology 50: 82.

BOOSALIS, M. G. 1962. Precocious sporulation and longevity of *Helminthosporium sativum* in soil. Phytopathology 52: 1172-1177.

BOWEN, G. D. 1961. The toxicity of legume seed diffusates toward rhizobia and other bacteria. Plant Soil 15: 155-165.

BOWEN, G. D., and A. D. ROVIRA. 1961. The effects of microorganisms on plant growth. I. Development of roots and root hairs in sand and agar. Plant Soil 15: 166-188.

BRIAN, P. W. 1960. Antagonistic and competitive mechanisms limiting survival and activity of fungi in soil. p. 117-129. *In* D. Parkinson and J. S. Waid [ed.], The ecology of soil fungi, Liverpool University Press, Liverpool.

BROWN, M. E., S. B. BURLINGHAM, and R. M. JACKSON. 1962. Studies on Azotobacter species in soil. 2. Populations of Azotobacter in the rhizosphere and effects of artificial inoculation. Plant Soil 17: 320-332.

BUXTON, E. W. 1960. Effects of pea root exudate on the antagonism of some rhizosphere micro-organisms towards *Fusarium oxysporum* f. *pisi*. J. Gen. Microbiol. 22: 678-689.

BUXTON, E. W. 1962. Control of fusarium wilt. Rothamsted Exptl. Sta. Ann. Rept. 1961: 118.

CARTER, P. H., and J. L. LOCKWOOD. 1957. Lysis of fungi by soil microorganisms and fungicides including antibiotics. Phytopathology 47: 154-161.

CHINN, S. H. F., and R. J. LEDINGHAM. 1957. Studies on the influence of various substances on the germination of *Helminthosporium sativum* spores in soil. Can. J. Botany 35: 697-701.

CHINN, S. H. F., and R. J. LEDINGHAM. 1961. Mechanisms contributing to the eradication of spores of *Helminthosporium sativum* from amended soil. Can. J. Botany 39: 739-748.

CHINN, S. H. F., R. J. LEDINGHAM, B. J. SALLANS, and P. M. SIMMONDS. 1953. A mechanism for the control of common root-rot of wheat. Phytopathology 43: 761.

DOBBS, C. G., and D. A. GRIFFITHS. 1961. Studies in soil mycology. IV. Mycostasis in soils. Forestry Comm. (London) Rept. Forestry Res. 1960: 87-92.

DOBBS, C. G., and D. A. GRIFFITHS. 1962. Studies in soil mycology. V. Mycostasis in soils. Forestry Comm. (London) Rept. Forestry Res. 1961: 95-100.

DOBBS, C. G., and W. H. HINSON. 1953. A widespread fungistasis in the soil. Nature (London) 172: 197.

DOBBS, C. G., W. H. HINSON, and J. BYWATER. 1960. Inhibition of fungal growth in soils. p. 130-147. *In* D. Parkinson and J. S. Waid [ed.], The ecology of soil fungi, Liverpool University Press, Liverpool.

ELKAN, G. H. 1962. Comparison of rhizosphere microorganisms of genetically related nodulating and non-nodulating soybean lines. Can. J. Microbiol. 8: 79-87.

ENSMINGER, L. E., and J. E. GIESEKING. 1942. Resistance of clay adsorbed proteins to proteolytic hydrolysis. Soil Sci. 53: 205-209.

ESTERMANN, E. F., G. H. PETERSON, and A. D. McCLAREN. 1959. Digestion of clay-protein, lignin-protein, and silica-protein complexes by enzymes and bacteria. Soil Sci. Soc. Am. Proc. 23: 31-36.

GRIFFIN, G. J. 1962. Production of a fungistatic effect by soil microflora in autoclaved soil. Phytopathology 52: 90-91.

HELY, F. W., F. J. BERGERSEN, and J. BROCKWELL. 1957. Microbial antagonism in the rhizosphere as a factor in the failure of inoculation of subterranean clover. Australian J. Agr. Res. 8: 24-44.

HENDERSON, M. E. K. 1960. Studies on the physiology of lignin decomposition by soil fungi. p. 286-296. *In* D. Parkinson and J. S. Waid [ed.], The ecology of soil fungi, Liverpool University Press, Liverpool.

HINSON, W. H. 1954. A study in the biology of soil moulds. Ph.D. Thesis, University of Wales.

HORST, R. K., and L. J. HERR. 1962. Effects of foliar area treatment on numbers of actinomycetes antagonistic to *Fusarium roseum* f. *cerealis* in the rhizosphere of corn seedlings. Phytopathology 52: 423-427.

JACKSON, R. M. 1958a. An investigation of fungistasis in Nigerian soils. J. Gen. Microbiol. 18: 248-258.

JACKSON, R. M. 1958b. Some aspects of soil fungistasis. J. Gen. Microbiol. 19: 390-401.

JACKSON, R. M. 1960. Soil fungistasis and the rhizosphere. p. 168-176. *In* D. Parkinson and J. S. Waid [ed.], The ecology of soil fungi, Liverpool University Press, Liverpool.

KALYANASUNDARAM, R. 1958. Production of fusaric acid by *Fusarium lycopersici* Sacc. in the rhizosphere of tomato plants. Phytopathol. Z. 32: 25-34.

KERR, A. 1956. Some interactions between plant roots and pathogenic soil fungi. Australian J. Biol. Sci. 9: 45-52.

KRASILNIKOV, N. A. 1939. The influence of soil bacteria on the growth of wheat. Mikrobiologiya 8: 523-530.

LINGAPPA, B. T., and J. L. LOCKWOOD. 1960. A chitin medium for isolation, growth and maintenance of actinomycetes. Nature (London) 189: 158.

LINGAPPA, B. T., and J. L. LOCKWOOD. 1961. The nature of the widespread fungistasis. J. Gen. Microbiol. 25: 473-485.

LINGAPPA, B. T., and J. L. LOCKWOOD. 1962a. Fungitoxicity of lignin monomers, model substances, and decomposition products. Phytopathology 52: 295-299.

LINGAPPA, B. T., and J. L. LOCKWOOD. 1962b. Relationship of soil microbes to the widespread soil fungistasis. Phytopathology 52: 739.

LOCKWOOD, J. L. 1958. *Streptomyces* spp. as a cause of natural fungistasis. Phytopathology 48: 393.

LUCAS, C. E. 1947. The ecological effects of external metabolites. Biol. Rev. Cambridge Phil. Soc. 22: 270-295.

MIRCHINK, T. G., and K. P. GRESHNYKH. 1962. Toxin formation in the soil by some fungal species of the genus Penicillium. Microbiology (U.S.S.R.) (Engl. transl.) 30: 851-854.

MISHUSTIN, E. N., and A. N. NAUMOVA. 1962. Bacterial fertilizers, their effectiveness and mode of action. Microbiology (U.S.S.R.) (Engl. transl.) 31:

MITCHELL, R., and M. ALEXANDER. 1961. The mycolytic phenomenon and biological control of Fusarium in soil. Nature (London) 190: 109-110.

MITCHELL, R., and M. ALEXANDER. 1962. Microbiological processes associated with the use of chitin for biological control. Soil. Sci. Soc. Am. Proc. 26: 556-558.

MOREAU, R., and R. SCHAEFFER. 1959. Sur la maladie du rond dans les Pessières Jurassiennes. Ann. Sci. Univ. Besançon. 2 Sér. Méd. et Pharm. 3: 112-120.

NASH, S. M., T. CHRISTOU, and W. C. SNYDER. 1961. Existence of *Fusarium solani* f. *phaseoli* as chlamydospores in soil. Phytopathology 51: 308-312.

PARK, D. 1960. Antagonism—the background to soil fungi. p. 148-159. *In* D. Parkinson and J. S. Waid [ed.], The ecology of soil fungi, Liverpool University Press, Liverpool.

PARK, D. 1961. Morphogenesis, fungistasis and cultural staling in *Fusarium oxysporum* Snyder and Hansen. Trans. Brit. Mycol. Soc. 44: 377-390.

PINCK, L. A., W. F. HOLTON, and F. E. ALLISON. 1961. Antibiotics in soil. I. Physico-chemical studies of antibiotic-clay complexes. Soil Sci. 91: 22-28.

PINCK, L. A., D. A. SOULIDES, and F. E. ALLISON. 1961. Antibiotics in soil. II. Extent and mechanisms of release. Soil Sci. 91: 94-99.

RANGASWAMI, G., and S. ETHIRAJ. 1962. Antibiotic production by *Streptomyces* sp. in unamended soil. Phytopathology 52: 989-992.

RISHBETH, J. 1950. Observations on the biology of *Fomes annosus*, with particular reference to East Anglian pine plantations. I. The outbreaks of disease and ecological status of the fungus. Ann. Botany (London) [N.S.] 14: 365-383.

RISHBETH, J. 1951a. Observations on the biology of *Fomes annosus*, with particular reference to East Anglian pine plantations. II. Spore production, stump infection, and saprophytic activity in stumps. Ann. Botany (London) [N.S.] 15: 1-21.

RISHBETH, J. 1951b. Observations on the biology of *Fomes annosus*, with particular reference to East Anglian pine plantations. III. Natural and experimental infection of pines, and some factors affecting severity of the disease. Ann. Botany (London) [N.S.] 15: 221-246.

ROBERTSON, N. F. 1954. Studies on the mycorrhiza of *Pinus sylvestris*. I. The pattern of development of mycorrhizal roots and its significance for experimental studies. New Phytologist 53: 253-283.

ROVIRA, A. D., and E. L. GREACEN. 1957. The effect of aggregate disruption on the activity of microorganisms in the soil. Australian J. Agr. Res. 8: 659-673.

SANTORO, T., and L. E. CASIDA. 1959. Antibiotic production by mycorrhizal fungi. Soc. Am. Bacteriologists, Bacteriol. Proc. 1959: 16.

SCHROTH, M. N., and W. C. SNYDER. 1961. Effect of host exudate on chlamydospore germination of the bean root rot fungus, *Fusarium solani* f. *phaseoli*. Phytopathology 51: 389-393.

SHREIBER, L. R., and R. J. GREEN. 1963. Effect of root exudates on germination of conidia and microsclerotia of *Verticillium albo-atrum* inhibited by soil fungistasis. Phytopathology 53: 260-264.

SOULIDES, D. A., L. A. PINCK, and F. E. ALLISON. 1961. Antibiotics in soils. III. Further studies on release of antibiotics from clays. Soil Sci. 92: 90-93.

SOULIDES, D. A., L. A. PINCK, and F. E. ALLISON. 1962. Antibiotics in soils. V. Stability and release of soil-adsorbed antibiotics. Soil Sci. 94: 239-244.

STEINBERG, R. A. 1950. The relation of certain soil bacteria to frenching symptoms of tobacco. Bull. Torrey Botan. Club 77: 38-44.

STEPANOVA, L. N., and E. M. FISH. 1958. [Toxic bacteria in sod-podzolic soils.] Izv. Akad. Nauk. SSSR. Ser. Biol. No. 3, p. 361-368.

STEVENSON, I. L. 1956. Antibiotic activity of actinomycetes in soil as demonstrated by direct observation techniques. J. Gen. Microbiol. 15: 372-380.

SUBBA-RAO, N. S., and D. L. BAILEY. 1961. Rhizosphere studies in relation to varietal resistance or susceptibility of tomato to Verticillium wilt. Can. J. Botany 39: 1747-1758.

THOMPSON, J. A. 1961. Studies on nodulation responses to pelleting of subterranean clover seed. Australian J. Agr. Res. 12: 578-592.

TIMONIN, M. I. 1940. The interaction of higher plants and soil microorganisms. II. Study of the microbial population of the rhizosphere in relation to resistance to soil-borne diseases. Can. J. Res., Sec. C, 18: 444-455.

TIMONIN, M. I. 1941. The interaction of higher plants and soil microorganisms. III. Effect of by-products of plant growth on activity of fungi and actinomycetes. Soil Sci. 52: 395-413.

TOUSSOUN, T. A., and Z. A. PATRICK. 1963. Effect of toxic substances from decomposing plant residues on root rot of bean. Phytopathology 53: 265-270.

TOUSSOUN, T. A., Z. A. PATRICK, and W. C. SNYDER. 1963. Influence of crop residue decomposition products on the germination of *Fusarium solani* f. *phaseoli* chlamydospores in soil. Nature (London) 197: 1314-1316.

TOUSSOUN, T. A., and W. C. SNYDER. 1961. Germination of chlamydospores of *Fusarium solani* f. *phaseoli* in unsterilized soils. Phytopathology 51: 620-623.

TVEIT, M., and R. K. S. WOOD. 1955. The control of Fusarium blight in oat seedlings with antagonistic species of Chaetomium. Ann. Appl. Biol. 43: 538-552.

VENKATA RAM, C. S. 1952. Soil bacteria and chlamydospore formation in *Fusarium solani*. Nature (London) 170: 889.

VENKATA RAM, C. S. 1960. Foliar application of nutrients and rhizosphere microflora of *Camellia sinensis*. Nature (London) 187: 621-622.

WHITE, N. H., G. A. CHILVERS, and G. EVANS. 1962. Antifungal activity of *Cylindrocarpon radicicola* Wr. Nature (London) 195: 406-407.

WINTER, A. G. 1961. New physiological and biological aspects in the interrelationships between higher plants. Mechanisms in biological competition. Symp. Soc. Exptl. Biol. Cambridge 15: 229-243.

WRIGHT, J. M. 1951. Phytotoxic effects of some antibiotics. Ann. Botany (London) [N.S.] 15: 493-499.

WRIGHT, J. M. 1956a. The production of antibiotics in soil. III. Production of gliotoxin in wheatstraw buried in soil. Ann. Appl. Biol. 44: 461-466.

WRIGHT, J. M. 1956b. The production of antibiotics in soil. IV. Production of antibiotics in coats of seeds sown in soil. Ann. Appl. Biol. 44: 561-566.

► DISCUSSION OF R. M. JACKSON PAPER

H. Stolp:

A special type of antagonistic relation among bacteria is represented by the parasitic action of a vibrio-like organism (Fig. 1) on susceptible host bacteria. The parasite is of minute size (0.3 × 0.8 μ approximately), and possesses a flagellum of about 50 mμ in diameter. It is highly motile and attaches with the nonflagellated end to the bacterial cell surface (Fig. 2), inducing in Gram-negative bacteria spheroplast formation and finally complete lysis (Fig. 3). In a bacterial lawn, the plating of a dilution of the parasite results (with appropriate dilutions) in the formation of "plaques" (Fig. 4) that externally are not distinguishable from the known phage-plaques. In liquid culture, the action of the parasite is accompanied by a reduction in optical density. The first strain, isolated in Berlin, shows activity restricted to bacteria belonging to the pseudomonads. Since then, in collaboration with M. P. Starr at the University of California, Davis, a number of strains of this parasite have been isolated that attack bacteria of different systematic position and that differ in their host-activity spectra (H. Stolp and M. P. Starr. Antonie van Leeuwenhoek J. Microbiol. Serol. 29: 217-248. 1963.). The possibility was indicated that this type of antagonism may have some ecological importance with respect to changes of bacterial equilibria.

S. Ishizawa:

I should like to comment on the distribution in soil of actinomycetes producing antibiotic substances against fungi or bacteria. Although the number of microorganisms decreases with depth, there exists some evidence

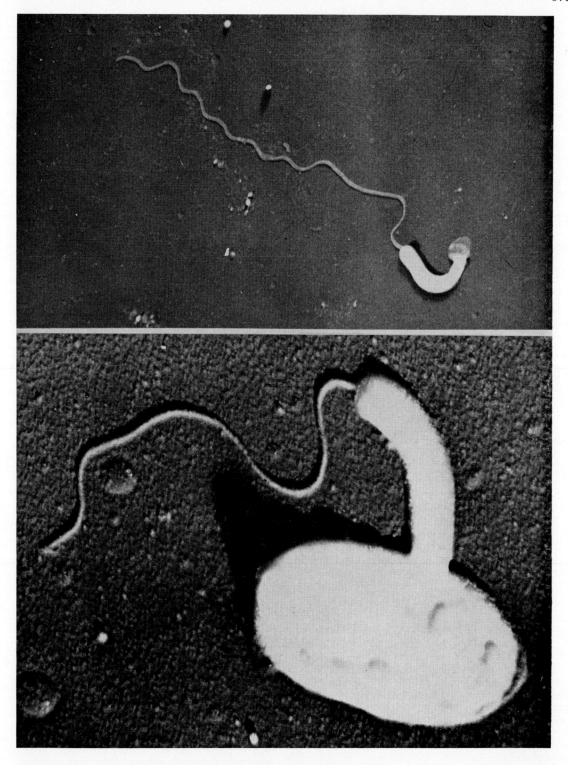

Figs. 1 and 2. Electron micrographs of *Bdellovibrio bacteriovorus* strain 100. (H. Stolp and M. P. Starr. Antonie van Leeuwenhoek J. Microbiol. Serol. 29: 217-248. 1963.) **Fig. 1** (upper). Single individual (× 18,000). **Fig. 2** (lower). *Bdellovibrio* attached to a host cell of *Erwinia amylovora* (× 33,000).

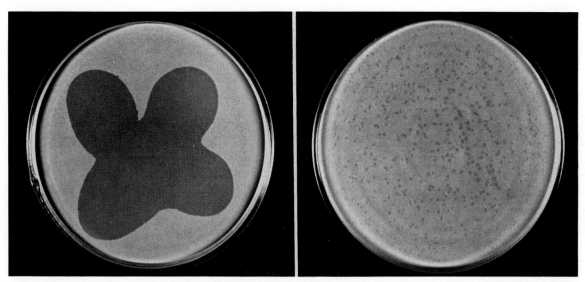

Figs. 3 and 4. Lytic effect of *Bdellovibrio bacteriovorus* on bacteria in culture. (H. Stolp and M. P. Starr. Antonie van Leeuwenhoek J. Microbiol. Serol. 29: 217-248. 1963.) **Fig. 3** (left). Lytic areas in a lawn of *Escherichia coli* B, produced by *B. bacteriovorus* strain Bd. 109. A suspension containing the parasites was dropped onto the bacterial lawn. **Fig. 4** (right). Single plaque formation by *Bdellovibrio* strain A3.12 on its homologous host, strain A3.12.

that the actinomycete flora differs considerably among horizons. For instance, according to one of the results obtained in our laboratory, the proportion of actinomycetes which inhibit strongly the growth of *Erwinia* is evidently larger in the lower horizon.

For biological control of plant pathogens in soil, study of the microbiological characterization of soil on the basis of the composition of soil population as well as on its activity should be intensified. It will be enhanced by combining microbiological criteria with chemical or physical criteria in the pedological classification of soil.

J. L. Lockwood:

I should like to discuss some of our results which may bear on the source of soil fungistasis. Natural soil amended with washed or unwashed conidia of any of several fungi gave increased oxygen uptake in Warburg flasks, as compared with nonamended soil. A portion of this increased respiration may be due to respiration of spores themselves, but stimulation of oxygen uptake can also be achieved by amending soil with sterile, aqueous washings from fungus spores. Similar results were obtained with autoclaved spores and dilute peptone solution.

Increased numbers of bacterial colonies were obtained in soil dilution plates after amendment of natural soil with spores and incubating for 8-16 hours.

Inhibition of germination of fungus conidia was obtained when a mixed population of bacterial cells was washed and centrifuged several times with dilute buffer, then incubated with the spores. But when the washed bacterial cells were incubated for 6 hours, then sterile-filtered, and conidia of *Helminthosporium* (which germinated in 2 hours) were placed in the filtrate, germination was not inhibited.

Germination of washed conidia on natural soil surfaces sometimes exceeded that of nonwashed conidia, and spores capable of rapid germination (e.g. rust uredospores) sometimes gave up to 50% germination on natural soil surfaces.

In some preparations of spores removed from natural soil surfaces on thin films, areas of bacterial proliferation could be seen.

These results are consistent with the concept that spores provide food for soil microbes, which, in turn, inhibit the spores in some manner.

C. G. Dobbs:

I prefer the word mycostasis to fungistasis. The phenomenon intervenes when and where other conditions for the initiation of growth are met, and it generally has a "competitive" relation with certain nutrients, notably sugars. It is important, however, to realize that many soils contain a residual mycostasis, not heat-sensitive or broken by sugars, and probably mainly inorganic in origin. This may well also exist in agricultural or treated soils and should always be investigated. It is now clear that many microorganisms may be involved in the production of the general, heat- and sugar-sensitive soil mycostases. Lockwood's evidence that freshly added spores may stimulate microbial soil extracts which show an increased inhibition when the soil is "fed" with washed spores of the test fungus, does not explain the continued inhibition of old spores in the soil. The concept of staling of the microhabitat cannot be excluded by work on fresh, cultured spores.

R. R. Baker:

It is essential in studies of soil fungistasis to indicate whether washed or unwashed material is used for testing, since nutrient may be carried over on the spores. Fungi found in soil should be used since these often have characteristics different from those not ordinarily found in this habitat. G. J. Griffin, in unpublished work, has further evidence for fungistasis being similar to staling. Sterile soil extracts, obtained with a pressure-membrane apparatus, contain inhibitory factors. Use of a sausage-casing membrane contributes nutrients tending to mask this, however. It is difficult to conceive of leakage of nutrients from propagules in soils promoting bacterial growth for long periods of time.

G. D. Pentland:

Dr. Kerr has noted the effect of discontinuous soil water on the availability of food for microorganisms, and on limiting bacteria to water pockets. Previously, Dr. Dobbs has gone on record as indicating that the fungistatic substance, or substances, in soil must be water-soluble. Would you comment on the effect of limited soil water on the availability of antibiotics or fungistatic substances—not so much in terms of production as in terms of diffusion through soil and contact with hyphal strands, especially when the water becomes discontinuous? We have been doing some experiments on the mycelial spread of *Coniophora puteana* from a wood food base through soil at different moisture levels. It will spread through the drier treatments but not through the wetter ones. We have visualized the reason for this as being connected with a discontinuity of the fungistatic substances in the drier soil.

R. M. Jackson:

Yes, it would seem likely that most antibiotics, or fungistatic substances, would depend on continuous water films for diffusion through soil. Under dry conditions, such diffusion would undoubtedly be impeded or prevented.

C. W. Emmons:

The fungi which cause systemic mycoses are saprophytes in soil or organic debris and these environmental sites, rather than infected man or animals, are the sources of infection for man and animals. In certain habitats these potential pathogens are very numerous. *Aspergillus fumigatus* may represent 95% of the viable spores at one stage in the succession of fungi in a compost pile. We have found 50,000,000 viable cells of *Cryptococcus neoformans* per g of an old pigeon nest. Here (at least ephemerally) competition seems to be absent or unimportant. On the other hand, *Histoplasma capsulatum* grows also in restricted habitats, but in the presence of many other fungi. We have been studying the occurrence of *H. capsulatum* around a house where human cases of histoplasmosis occurred, and in a small park adjacent to Pennsylvania Ave., Washington, D.C. The presence of house bats and roosting starlings, respectively, are the ecologic factors which enrich these soils and permit *H. capsulatum* to compete with other saprophytes. We should like to find a method of biological control which would eradicate or reduce the population of this pathogen without using general poisons which kill shrubbery and trees. We have isolated several species of *Streptomyces* from soil containing *Histoplasma.* These inhibit *Histoplasma* when grown in vitro with *Histoplasma,* but we have not been able to isolate an active antibiotic nor to demonstrate a change in the microflora of the soils supporting *Histoplasma* after heavy seeding, with and without organic amendments, with these strains of *Streptomyces.* We recognize that such a failure is a common experience.

J. Ulrich:

I should like to report on the activity of enzymes at the surfaces of colloids, as done in Dr. A. D. McLaren's laboratory. It was found that enzymatic activity was maintained even while the enzymes were ad-sorbed. If antibiotics were likewise adsorbed to soil colloids, they could possibly act from the adsorbed position and not necessarily have to be released to exert antibiotic activity on other organisms. Possibly the colloids would exert a "protective" action on the antibiotics.

J. Altman:

All discussion regarding fungistasis (mycostasis) seems to imply raw or nonsterile soil as being prerequisite, and from all pertinent discussion following your paper, a labile factor, also. Since this phenomenon is widespread and occurs under varying conditions, is reversed by nutrients, and affected by oxygen, is it not conceivable that every living microbe in soil is capable of releasing CO_2 in its metabolism? This CO_2 can readily be converted to H_2CO_3 in the water film or phase in soil. Secondly, some organisms might give off ethylene gas; both CO_2 and possibly ethylene can arise as a part of the glycolytic cycle. Sugar could overcome this fungistasis by stimulating growth of saprophytic microorganisms which could readily utilize CO_2 or break down ethylene.

Gerlind Eger: (A color motion picture was shown.)

Agaricus bisporus grows on composted or sterilized organic materials. As a rule, fructification occurs if the mycelium is covered with a layer of suitable unsterile casing material, for example, garden soil. By use of the *Halbschalentest* it is possible to obtain on a laboratory scale a quasi cross-section through the upper 6 inches of a mushroom bed. The mycelium is cultivated on sterilized compost in one half of a petri dish, the other half is filled with moist casing soil. After casing, the mycelium grows from the compost to the soil. After a few days of growth with normal speed, the growth becomes slower in certain areas as if it is being inhibited. In some instances, growth of the entire advancing front of mycelium slows down. Where the growth is inhibited, the mycelium forms minute white nodules, the fruitbody initials. The soil ahead of the initials mostly remains black because of the absence of mycelium growing on it. (Fig. 5, *A*.)

In some experiments, casing soil from the black areas of petri dishes, near where fruitbody initials were forming, was suspended in water. One part of the suspension was poured on heat-sterilized soil; this served to initiate fruitbodies in subsequent tests. The second part was filtered through paper filters and then poured on sterile soil, fruitbody formation also was initiated. The third part was sterilized by filtration through Seitz EK filters; no fruitbody initials were formed (Fig. 5, *B*). It is concluded that living microorganisms cause the initiation of fructification. On the other hand, growing mycelium of the cultivated mushroom inhibits the growth of microorganisms by means of a volatile substance. Evidence is given by the following experiments: Each of two series of agar plates in petri dishes was inoculated with 1 ml of the suspension of a microorganism. In one series growing mycelium of *Agaricus bisporus* was put on the lid. In the dishes containing growing mycelium, growth of the tested bacteria and molds was inhibited.

These and other experiments suggest that a specific microflora in the casing layer is selected by the volatile substance emitted by the mushroom mycelium when it grows under optimum conditions. If, however, the aeration is insufficient, the volatile substance accumu-

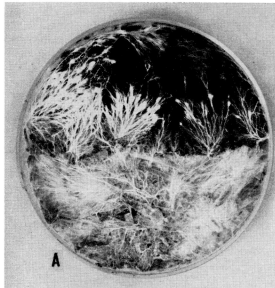

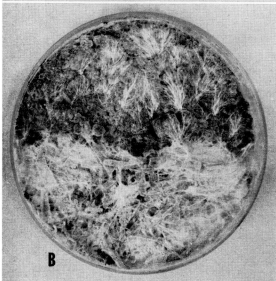

lates and even the growth of the favorable organisms is inhibited.

To obtain fructification of *Agaricus bisporus,* a balance must be maintained between the mushroom mycelium and the microflora in the casing layer.

L. C. Schisler:

I agree with Dr. Eger's findings of antibiotic activity of the mycelium of the cultivated mushroom, *Agaricus campestris* var. *bisporus.* This is readily observable and can be demonstrated in a variety of ways.

However, concerning her postulation that the microflora of the soil are responsible for the fruiting initiation in the cultivated mushroom, I have two questions:

1. What organisms are involved and can this effect be reproduced in pure culture?

2. How does she explain the initiation of fruiting under aseptic conditions observed by several investigators in this field?

G. Eger:

The organisms in question are bacteria or actinomycetes or both, but it has not yet been possible to obtain pure cultures.

There is no evidence, in some experiments with aerated cultures, that the conditions remained sterile until the end of the experiments. It is to be expected that the effect of the microorganisms in the casing layer of mushroom cultures can be replaced by chemical treatment under aseptic conditions. In my own experiments (Arch. Mikrobiol. 39: 313-334, 1961; Naturwissenschaft 49: 261, 1962) poor fruiting was obtained under sterile conditions with moist charcoal. Dr. E. Hauser (Switzerland) told me in 1959 that she had a mushroom strain that formed sporophores on sterile grain spawn in bottles. This is a great exception. Normal mushroom strains never do this. A single sporophore, even on horse-manure spawn, very scarcely occurs and was always reported to be a great exception. But in all these cases an incidental contamination was not excluded.

←——

Fig. 5. The *Halbschalentest* in which the mushroom grows on compost confined to the lower half of the dish. When casing soil is added to the upper half of the dish, mycelium grows over it: *A,* with nonsterile casing soil the strands form fruitbody initials in response to inhibition of growth. *B,* if the casing soil is sterile throughout fruitbody initials do not develop.

Parasitism and Predation of Soil Microorganisms[1]

M. G. BOOSALIS and REINHOLD MANKAU—*Department of Plant Pathology, University of Nebraska, Lincoln, and Department of Nematology, University of California, Riverside.*

The actual importance of parasitism and predation of soil microorganisms in their natural habitat is not known. This is because nearly all research on these types of antagonistic relations has been made in vitro (synthetic media and sterilized soil). One can only state from the evidence, largely of a descriptive nature, that biological control of root disease through parasitism and predation of the plant pathogen is a possibility worthy of increased study. In support of this statement we have necessarily drawn examples based primarily on studies in vitro and empirical observations.

Although occupying essentially the same habitat, the character, size, and mobility of nematodes cause them to be a step removed from the ecological relations common to fungal and bacterial pests; they are more aptly considered as members of the soil microfauna. Nevertheless, the basic principles involved in parasitism and predation of other soil microorganisms apply equally to the important nematode parasites of plants and justify their being considered as a group.

This paper is not intended to be a comprehensive review of the literature on intermicrobial parasitism and predation. Selected articles are cited, however, in presenting the major principles related to the topic. Several excellent papers on parasitism and predation of microorganisms have been published recently (DeVay, 1956; Sanford, 1959; Weindling, 1959; Darpoux, 1960; Brian, 1960).

MYCOPARASITISM.—*Terminology.*—The terms hyperparasitism, mycoparasitism, direct parasitism, and interfungus parasitism are used interchangeably to refer to the phenomenon of one fungus parasitic on another. The incitant is generally known as the hyperparasite or the mycoparasite.

Mycoparasites may be classified into several groups on the basis of the mode of parasitism and the effect

[1] The section on mycoparasites was published with the approval of the Director as Paper No. 1378, Journal Series, Nebraska Agricultural Experiment Station.

on the host. The destructive mycoparasites kill the host or its parts during their development, whereas the balanced parasites inflict little or no obvious damage to the host. Soil-borne fungi are attacked primarily by the destructive mycoparasites. This paper is concerned chiefly with the destructive mycoparasites.

Tropism.—In most instances mycoparasitism involves an intimate contact between the host and parasite. The ingenious experiments of Butler (1957) showed that parasitism of host hyphae by *Rhizoctonia solani* may be initiated by a tropic response involving a contact stimulus. Hyphae of *R. solani* responded thigmotropically to glass tubing and cotton fiber by coiling around these objects. Moreover, the hyphae occasionally penetrated the walls of the cotton fiber. The intensity of coiling and penetration, however, was considerably less than that on the host hyphae. This led to the conclusion that, in addition to thigmotropism, other factors may be contributing to the abundant development of hyphal coils and infection hyphae formed by the hyperparasite in contact with the host.

Mode of parasitism.—Parasitism by destructive mycoparasites may be initiated by direct penetration of the host or by coiling around the host hyphae with or without penetration. Examples of these types of attacks were noted by Butler (1957) for the mycoparasite *Rhizoctonia solani* on various hosts. In the case of *Penicillium vermiculatum* parasitizing *R. solani*, the penetration pegs develop either from coiling hyphae or from hyphae in direct contact with host mycelium (Boosalis, 1954, 1956). Recently Siegle (1961) reported that penetration of *Ophiobolus graminis* by *Didymella exitialis* is effected by penetration pegs boring through the cell wall or by the breakdown of the host wall induced by chitinase produced by appressoria.

After penetration, the parasites *Penicillium vermiculatum* and *Rhizoctonia solani* may develop infectious mycelium (Figs. 1-8). This structure usually grows and permeates part of the hypha or the entire mycelium of

Figs. 1-7. *Rhizoctonia solani* Kühn from decaying tomato fruit parasitizing *Rhizopus stolonifer* (Ehr. ex. Fr.) Vuill. and *Gilbertella persicaria* (Eddy) Hesseltine: **Fig. 1,** hypha of *R. solani* within sporangiophore of *G. persicaria* × 750; **Fig. 2,** *R. solani* within stolon of *Rhizopus stolonifer* × 375; **Figs. 3 and 5,** hyphae of *R. solani* within columellae and sporangiophores of *G. persicaria;* **Fig. 4,** penetration (see arrow) of internal hyphae of *R. solani* through the wall of a stolon of *Rhizopus stolonifer* (× 1000); **Figs. 6 and 7** show masses of hyphae of *R. solani* attacking a stolon of *Rhizopus stolonifer*. In **Fig. 6** (see arrow), an infection peg of *R. solani* in early stages of wall penetration (× 325). **Fig. 7** shows advanced stages of an attack of a hypha of *Rhizopus stolonifer*. (Photomicrographs kindly supplied by E. E. Butler.)

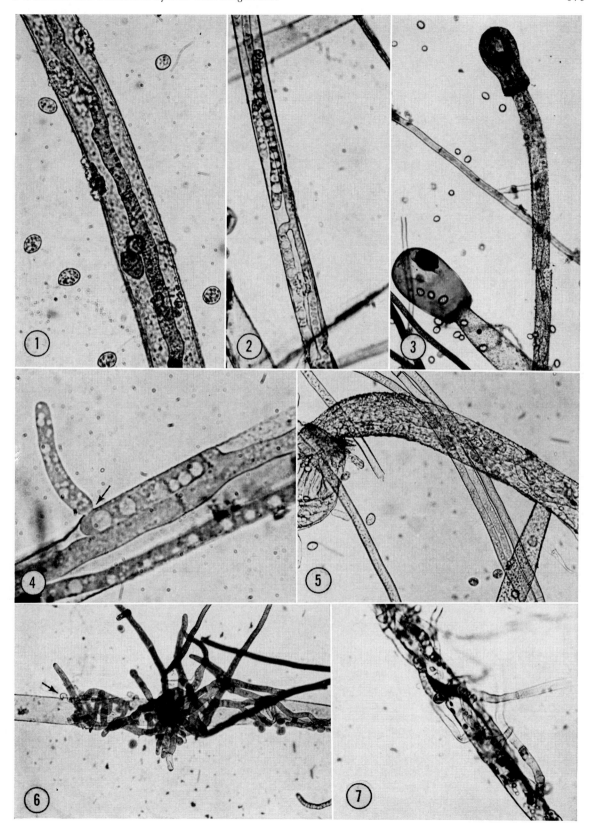

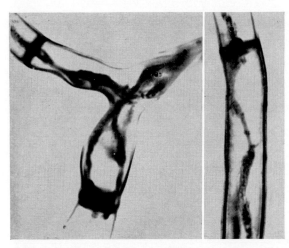

Fig. 8. Hyphae of *Rhizoctonia solani* invaded by *Penicillium vermiculatum* showing penetration through the septa, and branching of the parasitic hyphae. (M. G. Boosalis. Phytopathology 46: 473-478. 1956.)

the host (Boosalis, 1956; Butler, 1957). According to Butler, *R. solani* may infect a few host hyphae within 24 hours after contact, with maximum infection occurring at 48-72 hours. The rate and intensity of infection is profoundly affected by environmental conditions, particularly temperature and nutrition (Boosalis, 1956; Butler, 1957). Hyphal branching commonly develops within parasitized hyphae and may also occur at the junction of branching of the host hyphae. The number of hyphae produced by *P. vermiculatum* within the host varies from 1 to 4, most often 1 (Boosalis, 1956). Hyphae of *R. solani* and *P. vermiculatum* do not penetrate the hyphal wall of the host from the inside (Boosalis, 1956; Butler, 1957). Furthermore, although the wall of the parasitized host may collapse, it does not disintegrate.

Results from Siegle's (1961) studies revealed that the severity of take-all was markedly reduced by simultaneous inoculation of wheat seedlings with *Ophiobolus graminis* and *Didymella exitialis*. The pathogenicity of *O. graminis* is reduced by *D. exitialis* in two ways. First, the destructive mycoparasite can penetrate and kill the hyphae of *O. graminis* in the rhizosphere. This conclusion is based on the observations that the host mycelium is frequently disintegrated by an abundance of parasitic hyphae and that *D. exitialis* penetrates cell walls, grows into the host's thallus, and permeates its interior. As a result, the hyphae of *O. graminis* die and subsequently break down. Results from studies in vitro indicate that *D. exitialis* secretes the following free amino acids: aspartic acid, glutamic acid, alanine, leucine, and valine, and two other ninhydrin-positive substances. A solution of all these amino acids reduced the pathogenicity of *O. graminis* to about 40%, whereas individual amino acids caused a reduction of 20-30%. This constitutes the second way whereby *D. exitialis* reduces pathogenicity of *O. graminis*, but in this case without invading the host fungus. Siegle also reported that the reduction in pathogenicity caused by *Didymella* amino acids cannot be ascribed to growth-inhibition of

the runner hyphae of the pathogen. He suggested that the injury inflicted on *O. graminis* by the *Didymella* amino acids affects its nitrogen metabolism. Whether such changes in turn affect the enzyme systems such as cellulase production, must be demonstrated by more intensive biochemical work.

Several investigators (Boosalis, 1956; Butler, 1957; Siegle, 1961; Barnett and Lilly, 1962) state that destructive mycoparasites do not produce antibiotic or other deleterious materials that diffuse through the medium in advance of the hyphae. Unlike *Trichoderma lignorum* and other antibiotic-producing mycoparasites (Weindling, 1934, 1941), destructive hyperparasites do not initiate their parasitic activities at a distance. It appears that an intimate association of the host and parasite is a requisite for the production of chemical substances initiating parasitism. Additional information on the foregoing mechanism of parasitism, as well as other more subtle host-parasite relations, is presented in more comprehensive articles (Drechsler, 1943a; DeVay, 1956; Butler, 1957; Barnett and Lilly, 1958).

Effect of parasitism on the host and parasite.—Destructive mycoparasites usually cause disintegration of the host protoplasm (Boosalis, 1956; Butler, 1957; Barnett and Lilly, 1962). It is not always clear, however, whether death of the protoplasm occurs before or after penetration of the host. It is noteworthy that after destruction of the host protoplasm the internal hyphae of some parasites undergo autolysis (Godfrey, 1957; Butler, 1957). Drechsler (1938, 1943b) reported that after the parasitized oospores of certain hosts were gutted, the protoplasmic contents of the haustoria withdrew into the external hyphae of the parasite. These kinds of responses by the parasite and the host add to the difficulties of detecting mycoparasitism in natural habitats. It should be stated, however, that internal mycelium of other hyperparasites may persist long after the host protoplasm has disappeared.

Host structures parasitized.—In addition to mycelium, many other structures of the host are attacked by mycoparasites. *Gliocladium roseum* parasitizes and destroys conidia of many species of fungi (Barnett and Lilly, 1962). However, only immature conidiophores and conidia of *Helminthosporium sativum* are attacked by *G. roseum*. Campbell (1956) found that with *H. sativum* on synthetic media only the conidia were invaded and killed by *Myrothecium verrucaria*, both conidia and mycelia by *Epicoccum purpurascens*, but only the hyphae by *Phoma humicola*. Destructive mycoparasites grown in dual cultures and, in some instances, in sterilized soil grew within sporangiophores and sporangia (Butler, 1957), oogonia (Drechsler, 1943c), chlamydospores (Godfrey, 1957), oospores (Drechsler, 1938, 1943c), and zoospores (Barrett, 1912) of some species of the Phycomycetes. Tribe (1957) stated that the sclerotia of *Sclerotinia trifoliorum* were parasitized by *Coniothyrium minitans*. The excellent review article by DeVay (1956) on mycoparasitism lists additional mycoparasites and the specific host structures they infect.

Factors affecting parasitism.—It is self-evident that the degree of parasitism is greatly affected by innate factors and a variety of environmental factors. These factors are listed separately for reasons of convenience.

Innate factors.—Age of the host.—Parasitism may be contingent on the age of the host hyphae. Working with balanced mycoparasites, Barnett and Lilly (1958) noted that the age of the mycelium of several hosts does not influence the degree of susceptibility. On the other hand, only the young, rapidly growing host hyphae are highly susceptible to *Rhizoctonia solani* (Butler, 1957). Studies are needed on the chemical nature of the wall in order to explain the relation of susceptibility and age of the host hyphae.

Mechanical barriers.—Results from studies in vitro indicate that the host may resist infection by forming "mechanical barriers" against internal hyphae of mycoparasites. Infection hyphae of *Rhizoctonia solani* may be restricted by a protective sheath of wall-like material produced by the host, *Mucor recurvus* (Butler, 1957). The parasite may also be restrained by certain phycomycetous hosts by formation of septa ahead of the invading hyphae. Thickening of the inner side walls of some *Pythium* spp. at the site of appressorial attachment may also obstruct invasion by another *Pythium* sp. (Drechsler, 1943c).

Other factors.—Lysis of parasitic hyphae within host cells and the variability of host range of different isolates within one species of the parasite are also hereditary characteristics affecting parasitism.

Environmental factors affecting parasitism.—Nutrition.—One of the most important factors affecting mycoparasitism is nutrition. One reason for this is that the physiological system of the host relating to susceptibility is apparently influenced by the quantity or quality of nutrients or both. In the following studies reporting on nutrition, the susceptibility of the host was modified by varying the nutrients in synthetic media.

The kind or amount of carbohydrate can affect the incidence of mycoparasitism. The host, *Rhizoctonia solani,* was severely parasitized by *Penicillium vermiculatum* when grown on sand-cornmeal or on potato-dextrose agar containing a relatively high concentration of dextrose (20 g per liter) (Boosalis, 1954, 1956). On the other hand, when the host was cultured on PDA containing 10 g dextrose per liter, parasitism was negligible. It appeared that the high level of dextrose increased the incidence of parasitism by increasing the susceptibility of the host. Results from Butler's (1957) studies indicate that the kind of carbohydrate supplied to the host greatly affected the degree of parasitism. For example, *Mucor recurvus* is highly susceptible to *R. solani* on an inorganic-salt agar medium containing hexose or a di- or polysaccharide composed of hexose residues. This host was also highly susceptible when grown on the same base medium containing maltose, or on grain media of cornmeal, oats, or rice. Infection was sparse or absent on substrates containing pentose sugars, galactose, lactose, cellobiose, or on fresh peas or wheat germ.

Temperature.—In most studies on mycoparasitism involving destructive parasites, temperature was shown to affect the degree of parasitism. The optimum temperature for mycoparasitism is generally 25°-30°C (Boosalis, 1956; Butler, 1957; Brian, 1960). The incidence of parasitism on *Rhizoctonia solani* was considerably higher in green-manure-amended soil at 28°C than at 18° (Boosalis, 1956).

Light and pH.—Results from studies in vitro show that light and pH may also affect mycoparasitism. According to Butler (1957), infection of the host by *Rhizoctonia solani* was not altered by diffused daylight, but it was suppressed by artificial light of higher intensity.

Severe infection of *Pythium debaryanum* and *P. butleri* by *R. solani* occurred in a medium with a pH 5.5 or 7.7, whereas a pH 6.7 or 7.1 was not conducive to infection of *Rhizopus* spp. (Butler, 1957). Parasitism of *Armillaria mellea* by *Trichoderma* spp. was substantially reduced by adjusting the pH of the medium below 5.1; at pH 7.0 parasitism was inhibited (Aytoun, 1953).

Other Organisms.—Relatively little work has been done to determine what effect other microorganisms exert on the host-parasite relation in vitro. A significant investigation by Butler (1957) revealed that infection was completely inhibited, limited, or not affected by the presence of another fungus in culture with the host and parasite. We are not aware of any similar research in soil.

Host range.—There is an abundance of literature regarding the host range of different kinds of hyperparasites. A few of the more pertinent papers on host range are cited. Comprehensive compilations of mycoparasitic hosts are available elsewhere (DeVay, 1956; A. H. R. Butler, 1922).

Destructive mycoparasites vary in host range from those capable of attacking only one species (Backus, 1953; Boosalis, 1956), to those that parasitize fungi of two or more classes (DeVay, 1956; Butler, 1957). It has been suggested that perhaps the capacity of certain soil-inhabiting fungi to parasitize roots as well as other fungi is related to their effective survival in nature (Butler, 1957). The fact that a mycoparasite parasitic on phytopathogenic fungi can be attacked by other hyperparasites compounds the difficulties of devising biological control measures based on mycoparasitism.

Occurrence of mycoparasites in nature.—Systematic studies have not been pursued to determine the frequency of mycoparasitism in soil and other habitats. Consequently, it is not possible to accurately assess the importance of interfungus parasitism in nature. The presence of hyperparasitism in some habitats, however, is well documented.

Most of the evidence for the natural occurrence of mycoparasitism in soil is circumstantial. For example, hyperparasitism was established on glass slides buried in sterilized soil infested with pure cultures of the plant pathogen and its parasite (Warren, 1948). This certainly does not constitute incontrovertible proof of the existence of mycoparasitism in soil. Another report stated that sublethal dosages of carbon disulfide applied to natural soil stimulated *Trichoderma viride* to invade and kill *Armillaria mellea* (Darley and Wilbur, 1954). Infection of species of *Pythium* by chitridiaceous parasites was observed in natural soil (E. J. Butler, 1907). Drechsler (1943*b*) described destructive mycoparasitism of oospores of *Pythium graminicolum* on leaf mold. *Rhizoctonia solani,* introduced into unsterilized soil amended with green manure and kept at 28°C, was parasitized by soil-inhabiting fungi (Boosalis, 1956). Even under these favorable environmental conditions, only about 18% of the host hyphae were parasitized. In subsequent studies only 4 parasitized hyphae of *R. solani* were discerned out of 6000 screened in September from natural soil collected from six fields cropped with sugar beet (Boosalis, unpublished data).

Mycoparasitic control of soil-borne fungi.—Attempts to control root diseases through mycoparasitism have been very disappointing. In essence, these methods have consisted of adding copious amounts of the mycoparasite to the soil. In some instances in order to stimulate hyperparasitism, the pH of the soil was adjusted or the soil was amended with nutrients (Weindling and Fawcett, 1936; Boosalis, 1956). These treatments have not been adopted for the control of fungus diseases because they do not give consistent results or they are impractical on a commercial basis.

Antagonistic bacteria.—It has not been shown conclusively that bacteria can penetrate and parasitize intact, living fungi. Results from studies reporting damage to cereal-rust fungi by bacteria (Levine, Bamberg, and Atkinson, 1936; Pon et al., 1954) do not support the conclusion that such injury results from parasitism, involving an organic union of two different living organisms whereby one derives benefit at the detriment of the other. No evidence is presented in these studies to indicate whether lysis of the rust fungus, supposedly incited by parasitism, occurred before or after the bacteria invaded the hosts. It was suggested that under conditions of high temperature and high humidity antagonistic bacteria could affect the incidence of cereal rust (Pon et al., 1954).

There is good evidence to indicate that lysis of fungi may result from an antagonistic relation with bacteria (Kovoor, 1954; Krasil'nikov, 1958). In this instance, it was shown that certain bacteria in close association with the external surface of fungi incite lysis of the latter. No information was given regarding the mode of lysis. Noragrudskii (1948) believes that this type of antagonism is an important factor affecting the activity of soil fungi. More recently Mitchell and Alexander (1963) and Mitchell (1963) showed that lysis of several soil-borne fungi is associated with chitinase and laminarinase activity of *Bacillus cereus,* but some factor in addition to these enzymes is required for mycolysis. These workers also reported that lytic microbial flora could destroy fungus mycelium in sterile or unsterile soil amended with chitin or laminarin.

Stolp and Petzold (1962) stated that an obligatory parasite, morphologically similar to a *Vibrio,* caused lysis of many species of *Pseudomonas* and several species of *Xanthomonas*. These investigators noted that lysis is initiated by attachment of the nonflagellated pole of the parasite to the cell surface of a susceptible bacterium.

Bacteriophage.—The limited research on phage of phytopathogenic bacteria was recently reviewed by Darpoux (1960). He presents results from several investigations showing that phages can infect and incite lysis of phytopathogenic bacteria residing in soil. He states that attempts to control bacterial diseases of plants by applying phages to the soil or to plants were unsuccessful. Information on the biology and ecology of phages in soil is insufficient to draw conclusions as to the importance of viruses on other soil-inhabiting microorganisms.

PARASITES OF NEMATODES.—A number of reports of bacterial infections of soil nematodes occur in the literature (Dollfus, 1946), but almost all of them record the observation of bacteria within the body cavity, gut, and gonads of individual nematodes of various free-living species. In most cases it cannot be determined whether the bacteria involved are true parasites or saprophytic forms within injured nematodes. While an apparently transmissible bacterial infection was reported by Teunissen (in Schuurmans Stekhoven and Teunissen, 1938), no unequivocal observations of bacterial parasites of plant-parasitic nematodes appear to be known.

Loewenberg, Sullivan, and Schuster (1959) discovered what was believed to be a transmissible virus disease of the root-knot nematode *Meloidogyne incognita,* but apparently no further work has been reported.

Since viruses attack many groups of lower invertebrates and microorganisms, it would be surprising if nematodes were entirely free of such parasites.

Parasitic protozoa.—Among various protozoan infections reported for nematodes (Dollfus, 1946), only the minute sporozoans can be considered to be of any great importance as parasites. Sporozoan parasites of nematodes were probably first noted by Cobb in 1906 and again in 1918, but no attempt was made to identify the organisms. Micoletzky (1925) frequently observed sporozoans within nematodes in Europe and assigned them to the genus *Duboscquia* (Microsporidia, Nosematidae). *D. trilobica, D. de-mani* and *Duboscquia* sp., were described by Micoletzky from a variety of free-living nematodes. Although microsporidian parasites of nematodes parasitic in animals were known, among soil nematodes only microbivorous species were reported to be attacked until Thorne (1940) found a high percentage of the plant-parasite *Pratylenchus pratensis* (later identified as *P. brachyurus*), collected from soil in S. Carolina and Georgia, to be parasitized by a sporozoan which he tentatively named *Duboscquia penetrans.* Thorne reconstructed the probable development and life cycle of the parasite from preserved material and noted that errors may have been made which would need rectification.

Duboscquia penetrans (s. lat.) is undoubtedly widespread among plant-parasitic and other soil nematodes. Allen (1957) observed a high percentage of *Dolicho-*

dorus obtusus to be infected by parasites very similar to those described by Thorne. In lightly infected individuals the parasite was present almost exclusively in the reproductive system, but in heavily infected individuals most of the body was occupied. Allen also observed the parasite in the bodies of *Meloidogyne javanica* from Japan (Steinhaus and Marsh, 1962). Kuiper (1958) reported that *Duboscquia penetrans* was observed in the following nematodes in the Netherlands: *Pratylenchus pratensis, P. penetrans, Rotylenchus robustus, Tylenchorhynchus dubius,* in larvae of *M. arenaria;* and also in *Pratylenchus* sp. from Germany. Sporozoans have been observed in infected *Hoplolaimus* sp. from sugarcane fields near Karnal, India; in *Scutellonema* sp. from Nigeria, *Belonolaimus gracilis* from Florida, *Pratylenchus* spp. from Illinois, and in species of several genera from California, including *M. hapla* females completely filled with spores (Mankau, unpublished observations). In all cases the parasites appear to be *D. penetrans* described by Thorne. Williams (1960) found approximately 34% of root-knot-nematode females (*M. javanica* and *M. incognita acrita*) removed from roots of sugarcane in Mauritius to be filled with spores of *D. penetrans.* He made detailed observations on the development of the parasite in the host and observed that a form is released from the spore which multiplies prolifically by budding, and the daughter forms then develop by complicated nuclear rearrangement into spores.

The small size of the sporozoan and of its host makes it a difficult organism to study. The oval spores generally observed in or on nematodes were described as 2.5-3 μ long by Thorne (1940) while Williams (1960) reported them to measure 4-5 μ. More than one species may be involved among organisms described as *Duboscquia penetrans,* and there is some doubt as to the exact life cycle and the proper classification of the parasite. It probably belongs in the Haplosporidia of the Sporozoa. The manner in which spores are transmitted and penetrate the host is conjectural, but an infection plug probably penetrates the cuticle once the spore has attached to a nematode. The hemispherical configuration of the spore conforms closely to the cylindrical shape of the nematode. Usually spores attached to the cuticle are concentrated at the anterior end of the nematode and to a lesser extent at the posterior end. It seems reasonable that the underside of the spores are adhesive since they have no known means of locomotion. While they may be carried passively in the movement of soil-water films, they most likely attach to passing nematodes. Sedentary phytoparasitic nematodes such as *Meloidogyne* spp. may become infected during motile larval stages.

No experimental study of the effectiveness of sporozoans as biological control agents has yet been reported. Their ubiquitous occurrence and ability to sterilize and destroy their nematode hosts offer indications of the possible potential value of these organisms if their biology were better known. Occasional difficulty in maintaining *Pratylenchus* spp. in potted soil in the greenhouse has been experienced when the parasites were present (Mankau, unpublished data).

Parasitic fungi.—A number of phycomycetous fungi parasitize soil nematodes and the soil stages of nematodes parasitic in animals. Dollfus (1946) compiled the literature on these fungi, and Duddington (1955) reviewed much of the same material. *Catenaria anguillulae,* in the Blastocladiales; and *Myzocytium vermicola, Protascus subuliformis,* and *Haptoglossa heterospora* in the Lagenidiales are probably the most widespread and important of this group among the lower fungi. A few reports of species of *Lagenidium* attacking nematodes are given by Dollfus. Karling (1944) described *L. pathenosporum* from the bodies of *Heterodera* sp. in Brazil. A *Lagenidium* species has been observed to be a virulent parasite of *Xiphinema diversicaudatum* in Illinois, and another species occasionally attacks nematodes in California (Mankau, unpublished observations).

Catenaria anguillulae is a ubiquitous species frequently observed attacking nematodes removed from soil and kept for a time in water in the laboratory. Birchfield (1960) described a new species, *Catenaria vermicola,* as a virulent pathogen of several genera of nematodes in Louisiana. Birchfield's fungus may be a synonym of *C. anguillulae,* however, since his description fits those of Villot (1874) and the original description by Sorokine (1876), which were later confirmed by Sparrow (1932).

Catenaria anguillulae, frequently isolated from nematodes in California soils, is indistinguishable from *C. vermicola* or from *C. anguillulae* as originally described. The parasitic activity of this fungus was examined in a test in which it was added to a replicated series of small chambers containing groups of nematodes in water which were killed by exposure in a 60°C water bath for 1 hour, weakened by heating until convulsions occurred, and untreated, respectively. A control group did not receive fungus inoculum. All treatments were incubated at 26° for 48 hours. Of nine species of mainly plant-parasitic nematodes tested, 100% of the killed group were attacked by the fungus, while in the untreated group a very small percentage was attacked. Weakened nematodes were attacked to only a slightly greater degree than those untreated (Table 1). A few nematodes in the control series died among species which normally do not survive well in water at warm temperatures. No effects upon nematode populations could be noted when the fungus was added to soil. In nature this organism may be weakly parasitic, but it is probably largely saprophytic upon dead or injured members of the soil microfauna. The motile zoospores appear to be attracted to the mouth, excretory pore, vulva, or anus of inactive nematodes where they congregate, often in large numbers.

It has been observed over several years that nematodes of genera in the Dorylaimoidea are more easily attacked by parasitic fungi with motile zoospores than are the Tylenchida. This is especially evident among *Xiphinema* spp., which are members of the Dorylaimoidea. (Table 1). Whether this is due to the nature of the cuticle or other factors has not been determined.

Certain endozoic Phycomycetes appear to be important nematode parasites. *Protascus subuliformis* and

TABLE 1. The effect of *Catenaria anguillulae* on selected nematode species exposed to varying heat treatments

Nematodes	Percentage of nematodes infected by *C. anguillulae*			Percentage of nematodes dead when not heat-treated or exposed to *C. anguillulae*
	Killed by heat	Weakened by heat	No heat treatment	
Aphelenchus avenae	100	7.3	3.0	0
Hemicycliophora arenaria	100	1.3	1.3	0
Cephalobus sp.	100	1.6	1.3	1.3
Pratylenchus scribneri	100	12.0	4.0	0
Trichodorus christiei	100	16.0	12.0	12.0
Tylenchulus semipenetrans	100	6.0	10.0	0
Heterodera schachtii	100	16.0	6.0	0
Meliodogyne sp.	100	16.0	0	0
Xiphinema index	100	65.0	57.0	0

Haptoglossa heterospora are common in California soils. These two species differ from other Lagenidiales in their nonmotile adhesive spores but apparently are not themselves closely related. Dollfus (1946) cites several reports of Phycomycetes attacking helminth eggs in soil, and Ellis and Hesseltine (1962) have recently reported the parasitism of *Rhopalomyces* on nematode eggs.

PREDATORS OF SOIL NEMATODES.—A variety of soil organisms ranging from protozoa to microarthropods are predators of nematodes. The amoeboid proteomyxan organism, *Theratromyxa weberi,* was observed to prey on nematodes in the genera *Heterodera, Meloidogyne, Pratylenchus, Rhabditis,* and *Hemicycliophora* in the Netherlands (Weber, Zwillenberg, and van der Laan, 1952; van der Laan, 1954). Similar organisms have been found associated with the cysts of the golden nematode (*H. rostochiensis*) in England and the sugar-beet nematode (*H. schachtii*) in Canada (Winslow and Williams, 1957). Root-knot nematodes (*Meloidogyne* sp.) were observed to be attacked and consumed by plasmodial organisms, presumably myxomycetes, in Russia (Paramonov, 1954). In each case the larger soil nematodes were apparently not attacked by such organisms.

While van der Laan (1954) observed as many as 128 *Heterodera* larvae in one digestive cyst of *Theratromyxa weberi* with a diameter of 350 μ, he concluded that due to the nonspecific character of the organism's prey, their slow rate of spread, and susceptibility to desiccation, they were not likely to prove of practical importance in control of plant-parasitic nematodes.

A ciliate protozoan was observed to ingest nematodes (Doncaster and Hooper, 1961), but apparently this is only a chance occurrence since the ingestion of nematodes usually resulted in damage to the organism. Although some soil ciliates attain an appreciable size, it is unlikely that this group of organisms is of any consequence as predators of nematodes.

Predacious nematodes.—A large variety of carnivorous nematode species comprise one of the most important and least-studied groups of organisms predacious upon soil and plant-parasitic nematodes. Genera such as *Odontopharynx, Butlerius, Onchulus, Monochulus,* and *Ironus,* have generally unknown food habits but are

considered to be predatory on the basis of their morphology. Large nematodes of the genera *Labronema, Aporcelaimus, Sectonema, Actinolaimus, Carcharolaimus, Nygolaimus,* and possibly others are known to feed on enchytraeid worms and may also attack enlarged sedentary plant-parasitic nematodes exposed on the surface of roots. Many species of *Discolaimium, Discolaimus, Eudorylaimus* (Fig. 9), *Mononchus, Tripyla,* and *Seinura* have been observed to feed on other nematodes (Christie, 1960).

Linford and Oliveira (1937) observed that small predatory species of *Seinura* were capable of paralyzing their prey, probably by an injection of saliva, and thus compensate for their small size. They successfully attacked larvae of *Meloidogyne* sp. and *Pratylenchus* sp., both important plant parasites. *Seinura* sp. can be reared in vitro when it is supplied with a sufficient population of prey such as a fungivorous nematode feeding upon a fungus in agar culture. Under such conditions the population of predators can multiply more than 1,000-fold during approximately 2 weeks (Linford, 1959). None of the plant-parasitic nematodes multiply as rapidly.

Some predacious nematodes are probably omnivorous and consume a variety of organisms. *Eudorylaimus ettersbergensis* feeds upon blue-green algae (*Chrococcus* sp.), green algae (*Chlorella vulgaris* and *Tetraedon* sp.), a protozoan (*Drepanomonas* sp.), and a fungus (*Cephalothecium* sp.) (Hollis, 1957). Unidentified *Eudorylaimus* spp. have occasionally been observed to feed on fungi as well as nematodes (Mankau, unpublished observations). Similarly, the usually fungivorous nematode, *Aphelenchus avenae,* was observed to pierce and suck out the contents of eggs of *Cephalobus* sp. within agar in petri dishes.

In some southern California citrus-orchard soils, substantial numbers of *Thornia* sp. are occasionally found associated with citrus-nematode infestations. This nematode was observed to feed on *Tylenchulus semipenetrans* larvae, *Aphelenchus avenae,* and various microbivorous nematodes, encysted amoebae, and several fungi, including yeast cells in agar cultures. It reproduces abundantly in petri dishes on species of the fungi *Alternaria* and *Pyrenochaeta. Thornia* sp. was used in an experiment with potted citrus seedlings to determine whether it exerted a degree of biological control on the citrus nematode. One group of potted seedlings was

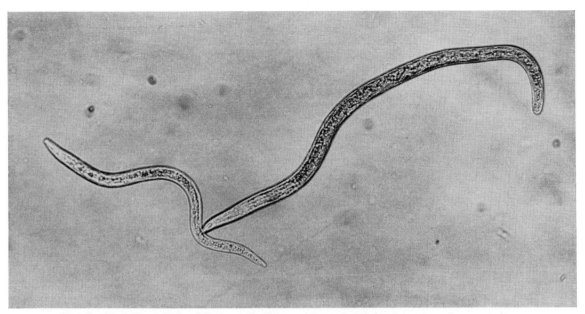

Fig. 9. Predacious *Eudorylaimus* sp. feeding on larva of *Aphelenchus avenae* in agar culture.

infested with the citrus nematode and *Thornia* sp., another with *Thornia* sp. without the citrus nematode, another with just the citrus nematode, and a control group was left free of both nematodes. Each treatment was replicated eight times. No significant differences occurred in the fresh top weights of the seedlings in the various treatments after 17 months, nor were there significant differences in citrus-nematode numbers in treatments to which they were added, although more occurred in the treatment which also contained *Thornia* sp. (Table 2). The *Thornia* sp., however, were numerous when associated with the citrus nematode but only a trace occurred in pots free of the plant parasite. After an additional 12 months during which the plants developed new top growth, an increase of *Thornia* sp. occurred in both treatments to which they had been added, but the increase was almost 7-fold when the citrus nematode was present. The plant parasite's population had dropped in the treatment with *Thornia* sp. but not to a statistically significant degree. Under certain conditions the predation of *Thornia* sp., combined with that of other nematodes, Collembola, nematode-trapping fungi, and possibly predacious mites, may amount to a significant degree of natural control of the citrus nematode. Individual factors in such biological equilibria are difficult to assess accurately.

Christie (1960) has pointed out that up to now opinions regarding the effects of predacious nematodes are based upon observations largely unsupported by experimental data of any kind, and that this is an attractive and unexplored field awaiting investigation.

Miscellaneous predators.—Tardigrades were reported attacking nematodes in the United States and Ceylon by Hutchinson and Streu (1960). Doncaster and Hooper (1961) observed *Macrobiotis* sp. making distinct tears in the nematode cuticle and possibly injecting a toxic secretion that immobilized the prey. Large and vigorously moving mononchids were successfully attacked. The food of these unusual members of the soil microfauna may be varied, but apparently certain species are carnivorous and withdraw the body contents of victims with an oral stylet. In southern California soils they are occasionally abundant and have also been observed to attempt to feed on nematodes. Tardigrades, however, probably have only an incidental relation to soil nematode populations.

Enchytraeid worms in the genera *Fridericia* and *Enchytraeus* were reported to control populations of *Heterodera schachtii* in sugarbeet roots when both the nematodes and worms were added to sterilized soil in a pot test (Schaerffenberg and Tendl, 1951). The en-

TABLE 2. The effect of a predacious nematode (*Thornia* sp.) on a citrus nematode (*Tylenchulus semipenetrans*) infestation

Treatment (nematodes added)	17-month period			29-month period		
	Av. citrus top wt, g	Nematodes, av. per 50 cc soil		Av. citrus top wt, g	Nematodes, av. per 50 cc soil	
		Citrus	*Thornia* sp.		Citrus	*Thornia* sp.
Tylenchulus semipenetrans and *Thornia* sp.	256.7	8,607	61	182.5	2,489	87
Tylenchulus semipenetrans	269.0	5,522	0	165.6	3,956	0
Control	287.6	0	0	194.5	0	0
Thornia sp.	295.1	0	1	184.2	0	13

chytraeids were said to penetrate the epidermis of the roots and feed on the immature sugarbeet nematodes. These results are somewhat questionable in that Enchytraeidae are normally saprophagous and *Heterodera* spp. require relatively sound cortical and stelar tissues to accomplish their specialized host-parasite relation (Mankau and Linford, 1960); in this position they are probably unavailable to enchytraeid worms, which have no special organs for penetrating roots. The worms may dislodge developing nematodes in highly decomposed roots, but such conditions are also unfavorable for the parasite.

Some true gamasid mites (Parasitidae) are abundant in soil and are frequently predators of small enchytraeid worms, insect eggs, and other mites. Although little of the biology of these and other predacious mites is known, nematodes are believed to form a portion of their diet (Kevan, 1962).

The minute Collembola, or springtails, are among the most numerous of all soil arthropods and are frequently recovered with techniques used to extract nematodes from soil. They are not generally considered to be predacious, but some are known to eat nematodes (Brown, 1954). Murphy and Doncaster (1957) reported voracious feeding by *Onychiurus armatus* (s. lat.) and occasional feeding by several other species of Collembola on *Heterodera* females and cysts (Fig. 10). They determined that 6.9% of *H. cruciferae* individuals recovered from 247 g of soil and roots from a cabbage plant were definitely damaged by *O. armatus*. Predatory activity may have been much greater, for it is probable that during extraction many remnants of the more fragile white females were lost or damaged beyond recognition. Collembola have also been observed feeding on nematodes in agar plates containing soil and root fragments which were being examined for the presence of nematode-trapping fungi (Mankau and Clarke, 1959). Colonies of Collembola have subsisted for periods of over 6 months in plates in which nematodes were reproducing. No particular orientation toward nematodes was apparent since the Collembola walk over or touch many nematodes with their antennae without any attempt to feed but occasionally grasp a nematode, usually at one end and smoothly and rapidly ingest it with a chewing action of the mandibles. In experiments in which soil was amended with organic materials, large numbers of springtails developed in association with large increases in the nematode fauna (Mankau, 1962a). Collembola which feed on nematodes may be omnivorous in habit and utilize a variety of soil organisms as food. They are often observed associated with citrus roots heavily infested with the ex-

Fig. 10. Two Collembola (*Onychiurus armatus*) feeding on mature female *Heterodera cruciferae*. The predators perforate the nematode cuticle and consume the body contents. (Photo kindly supplied by C. C. Doncaster.)

posed females of the citrus nematode (*Tylenchulus semipenetrans* Cobb).

Predacious fungi.—Fungi which capture and consume nematodes are one of the most unusual and interesting groups of organisms to be found in the soil. They are widely distributed and especially abundant in surface litter and decaying organic matter. Over 50 species are known to attack nematodes, and many other related species prey upon protozoa, rotifers, Collembola, and undoubtedly other members of the soil micro- or meiofauna. The most important of these occur in several genera of the Hyphomycetes, *Arthrobotrys*, *Dactylella*, and *Dactylaria*. Many nematode-trapping species are also found in the Zoopagales, an order of Zygomycetes consisting mainly of fungi that prey on amoebae and other protozoa.

About 1933, Charles Drechsler began a monumental study of predacious fungi which, to date, has resulted in a classic series of descriptions and observations on these organisms. The majority of the species known today were described and admirably illustrated by him. Early literature on predacious fungi was comprehensively reviewed by Drechsler (1941) and later brought up to date by Duddington (1955, 1960).

Duddington (1955) has reviewed the large number of fungus species of parasitic habit among the Hyphomycetes, and little can be added to his treatment of the group. Adhesive spores which adhere to the integument of the nematode are common to most of this group. The main vegetative mycelium is within the body of the host, only the fertile hyphae being external. The genus *Nematoctonus*, with clamp connections on its fertile hyphae, is unique in this series; it is probably an imperfect basidiomycete. Interestingly, several species of *Nematoctonus* have been isolated in California from the dung of desert mammals invaded by nematodes.

Species of *Harposporium* have tortuously shaped spores with a remarkable parasitic relation to nematode hosts. Although Duddington (1955) thought the sickle-shaped spores of *H. anguillulae* may pierce the nematode integument, it has been observed that spores of isolates frequently obtained from California soils must be ingested by nematodes to become infective. Aschner and Kohn (1958) have demonstrated the germination of *H. anguillulae* conidia in the esophagus of microbivorous nematodes. The elaborately shaped and sharp-pointed conidia of some species in this genus become lodged in the lumen of the muscular esophagus of nematodes which can ingest them. A germ tube penetrates into the body cavity and within a short time the nematode is filled with trophic hyphae. Such fungi cannot parasitize plant-parasitic nematodes, which suck in cellular fluids through the minute lumen of the buccal spear. Endozoic Hyphomycetes are frequently referred to as predacious, but this designation is more appropriate to the fungi with specialized trapping organs.

The traps by which nematophagous fungi capture their prey have been described in detail by Drechsler (1941) and Duddington (1957). Briefly, they fall into two main categories: adhesive processes and mechanical traps. Of the former, the most common type is a sticky hyphal network formed by anastomosing hyphal loops or bails in three-dimensional systems. Nematodes become enmeshed in the adhesive network and struggle for a time but within a few hours are penetrated by an infection bulb, from which trophic hyphae grow out to consume the body contents. Other types include adhesive lobes or lateral branches which in some species join in latticelike arrangements along the hyphae (Fig. 11); still others possess sticky spherical knobs on short stalks along the hyphae. All these adhesive organs operate in basically the same way.

Mechanical nematode traps include nonconstricting and constricting rings. The former are formed by a branch from the mycelium which curls round upon itself and forms a three-celled ring, attached to the parent hypha by a slender stalk, also usually of three cells. The somewhat tapered form of a wandering nematode becomes wedged in the ring as it passes along the hypha and is held securely. Frequently the struggles of the prey dislodge the trap from the hypha and allow the nematode to escape, but the ring is generally firmly fixed over the body of the victim and within a short time an infection plug from the cells of the ring penetrate and kill the nematode.

The constricting ring forms in the same way as the nonconstricting type. The stalk bearing the three-celled ring consists of only two cells, however, and is somewhat thicker than the nonconstricting type. The traps generally form at a right angle to the hyphae. The closure of the ring is a tactile response: when a nematode enters the ring the cells suddenly inflate and ensnare the victim by a firm constriction of its body. Trophic hyphae grow out from the cells of the ring and absorb the body contents of the nematode (Fig. 12).

When the movement of nematodes through soil is observed microscopically, as with the observation boxes described by Lindford (1942), they can be seen to frequently utilize strands of fungus hyphae to traverse soil pore spaces. When such hyphae are those of predacious fungi, the marvelous efficiency of the traps described can be readily appreciated.

The process by which constricting ring traps are stimulated and operate instigated several interesting investigations, which have been reviewed by Duddington (1955, 1957). In a recent detailed study, Muller (1958) tested experimentally various theories proposed on the physiological mechanism of ring constriction and concluded on the basis of known facts that a change in wall structure occurs, producing a sudden decrease in pressure on the wall, and an increase in permeability of the cell membrane to water. The amount of osmotically active material in a ring cell then trebles, but the rate and timing of this increase in relation to the inflation process is as yet unknown. The stimulus-sensitive part of the cell wall is assumed to have a rather special structure in which the protoplast and cell wall, and membrane permeability and changes in wall structure, are uniquely and intimately interrelated and may thus reasonably be expected to be triggered by the same stimulus.

Most predacious fungi do not produce trapping organs in pure culture, and factors which induce trap forma-

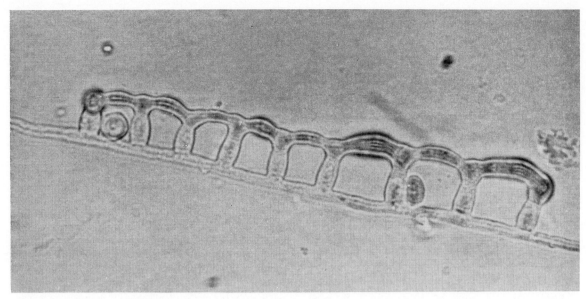

Fig. 11. Adhesive scalariform hyphal processes of the nematode-trapping fungus *Dactylella gephyropaga*. (Approx. × 1750.)

tion are of importance in understanding their biology. Feder, Everard, and Duddington (1960) have demonstrated genetic variability in the ability of *Dactylella doedycoides* to produce traps due to the heterocaryotic nature of its mycelium and conidia. Certain isolates of *Arthrobotrys dactyloides* obtained in California produce traps in pure culture, while others do not. Pramer and Stoll (1959) discovered that a morphogenic substance, which they named nemin, caused trap formation in *A. conoides*. An assay procedure for the study of

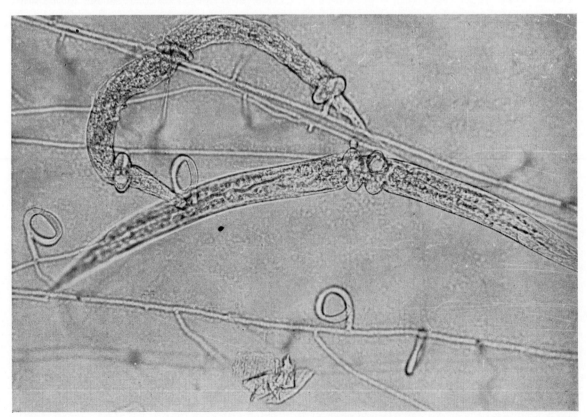

Fig. 12. Citrus nematode larvae, *Tylenchulus semipenetrans*, trapped and penetrated by *Arthrobotrys dactyloides*. This predacious fungus occurs commonly in the rhizosphere of nematode-infested citrus plants.

the chemical nature of this substance was developed by Winkler, Kuyama, and Pramer (1961), and a protein having the activity of nemin was later purified and its properties determined (Kuyama and Pramer, 1962). Feder, Everard, and Wooten (1963) demonstrated that each of several predacious fungi has a different reactive threshold to the neminlike complex and speculated upon trap-formation patterns in these fungi. The formation of traps by conidia exposed to soil solutions may be the result of the response of a poorly competitive fungus to soil fungistasis (Mankau, 1962b). Several factors may stimulate trap formation among various predatory fungi.

Despite the ability of *Arthrobotrys conoides* to capture, kill, and subsist on nematodes, Coscarelli and Pramer (1962) demonstrated that the nutritional needs of the fungus do not differ essentially from the pattern of other microorganisms. Biotin, thiamine, and zinc were required for growth in a glucose-inorganic-salts medium.

Attempts at biological control of noxious nematodes with parasites or predators have been limited almost entirely to experiments with predacious fungi. As early as 1888, W. Zopf considered the use of *Arthrobotrys oligospora* Fres. against the wheat nematode, but little further work was undertaken until a series of studies by Linford and co-workers in Hawaii, and by several French workers in the early 1940's, investigated the activity of nematode-trapping fungi against parasitic nematodes. Duddington discussed this work in several excellent reviews (1955, 1957, 1960) and has provided a great stimulus for study of fungus control of nematodes. While Duddington (1960) indicated that the results of attempts to achieve biological control by adding predacious fungi to soil have been largely inconclusive, a few promising findings led him to conclude that in the predacious fungi exist a potential means for reducing nematode damage to crops. Gorlenko (1956) reviewed Russian activity in this field and implied that the results have stimulated further research and development of the utilization of nematode-trapping fungi. Soprunov (1958) published a 365-page book on the subject, with extensive experimental data and descriptions of new predacious Russian fungi. Biological control of nematodes with predacious fungi received further support in recent years from Feder (1959), who stressed the need for investigations of their role in the natural associations of the rhizosphere microflora and fauna; and from Scognamiglio (1959), who discussed means of achieving more dependable control.

The results obtained by the experimental use of fungi for biological control of nematodes have been neither impressive nor consistent and have never approached control obtained by soil fumigation. Hutchinson and Mai (1954) concluded that the trapping devices of the fungus *Dactylaria eudermata* Drechs. did not effectively control the golden nematode; and Duddington and co-workers also did not obtain obvious control of this nematode (Duddington, Jones, and Williams, 1956) or of the sugarbeet nematode (Duddington, Jones, and Moriarty, 1956). Hams and Wilkin (1961) showed that

use of predacious fungi in pot tests resulted in sufficient control of cyst nematodes, but that such control was not apparent in field tests. Protection against root-knot nematode damage by efficient nematode-trappers was not observed in pot or microplot experiments (Mankau, 1961a,b); and Tarjan (1961) failed to reduce numbers of *Radopholus similis* in roots of citrus seedlings or mature trees in a series of greenhouse and field tests. Both the latter authors encountered difficulty in establishing fungi in soil and attributed this to the presence of antagonistic microorganisms (Mankau, 1961c). An apparently widespread fungistatic response of spores of several predacious Hyphomycetes in soils was demonstrated; the response could be altered somewhat with soil amendments (Mankau, 1962b). Tarjan (1961) found the normal soil inhabitants, *Trichoderma* sp. and *Gliocladium* sp., to be antagonistic to *Arthrobotrys musiformis*.

Although the effects of nematode-trapping fungi are generally believed to be beneficial, W. B. Cooke and Ludzack (1958) observed an impairment in the functioning of several laboratory activated-sewage-sludge units by the predacious fungus *Zoophagus insidians*. The fungus eliminated populations of browsing rotifers (*Monostyla* sp.), which maintained a favorable condition of the activated sludge by control of bacterial populations.

An increasing amount of evidence indicates that organic manuring may protect host crops and relatively suppress the reproduction of plant-parasitic nematodes in soil (Oostenbrink, 1960). Recent studies (Lear, 1959; Duddington and Duthoit, 1960; Mankau and Minteer, 1962; and Johnson, 1962) have shown that the addition of large amounts of organic materials reduce populations of phytophagous nematodes. Although there is no direct evidence, the activity of nematode-trapping fungi or other predators is believed to be a factor. The rapid reproduction of microbivorous soil nematodes and the attendant increase in natural enemies stimulated by the addition of organic matter was viewed by Linford, Yap, and Oliveira (1937) as an important deterrent to plant-parasitic nematodes in soil. Hutchinson, Reed, and Pramer (1960), however, found no apparent correlation between numbers of predacious nematodes and nematode-trapping fungi in areas in which parasitic nematode populations were lower owing to the presence of organic residue. Duddington, Everard, and Duthoit (1961) experienced significant reductions of *Heterodera avenae* by the addition of a green manure and a predacious fungus, *Dactylaria thaumasia*, to infested soil. In an experiment with the same fungus and a straw mulch and steer manure, control of the root-knot nematode was not obtained (Mankau, 1961b). While there is ample indication that organic manuring may stimulate biological-control agents, there is as yet no definite, dependable, and economic practice which can be recommended to achieve consistent results. Van der Laan (1956) suggested that a physiological change in the plant, resulting in slight resistance to nematode attack, may be brought about by organic amendments.

CONCLUSIONS.—*Indicated lines of research in myco-parasitism.*—A large body of information on mycoparasitism has been gained from studies in vitro employing synthetic media and, in some instances, sterilized soil. Through these investigations, precise observations were made on the mode of penetration and parasitism of the host under different environmental conditions. Temperature and nutrition have been most extensively studied in relation to hyperparasitism. Although results from more recent research demonstrate unequivocally that the degree of mycoparasitism can be markedly affected by altering the physical environment or by changing either the concentration or the kind of nutrition of the host, these experiments fail to show how changes in susceptibility are mediated. This is especially the case with dual-culture studies in vitro with destructive mycoparasites isolated from soil or diseased roots. This does not mean that studies in vitro should be discontinued. On the contrary, it points up the need for more basic work in vitro to elucidate the physiological and biochemical mechanisms of parasitism and to show how these mechanisms relate to susceptibility of the host fungus in response to environment. In this connection, the pioneer work of Barnett and Lilly (1958) and Shigo, Anderson, and Barnett (1961) with balanced mycoparasites indicates that susceptibility is correlated with the presence of a growth-promoting substance and with high amounts of soluble nitrogen within the host mycelium. These investigators also noted that susceptibility was increased by adding microelements to the substrate. However, the role of the unidentified growth-promoting substance, as well as the soluble nitrogen and the microelements, is not known. It is important to learn whether similar materials relate to susceptibility of those hosts attacked by destructive mycoparasites from the soil. Research along these lines would provide the framework for subsequent investigations in vitro and in soil on the physiology and ecology of mycoparasitism.

Before biological control of root diseases can be achieved through mycoparasitism, a better understanding of this antagonistic phenomenon in natural soil is needed. Any studies on mycoparasitism in soil, however, should be preceded by research to determine whether interfungus parasitism exists in soil. This determination is imperative for it is indeed an astonishing fact that only a few fungi shown to be mycoparasitic in synthetic media are known to parasitize fungi to any appreciable extent in natural, unamended soil. In fact, circumstantial evidence from studies in vitro with mixed cultures and from microscopic examination of hyphae from natural soil suggests that destructive mycoparasitism is not common in soil per se. Such evidence, however, is too insubstantial to draw any conclusions as to the importance and prevalence of mycoparasitism in the multitude of microhabitats of the soil.

Although any studies to ascertain the importance of mycoparasitism in soil would employ the use of recently devised methods, in all probability more sophisticated techniques will have to be designed for obtaining parasitized fungi from the various soil habitats. It may

well be that hyperparasitism is prevalent only in habitats that are commonly colonized by a large array of fungi and other microorganisms. Such habitats may be associated with plant residues and with other organic materials and with the rhizosphere and rhizoplane.

Systematic research to locate the site of mycoparasitism should be made throughout the year and under varying conditions of soil moisture. Fields with crop residues known to reduce the incidence of root diseases of plants might also comprise habitats with microenvironments conducive to mycoparasitism. It would not be surprising to find that several different kinds of antagonistic relations with soil-borne phytopathogenic fungi are stimulated by crop residues which alleviate root diseases.

Proof that destructive mycoparasitism exists in soil would, in all likelihood, lead to other research on the ecology and physiology of interfungus parasitism. The success of such investigations in soil will also be contingent on the efficacy of the techniques and methods used. It will be necessary to develop methods for infesting the soil without using foreign materials for the deposition of the host fungus. Furthermore, the method should enable the quick recovery of the host fungus from the infested soil after any prescribed incubation period. Such a method, recently designed for studying conidia of *Helminthosporium sativum* in soil, has yielded new information regarding the mode of conidial germination in natural soil and the longevity of spores in different soils (Boosalis, 1960).

Knowledge gained from the proposed studies on mycoparasitism in vitro and in soil may provide a sound basis for devising effective biological control of root diseases through crop rotation, soil amendments, cultural practices, or some other means.

It has not been conclusively shown that bacteria invade fungi. However, bacteria are known to cause lysis of fungi. Further research is required to show the importance of this type of microbial antagonism in relation to the survival and growth of phytopathogenic fungi in soil.

Although phages have been discovered on plant-pathogenic bacteria, little is known about their relation to microorganisms of the soil. Exploration of this area of soil biology may help to solve some of the problems concerned with the ecology of soil-borne microorganisms.

Nematode parasites and predators.—There is abundant empirical evidence that phytoparasitic nematodes are attacked by numerous and varied soil organisms, but the activity of such organisms in nature and their effect upon nematode population dynamics is little understood as yet, either in agricultural or nonagricultural soils. Most soils are inhabited by parasites and predators of nematodes; however, these organisms are largely nonspecific in character. Members of the soil microfauna predacious on nematodes are probably general carnivores and do not depend specifically on nematodes for food. Sedentary plant-parasitic nematodes protruding from roots, however, may be especially vulnerable to these predators. All of the known parasites of phytoparasitic nematodes also attack other widely diversified types of soil nematodes. Some of the most specific parasitic fungi are those (*Harposporium* spp.) in which the spores must be ingested by nematodes and are limited to microbivorous forms of little or no economic importance. The nematode victims of predatory fungi are mainly selected by chance contact. Large, robust nematodes may escape from such traps, but most soil nematodes are within the range which can be held fast by trapping fungi. High specificity between host and parasite or even predator is generally considered to be an important factor in effective biological control.

The contrived use of biotic agents to control plant-parasitic nematodes has had only cursory beginnings and no remarkable advances have as yet been made in this area. The greatest emphasis has been placed upon the use of predacious fungi and while their effectiveness in vitro and in pot tests has been encouraging, their application on a field scale has been singularly disappointing. Although annual cultivation may reduce the density of predatory fungi in agricultural soil, such fungi are apparently already abundant even in these locations. In the relatively undisturbed soil of citrus orchards, for example, three or four species of nematode-trapping fungi are frequently intimately associated with infestations of the citrus nematode (Mankau and Clarke, 1959). The application of nematophagous fungi to soil would seem to be appropriate only if they were absent from the soil to be treated, or if it were known that a given species was more effective against a particular nematode pest than those already present, or if greater population densities of the fungi would result. The latter condition may be difficult to attain in view of demonstrated antagonisms to predacious fungi in soils. The activity of predacious fungi in the natural soil environment is still little understood, and some evidence has been presented to indicate that an increase in predacious activity occurs for only a short time after the addition of organic matter and then declines (R. C. Cooke, 1962). There is some evidence from laboratory tests (R. C. Cooke, 1963) that various species of nematode-trapping fungi differ considerably in their ability to trap nematodes in soil. This may account for the inconsistent results obtained with these organisms.

The effectiveness of predators and parasites is probably limited by mobility, by the ability to seek out prey or hosts, and by population densities. Very scant information is available on these aspects of their biology. In the confined biotic community of the soil, the production of large quantities of motile spores which spread in the soil-water films would be a distinct advantage to an effective biological control agent; however, little is known about the occurrence and biology of organisms fitting this description. Similarly, almost no work has been undertaken on factors which may influence the susceptibility of nematodes to parasitism and predation.

Since parasites and predators of nematodes appear to be very widespread, biological-control studies should be essentially ecological in nature and should aim at the modification of the biotic characteristics of the environment of a pest in such a way as to influence its population density. Despite ever-increasing effort in the special area of soil biology dealing with nematodes, our ignorance about fundamental factors which affect the biological equilibrium and biotic potential of nematode pests is enormous. The great lack of experimental data relative to the influence of nematode parasites and predators should of itself be a stimulation for more attention to the possibilities which exist here.

LITERATURE CITED

ALLEN, M. W. 1957. A new species of the genus *Dolichodorus* from California (Nematoda: Tylenchida). Proc. Helminthol. Soc. Wash. D.C. 24: 95-98.

ASCHNER, M., and S. KOHN. 1958. The biology of *Harposporium anguillulae*. J. Gen. Microbiol. 19: 182-189.

AYTOUN, R. S. C. 1953. The genus Trichoderma: its relationship with *Armillaria mellea* (Vahl ex Fries) Quél and *Polyporus schweinitzii* Fr., together with preliminary observations on its ecology in woodland soil. Trans. Proc. Botan. Soc. Edinburgh 36: 99-114.

BACKUS, M. P., and E. A. STOWELL. 1953. A Fusidium disease of Xylaria in Wisconsin. Mycologia 45: 836-847.

BARNETT, H. L., and V. G. LILLY. 1958. Parasitism of *Calcarisporium parasiticum* on species of Physolospora and related fungi. West Virginia Agr. Expt. Sta. Bull. 420T, 36 p.

BARNETT, H. L., and V. G. LILLY. 1962. A destructive mycoparasite, *Gliocladium roseum*. Mycologia 54: 72-77.

BARRETT, J. T. 1912. Development and sexuality of some species of Olpidiopsis (Cornu) Fisher. Ann. Botany (London) 26: 209-238.

BIRCHFIELD, W. 1960. A new species of Catenaria parasitic on nematodes of sugarcane. Mycopathol. Mycol. Appl. 13: 331-338.

BOOSALIS, M. G. 1954. *Penicillium* sp. parasitic on *Rhizoctonia solani* (Abstr.). Phytopathology 44: 482.

BOOSALIS, M. G. 1956. Effect of soil temperature and green-manure amendment of unsterilized soil on parasitism of *Rhizoctonia solani* by *Penicillium vermiculatum* and *Trichoderma* sp. Phytopathology 46: 473-478.

BOOSALIS, M. G. 1960. A soil infestation method for studying spores of *Helminthosporium sativum*. Phytopathology 50: 860-865.

BRIAN, P. W. 1960. Antagonistic and competitive mechanisms limiting survival and activity of fungi in soil. p. 115-129. *In* D. Parkinson and J. S. Waid [ed.], The ecology of soil fungi, Liverpool University Press, Liverpool.

BROWN, W. L. JR. 1954. Collembola feeding upon nematodes. Ecology 35: 421.

BULLER, A. H. R. 1922. Researches on fungi. vol. 2. Longmans, Green, and Co., London, England. 492 p.

BULLER, E. J. 1907. An account of the genus Pythium and some Chytridiaceae. India Dept. Agr. Mem., Botan. Ser. vol. 1, No. 5.

BUTLER, E. E. 1957. *Rhizoctonia solani* as a parasite of fungi. Mycologia 49: 354-373.

CAMPBELL, W. P. 1956. The influence of associated microorganisms on the pathogenicity of *Helminthosporium sativum*. Can. J. Botany 34: 865-874.

CHRISTIE, J. R. 1960. Biological control—predaceous nematodes. Ch. 46, p. 466-468. *In* J. H. Sasser and W. R. Jenkins [ed.], Nematology, fundamentals and recent advances with emphasis on plant parasitic and soil forms, University of North Carolina Press, Chapel Hill, N. C.

COBB, N. A. 1906. Fungus maladies of the sugar cane, with notes on associated insects and nematodes. Rept. Expt. Sta. Hawaiian Sugar Planters Assoc., Hon. Bull. 5, 254 p.

COBB, N. A. 1918. Nematodes of the slow sand filter-beds of American cities. p. 189-212. *In* Contributions to a science of nematology VII, Waverly Press, Baltimore, Md.

COOKE, R. C. 1962. Behavior of nematode-trapping fungi during decomposition of organic matter in the soil. Trans. Brit. Mycol. Soc. 45: 314-320.

COOKE, R. C. 1963. The predaceous activity of nematode-trapping fungi added to soil. Ann. Appl. Biol. 51: 295-299.

COOKE, W. B., and F. J. LUDZACK. 1958. Predacious fungus behavior in activated sludge systems. Sewage Ind. Wastes 30: 1490-1495.

COSCARELLI, W., and D. PRAMER. 1962. Nutrition and growth of *Arthrobotrys conoides*. Jour. Bacteriol. 84: 60-64.

DARLEY, E. F., and W. D. WILBUR. 1954. Some relationships of carbon disulfide and *Trichoderma viride* in the control of *Armillaria mellea* (Abstr.). Phytopathology 44: 485.

DARPOUX, H. 1960. Biological interference with epidemics. vol. 3, p. 521-565. *In* J. G. Horsfall and A. E. Dimond [ed.], Plant pathology, an advanced treatise, Academic Press, New York and London.

DeVAY, J. E. 1956. Mutual relationships in fungi. Ann. Rev. Microbiol. 10: 115-140.

DOLLFUS, R. P. 1946. Parasites (animaux et vegetaux) des Helminthes. Encyclopedie biologique. vol. 27. Lechevalier, Paris. 481 p.

DONCASTER, C. C., and D. J. HOOPER. 1961. Nematodes attacked by Protozoa and Tardigrades. Nematologica 6: 333-335.

DRECHSLER, C. 1938. Two hyphomycetes parasitic on oospores of root-rotting Oomycetes. Phytopathology 28: 81-103.

DRECHSLER, C. 1941. Predaceous fungi. Biol. Rev. 16: 265-290.

DRECHSLER, C. 1943a. Antagonism and parasitism among some Oomycetes associated with root rot. J. Wash. Acad. Sci. 33: 21-28.

DRECHSLER, C. 1943b. Another hyphomycetous fungus parasitic on Pythium oospores. Phytopathology 33: 227-233.

DRECHSLER, C. 1943c. Two species of Pythium occurring in southern states. Phytopathology 33: 261-299.

DUDDINGTON, C. L. 1955. Fungi that attack microscopic animals. Botan. Rev. 21: 377-439.

DUDDINGTON, C. L. 1957. The friendly fungi. A new approach to the eelworm problem. Faber & Faber, London. 188 p.

DUDDINGTON, C. L. 1960. Biological control—predaceous fungi. Chapter 45. *In* J. N. Sasser and W. R. Jenkins [ed.], Nematology, fundamentals and recent advances with emphasis on plant parasitic and soil forms, University of North Carolina Press, Chapel Hill, N. C.

DUDDINGTON, C. L., and CECILY M. G. DUTHOIT. 1960. Green manuring and cereal root eelworm. Plant Pathol. 9: 7-9.

DUDDINGTON, C. L., C. O. R. EVERARD, and CECILY M. G. DUTHOIT. 1961. Effect of green manuring and a predacious fungus on cereal root eelworm in oats. Plant Pathol. 10: 108-109.

DUDDINGTON, C. L., F. G. W. JONES, and F. MORIARTY. 1956. The effect of predacious fungus and organic matter upon the soil population of beet eelworm, *Heterodera schachtii* Schm. Nematologica 1: 344-348.

DUDDINGTON, C. L., F. G. W. JONES, and T. D. WILLIAMS. 1956. An experiment on the effect of a predacious fungus upon the soil population of the potato root eelworm, *Heterodera rostochiensis* Woll. Nematologica 1: 341-343.

ELLIS, J. J., and C. W. HESSELTINE. 1962. *Rhopalomyces* and *Spinellus* in pure culture and the parasitism of Rhopalomyces on nematode eggs. Nature (London) 193: 699-700.

FEDER, W. A. 1959. The possibilities of biological control of plant-parasitic nematodes in tropical and sub-tropical areas. Proc. Soil & Crop Sci. Soc. Florida 19: 452-463.

FEDER, W. A., C. O. R. EVERARD, and C. L. DUDDINGTON. 1960. Heterocaryotic nature of ring formation in the predaceous fungus *Dactylella doedycoides*. Science 131: 922-924.

FEDER, W. A., C. O. R. EVERARD, and L. M. O. WOOTEN. 1963. Sensitivity of several species of the nematophagous fungus *Dactylella* to a morphogenic substance derived from free-living nematodes. Nematologica 9: 49-54.

GODFREY, R. M. 1957. Studies of British species of Endogone. II. Fungal parasites. Trans. Brit. Mycol. Soc. 40: 136-144.

GORLENKO, M. V. 1956. Predatory fungi and their utilization in nematode control. Nematologica 1: 147-150.

HAMS, A. F., and G. D. WILKIN. 1961. Observations on the use of predacious fungi for the control of *Heterodera* spp. Ann. Appl. Biol. 49: 515-523.

HOLLIS, J. P. 1957. Cultural studies with *Dorylaimus ettersbergensis*. Phytopathology 47: 468-473.

HUTCHINSON, S. A., and W. F. MAI. 1954. A study of the efficiency of the catching organs of *Dactylaria eudermata* (Drechs.) in relation to *Heterodera rostochiensis* (Wr.) in soil. Plant Disease Reptr. 38: 185-186.

HUTCHINSON, M. T., J. P. REED, and D. PRAMER. 1960. Observations on the effects of decaying vegetable matter on nematode populations. Plant Disease Reptr. 44: 400-401.

HUTCHINSON, M. T., and H. T. STREU. 1960. Tardigrades attacking nematodes. Nematologica 5: 149.

JOHNSON, L. F. 1962. Effect of the addition of organic amendments to soil on root knot of tomatoes. II. Relation of soil temperature, moisture, and pH. Phytopathology 52: 410-413.

KARLING, J. S. 1944. New lagenidiaceous parasites of rotifers from Brazil. Lloydia 7: 328-342.

KEVAN, D. K. McE. 1962. Soil animals. H. F. & G. Witherby Ltd. London. 237 p.

KOVOOR, A. T. A. 1954. Some factors affecting the growth of *Rhizoctonia bataticola* in the soil. J. Madras Univ. 24B: 47-52.

KRASIL'NIKOV, N. A. 1958. Soil microorganisms and higher plants. Academy of Sciences, USSR. 474 p.

KUIPER, K. 1958. Parasitering van aaltjes door protozoen. Tijdschr. Plantenziekten 64: 122.

KUYAMA, S., and D. PRAMER. 1962. Purification and properties of a protein having nemin activity. Biochim. Biophys. Acta 56: 631.

LAAN, P. A. VAN DER. 1954. Na der onderzoek over het aaltjesvangende amoeboide organisme *Theratomyxa weberi* Zwillenberg. Tijdschr. Plantenziekten 60: 139-145.

LAAN, P. A. VAN DER. 1956. The influence of organic manuring on the development of the potato root eelworm, *H. rostochiensis*. Nematologica 1: 112-125.

LEAR, B. 1959. Application of castor pomace and cropping of castor beans to soil to reduce nematode populations. Plant Disease Reptr. 43: 459-460.

LEVINE, M. N., R. H. BAMBERG, and R. E. ATKINSON. 1936. Microorganisms antibiotic or pathogenic to cereal rusts. Phytopathology 26: 99-100.

LINFORD, M. B. 1942. Methods of observing soil flora and fauna associated with roots. Soil Sci. 53: 93-103.

LINFORD, M. B. 1959. Biological control of plant nematodes. Illinois Research (Illinois Agr. Expt. Sta.) 1: 10-11.

LINFORD, M. B., and J. M. OLIVEIRA. 1937. The feeding of hollow-spear nematodes on other nematodes. Science 85: 295-297.

LOEWENBERG, J. R., T. SULLIVAN, and M. L. SCHUSTER. 1959. A virus disease of *Meloidogyne incognita incognita,* the southern root-knot nematode. Nature (London) 184: 1896.

MANKAU, R. 1961a. The use of nematode-trapping fungi to control root-knot nematodes. Nematologica 6: 326-332.

MANKAU, R. 1961b. An attempt to control root-knot nematode with *Dactylaria thaumasia* Drechsler and *Arthrobotrys arthrobotryoides* Lindau. Plant Disease Reptr. 45: 164-166.

MANKAU, R. 1961c. Antagonisms to nematode-trapping fungi in soil. (Abstr.) Phytopathology 51: 66.

MANKAU, R. 1962a. The effect of some organic additives upon a soil nematode population and associated natural enemies. Nematologica 7: 65-73.

MANKAU, R. 1962*b*. Soil fungistasis and nematophagous fungi. Phytopathology 52: 611-615.

MANKAU, R., and O. F. CLARKE. 1959. Nematode-trapping fungi in southern California citrus soils. Plant Disease Reptr. 43: 968-969.

MANKAU, R., and M. B. LINFORD. 1960. Host-parasite relationships of the clover cyst nematode, *Heterodera trifolii* Goffart. Illinois Agr. Expt. Sta. Bull. 667, 50 p.

MANKAU, R., and R. J. MINTEER. 1962. Reduction of soil populations of the citrus nematode by the addition of organic materials. Plant Disease Reptr. 46: 375-378.

MICOLETZKY, H. 1925. Die freilebenden Süsswasser- und Moornematoden Dänmarks nebst Anhang über Amobosporidien und andere Parasiten bei freilebenden Nematoden. Mem. Acad. Roy. Sci. Lettres Dänemark (Copenhagen). Sec. Sci. 8e ser. t. X, no. 2, p. 55-310.

MITCHELL, R. 1963. Addition of fungal cell-wall components to soil for biological disease control. Phytopathology 53: 1068-1071.

MITCHELL, R., and M. ALEXANDER. 1963. Lysis of soil fungi by bacteria. Can. J. Microbiol. 9: 169-177.

MULLER, H. G. 1958. The constricting ring mechanism of two predacious hyphomycetes. Trans. Brit. Mycol. Soc. 41: 361-364.

MURPHY, P. W., and C. C. DONCASTER. 1957. A culture method for soil meiofauna and its application to the study of nematode predators. Nematologica 2: 202-214.

NOVOGRUDSKII, D. M. 1948. The colonization of soil bacteria on fungal hyphae. (In Russian with English title.) Mikrobiologiya 17: 28-35.

OOSTENBRINK, M. 1960. Population dynamics in relation to cropping, manuring, and soil disinfection. Ch. 49, p. 439-442. *In* J. N. Sasser and W. R. Jenkins, Nematology, fundamentals and recent advances with emphasis on plant parasitic and soil forms, University of North Carolina Press, Chapel Hill, N. C.

PARAMONOV, A. A. 1954. [An amoeboid organism destroying infective larvae of the root-knot nematode.] Tr. Gelmintologicheskoi Laboratorii. Akad. Nauk USSR 7: 50-54.

PON, D. S., C. E. TOWNSEND, G. E. WESSMAN, C. G. SCHMITT, and C. H. KINGSOLVER. 1954. A Xanthomonas parasitic on uredia of cereal rusts. Phytopathology 44: 707-710.

PRAMER, DAVID, and N. R. STOLL. 1959. Nemin: a morphogenic substance causing trap formation by predaceous fungi. Science 129: 966-967.

SANFORD, G. B. 1959. Root-disease fungi as affected by other soil organisms. p. 367-376. *In* C. S. Holton et al. [ed.], Plant pathology, problems and progress 1908-1958. University of Wisconsin Press, Madison, Wisc.

SCHAERFFENBERG, B., and H. TENDL. 1951. Untersuchung über das Verhalten der Enchytraeiden gegenüber dem Zuckerrubennematoden *H. schachtii* Schm. Z. Angew. Entomol. 32: 476-488.

SCHUURMANS STECKHOVEN, J. H., and R. J. H. TEUNISSEN. 1938. Nematodes libres terrestres. Exploration du Parc National Albert. Missions G. F. DeWitte (1933-1935). Fasc. 22. Bruxelles. 229 p.

SCOGNAMIGLIO, A. 1959. [Biological control of nematodes.] Italia Agr. 96: 815-819.

SHIGO, A. L., C. D. ANDERSON, and H. L. BARNETT. 1961. Effects of concentration of host nutrients on parasitism of *Piptocephalis xenophila* and *P. virginiana*. Phytopathology 51: 616-620.

SIEGLE, H. 1961. Über Mischinfektionen mit *Ophiobolus graminis* und *Didymella exitialis*. Phytopathol. Z. 42: 305-348.

SOPRUNOV, F. F. 1958. [Carnivorous hyphomycetous fungi and their use in control of pathogenic nematodes.] Akademiya Nauk Turkmenskoi USSR, Ashkhabad. 365 p.

SOROKINE, N. 1876. Note sur les vegetaux parasites des Anguillulae. Ann. Sci. Nat. Botan. 4: 62-71.

SPARROW, F. K. 1932. Observations on the aquatic fungi of Cold Spring Harbor. Mycologia 24: 268-301.

STEINHAUS, E. A., and G. A. MARSH. 1962. Report of diagnoses of diseased insects, 1951-1961. Hilgardia 33: 349-490.

STOLP, H., and H. PETZOLD. 1962. Untersuchung über eine obligat parasitischen Mikroorganismus mit lytischer Aktivität für Pseudomonasbakterien. Phytopathol. Z. 45: 364-390.

TARJAN, A. C. 1961. Attempts at controlling citrus burrowing nematodes using nematode-trapping fungi. Soil Crop Sci. Soc. Florida Proc. 21: 17-36.

THORNE, G. 1940. *Duboscquia penetrans,* n. sp. (Sporozoa, Microsporidia, Nosematidae) a parasite of the nematode *Pratylenchus pratensis* (de Man) Filipjev. Proc. Helminthol. Soc. Wash. D.C. 7: 51-53.

TRIBE, H. T. 1957. On the parasitism of *Sclerotinia trifoliorum* by *Coniothyrium minitans*. Trans. Brit. Mycol. Soc. 40: 489-499.

VILLOT, A. 1874. Monographie des Dragonneaux. Arch. Zool. Exptl. Gén. 3: 184-185.

WARREN, J. R. 1948. An undescribed species of Papulospora parasitic on *Rhizoctonia solani* Kuhn. Mycologia 40: 391-401.

WEBER, A. P., L. O. ZWILLENBERG, and P. A. VAN DER LAAN. 1952. A predacious amoeboid organism destroying larvae of the potato-root eelworm and other nematodes. Nature (London) 169: 834-835.

WEINDLING, R. 1934. Studies on a lethal principle effective in the parasitic action of *Trichoderma lignorum* on *Rhizoctonia solani* and other soil fungi. Phytopathology 24: 1153-1179.

WEINDLING, R. 1941. Experimental consideration of the mold toxins of Gliocladium and Trichoderma. Phytopathology 31: 991-1003.

WEINDLING, R. 1959. Role of parasitism in microbial antagonisms. p. 623-626. *In* Recent Adv. Botany (Canada) (9th Intern. Botan. Congr., Montreal) University of Toronto Press, Toronto.

WEINDLING, R., and H. S. FAWCETT. 1936. Experiments in the control of *Rhizoctonia* damping-off of citrus seedlings. Hilgardia 10: 1-16.

WILLIAMS, J. R. 1960. Studies on the nematode soil fauna of sugarcane fields in Mauritius. 5. Notes upon a parasite of root-knot nematodes. Nematologica 5: 37-42.

WINKLER, E. J., S. KUYAMA, and D. PRAMER. 1961. A nemin assay procedure. Nature (London) 191: 155-156.

WINSLOW, R. D., and T. D. WILLIAMS. 1957. Amoeboid organisms attacking larvae of the potato root eelworm (*Heterodera rostochiensis* Woll.) in England and the beet eelworm (*H. schachtii* Schm.) in Canada. Tijdschr. Plantenziekten 63: 242-243.

► DISCUSSION OF M. G. BOOSALIS AND R. MANKAU

M. Alexander:

Our work in the area of mycolysis is based upon three assumptions: (1) mere inoculation of an antagonist into soil will not lead to significant control; (2) mycolysis does occur in soil; and (3) the initial step in lysis is an enzymatic digestion of constituents of the fungal wall. On this basis, we have undertaken investigations of the constituents of fungal walls and of the enzymes concerned with lysis of pathogenic fungi. Two wall components and enzymes acting upon them have been characterized, and addition of the two constituents chitin and laminarin has led to significant control of several diseases; we have as yet, however, no adequate evidence to support the contention that the control associated with chitin or laminarin really results from a selective stimulation of mycolytic bacteria or actinomycetes.

M. G. Boosalis:

How do you detect the presence of chitinase, and do you feel that this is an accurate method?

M. Alexander:

The method is grossly inaccurate because most of the chitinase is undoubtedly adsorbed to soil particles. The procedure which we are using is making a soil suspension and assaying in a very short period of time the amount of N-acetyl-D-glucosamine or hexoses produced from chitin. This we feel is a reflection of the activity but is not an accurate measure because of the adsorption problems.

J. D. Menzies:

Mycoparasitism and predation of pathogens may have little practical value in controlling pathogens capable of saprophytic increase in soil, but must be an important attrition factor on pathogens that survive by resting structures only.

A. Burges:

In dealing with fungal-fungal parasitism one must not overlook examples such as *Cordyceps* parasitising truffles, and *Boletus parasiticus* and *Nyctalis* spp., which attack higher Basidiomycetes.

H. Katznelson:

Bacteriophages are certainly present in soil, and for many bacteria, including bacterial plant pathogens. They are, however, usually at low titres due to adsorption on soil clays, inactivation by various organisms including fungi, and general inability to multiply on the relatively inactive bacterial flora except when it is stimulated by addition of organic matter and possibly in the rhizosphere, an area which has not been studied extensively in this connection. The activity of phages in soil is limited also because of the development of resistant strains of bacteria. Attempts to control bacterial plant pathogens such as those causing blights with phages have not been successful, at least in our hands. In experiments to determine if phage interfered with the ability of nodule bacteria to produce nodules in sand and soil cultures, we found that nodule bacteria were not affected, for good nodulation occurred. Perhaps we were working with a strain of bacteria resistant to the phage. Consequently, I would be somewhat dubious about the use of bacteriophage to control bacteria in soil and even on plants.

M. G. Boosalis:

I concur with Dr. Katznelson's comment regarding the attempts to control bacterial plant pathogens by phages. I am not aware of any successful biological control of plant-pathogenic bacteria by means of phages.

J. L. Lockwood:

A simple and dramatic demonstration of mycolysis by natural soil can be made by placing mycelia of various fungi on the surface of soil in petri dishes. In our work, virtually all the mycelium of several plant-pathogenic fungi was destroyed within a few days after being added to soil. This mycolytic property of soil can be reproduced by inoculating sterilized soils

with isolates of *Streptomyces*. The mycolytic action of actinomycetes appears to occur at a distance from the mycelium, and not require close proximity with hyphae, as bacterial lysis of fungi often does. This can be demonstrated in agar cultures by zones cleared of fungal hyphae surrounding the *Streptomyces* colony.

E. E. Trujillo:

The work of Snyder and colleagues has shown that plant pathogens such as the wilt fusaria are present in the soil as resting structures. Other organisms such as the pythiaceous fungi produce resting structures with thick outer walls which are not easily destroyed by microbial activity. Our evidence with *Pythium aphanidermatum* in soil seems to indicate that lysis of the growing hyphae occurs quite frequently; however, we find that previous to this oospores or resting sporangia had formed and they survive quite well in spite of other soil-microflora activity. Would you comment on the possible significance of the resting structure in this respect?

M. G. Boosalis:

There are indeed a number of soil-inhabiting fungi, such as you mentioned, which produce various kinds of resting structures in soil. However, little is known about the mechanism which enables these fungus structures to persist in soil. I do not believe the longevity of resting fungus structures can be ascribed entirely to their thick walls. If this were the case, then the thick-walled chlamydospores of *Ustilago tritici* would remain viable in soil longer than a few weeks. The chemical nature of the walls, coupled with a distinct physiological mechanism of the fungus resting structure, undoubtedly also contributes to the resistant nature of these bodies.

Dr. Trujillo's finding, indicating that lysis of growing hyphae of *Pythium aphanidermatum* in soil is preceded by sporulation, is of great significance. This means, then, that it cannot be assumed that lysis of growing hyphae in soil inevitably results in reduction of potential inoculum. The production of various resting structures, such as spores, prior to the destruction of hyphae, may be a common phenomenon in soil. In this connection, results from our studies indicated that *Helminthosporium sativum* sporulates profusely in soil. Furthermore, conidial formation of this fungus commenced when hyphal growth was arrested. Consequently, sporulation occurred at all stages of hyphal development, ranging from a very short germ-tube-like structure with a single conidium at its tip to a branched hypha bearing many spores. A detailed description of the mode of sporulation of *H. sativum* in soil is given in *Phytopathology* (52: 1172-1177, 1962).

The capacity of fungi to sporulate quickly when conditions are inimical to vegetative growth is an important safeguard against drastic reduction of inoculum in the fluctuating environment of the soil.

D. W. Burke:

I should like to know more about the possible importance of nematodes predatory on fungi. On two occasions I have observed nematodes appearing to be full of macroconidia of *Fusarium solani* f. *phaseoli* around colonies of this fungus which had been "plucked clean" of conidia.

R. Mankau:

There are probably some microbivorous nematode species which may feed largely by ingesting fungus spores or even hyphae. We know very little of such nematodes. The more important fungivorous nematodes are stylet-bearing forms which suck out the protoplasm from fungus hyphae or other structures. These species are very common in many soils and undoubtedly of some importance in reducing the density of fungi in soil. A few instances of nematodes depressing the incidence of diseases incited by fungi have been noted (H. L. Rhoades and M. B. Linford. Plant Disease Reptr. 43: 323-328, 1959; A. F. Schindler and R. N. Stewart. Phytopathology 46: 469, 1956). In our laboratory at Riverside we have demonstrated (R. Mankau and K. Mankau, The role of mycophagous nematodes in the soil. I. The relationships of *Aphelenchus avenae* to phytopathogenic soil fungi. *In* J. van der Drift and J. Doeksen, *Soil Organisms,* Proc. Colloq. Soil Fauna, Soil Microflora and Their Relationships, North-Holland, Amsterdam. 1963. 450 p.) that the ubiquitous fungivorous nematode, *Aphelenchus avenae,* is an obligate fungivore and feeds primarily and voraciously on important root-rotting fungi. In some instances it is probably an important factor in reducing the damage by phytopathogenic fungi.

A. Burges:

Would Dr. Mankau comment on the growth form of nematode-trapping fungi in the soil? In culture they produce an extensive mycelium. Do they do this in the soil?

R. Mankau:

My experience with these fungi leads me to believe that they do not ordinarily produce extensive mycelial growth in the soil. They may do so temporarily when organic matter is mixed with soil, in which case they probably behave as saprophytes and then extend their activity in a predacious phase as nematode populations build up. Nematode-trapping fungi are seldom, if ever, observed in soil-dilution plating but can easily be recovered, if present, with plating techniques which allow the gradual buildup of nematode numbers without too much bacterial and saprophytic-fungus development. We have observed that they are poor colonizers of natural soils and that many common soil microorganisms are antagonistic to them on agar plates. When spores of some predacious fungus species have been exposed on agar disks to soil solutions, lysis of germ tubes and mycelia has occurred. Several species of nematode-trapping fungi can be easily isolated from the rhizosphere of nematode-infested citrus roots, for example, but one has much less success with nonrhizosphere soil from the same area.

D. Pramer:

Dr. Burges, there is some evidence in the literature for trap formation by predacious fungi in soil. Dr. Tribe has reported and photographed these structures as part of the sequence of organisms that invade and decompose cellulose that is buried in soil. In addition, nematodes isolated from soil and examined microscopically were found in some few cases to be encircled by the organelles of capture formed by predacious fungi.

A. S. Sussman:

Ingestion of spores by certain animals like slugs has been reported to result in the breaking of dormancy of these cells. Has any work been done on spores ingested by nematodes which relates to the possibility of activation of dormant cells?

R. Mankau:

There has been no work, to my knowledge, on the activation of fungal spores by the passage through the intestinal tract of nematodes. Many of the free-living, non-stylet-bearing soil nematodes are bacterial feeders with buccal openings too small to ingest any but the very smallest spores. Some species can evidently ingest spores easily but it is not known whether they pass through the nematode's body undamaged. Many of the nematodes without a stylet have one or more large puncturing teeth or smaller grasping teeth or both, which may destroy any ingested spores. They are generally considered to be carnivorous species which feed on protozoa, rotifers, nematodes, and other members of the soil microfauna. The anal opening in even very large nematode species is very small and it seems unlikely that the spores of any particular fungus pass through the body of a nematode commonly found in soil with any regularity.

J. D. Menzies:

In view of the vast numbers of bacteria ingested by soil protozoa it is amazing to me that pathogenic bacteria can survive for so long a time in soil, unless saprophytic multiplication is more common than we think.

PART VII

◄

THE SOIL INOCULUM

The Dynamics of Inoculum[1]

RALPH BAKER—*Department of Botany and Plant Pathology, Colorado State University, Fort Collins.*

▶

Pathologists have devoted much thought to attempts to define those events revolving about the process of inoculation. Even the term inoculate, however, has been used in various ways. Thus, it may be used in a broad sense meaning, placing "a microorganism . . . into an organism or a substratum" (Ainsworth and Bisby, 1950) or in a stricter sense, "the transference of inoculum from the place of its production or origin to the infection court" (Whetzel et al., 1925). By the latter definition, suscepts could be "inoculated," soils "infested." Since a plant merely comes in contact by some means with a pathogen during inoculation, it has been suggested that the simple term expose is appropriate (Raabe et al., 1962). This concept has the advantage of simplicity. The term inoculate is very well established, however, whatever shade of meaning is applied.

The various definitions of the term "inoculum potential" have been reviewed most recently by Dimond and Horsfall (1960) and Garrett (1960). From these treatments, it is apparent that modern pathologists utilize at least two different concepts in defining the term. In a broad sense it may be used as "the resultant of the action of the environment, the vigor of the pathogen to establish an infection, the susceptibility of the host and the amount of inoculum present" (Dimond and Horsfall, 1960). A knowledge of all these components would indeed enable the researcher to forecast and describe the nature of epidemics. In general, however, the soil microbiologist has been more interested in the potentiality or degree of infectivity of a pathogen as it stands poised at the surface of its substrate (Garrett, 1956, 1960). Ultimately this can be viewed as a concept involving biological energy available for colonization of a host and would be a function of inoculum density or intensity (mass or units of inoculum per unit of soil), available nutriment (both internal and external to the propagule), environmental factors, and genetic capacity of the organism (Martinson, 1963). This definition has the advantage of confining inoculum potential to an expression of energy of the pathogen at a specific place in time and space and will be used in this paper unless otherwise indicated.

[1] Published with the approval of the Director of the Colorado Agricultural Experiment Station, as Scientific Series, Paper No. 875.

Using this concept for prediction of disease severity, the sum of all intensity and capacity factors (Dimond and Horsfall, 1960) influencing the *inoculum* would first be determined. This value would be the inoculum potential sensu Garrett. For any particular host, another set of factors could be applied to this value, namely, the resistance of the host during its entire life cycle and the influence of environment on this resistance. Combining all these factors should give a predictive index of disease severity: truly an ambitious undertaking but not beyond the reach of modern technology.

CONSIDERATIONS IN MEASURING INOCULUM POTENTIAL.—*Use of host indicators.*—Classically, inoculum potential has been measured with hosts as indicators (MacFarlane, 1952; Maloy and Alexander, 1958; Petersen, 1959; Reiling, King, and Fields, 1960; Wilhelm, 1951). Since the concept carries with it the disease-producing ability of inoculum in a particular environment, this is the most concrete assessment applied. Measurements of this type, however, often have severe limitations in critical experiments.

To assess the actual potential of inoculum by using a host, all of the factors mentioned above in the broader concept of inoculum potential (sensu Dimond and Horsfall) must be utilized. For instance, a sudden or even subtle change in environment during the incubation period between inoculation and symptom expression may result in profound alteration in disease index. Thus, the symptoms may reflect potentials in the infection process rather than energy of the inoculum at the host surface. In well-controlled experiments, environmental conditions may be held constant during this critical period, but there are other difficulties. Those pathologists who go down to the soil to study root rots are aware of the additional difficulties involved in objectively assessing disease severity. Infections involving parenchyma tissue in which death of the host does not occur or is delayed are especially treacherous. Usually the investigator resorts to disease classes (Horsfall and Barratt, 1945) based on number or size of lesions or other symptoms. This may give false impressions of severity. Stems or roots may be girdled superficially. This may not be so important as, for example, a penetration of normally resistant vascular tissues (Christou and Snyder, 1962) or toxin production by a well-established pathogen (MacWithey, 1961). Thus, the difficult assessment of extent of infection in three dimensions, including the location in host tissues, is essential in assessing disease severity.

Another pitfall in determining inoculum potential by host reaction is variation in the relative physiological ability of a host to contract disease at different stages of its life history. This phenomenon has been called "disease potential" by Grainger (1956). Thus, host reactions over a period of time may vary widely with identical inoculum potentials (sensu Garrett). Examples of this are abundant. For instance, MacWithey (1963) has shown that apparent infection of sugar beets by *Aphanomyces cochlioides* Drechs. is dependent upon the age of the seedling at the time of inoculation. This is also illustrated in Figs. 1*A* and 1*B*. Here two varieties of carnation were inoculated with various inoculum densities of *Fusarium roseum* f. *cerealis* (Cke.) Snyd. & Hans. conidia at different times after "striking" nonrooted cuttings for propagation. For both varieties resistance increased until 15 days after the beginning of propagation, when the cuttings became more susceptible. Twenty days after striking, when the cuttings were ready for transplanting, resistance had increased again.

Fig. 2 shows representative plants from the above experiment of the variety William Sim. It is interesting to note (from visual aboveground symptoms alone) that increasing resistance from the beginning of the propagative period was most evident with an inoculum density of 1 conidium per cc of propagative medium. In contrast, increased susceptibility after 15 days is exhibited by plants inoculated with 10 or 100 conidia per cc. This demonstrates the value of using various inoculum densities for the detection of subtle differences in behavior of inoculum and host over a period of time. Thus, the conclusions mentioned above could not have been made if an inoculum density of 1,000 conidia per cc had been used. This has significance for a variety of research areas. For example, extreme caution is necessary in interpretation of data obtained by inoculating plants in a germ-free or near germ-free environment. Even weak or nonvirulent microorganisms at low inoculum densities operating without an antagonistic microflora or in superoptimum environments can induce substantial and atypical damage (Schwinghamer, 1956).

As shown in Fig. 1, resistance of carnation varieties increased after being placed in the propagative bed until 10 days after striking. This resistance fell off at 15 days and increased again at 20 days. Increased susceptibility at 15 days coincides with the emergence of adventitious roots. Phillips (1962) has captured in a photograph *Fusarium roseum* f. *cerealis* in the act of penetrating cells in the stem damaged by an emerging root during this period; this provides an explanation for increase in susceptibility.

Fig. 3 illustrates again the value of critically assessing host resistance over a period of time. Resistance of two varieties of carnation to *Fusarium* stem rot was compared in the period following transplanting from the propagative bench. The variety Miller's Yellow was more susceptible than William Sim, but this is not evident at all times, e.g. inoculations made at 0 days and 20 days after transplanting. Both varieties were com-

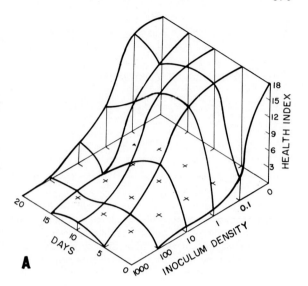

A

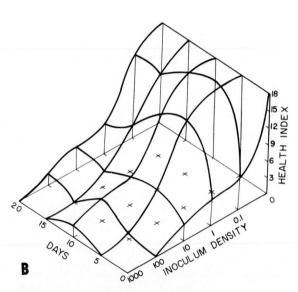

B

Fig. 1. Health indices of 2 varieties of carnation, William Sim (*A*) and Miller's Yellow (*B*), inoculated at striking and at successive 5-day intervals thereafter at various inoculum densities. Health index on 0-18 scale: 0 = plant dead, 18 = plant symptomless. This is a representative experiment based on averages from 36 plants per treatment divided into 4 replications.

paratively resistant 20 days after transplanting; however, Miller's Yellow apparently recovered more slowly (Baker, 1957).

It is essential then that rigorous criteria be established if inoculum potential is to be properly assessed by host reaction. The resistance or susceptibility of the host must be known; indeed it is just as important to have an intimate knowledge of host resistance during its life cycle as to know the capabilities of the pathogen. Again, objective measurements of the degree of infec-

Fig. 2. Disease induced by *Fusarium roseum* f. *cerealis* on carnation cuttings at inoculum densities of 1, 10, 100, and 1,000 conidia per cc of soil and inoculated at striking and at successive 5-day intervals thereafter.

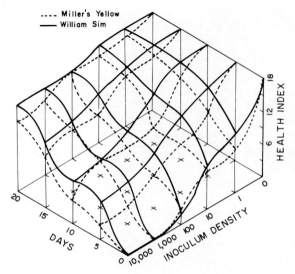

Fig. 3. Fusarium stem rot developing in a resistant variety (William Sims, solid lines) and a more susceptible variety (Miller's Yellow, dotted lines) inoculated at various intervals after transplanting and at various inoculum densities. Health index computed as in Fig. 1.

tion should be carefully worked out. Quantitative techniques borrowed from our friends engaged in research on viruses and leaf spots could well be used through counts of infection foci (Petersen, 1959) or lesions (Nash, Christou, and Snyder, 1961). Total dry-weight depression or yield data may also be valuable except for short-term experiments. Very good measurements of disease severity may be collected from emergence (Chi and Hansen, 1962; Leach, 1947; Martinson, 1963) or survival (Luke and Pfahler, 1962) data. The incubation period may also be used for objective assays of inoculum density in some instances. Phillips (1962) noted a direct correlation between the time required for symptoms to appear on carnation cuttings and the inoculum density of conidia of *Fusarium roseum* f. *cerealis*.

Another technique used to estimate objectively the populations of pathogenic fungi in soil by using an appropriate host is the "most probable number" method (Maloy and Alexander, 1958). The numbers of diseased bean plants occurring in various spore-dilution series of *Fusarium solani* f. *phaseoli* (Burk) Snyd. & Hans. or *Thielaviopsis basicola* (Berk. & Br.) Ferr. was noted and from a table of most probable numbers the population was estimated. Other applications (Jenkins, 1962; Tsao, 1960) will be treated later. This statistical method, though cumbersome, may find wide application in inoculum-potential studies.

Correlations with activity or inoculum density.—If inoculum-potential values are confined to the surface of the substrate, it should not be necessary to use a host for measurement of the energy available for infection. Thus, Martinson (1963) correlated inoculum potential of *Rhizoctonia solani* Kühn on radish with frequency of invasion of soil microbiological sampling tubes. Papavizas and Davey (1959) demonstrated that fre-

quency of isolation of the same pathogen from buckwheat stem pieces in soil increased with higher inoculum densities. These methods offer exciting possibilities because they eliminate uncertain host responses due to fluctuating resistance, require relatively little time and less space, and in some cases are extremely sensitive.

In equating inoculum potential with frequency of isolation in "baiting" techniques, there is a basic assumption that saprophytic activity is identical with pathogenicity. This is not necessarily true. The pioneering work of Jones, Johnson, and Dickson, (1926) demonstrated that optimum temperatures for enzymes inducing parasitism may be different from those important in saprophytic activity. More recently Cochrane (1958) has also postulated that pathogenicity and growth may not be affected similarly by temperature. As Martinson (1963) has suggested, close correlations between inoculum potential and saprophytic activity among the fungi are most likely with primitive parasites having good competitive saprophytic ability and a high mycelial growth rate.

Baiting techniques frequently employ short-term exposure of substrates for invasion by pathogens. At certain temperatures below or above the optimum for saprophytic activity of a pathogen, these substrates may be invaded very slowly. This would result in low predictive values for inoculum potential. High values have resulted in these instances, however, when a host has been used to measure potentials. Martinson (1963) has demonstrated this phenomenon using soil microbiological tubes to provide predictive damping-off indices. The tubes were in the soil at 15°C for only 72 hours and were invaded at a very low frequency at any inoculum density by *Rhizoctonia solani*. A high incidence of damping-off of radish seedlings, however, was noted under these conditions. Martinson suggested that radish seedlings had a low coefficient of velocity of emergence, sensu Kotowski (1927) and Leach (1947), at 15°C and therefore were exposed to the fungus for a longer period of time prior to emergence.

Measuring inoculum potential without indicator hosts may be more difficult for specialized parasites not readily isolated with baiting techniques. Fortunately, methods have been developed for determining inoculum density for many soil microorganisms: for instance, by dilution techniques for *Fusarium solani* (Mart.) Appel. & Wr. f. *phaseoli* (Burk.) Snyd. & Hans. (Nash and Snyder, 1962), *F. oxysporum* Schlect. f. *pisi* (Linford) Snyd. & Hans., race 2, *F. solani* (Mart.) Appel & Wr. f. *pisi* (Jones) Snyd. & Hans. (Worf and Hagedorn, (1961), and *Verticillium albo-atrum* Reinke & Berth. (Nadakavukaren and Horner, 1959); and screening sclerotia of *Sclerotium rolfsii* Saccardo (Leach and Davey, 1938). Ultimately it should be possible to couple these with the influence of the most important capacity factors on inoculum potential (e.g. Chi and Hansen, 1962). Mathematical relations could be established, and predictive indices of inoculum potential for any set of environmental conditions could be computed. For example, the most important soil factors influencing inoculum potential of *F. solani* f. *phaseoli* are probably inoculum density and the capacity factors associated with C:N ratio and temperature of the soil. Preliminary work at Colorado State University has established the relations between these factors, and data are being accumulated for computations.

The capacity factors for inoculum potential have received little attention (Dimond and Horsfall, 1960). Certainly these may become important in certain instances as demonstrated by the work of Leach (1947) with the temperature factor of inoculum potential. Even so, Martinson (1963) has reported that damping-off incited by *Rhizoctonia solani* was primarily influenced by inoculum density. While some influence due to temperature was noted, the relative growth rates of host and pathogen at various temperatures (as reflected in the H:P ratio) were not of great importance in computing a predictive index of disease severity.

Alternatively, a more basic knowledge of the mechanisms involved in the "attraction" of pathogens to host tissue may lead to more efficient baiting techniques for isolation of some parasites. For example, modification of media in soil microbiological sampling tubes with tomato exudates yielded a *Phytophthora* sp. not isolated by any other modification of the method (Martinson and Baker, 1962).

Detached portions of the host may provide means of measuring activity of pathogens not easily isolated from soils. An excellent example of the potentialities of such a method has been reported by Tsao (1960) working with *Phytophthora citrophthora* (R. E. Sm. & E. H. Sm.) Leonian. Using lemons to detect the pathogen, he developed a serial-dilution endpoint technique similar to the most-probable-number method (Maloy and Alexander, 1958) for assaying disease-producing ability of various soils. Jenkins (1962) also applied the same principles for estimating populations of *P. parasitica* Dast. var. *nicotianae* (Breda de Haan) Tucker, using tobacco leaves as indicators. Since actual host tissue is used, activity under any given environmental condition should give reliable predictive values.

Biological energy.—In Garrett's (1956) definition of inoculum potential, there is an intriguing element suggesting that potential might eventually be measured in fundamental units of biological energy. As applied in this instance, energy may be exceedingly difficult to measure in an absolute sense. Even so, advances are being made along this line in other fields (King and Farmer, 1961; Lifson, Gordon, and McClintock, 1955; McClintock and Lifson, 1958), and current methodology should yield reasonably reliable data. There has long been a need for fundamental and unifying concepts in the field of biology. Such procedures designed to establish a fundamental concept of energy as the basis for the potential of pathogens to invade host tissue may find wide application in animal as well as plant pathology.

Martinson (1959), in studies with *Rhizoctonia solani*, has attempted to measure energy indirectly at different inoculum levels. A correlation was noted between inoculum density in raw soil and evolved CO_2. Since the inoculum used was increased originally in a dilute corn-meal-sand mixture, a certain amount of substrate was introduced into the soil. Thus much of the increase in CO_2 evolution could have resulted from stimulated activity of the soil microflora of the raw soil. Since a pathogen is such a small part of the total population in soil, it is evident that extremely sensitive methods must be employed to measure its energy. Calorimetry (Daggs and Halcro-Wardlaw, 1933; Magee, et al., 1939), with the use of isotopes (Wheeler, 1953) and combustion methods, is now being evaluated and promises a chance of success. Inherent difficulties may arise but the challenge is there awaiting resolution.

FACTORS INFLUENCING ENERGY LEVEL OF INOCULUM.—Having treated the means by which inoculum potential may be measured, it is appropriate to take up in some detail the factors affecting energy level in the vicinity and at the surface of the host substrate. We are fortunate, as evidenced by the literature in general and this symposium in particular, in having substantial contributions in this area. Obviously there are gaps in our knowledge. This symposium should stimulate research designed to breach these gaps—and inevitably open others.

Some of the major factors influencing the energy level of inoculum can be organized into a schematic diagram (Fig. 4).

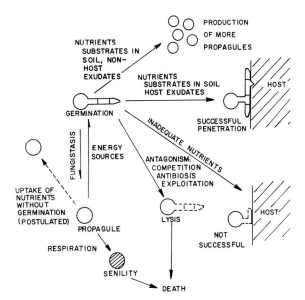

Fig. 4. Diagram illustrating major factors influencing energy level of inoculum.

The basic unit may be considered as the propagule, be it chlamydospore, resistant hypha, sclerotium, or other dormant structure. Each unit contains a certain amount of nutrient derived from the parent mycelium. It also carries genetic factors concerned with virulence. Thus, the energy available for penetration and infection at this point would be the product of the density of inoculum, the energy stored in fats and other compounds, and the inherent genetic potential of the propagules.

Mathematical relations connected with inoculum will

be presented in the next paper by Dr. Dimond. At this point, however, it may be well to take up some of the relations connected with orientation of propagules in the soil. The simplest three-dimensional geometric figure representing propagules in a three-dimensional medium is a tetrahedron (Fig. 5). The surface of a tetrahedron

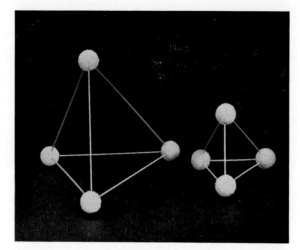

Fig. 5. Space relations obtained by reducing the distance between spores. The tetrahedron at the left has 8 times the volume, but the balls (representing spores) are only twice as far apart as the one at the right.

consists of four equilateral triangles; thus one apex is equidistant from the other three apices. If each of the four apices represents a spore, then the distance between spores (the edges of the tetrahedron) with random distribution is a constant, D. The volume of the tetrahedron can be determined by the formula:

$$V = 0.11785D^3$$

The distance between propagules is thus associated with the three-dimensional volume enclosed within the tetrahedron. Now let the distance between spores be reduced to $\frac{1}{2}$ the original, or $D/2$. Using the equation for the volume of the tetrahedron with the edges representing the distance between spores (in this case $D/2$) the volume would be:

$$V = 0.11785 \ (D/2)^3$$
$$= \frac{0.11785D^3}{8}$$

Thus, the volume has been reduced to $\frac{1}{8}$ of its original size by decreasing the distance between propagules by $\frac{1}{2}$; or 8 times the number of spores must be added to a constant volume to decrease the distance between them by $\frac{1}{2}$. It should also follow that the effective distance between inoculum and root or underground stem is decreased by the same factor. Thus in a hypothetical system, with the surface of the root essentially a plane inserted in the soil, an 8-fold increase in number of propagules would result in only a 2-fold increase in units touching the plane; if propagules were induced to germinate in the rhizoplane only, doubling of successful infections would require 8 times the amount of inoc-

ulum. This relation between the propagules and infection can be expressed:

$$D = k(I)^{1/3}$$

where D is the theoretical successful infection resulting in disease, k the constant of proportionality, and I is the inoculum density, or number of propagules. The slope of the curve resulting when D is plotted against I is constantly changing but can be determined at any single point by the equation:

$$\text{slope} = \frac{k}{3(I)^{2/3}}$$

For a linear relation between the number of infections and units of inoculum, log D can be plotted against log I, or

$$\log D = 1/3 \log I + \log k$$

where log $D = y$, log $I = x$, and log $k = c$; the equation for the straight line is:

$$y = 1/3 \ x + c$$

The graph of this equation has a slope of 1/3 and crosses the y axis at point c.

Alternatively, the root could be considered as exuding substances capable of promoting germination of propagules and probably furnishing directional stimulus. Thus the volume of influence (the rhizosphere) would be in the form of a hollow cylinder. In a hypothetical system reducing the distance between spores by $\frac{1}{2}$ would add 8 times as many units in this volume and increase energy by this factor. In this instance, increase of 8 times the inoculum should increase infection 8 times, and the slope of the curve should be 1.

Critical experiments establishing the relations mentioned above should yield interesting information on the influence of the root on inoculum.

Does a propagule, awaiting the presence of a suitable host substrate, merely lie dormant losing energy until senility and death finally call it to its mycological heaven?

Certainly many dormant structures can germinate in the presence of substrates other than the host (Martinson and Horner, 1962; Schroth and Hendrix, 1962; Schroth and Snyder, 1961). In many cases, these may form more resting structures after a brief period of activity. Thus inoculum density can be maintained or can even increase.

Preliminary studies may suggest a more subtle method whereby propagules may increase their energy level over long periods of time without germination and active growth. There is good evidence that many propagules in the soil require at least a carbon and nitrogen source for germination (Cochrane, 1958). It has also been established that the soil solution is capable of supplying these requirements for germination if fungistasis is removed (Griffin, 1962b). There are exceptions to this, as when nitrogen immobilization occurs owing to incorporation of amendments with a high C:N ratio; but the soil solution in "normal" equilibrium is not a barren desert devoid of sources of nutrients.

If conidia of *Fusarium solani* f. *phaseoli* are washed and placed in distilled water containing 300 ppm sucrose, they do not germinate, since other nutritional factors are required. There is oxygen uptake, however, and after 12 hours, a pigment having properties of anthocyanin is produced in the medium (Griffin, 1962*b*). The spores also stain more intensely with Sudan III, indicating an increase in lipid synthesis. Translating this to what actually occurs in soil would certainly be speculative at this point, but it may be postulated that propagules do not remain dormant in the soil slowly losing potential. They cannot germinate because of fungistatic factors, but some may be able to accumulate energy from nutrient sources in the soil solution over long periods of time. Demonstration of increased inoculum potential due to treatment in vitro with carbon sources as above may be relatively easy with sensitive materials and methods; development of experimental evidence of the situation as it occurs in soil is likely to be more difficult.

There is evidence indicating that different reproductive units of the same fungus may contain different potentials for inducing disease. Prasad (1949) and Sims (1960) have noticed differences in virulence following culture of pathogens on various vitamin-amended substrates. Variations in available carbon and nitrogen, however, are most likely in soils. D. J. Phillips (unpublished data) has demonstrated that disease severity resulting from inoculation with conidia of *Fusarium roseum* f. *cerealis* grown on media low in carbon was significantly lower than with propagules produced with high carbon. In these experiments inoculum variation was carefully controlled with respect to density, viability, and mutation. Thus the conidia produced by substrates high in available carbon apparently contained more energy for colonization of the host. Again, Isaac (1957) found that isolates of *Verticillium* grown on media adequately supplied with sodium nitrate induced wilt more rapidly in *Antirrhinum* than nitrogen-starved isolates.

With an appreciation of the zymogenous characteristics of many of the commonly occurring soil pathogens, researchers have begun to concentrate efforts on studies of spore germination in soil. The discovery of a fungistatic factor in soil (Dobbs and Hinson, 1953) contributed significantly to the knowledge of fundamental ecological relations. There are conflicting views of the mechanisms involved in this phenomenon (Griffin, 1962*a,b*; Lingappa and Lockwood, 1961), but there is no doubt that the level of nutrients in the soil must increase or the level of fungistatic materials must fall below a certain point before germination of the propagules of many species occurs. The addition of energy sources such as residues (Dobbs and Hinson, 1953; Stover, 1958) or plant exudates (Jackson, 1957; Schroth and Snyder, 1961) provides an increase in nutrients sufficient for germination. If fungistasis is related to the constant renewal and accumulation of low levels of metabolic products of the soil microflora (Griffin, 1962*a*), in time the concentration of these materials might increase, especially in the vicinity of

substrates (Brian, 1960) so that a higher nutrient level is needed to promote germination and growth.

Once the propagule of the pathogen has germinated, subsequent adventures may modify its energy and thus its ability to induce infection. In the presence of residues or nonhost tissue, it may form more units such as chlamydospores (Schroth and Hendrix, 1962) or sclerotia (Martinson and Horner, 1962). Alternatively, lysis may occur (Burke, 1956) dropping the potential to 0.

If the exudates from a suitable host have induced germination, there is, of course, possibility for successful penetration and infection, and return to dormancy is delayed until the host tissue has been colonized for some time (Christou and Snyder, 1962). As the organism approaches the surface of the host, however, a great many factors augmenting or inhibiting its progress are operating. Energy is being expended in respiration, and antagonism from other organisms depresses inoculum potential. Nutrients from substrates and host exudates compensate, at least in part. Penetration and infection may require differentiated structures such as formation of infection cushions and hyphal pegs (Kerr and Flentje, 1957; Christou and Snyder, 1962). There is evidence that success requires at least suitable carbon and nitrogen sources in some cases (Toussoun, Nash, and Snyder, 1960).

The pathogen is at the surface of its host. This is one of the most important moments in the development of the disease from the arrival of inoculum in the infection court to the final development of symptoms. At this point the biological energy available is the culmination of a dynamic process involving the genetic and nutritional status of the thallus modified by the environment and the density of the inoculum. Future work evaluating these processes and establishing fundamental concepts based on energy for the potential of pathogens to invade host tissue should prove to be of great value. Additional research establishing quantitative relations will furnish the basis for work on biometrics and physical models providing or greatly clarifying fundamental and unifying concepts in the field of biology.

ACKNOWLEDGMENTS.—For critical and helpful discussion of the topics covered in this paper, I wish to thank the following: Douglas J. Phillips, Donald Lindsey, Charlie Martinson, and Gary Griffin. Appreciation is also expressed to Charles Maurer for assistance in preparing figures and Jon Dodson and G. M. Angleton for aid in mathematical computations.

LITERATURE CITED

AINSWORTH, G. C., and G. R. BISBY. 1950. A dictionary of the fungi. Butler & Tanner, Ltd., Frome and London. 447 p.

BAKER, R. R. 1957. Comparative studies on the resistance of two carnation varieties to Fusarium stem rot. (Abstr.) Phytopathology 47: 3.

BRIAN, P. W. 1960. Antagonistic and competitive mechanisms limiting survival and activity of fungi in soil. p. 168-188. *In* D. Parkinson and J. S. Waid [ed.], The ecology of soil fungi, Liverpool University Press, Liverpool.

BURKE, D. W. 1956. Soil microflora relationships in the

development of bean root rot in Columbia basin soils. Ph.D. thesis, Washington State University.

CHI, C. C., and E. W. HANSEN. 1962. Interrelated effects of environment and age of alfalfa and red clover seedlings on susceptibility to *Pythium debaryanum*. Phytopathology 52: 985-989.

CHRISTOU, T., and W. C. SNYDER. 1962. Penetration and host-parasite relationships of *Fusarium solani* f. *phaseoli* in the bean plant. Phytopathology 52: 219-226.

COCHRANE, V. W. 1958. Physiology of fungi. John Wiley & Sons, Inc., New York. 524 p.

DAGGS, R. G., and H. S. HALCRO-WARDLAW. 1933. The conversion of fat to carbohydrate in the germinating castor bean. II. The combustion respiratory quotient as determined by a modified oxycalorimeter. J. Gen. Physiol. 17: 303-309.

DIMOND, A. E., and J. G. HORSFALL. 1960. Inoculum and the diseased population. vol. 3, p. 1-22. *In* J. G. Horsfall and A. E. Dimond [ed.], Plant pathology, an advanced treatise, Academic Press, New York and London.

DOBBS, C. G., and W. H. HINSON. 1953. A widespread fungistasis in soils. Nature (London) 172: 197-199.

GARRETT, S. D. 1956. Biology of root-infecting fungi. Cambridge University Press, London and New York. 292 p.

GARRETT, S. D. 1960. Inoculum potential. vol. 3, p. 23-56. *In* J. G. Horsfall and A. E. Dimond [ed.], Plant pathology, an advanced treatise, Academic Press, New York and London.

GRAINGER, J. 1956. Host nutrition and attack by fungal parasites. Phytopathology 46: 445-456.

GRIFFIN, G. J. 1962a. Production of a fungistatic effect by soil microflora in autoclaved soil. Phytopathology 52: 90-91.

GRIFFIN, G. J. 1962b. Physiological studies of conidial germination in soil. Ph.D. thesis, Colorado State University.

HORSFALL, J. G., and R. W. BARRATT. 1945. An improved grading system for measuring plant diseases. (Abstr.) Phytopathology 35: 655.

ISAAC, IVOR. 1957. The effects of nitrogen supply upon Verticillium wilt of Antirrhinum. Ann. Appl. Biol. 45: 513-515.

JACKSON, R. M. 1957. Fungistasis as a factor in the rhizosphere phenomenon. Nature (London) 180: 96-97.

JENKINS, S. F., JR. 1962. Preliminary studies for estimating the disease potential of *Phytophthora parasitica* var. *nicotianae* in infested tobacco soils. Plant Disease Reptr. 46: 825-826.

JONES, L. R., J. JOHNSON, and J. G. DICKSON. 1926. Wisconsin studies upon the relation of soil temperature to plant disease. Wisconsin Agr. Expt. Sta. Bull. 71, 144 p.

KERR, A., and N. T. FLENTJE. 1957. Host infection in *Pellicularia filamentosa* controlled by chemical stimuli. Nature (London) 179: 204-205.

KING, J. R., and D. S. FARMER. 1961. Energy metabolism, thermo regulation and body temperature. vol. 2, p. 215-288. *In* A. J. Marshall [ed.], Biology and comparative physiology of birds, Marshall Academic Press, New York.

KOTOWSKI, F. 1927. Temperature relations to germination of vegetable seed. Proc. Am. Soc. Hort. Sci. 23: 176-184.

LEACH, L. D. 1947. Growth rates of host and pathogen as factors determining the severity of pre-emergence damping-off. J. Agr. Res. 75: 161-179.

LEACH, L. D., and A. E. DAVEY. 1938. Determining the sclerotial production of *Sclerotium rolfsii* by soil analysis and predicting losses of sugar beets on the basis of these analyses. J. Agr. Res. 56: 619-631.

LIFSON, N., G. B. GORDON, and R. MCCLINTOCK. 1955. Measurement of total carbon dioxide by means of D_2O^{18}. J. Appl. Physiol. 7: 704-710.

LINGAPPA, B. T., and J. L. LOCKWOOD. 1961. The nature of the widespread soil fungistasis. J. Gen. Microbiol. 26: 473-485.

LUKE, H. H., and P. L. PFAHLER. 1962. Quantitative measurement of host-pathogen interactions. Phytopathology 52: 340-343.

MACFARLANE, I. 1952. Factors affecting the survival of *Plasmodiophora brassicae* Wor. in the soil and its assessment by a host test. Ann. Appl. Biol. 39: 239-256.

MACWITHEY, H. S. 1961. *In vitro* inoculation of sugar beet seedlings with *Aphanomyces cochlioides* Drechs. J. Am. Soc. Sugar Beet Technologists. 11: 309-312.

MACWITHEY, H. S. 1963. The relationship of exposure time to Aphanomyces inoculum and the age of the sugar beet seedling to symptom severity and subsequent growth. J. Am. Soc. Sugar Beet Technologists 11: 309-312.

MAGEE, J. L., T. W. DEWITT, E. C. SMITH, and F. DANIELS. 1939. A photocalorimeter. The quantum efficiency of photosynthesis in algae. J. Am. Chem. Soc. 61: 3529-3533.

MALOY, O. C., and M. ALEXANDER. 1958. The "most probable number" method for estimating populations of plant pathogenic organisms in the soil. Phytopathology 48: 126-128.

MARTINSON, C. A. 1959. Inoculum potential studies of *Rhizoctonia solani*. M.Sc. thesis, Colorado State University.

MARTINSON, C. A. 1963. Inoculum potential relationships of *Rhizoctonia solani* measured with soil microbiological sampling tubes. Phytopathology 53: 634-638.

MARTINSON, C., and R. BAKER. 1962. Increasing relative frequency of specific fungus isolations with soil microbiological sampling tubes. Phytopathology 52: 619-621.

MARTINSON, C. A., and C. E. HORNER. 1962. Importance of non-hosts in maintaining the inoculum potential of Verticillium. (Abstr.) Phytopathology 52: 742.

MCCLINTOCK, R., and N. LIFSON. 1958. Determination of the total carbon dioxide outputs of rats by the D_2O^{18} method. Am. J. Physiol. 192: 76-78.

NADAKAVUKAREN, M. J., and C. E. HORNER. 1959. An alcohol agar medium selective for determining Verticillium microsclerotia in soil. Phytopathology 49: 527-528.

NASH, SHIRLEY M., and W. C. SNYDER. 1962. Quantitative estimations by plate counts of propagules of the bean root rot Fusarium in field soils. Phytopathology 52: 567-572.

NASH, SHIRLEY M., T. CHRISTOU, and W. C. SNYDER. 1961. Existence of *Fusarium solani* f. *phaseoli* as chlamydospores in soil. Phytopathology 51: 308-312.

PAPAVIZAS, G. C., and C. B. DAVEY. 1959. Isolation of *Rhizoctonia solani* Kühn from naturally infested and artificially inoculated soils. Plant Disease Reptr. 43: 404-410.

PETERSEN, L. J. 1959. Relations between inoculum density and infection of wheat by uredospores of *Puccinia graminis* var. *tritici*. Phytopathology 49: 607-614.

PHILLIPS, D. J. 1962. Histochemical and morphological studies of carnation stem rot. Phytopathology 52: 323-328.

PRASAD, N. 1949. Variability of the cucurbit root-rot fungus, *Fusarium (Hypomyces) solani* f. *cucurbitae*. Phytopathology 39: 133-141.

RAABE, R. D., W. A. KREUTZER, S. WILHELM, and E. K. VAUGHAN. 1962. "What do we mean"—a panel discussion, p. 9-11. *In* Proc. of 9th Annual Conf. on the Control of Soil Fungi. San Francisco. (Mimeo.)

REILING, T. P., T. H. KING, and R. W. FIELDS. 1960. Soil indexing for pea root rot and the effect of root rot on yield. Phytopathology 50: 287-290.

SCHROTH, M. N., and F. F. HENDRIX, JR. 1962. Influence of nonsusceptible plants on the survival of *Fusarium solani* f. *phaseoli* in soil. Phytopathology 52: 906-909.

SCHROTH, M. N., and W. C. SNYDER. 1961. Effect of host exudates on chlamydospore germination of the bean root rot fungus, *Fusarium solani* f. *phaseoli*. Phytopathology 51: 389-393.

SCHWINGHAMER, E. A. 1956. Physiologic specialization in *Colletotrichum linicolum*. Phytopathology 46: 300-305.

SIMS, A. C., JR. 1960. Effect of culture substrate on the virulence of single-basidiospore isolates of *Pellicularia filamentosa*. Phytopathology 50: 282-286.

STOVER, R. H. 1958. Studies of Fusarium wilt of bananas. III. Influence of soil fungitoxins on behavior of *F. oxysporum* f. *cubense* in soil extracts and diffusates. Can. J. Botany 36: 439-453.

Toussoun, T. A., Shirley M. Nash, and W. C. Snyder. 1960. The effect of nitrogen sources and glucose on the pathogenesis of *Fusarium solani* f. *phaseoli*. Phytopathology 50: 137-140.

Tsao, P. H. 1960. A serial dilution end-point method for estimating disease potentials of citrus phytophthoras in soil. Phytopathology 50: 717-724.

Wheeler, H. E. 1953. Detection of microbial toxins by the use of radioisotopes. Phytopathology 43: 236-238.

Whetzel, H. H., L. R. Hesler, C. T. Gregory, and W. H. Rankin. 1925. Laboratory outlines in plant pathology. 2nd ed. W. B. Saunders, Philadelphia. 231 p.

Wilhelm, S. 1951. Effect of various soil amendments on the inoculum potential of the Verticillium wilt fungus. Phytopathology 41: 684-690.

Worf, G. L., and D. J. Hagedorn. 1961. A technique for studying relative soil populations of two Fusarium pathogens of garden peas. Phytopathology 51: 805-806.

[*For discussion of Ralph Baker's paper, see the discussion following the A. E. Dimond and J. G. Horsfall paper*]

The Theory of Inoculum

A. E. DIMOND and J. G. HORSFALL—*Department of Plant Pathology and Botany, The Connecticut Agricultural Experiment Station, New Haven.*

▶

Inoculum is of interest to us because it is capable of producing disease. Our assignment is to deal with the quantitative aspects of inoculum, to discuss principles, to relate these principles to one another, and to suggest new approaches. We hope that this will encourage some investigators to think further about the subject.

To deal with the inoculum of soil-borne pathogens in a quantitative way is a challenge. With air-borne pathogens, one can estimate inoculum by trapping spores. With soil-borne pathogens, estimation is very difficult. With air-borne pathogens, one can apply inoculum directly to the host surface and measure the quantitative relation between inoculum density and disease production. With soil-borne pathogens, the experiment is more difficult. With air-borne inoculum, the interaction with other microflora is usually small. With soil-borne inoculum, this interaction is the essence of antibiosis. With air-borne inoculum, a reasonably satisfactory theory exists for predicting the distribution of inoculum. We know that this same theory is inapplicable to soil-borne pathogens and at present we have no satisfactory alternative theory to account for the distribution of inoculum in soils. Yet soil- and air-borne pathogens have many similarities.

THE ORGANIZATION OF INOCULUM INTO UNITS.— Inoculum is viable material of any nature that can infect a host. Inoculum may also serve to produce more inoculum, whether or not disease intervenes. The form and state of inoculum govern how long it persists, how much of it is germinable at any time, how well it resists adversity, and how efficient it is in producing infection.

A unit of inoculum is simply the parcel in which viability is dispersed. In multicellular units, inoculum may be more efficient in surviving, in the storage and use of food materials, and in producing infections. Studies by Isaac and MacGarvie (1962) present evidence for the division of function of microsclerotial cells of *Verticillium dahliae*, some but not all being able to germinate. Garrett (1956a), in discussing sclerotia, has noted the specialization of cellular function. In many sclerotia the outer cells form a rind that has a protective function. Presley (1939) also has noted beneath the rind in the sclerotia of many fungi the specialized cells that have a germinative function. By contrast, all cells of the sclerotia of *Phymatotrichum*

omnivorum are capable of germination. Sclerotia represent an organizational economy that is efficient in the storage and use of foods. Ergle and Blank (1947) demonstrated that the sclerotia of *P. omnivorum* store about half of their dry weight as carbohydrate, double the quantity present in mycelium.

The rhizomorph illustrates the effectiveness of organizing individual strands into groups. Garrett (1956a) points to the significance of mycelial aggregation. The translocative function of the rhizomorph is an obvious consequence of the necessity for attachment to a food base if the rhizomorph is successfully to infect its host (Bliss, 1941; Garrett, 1956a).

We can estimate the advantage of mycelial aggregation, considered as a protective function. This can be done by calculating the surface exposed by a rhizomorph to that exposed by the same number of mycelial strands. The ratio of surface to volume in the rhizomorph at varying degrees of complexity of organization is another index of the advantage of aggregation. These two ratios prove to be almost identical and decrease steadily as rhizomorphs increase in complexity (Table 1). In a complex rhizomorph, the surface exposed per

TABLE 1. Surface relations of rhizomorphs and individual mycelial strands

Number of strands	Ratio of surfaces, rhizomorph:mycelium*
1	1.00
7	0.57
19	0.37
37	0.27
61	0.21
91	0.18
397	0.08
1,657	0.04

* The corresponding surface:volume ratios per unit length for rhizomorphs are only slightly lower.

unit length may be 1/25th of that exposed by naked mycelium.

The organization of inoculum into more complex units can be advantageous in other ways. In a cluster of cells, the inner ones are protected against toxic materials and drought, and when a single germ tube is produced, adjacent cells may contribute to its development. When a multicellular unit of inoculum produces several germ tubes, these together will produce more of an enzyme needed for invasion of the host than a single cell. In this circumstance the defense of the host must be that much more efficient if infection is to be prevented. These are numerical aspects of the concept of energy that Garrett (1956a, 1956b, 1960) has associated with the term inoculum potential.

THE QUANTITY OF INOCULUM.—*Multiplication of inoculum.*—Logarithmic nature of reproduction.— Inoculum presents a hazard to the host according to its abundance, other things being equal. When a bacterium divides, it produces two offspring, and these by division produce four. This is an example of logarithmic growth. When a fungus spore infects the host and produces a crop of spores in the lesion, and when these spores reinfect and produce yet another crop of spores, the increase in inoculum is also logarithmic. As a specific example, Lin (1939) determined the average number of pycnidiospores in a pycnidium of *Septoria apii* as 3,675 and the average number of pycnidia per lesion as 56. Thus, some 200,000 spores are formed in a single lesion, and each of these is potentially capable of producing a like number of spores on reinfecting a population of host leaves. Even if the majority of spores fail to produce new lesions, the increase in inoculum is logarithmic.

Such a process of increase can be expressed in exponential form as $I = I_0 e^{rt}$ or in logarithmic form as $\log I = \log I_0 + rt, \log_e 10$ in which I is the amount of inoculum at time t, I_0 is the amount initially present, and r is the rate of multiplication. The second equation is in linear form, that is, the logarithm of I plotted against t gives a straight line. The position of the line is determined by $\log I_0$ and the slope of the line is $2.3 r$. Thus the slope is a measure of the rate of multiplication, the proportional increase in the population per unit of time.

Changes in the environment will alter the value of r, which may be large in a favorable situation or small in a poor one. When the environment is very poor, r may have a negative value and the amount of inoculum decreases with time. This is what happens in the field when *Phytophthora infestans* encounters hot, dry weather. The amount of inoculum decreases logarithmically.

Multiplication of Inoculum in Nonpathogenic Lesions.—The formation of lesions on host tissue serves to supply energy to mycelium and to increase the amount of inoculum. The amount of inoculum available influences the chance of infection in a new area and the survival of inoculum until a new susceptible crop is planted. Apparently, soil-borne pathogens sometimes form lesions without producing significant damage to the host, that is, they can be parasitic without being pathogenic. Thus, Webb (1949) found zoosporangia, probably of *Plasmodiophora brassicae*, developing in root hairs of noncrucifers. Martinson and Horner (1962) have demonstrated that new microsclerotia are produced by *Verticillium* in a soil on the roots of plants that are not hosts. This evidence aids in accounting for Wilhelm's (1955) finding *Verticillium* in field soils for 14 years after a known host had been planted, and Presley's (1950) finding *Verticillium* in virgin soils

where no cultivated crops had been grown. Wilhelm's (1956) sand-culture technique for isolation of fungi associated with roots has proved helpful in studying this relation.

The Law of Lesion Size.—Van der Plank (1960) has discussed the importance of the multiplication rate of inoculum in the development of disease. The size of a lesion is related to the potential rate of multiplication of inoculum. When lesions are small and remain localized, the pathogen generally fruits in a short time, but when a lesion occupies the entire plant, as it does in a systemic disease, inoculum multiplies more slowly. When lesions are small, infections can occur repeatedly through successive cycles in a growing season, and the amount of inoculum can then increase prodigiously. Van der Plank (1959, 1960) has expressed this relation as the law of lesion size, according to which the highest potential multiplication rates are possessed by pathogens that produce small lesions. We need think only of late blight and wheat rust in contrast with Dutch elm disease and oak wilt to illustrate this principle. It is the same with soil-borne pathogens: that of root knot versus those of verticillial or fusarial wilt. The lesion of root knot is small; that of fusarial wilt involves the entire plant. The multiplication rate of *Meloidogyne* is high; that of *Fusarium* is low, relatively speaking. But here arises an interesting matter.

The dispersal of soil-borne pathogens is restricted. In the soil, nothing comparable to eddy diffusion aids dispersal of spores, and only conduction of inoculum can function to extend its range. Conductive processes include the transport of inoculum in water, and the growth of mycelium or rhizomorph through soil, or the corresponding growth of host roots toward inoculum, followed by growth of inoculum over the surface of host roots in the rhizosphere.

Dispersal by water, not on but within the soil, is probably not very efficient. If growth is a principal means of dispersal in the soil, then the production of local lesions serves no purpose subsequently in dispersal of the inoculum produced there, but only provides a food base for mycelium and increases the abundance of inoculum at a point. The fungus pathogens that form small local lesions in which multiplication of inoculum can occur rapidly are air-borne. The infrequency of local lesion formation by soil-borne pathogens, in the sense of the law of lesion size, is probably significant. Local lesions serve no purpose in the dispersal of propagules. The local lesions associated with damping-off are no exception because the lesions are nonrecurrent through the growing season. But because *Meloidogyne* is locomotive, lesion formation is a step in dispersal. This may be the reason why the nematodes provide the best examples of soil-borne pathogens that form local lesions.

The longevity of inoculum.—Dormancy.—We may define dormancy as the result of intrinsic factors and fungistasis as the result of external factors that postpone the time when germination and growth occur readily. The causes of dormancy are varied and have been discussed by Sussman in this symposium and by

Gottlieb (1950) and Cochrane (1958), and the principles involved in fungistasis have been discussed by Lockwood earlier in this symposium. At the moment, however, we are not so much concerned with the causes of dormancy and fungistasis as their effects, which Garrett (1944, 1956a) has recognized and discussed.

Dormancy increases the longevity of inoculum and its resistance to toxic materials. When a population of propagules loses its dormancy, it does so irregularly, and causes infections over a longer time than nondormant inoculum. Thus, the net effect of dormancy is to reduce the danger to a crop at any given time but to prolong the time over which danger exists. In a population of propagules, dormancy increases both resistance and variability of resistance to toxic agents. This reduces our control over inoculum at any given time and makes it necessary that our control measures be exerted over a longer time. Both of these effects are disadvantageous in the control of soil-borne pathogens.

To overcome these effects, dormancy must be broken. The principles involved can be illustrated from the work of Miller and Stoddard (1958) on the tobacco-cyst nematode. Cysts of this nematode are highly resistant to nematocides and persist in the soil for a long time. Miller and Stoddard have found that a variety of compounds, among them nabam and zineb, break the dormancy and promote the hatching of eggs. This causes the inoculum to be more vulnerable to soil fumigation. To the extent that nabam acts uniformly upon the population of propagules, it reduces its longevity and thereby reduces the period necessary for crop rotation. When nabam is applied to an infested soil that is cropped with tobacco, the population of cyst nematodes increases rapidly. When nabam is applied in the absence of a host, the amount of inoculum in the subsequent season is reduced. When nabam is applied and the field is subsequently fumigated, the inoculum is drastically reduced. These same principles may be useful in control of dormant inoculum of other soil-borne pathogens when dormancy can be broken by chemical means.

Survival of Inoculum.—In discussing the multiplication of inoculum in lesions, we saw that the multiplication rate may become negative in a poor environment. When this happens, inoculum decreases. Spores in the population die faster than new ones are formed. Thus, when inoculum in the soil cannot reproduce, it dies with the passage of time; the equation describing the survival of inoculum is still $\log I = \log I_o + rt \log_e 10$, but r is now negative in value and describes the rate of death. This relation can also be expressed as $\log (I/I_o) = 2.3\ rt$. The right-hand side of the equation is negative, I/I_o is the proportion of survivors, and its logarithm is proportional to time as well as the rate of death.

Rahn (1945) has presented the argument and a body of evidence for a logarithmic order of survival of bacteria. The inactivation rate of viruses also closely approximates this law. The death of *Plasmodiophora*

brassicae in the soil also occurs logarithmically, so that a few propagules persist for a long time (Macfarlane, 1952).

The half-life of inoculum has been proposed to measure its longevity by Yarwood and Sylvester (1959). The half-life concept implies a logarithmic rate of death of the population. The half-life, the time required for half of the inoculum to die, can be obtained graphically by plotting values of I/I_o on semilog paper against t and noting the time corresponding to a survival of half of the population. The half-life of inoculum can also be calculated from the standard equation when the death rate is a constant, but use of the equation to calculate the half-life of inoculum can be misleading because variations in the death rate will pass unnoticed.

In fact, when organisms are complex, the death rate is not a constant. Death begins only after a lapse of time. Then, at some time after the onset of death, r becomes a constant. An example (Fig. 1) is the killing

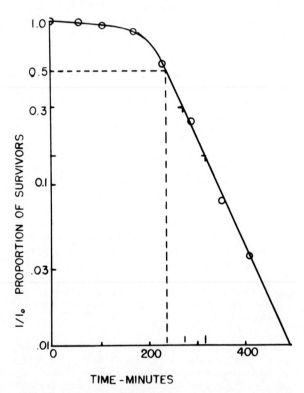

Fig. 1. The killing of *Botrytis cinerea* spores at 37°C (data from Smith, 1923). For explanation see text.

of *Botrytis cinerea* spores by heat (Smith, 1923). In this case, presumably, the departure from a constant death rate arises from the multinuclear nature of the spores. If a spore survives after the destruction of one or more nuclei, the lag represents the time required to inactivate a number of nuclei before the number of nuclei remaining limits germination.

In practice, when the half-life of such inoculum is determined, allowance must be made for this lag before dying begins. The half-life of *Botrytis* spores at 37°C proves to be some 235 min when the graphic method is used and some 45 min after the death rate becomes constant (Fig. 1). The latter, 45 min, is the value obtained by use of the standard equation. To ignore the initial lag would have practical consequences. Suppose, for example, that one used the relation that after 10 half-lives the viable inoculum remaining would be reduced to approximately 0.1% of the initial amount. The calculated value of 45 min would suggest that there would be 0.1% of survivors after 450 min. When one allows for the initial lag, the answer is 640 min. In reality, after 450 min there would be some 1.6% survivors instead of 0.1%. In a practical situation, where rotation practice was based on calculations of this sort, the error would result in readily observable differences in rate of reinfestation of the field because there would be some 16 times as much viable inoculum as had been estimated.

When units of inoculum are multicellular, a departure from a constant death rate can be expected. The death of one or more cells of the unit of inoculum obviously does not destroy its viability, and when the cells comprising the unit are also multinuclear, the lag can be expected to be greater still.

Experimental data exist to illustrate this idea. Wyckoff and Rivers (1930) irradiated bacteria on nutrient agar plates immediately after seeding and another group after they had an opportunity to multiply to aggregates of from four to sixteen cells. When counts of survivors were appropriately plotted against time of irradiation, the survival curve was linear for the first group, but in the second, the curve showed the lag before the onset of death that is characteristic of a complex system. We may conclude, then, that for multicellular inoculum, the departure from a constant death rate may extend into the region of 50% survival and make the determination of half-life a difficult matter, except when graphical methods are used.

In passing, we may note that the lag before dying begins is characteristic of multicellular units of inoculum. This is an illustration of the greater survival value of inoculum organized into multicellular units. The data of King and Eaton (1934) on sclerotia of the cotton-root-rot pathogen and of Isaac and Heale (1961) on *Verticillium albo-atrum* illustrate this principle at work in a rough way.

The half-life concept is a better way of looking at the survival of inoculum of soil-borne pathogens than has been used in the past, but it is not a foolproof procedure. When inoculum is multinucleate or multicellular, departures from a logarithmic law of survival may be expected and half-life may not bear a constant relation to quarter-life.

The extinction of inoculum.—The rate of reproduction and the rate of death of inoculum taken together determine how successful a population of inoculum may become. Multiplication and death proceed simultaneously in a real world. The problem of extinction is familiar to us all in terms of the chance that the name of a family will not die out. Waggoner (1962) has dealt with this matter in relation to inoculum.

Three matters are critical in determining the outcome. First is the number of spores, the quantity of inoculum present, I_0. Second is the probability, P_0, that this inoculum will fail to multiply. The probability that it will succeed is $1 - P_0$. Finally, the number of offspring, m, of a parent that has any children is critical, or, in our case, the number of spores produced in a lesion. The factor $m(1 - P_0)$ corresponds to I/I_0 for a single generation in the equation of growth. In terms of survival of a family name, these factors correspond to how many males there are with the surname Smith; of these, what proportion fail to have children; and how many children are there in the average family of the Smiths that do have children. The product $m(1 - P_0)$ gives the average change in population per generation, and if this product is less than 1, extinction is certain to occur, perhaps not at once, but eventually. When the product is greater than 1, the probability of extinction decreases, especially as I_0 increases (Table 2).

TABLE 2. The probability of extinction of inoculum*
(The probability that a line of inoculum will be extinguished when there are I_0 spores, which fail to multiply with a probability P_0, or succeed, giving an m-fold increase)

Multipli- cation, m	Initial number of spores, I_0				
	1	2	4	16	256
$P_0 = 0.75$					
$\leqslant 4$	1.00	1.00	1.00	1.00	1.00
5	0.89	0.79	0.63	0.16	<0.01
7	0.80	0.64	0.41	0.03	<0.01
∞	0.75	0.56	0.32	0.01	<0.01
$P_0 = 0.9$					
$\leqslant 10$	1.00	1.00	1.00	1.00	1.00
11	0.97	0.94	0.89	0.61	<0.01
16	0.92	0.85	0.72	0.26	<0.01
∞	0.90	0.81	0.65	0.18	<0.01

* From: P. E. Waggoner. Phytopathology 52: 1100-1108.

The pertinence of this matter for soil-borne pathogens is obvious. Infection centers may frequently fail to persist in an inhospitable soil, and a massive inoculum is but one way in which extinction can be avoided. The spores of some soil-borne pathogens are found in the air. How frequently do these establish new, persistent centers of infection? In this case, the initial number of spores, I_0, that land at a site is likely to be low, their chance of failure to multiply, P_0, is usually high, and only a large value of m, the multiplication factor, will permit the colony to persist. On this basis, one might expect that the contribution of air-borne inoculum to persistent outbreaks of soil-borne pathogens would be small; such outbreaks probably occur, but persist infrequently. Quite obviously, the concept of extinction applies to ship-borne, plow-borne, and transplant-borne colonists as well, and their eventual success is determined by the factors already discussed.

INOCULUM AND DISEASE.—*Inoculum density relations.*—We have discussed variations in the quantity of inoculum, apart from the host plant, but inoculum is important because it produces disease. In general we know that in a favorable environment, the amount of disease increases as inoculum increases. But only in exceptional cases is there a direct proportionality between these two variables.

The Semilogarithmic Transformation.—To analyze the situation, let us examine a model in a form modified from that given by Youden, Beale, and Guthrie (1935). A bacterial suspension is prepared, containing x bacteria in N ml, and 1-ml samples are transferred into each of N petri dishes. Each sample is mixed with nutrient agar and incubated. After a suitable time, the number of sterile plates, z, is counted. The proportion of sterile plates, z/N, depends on the average number of bacteria per sample, x/N, according to the relation

$$z/N = e^{-x/N} \qquad (1)$$

In logarithmic form, this equation is $\log z = \log N - 2.3\, x/N$, where 2.3 equals $\log_e 10$. Thus, when $\log z$ is plotted against x, the relation is linear with a negative slope equal to $-2.3/N$ (Fig. 2). In this model, healthy plants can be equated to sterile plates and diseased plants to plates bearing colonies.

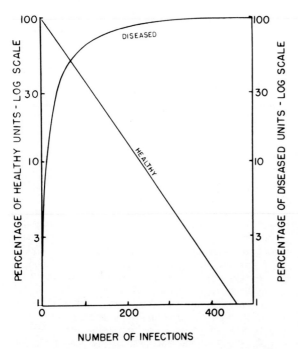

Fig. 2. Relation between logarithms of percentage of diseased units and number of infections, and relation between logarithms of percentage of healthy units and number of infections.

Alternatively, we may count the number of plates, y, that contain bacterial colonies and determine the proportion, y/N, that are not sterile. If the proportion of sterile plates equals $e^{-x/N}$, then the proportion that is not sterile is $1 - e^{-x/N}$, and this gives the equation

$$y/N = 1 - e^{-x/N} \qquad (2)$$

Unlike the proportion of sterile plates, the proportion of nonsterile plates bears no simple relation to x, that is, $\log y/N$ is not simply related to x (Fig. 2).

Mathematically, $e^{-x/N}$ can be evaluated by determining the sum of the series

$$e^{-x/N} = 1 - x/N + \frac{x^2 N^2}{2!} - \frac{x^3/N^3}{3!} + \ldots$$

By substituting this sum into equation (2), we obtain

$$y/N = (x/N - \frac{x^2/N^2}{2!} + \frac{x^3/N^3}{3!} - \ldots).$$

When values of x are very small, the second and higher terms of the series can be neglected. Thus, for dilute suspensions,

$$y/N = x/N \qquad \text{or} \quad y = x \qquad (3)$$

This analogy is comparable with the situation when inoculum is distributed at random in a field, and the Poisson distribution applies to multiple infections. N now corresponds to the total number of plots, which may be plants or leaves or unit lengths of root. Corresponding to the number of healthy plots is z, and y is now the number of diseased plots of the same area, so that $z = N - y$. The total inoculum per plot corresponds to the inoculum per petri dish and is x/N. Equations (1) and (2) now apply to the proportion of healthy plants, z/N, and the proportion of diseased ones, y/N. Note that it is the proportion of healthy plants that bears a simple relation exponentially to the amount of inoculum, not the proportion of diseased plants. Equation (3) states that there is a simple relation between the proportion (or number) of diseased plants and the average amount of inoculum when the amount of inoculum is low and less than 10% of the plants are diseased. This treatment implicitly assumes that a single spore can produce an infection.

There are good data to suggest a simple relation between amount of inoculum and number of infections when the amount of inoculum is small. Rowell and Olien (1957) have shown the simple proportionality between number of urediospores deposited on wheat leaves and the number of uredia developing. Further, a linear relation between the logarithm of the concentration of spores applied and the logarithm of the number of lesions developing was shown over a more extended range of spore concentrations by McCallan and Wellman (1943) for early blight, late blight, and *Septoria* leaf spot of tomato and by Last and Hamley (1956) for *Botrytis* on broad bean. Thus the number of lesions that develop can be assumed to be directly related to the amount of inoculum, within limits.

When inoculum is more abundant, the number of infections is not simply related to the number of diseased plants because a plant will become infected a second or a third time but still be counted as merely diseased. This is the multiple-infection problem, discussed by Gregory (1948). When disease is measured as the percentage of diseased plants (or plots), it becomes important to know the number of infections that have taken place. Equation (2) can be expressed explicitly in terms of x in the form

$$x = 2.3 \ N \ [\log \ N - \log \ (N - y)].$$

Gregory (1948) has used this equation to compute the number of infections corresponding to different percentages of plots that are diseased, when N is 100, y is the number of diseased plots, and x is the number of infections. This is the multiple-infection transformation. Its use permits an accurate assessment of the increase in amount of disease with inoculum. By contrast, when data are expressed as percentage of diseased plants, the multiple infections are ignored, and the increase in disease with inoculum is underestimated, except when the proportion of diseased plants is less than 0.1.

The relation upon which the multiple-infection transformation is based can be transposed to $\log \ (N - y) - \log \ N = -x/ \ (2.3 \ N)$, and, remembering that $N - y = z$, the number of healthy plants, and that $\log \ z - \log \ N$ equals z/N, we return to the relation expressed in equation (1) in logarithmic form.

When one uses entire plants as plots, the argument is straightforward. Smaller units, such as leaves or unit lengths of root, may be used as plots, so long as they are of the same size and susceptibility. The number of healthy plots is inversely proportional to inoculum density, and, at low inoculum densities, the number of diseased plots is directly related to inoculum density. As inoculum density increases, the number of multiple infections also increases. As the size of the plot decreases, the problem of multiple infections are fewer for a given inoculum density. At very high inoculum densities, inoculum may compete for a single susceptible site, the minimum unit plot that can be taken. This last case is familiar to virologists, and Youden, Beale, and Guthrie (1935), Bald (1950), and Kleczkowski (1950) have all dealt with the relation between the virus concentration and the number of lesions produced.

The literature contains another suggested relation between the proportion of infected units and the amount of inoculum: that there is a simple linear relation between the logarithm of the percentage of diseased plots and the logarithm of the inoculum density. There is an apparent conflict here. The amount of inoculum obviously cannot be related simply to the proportion of healthy tissue, on the one hand, and the proportion of diseased tissue, on the other. This matter can be resolved if one plots values of the percentage of diseased plots against the amount of inoculum from the multiple-infection transformation on a log-log grid (Fig. 3). Such a plot shows the relation to be neither linear nor simple, but rather that proportions of disease less than 60% deviate from $\log \ y/N = k \ \log \ x/N$ by so small an amount that the deviation is usually undetectable. At very high levels of disease, where multiple infection is high, the deviation from this relation is obvious.

We have assumed by this approach that inoculum is distributed randomly, that multiple infections occur according to a Poisson distribution, and that the susceptibilities of areas are uniform or that their variation

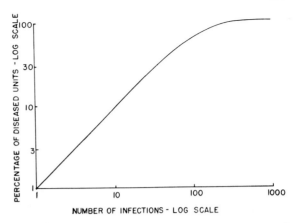

Fig. 3. Relation between logarithm of percentage of diseased units and logarithm of number of infections.

can be ignored. Varying numbers of units of inoculum are assumed to cause a single infection simply because of multiple infections, but potentially one unit of inoculum, or a constant multiple of inoculum units, is assumed to be capable of causing an infection (Kleczkowski, 1950; Druett, 1952; Peto, 1953).

The Logarithmic-Probability Transformation.—Biologists are well aware of the variability of organisms, and to assume that either a population of inoculum is uniform in virulence or a population of infectible sites is uniformly susceptible does violence to their experience. An alternative hypothesis that leads to linear relations between the percentage of healthy units and the amount of inoculum is the logarithmic-probability transformation. According to this idea, subjected many times to experimental test, the susceptibilities in a population are normally distributed in accordance with the logarithm of the dosage of the damaging agent (Finney, 1947; Horsfall, 1956; Wilcoxon and McCallan, 1939; Kleczkowski, 1950). As a consequence, the percentage of survival in probit units is linearly related to the inoculum density when data are plotted on a log-probit grid. Because the ordinate is symmetrical about the ED_{50}, data can be plotted as percentage of healthy units or percentage of diseased units—either leads to a linear relation, but the slope in one case is the reciprocal of the other. The applicability of the log-probit grid to occurrence of plant disease in the field has been shown with fungicidal dosages (Dimond et al., 1941). The relation was also shown to hold for inoculum levels as well as fungicides, using data of Heald (1921) and Twentyman (1931) on spore load of bunt in relation to the percentage of smutted wheat in the field (Dimond et al., 1941).

The results from use of the semilog transformation and the log-probit transformation, both much used in bioassays, have been considered by Peto (1953) in relation to infectious pathogens attacking a host. He concludes that when the amount of inoculum is expressed in multiples of the ED_{50}, the two methods lead to assessments that differ but slightly, and the validity of the two assessments cannot be distinguished without the use of a very large number of host organisms. Peto prefers the semilog transformation because an economy in use of host organisms is possible. Kleczkowski (1950), although recognizing the essential equivalence of the two approaches, considers the assumptions underlying the logarithmic-probability transformation as the more realistic, and so do we.

We may, therefore, add a fourth relation between the percentage of healthy units (or, now, the percentage of diseased units) and the quantity of inoculum, which is

$$\text{probit } z/N \text{ (or probit } y/N) = a \ (\log x) + b, \quad (4)$$

in which a is the slope of the dosage-response curve, and b is the position, commonly measured in terms of ED_{50}. The slope, a, is a measure of the nature of the distribution of susceptibility in the population, and is related to the variability in susceptibility of the population.

Use of the log-probit transformation requires the use of percentages to measure the response of the host unit. As Gregory (1948) has shown, use of percentages leads to artificial flattening of curves because the multiple infections are ignored. Log-probit dosage-response curves are characteristically flat and the multiple infections can be evaluated only by resorting to the semilog transformation!

The Number of Spores Necessary to Produce a Lesion.—Gäumann (1950) defines the numerical threshhold of infection as the number of individual parasites which, under favorable conditions, is necessary to establish infection. On the basis of the foregoing discussion, there are two obvious ways of viewing infection.

According to the ideas behind the semilog transformation, the infectible sites of the host do not vary in susceptibility and the inoculum does not vary in aggressiveness—at least not significantly. According to this view, the numerical threshhold of infection is a single number for each organism and host, frequently 1, and there are many instances in the phytopathological literature where a single propagule has been seen to establish a lesion. Ayers (1944), for example, describes clubroot infection by a single zoospore of *Plasmodiophora*.

But in practice, infection is best thought of as a matter of probability, and the log-probit transformation allows for variation in aggressiveness of the pathogen, and in susceptibility of infectible sites on the host, and also allows for the probability of successful colonization. The number of spores necessary to produce a lesion will vary with circumstances. Thus, Rowell and Olien (1957), under conditions later found suboptimal for infection, obtained one lesion for each 400 urediospores applied to wheat; and McCallan and Wellman (1943) obtained one late-blight lesion per 15.3 spores, one early-blight lesion per 57.4 spores, and one septoria-leaf-blight lesion on tomato per 525 spores. These are all sizable numbers and reflect the distribution of inoculum over many sites that are not susceptible and competition for susceptible sites by more than one unit of inoculum. Glynne (1925) has found that some 231 sporangia per g of soil are necessary to cause infection by the potato-wart organism.

The number of spores required to produce a lesion

may be viewed as an ED_{50} value, the number of inoculum units that will produce a lesion in 50% of the susceptible sites that have been exposed. We shall see later, in discussing measures of inoculum potential, that shifts of ED_{50} values without a shift in slope of log-probit curves of inoculum density and response do, in fact, give a measure of the quantity of inoculum required to produce infection. Rather than setting a "threshhold," we shall simply say that infection is chancy, and many colonists die for each success.

Number of Lesions versus Damage.—A single girdling lesion can kill a plant. A lesion that weakens the plant mechanically can be responsible for lodging and complete loss of the plant in terms of yield. A single systemic lesion often kills a plant. These dramatic examples suggest that there is no regular and quantitative relation between the number of lesions on a plant and the damage done. But estimates of damage are necessary and when lesions are of a like kind, quantitative relations may properly be sought.

Garrett (1956a) has referred to sugar-loving fungi in the soil. These constitute a group in which the lesions are localized and infected tissues apparently suffer more as a result of enzymatic maceration than from toxic materials that derange metabolic processes in a more subtle way. *Rhizoctonia solani* is an example of such a pathogen. Rich and Miller (1963) have counted the number of rhizoctonia fragments adhering to a 5 cm length of root of strawberry plants and related this number to the number of rooted plants at the end of the growing season, including new runner plants. They obtained a highly significant linear regression, whether data were plotted as the number of fragments per unit length of root or their logarithms against the number of plants at the end of the growing season. It was not possible to judge the better method of plotting by goodness of fit, but the two types of plotting led to considerably different estimates of damage at high and at very low levels of infection. As many as 5 fragments per cm of root reduced the number of plants at the end of the season below that at the start and 1 fragment per cm permitted some increase by runners but reduced the expected number. Data of this type will permit us to develop more adequate methods of estimating damage quantitatively in studies on root diseases. With such methods, it will be possible to estimate the amount of inoculum present when the damage and cause are known.

Time relations.—During the course of a season as disease develops in a field, the percentage of disease in probit units is proportional to the time elapsing, as Barratt (1945) and Barratt and Richards (1944) have noted. The reason for this is straightforward. In a favorable environment, inoculum multiplies logarithmically with time, and the logarithm of the inoculum is proportional to time. Thus, disease is related to inoculum density on a log-probit grid and to time on an arithmetic-probit grid. Van der Plank (1960) has presented the data of Large (1945), showing that the relation between percentage of infection and time is a symmetrical, sigmoid curve. The plotting of these same data on an arithmetic-probability grid will convert the curve to a straight linear relation.

Disease gradients.—Random distribution of infections.—The distribution of inoculum can be deduced from disease gradients. The relation between the number of lesions and distance can be expected to vary with the disease, depending on the method of dissemination, which determines the pattern of dispersal. The various relations used to describe disease gradients are partly a reflection of different methods of dispersal, and partly different ways of describing the same relation because of differing hypotheses that have been used for interpretation.

Using a log-probit grid, Zentmyer and his colleagues (Zentmyer, Horsfall, and Wallace, 1943, 1944; Zentmyer, Wallace, and Horsfall, 1946) obtained a linear relation between the percentage of infection and distance for the spread of Dutch elm disease by bark beetles from a single diseased tree as a source. For an insect-borne virus, Frampton, Linn, and Hansing (1942) obtained a linear relation between the distance from the source and the logarithm of the percentage of infection. Wilson and Baker (1946a,b) dealt with the number of infections, rather than the percentage, and, for air-borne spores, related the number of infections inversely as the square of the distance. This involves a negative linear correlation between the logarithm of the frequency of infection and the logarithm of the distance. Wolfenbarger (1946) has assumed that the amount of disease varies with the logarithm of the distance.

Gregory (1945) showed that the dispersal of air-borne spores approximates an inverse power law but that the precise distribution is related to distance in a complex way. The power approaches 2 as air becomes more turbulent. In general, however, the relation is of the same form as that of Wilson and Baker, and the relation is linear when the logarithm of spore number is plotted against the logarithm of distance.

In discussing disease gradients, van der Plank (1960) also assumes a log-log relation between the number of infections and distance, i.e. an inverse-power law. But none of van der Plank's examples are strictly linear and the data would appear to fit a more nearly linear relation if distance were used instead of the logarithm of distance. Gregory (1961) has plotted the data of Waggoner (1952) in this form. Both Waggoner's and Gregory's expressions relating incidence of disease to distance from the source show that it is a complex phenomenon.

Disease gradients have been well discussed by van der Plank (1960). The slopes of his gradient lines suggest an inverse-power law with an exponent of between 3 and 4. Dispersal data (Gregory, 1961) would not predict such a steep gradient, but rather an inverse-power relation having an exponent less than 2. This limit of 2 is a well-known meteorological characteristic for the dispersal of a cloud that is not depleted by trapping. Trapping, of course, speeds depletion and steepens the disease gradient.

The dispersal of spores is a physical affair and no judgment need be made of the viability of spores on arrival. Disease gradients, on the other hand, are a resultant of the physical dispersal, and of two biological processes: loss of viability of inoculum in transit and failure of viable units to produce a lesion on arrival. The number of spores arriving at a site varies inversely as a power of the distance. The logarithm of the proportion of viable spores remaining after exposure to hot, dry air decreases as the time of exposure and the rate of death. The number of lesions produced is related to the number of viable spores arriving when multiple infection of sites is not a problem. A disease gradient, then, will be the resultant of these several factors, and the gradient will be steeper than can be accounted for by depositional effects alone.

Van der Plank (1960) has shown that disease gradients of Dutch elm disease follow an inverse-cube line and gradients of late blight and downy mildew of onion follow an inverse fourth-power relation. The pathogen of Dutch elm disease is carried by an insect and the mortality of spores in transit should be less than for the fragile spores of the downy mildews borne by air. Among soil-borne pathogens, exposed to fungistatic, antibiotic, and fungilytic principles, the mortality of inoculum in transit (if and when transit occurs except by growth) must be high and gradients very steep. Further, depletion by trapping would be extremely high, steepening the gradient even more.

Nonrandom Distribution of Infections.—The fundamental equation of the multiple-infection transformation may be rearranged in the form $\log [(N-y)/N] = -x/2.3 N$. This is another form of equation (1). Thus, when data are expressed in percentages, N may be taken as 100 on the right-hand side of the equation. Accordingly, when the logarithms of the percentages of healthy plants are plotted against the number of infections, the line relating the variables should have a constant slope of $-1/230$ or -0.004343. This relation assumes a random distribution of inoculum. The relation is still linear when inoculum is not distributed at random, but the slope of the line is changed, according to the nature of the departure from random distribution (Gregory, 1948).

This same relation was used by Blackman (1942) in studying the distribution of species in ecological studies. Blackman found that higher plants are not distributed in purely random fashion, but occur in clusters. He suggested that the ratio of the slope of the observed line to the expected slope was a useful measure of the nature of distribution, and called this ratio K. When K is greater than 1, species or lesions are clustered in groups, and when K is less than 1, the lesions are "underdispersed," indicating something akin to repulsion between units of inoculum (Gregory, 1948).

Fracker and Brischle (1944) found that the distribution of *Ribes*, although plotted as a linear log-probit relation, departed from a Poisson distribution and showed the aggregation or clustering that is characteristic of a contagious distribution. Neyman (1939) has described a distribution, perhaps more suitable for the pattern that contagious material follows, with clustering in groups upon a background of more general distribution at random, and Archibald (1948) has found this useful in describing the distributions of populations of plants. Beale and Rescia (1953) have modified the formulation of the Neyman contagious distribution to a more generalized form.

The distribution of soil-borne pathogens, even more than of those living aboveground, might be expected to be nonrandom. Data on disease gradients for these organisms are uncommon. Let us speculate. Geiger (1950) has said that the effectiveness of eddy diffusion in transfer of heat in air is some 10 to 10,000 times greater than that of conduction. Probably the role of eddy diffusion in dispersal of spores in air is similarly greater than of other mechanisms of dispersal. In the soil, nothing comparable to eddy diffusion exists, and growth of mycelium or of host roots must have an important part in the dispersal process. Also in contrast with the aerial dispersal process, trapping of spores is highly efficient, and the extinction of pockets of inoculum must be a common occurrence. These processes lead to steep gradients, but dispersal of such pathogens as *Verticillium* on cultivating equipment in a nonrandom manner has been dramatically portrayed by Keyworth (1942).

All of these considerations suggest a nonrandom distribution of inoculum, a highly clustered situation characteristic of a contagious distribution. Values of K much greater than 1 would be a characteristic of this situation. Truly, here is a unique opportunity for advancing conceptual knowledge of distributions and their interpretation.

INOCULUM POTENTIAL.—From the time the term was coined (Horsfall, 1932), the concept of inoculum potential has grown. How the concept has changed has been discussed by Garrett (1960) and by us (Dimond and Horsfall, 1960; Horsfall and Dimond, 1963). There is no need to review this material again. The present discussion will summarize a different aspect of the subject.

Inoculum potential measures the ability of the pathogen to infect its host. Infection is a manifestation of that potential and is analogous to work. The ability of the pathogen to infect is conditioned by the amount of inoculum, its virulence, the environment, and the susceptibility of the host. The discussion on the log-probit transformation has already dealt with how amount of inoculum, its virulence, and susceptibility of the host are allowed for.

The use of log-probit curves for measuring inoculum potential in the field was suggested in 1941 (Dimond, 1941). The amount of disease bears a linear relation to the amount of inoculum or to dosage of fungicide (which reduces inoculum) on a log-probit grid. A shift in the environment causes the slope of this curve to change (Dimond et al., 1941). More recently, with the realization that dosage-response curves can be used in studies on inoculum potential under restricted conditions and that other aspects of the host-pathogen interaction can also be clarified thereby, this approach to inoculum potential has been reappraised (Horsfall and Dimond, 1963).

A consideration of the characteristics of dosage-response curves is useful to this discussion. In evaluating fungicides, a linear dosage-response curve is obtained when mortality of spores is plotted against dosage of fungicide on a log-probit grid. The curve has two significant characteristics, slope and position. Two closely related fungicides will yield curves of identical slope but different position, and this situation suggests a similar mode of fungicidal action. Less closely related materials may have dosage-response curves that differ in slope, and this suggests that the mode of action of the two fungicides is different. The distribution of susceptibilities of the spores to the fungicides differs in the two cases.

In an inoculum-density–disease curve, used for measuring inoculum potential, the inoculum is analogous to the fungicide and is varied in dosage. The host plants correspond to the spore population in the fungicidal test and their response is measured in terms of percentage infection. When populations of two varieties of host are subjected to a range of concentrations of inoculum, the resulting inoculum-density–response curves will be linear. Two situations may arise. If the two curves are parallel, then each increment of inoculum produces an identical increase in disease on the two varieties of host. The hosts respond similarly to an increment of inoculum, and this reflects a similar "mode of action" of the pathogen on the two varieties. When the two curves are not parallel, then the nature of the pathogenic process differs on the two varieties. These two situations indicate quantitative differences in response (or resistance) when curves are parallel, and qualitatively different pathogenesis (or resistance) when slopes are not parallel (Horsfall and Dimond, 1963).

Quantitative differences.—When a given quantity of inoculum is distributed randomly over a field, the number of plants affected declines as plants are more widely spaced, as Shapovalov, Blood, and Christensen (1941) have found for curly top of sugar beets, Linford (1943) for pineapple yellow spot, and van der Plank and Anderson (1945) for kromnek disease of tobacco.

The nature of environmental effects on susceptibility to disease can also lead to quantitative differences. Macfarlane (1952) imposed differing nutritional levels on cabbage exposed to varying concentrations of inoculum of the club-root pathogen. The resulting curves are parallel in such a manner that the ED_{50} of the inoculum decreases as nutritional level of the host increases. The amount of "work" necessary, that is, the number of spores expended per infection of a succulent root hair is apparently less than for a poorly nourished one, but the basic process is the same in both cases.

Deverall and Wood (1961), studying infection of broad bean by *Botrytis fabae*, present data illustrating that more spores are required to infect plants on a high level of calcium nutrition than on a low one. That is, the curves are parallel, but the ED_{50} is higher for plants fed on higher levels of calcium. More spores are required to produce a lesion. We may speculate on the reason. *Botrytis* is known to produce pectolytic enzymes, which are probably involved in the infection process. When pectic compounds in host cells have a high calcium content, they are less available to macerating enzymes than when calcium content is low. This necessitates more enzyme for infection. Because a single germinating spore can produce pectolytic enzymes only at a given rate, a greater quantity of germinating spores is required to cause a lesion on a plant with a high calcium content than on a calcium-deficient plant.

Colhoun's (1961) data show that crucifers grown under a high light intensity require more inoculum for 50% infection than plants grown in dim light, but the slopes of the curves are parallel.

Quantitative effects arise when the inoculum-density–disease curve is displaced without a change in slope. This shift simply means that the number of spores required to produce a lesion is changed by an operation, whether the operation involves planting density, nutrition of the host, or a change in the variety of the host. A displacement to the right means that inoculum is less efficient in producing disease and that the pathogenic process is not changed. Such a manifestation for a soil-borne pathogen means a lower potential in the soil.

Qualitative differences.—The manifestation of inoculum potential can change in another way. According to the ideas underlying the logarithmic-probability transformation, the susceptibility of infectible sites of the host is normally distributed in accordance with the logarithms of inoculum density if pathogenicity is constant. To broaden the idea to include pathogenicity as well, we may speak of the "pathogenicity × susceptibility" interaction in like manner. Normal curves vary in shape as measured by the standard deviation, so that a curve may reflect a broad or narrow distribution of "pathogenicity × susceptibility." When the distribution is broad, the slope of the linear inoculum-density–disease curve will be flat, and when the distribution is narrow, this curve will have a steep slope. When the slope of the inoculum-density–disease curve is changed, it reflects a change in inoculum potential. One cannot say, however, that the potential is halved or doubled, but that it is changed qualitatively.

When the quality of the disease process differs among varieties, the slopes of the inoculum-density–disease curves should differ. Heald (1926) notes that bunt causes the heads of *Triticum compactum* to become more slender than those of *T. vulgare,* and the infected heads of the latter are more loose and open and the leaves a darker green than those of *T. compactum.* Heald (1921) and Heald and Boyle (1923) varied the inoculum density of bunt on wheat and determined the percentage of disease subsequently developing. Curves plotted from these data are steeper for the varieties of wheat originating from *T. compactum* than for those originating from *T. vulgare.* These data suggest the potential value of using inoculum-density–disease curves in discriminating qualitatively different mechanisms of resistance as between resistant varieties of a host or of pathogenesis between races of a pathogen.

Marquis wheat is known to be more resistant to bunt than Wilter Fife, and both are *Triticum vulgare* types. The inoculum-density–disease curves for these two varieties are parallel, and the higher resistance of Marquis may result from a thicker mechanical barrier to penetration or from other physical cause.

Age of host tissue may result in curves that differ in slope. Normally, we think of young apple leaves as more susceptible to apple scab than old ones. The slope of the inoculum-density–disease curve was steeper in July than in June (Dimond et al., 1941). The difference is ascribed to age of tissues (Horsfall and Dimond, 1963).

Low pH of the soil is known to favor clubroot. Data of Samuel and Garrett (1945) show that as pH of soil is increased, the slope of the inoculum-density–disease curve steepens. In turn this effect suggests that the mechanism of disease induction changes for club root with pH of the soil.

In summary, then, the slope of the inoculum-density–disease curve may prove to be a useful index for measuring inoculum potential and allied attributes of plant populations exposed to inoculum. When curves have different slopes, this indicates differing pathogenic mechanisms or differing resistance mechanisms. If this thesis proves tenable, the method will prove useful in discriminating between similar and dissimilar mechanisms of disease resistance.

ACKNOWLEDGMENTS.—We acknowledge with thanks the help of Dr. Saul Rich and Dr. Paul E. Waggoner in offering useful suggestions concerning the manuscript.

LITERATURE CITED

ARCHIBALD, E. E. A. 1948. Plant populations. I. A new application of Neyman's contagious distribution. Ann. Botany (London) [N. S.] 12: 221-235.

AYERS, G. W. 1944. Studies on the life history of the club root organism, *Plasmodiophora brassicae.* Can. J. Res., Sec. C, 22: 143-149.

BALD, J. G. 1950. Measurements of the concentration of plant virus suspensions. p. 17-29. *In* M. Delbrück [ed.], Viruses 1950, California Institute of Technology, Pasadena.

BARRATT, R. W. 1945. Intraseasonal advance of disease to evaluate fungicides or genetic differences. Phytopathology 35: 654.

BARRATT, R. W., and M. C. RICHARDS. 1944. Alternaria blight versus the genus Lycopersicon. New Hampshire Agr. Expt. Sta. Tech. Bull. 82, 25 p.

BEALL, G., and R. R. RESCIA. 1953. A generalization of Neyman's contagious distributions. Biometrics 9: 354-386.

BLACKMAN, G. E. 1942. Statistical and ecological studies in the distribution of species in plant communities. I. Dispersion as a factor in the study of changes in plant populations. Ann. Botany (London) [N. S.] 6: 351-370.

BLISS, D. E. 1941. Artificial inoculation of plants with *Armillaria mellea.* Phytopathology 31: 859.

COCHRANE, V. C. 1958. Physiology of fungi. Wiley & Sons, New York. 524 p.

COLHOUN, J. 1961. Spore load, light intensity and plant nutrition as factors influencing the incidence of club root of Brassicae. Trans. Brit. Mycol. Soc. 44: 593-600.

DEVERALL, B. J., and R. K. S. WOOD. 1961. Infection of bean plants (*Vicia faba* L.) with *Botrytis cinerea* and *B. fabae.* Ann. Appl. Biol. 49: 461-472.

DIMOND, A. E. 1941. Measuring inoculum potential and coverage index of sprays. Phytopathology 31: 7.

DIMOND, A. E., and J. G. HORSFALL. 1960. Prologue—Inoculum and the diseased plant. vol. 3, p. 1-22. *In* J. G.

Horsfall and A. E. Dimond [ed.], Plant pathology, an advanced treatise, Academic Press, New York and London.

DIMOND, A. E., J. G. HORSFALL, J. W. HEUBERGER, and E. M. STODDARD. 1941. Role of the dosage-response curve in the evaluation of fungicides. Connecticut Agr. Expt. Sta. (New Haven) Bull. 451, p. 635-667.

DRUETT, H. A. 1952. Bacterial invasion. Nature (London) 170: 288.

ERGLE, D. R., and L. M. BLANK. 1947. A chemical study of the mycelium and sclerotia of *Phymatotrichum omnivorum*. Phytopathology 37: 153-161.

FINNEY, D. J. 1947. Probit analysis. Cambridge Univ. Press, Cambridge, England. 256 p.

FRACKER, S. B., and H. A. BRISCHLE. 1944. Measuring the local distribution of Ribes. Ecology 25: 283-303.

FRAMPTON, V. L., M. B. LINN, and E. D. HANSING. 1942. The spread of virus diseases of the yellows type under field conditions. Phytopathology 32: 799-808.

GARRETT, S. D. 1944. Root disease fungi. Chronica Botanica, Waltham, Mass. 178 p.

GARRETT, S. D. 1956a. Biology of root-infecting fungi. Cambridge University Press, London and New York. 292 p.

GARRETT, S. D. 1956b. Rhizomorph behavior in *Armillaria mellea* (Vahl.) Quél. II. Logistics of infection. Ann. Botany (London) [N. S.] 20: 193-209.

GARRETT, S. D. 1960. Inoculum potential. vol. 3, p. 23-57. *In* J. G. Horsfall and A. E. Dimond [ed.], Plant pathology, an advanced treatise, Academic Press, New York and London.

GÄUMANN, E. 1950. Principles of plant infection. Transl. by W. B. Brierley. Hafner, New York. 544 p.

GEIGER, R. 1950. Climate near the ground. Harvard University Press, Cambridge, Mass. 482 p.

GLYNNE, MARY D. 1925. Infection experiments with wart disease of potatoes, *Synchytrium endobioticum* (Schilb.) Perc. Ann. Appl. Biol. 12: 34-60.

GOTTLIEB, D. 1950. Physiology of spore germination in fungi. Botan. Rev. 16: 229-257.

GREGORY, P. H. 1945. The dispersion of air-borne spores. Trans. Brit. Mycol. Soc. 28: 26-72.

GREGORY, P. H. 1948. The multiple-infection transformation. Ann. Appl. Biol. 35: 412-417.

GREGORY, P. H. 1961. The microbiology of the atmosphere. Interscience, New York. 252 p.

HEALD, F. D. 1921. The relation of spore load to the per cent of stinking smut appearing in the crop. Phytopathology 11: 269-278.

HEALD, F. D. 1926. Manual of plant diseases. McGraw-Hill, New York. 891 p.

HEALD, F. D., and L. W. BOYLE. 1923. Further notes on the relation of the spore load to the percentage of stinking smut appearing in the crop. Phytopathology 13: 334-337.

HORSFALL, J. G. 1932. Dusting tomato seed with copper sulfate monohydrate for combating damping-off. N. Y. Agr. Expt. Sta. (Geneva, N. Y.) Tech. Bull. 198, 34 p.

HORSFALL, J. G. 1956. Principles of fungicidal action. Chronica Botanica, Waltham, Mass. 280 p.

HORSFALL, J. G., and A. E. DIMOND. 1963. A perspective on inoculum potential. Festschr. to honor Prof. P. Maheshwari. J. Indian Botan. Soc. 42A: 46-47.

ISAAC, I., and J. B. HEALE. 1961. Wilt of lucerne caused by species of Verticillium. III. Viability of *V. albo-atrum* carried with lucerne seed; effects of seed dressings and fumigants. Ann. Appl. Biol. 49: 675-691.

ISAAC, I., and Q. D. MACGARVIE. 1962. Germination of resting bodies of Verticillium species. Nature (London) 195: 826-827.

KEYWORTH, W. G. 1942. Verticillium wilt of the hop (*Humulus lupulus*). Ann. Appl. Biol. 29: 346-357.

KING, C. J., and E. D. EATON. 1934. Influence of soil moisture on longevity of cotton root rot sclerotia. J. Agr. Res. 49: 793-798.

KLECZKOWSKI, A. 1950. Interpreting relationships between the concentration of plant viruses and numbers of local lesions. J. Gen. Microbiol. 4: 53-69.

LARGE, E. C. 1945. Field trials of copper fungicides for the control of potato blight. I. Foliage protection and yield. Ann. Appl. Biol. 32: 319-329.

LAST, F. T., and ROSEMARY E. HAMLEY. 1956. A local-lesion technique for measuring the infectivity of conidia of *Botrytis fabae* Sardina. Ann. Appl. Biol. 44: 410-418.

LIN, K. H. 1939. The number of spores in a pycnidium of *Septoria apii*. Phytopathology 29: 646-647.

LINFORD, M. B. 1943. Influence of plant populations upon incidence of pineapple yellow spot. Phytopathology 33: 408-410.

MACFARLANE, I. 1952. Factors affecting the survival of *Plasmodiophora brassicae* Wor. in the soil and its assessment by a host test. Ann. Appl. Biol. 39: 239-256.

MARTINSON, C. A., and C. E. HORNER. 1962. Importance of nonhosts in maintaining the inoculum potential of Verticillium. Phytopathology 52: 742.

MCCALLAN, S. E. A., and R. H. WELLMAN. 1943. A greenhouse method of evaluating fungicides by means of tomato foliage tests. Contrib. Boyce Thompson Inst. 13: 93-134.

MILLER, P. M., and E. M. STODDARD. 1958. Increasing the hatching of eggs of cyst and rootknot nematodes with nabam. Science 128: 1429-1430.

NEYMAN, J. 1939. On a new class of "contagious" distributions, applicable in entomology and bacteriology. Ann. Math. Statistics 10: 35-37.

PETO, S. 1953. A dose response equation for the invasion of microorganisms. Biometrics 9: 320-335.

PRESLEY, J. T. 1939. Unusual features in the behavior of sclerotia of *Phymatotrichum omnivorum*. Phytopathology 29: 498-502.

PRESLEY, J. T. 1950. Verticillium wilt of cotton with particular emphasis on variation of the causal organism. Phytopathology 40: 497-511.

RAHN, O. 1945. Injury and death of bacteria by chemical agents. Biodynamica Monographs (Normandy, Mo.) 3, 183 p.

RICH, S., and P. M. MILLER. 1963. Efficiency of infective propagules of *Rhizoctonia solani* in reducing vigor of strawberry plants. Nature (London) 197: 719-720.

ROWELL, J. B., and C. R. OLIEN. 1957. Controlled inoculation of wheat seedlings with urediospores of *Puccinia graminis* var. *tritici*. Phytopathology 47: 650-655.

SAMUEL, G., and S. D. GARRETT. 1945. The infected root-hair count for estimating the activity of *Plasmodiophora brassicae* Woron. in the soil. Ann. Appl. Biol. 32: 96-101.

SHAPOVALOV, M., H. L. BLOOD, and R. M. CHRISTENSEN. 1941. Tomato plant populations in relation to curly-top control. Phytopathology 31: 864.

SMITH, J. HENDERSON. 1923. The killing of *Botrytis cinerea* by heat, with a note on the determination of temperature coefficients. Ann. Appl. Biol. 10: 335-347.

TWENTYMAN, R. L. 1931. Experiments on the control of "stinking" smut or bunt. a. Tests of the dry copper powders. J. Agr. (Victoria) 29: 235-248.

PLANK, J. E. VAN DER 1959. Some epidemiological consequences of systemic infection. p. 566-573. *In* C. S. Holton et al. [ed.], Plant pathology: problems and progress 1908-1958, University of Wisconsin Press, Madison, Wisc.

PLANK, J. E. VAN DER 1960. Analysis of epidemics. vol. 3, p. 229-289. *In* J. G. Horsfall and A. E. Dimond [ed.], Plant pathology, an advanced treatise, Academic Press, N. Y.

PLANK, J. E. VAN DER, and E. E. ANDERSON. 1945. Kromnek disease of tobacco: a mathematical solution to a problem of disease. Union S. Africa Dept. Agr. and Forestry Sci. Bull. 240, 6 p.

WAGGONER, P. E. 1952. Distribution of potato late blight around inoculum sources. Phytopathology 42: 323-328.

WAGGONER, P. E. 1962. Weather, space, time, and the chance of infection. Phytopathology 52: 1100-1108.

WEBB, P. C. R. 1949. Zoosporangia, believed to be those

of *Plasmodiophora brassicae,* in the root hairs of non-cruciferous plants. Nature (London) 163: 608.

WILCOXON, F., and S. E. A. McCALLAN. 1939. Theoretical principles underlying laboratory toxicity tests of fungicides. Contrib. Boyce Thompson Inst. 10: 329-338.

WILHELM, S. 1955. Longevity of the Verticillium wilt fungus in the laboratory and field. Phytopathology 45: 180-181.

WILHELM, S. 1956. A sand-culture technique for the isolation of fungi associated with roots. Phytopathology 46: 293-295.

WILSON, E. E., and G. A. BAKER. 1946a. Some features of the spread of plant diseases by air-borne and insect-borne inoculum. Phytopathology 36: 418-432.

WILSON, E. E., and G. A. BAKER. 1946b. Some aspects of the aerial dissemination of spores, with special reference to conidia of *Sclerotinia laxa.* J. Agr. Res. 72: 301-327.

WOLFENBARGER, D. O. 1946. Dispersion of small organisms, distance dispersion rates of bacteria, spores, seeds,

pollen, and insects; incidence rates of diseases and injuries. Am. Midland Naturalist 35: 1-152.

WYCKOFF, R. W. G., and T. M. RIVERS. 1930. The effect of cathode rays upon certain bacteria. J. Exptl. Med. 51: 921-932.

YARWOOD, C. E., and E. S. SYLVESTER. 1959. The half-life concept of longevity of plant pathogens. Plant Disease Reptr. 43: 125-128.

YOUDEN, W. J., HELEN P. BEALE, and J. D. GUTHRIE. 1935. Relation of virus concentration to the number of lesions produced. Contrib. Boyce Thompson Inst. 7: 37-53.

ZENTMYER, G. A., J. G. HORSFALL, and P. P. WALLACE. 1943. Logarithmic-probit relation of spore dosage and response in Dutch elm disease. Phytopathology 33: 1121.

ZENTMYER, G. A., J. G. HORSFALL, and P. P. WALLACE. 1946. Dutch elm disease and its chemotherapy. Connecticut Agr. Expt. Sta. (New Haven) Bull. 498, 70 p.

ZENTMYER, G. A., P. P. WALLACE, and J. G. HORSFALL. 1944. Distance as a dosage factor in the spread of Dutch elm disease. Phytopathology 34: 1025-1033.

► DISCUSSION OF THE A. E. DIMOND AND J. G. HORSFALL AND THE R. R. BAKER PAPERS

J. G. Bald:

The biological systems normally investigated by students of soil-borne plant pathogens are exceedingly complex. The number of variables is generally too great to be covered by simple equations. The amount of data needed for accurate quantitative description of these complex experiments may be more than the experimenter can gather. It may be necessary to limit and define the range of data and reduce the number of variables before accurate quantitative description is possible. To accomplish this the advice of a mathematician in designing the experiments is advisable.

G. Semeniuk:

It seems to me your theoretical treatment of inoculum potential relates potential more to planar situations than to spatial situations that exist in soil. In soil, inoculum propagules are spatially distributed. Assuming random distribution of propagules, the probability of placing a seed, root, or a dead organic particle close to a propagule will depend on the abundance of propagules per unit volume of soil. Accordingly, if a given natural soil containing inoculum propagules is diluted in stepwise series with another natural soil devoid of inoculum propagules, then the propagules in the first soil will be separated at greater distances from one another, and the probability of placing a seed, root, or a dead organic particle close to a propagule in the dilution series will decline correspondingly. Further, as soil essentially is fungistatic toward propagules, and as seed, root, or dead organic particles promote the growth of propagules to infect themselves, the distance propagules have to grow to reach the particle becomes all important.

To illustrate the operation of this principle, I should like to cite our attempts to evaluate the relative amounts of inoculum of *Pythium ultimum* in seed and seedling rot of alfalfa in natural soils of South Dakota. Test soils were diluted in series with a diluent soil to give test-soil concentrations of 100, 50, 25, 12.5, 6.25, and 3.25%. Healthy stands were better as the dilutions increased. To compare soils statistically, linear regressions were needed between stands and dilution. Such regressions were obtained only when test-soil concen-

tration values were converted to the reciprocal of their cube root (i.e. the reciprocal of the cube root of 100, 50, 25, etc.). Differences in position and slope of lines among soils were obtained. This indicated there were differences among soils in amounts of alfalfa seed and seedling rot (*Pythium*) propagules; also, that distance between a propagule and the article of invasion was basic to the ability of the propagule to function.

A. E. Dimond:

The treatment of inoculum potential that has been presented applies to three-dimensional situations. Plants grow in three dimensions aboveground as well as in the soil. The denser medium of the soil as compared with the atmosphere does not alter the treatment, so long as inoculum is randomly distributed. One can use standard lengths of root as the unit which is classed as infected or healthy and express the results as the percentage that is healthy or diseased. One can also use entire plants.

In the experiment that Dr. Semeniuk has discussed, he has measured the number of plants emerging. This represents the number of healthy plants, but the total number of seeds planted is not given, so that data cannot be expressed as percentages. Dr. Semeniuk then found the number of plants emerging was linearly proportional to the reciprocal of the cube root of the concentration of infested soil (which is equivalent to the density of inoculum of *Pythium*). His observed relation may be expressed as $y = a N^{-1/3} + b$, where y is the number of plants emerging, N is the concentration of infested soil, a is the slope of the line, and b is the number of plants emerging when no inoculum is present. This equation can be rewritten for convenience as $b - y = -1/3 \log N - \log a$. When y is plotted against $N^{-1/3}$, or when $\log (b - y)$ is plotted against $-1/3 \log N$, the data are linearly related. These two methods of plotting are equivalent to one another mathematically; but note that, even if equivalent, it is not $\log y$, but $\log (b - y)$ that must be plotted to yield a straight line. Further, $\log (b - y)$ is also linearly related (straight line) to $-\frac{1}{2} \log N$ or to $\log N$ or to $2 \log N$. Thus, the reciprocal of the cube root has no greater significance than the reciprocal of the square root of the concentration of infested soil, or the logarithm of the concentration or the square of the concentration. This line of reasoning suggests that one might be erroneous in concluding that the reciprocal of the cube root of the concentration of inoculum has a unique relation to stand because of a three-dimensional spatial relation.

C. E. Yarwood:

I agree that van der Plank's principle, as expounded by Dr. Dimond, that the rate of increase of disease is inversely related to the size of the lesion, is a great contribution to plant pathology. This, however, is only true for the disease, not for increase in the pathogen. The best example I know is the contrast of wheat stem rust or bean rust (small lesions) and systemic infections of tobacco mosaic in tobacco (large lesions). Under field conditions tobacco mosaic multiples less rapidly than bean rust, in accordance with van der Plank's principle. Under favorable conditions tobacco-mosaic virus multiplies (doubles) about twice as fast as does bean rust. Can Dr. Dimond reconcile the apparent discrepancy when the rate of the increase of the pathogen is compared with the rate of increase in disease?

A. E. Dimond:

In general terms, van der Plank's principle covers both the rate of increase of inoculum and of disease when inoculum is dispersed and available to produce infection. Just as with the gas law, the law of lesion size describes what happens in ideal circumstances. Rates of multiplication of inoculum and of disease follow the principle when diseases have a comparable means of dissemination. When dispersal is efficient, comparisons can be made even if the methods of dispersal differ.

In the case of wheat and bean rusts, the air-borne inoculum is dispersed as it is produced and is available to produce new infections. In the case of aphid-borne viruses, the dispersal depends upon the abundance of the aphid population and its efficiency as a vector. In the case of tobacco-mosaic virus, dispersal is by a mechanical process, and increase in disease is delayed until dispersal has occurred. When there is a long delay in dispersal, the rate of multiplication of disease will be affected. But in any case, the rate at which disease multiplies will not be the same as the rate at which inoculum does. Rates of disease multiplication will always be lower than of inoculum increase.

Van der Plank has discussed the law of lesion size as it applies to two systemic, aphid-borne viruses that attack plants of differing size and shown that the principle applies in this circumstance also. But the principle cannot be applied to virus diseases where local lesions are self-limiting, and it should probably not be expected to apply in a comparison between a virus, on the one hand, and a bacterium or fungus, on the other.

S. Wilhelm:

The first use of the term inoculum potential in the literature was by J. G. Horsfall for the mass of inoculum per unit volume of soil. There is a great deal of published information on the relation between this mass of inoculum, which is often a measurable thing, and the amount of subsequent disease it produces. Perhaps R. R. Baker is now using the term "inoculum density" in this sense, but if he is, surely not everyone is. It seems to me that including such things as host resistance, distance between hosts, and the influence of the environment, in the term inoculum density is outside the concept of inoculum. This is a disease phase, and the term disease potential, is a perfectly acceptable term for us, but "inoculum potential" is not. As Dr. Horsfall used the term potential, it had the meaning of mass. Now of course it means energy too, but if we use the concept of energy here we simply destroy the term as something we can actually measure. We can count propagules, as L. D. Leach did with *Sclerotium rolfsii*, and we can show a relation between the number of these propagules and the disease. This doesn't mean that a given number of propagules will always result in a given amount of disease. Confusing environmental factors here come into play, but we should state the number of particles of inoculum wherever possible.

W. C. Schnathhorst:

The study of the variation in virulence of 12 isolates of *Verticillium albo-atrum* from 12 different host species indicated little or no physiological specialization, but rather a direct relation between virulence and the inoculum potential of the inoculating suspension for each isolate. From this study a definition of inoculum potential was derived that can be expressed in several ways:

(1) $I = VN$
where I is inoculum potential, V is the percentage of viable conidia, and N is the number of conidia per cc of suspension;

(2) $I = VT$
where I and V have the usual meaning (above) and T is the turbidity of the conidial suspension as determined on a spectrophotometer. T is another measure of the number of units of the pathogen in the suspension.

In addition, the percentage of infection of viable units may be a necessary consideration and may affect the above formulas. Infectivity is assumed to be a constant in the above expressions. A closer approximation to I may be the following:

(3) $I = VNIn$ or $I = VTIn$
where I, V, N, and T have the usual meaning (above) and In is the percentage of viable units that actually infect the host. This is rather easily determined with many foliar pathogens but would appear to be rather difficult with many soil pathogens.

From Figs. 4, 5, and 6 it can be seen that disease severity (S) is proportional to the log of the inoculum potential (I), i.e. S is proportional to $\log I$. From this, a formula can be derived that will predict S when I is known:

$$\frac{S}{\log I} = K \text{ (proportionality constant)}$$

(4) $S = K \log I$

This formula requires that a curve for each pathogen be worked out similar to Figs. 5 and 6 before I of an inoculating suspension or of a soil sample etc. can be used to predict disease severity.

This derivation is identical with the psychophysical

Fig. 4. Cotton plants (*Gossypium hirsutum* var. Delta Pine 15) inoculated by root-dip method with full-strength conidial suspensions of different isolates of *Verticillium albo-atrum* (microsclerotial form) from different hosts. The reaction of this variety to the various isolates of the fungus demonstrates the direct relation between inoculum potential and disease severity. The isolates and their respective inoculum potentials are from left to right: cotton, 13,000; almond, 5,000; honeydew melon, 1,600; watermelon, 1,000; cherry, 300; and flax, 75. For calculation of inoculum potential and prediction of disease severity, see accompanying graphs and formulas (pp. 416, 418).

law called the Weber-Fechner Law, which Horsfall invoked in an earlier scheme of measuring disease severity.

R. R. Baker:

This computation would more nearly measure inoculum *density* in the terms just used in this paper unless *K* included capacity factors.

P. H. Tsao:

Dr. Baker, what is your reason for placing the most-probable-number method (for *Fusarium solani* f. *phaseoli* and *Thielaviopsis basicola*) in the group of methods used for assessing "inoculum potential" and for placing the serial-dilution-endpoint method (for *Phytophthora parasitica* and *P. citrophthora*) in the group of methods used for assessing "inoculum density"? In my opinion, these two methods are quite similar in nature in that both involve a procedure in which a quantitative manipulation of the soil is followed by a qualitative detection of the pathogen by the use of a selective trap-host—bean seedlings, carrot disks, or lemon fruit, depending on the pathogens involved. There might be disagreements in terminology, but one should never consider the serial-dilution-endpoint method as a method for determining *inoculum density*, as it was never meant to be.

R. R. Baker:

I apparently did not make myself clear. The serial-dilution endpoint is not necessarily a method for determining inoculum density, and is not so treated in my paper. But the most-probable-number method reflects both inoculum potential and inoculum density.

A. Kerr:

A common method of testing the pathogenicity of a soil fungus is to grow the fungus on cornmeal sand or similar substrate and mix this with soil in which test plants are then grown. Generally 1 to 5% inoculum is used, but from my work on *Pythium ultimum* and *Fusarium oxysporum* f. *pisi* this level of inoculum results in a soil population of the pathogen 10 to several hundred times higher than is likely to occur in a natural soil. Much useful information is lost by using such high levels of inoculum—such high inoculum density, if you will.

C. E. Horner and R. L. Powelson:

Inoculum density (the number of functional propagules per unit volume of soil), inoculum potential (sensu Garrett), and disease as measured by an index of incidence or severity, as used by McKinney, Heuberger and Horsfall, Wilhelm and others, are intimately related. Two of these factors, i.e. inoculum density and disease, can be measured quantitatively for a large number of soil-borne plant pathogens. Inoculum potential, while fundamentally important, is difficult to measure, since it is a product of the complex interaction of the individual in relation to its environment.

We submit, therefore, that for the practicing plant pathologist, inoculum density, and disease as determined by a disease or infection index, will be the most useful.

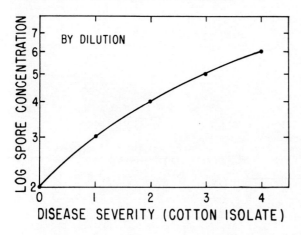

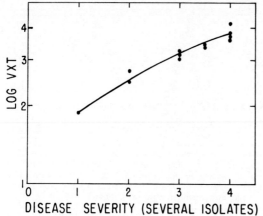

Fig. 5 (upper). The relation between conidia per cc of inoculating suspension and disease severity in Delta Pine 15 cotton. The isolate used was the highly pathogenic cotton isolate of *Verticillium albo-atrum*. The full-strength suspension was serially diluted and spore numbers determined with a hemacytometer. Viability of conidia in this case is a constant. Disease severity rating was based on a visual scale of 0-4, 0 being no visual symptoms, and 4 being an early lethal reaction. The line on the graph can be straightened by plotting log of spore concentration and disease-severity rating on a log-log scale or on a simple arithmetic scale on both axes.

Fig. 6 (lower). The relation between the log of inoculum potential and disease severity in Delta Pine 15 cotton with 12 different isolates of *Verticillium albo-atrum*. Inoculum potential in this case is given by $V \times T$, where V is the percentage of viable conidia and T is the turbidity of the conidial suspension as determined in a spectrophotometer. As in Fig. 5, the line on the graph can be straightened by plotting log $V \times T$ and disease severity on a log-log scale or on a simple arithmetic scale on both axes. Note the almost identical slopes in Figs. 5 and 6.

Disease is the result of the potential of a pathogen to produce disease in that particular environment. In general, inoculum density and disease index can be assayed quantitatively. These two parameters are useful workable tools with positive practical application.

J. Tammen:

The term inoculum potential as presented and currently used would seem to involve at least four separate, but interdependent, concepts relating to the occurrence of plant disease:

1. The concept of *inoculum potential,* as originally conceived by Horsfall (1932, cited in the Dimond and Horsfall paper).
2. The concept of *infection potential,* which relates to the energy of growth available for infection at the infection court (Garrett, 1956, cited in the Baker paper).
3. The concept of *susceptibility,* in the sense of the innate susceptibility of the host.
4. The concept of *disease proneness,* which relates to the alteration of susceptibility by the action of the environment.

Concepts 1 and 2 relate to the pathogen; concepts 3 and 4 relate to the suscept. A fifth term, *disease potential,* would relate to the interaction of inoculum potential, infection potential, susceptibility, and disease proneness.

It is an error, it seems to me, to bring these concepts together in the single expression "inoculum potential" for at least three reasons:

1. It corrupts the term in its original sense and causes it to appear in the literature with two different meanings dependent upon date of publication.
2. It would require the use of a "new" term to cover the original concept (i.e. inoculum density).
3. Because it does involve at least four concepts, the issue is clouded and the proposal of new hypotheses necessary for specific research is made increasingly difficult.

It is proposed, therefore, that the term inoculum potential be retained in its original sense and that new terms be derived to cover new concepts as they appear.

R. R. Baker:

I would agree that all these terms brought together in a single phrase, "inoculum potential," would not be justified. As pointed out, inoculum pertains to the pathogen and does not involve the host. Potential, however, denotes action or power, and density of inoculum would not be the only thing involved in the "power" of the pathogen to incite disease just before it invades the host. I see no reason for conserving the original definition of inoculum potential since (1) by adding the concept of capacity (environmental) factors, it is better defined, and (2) Horsfall has now redefined his term in an entirely different sense (Dimond and Horsfall, 1960, cited in my paper, as are the other references in this paragraph). I am by no means trying to add new terms. Inoculum density needs no definition; it is self-defined. "Infection potential," as you define it, appears to be inoculum potential as defined by Garrett (1956). Disease potential has been used with so many shades of meaning that it is difficult to pin down (see, for example, Grainger, 1956; Tsao, 1960). I like Grainger's concept of this term designating the susceptibility of a host at different stages of its life history. Actually, combining your four terms we should end up with the concept of "disease severity," now in very common use in the literature.

The present state of confusion of terms is shown on page 419 in short form.

For the reasons stated above, it would seem best to sum this up in a very simple expression: disease severity is the resultant of the inoculum potential, sensu Garrett (1956) and the disease potential, sensu Grainger (1956).

Disease severity, or inoculum potential sensu Dimond and Horsfall (1960)

Pathogen's "power" or energy to incite disease

1. Inoculum potential sensu Horsfall (1932), or inoculum density sensu Petersen (1959), or intensity sensu Dimond and Horsfall (1960).

2. Environmental effect, or capacity sensu Dimond and Horsfall (1960).

Inoculum potential sensu Garrett (1956)

Ability of host to contract disease

1. Susceptibility at different stages.

2. Environmental effect or disease proneness.

Disease potential sensu Grainger (1956)

PART VIII

◄

INTERACTIONS BETWEEN SOIL,
MICROORGANISMS, AND PLANT

Crop Sequence in Relation to Soil-borne Pathogens

MARY D. GLYNNE—*Plant Pathology Department, Rothamsted Experimental Station, Harpenden, England.*

▶

CROP ROTATION.—Some soil-borne pathogens are especially important because they have contributed to make rotation of crops an integral part of farming practice for at least two thousand years. With the development of new techniques the necessity for crop rotation is questioned, and it becomes increasingly important to understand its effects on all the factors that influence yield. A brief survey of the development of crop rotation in Europe is relevant.

The Romans recognised the value of rotation as a means for maintaining crop yields. Virgil praises it in his delightful didactic poem "The Georgics," written on his Mantuan farm (30-37 B.C.). C. Day Lewis' (1941) translation reads:

> See, too, that your arable lies fallow in due rotation,
> And leave the idle field alone to recoup its strength:
> Or else, changing the seasons, put down to yellow spelt
> A field where before you raised the bean with its rattling pods
> Or the small-seeded vetch
> Or the brittle stalk and rustling haulm of the bitter lupin.
> . . . .
> So too are the fields rested by a rotation of crops,
> And unploughed land in the meanwhile promises to repay you.

Arriving in Britain in 55 B.C., the Romans introduced a rotation already well established on the continent of Europe (Sanders, 1944).

Autumn cereal   (wheat, rye)
Spring cereal   (oats, barley, peas)
Fallow   (grazed till midsummer, then ploughed)

This sequence, enforced under the old manorial system, persisted in England until the eighteenth century; then the introduction of new crops, notably turnips, and new methods of husbandry led to the development of new rotations, such as the well-known Norfolk four-course.

The introduction of mineral fertilisers and later of mechanical power on the farm in the nineteenth century made it possible to depart from the four-course and similar rotations and still maintain and even increase yields. Urgent needs for particular kinds of crops during two world wars, and great economic changes, necessitated frequent abandoning of consistent crop rotations, and led to a great range of crop sequences. New techniques have been developed, especially in the last two decades; they are being improved and applied at an ever-increasing tempo. Mechanisation is used for land cultivation and drying and storing of crops; selective weed killers help to control weeds; chemicals and the use of resistant varieties control some pests and diseases. The large capital outlay and costs are often more than compensated for by annual saving in the ever-rising wages bill. Many progressive farmers therefore want to adopt the most efficient and labour-saving methods of mechanised farming; this can be most profitable where one or only a few crops, requiring the same kind of machinery, are grown. Impatient of the restrictions imposed by the old systems of crop rotation, they would like to abandon them and use other methods to obtain the yields in the past obtainable only by prescribed crop rotations.

This is often attempted. But all over the world are found instances of decline in yield of many different kinds of crops, as diverse as rice, sugarcane, beans, and wheat, when one is grown continuously or very frequently on the same land; the reasons for the decline are not fully understood.

So this generation is faced with a revolution in agricultural methods proceeding at a rate unprecedented in history. It is also faced with an urgent world-wide need to increase production of food. We therefore need to determine the potential yield of each crop under the conditions which suit it best, and the combination of crops and factors which give maximum productivity of the land. This will set standards whereby the relative advantages of different systems can be compared. Some will be more productive in some places, others elsewhere, and everywhere their application will be greatly influenced by economic factors, which are also changing. We need to know, not only how much each system influences yield, but what factors are involved and how they can be controlled. Studies of the effects that different crops have on the soil, and through the soil on subsequent crops, are therefore of vital importance today.

Preceding crops may influence yield by different means according to the kind of crops, climate, and soil. Important effects may be physical, affecting soil moisture and texture; chemical, affecting soil nutrients; and biological, affecting weeds, pests, diseases, and the soil microflora and fauna; and all these factors may interact with each other.

SOIL-BORNE PATHOGENS.—The control of soil-borne pathogens by means of crop sequence depends on the degree of control required and on the ability of the pathogen to survive. Complete elimination from soil may be required and may take many years for fungi which have long-lived resting bodies, e.g. *Synchytrium endobioticum,* causing wart disease of potatoes, and *Plasmodiophora brassicae,* causing club root of crucifers. But some pathogens are easily brought to the level where their effects are relatively unimportant; these include the pathogens that survive mainly on the residues of infected crops. Many of these are not very active saprophytes and do not have long-lived resting bodies; as the plant residues decay, the amount of surviving inoculum falls below the level which materially affects the next susceptible crop, although the fungus may not be entirely eliminated.

This group includes those pathogens that are influenced by crop rotation and have helped to make it so important a part of agricultural practice. There are two complementary methods for studying them. One uses microbiological techniques to study the pathogen, and gives precise information about how it behaves in culture and in soil; but it is often difficult to relate these results with behaviour of pathogen and crop in the field. The second method begins by studying field crops and attempts to evaluate the effects of different factors, including pathogens, on yield. This method sometimes indicates which problems are vitally important in agriculture, and often shows how the diseases can be controlled and yields increased, but seldom, if ever, provides unequivocal evidence of how this is achieved. This deeper understanding awaits investigation by the precise methods of microbiology. Integration of results obtained by the two methods is an imperative need today.

SOIL-BORNE PATHOGENS OF WHEAT AT ROTHAMSTED.—We will now consider some results and problems raised, using the second method to study factors which influenced yields of winter wheat in the last quarter of a century at Rothamsted. This began with disease surveys of winter wheat in existing experiments. Most of the long-term experiments, which continued for at least 30 years, were designed to study effects of fertilisers on yields in the varying weather of different years. They also provided unique opportunities for observing behaviour of pathogens in crops that each year received almost the same treatments. The surveys showed that the two most important soil-borne diseases of wheat at Rothamsted were eyespot, caused by *Cercosporella herpotrichoides,* and take-all, caused by *Ophiobolus graminis.* Brown footrot, caused by *Fusarium* spp., and sharp eyespot, caused by *Rhizoctonia solani,* occurred but were only occasionally severe enough to cause obvious loss. The incidence of eyespot and take-all was influenced by weather and cultural treatments, and differed in experiments with different crop sequences, which also showed great differences in yield. These surveys showed the need for measurements, within the same experiments, of the effects of crop sequence on pathogens and on yields. A series of relatively short-term, 3- to 8-year, rotation experiments, begun in 1950, was therefore designed to measure the effects of preceding crops on disease and on other factors influencing yields of winter wheat (and more recently of barley).

THE LONG-TERM EXPERIMENTS.—*Broadbalk.*—On Broadbalk field, where wheat has been grown annually since 1843, weeds soon become troublesome, but were partially controlled by hoeing and even hand-weeding, when labour was cheap. By the 1920's the weeds had become so prevalent that drastic methods were needed if the experiment was to continue. A fallowing system was therefore begun whereby a fifth of each plot was fallowed each year in succession (Fig. 1). Since 1932

Fig. 1. Broadbalk wheat field; aerial view, 1954.

it has therefore been possible to compare the first, second, third, and fourth crops after 1-year fallow in a series of plots receiving different fertiliser treatments. To restore the sequence of continuous cropping, one half of section I has been sown with wheat each year since autumn 1951; it has now carried eleven consecutive wheat crops (with chemical weed killers).

Four-course, six-course, and ley arable experiments.— Other long-term experiments included the four-course, in which four crops (potatoes, *barley,* ryegrass or beans, *wheat*) were grown on adjacent blocks each year and followed each other in the same order on each block; and, on another field, the six-course, in which six crops (potatoes, *rye,* sugar beet, *barley,* clover, *wheat*) were grown in the same way, each with a variety of manurial treatments. In both experiments a cereal (wheat, barley or rye) was grown in alternate years with other crops intervening, so that wheat followed a 1-year break after barley.

The more recent ley arable experiments (in which 3 years arable, including wheat, follows grass ley or lucerne) were the only long-term experiments in which more than a 1-year break separated susceptible crops and in which different crop sequences were followed within one experiment.

EYESPOT.—The eyespot fungus, *Cercosporella herpotrichoides,* can survive for several years as mycelium on infected straw buried in the soil (Macer, 1961). When infected straws are brought to the surface by ploughing, cultivation, or weathering, vast numbers of spores are produced in cool damp weather (Fig. 2). The

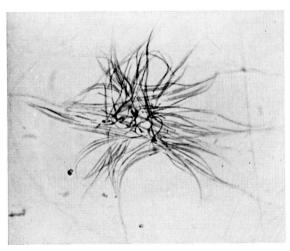

Fig. 2. Mycelium with spores of *Cercosporella herpotrichoides* growing on slide.

spores seem not to move in dry air, but are splashed on to young plants, which they infect and on which they produce lesions and fresh crops of spores; these in turn are splashed on to surrounding plants, so spreading the disease through the crop. Spore production stops in warm or dry weather, and dispersal depends on rain. Thus weather is a most important factor influencing both primary infections from straw and secondary infections from young plants. Early infections allow most time for the slow-growing fungus to penetrate deeply into the plant and so to produce severe lesions by harvest (Fig. 3); ears borne on straws (culms) with severe lesions yield, on an average, about half as much grain as those on straws free from or only lightly infected. Late infections produce a larger proportion of slight or superficial lesions (Fig. 4), which have negligible effect on yield, but contribute to the amount of infectious material left on the land.

Effect of fallow.—Eyespot incidence depends on two main factors: the amount of infectious material left by preceding crops and the weather.

Disease surveys, in the 20 years 1938-1957, of eight Broadbalk plots (2B, 3, 5, 6, 7, 8, 17, 18) with different fertiliser treatments, showed that although there were manurial effects, they were small compared with those of a 1-year fallow. The first crop after fallow had an average of less than half as many straws with severe eyespot lesions at harvest as the second, third, or fourth crops (20% as compared with a mean of 44%) (Fig. 5). There was, however, little difference in the proportion with slight eyespot lesions (18% as compared with 22%) (Fig. 5).

The incidence of severe eyespot in the first crop is less than on subsequent crops after fallow because

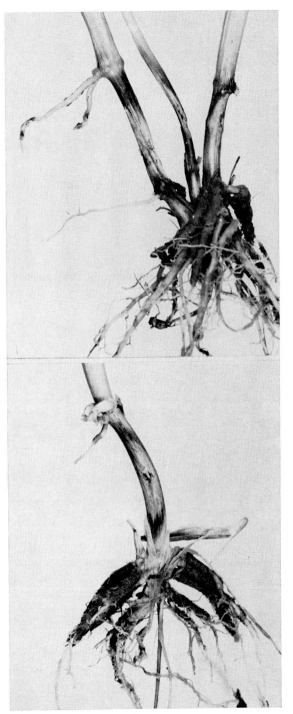

Figs. 3 and 4. Eyespot on ripe wheat straw, caused by *Cercosporella herpotrichoides:* **Fig. 3** (upper), severe lesions from early infections; **Fig. 4** (lower), slight lesions from late infections.

infectious material decays during the period after fallow. This decay was measured on Broadbalk plots by Miss J. Cox (Cox and Cock, 1962). In the spring of 1958, she counted the number of straw bases on measured areas in sections after wheat and after fallow,

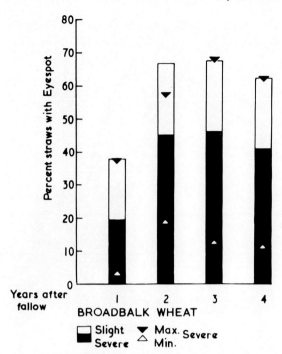

Fig. 5. Broadbalk wheat: per cent straws with eyespot lesions at harvest, mean of 8 plots, 20 years, 1938-1957.

and used a sporing test (Glynne, 1953) to determine the proportion able to produce spores of *Cercosporella herpotrichoides*. On equal areas she found an average of 22 potentially infective wheat straws in sections after wheat and only 1 after fallow (Table 1).

TABLE 1. Eyespot of Broadbalk wheat in relation to previous crops and number of infective straw bases on soil surface in January-March, 1958*

			Per cent with eyespot	
Previous crops		Number of potentially infective straw bases on 5 yd²	Plants in April	Straws with severe lesions in July
1956	1957			
Wheat	Wheat	22	17	40
Wheat	Fallow	1	1	10

* Data from Cox and L. J. Cock, 1962.

The number of early infections that produced lesions on young plants by April was closely related to the number of potentially infective straws on the soil surface. After April, eyespot increased in all plot sections, diminishing the difference between them, but still giving in 1958 four times as many severe lesions in wheat after wheat as after fallow. The difference in number of severe lesions between the first and subsequent crops is thus accounted for by difference in the amount of inoculum on the soil surface. Subsequent spread of the disease differs greatly in different years, depending largely on weather. Where there were many primary foci of infection, many late infections causing slight lesions were superimposed on, and masked by, earlier infec-

tions causing severe lesions; but where there were few early infections there were more uninfected plants which could show slight lesions. So, on an average, a similar proportion of straws had slight lesions at harvest after wheat and after fallow (Fig. 5).

The great annual variation in severe eyespot lesions within the same crop sequences (2 to 43% after fallow, 13 to 63%, mean, after wheat) can be attributed mainly to weather influencing spread and development of the disease.

In some years the highest level of infection was attained in the second consecutive wheat crop, showing that adequate inoculum had been left by the preceding first crops after fallow; but in other years, including those which followed a year of low eyespot incidence, there does not seem to have been enough inoculum to reach maximum infection in the second crop, but there was in the third; the 20-year means showed almost the same average of 46% with severe lesions in the second and third crops. The fourth crop, however, averaged 5% less; it seems likely that this decrease is significant because it occurred in 17 years.

Comparison of the first to fourth consecutive wheat crops with the fifth to eleventh crop, on that part of section I cropped with wheat continuously from 1956 to 1962 (including Miss J. Cox's records from 1958, given in the Rothamsted Experimental Station Reports for 1958 to 1962) showed the highest level of infection was attained in some years in the third, in others not until the fourth consecutive crop; this slower development was associated with a lower eyespot incidence than in the earlier (1938-1955) records, partly the result of later sowing. In every year the fifth to eleventh crop had fewer eyespot lesions than the fourth (or the third) with a 7-year mean difference of 11% (Fig. 6). Though the possible influence of weed killer (applied only to the section carrying the fifth to eleventh crop) cannot be excluded, there is here an

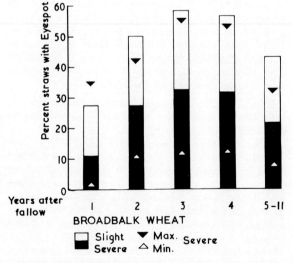

Fig. 6. Broadbalk wheat: per cent straws with eyespot lesions at harvest, mean of 3 plots, 7 years, 1956-1962. (Yearly records in Rothamsted Experimental Station Reports, 1956-1962, Glynne and Cox.)

indication that eyespot, after an initial increase, may then tend to decrease in consecutive wheat crops. This is supported by results of rotation experiments (Figs. 8, 9, 10), though in these decline in eyespot was associated with increase in take-all.

Effect of other crops.—In the four- and six-course experiments wheat was preceded by a 1-year break after barley, which was sown in spring and was therefore much less severely infected than wheat. Eyespot was more often severe and had a higher mean percentage of infected straws than after a 1-year fallow on Broadbalk; this may be partly because the self-sown barley in the crop preceding wheat carried the fungus. In the six-course experiment, rye (less susceptible than barley but sown in autumn) was about as severely infected as barley; the smaller frequency of severe eyespot and the lower mean percentage infected in the six- than in the four-course experiment may reflect the longer interval between the more heavily infected wheat crops, and slower buildup of infectious material in the six-course experiment (Glynne, 1963) (Fig. 7).

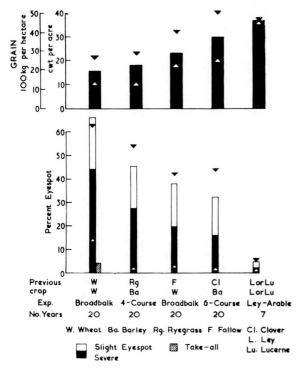

Previous crop	W W	Rg Ba	F W	Cl Ba	L or Lu L or Lu
Exp.	Broadbalk	4-Course	Broadbalk	6-Course	Ley-Arable
No. Years	20	20	20	20	7

W. Wheat Ba. Barley Rg. Ryegrass F. Fallow Cl. Clover
L. Ley
Lu. Lucerne

☐ Slight Eyespot   ▨ Take-all
■ Severe

Fig. 7. Yield and per cent straws with eyespot on wheat in long-term experiments at Rothamsted.

The 3-year interval under grass or lucerne, or under arable crops excluding wheat and barley in the ley-arable experiments, sufficed to make eyespot unimportant without altogether eliminating it (Salt, 1959).

EYESPOT AND YIELD.—*Long-term experiments.*—The old varieties of wheat, Squarehead's Master and Yeoman, which have similar potential yields (at Rotham-

sted, about 40 cwt, 4480 lb, or 71 bu per acre, or 5,022 kg per hectare) were grown for 7 years in the ley-arable and throughout the 20 years of the other experiments. Although the long-term experiments were on four different fields and included a range of fertiliser treatments, it seemed worth while to take means of all treatments within each experiment and compare the long-term averages in the incidence of eyespot and yield of grain. In all these experiments take-all appeared negligible, averaging less than 1% infected plants except on Broadbalk where wheat followed wheat. The very close relation (Fig. 7) between much severe eyespot and small yields means that in these experiments the conditions which resulted in severe eyespot were also those which gave small yields. Such figures emphasised the need for controlled experiments designed to measure, within the same experiments, the effects of crop sequences on disease and other factors influencing yield.

Short-term experiments.—The short-term rotation experiments begun in 1950 have shown that, at Rothamsted, 1 year free from the susceptible crops, wheat and barley, reduced but was not enough to control eyespot. On land already infested, 2-year breaks were enough and almost as effective as 3 years in bringing eyespot to a level at which it did little harm, provided the land was kept free from self-sown susceptible plants. Oats, though slightly susceptible to the eyespot fungus, were about as efficient as fallow or nonsusceptible crops such as beans or potatoes, in clearing land infested by eyespot, take-all, and weeds (Fig. 8). Control of the two diseases was accompanied by spectacular increases in yield from 15½ cwt to 37 cwt per acre (Fig. 8). (They were remarkably similar to the yields of wheat after wheat on Broadbalk and the mean of those after ley or lucerne in the ley-arable, which were respectively 15½ and 37½ cwt per acre; Fig. 7.) Because small grains ("tail corn") increased with greater incidence of eyespot and take-all, the amount of dressed grain was about three times as great in plots with little disease as in those with much (Glynne, Salt and Slope, 1954) (Fig. 8).

The development of diseases in consecutive wheat crops on relatively clean land after 2 years under nonsusceptible crops is shown in a replicated experiment (Glynne and Slope, 1959), in which the old variety Holdfast was compared with the newer, high-yielding variety Cappelle.

In 1955 both eyespot and take-all developed more quickly than usual on this land and were severe in the second wheat crop, which yielded only about a third as much as the first (Figs. 9 and 10). In 1956 the results seemed more typical of Rothamsted land, when in both varieties the second crop yielded about three quarters as much and the third about half as much as the first. Decreased yields were again associated with increase in eyespot; the lowest yields with eyespot and take-all, and with fewer ears. Eyespot and take-all, as well as pests, such as wheat bulb fly, all decrease the number of ears. The variety Cappelle yielded an average of about 10 cwt per acre more than Holdfast. It was less severely affected by eyespot, but consistently

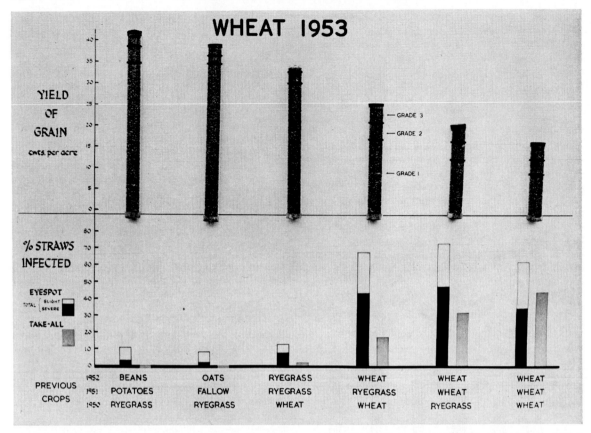

Fig. 8. Effects of previous crops on yield and per cent straws with eyespot and take-all on land previously (1949) infested by eyespot, take-all, and weeds. (Glynne, Salt, and Slope, Rothamsted Exptl. Sta. Rept. 1953: 94. 1954.)

more severely affected by take-all, although the effect did not reach the level for significance, possibly because the disease was so unevenly distributed.

TAKE-ALL.—In all these experiments, take-all, caused by *Ophiobolus graminis*, seemed important only when wheat followed wheat or barley. This conformed with the widespread experience of other workers that take-all is usually controlled by 1 year free from crops or self-sown plants of wheat or barley and from susceptible perennial grass weeds such as *Agropyron repens, Holcus lanatus*, and *Agrostis stolonifera*. Take-all thus contrasts with eyespot, which was often severe after a 1-year break. This difference may depend partly on the more rapid decomposition in soil of roots and crowns affected by take-all than of the higher stronger parts of the straw that carry eyespot lesions. It also depends on the different modes whereby the two fungi attack and spread through the crop. The dispersal of *Cercosporella herpotrichoides* through the air by means of splash-dispersed spores enables it to spread rapidly from a few foci of infection in the spring, infecting the plants at or just above soil level. The take-all fungus survives on pieces of infected roots and crowns buried in the soil and usually infects seminal roots first. It grows along them, sometimes reaching crown roots, which may also be infected independently, and less often reaches the crown (Figs. 11 and 12).

The effects of take-all on the crop differ greatly in intensity; in late spring it may cause yellowing of leaves very like the symptoms of nitrogen deficiency; in dry weather the green leaves of infected crops may show drought symptoms with rolling of leaves, while nearby heavier crops with little or no take-all show no such symptoms. The disease may cause early ripening or whiteheads of few or many ears; invasions of dead ears by saprophytic fungi in damp weather may cause greying; the most severe symptoms appear as patches in the crop in which the plants are severely dwarfed and have few ears with little grain in them. Although many grasses are susceptible to *Ophiobolus graminis* (Garrett, 1941; Buddin and Garrett, 1944; Wehrle and Ogilvie, 1955) a 1-year break under a grass ley controlled take-all almost as well as a year under a nonsusceptible crop. At Rothamsted the disease seemed to develop more quickly in consecutive wheat crops on old arable land than on ploughed-up pasture, and it developed most quickly, even after a 2-year cleaning period, on land where there had previously been a severe attack. This suggests that deeply buried inoculum may survive to form a reservoir of infective material.

Where wheat was grown without a break after take-all had been severe, the disease sometimes decreased in severity in succeeding crops. In our experiments this was first observed in 1933 in the continuous wheat experiment (begun in 1887 to compare with Broadbalk)

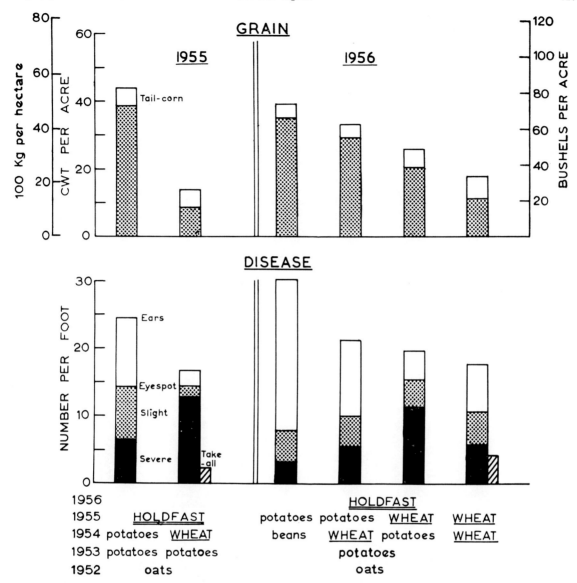

Fig. 9. Yield and number straws with eyespot and take-all on winter wheat in rotation experiment; Holdfast. (Sown 3 bu per acre.) (Data from M. D. Glynne and D. B. Slope, Ann. Appl. Biol. 47: 187-199. 1959.)

on the light sandy soil of the Woburn Experimental Farm. Severe infestation by weeds had necessitated a 2-year cleaning period under fallow; then no manures were applied but residual manurial effects observed. Take-all appeared in many plots in the third consecutive wheat crop in 1931 and increased in all these plots in 1932; but in 1933 the disease increased in plots which had less but decreased in all plots more than 35% infected the previous year (Glynne, 1935).

Its behaviour on Broadbalk is interesting. The fungus is commonly found in spring on roots of wheat following wheat on plots at all levels of fertility. It is also found at harvest; but the 20-year mean showed an average of only 4% straws with take-all obvious on the roots, with no significant differences between the second, third, and fourth crops after fallow. The symptoms of take-all on Broadbalk wheat are normally not nearly so

severe as in other fields where consecutive wheat crops are grown for a few years; for example, on Little Knott field the second and third wheat crops after a 1-year break were seriously affected and had respectively 30% and 34% straws with severe take-all on roots in 1953, when the same variety on Broadbalk had only 2% infected in the second and third crops after fallow. These differences suggested that there may be physical, chemical, or biological factors that check development of take-all in Broadbalk soil. In studying this, Miss Cox (1963) compared development of the disease on roots in the fourth wheat crop on Broadbalk with a comparable crop in a short-term rotation experiment on crop sequence. Early infection occurred in both, but few new lesions developed after April on wheat on Broadbalk, whereas in the short-term wheat they continued to increase and produced severe symptoms by harvest.

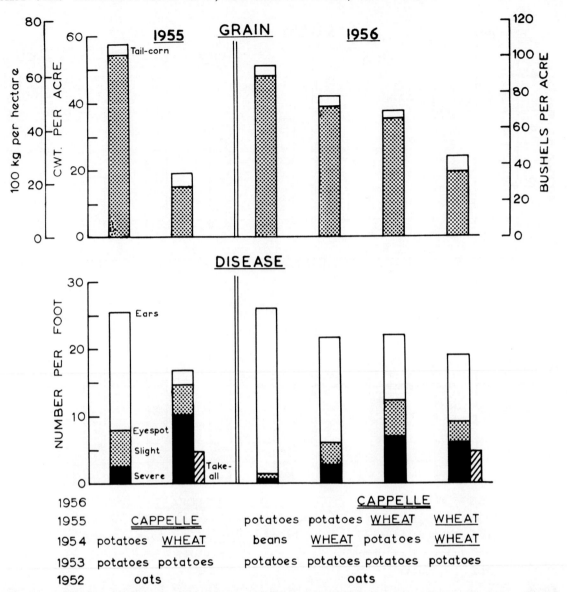

Fig. 10. Yield and number straws with eyespot and take-all on winter wheat in rotation experiment; Cappelle. (Sown 4 bu per acre, giving the same number of seeds as 3 bu of the smaller-seeded variety Holdfast.) (Data from M. D. Glynne and D. B. Slope, Ann. Appl. Biol. 47: 187-199. 1959.)

The evidence at present available suggests that inhibition acts by preventing establishment of new lesions after initial infection has taken place.

There was, however, one year, 1957, in the last 25 years when severe symptoms with stunted plants in patches appeared on limited areas of Broadbalk field. This followed the application of ground chalk in 1954 to counteract the growing acidity on plots receiving annual dressings of ammonium sulphate.

Effect on yield.—The effect of take-all on yield and the decline of the disease in consecutive wheat crops became apparent in a pot experiment begun in the autumn of 1952. Although the disease sometimes increased at different rates in replicate pots, the trend showed an increase, then a decrease in take-all, with corresponding effects on yield. The first crop after fallow always had the largest yield and take-all was negligible; the disease became severe in the second or third crop and decreased in subsequent crops. Thus in 1958 the sixth consecutive wheat crop had fewer plants with severe take-all and yielded more than the second wheat after 4 years' fallow; and in the next 2 years the seventh and eighth consecutive crops had less take-all and yielded more than the third (Table 2).

In the field, this effect showed most clearly in an experiment in which cereals and beans were grown in the same sequences in consecutive years on adjacent areas (Slope, 1963). The test crops showed that take-all, very slight in the first wheat after a 2-year break, was severe in the second and third crops, when yields were

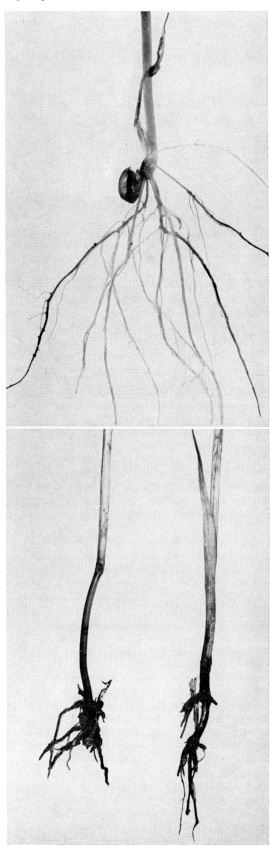

correspondingly smaller; but the fourth wheat crop showed partial recovery, with less severe take-all and an average of about 7 cwt per acre more grain than the second and third, but 15 cwt per acre less than the first (Fig. 13).

The factors influencing this partial control are still obscure, and have not hitherto been related to the microbiological antagonism known to develop in pot experiments when sterilised soil becomes invaded by other organisms. Our observations suggest that there may be a similar but smaller decline of eyespot in the field, and there is some evidence that suggests that cereal root eelworm, *Heterodora avenae* Woll., may increase and then decrease in successive oat crops (Collingwood, 1962). It may be that these illustrate a principle that applies to other pathogens. The extent to which it occurs and its effect on yield will determine whether or not it may be useful in agricultural practice. The factors responsible need investigation both in the soil and on the plants.

D. B. Slope and Judith Cox (unpublished data), studying development of the fungus on the roots of winter wheat in field plots, find that infection occurs throughout the winter, but that spread of the disease through the root system of an infected plant is very slow until April or May. At this time the disease often develops rapidly, but in some seasons little or no further development occurs; so similar levels of infection in spring lead to very different degrees of severity at harvest. Concentrated research at the time of rapid development in spring should help to throw light on the factors which determine whether, after initial infection, take-all becomes severe or not.

EFFECTS OF TREATMENTS ON YIELD AND DISEASE.— Some idea of the relative values of different treatments is obtained by comparing their effects on crop yield.

The decline of disease observed under continuous cultivation of wheat may mitigate the worst effects of monoculture, but much smaller yields are obtained than under crop rotation. Thus the most fertile plots on Broadbalk (7, 8, 2B) following wheat yielded an average (1938-57) of 19-23 cwt per acre, whereas the same variety on other fields receiving comparable treatments, but following 2 or 3 years free from susceptible crops, yielded 36-40 cwt per acre.

The same treatments sometimes had different effects according to the crop sequence and the consequent incidence of disease. Thus the high-yielding variety Cappelle consistently yielded more than Holdfast, but the difference in yield between the two varieties was greatest where disease was least. Thus in 1955 and 1956, Cappelle, after 2 years free from susceptible crops, yielded 14 cwt per acre more than Holdfast, but only 5 cwt per acre more in the most severely infected crops following wheat (Glynne and Slope, 1959).

For healthy crops, optimum seed rate would seem to be about that normally used, but in close cereal cropping, where eyespot and take-all are severe, smaller

Figs. 11 and 12. Take-all of wheat caused by *Ophiobolus graminis:* Fig. 11 (upper), on roots in spring; Fig. 12 (lower), severe take-all at harvest.

TABLE 2. Grain yield and take-all in consecutive wheat crops; pot experiment 1953-1960.*

Preceding years					1957	1958	1959	1960
1953	1954	1955	1956					
Fallow	Fallow	Fallow	Fallow	Grain, g per pot	Fallow	22	17	8
				% Take-all	—	0	30	48
Fallow	Fallow	Fallow	Fallow	Grain, g per pot	21	7	5	14
				% Take-all	0	79	80	21
Wheat	Fallow	Wheat	Fallow	Grain, g per pot	19	—	20	—
				% Take-all	4	—	3	—
Wheat	Wheat	Wheat	Wheat	Grain, g per pot	9	16	16	15
				% Take-all	59	32	15	13

* Large pots, 36 lb soil, outdoors in birdproof cage.

seed rates sometimes give larger yield. Halving the normal seed rate in 1955 and 1956 decreased yield of the healthiest crops by about 4½ cwt per acre, but increased yield of crops severely infected by eyespot and take-all by about 1 cwt per acre. Halving the normal seed rate in 1953 decreased the incidence of

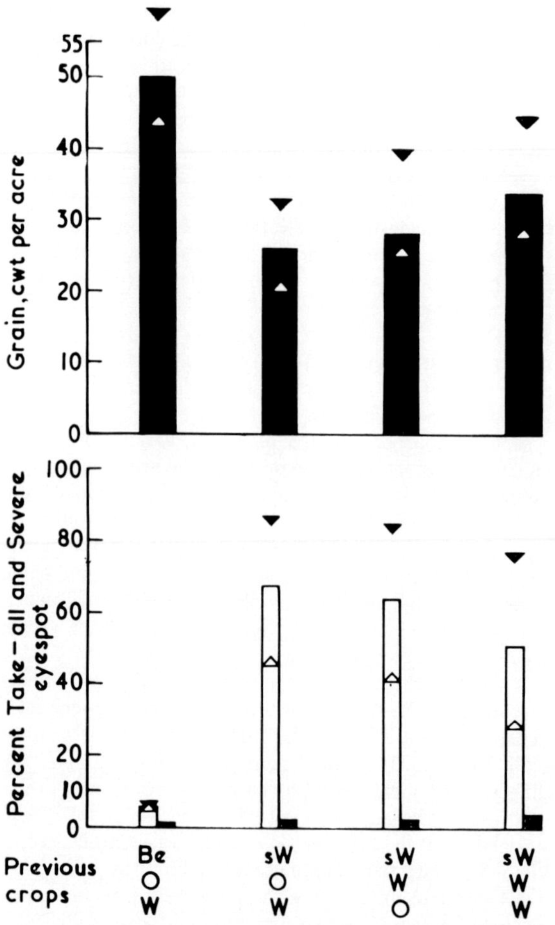

Fig. 13. Yield of grain and per cent take-all in test wheat crops, 1960-1962, following different crop sequences. Great Field test. Wheat crops for 3 years, 1960-1962. *Be* = beans; *O* = oats; *sW* = spring wheat; *W* = winter wheat. White bars = mean per cent take-all, black bars = mean per cent severe eyespot. Maxima shown by black triangles, minima by white triangles. (D. B. Slope. Rothamsted Exptl. Sta. Rept. 1962: 116-117. 1963.)

take-all and increased yield by over 8 cwt per acre in nitrogen-deficient soil (Salt, 1957).

Late sowing gives less time than early sowing for the fungus causing eyespot to spread in the crop before drier warmer weather prevents spore production; it also gives more time for decay of infected debris carrying take-all. Where these diseases are negligible, early sowing usually increases yield; but where the diseases are prevalent, the loss of yield from late sowing can be more than offset by a smaller loss from disease. This partly accounts for the fact that successive crops of spring barley can be profitably grown in southern and eastern parts of Britain, though the actual incidence of diseases and their effects on yield still need to be critically measured. The practice is less likely to succeed in the northern and western regions, where cooler and wetter weather favour the rapid spread of eyespot, which is much more severe in spring-sown crops in Scotland and Ireland than in southeast England.

Response to nitrogenous fertilisers may be decreased by eyespot, which increases the tendency to lodge by weakening the straw bases. By contrast take-all causes most loss in crops deficient in nitrogen and may therefore increase actual response to nitrogenous fertiliser, although the diseased crop still yields less than the healthy.

With adequate basal fertilisers, yield responses were less in our rotation experiments than those on Broadbalk with its extreme range of fertiliser treatments. One plot given complete fertiliser every year yielded a 20-year (1938-57) average of 22.4 cwt per acre; whereas a plot given no fertiliser since 1843, yielded 9.6 cwt per acre in wheat following wheat; in the first crops after fallow the two plots yielded respectively 27.5 and 17.5 cwt per acre.

Annual variation, chiefly ascribed to weather, affected yield as much as the extremes of fertiliser treatments shown, the largest mean yield (in eight representative plots) on Broadbalk being between two and three times as great as the smallest, the difference between the largest and the smallest mean yield (20 years) was about 12 cwt per acre after wheat, 16 cwt per acre after fallow. The same weather often had different effects, giving yields above average in one crop sequence, below average in another. There was least annual variation in yield of wheat and least eyespot and take-all after two nonsusceptible crops (Glynne, 1963).

Preceding wheat or barley had at least as much effect

as fertilisers or weather; after two nonsusceptible crops yields were between two or three times as great as after several susceptible cereals, the difference amounting to 22 and 32 cwt per acre in 1955 and 1956 respectively (Figs. 9 and 10).

DISCUSSION.—By concentrating attention on effects of crop sequence on eyespot, take-all, and yield of winter wheat at Rothamsted, we have seen a fairly consistent pattern of behaviour. The pattern is similar in other parts of southern England (Batts and Fiddian, 1955; Doling and Batts, 1960; Lewis, Procter, and Hood, 1960; Hood and Procter, 1961), but it differs elsewhere. Thus, whereas in southern England a preceding oat crop controls take-all, it does not do so in Wales, Scotland, and Ireland because the strain *Ophiobolus graminis* var. *avenae* occurs there and attacks both wheat and oats. Likewise in the north and west of Britain and northern European countries, substituting spring wheat or barley for winter wheat is less effective in checking eyespot than it is in the drier south.

Where the range of climate is greater, other effects become evident. Extreme cold may delay decay of infected plant residues and prolong the period under nonsusceptible crops needed to control the disease. In the dryland areas of North America eyespot and take-all disappear, and *Helminthosporium sativum* and *Fusarium* spp. become the dominant fungi causing foot-rot of wheat; in the colder north, other fungi, such as *Calonectria graminicola* and *Typhula* sp., may become important. The possibility of controlling these and other diseases by crop sequence must depend on the susceptibility of different hosts, the mode and time of survival of each pathogen without the host, and the pathogens' ability to spread in the crop. Climate may also alter the relative importance of pathogens and of other factors. Thus, for example, soil moisture may be the most important factor in the dryland areas, but here irrigation would alter the pattern.

Other crops with different diseases show different patterns of behaviour. When one crop, or crops with similar susceptibilities, are grown frequently on the same land, yields, though accepted as adequate, may be much lower than those obtained under crop sequences that control the pathogens.

Planned experiments are needed to measure effects of different crops on the soil and through the soil on subsequent crops. Simultaneous studies are needed on the effects of each crop on soil moisture, nutrients, and biological factors such as weeds, nematodes, insects, and pathogens. Their effects must be measured on subsequent crops: on root and shoot development, and on each of the two components of yield, number of productive units (e.g. ears of cereals) and weight of each. Such studies would help to integrate the many factors that determine yield.

New knowledge of the factors influencing decline in disease under continuous cropping may make it possible to expedite and exploit this partial recovery. Greater and more immediate increases in yield are likely to follow studies of effects of different crop sequences on pathogens and on yield; and the studies of effects on yield, within each crop sequence, of varying treatments such as dates of ploughing and of sowing, of seed rate and fertilisers and their interactions with pathogens.

Few methods of biological control seem to offer such rich rewards in terms of increased yield of individual crops and increased productivity of land as does the use of crop sequence to control soil-borne pathogens.

LITERATURE CITED

BATTS, C. C. V., and W. E. H. FIDDIAN. 1955. Effect of previous cropping on eyespot in four varieties of wheat. Plant Pathol. 4: 25-28.

BUDDIN, W., and S. D. GARRETT. 1944. Take-all of cereals in 1943. Agriculture (London) 51: 108-110.

COLLINGWOOD, C. A. 1962. Continuous corn growing and cereal root eelworm in the south west. Natl. Agr. Advisory Serv. Quart. Rev. 14: 59-64.

COX [JUDITH]. 1963. Take-all on Broadbalk. Rothamsted Exptl. Sta. Rept. 1962: 117-118.

COX, JUDITH, and L. J. COCK. 1962. Survival of *Cercosporella herpotrichoides* on naturally infected straws of wheat and barley. Plant Pathol. 11: 65-66.

DOLING, D. A., and C. C. V. BATTS. 1960. Effect of previous cropping on eyespot and take-all in four varieties of winter wheat. Plant Pathol. 9: 115-118.

GARRETT, S. D. 1941. Soil conditions and the take-all disease of wheat. VII. Survival of *Ophiobolus graminis* on the roots of grasses. Ann. Appl. Biol. 28: 325-332.

GLYNNE, MARY D. 1935. Incidence of take-all on wheat and barley on experimental plots at Woburn. Ann. Appl. Biol. 22: 225-235.

GLYNNE, MARY D. 1953. Production of spores by *Cercosporella herpotrichoides*. Trans. Brit. Mycol. Soc. 36: 46-51.

GLYNNE, MARY D. 1963. Eyespot *Cercosporella herpotrichoides* and other factors influencing yield of wheat in the six-course rotation experiment at Rothamsted (1930-60). Ann. Appl. Biol. 51: 189-214.

GLYNNE, [MARY D.], [G. A.] SALT, and [D. B.] SLOPE. 1954. Cereal foot and root rots. Rothamsted Exptl. Sta. Rept. 1953: 94.

GLYNNE, MARY D., and D. B. SLOPE. 1959. Effects of previous wheat crops, seed-rate and nitrogen on eyespot, take-all, weeds and yields of two varieties of winter wheat: field experiment 1954-56. Ann. Appl. Biol. 47: 187-199.

HOOD, A. E. M., and J. PROCTER. 1961. An intensive cereal-growing experiment. J. Agr. Sci. 57: 241-247.

LEWIS, A. H., J. PROCTER, and A. E. M. HOOD. 1960. A comparison of ley and arable farming systems. J. Agr. Sci. 54: 310-317.

LEWIS, C. DAY. 1941. The Georgics of Virgil. A new translation. Book 1. 2nd impression. Jonathon Cape, Ltd., London. p. 17.

MACER, R. C. F. 1961. Survival of *Cercosporella herpotrichoides* Fron. in wheat straw. Ann. Appl. Biol. 49: 165-172.

SALT, G. A. 1957. Effects of nitrogen applied at different dates and of other cultural treatments on eyespot, take-all and yield of winter wheat. Field experiment 1953. J. Agr. Sci. 48: 326-335.

SALT, G. A. 1959. Eyespot on wheat in ley-arable rotation experiments at Rothamsted, 1952-58. Plant Pathol. 8: 59-61.

SANDERS, H. G. 1944. Rotations. Min. Agr. and Fish. Bull. 85, 18 p. H.M. Stationery Office, London.

SLOPE, [D. B.] 1963. Cereal-bean experiment. Rothamsted Exptl. Sta. Rept. 1962: 116-117.

WEHRLE, V. M., and L. OGILVIE. 1955. Effect of grass leys in the carryover of take-all. Plant Pathol. 4: 111-113.

► DISCUSSION OF M. D. GLYNNE PAPER

T. Kommedahl:

Can the effect of changing the crop variety be substituted for the effect from changing the crop on those that follow? We have evidence from greenhouse experiments at the University of Minnesota that by selecting an appropriate root-rot resistant variety, we can obtain the same beneficial effect on crops that follow as are obtained from a different crop. With respect to root diseases caused by *Helminthosporium* and *Fusarium*, varietal sequence in a given crop may be as effective as crop sequence.

M. D. Glynne:

All known wheat and barley varieties are susceptible to *Ophiobolus graminis* and *Cercosporella herpotrichoides;* differences in susceptibility are too small for varietal sequence to be substituted for crop sequence. It is, however, possible that different varieties may leave different quantities of residues infected by either fungus, and thus vary in effectiveness in carrying one or the other fungus to subsequent crops; this possibility has not been investigated.

S. D. Garrett:

As Dr. Glynne has shown, both eyespot and take-all diseases of cereals at first increase with continuous cultivation of a susceptible crop, but after a few years significantly decline. This also happens with *Phymatotrichum* root-rot of cotton. This may be due in part to an earlier killing of crop plants in later years of the crop sequence, so that this period of saprophytic survival of the pathogen is shorter, but this is probably only part of the explanation.

M. D. Glynne:

The effects of the amount of inoculum and of other factors on the decline of disease under continuous cropping needs to be measured for each disease.

Although a few plants may be killed in spring by *Cercosporella herpotrichoides*, the amount of inoculum left by preceding crops seems to be more than adequate for maximum infection, so that the decline of this disease, suggested by observations at Rothamsted, seems likely to depend more on other factors than on decrease in inoculum.

There are instances where this might be true of take-all, but this needs investigation, with measurements of the amount of inoculum needed for severe infection.

J. E. DeVay:

I would like to add that corn is commonly cropped continuously on the same fields in Minnesota; if soil fertility is maintained and root worms (*Diabrotica longicornis*) are controlled by soil insecticides, no increase in diseases such as root- and stalk-rot is apparent. Yields of corn from fields continuously cropped to corn are comparable to those from similar stalk populations on fields involved in various crop rotations.

J. W. Oswald:

I would also like to add to the list of diseases showing this phenomenon. We have potato rotation plots now that are in their 14th year which showed a buildup of potato scab to a maximum in about the fifth year, and then a gradual decline. The intensity at the end

of the fourteenth year is about half that at its maximum. We have pondered a great deal as to what was involved, and the suggestion that Dr. Garrett has given certainly would not enter the case of potato scab, where there has been no effect on the actual crop itself. We have suspected that perhaps in the process of the buildup of the organism there has been associated with it perhaps also a buildup of certain antagonists, and that perhaps some type of an equilibrium has been reached, but we of course have no evidence for this.

M. D. Glynne:

I think that is also true of eyespot, but with the decay of inoculum, there may be a little less inoculum in the fourth, fifth, and sixth crop. There was still enough inoculum to cause maximum infection; it doesn't fall below the level at which the amount of inoculum is critical.

E. W. Hanson:

How frequently does the take-all disease occur in more than trace amounts at Rothamsted? Is it an important disease in England? What have been the effects of continuous cropping to wheat on the severity of seedling diseases? Have these been similar to the effects on older plants?

M. D. Glynne:

At Rothamsted, take-all occurs often where winter wheat follows winter- or spring-sown wheat or barley; this is usually in planned experiments.

The disease is important in England, because mechanisation and financial factors make it profitable to grow cereals, so farmers want to grow as many as possible in succession on the same land, and the present acreage under cereals is very high. To meet urgent needs to produce more food in the 1940's, consecutive wheat crops were grown, but serious outbreaks of take-all and eyespot occurred. The danger of growing consecutive wheat crops is now generally recognized. But spring-sown barley involves less risk, and is now extensively grown in succession in south and east England, giving yields which are profitable. There is, however, some evidence that indicates a decline in yield in the third or fourth crops associated with subclinical development of take-all. A field experiment is now in progress at Rothamsted to measure effects of crop sequence on barley (D. B. Slope). The test crops of barley in 1963 should give the first of a series of results.

Eyespot and take-all sometimes kill a few seedling plants in spring, especially on plots deficient in nutrients. Fewer plants may survive and fewer ears are produced in wheat grown continuously than in wheat following two nonsusceptible crops.

F. F. Hendrix Jr.:

In North Carolina, several formae of *Fusarium oxysporum* were found to invade the roots of nonsusceptible plants. These roots were not diseased. In later work in California, chlamydospores of *F. solani* f. *phaseoli* were found to germinate, grow a little, and form additional chlamydospores in the rhizosphere of nonsusceptible crops, and in the area immediately surrounding plant debris in soil. These observations were followed by plate counts which indicated a buildup of the fungus in the rhizosphere.

Both of these examples are suggested as a mechanism of a long-term survival, and not as a means of buildup of the fungus in soil. Do you feel that this phenomenon is occurring in your plots?

M. D. Glynne:

We have no evidence that this interesting phenomenon occurs in our plots. Survival of the fungi causing eyespot and take-all is rather similar under clean, bare fallow and under nonsusceptible crops, and any differences can generally be attributed to the presence, in nonsusceptible crops, of self-sown, susceptible wheat or barley or susceptible grass weeds. It has not hitherto been associated with survival on roots of nonsusceptible plants.

T. C. Vanterpool:

In the part of your paper dealing with take-all root-rot you showed some graphs which gave the incidence of take-all in rotations containing oats and wheat. Could you tell us whether one or both of the *avenae* and *tritici* varieties of *Ophiobolus graminis* are present in the soil at Rothamsted?

M. D. Glynne:

Ophiobolus graminis var. *avenae*, causing take-all on oats, occurs in the north and west of Britain, in Scotland, Wales, and Ireland, where oats are grown more often than in the south and east. It has not been found at Rothamsted, where oats are about as effective as other nonsusceptible crops in freeing land from take-all.

E. K. Vaughan:

The suggestion was made that under continuous cropping to a single crop (wheat), the losses due to a fungus disease gradually diminish. This was supported by Oswald and others.

In Oregon onions are grown in two areas. In western Oregon they have been grown continuously in many fields for at least 65 years in pure organic soil (deep peat), of very low pH, which remains wet and cool most of the year. Under these conditions pink root, *Pyrenochaeta terrestris,* is always present, yet good yields are obtained. This tends to support the suggestion.

In eastern Oregon onions are grown, under desert conditions, in strictly mineral soils of pH 8-8.5. In winter the soil is frozen and during the summer is flood-irrigated at fairly frequent intervals. Under these conditions, if onions are planted more than 2 years in succession, pink-root disease is so severe that the crop is unprofitable. Severity of the disease does not decrease if onions are planted year after year.

Our experiences indicate that nature of the soil, pH, temperature, moisture, etc., all influence development of the parasites and of the competing fungi. While it is undoubtedly true that certain disease fungi do reach an equilibrium with their fellow microorganisms, under certain conditions they do not always, or necessarily, do so.

M. D. Glynne:

The fields at Oregon where onions have been grown continuously for 65 years provide an excellent opportunity for crop-sequence experiments in which, in the same field, the effects of different crops on yields and disease incidence of subsequent onion crops, are compared.

Besides the possible decline in disease under continuous cropping, soil texture, moisture, and pH may, as suggested, be partly responsible for the contrast in behaviour in western and eastern Oregon.

There seems to be a level of pH between 4 and 5 at which wheat grows well, and take-all does not. Increase in acidity damages wheat, decrease is followed by loss from take-all.

C. Maier:

I should like to describe two situations which exist in New Mexico with *Phymatotrichum omnivorum* and cotton, then to suggest their possible significance. In the Rio Grande Valley centered at Las Cruces, some 160,000 acres under irrigation are liberally infested with the cotton-rot fungus. This soil is a heavy silt-clay loam called Gila adobe. Cotton has rarely been affected by this fungus, although severe damage to ornamentals occurs throughout the valley. *Phymatotrichum* can be readily recovered from the roots of mesquite and other desert flora on this soil. Cotton roots are rarely affected and disease loss, even where infection is present, is nil.

In the Mimbres Valley, an intermountain valley near Deming, *Phymatotrichum* is often a serious threat to cotton in new land just put under cultivation. After 2 or 3 years under cotton culture the disease ceases to be economically important. The soil in this valley is a medium sandy loam.

These two situations serve, I suggest, to illustrate successful biological control by soil fungistasis, as suggested by Dr. Jackson and others in the first situation, and by the beneficial effects of monocropping on the rhizosphere microflora, as described by Dr. Mary Glynne in the second.

Summary and Synthesis of Papers on Antagonism and Inoculum Potential

GEORGE C. PAPAVIZAS—*Crops Research Division, Agricultural Research Service, United States Department of Agriculture, Beltsville, Maryland.*

It is a great privilege for me to summarize the lessons of yesterday's papers, which have exhaustively reviewed several aspects of microbial antagonism and its relation to biological control of soil-borne plant diseases. In my summary I shall not detail all the presented concepts and ideas on the mechanisms of antagonism. Instead, I shall simply discuss some of the highlights and some of the less usual instances. Also I shall raise a number of questions for which I have no answers. This kind of presentation may lack the over-all coherence of a conventional summary. However, if I restrict myself to what is already *terra cognita* to all of us from yesterday's papers, I should miss the opportunity of suggesting certain points of interest on the functioning mechanisms.

I propose to place the papers on antibiosis, mycoparasitism and predation, and competition, presented by Jackson, Boosalis and Mankau, and Clark, respectively, under the general term of antagonism and to accept this term in its broadest meaning, i.e. as encompassing all possible microbial associations and interactions in which at least one of the interacting microbes is harmed. To do this I must consider competition in a strict sense as an associative effect in which one organism adversely affects another in the struggle for some limiting factor of the environment. The word competition is derived from the latin verb *competere*, which, according to the Oxford English Dictionary, means "the action of endeavouring to gain what another endeavours to gain at the same time, the striving of two or more for the same object, rivalry." The Greek word antagonism, however, is broader in meaning: it means struggling to predominate by every possible offensive and defensive means available.

It became obvious from Clark's presentation that soil microbiologists, when compared with botanists and zoologists, lag in the amount of knowledge they have accumulated on competition. This lag is due to at least the following: (1) It is immensely more difficult to observe competition among different groups of microbes than competition between higher plants and animals; (2) it is difficult to select a suitable microbial association, find appropriate parameters, and measure the performance of various components in that association by simply comparing these parameters, as the botanists and zoologists have often tended to do with the index of density, growth, and time; (3) several investigators believe that soil solutions contain sufficient nutrients for fungal growth and thus overlook the possibility of rapid utilization of energy-yielding substrates by a group of organisms and the possibility of immobilization of available nutrients by these microorganisms; and (4) the word competition is rather loosely used to define any detrimental interaction between microbes. The word competition must not be accepted as an omnibus term, but must be restricted to one unambiguous meaning.

Before closing on competition, I shall raise a number of questions for future consideration. Is there any specific selective effect on competitive interactions exercised by the host plant, especially through elaboration of microbial growth-promoting substances, which are either essential for or stimulatory to other microbes in the immediate vicinity of roots? Is it more important to study competition for energy-yielding material in the bulk of soil or at the soil-root interfaces where systems of associative relations are immensely more intricate? In what ways does competition for food among microbes regulate their numbers? What are the differences in the biology of individual microbial species that determine success or failure in competition for energy-yielding substrates? What role does production of or tolerance to microbial metabolites play in successful substrate utilization?

Antibiosis was recognized in Jackson's presentation as being mediated by specific or nonspecific toxic metabolites of microbial origin, by lytic agents, and by soil mycotoxins. The evidence that antibiosis, mediated by specific or nonspecific toxic substances of microbial origin, is important in biological control of soil-borne plant pathogens is still mainly speculative. However, the examples given by Jackson or discussed by others on several occasions this week are clearly suggestive that specific or nonspecific toxic products of microbial metabolism may account for suppression of certain pathogens in soils. The significant line of circumstantial evidence is based on the fact that conditions necessary for biological control and requirements essential for antibiotic production in soil are parallel.

Although the evidence for antibiotic production in mineral soil is still questionable, the evidence for antibiotic production and accumulation in soil organic microhabitats is becoming increasingly convincing. In specific soil microhabitats such as segments of organic debris, plant residues, seed coats, and soil-root inter-faces, where pathogenic microorganisms may rest or accumulate by necessity or choice, antibiotic substances may attain a local concentration sufficiently high to exert a profound effect, even though the over-all con-centration is too small to be detected by ordinary ex-traction procedures. On the other hand, whether anti-biotics are produced or not in mineral soil perhaps is only of academic interest in connection with practical biological control. If, however, antibiotics are produced in natural amended soil or in natural soil microhabitats, this fact is of extraordinary practical significance, be-cause production after amendments is a result of upset-ting the dynamic soil equilibrium by a treatment ap-plied by man.

Evidence was brought forward by Jackson that anti-biosis may assume the form of a natural toxicity to fungi in natural soils manifested by nonspecific inhibi-tion of spore germination and by lysis of fungal germ tubes and mycelium. Despite extensive studies on myco-stasis believed to be of biological origin, there still remains the question of specific origin and nature of the widespread mycostat in soil. In the attempts to interpret mycostatic phenomena in strict chemical terms, very little progress has been made since Neilson-Jones (1941) a little over 20 years ago described soil toxicity to mycorrhizal fungi.

If the origin of mycostasis is biological, is it due to specific antibiotics, to nonspecific diffusible toxins of biological origin, to staling substances produced by an-tagonistic or nonantagonistic microbes, to accumulation in soil of lignin decomposition products, or merely to inhibition of spore germination by soil bacteria and actinomycetes activated around fungal spores? If spe-cific antibiotics, production of which is favored in soil by energy-yielding substrates, account at least to some extent for mycostasis, why do carbohydrates overcome the mycostatic effect? On the other hand, if we are to accept that episporic microflora is responsible for myco-stasis, in all probability we must assume that spores provide adequate nutrients to stimulate rapid bacterial growth, exclude fungi from the list of suspects, and assign the mycostatic role to bacteria and actinomycetes only. Further substantial evidence was brought forward by Lockwood on the significance of the episporic micro-flora. Stolp's report on vibriolike bacteria lysing patho-genic bacteria producing lysozymes only in the presence of the host is also significant. If we assign the myco-static role to this kind of microflora, however, how can we explain the reduction, removal, or overcoming of mycostasis by addition to soil of nutrients or even better by organic solvents, or elution with citrate-phosphate buffer? How can we interpret the phenom-enon of restoring mycostasis by inoculating sterilized soils with certain fungi?

Jackson said that mycostasis plays a significant role in the survival of primary saprophytes in soil. On the other hand, stimulation of spore germination by root exudates, organic materials, and other means of over-coming mycostasis is also of great ecological signifi-cance, because this mechanism encourages spore germi-nation of saprophytes, which may in turn be responsible

for suppression of root pathogens in soil microhabitats. This principle is also suggested by the stimulatory effect of seedling roots or organic amendments on sclerotium, chlamydospore, or resting-spore germination. But this mechanism of inoculum fluctuations in soil could work both ways. Several investigators suggested that in an environment not conducive to normal sporulation, "pre-cocious" sporulation of propagules of pathogenic fungi as a result of overcoming mycostasis may be an impor-tant mechanism in increasing rather than decreasing inoculum potential.

In the attempts to isolate a single mycostat from soils, other possibilities such as that of mycotoxins being antibiotic-toxin-clay or antibiotic-toxin-lignin complexes were perhaps overlooked. Antibiotics, toxins, and lignin-breakdown products adsorbed on clay col-loids may still be functional by a slow exchange mech-anism in wet soil. Such a mechanism for antibiotic exchange was recently demonstrated (Pinck, Soulides, and Allison, 1961; Soulides, Pinck, and Allison, 1961, 1962). The possible significance of excretion by fungal spores of germination activators or inactivators inter-acting with mycostatic principles or a possible relation between mycostasis and organic-substrate breakdown products was also overlooked. Fungi may not only be differentially sensitive to such complexes, but genetic differences may also exist within spores of a species. Methods must be developed that will reveal the effect of natural concentrations of mycotoxins on fungi grow-ing in soil.

Boosalis and Mankau stated that practical biological control of root diseases and plant-parasitic nematodes through mycoparasitism and predation of the causal organism, though a possibility in the future, is not promising at the present. While a great deal is known about the phenomena in vitro and in sterile soil, we quickly pass into the realm of speculation when we consider the evidence obtained under natural conditions. As Boosalis and Mankau noted, we need to know whether interfungus parasitism really exists in natural soil before we attempt any detailed studies of this phenomenon. It must be remembered, however, that these authors discussed parasitism of the pathogen only, without implying that competition or antibiosis may not provide a practical approach to biological control.

Balanced mycoparasitism is affected by growth-pro-moting substances, nitrogen, and microelements. The question that immediately comes to mind is whether similar materials increase or decrease the susceptibility of fungal hosts to destructive mycoparasites. If there is a biochemical basis for destructive mycoparasitism mediated by accessory growth-promoting substances and inorganic elements, its study and demonstration will be of extraordinary significance, and much effort therefore must be directed to that end. Progress in understanding of intermicrobial parasitisms and their mechanisms appears most likely through biological and biochemical research on a number of individual rela-tions by means of new sophisticated techniques. We also need to know more about the host-parasite relations as mediated by the effect of other microbes through the year and under all conditions in soil, soil-root interfaces, and other microhabitats.

Accumulating evidence suggests that soil predacious fungi constitute potential means of reducing nematode damage to crops. Reference was already made by Boosalis and Mankau to the evidence indicating that organic amendments suppress the rate of infestation and reproduction of plant-parasitic nematodes. Do organic amendments really bring about biological control by stimulating nematode-trapping fungi or by increasing host resistance to nematode attack? This is a good question for future study, but it must be realized that to study correlations between population dynamics of plant-parasitic nematodes and those of nematode-trapping fungi, the necessary tools and techniques must first be developed. In seeking to control nematodes by means of nematode-trapping fungi, we need to understand the factors mediating the specificity between host and nematode parasite as well as those influencing the susceptibility of nematodes to parasitism and predation. We also need to understand the importance of mycostasis on spore germination of predacious fungi and the biotic potential of these organisms.

Before closing the remarks on the mechanisms of microbial antagonism, perhaps it is appropriate for me to suggest that it is an oversimplification of biological facts when we search for single mechanisms to account for biological control. Let us visualize a series of competitive interactions triggered by the success of a particular group of microbes in utilizing energy-yielding materials. Successful competition for food does not preclude formation of antibiotic substances during utilization of a substrate or Garrett's concept of starvation. In fact, successful competition for energy-yielding materials may be a cause for antibiotic production, starvation, and lysis of fungal mycelium in soil, as autolysis occurs more frequently in poor media than in rich.

After presentations and discussions of the mechanisms of antagonism, Baker introduced and successfully linked the subject of dynamics of inoculum with current concepts of microbial antagonism. The greatest part of his talk was concerned with definitions of inoculum potential, the quantitative and qualitative relations of inoculum potential, various aspects of energy level of the inoculum, and the degree of its infectivity as modified by nutrients, mycostatic factors, and root excretions.

Determinations of the actual fluctuations of inoculum potential are of great importance if we are to understand the impact of environmental factors on the parasitic and saprophytic activities of soil-borne plant pathogens. Estimations of inoculum potential on the basis of "host indicators" is the most widely used method, but even with its modifications, it may not be the most satisfactory one, because it is conditioned by host specificity and by a large number of other variables. Absence of infection does not necessarily indicate absence of the pathogen in soil. Neither does the presence of a particular strain pathogenic to a particular host reflect the entire population of the pathogen in soil. The principal limitation of the "host indicator" method

lies in the fact that it is rather poorly adapted for use in studies on the effect of soil treatment, since virtually any soil treatment will also affect the plants used.

Although the property of being potentially able to cause infection is the most essential characteristic of the inoculum, yet in studying a disease in the field, we must also be concerned with the multiplication, longevity, and quantity of inoculum; with its dispersal, infectibility, distribution of infections, and time relations; and with environmental factors.

The presentation by Dimond and Horsfall very effectively showed the intricacies and mathematical relations concerning inoculum potential. Although the concepts put forward are based mostly on air-borne inoculum and may not be entirely applicable to soil-borne pathogens, they may be used as extremely useful guidelines for formulating inoculum-density–disease-severity curves for soil-borne diseases. The fundamental clue as to how the mechanisms of antagonism will work in a given situation is derived from the numerical value of r, which Dimond and Horsfall in survival studies define as the death rate of inoculum per unit of time. In biological control measures we must aim at either increasing the value of r or decreasing the nutritional status or both, since it is very difficult, if not impossible, to destroy inoculum completely by biological means.

Very few practical instances are known in which biological measures have been used successfully for biological control. One such case was reported by Fox in the replantings of rubber trees in Malaya. Biological eradication of *Fomes lignosus* and other fungi, which is encouraged by tree or stump poisoning and the establishment of a good cover of creeping legumes, is an approach suitable for rhizomorphic root-infecting fungi with an ectotrophic growth habit and with rhizomorphs epiphytic for a considerable distance in advance of penetration. Fox attributed biological eradication of rubber-tree root-infecting fungi to the following: (1) the covercrop provides conditions under which the pathogen consumes its energy of growth in harmless activities; (2) cover plants act as decoys diffusing the inoculum potential; and (3) beneath the covercrops the soil develops mycostatic principles against the pathogens.

Glynne noted that crop sequence is by all odds the best known, the most widely adopted, and perhaps the oldest method of controlling soil-borne plant pathogens. She reported in considerable detail a series of long- and short-term crop-sequence experiments to control take-all and eyespot of wheat in Great Britain. Glynne brought up a very interesting point, namely that monocultures may eventually result in disease reduction and increased yields. This very interesting development was also reported by others, including Garrett and Oswald. This is likely to be a very profitable area for future studies. Undoubtedly there are several other good instances of successful biological control of soil-borne pathogens.

Biological control through crop sequence has been variously ascribed to antagonistic effects of natural soil microfloras associated with crop residues and root excretions, to effects of nutrients, to accumulation or depletion of toxic ions, to decoying activities of root excretions and organic supplements, to increasing host resistance, sometimes to reducing the inoculum potential of the pathogen, or to preventing the contiguity in time and space of susceptible plants and aggressive pathogens. Crop-sequence measures have occasionally been dramatically effective, but they are inherently difficult to identify, develop, and practice.

The effectiveness of control by crop sequence and soil management is often very erratic, revealing great voids in our knowledge of scientific principles and in the advancement of the arts of management. All too frequently crop sequence is chosen by trial and error and the methods employed are empirical and do not seriously assist our attempts to disentangle the multiplicity of variables encountered. Satisfactory progress in biological control through crop sequence and agricultural management will be achieved only through meticulous and fundamental researches on the biology of root diseases, coupled with close observations of the effects of ancillary factors.

Cruickshank's presentation on phytoalexins was interesting because, in addition to giving exciting news on pisatin, he stimulated a number of questions in our minds. Is there any factor (or factors) which, upon release by some fungi into the host cells, stimulates the formation of phytoalexins? If plants possess precursors of phytoalexins, could we simulate the attack of the pathogen by introducing the factor stimulating phytoalexin production? Do plants produce phytoalexins under the constant attack of their roots by "low-grade" parasites? Do plants produce phytoalexins

under the attack of mixed populations of microorganisms?

Physiological contact between host tissue and parasite is a prerequisite in phytoalexin formation, according to Cruickshank. Let us now visualize a modification of this concept to include biological responses exclusive of the parasite. Can we modify plant metabolism through external factors such as foliar or root applications of growth regulators, accelerators of metabolism, precursors, inhibitors, or even common nutrients to induce formation of phytoalexinlike substances? We cannot answer these questions; we can only raise them.

In conclusion, it is hoped that some of the questions touched upon in this summary will be taken up in the near future and with the extraordinary progress in modern microbiological and biochemical techniques our knowledge would be widened considerably. The elucidation of some of the big problems that beset us will undoubtedly have great theoretical and practical applications to agriculture.

LITERATURE CITED

NEILSON-JONES, W. 1941. Biological aspects of soil fertility. J. Agr. Sci. 31: 379-411.

PINCK, L. A., D. A. SOULIDES, and F. E. ALLISON. 1961. Antibiotics in soils: II. Extent and mechanism of release. Soil Sci. 91: 94-99.

SOULIDES, D. A., L. A. PINCK, and F. E. ALLISON. 1961. Antibiotics in soils: 3. Further studies on release of antibiotics from clays. Soil Sci. 92: 90-93.

SOULIDES, D. A., L. A. PINCK, and F. E. ALLISON. 1962. Antibiotics in soils: V. Stability and release of soil-adsorbed antibiotics. Soil Sci. 94: 239-244.

► DISCUSSION OF G. C. PAPAVIZAS PAPER

A. E. Dimond:

Dr. Papavizas considers the treatment of "Theory of Inoculum" as derived from considerations of airborne pathogens and possibly not entirely applicable to soil-borne pathogens. Plants grow in air in three dimensions, and the fact that roots exist in a denser medium than leaves and stems does not alter the theory. If inoculum is randomly distributed, and if measurements are made on the *percentages* of unit lengths of root that are or are not infected after a suitable incubation

period, the considerations presented in "Theory of Inoculum" will be found as applicable to soil-borne pathogens as to aerial pathogens. Thus, Rich and Miller (1963; cited in the Dimond and Horsfall paper) have recently measured *Rhizoctonia* infections by counting the number of mycelial fragments adhering to a unit length of root as a measure of severity of infection. If their data are expressed as the number of units that are infected (or healthy) in relation to the total observed, these will be in the form applicable for the equations developed.

►

Plant Residues and Organic Amendments in Relation to Biological Control

Z. A. PATRICK and T. A. TOUSSOUN—*Research Station, Canada Department of Agriculture, Harrow, Ontario, and Department of Plant Pathology, University of California, Berkeley.*

►

One of the more promising and most frequently used methods of attaining biological control of soil-borne plant pathogens is with the aid of plant residues and organic amendments added to the soil. Reduction in disease severity can often be obtained with such substances, apparently through their effects on antagonisms, antibiosis, microbial competition, or other mechanisms, which in some manner are ultimately detrimental to the pathogen. The striking successes in reducing some root diseases often obtained in the laboratory or simple pot experiments are, however, usually only partially realized or are disappointing under natural field conditions. Sometimes, too, undesirable effects, such as increases in disease severity and phytotoxicity, have been obtained. Why a given treatment may have both beneficial and detrimental effects or may control root disease in some instances and not in others, remains largely unresolved.

The literature on both the beneficial and the detrimental effects of plant residues on root disease is extensive but, because of the wide variability in results, confusion is common. We will attempt to deal, in part, with both these effects in the hope this might help in understanding some of the mechanisms involved so that eventually we may be able to exploit the former and avoid or moderate the latter. In this discussion consideration of the beneficial effects will be restricted mainly to the phenomenon of stimulated antagonism as it affects fungal pathogens in soil, while the detrimental effects will deal with the phenomenon of phytotoxicity and its possible significance in the etiology of root rots.

BENEFICIAL INFLUENCE OF PLANT RESIDUES AND ORGANIC AMENDMENTS ON BIOLOGICAL CONTROL.—Garrett (1959) has stated: "Root disease investigators have before them the elusive lure of biological control, but this is likely to remain elusive until the microbial ecology of the soil is better understood—a prospect possibly remote." This "lure" is made attractively challenging by the demonstration that biological control can, at times, operate in the field. Thus, organic materials have been shown to be effective in reducing the intensity of such diseases as take-all of wheat (Fellows, 1929), *Phymatotrichum* root rot of cotton (King, Hope, and Eaton, 1934), potato scab (Millard, 1923), root rot of strawberry (Hildebrand and West, 1941), and

Phytophthora root rot of avocado (Zentmyer and Paulus, 1957). One should also mention in this connection, the efficacy of crop rotation in controlling the severity of a variety of soil-borne diseases. The benefit gained by this practice may be due not only to the "starvation" of the pathogen brought about by the absence of the host but also to the stimulation of the antagonistic properties of the soil microflora in the presence of the nonhosts and their remains.

While such evidence may make Garrett's statement appear unduly pessimistic, it is well to point out that many of these practices were arrived at empirically; in some cases, well before much knowledge about the microbial ecology of the soil was available (Pammel, 1890; Tepper, 1893). In many instances, too, these practices and the benefits derived are purely regional in application. Thus, while *Phymatotrichum* root rot of cotton and take-all of wheat have been the foci of intensive interest on the part of plant pathologists, mycologists, and soil microbiologists for many years, the mechanisms by which biological control of these diseases has been achieved is still a matter of controversy. Similarly, a glance at the literature concerning the benefits of a certain organic residue for the control of potato scab, for example, will show that while the residue appears to control the pathogen in one area it may not do so in another. Obviously, such erratic results will continue until a better understanding of the mechanisms involved in biological control is obtained.

Antagonism as a potential force for the control of soil-borne diseases.—Nowhere else in the world, with the possible exception of certain areas of the sea, is there such a concentration and diversity of organisms as in the soil. As a result, competition for substrates and environments capable of supporting life is intense. In the competition for nutrients and space, all organisms interact directly or indirectly with other organisms with which they come in contact. In such a highly competitive system an organism which in some way can exert an unfavorable influence against another organism growing in association with it, would probably have some advantage. This, in essence, is the phenomenon of antagonism (Wood and Tveit, 1955; Snyder, 1960). As stated by Snyder, "Antagonism is the sum total of the unfavorable influences which one organism exerts against another." Although neither the exact nature nor the mechanism of action of antagonism is fully understood, there is sufficient information available to suggest that this phenomenon holds great promise for the future as an effective means of disease control in the soil (Snyder, 1960). The main problem at present is to learn in greater detail how to successfully influence the course of antagonism to this end.

Problems associated with the use of introduced antagonists.—The work of Millard (1923) and of Sanford (1926) and their associates on the control of potato scab by green manuring signaled the beginning of intensified interest in antagonisms among microorganisms and in the application of such discoveries to the control of soil-borne diseases. Suppression of the pathogen by selected antagonists was often demonstrated in simple systems such as sterilized soil, but attempts at duplicating such results in the field failed or were effective for only short periods after inoculation even when the soil was amended in favor of the antagonist (Wood and Tveit, 1955). The difficulties involved in the introduction, distribution, and maintenance of an effective population of selected microorganisms in natural soil are a very great obstacle to the successful use of known antagonistic organisms in biological control.

Since food substrates in the soil are generally in short supply, there is great competition among soil microorganisms for the available substrates. Similarly the soil environment, because of the accumulation of inimical metabolic by-products, is frequently rendered inhospitable to the continued growth of microorganisms. As a result of these conditions, whose existence was demonstrated by Dobbs and Hinson (1953), it has been shown by Warcup (1955, 1957) and others that fungi spend a good part of their existence in soil in a state of enforced inactivity. Such knowledge makes us realize that the struggle for existence in soil is stiff indeed and that its concomitant, antagonism, is a widespread and many-faceted phenomenon of the soil environment. The addition of inoculum to such a hostile environment must, therefore, be accompanied by a change in this environment to favor the introduced organism if it is to be successful. For this to be accomplished, a knowledge of the ecology of the organism is required and techniques must be developed to keep the environment favorable. These are formidable tasks. Although the host range of soil-borne plant pathogens has received considerable attention, relatively little is known about the "substrate ranges" of well-known saprophytes. The very ubiquity of saprophytes tends to lead us to the false assumption that they can build up on anything anywhere. Yet the known facts on the succession of fungi during the decomposition of various residues clearly point in the opposite direction and show that the "substrate range" of saprophytes may be narrower than supposed and that consequently the periods during which such an organism can build up its population are fleeting. Clearly then, the addition of a favorable substrate together with an antagonist to the soil is not sufficient to guarantee the survival of that organism. Other organisms will compete with it, will succeed it as decomposition progresses, and may overwhelm it.

Thus, for example, the practice of adding cornmeal-sand cultures to soil may be unsatisfactory, for not only may the substrate be more favorable to certain components of the soil microflora (Chilvers, 1962) but it may also, if the incubation period is long enough, be rendered unfavorable to the organism that is cultured on it by the accumulation of its own staling products.

The population of a pathogen is frequently built up by cropping repeatedly to a susceptible host. It is thus possible that the repeated turning under of an appropriate residue may in a like manner favor the buildup of a selected antagonist. It is doubtful, however, that such a procedure would be a practical agricultural practice. Recently Kerr (1961) tried to circumvent these problems by using the growing root system as a substrate for an introduced antagonist. He isolated a bacterium antagonistic to *Verticillium albo-atrum* from the rhizosphere of tomato and attempted to obtain biological control by inoculating the seeds and roots of young tomato seedlings with the antagonist. Unfortunately, however, no control was obtained and the population of the antagonist declined rapidly with time.

Failure to establish a microorganism in soil may be due to other factors. For example, the wrong type of inoculum may have been used. Schreiber and Green (1962) found that *Verticillium albo-atrum* survived in a mineral soil when it was introduced as microsclerotia but did not survive when it was introduced as mycelium and conidia. Soil aeration and type of inoculum may also have an important bearing on establishment and subsequent survival. For example, S. M. Nash (unpublished data) found that while only 25% of the macroconidia of *Fusarium solani* f. *phaseoli* added to natural soil were able to convert into chlamydospores, this number could be increased to 40% by aerating the soil at intervals after inoculation.

Since microorganisms are generally increased in pure culture prior to their addition to soil, the quality and quantity of the nutrients used can also influence establishment and survival. For example, C. E. Horner (unpublished data) found that microsclerotia of *Verticillium* obtained from naturally infected potato stems survived indefinitely when added to natural soil, whereas those obtained from pure cultures did not. The mere presence of a thick wall, therefore, does not necessarily guarantee survival of the pathogen. Other factors associated with the living protoplasm probably play an important role in the mechanism of survival; these may often be dependent on nutrition.

The effectiveness of antagonists in biological control requires that they not only be present in high enough populations but also be in an active state. This presupposes that conditions must be favorable for their growth in the presence of the pathogen so that substances or other factors that may be necessary for antagonism can be produced. Greenhouse-grown crops would appear to offer better prospects for the use of selected antagonists in biological control. This is so because under greenhouse conditions the environment can be controlled and also because the limited amount of soil involved can be manipulated with relative ease.

Even in such cases, however, biological control must be combined with other methods to be fully effective. Ferguson (1957) for example, has shown that pepper plants sown in flats of steam-sterilized soil could be effectively protected from the danger of accidental contamination by *Rhizoctonia solani*, if antagonistic fungi such as *Myrothecium* sp., *Penicillium* sp., or *Trichoderma* sp. were introduced into the soil immediately after sterilization. Even under such conditions, however, complications can arise. Ferguson further found that the protection gained was temporary. If the population of *Myrothecium* was increased to lengthen the periods of control, stunting of the pepper seedlings occurred. He also showed that in dense plantings and under conditions of high humidity, *Rhizoctonia* could "escape" the *Myrothecium* antagonist by spreading from plant to plant above the soil surface. These results again illustrate that controlled colonization of soil by selected antagonists is difficult to achieve, and does not appear to be amenable to routine commercial application. Other methods of biological control such as the use of low-potency fungicides or soil pasteurization as advocated by Baker (1962) may prove to be more practicable. These methods would eliminate the pathogens with the least disturbance to the other members of the soil microflora, which would then offer protection against accidental recontamination by pathogens.

With all these difficulties in mind, it would thus appear that the most profitable avenue of approach to biological control is to learn how the biological equilibrium in the soil can be modified to the detriment of the pathogens themselves or of their activities. One approach is by manipulating the soil environment so as to draw on the maximum antagonistic potential of the soil microflora. Such an end can often be attained by increasing the activity of the microflora through the addition of crop residues. It may sometimes be obtained by such practices as crop rotation, bare fallowing, or flood fallowing. These practices prevent the pathogen from "escaping" into a host or lower its vitality or both. These mechanisms may operate during the resting or the active phase of the pathogen.

Stimulated antagonism of the soil microflora during the resting phase of the pathogen.—While the longevity of the resting structures of various pathogens have been extensively studied, not much evidence is available on the natural conditions that curtail this activity in the absence of germination. Still less is known about the role of antagonism on the longevity. Ferguson (1953) showed that nutrient-rich sclerotia of *Sclerotium delphinii* and *S. sclerotiorum* were rarely colonized except by *Penicillium* and *Trichoderma* species. Killed sclerotia, on the other hand, were readily colonized by bacteria, fungi, protozoa, mites, nematodes, and small annelids. Tribe (1957) found that *Coniothyrium minitans* actively parasitized and destroyed sclerotia of *Sclerotinia trifoliorum* in soil. Clark (1942) found that the activity of the soil microflora appeared to be essential for the destruction of the sclerotia of *Phymatotrichum omnivorum* in soils amended with organic

materials since viability remained high under similar but sterile conditions.

While it may be possible to "starve out" a pathogen by withholding its hosts, more drastic manipulations of the environment such as flood fallowing usually appear necessary to destroy resting structures. Moore (1949) has advocated this approach as a means of killing sclerotia of *Sclerotinia sclerotiorum*. Flooding has also been successful to some degree with *Fusarium oxysporum* f. *cubense* (Stover, 1962). Flooded soils, however, have a lowered population of organisms; thus the problem of recontamination can be serious, particularly if the pathogen has a strong competitive saprophytic ability.

It has been assumed that death in flood-fallowed soils is by "asphyxiation." But the possibilities of stimulated antagonism by anaerobic microorganisms should not be overlooked. Thus Stover (1962) noted that *Fusarium oxysporum* f. *cubense* in submerged fresh banana stems was quickly destroyed as a result of a highly putrefactive decay. Menzies (1962) has shown that the destruction of microsclerotia of *Verticillium* in flooded soil was accelerated by the addition of glucose or alfalfa meal, that the killing effect moved upward and destroyed sclerotia in soil layers that were never anaerobic, and that the lethal principle persisted for several days after the soil had been returned to aerobic conditions. Although it may be difficult to maintain strictly anaerobic conditions in the field, it is possible that localized areas of anaerobiosis may persist, especially in buried residues, long enough to be detrimental to the pathogen. Thus anaerobic microsites may be important in the destruction of pathogens when crop residues are decomposing. This type of antagonism merits further investigation.

Host residues are the reservoirs of propagules of the pathogen. Conditions which would accelerate the decomposition of such materials presumably would eliminate much of the inoculum of the pathogen. This may not always be the case, however. Butler (1961) showed that increased soil fertility brought about by rotation with legumes depressed the survival of *Helminthosporium sativum*, presumably because of the increased decomposition of the host residues. On the other hand, the survival of *Ophiobolus graminis* was enhanced under such conditions. Garrett (1956) has shown that survival of *O. graminis* was high under high-nitrogen conditions even though straw decomposition proceeded rapidly, and that survival was reduced under low-nitrogen conditions even though the straw showed almost no signs of decomposition. Garrett suggested that nitrogen allowed *O. graminis* to continue a slow saprophytic growth in the straw but that *H. sativum* was not able to do so. The differences between the two organisms may be due not to differences in their competitive saprophytic ability but to the ability of the protoplasm of the resting mycelium to utilize the nutrients for the elaboration of compounds required for resistance against attack from antagonists. The production of antifungal substances is possible without any new growth, as was shown by the results of Ferguson (1953) with species of *Sclerotinia*. Where large reserves of nutrients are not available, such as in resting mycelium, the type and quantity of nutrients available in the soil may determine whether or not a pathogen in the resting stage can withstand the onslaught of organisms decomposing the surrounding residue.

Stimulated antagonism of the soil microflora during the active phase of the pathogen.—There is more evidence in the literature on biological control during the active growth of the pathogen, i.e. after germination and before penetration or the formation of resistant structures. Mitchell, Hooten, and Clark (1941) found that sclerotia of *Phymatotrichum* were stimulated to germinate by the addition of organic materials and that destruction of the mycelium soon followed. Chinn et al. (1953) and Chinn and Ledingham (1957) showed that the addition of soybean meal and other amendments caused the normally dormant spores of *Helminthosporium* to germinate but the hyphae of the pathogen soon became lysed and perished. Similar observations have been made for *Fusarium oxysporum* f. *cubense* (Sequeira, 1962), and for *F. solani* f. *phaseoli* (Toussoun et al., 1963). With both of these fungi stimulation of chlamydospore germination by the addition of nutrients and other organic amendments was observed to be frequently accompanied by lysis of germ tubes and hyphae. The amount of destruction obtained varied with the type of amendment used and stage of decomposition, generally being most severe in the presence of carbohydrates or of materials with a high C:N ratio. Lysis in these cases may thus be partly due to nitrogen starvation. The elimination of such pathogens in soils amended with large amounts of carbohydrates may also be due to the fact that, while chlamydospores are stimulated to germinate, the hyphae so formed are unable to form new chlamydospores (Sequeira, 1962) and therefore die in the absence of a host. This is supported by experiments in pure cultures (Toussoun, unpublished) which showed that colonies grown on media high in sugar failed to form chlamydospores.

While it would seem from these and other experiments that the destruction of hyphae and mycelia is brought about primarily by the "wasting away" of the pathogen, it should be noted that antagonistic microorganisms may play an important role in this process. Winter, Peuss, and Schönbeck (1960) stated that hyphae create around themselves an environment akin to the rhizosphere. Lingappa and Lockwood (1962) think spore-surface bacteria may contribute to fungistasis. It is possible, therefore, that these organisms may hasten the death of the host mycelium through competition for nutrients. The effects of this flora may be even more direct. Mitchell and Alexander (1961*a,b*) isolated several strains of *Bacillus* and *Pseudomonas* that attacked living and dead mycelia of *Fusarium oxysporum* f. *cubense*. They found that these bacteria could utilize chitin as a sole source of carbon. They reported control of *Fusarium* wilt of radish by the addition of chitin to soil. The effect of high-carbon amendments on *Fusarium*, therefore, appears to be twofold. On the one hand, increased antagonism occurs; on the other, the pathogen is prevented from forming

resistant structures and therefore cannot "escape." It is possible that the effects of amendments on the suppression of other pathogens may follow the same pattern, especially if these pathogens have a lower competitive saprophytic ability than the fusaria just discussed.

The value of crop rotation as a control measure may be due, as mentioned earlier, not only to the "starving out" of the pathogen but also to the increased activity of the soil flora which occurs soon after the crops are turned under. Lyle et al. (1948) have shown that Texas root rot of cotton can be controlled by the use of a sweet clover rotation even though the clover was susceptible to *Phymatotrichum*. While the influence of the increased soil fertility on the cotton cannot be disregarded, the results obtained by these workers suggest that the activity of the pathogen was depressed by the increased antagonism during the decomposition of the sweet-clover residues. More direct evidence on this type of effect of crop rotation has been obtained by Nash and Snyder (1962) with *Fusarium solani* f. *phaseoli*. In a study extending over a period of several years on the fluctuation of populations of the pathogen in several fields, they found that the count of the propagules in a field which had only beans for 3 years with a winter fallow between crops was lower than in an adjacent field where a barley rotation was practiced. Similar increases in propagules of the pathogen following a barley crop were also noted in other fields. Yet histories of these fields showed that *Fusarium* root rot of bean is decreased after a barley rotation. Here then is an apparently anomalous example where inoculum of a pathogen is increased by a rotation, yet the disease is decreased.

While it may appear ridiculous at first sight to employ in rotations, crops which increase the population of the pathogen, it should be remembered that the effect of the residues of such a crop may be quite different from that which occurs while the crop is growing. The preponderant effect may well occur during decomposition of the residues, particularly since this effect often occurs at the most propitious time, namely prior to and during the planting and growth of the host. Furthermore, residues may have entirely different effects on the pathogen depending on the condition and stage of their decomposition (Toussoun, Patrick, and Snyder, 1963). Increase of the pathogen may occur initially; but if the pathogen is increasingly antagonized as decomposition progresses, if it is lysed as it germinates in the presence of the host, or if it is robbed of its nutrients for pathogenesis, then disease does not ensue. Snyder, Schroth, and Christou (1959) and Weinke (1962) have shown that the incorporation of materials with high C:N ratio decreased bean root rot caused by *Rhizoctonia solani*, *Thielaviopsis basicola*, and *Fusarium solani* f. *phaseoli*. The residues had to be incorporated 1-2 weeks prior to planting in order for disease suppression to take place. Control was apparently due to nitrogen starvation of the pathogen brought about by the saprophytes multiplying on the residue. This was corroborated by further experiments (Toussoun, Nash, and Snyder, 1960), which showed that nitrogen-starved thalli produced fewer lesions than those fed with adequate nitrogen.

It is possible too, that other mechanisms are at work here. Indeed, considering the state of our knowledge, it is doubtful whether we can differentiate the various phenomena which make up antagonism as it occurs in the soil. Blair (1943) showed that the depressive effect of wheat straw or dried grass on the pathogenicity of *Rhizoctonia* could be attributed in part to the nitrogen starvation of the mycelium brought about by the saprophytes multiplying on the residues. He also reported that increased CO_2, brought about by increased respiration of the microorganisms, may have contributed to the depressive effect on the pathogen. Not much work has been done on this form of antagonism, but it is now known (Durbin, 1959) that isolates of *Rhizoctonia* differ in their sensitivity to CO_2 concentrations. Papavizas and Davey (1962) have shown that in colonized substrate segments the pathogenic phase of *Rhizoctonia* was more sensitive to CO_2 than its saprophytic phase, which in turn was more sensitive than its resting phase. The CO_2 aspect of crop-residue decomposition should be explored more fully, for it is quite possible that under field conditions the composition of the soil atmosphere may become a factor as limiting as food supply.

Much interest in the effect of the rhizosphere microflora on the incidence of root diseases has followed the work of Lochhead and his associates in Canada (Lochhead, 1959). Attempts have been made to demonstrate that the effects of various organic amendments could be ascribed to an increase in the population of antagonistic organisms in the rhizosphere, but conclusive evidence appears to be meager. Lochhead and Landerkin (1949) ascribe their control of potato scab with soybean residues to the greater number of antagonistic actinomycetes in the rhizosphere. Clark (1939) and Clark and Thom (1939), on the other hand, found that the rhizospheres of wheat and cotton were not affected by organic manuring. It remains to be seen, therefore, whether the number of specific antagonists can be increased in the rhizosphere by means of crop residues. It is more likely, as Garrett (1956) has pointed out, that green manuring permits the growth of rhizosphere microorganisms in soil distant from the roots. This would then result in a widened zone of competition around the plant.

The importance of this zone in root disease is due not only to its placement, i.e. at the infection court, but also to the fact that many pathogens, especially root-inhabiting fungi, have an ectotrophic growth habit (Garrett, 1956), a habit which puts them in direct competition with the rhizosphere microflora. It should also be mentioned that a saprophytic growth phase on the surface of the host prior to penetration has been found to be a characteristic of such soil-inhabiting fungi as *Rhizoctonia* (Flentje, 1957) and *Fusarium solani* f. *phaseoli* (Christou and Snyder, 1962). It has been shown with the latter that the incorporation of mature barley straw not only increases lysis of germ tubes, as mentioned previously, but also affects saprophytic growth on the host. Thus Cook (1962) has found that the number of thalli formed on the host surface in

barley-straw-amended soil was less than in the control soil and the thalli which did form remained small. In contrast, those formed in the unamended soil showed substantial daily increases. It would seem therefore that the biological control brought about by crop residues can make itself felt up to and even following penetration.

It would appear that in any consideration of the effect of stimulated antagonism on plant pathogens, in which the end result, hopefully, is the control of the disease, we cannot ignore the host. The beneficial aspects of crop residues, just dealt with, may be obtained through their influence on the host as well as on the pathogen, but the separation of these effects can be complicated in the extreme. The benefits derived from crop rotation, for example, may accrue from its harmful effect on the pathogen either while the crop is growing or while its residues are decomposing in the soil. It may also result from beneficial effects derived by the host either directly through the increase of soil nitrogen or indirectly through the improvement of soil tilth and other agronomic factors. What decides whether disease is controlled under such circumstances is generally not one single factor but the sum of many factors which make up the reactions and interactions of the triangle composed of pathogen, host, and environment. A glimpse of this complex picture has been given us by Garrett's (1938, 1940, 1941) and Garrett and Mann's (1948) elucidation of the role of nitrogen in the take-all disease of wheat. It was shown that while the nitrogen liberated from organic manures increased the survival of the pathogen in the crop residues, it also increased the tillering capacity of the host. In this instance nitrogen lessened the disease because the effect on the host outweighed that on the pathogen. Many more examples of such interrelations could be given. It is obvious here as elsewhere that the combined efforts of specialists in several disciplines are required before a complete picture of all the interactions involved can be elucidated. While we realize that this is so, a start has to be made, and as plant pathologists we have attempted to focus our discussion of control by means of crop residues on the pathogen itself. In so doing we have omitted many cases of successful control mentioned in various reviews (Berkeley, 1944; Wood and Tveit, 1955; Simmonds, 1941, 1953; Garrett, 1956; Sanford, 1959, Darpoux, 1960; Menzies, 1963) not because of any lack of merit but simply because not much is known about the manner in which the control is achieved. Such work, therefore, is still in the empirical stage. While this in no way detracts from the value of the results obtained, it does not as yet provide a scientific basis for further progress.

While our understanding of the mechanisms involved in biological control is at present severely limited by a lack of detailed knowledge of the life cycles of pathogens under natural conditions, certain aspects of disease control by means of crop residues are perhaps becoming clearer. A pathogen, be it a soil inhabitant or a root inhabitant, can escape competition in soil in two ways: by the formation of resistant structures or by the invasion of a host. Competitive saprophytic ability, therefore, is not only the ability to grow through soil and to colonize new substrates in the presence of antagonists but is also the ability to increase the number of resistant propagules. A major difference between soil inhabitants and root inhabitants lies in the range of environmental conditions in which this latter process can take place. These propagules, then, are the foci for the control measures we have discussed. If they are destroyed or sufficiently reduced in number, disease is generally lessened. It is interesting to note that the means by which this may be accomplished through stimulated antagonism of the soil microflora is frequently the same whether we deal with soil-inhabiting or root-inhabiting pathogens.

It would appear, in general, that the direct destruction of resistant structures is difficult to achieve. More frequently such destruction takes place after germination. The tolerance of pathogens to antagonism, therefore, is at its weakest just after germination and it is at its strongest in the resting stage. If this is so, then the effect of crop residues in suppressing the pathogen is exercised not only in stimulating the growth of the general soil microflora but also in stimulating the germination of the resting propagules of the pathogen and

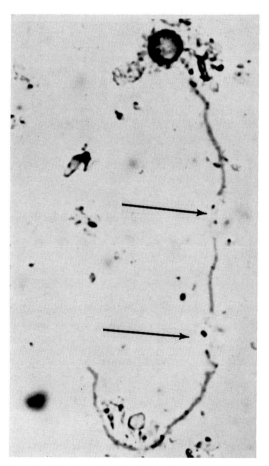

Fig. 1. Germination of chlamydospores of *Fusarium solani* f. *phaseoli* stimulated in the vicinity of decomposing plant residues; this is often followed by lysis (indicated by arrows).

thereby exposing it to antagonism at its most vulnerable stage. An example of this is shown in Fig. 1. Here the germination of chlamydospores of *Fusarium solani* f. *phaseoli* is markedly stimulated on the surface and immediate vicinity of plant-residue fragments decomposing in natural field soil. As indicated by arrows, this is often followed by lysis of the hyphae (Toussoun, Patrick, and Snyder, 1963).

Since nutrients comprise an important segment of the soil environment that frequently becomes limiting, competition for nutrients may be regarded as one of the more successful methods of control that can be obtained by means of crop residues. In this connection it should be pointed out that the nutrition of the pathogen, as it affects its behavior in the soil, has been frequently ignored. We are not speaking here of conditions that lead to starvation but rather of the necessity, shown with *Fusarium solani* f. *phaseoli*, for a balanced nutrition without which the fungus is apparently unable to attack its host or form new chlamydospores (Toussoun, Nash, and Snyder, 1960). In this case competition for nitrogen seems to play an important role and it is apparently for this reason that the decomposition of residues having a high C:N ratio depress the disease. Other nutrients may play similar roles in other cases. This may explain, for example, why soybean residues have been used successfully in the control of several diseases while residues from red clover, rye, barley, and other crops have often increased disease severity (Millard, 1923; Hildebrand and West, 1941; Chinn et al., 1953; Snyder, 1960).

Competition for nutrients is not of course the sole mechanism at work, and we have commented on the difficulties involved in distinguishing between this and such closely allied phenomena as antibiosis. Although antibiotic production per se has shown spectacular results in simple systems, it still remains to be proved that it is of major significance in the general competition of the soil flora. Perhaps the spectacular antibiotic is overshadowed in nature by the less potent but more abundant staling products.

While detailed information on many of the mechanisms involved in biological control are still fragmentary, some of the general principles are known to us. It may seem surprising, therefore, that control of root pathogens by means of crop residues has only had limited success when used against specific diseases. As with other control measures, however, the method has its strengths and weaknesses and perhaps, with the present state of knowledge on the subject, our expectations should be more limited, both as to the diseases it is possible to control and the degree of control that can be attained by this means. An example of this is suggested by the work of Oswald and Lorenz (1956) and Weinhold et al. (1964) on the control of potato scab by means of green manures. In their study, extending over a period of 12 years, it was found that the incorporation of soybean residues prevented the build-up of scab incidence in fields with low initial infestation but failed to control scab once the pathogen was well established. Barley residues, on the other hand, always increased disease severity. These results suggest that perhaps the value of soil amendments lies principally in preventing pathogen buildup rather than in eliminating the disease once the causal organism becomes well established. It may be that for practical agricultural use, biological means of disease control should be integrated with other methods, each supplementing the other. Soil fungicides and other effective methods should be used for immediate disease suppression, then a more permanent long-term disease suppression can be attained through proper use of plant residues.

DETRIMENTAL EFFECTS OF PLANT RESIDUES AND ORGANIC AMENDMENTS ON PLANTS.—Some of the reasons for the unfavorable effects of plant residues and organic amendments on plants and their diseases are quite obvious. Often they may have a direct effect on the pathogen by increasing inoculum, improving growth or survival, or providing a food base (Garrett, 1956). Sometimes, as discussed by Ripley (1941), Bear (1951), Millar (1955), Miller, Turk, and Foth (1958), and others, injurious effects may be due to the depletion of nutrients or oxygen, immobilization of nitrogen and phosphorus, or an excess of carbon dioxide, ammonia, or other gases in the soil brought about by microorganisms during the decomposition of the residues. It is not within the scope of this discussion, however, to consider all these factors even though many have a bearing on the problem of root diseases and biological control. This discussion will be confined mainly to instances where extractable chemical agents, referred to as phytotoxins, appear to be the dominant injurious cause.

A discussion of this subject would not be complete without some mention of the so-called soil-toxin theory. Historically it is one of the oldest, most intriguing, and still most controversial concepts advanced to explain the detrimental effects of plant residues on plants. The soil-toxin theory implies that phytotoxic substances may be produced by plant roots; they may also be derived from other plant tissues or produced during the decomposition of plant remains. Reviews and critical evaluation of the subject have been prepared by Loehwing (1937), Bonner (1950), Martin (1957), Krasil'nikov (1958), Börner (1960), Woods (1960), Garb (1961), Winter (1961), and others. After examining the available evidence these investigators concluded that under certain conditions substances toxic to living plants may be liberated from plant residues during their decomposition and also can originate from excretions of roots and underground stems of some plants. Information as to the chemical nature of these substances or whether they could possibly accumulate to any effective concentration under natural field conditions and be significant in the etiology of root diseases is, however, either fragmentary, contradictory, or lacking.

Phytotoxic properties of plant residues are usually demonstrated by use of leachings of the plants in question or by aqueous extracts of the macerated plant material. The crude extracts, after filtration and some purification, are tested for phytotoxic effects on various test plants. In the laboratory some of these extracts inhibit the germination of seed, cause stunting of seed-

lings, or produce root injury, wilting, or other deleterious effects on plants. From such results it seems logical to assume that many of these compounds, since they eventually must reach the soil by leaching and during rotting of the plant tissues, presumably come in contact with living plants and produce similar effects in nature. In the opinion of many investigators, however (Loehwing, 1937; Bonner, 1950; Börner, 1960; Winter, 1961; Grümmer, 1961), only in a few exceptional circumstances have the laboratory results been satisfactorily confirmed under natural field conditions. Nor have many specific phytotoxins been isolated in effective concentrations from the soil environment and identified. In addition, it has been observed in the laboratory and in the field that decomposition of apparently similar plant residues is accompanied by formation of phytotoxic substances at one time and not at another. In our opinion, one of the main reasons for some of the difficulties and the unconvincing results may be due to a lack of reliable, sensitive, and rapid assay techniques. Satisfactory assay methods are particularly important with problems of this nature since decomposition of plant residues or any organic substrate in the soil is a continuing process and the types of products that arise depend on so many factors. As pointed out by Waksman (1952), Krasil'nikov (1958), and Winter (1961), substances arising from a given type of plant material under one set of conditions may be very toxic to plants while at another time under different conditions they may be beneficial. Similarly, most of the compounds, no matter how toxic they may be, are subject to rapid deactivation, destruction, or transformation by the soil microflora. Owing to the nonspecific nature of action of many of these compounds and their relatively rapid inactivation, it is evident that, in the absence of suitable methods of detection, their occurrence might not be apparent and many of the injurious effects would thus be attributed to some other more obvious cause. Rapid and sensitive assay methods are essential for detecting such substances during the interval between their production and their disappearance.

Type of phytotoxic substances formed during decomposition of plant residues in soil.—As indicated by the various reviews (Skinner, 1918; Bonner, 1950; Audus, 1953; Börner, 1960; Garb, 1961; and Winter, 1961), in the long list of the identified chemicals there are found aromatic aldehydes including vanillin, and salicylaldehyde. According to Norman (1943), Brauns (1952), and Winter (1961), aldehydes of this type are among the first products of the microbial degradation of lignin. Skinner (1918) isolated from unproductive soils a range of phytotoxic organic compounds including protein-degradation products. Phytotoxic substances originating as degradation products of cellulose and other plant constituents have also been found (Millar, 1955; Miller, Turk, and Foth, 1958). Börner (1960) showed that cold-water extracts of barley, rye, and wheat straw contain ferulic acid (4-hydroxy-3-methoxycinnamic acid), *p*-coumaric acid (4-hydroxycinnamic acid), vanillic acid (4-hydroxy-3-methoxybenzoic acid) and *p*-hydroxybenzoic acid. New compounds with phytotoxic properties are discovered quite regularly.

Parenthetically, it should be noted that although a number of specific chemical substances have been identified and postulated to be the specific phytotoxins involved, most of the evidence is based on laboratory isolations and manipulations. There is no direct evidence whether many of the identified compounds occur as such in nature. As indicated by Norman (1943), Bonner (1950), and Winter (1960, 1961), no one has ever succeeded in extracting a chemically defined substance of biotic origin in effective quantities from natural soils. Similarly, the biochemistry of the rotting of plant residues in the soil has not been followed in any detail because of the lack of suitable experimental methods. This is made even more difficult because all biological processes in the soil are in a dynamic state, continually changing, and the process also includes synthesis of microbial products. Thus correlations between the observed phytotoxicity in nature and the isolation of a certain compound are always open to interpretation difficulties. Whether the biochemistry and true identity of many of these compounds can ever be completely known is, in our opinion, highly questionable.

It is well known that in the majority of cases the decomposition of plant residues in the soil is not accompanied by phytotoxic effects on the succeeding crops. The reasons why decomposition of a given plant residue is accompanied by phytotoxin formation at one time and not at another are often not clear. Predictions of the effect of a plant residue or organic amendment on the growth of the subsequent crop or its ultimate value for biological control are, therefore, in many instances, impossible. As pointed out by Skinner (1918), Doran (1928), Ripley (1941), and Millar (1955), soil toxins due to organic constituents are mainly associated with heavy soils characterized by poor aeration, excessive moisture, and relatively cool temperature conditions. If oxygen is deficient in the soil, cellulose, lignin, proteins, and other constituents of plant tissues are believed to give rise to a variety of intermediate reduction compounds, many of which are phytotoxic. These views are supported by our studies (Patrick and Koch, 1958). It was found that water extracts of soils containing residues from rye, corn, timothy, and tobacco plants were phytotoxic when such residues had been decomposing in the soil for 5 to 30 days under saturation conditions. Saturation conditions, however, did not have to be maintained throughout the whole decomposition period to give rise to phytotoxic products. Flooding of the soil for 3 to 5 days also gave rise to extracts that were highly toxic. When all recognizable plant residue was removed from the soil, no phytotoxicity was detected in extracts either from soil maintained at field capacity or from saturated soil.

The question as to what may constitute adequate soil aeration is a complex one and much remains to be clarified. Although we cannot enter into a discussion of soil aeration, this question is of immense importance. Directly or indirectly it affects all plants and microorganisms in the soil (Waksman, 1952; Russell, 1957; Bergman, 1959). Because of the soil's limited capacity for air, its oxygen supply is frequently at a critical level (Bergman, 1959; Currie, 1962; Lemon, 1962). The numerous studies on this subject suggest that oxygen deficiencies may be a relatively common occurrence in most soils, and localized pockets of anaerobiosis are widespread (Bergman, 1959; Greenwood, 1961; Hawkins, 1962; Lemon, 1962; Parr and Reuszer, 1962). It is evident, too, that when microbial activity is intense (as might occur during the early stages of decomposition of plant residues), the demand for oxygen may be higher than the supply and anaerobic conditions may occur quite often. Thus it is probable that the conditions of decomposition of plant residues in the soil that are highly suitable to phytotoxin formation may be more common than is generally realized. This view is supported by our more recent studies (Patrick, Toussoun, and Snyder, 1963; Patrick and Koch, 1963). The studies were conducted under natural field conditions at Harrow, Ontario, Canada, and Salinas, California, in growers' fields and field plots. They involved the use of residues from barley, rye, wheat, timothy, corn, tobacco, broccoli, and broadbean plants. The fields were treated in the normal way by the grower; the covercrop was fertilized, disked or plowed, and the subsequent crops were planted in 2 to 8 weeks. The fields were sampled at regular intervals after these crops were turned under.

In general, our studies showed that substances possessing phytotoxic properties may be formed during the decomposition of the above-mentioned plant residues under natural conditions in the field. Such substances are most likely to be formed during relatively early stages of the decomposition process. In our tests, peak of phytotoxicity was attained when the residues had been decomposing in the soil for periods of 10 to 25 days. At this stage of decomposition aqueous extracts of the various residues inhibited germination and growth of lettuce by 30 to 70%. Respiration of 6-day-old tobacco seedlings (after exposure to the extracts for 5 hours) was inhibited by 30 to 75%. Extracts were also obtained which completely inhibited the germination of lettuce, barley, corn, bean, and tobacco seed and reduced the respiration of corn root tips and tobacco seedlings by up to 95%. After the period of high phytotoxicity, the activity declined, and stimulatory effects were frequently obtained with extracts of residues that had been decomposing in the soil for 30 to 60 days. Some phytotoxicity was obtained with aqueous extracts of undecomposed residues, but inhibition of germination and growth of lettuce rarely exceeded 30% with such extracts. There were also considerable differences between fields as to the time peak toxicity was reached, the relative amount of toxicity attained, and the length of time peak phytotoxicity was maintained. In many fields the phytotoxicity rarely exceeded 30% inhibition throughout the whole decomposition period, which was considered as terminated when the plant residue could no longer be recognized. In other fields, however, peak of phytotoxicity (inhibition values over 50%) was reached in 5 to 10 days and was maintained at this level for up to 30 days. The phytotoxicity then declined, sometimes gradually but usually quite rapidly. It was further found that phyto-toxicity could be detected only in extracts of the plant residue and only if the decomposing residue had been freed of most of the soil prior to extraction. Little or no phytotoxicity was detected in aqueous extracts of the soil and plant-residue mixture in the proportions obtained directly from the field. Apparently any phyto-toxic compounds released during the decomposition of the residue were inactivated or adsorbed by the soil and very little diffusion of the substances occurred outside the immediate area of localized production. Considerable phytotoxicity could be found, however, in aqueous extracts of the soil in contact with the residue. On the other hand, no activity and sometimes a stimulation of root growth was obtained with aqueous extracts of soil that was not under the immediate influence of the decomposing plant material.

These results may explain, in part, the lack of agree-ment often found in the literature concerning the pro-duction and existence of phytotoxic substances in the soil. Our results illustrate the range of results it is pos-sible to obtain with the same sample of soil containing the same decomposing plant material. It is evident, too, from parallel researches on antibiotic formation in natural soil (Wright, 1956; Brian, 1957, 1960) that many other substances produced during the decomposi-tion of plant residues are probably just as rapidly in-activated or adsorbed by the soil colloidal matter or masked by the relatively large soil mass. It would appear, therefore, that a more logical way to examine the biological activity and types of substances produced during the decomposition of plant residues or other organic material is to separate the residue fragments from the soil prior to extraction and deal with these individually rather than with the total soil mass.

Distribution of phytotoxins in field soil.—In accord-ance with the evidence presented so far, injury to plant roots should be most frequently found in the vicinity of decomposing plant material. In normal field practice during the plowing or disking of a covercrop, the plant material is unevenly distributed throughout the soil and occurs on and in the soil in clumps of varying size. There may be micro- and macrolocations where rela-tively large quantities of residue are clumped together and others where it may be sparse. Similarly, as far as the roots of plants are concerned, during their growth through the soil they come into contact with the pieces of plant residue and so would be beneficially or adversely affected by the types of substances which are being produced at that particular time in association with that piece of residue. Thus the extent of root injury should be primarily dependent on the frequency of chance encounters of a growing root system with fragments of plant residue when the decomposition products are toxic. Under most field conditions, there-fore, the injurious effects to plants would be unevenly distributed, the severity being related to the amount of residue in the immediate vicinity of the plant. The possible exception might be in instances where ab-normally large quantities of plant residue had been added to the soil. In such cases, and if decomposition

conditions were such as to lead to toxin formation, the phytotoxic effects may be widespread and severe.

In most of our studies we attempted to support lab-oratory results by direct studies in the field. Detailed observations were carried out in fields containing plant residues at various stages of decomposition and were conducted on tobacco, lettuce, spinach, corn, and broc-coli seed and seedlings subsequently planted. A few of the more interesting observations will be described briefly. As is usual for a majority of field observations, there was considerable variability in the results. When fields with growing plants were examined, one was im-pressed by the considerable quantities of recognizable plant debris at various stages of decomposition present in many of the fields with the living roots closely inter-mingled with it. This condition was most common in the early part of the growing season when the plants were in the seedling stage and becoming established. In many instances where a root was growing in contact with or close proximity to fragments of decomposing plant debris, a discolored or sunken lesion would be found on that region of the root. Root-observation boxes revealed the same phenomenon and, as shown in Fig. 2, injury to plant roots was most severe on seg-ments of roots found growing in contact with and in the immediate vicinity of decomposing plant residues. There were also many instances of browning of the apical meristems and other radicle injury, characteristic of injury found in the laboratory; again these were found near fragments of decomposing plant debris. There were exceptions, too, and some roots were found growing through the residue without visible injury. When isolations were made from many of the lesions associated with the residue, no single known pathogen was consistently obtained. A variety of organisms were isolated from such lesions. These were predominantly common soil saprophytes.

Our studies (Patrick and Koch, 1958; Patrick, Tous-soun, and Snyder, 1963) suggest that under most field conditions, production and effective toxicity of residue decomposition products are limited mainly to the loci where suitable substrates occur, namely the micro-environments of the plant-residue fragments. Because of adsorption and inactivation in the soil, such sub-stances occur in relatively high concentrations only in and around the loci of production. In most fields be-cause of the uneven and relatively sparse distribution of plant debris, the injurious effects on plants would be limited to chance encounters of roots with loci of toxin formation.

Specific effects of phytotoxins on plants.—We would like to describe briefly some of the effects that phyto-toxic substances may produce on living plants. It has been shown (Skinner, 1918; Cochrane, 1948; Bonner, 1950; Audus, 1953) that a wide range of injurious effects may be induced by the phytotoxins on plants, apparently in the absence of other causal factors. These include delay or complete inhibition of seed germination, reduction of growth of seedlings, root injury, and wilt-ing. It was also found, by these and other investigators, that some plant species are more sensitive than others

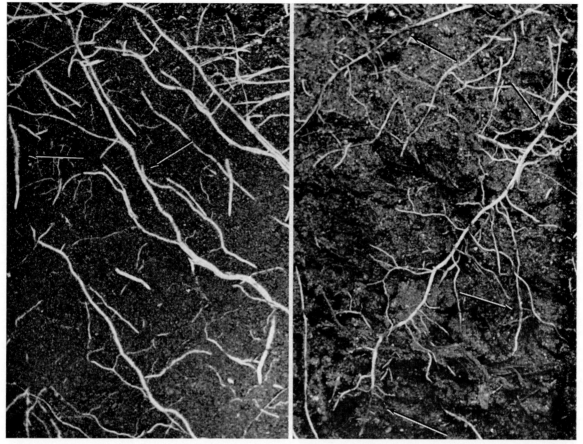

Fig. 2. Effect of decomposition of rye residue on black root rot (*Thielaviopsis basicola*) severity on Burley 1 tobacco. Left, naturally infested soil without residue; right, rye residue decomposing 15 days in same soil. Note that lesions, shown by arrows, are most severe on roots near decomposing residue.

to these substances. Similarly, as shown by Audus, some toxins are highly specific to certain plants and apparently harmless to others. We obtained a similar range of phytotoxic effects with many of the extracts obtained from decomposing plant residues (Patrick and Koch, 1958; Patrick, Toussoun, and Snyder, 1963). One of the more interesting effects noted in our studies was the rapid inhibiting effect on respiration of the test plants (corn, peach, and tobacco root tips and 5-day-old tobacco seedlings) produced by many of the extracts. Some extracts were so potent that the inhibiting effects on respiration could be measured when seedlings had been exposed to the extracts for less than 1 hour. Another striking observation was the highly selective effects of these toxins on roots. Root-hair formation was greatly inhibited (Fig. 3). The primary root or radicle appeared to be especially sensitive to such substances. The growth of the radicle was either completely or partially inhibited, while the hypocotyl often was only slightly affected. The apical-meristem region of the root became discolored and apparently was killed (Fig. 3). The effect on the apical meristems was rapid; browning was observed when the roots were exposed for less than 1 hour to the more toxic extracts. The apical-meristem injury was a consistent character-

istic effect of phytotoxins on roots. This type of injury was observed in laboratory tests and on plants growing in the field and may prove to be of great importance for diagnostic determination of phytotoxin injury in the field. Most of the injurious effects described appeared to be irreversible; there was no recovery when the seed or seedlings were removed from the toxic solutions.

When small drops of the more toxic extracts were placed on roots of lettuce, bean, or tobacco, injury in the form of depressions and discoloration were noted beneath these drops in less than 1 hour. If the root was small the region of the root under the drop collapsed and shriveled. The toxins also appeared to affect the permeability of the plant cells. Chromatographic analyses of bean stems exposed to the various toxins showed (Toussoun and Patrick, 1963) that exudation of ninhydrin-positive substances and sugars was greatly increased in those areas in contact with the toxic extracts. This occurred in the absence of any pathogen.

The role of plant-residue-derived phytotoxins in root disease.—In view of the universal occurrence of plant residues at various stages of decomposition in arable soils, the indication that among the substances derived

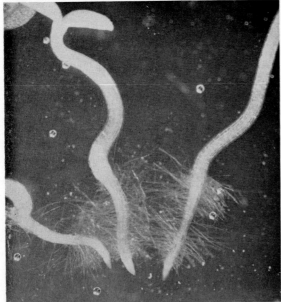

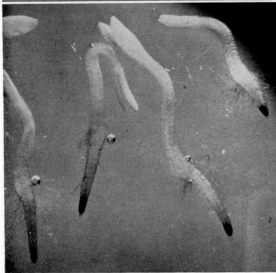

Fig. 3. Bottom, tobacco seedlings exposed to phytotoxins from decomposing plant residues showing brown and necrotic apical meristems, and inhibition of root growth and root-hair development. Top, seedlings exposed to nontoxic extracts.

from such residues some have phytotoxic properties, and the broad spectrum of injurious effects they produce on plants, it is not unreasonable to assume that phytotoxins from plant residues may, at times, be involved in the etiology of certain root diseases. There are, however, very few well-documented instances of the participation of this group of toxins in specific root diseases, either as primary causal agents or by predisposing the host to invasion by a pathogen. This, perhaps, is not altogether surprising since the existence and effective activity of phytotoxins in nature has also been difficult to prove conclusively. Some evidence is available, however; for example, Rands and Dopp (1938) showed that apparently noninjurious amounts of salicyl-

aldehyde, a phytotoxin from soil (Skinner, 1918), predisposed sugarcane to *Pythium* root rot. Graham and Greenberg (1939), made similar observations in connection with *Pythium* root rot of wheat. Their results, however, have not been fully confirmed. This may be somewhat surprising since the importance of toxins in the etiology of most plant diseases is becoming increasingly apparent. The subject has been discussed by Dimond and Waggoner (1953), Brian (1955), Ludwig (1960), and others. As indicated in these reviews, however, most of the toxins involved are products of a specific microorganism (usually the pathogen) or a microorganism-host interaction. These are beyond the scope of our present discussion.

Irrespective of the source of these toxins, however, they appear to act in a similar manner, i.e. by predisposing the plant to invasion. Ludwig (1960), in discussing the mechanism of action of toxins, states that "A variety of physiological processes in the host are affected and the over-all effect can best be summarized by saying that they induce premature 'senescence.' In this, resistance factors of the host may be overcome or specific nutrients required by the microorganisms may become available." In many such instances, as shown by Kerr (1956), the initial production of the toxin may be external to the host and the effect one of preconditioning the host to the advance of the pathogen. It was further shown by Ludwig and his associates (Ludwig et al., 1956; Ludwig, 1957) that the induction of the seedling-blight phase of barley inoculated with *Helminthosporium sativum* is associated with the production by the fungus of toxic substances that are not only prerequisite for the infection of the host tissue by the pathogen, but may also predispose the roots and the basal parts of the plant to attack by other organisms not normally regarded as strong pathogens. It would thus appear that this group of externally active toxins, in many instances, would be nonspecific to the organism they aid or the host they injure. Our studies (Patrick and Koch, 1958, 1963; Patrick, Toussoun, and Snyder, 1963; Toussoun and Patrick, 1963) suggest, too, that the toxins need not necessarily be formed by the specific pathogen growing saprophytically on the host or in the soil on an organic food base. They can also be derived independently from plant residue during decomposition. In each instance the initial effect of the toxins is primarily on the host. As a consequence, it is quite possible that an invasion by a given organism need not always be directly correlated with its own capacity for toxin production and the pathogen need not become established solely through its own efforts. The role of toxins in root infection, therefore, should not be thought of as being the sole province of the pathogen because phytotoxic substances from other sources in the soil may be important in the infection phenomenon. This is clearly illustrated by root rots of bean caused by *Fusarium solani* f. *phaseoli, Rhizoctonia solani,* and *Thielaviopsis basicola* (Toussoun and Patrick, 1963), and by black root rot of tobacco caused by *Thielaviopsis basicola* (Patrick and Koch, 1963).

Our studies (Toussoun and Patrick, 1963) showed that root rot of bean was greatly increased when, previous to inoculation with each of the pathogens, the roots were exposed to toxic extracts obtained from decomposing plant residues. The disease-enhancing activity of the various toxic extracts was demonstrated in laboratory experiments with *Fusarium solani* f. *phaseoli*. As shown in Fig. 4, lesions developed more rapidly and

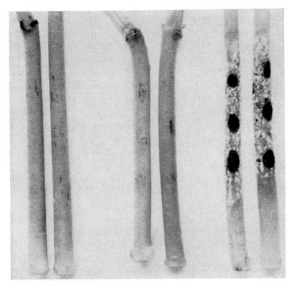

Fig. 4. Lesions on bean stems treated with phytotoxins and *Fusarium solani* f. *phaseoli*. Treatment in pairs, left to right, pathogen alone; toxin alone; pathogen + toxin.

Fig. 5. Effect of phytotoxins from decomposing plant residues on severity of black root rot (caused by *Thielaviopsis basicola*) on moderately resistant (top) and highly resistant (bottom) tobacco varieties. Treatments, left to right: control; toxin; toxin + pathogen; pathogen alone. Note that the resistance was considerably reduced by pretreatment with toxin.

were more extensive in the presence of toxic decomposition products than in the distilled water controls. The toxins, also, altered the permeability of the host tissues and resulted in increased exudation of amino acids and probably other substances.

A similar disease-enhancing activity of toxins from plant residues was illustrated for black root rot of tobacco caused by *Thielaviopsis basicola* (Patrick and Koch, 1963). When one group of healthy tobacco plants was exposed to toxins, and then it and the control group were inoculated with the same pathogenic isolates of *T. basicola* and subjected to the same environmental conditions, invasion, colonization, and disease development were considerably more severe in the plants which had been pretreated with the toxins (Fig. 5). There were no significant differences between the 16 different tobacco varieties tested or the different isolates of *T. basicola*. The disease was equally destructive to roots of the resistant and the susceptible varieties after the toxin treatment. Exposure to the toxins resulted in an apparent breakdown of resistance. The effect of the toxins appears to be primarily on the host plant rather than on the fungus. Colonization of tissues and sporulation of the fungus were considerably more extensive in the roots treated with the toxins. Apparently relatively noninjurious concentrations of toxins are effective for this purpose. The precise manner in which the toxins predispose the tobacco roots to fungal invasion, or what biochemical and physiological changes are involved in increased host susceptibility are not clear.

Considerably more direct evidence is desirable on relative frequency of formation, concentration, and activity of plant-residue-derived phytotoxins in field soils. Nevertheless, there is sufficient evidence to suggest that in addition to their direct toxic action, involvement in the etiology of root disease is one of their most important roles. They appear to be of particular importance in root diseases caused by the more primitive, soil-inhabiting, unspecialized parasites. Such organisms have a wide distribution in the soil. They constitute part of the normal microbiological environment of the roots of plants. A simple and direct host-parasite causal relation does not usually hold for this group of root parasites. A prerequisite to the establishment of a successful and progressive root infection by such parasites is that the passive and active resistance of the host be overcome by other factors—the host must be predisposed to infection. This can be accomplished in many ways and many factors appear to be involved. As indicated by Ludwig (1960) and others, phytotoxins produced by the parasite or, as shown here, phytotoxins derived independently during crop-residue decomposition are equally effective as host-conditioning factors.

It is also known (Garrett, 1956; Yarwood, 1959) that physical environment and other soil factors that have adverse effects on the growth of the plant will also increase root-rot severity. For example, *Thielaviopsis basicola* is destructive only to young plants and those growing under adverse conditions (Lucas, 1958). Cold, wet, heavy soils or other conditions unfavorable for the growth of tobacco usually result in a marked increase in disease severity. Decomposition of rye, timothy, and other crops used in the tobacco rotations is often accompanied by the formation of phytotoxic substances. Such substances are produced most consistently and at highest concentrations under conditions of high soil moisture, in relatively heavy soils, and at cool temperatures. The similarity of environmental conditions causing severe black root rot to those that are most favorable for the type of plant-residue decomposition which gives rise to the formation of phytotoxic substances suggests possible relations between increased susceptibility of tobacco to the pathogen and the occurrence of phytotoxic substances in the soil.

Similarly, as pointed out by Wilhelm (1959), as more knowledge about root rots is obtained the demarcation line between pathogens and saprophytes becomes increasingly indistinct. It is becoming apparent also that certain root rots may not be caused by a specific pathogen but may often be due to organisms that ordinarily cause little damage but which are able, when conditions are favorable, to become suddenly more aggressive. Among the factors of the soil environment most likely to cause this shift in behavior could be the conditions which determine the production of toxic products during the decomposition of plant residues. The formation of these compounds and their weakening effect on the plant root may be all that is necessary to trigger the dormant pathogenic activity of a number of organisms lying in or about the root and which would lead to a root rot of the kind which would be attributed to a "complex" rather than a specific pathogen. Crop residues have been shown to be important in the practical control of certain root rots. It is also evident that residues of a crop that while growing has suppressive effect on a given pathogen, can later enhance the invasive capacity of this very same pathogen. These differences in effects apparently are dependent on the environmental factors that rule the ecological niche at that particular time. Since toxic products are most often obtained from crop residues that had been decomposing under cold, wet, or anaerobic conditions, it seems reasonable to postulate that conditions not associated with the formation of phytotoxic substances, may prevent the disease, while decomposition conditions conducive to the formation of these compounds would tend to increase root-rot severity. The results presented, along with the other discussions, may thus have important implications with respect to biological control of soil-borne plant pathogens through proper use of plant residues. Some of the positive and negative aspects that might be encountered have been brought out which may explain why in some instances an apparently similar practice may give rise to contradictory results.

Phytotoxicity associated with specific plants.—Of general interest to the problem of plant-derived phytotoxins is the question of the precise source of such substances. It is often important to know whether the main phytotoxic components are the result of specific toxic compounds characteristic of the plant species,

intermediate reduction products formed when decomposition of plant residues takes place under adverse soil conditions, or synthesis products of soil microorganisms using plant material as substrate. As pointed out in this discussion and as indicated by other investigators (Bonner, 1950; Audus, 1953; H. Martin, 1957; Börner, 1960; Woods, 1960; Winter, 1961), it is impossible to generalize on this question. Many plant species are known to contain specific toxins; thus each species must be considered separately. In most instances, however, it would appear that the phytotoxicity may be the combination of all the sources mentioned.

As far as practical field applications are concerned, a distinction of the precise source of phytotoxins may appear to be relatively unimportant since, irrespective of source, they eventually reach the soil and affect plants in their characteristic ways. This is not entirely true, however, particularly in selecting a suitable plant residue for use in biological control. It is obvious that use of residues of plants that are known to contain toxins would be undesirable. It is conceivable, too, that some of the disappointing results obtained with certain plant residues or organic amendments used in biological control may have been due to this phenomenon. Phytotoxic substances have been obtained from water extracts of barley, rye, wheat and oat straw, soybean, clover and timothy hay, corn and sorghum stalks, bromegrass, sweetclover stems, and many other plants among those most likely to be used in crop rotations as sources of organic amendments (H. Martin, 1957; Börner, 1960; Woods, 1960; Nielsen, Cuddy, and Woods, 1960; Guenzi and McCalla, 1962). The significance of some of these compounds in stubble-mulch farming has been pointed out by McCalla and Duley (1950), Nielsen, Cuddy and Woods, and Guenzi and McCalla. Their results suggest that these substances may be of importance in inhibiting germination of seed and the initial growth of seedlings.

We should also consider briefly a few of the problems of phytotoxicity most frequently associated with specific plants and the evidence for specific crop sequences and associations. Over the centuries, largely through empirical trial and error, growers observed certain definite crop-to-crop influences, often with high specificities in the relations. This is often true in the case of certain weeds and, although they are not usually used in the rotations, they are rarely absent and should be considered. There is no doubt that weeds are injurious to crops, but the mechanism of such injury is in doubt. A common explanation has been one of competition for space, light, and nutrients (Welbank, 1961, 1962). Often, however, additional mechanisms, suggestive of phytotoxins, appear to be involved (Garb, 1961). As shown by Mann and Barnes (1947, 1952), the presence of twitch grass (*Holcus mollis* L.) halved the growth of barley even when the plants were grown so thinly that the competition for root space was avoided. From their experiments they concluded that the injurious effect of one grass on another seems to be proved, but that the effect varies from one grass to another and seems to be a specific property of each grass. As indicated by Audus (1953), phytotoxic substances have also been found in the tissues of many weeds, including couch grass [*Agropyron repens* (L.) Beauv.], the hawkweeds (*Hieracium* spp.), and the goldenrods (*Solidago* spp.). According to Welbank (1961), however, in many of these instances, experimental evidence is insufficient to support the interpretation either in the matter of toxin production or effectiveness in nature. On the other hand, Grümmer (1961) found that growth of many cultivated plants is severely reduced by the presence of *Agropyron repens* even in small amounts. Some plants frequently are only slightly affected. Little is known of the chemical nature of the toxic principle. Grümmer isolated several phenolic substances, including *p*-hydroxybenzoic and vanillic acids, and agropyrene from the roots and rhizomes of *Agropyron*. He also found that while many of the phenolic substances are set free on the death of the organs, only negligible amounts were given off into the surrounding medium by living roots. Welbank (1960) showed that greater toxic effects are produced by the decay of *Agropyron* residues under anaerobic than under aerobic conditions.

The inhibiting effects of black walnut trees (*Juglans nigra* L.) and butternut (*J. cinerea* L.) on tomatoes, potatoes, alfalfa, apple, and other plants is another well-known example of phytotoxic effects associated with specific plants (Massey, 1925; Davis, 1928; Gries, 1943; H. Martin, 1957). Bode (1958) showed that the major source of the toxic substances (juglone and probably some tannins) diffusing into the soil may be from the leaves.

We do not wish to catalog the many other examples of phytotoxic effects associated with specific plants that have been described, since these may be found in the recent reviews. Similarly, some of the plants concerned are not those that are likely to be used as sources of plant residues or organic amendments for biological control. We will, however, refer briefly to the so-called "soil-sickness" or "replant" problems that are associated with specific crops of economic importance. A general characteristic of this group of problems is that when a crop is grown in the same soil for long periods of time subsequent plantings often grow poorly in comparison with similar plantings in virgin soil or in soil never cropped to the species concerned. The condition is usually species specific and other crops grow well in the same soil. A number of crops are subject to this phenomenon. The better known examples include flax (*Linum* spp.), bromegrass (*Bromus inermis* Leyss.), guayule (*Parthenium argentatum* A. Gray), apple, peach, and citrus. The main causes of these phenomena are not well understood even though they have been subjects of extensive investigations. The main theories advanced to explain the difficulties are the usual ones, namely: nutritional deficiency, some parasitic organism yet undetected, or production of toxins either directly by the plant or through microbial decomposition of the residues. When the cause can be identified, it may be any one of these or involve all three, in which case we have the so-called "complex."

With bromegrass, Benedict (1941) showed that the condition known as "sodbinding," in which old stands of bromegrass thin out, was due to phytotoxins from the plant. He showed that leachings of dried roots of bromegrass or from decomposing plant material are inhibitory, even in small amounts, to growth of bromegrass seedlings. Meyers and Anderson (1942) tried to identify the condition with nitrogen deficiency and, although they obtained some improvement with nitrogen application, they found that even in well-fertilized bromegrass soils the yields were much smaller than from soils in which bromegrass had not previously been grown. A phytotoxin also appears to be the main cause of the self-inhibition of guayule plants. Bonner and Galston (1944) and Bonner (1946, 1950) provided well-documented evidence showing that a phytotoxic substance leached from guayule plants strongly inhibited the growth of guayule seedlings They isolated a crystalline compound, transcinnamic acid, from the leachings of guayule roots which they believed to be the main toxic component involved. Guayule seedlings were 100 times more sensitive to this compound than tomato seedlings.

The "soil-sickness" or "replant" problems of apple, peach, and citrus are problems of economic importance, particularly in areas where it is uneconomical to abandon the old sites or when the old orchards have to be renovated. As indicated by Börner (1959, 1960), replant phenomena occur in many areas of the world. Difficulties in replanting apples have been reported from Europe, peach in Canada and California, and citrus in California.

In many areas of Europe (Grümmer, 1955; Schander, 1956; Börner, 1959) young apple replants cannot be planted in old apple-orchard sites. Apple trees planted in such locations show retarded growth and shortened internodes, the roots show varying degrees of discoloration, and growth of the taproot is reduced. The plants recover when they are moved to soil that had not been used for growing apples. Börner, in summarizing the present status of the subject, writes, "The existing publications state that, besides an impoverishment of soils of microelements and a damage of apple roots by nematodes, the root residues remaining in the soil play an important role in this problem." Fastabend (1955) showed that residues from apple roots or water leached through the affected soils produced the toxicity symptoms in seedlings when added to healthy soil. Börner identified phlorizin as a natural constituent of apple-root bark. The compound is apparently broken down in the soil, giving rise to phloretin, phloroglucinol, *p*-hydroxyhydrocinnamic acid, and *p*-hydroxybenzoic acid, all of which showed varying degrees of phytotoxicity to apple seedlings. Börner (1959, 1960) was unable to determine, however, "whether the direct action of phlorizin and its breakdown products are the main causes of apple soil sickness."

An apparently similar problem in California on citrus has been investigated by J. P. Martin and his associates (Martin, 1948, 1950; Martin and Batchelor, 1952; Martin, Aldrich, et al., 1953; Martin and Ervin, 1958). The primary causes of the "slow decline of citrus," as the condition is commonly called, is as yet not clear and many factors appear to be involved.

The peach-replant problem has been reported by

Proebsting and Gilmore (1941) from California, and Upshall and Ruhnke (1935) and Koch (1955) from Canada. Proebsting and Gilmore suggested that one of the causes of tree failure is a phytotoxin produced from root residues of old peach trees. We have investigated this problem extensively in Harrow and find that a number of factors appear to be involved (Patrick, 1955; Wensley, 1956; Ward and Durkee, 1956; Mountain and Boyce, 1958; Harrison, 1958; Mountain and Patrick, 1959). It was found (Patrick, 1955; Ward and Durkee, 1956) that peach-root bark contains a cyanogenic glucoside, amygdalin, in relatively large amounts. Amygdalin is also present in living roots along with the hydrolyzing enzyme, emulsin. Amygdalin, as such, is not toxic to peach roots or peach seedlings, but its degradation products, benzaldehyde and hydrogen cyanide, are highly toxic. Breakdown of amygdalin into the toxic components is readily accomplished by microorganisms normally found in peach soil and by the enzymes (emulsin and perhaps others) in the peach-root cells. It was further found (Mountain and Patrick, 1959) that the nematode *Pratylenchus penetrans,* found in peach soils of southwestern Ontario in large numbers, can bring about hydrolysis of amygdalin. This it can do directly, by means of its own enzyme systems, and indirectly through mechanical damage of the root cells. This allows amygdalin and the enzyme to be brought together and thereby releases the toxic components. On the basis of these studies, it is suggested that the peach-replant problem is a true root-rot complex in that many causal factors appear to be involved, none of which alone can produce the entire disease syndrome. Any lesion-producing agency, however—nematodes, fungi or insects—that could bring about the rupturing of the cells containing the two potentially toxic components could act as an incitant. Superimposed upon the pathology of root necrosis are the phytotoxic effects of root residues of the former trees. It is evident, however, that irrespective of the causal organism involved the production of phytotoxic substances through the hydrolysis of amygdalin is the main mechanism involved in the entire etiological sequence of degeneration of peach roots.

CONCLUSIONS.—There is no doubt that the beneficial effects of plant residues far outweigh their detrimental effects, but we have chosen to stress the latter, since these usually are overlooked. We attempted to show how these may operate, when they occur, and the best means of avoiding them so that the full beneficial potential of plant residues as biological-control agents can be attained. It is evident that on adding a certain plant residue or organic amendment to the soil a wide range of effects must be expected. In the early stages of decomposition and with reduced oxygen, phytotoxic effects appear to predominate. The planting of subsequent crops should thus be avoided during this critical time.

It is impossible to generalize, however, as to the waiting period necessary or the best crop to use as the organic amendment, since plant species and maturity, soil type, decomposition conditions, cultural practices, and other environmental factors operating at

that particular time often determine whether the end result is beneficial or detrimental. Since, however, phytotoxicity is associated mainly with the decomposing plant residues, it is a relatively simple matter to test these for phytotoxicity even in the field. The subsequent planting can thus be delayed until peak phytotoxicity has passed. Some plant residues are more toxic than others to certain crops while others contain specific toxins; these should be avoided as organic amendments. Similarly, certain crops, soils, cultural practices, and environmental conditions maintain the phytotoxic effect for longer periods, and each crop, disease, and locality must be evaluated individually. The phytotoxic effects do not persist indefinitely and eventually disappear from most soils.

Thus although plant residues and organic amendments may aid in the biological control of soil-borne plant pathogens, this effect may, at times, be modified or negated. More information is required, therefore, on the effect of such substances on root disease before accurate predictions can be made on the final outcome resulting from their use.

LITERATURE CITED

AUDUS, L. J. 1953. Plant growth substances. Leonard Hill, Ltd., London. 465 p.

BAKER, K. F. 1962. Principles of heat treatment of soil and planting material. J. Australian Inst. Agr. Sci. 28: 118-126.

BEAR, F. E. 1951. Soils and fertilizers. John Wiley & Sons Inc., New York; Chapman & Hall, Ltd., London. 374 p.

BENEDICT, H. M. 1941. The inhibiting effect of dead roots on the growth of bromegrass. J. Am. Soc. Agron. 33: 1108-1109.

BERGMAN, H. F. 1959. Oxygen deficiency as a cause of disease in plants. Botan. Rev. 25: 417-485.

BERKELEY, G. H. 1944. Root rots of certain non-cereal crops. Botan. Rev. 10: 67-123.

BLAIR, I. D. 1943. Behaviour of the fungus *Rhizoctonia solani* Kühn in the soil. Ann. Appl. Biol. 30: 118-127.

BODE, H. R. 1958. Beiträge zur Kenntnis allelopathischer Erscheinungen bei einigen Juglandaceen. Planta 51: 440-480.

BONNER, J. 1946. Further investigation of toxic substances which arise from guayule plants: relation of toxic substances to the growth of guayule in soil. Botan. Gaz. 107: 343-351.

BONNER, J. 1950. The role of toxic substances in the interactions of higher plants. Botan. Rev. 16: 51-65.

BONNER, J., and A. W. GALSTON. 1944. Toxic substances from the culture media of guayule which may inhibit growth. Botan. Gaz. 106: 185-198.

BÖRNER, H. 1959. The apple replant problem. I. The excretion of phlorizin from apple root residues and its role in the soil sickness problem. Contrib. Boyce Thompson Inst. 20: 39-56.

BÖRNER, H. 1960. Liberation of organic substances from higher plants and their role in the soil sickness problem. Botan. Rev. 26: 393-424.

BRAUNS, F. E. 1952. The chemistry of lignin. Academic Press, New York. 808 p.

BRIAN, P. W. 1955. The role of toxins in the etiology of plant diseases caused by fungi and bacteria. *In* Microbial ecology, Symp. Soc. Gen. Microbiol. 5: 294-319.

BRIAN, P. W. 1957. The ecological significance of antibiotic production. *In* Microbial ecology. Symp. Soc. Gen. Microbiol. 7: 168-188.

BRIAN, P. W. 1960. Antagonistic and competitive mechanisms limiting survival and activity of fungi in soil.

p. 115-129. *In* D. Parkinson and J. S. Waid [ed.], Ecology of soil fungi, Liverpool University Press, Liverpool.

BUTLER, F. C. 1961. Root and foot rot disease of wheat. N. S. Wales Dept. Agr. Sci. Bull. 77, 98 p.

CHILVERS, G. A. 1962. A particulate inoculum for non-sporing fungi. Nature (London) 195: 93-94.

CHINN, S. H. F., and R. J. LEDINGHAM. 1957. Studies on the influence of various substances on the germination of *Helminthosporium sativum* spores in soil. Can. J. Botany 35: 697-701.

CHINN, S. H. F., R. J. LEDINGHAM, B. J. SALLANS, and P. M. SIMMONDS. 1953. A mechanism for the control of common root rot of wheat. Phytopathology 43: 701.

CHRISTOU, T., and W. C. SNYDER. 1962. Penetration and host-parasite relationships of *Fusarium solani* f. *phaseoli* in the bean plant. Phytopathology 52: 219-226.

CLARK, F. E. 1939. Effects of soil amendments upon the bacterial populations associated with roots of wheat. Trans. Kansas Acad. Sci. 42: 91-96.

CLARK, F. E. 1942. Experiments toward the control of the take-all disease of wheat and the *Phymatotrichum* root rot of cotton. U.S. Dept. Agr. Tech. Bull. 835, 27 p.

CLARK, F. E., and C. THOM. 1939. Effects of organic amendments upon the microflora of the rhizosphere of cotton and wheat. Trans. 3rd. Com. Intern. Soc. Soil Science, p. 94-100.

COCHRANE, V. W. 1948. The role of plant residues in the etiology of root rot. Phytopathology 38: 185-196.

COOK, R. J. 1962. Influence of barley straw on the early stages of pathogenesis in Fusarium root rot of bean. (Abstr.) Phytopathology 52: 728.

CURRIE, J. A. 1962. The importance of aeration in providing the right conditions for plant growth. J. Sci. Food Agr. 13: 380-385.

DARPOUX, H. 1960. Biological interference with epidemics. p. 521-565. *In* J. G. Horsfall and A. E. Dimond [ed.], Plant pathology, an advanced treatise, Academic Press, New York.

DAVIS, E. F. 1928. The toxic principle of *Juglans nigra* as identified with synthetic juglone, and its toxic effects on tomato and alfalfa plants. Am. J. Botany 15: 620.

DIMOND, A. E., and P. E. WAGGONER. 1953. On the nature and role of vivotoxins in plant disease. Phytopathology 43: 229-235.

DOBBS, C. G., and W. H. HINSON. 1953. A widespread fungistasis in soils. Nature (London) 172: 197-199.

DORAN, W. L. 1928. The growth of tobacco and brown root rot of tobacco as affected by timothy infusions of different ages. J. Agr. Res. 36: 281-287.

DURBIN, R. D. 1959. Factors affecting the bacterial distribution of *Rhizoctonia solani* with special reference to CO_2 concentration. Am. J. Botany 46: 22-25.

FASTABEND, H. 1955. Über die Ursachen der Bodenmüdigkeit in Obstbaumschulen. Landwirtschaft-Angewandte Wissenschaft. Sonderheft Gartenbau IV, Landwirtschaftsverlag, Hiltrup/Münster. 95 p.

FELLOWS, H. 1929. Studies of certain soil phases of the wheat take-all problem. Phytopathology 19: 103.

FERGUSON, J. 1953. Factors in colonization of sclerotia by soil organisms. (Abstr.) Phytopathology 43: 471.

FERGUSON, J. 1957. Beneficial soil microorganisms. p. 237-254. *In* K. F. Baker [ed.], The U. C. System for producing healthy container-grown crops. California Agr. Expt. Sta. Manual 23, 332 p.

FLENTJE, N. T. 1957. Studies on *Pellicularia filamentosa* (Pat.) Rogers III. Trans. Brit. Mycol. Soc. 40: 322-336.

GARB, S. 1961. Differential growth-inhibitors produced by plants. Botan. Rev. 27: 422-443.

GARRETT, S. D. 1938. Soil conditions and the take-all disease of wheat. III. Decomposition of the resting mycelium of *Ophiobolus graminis* in infected wheat stubble buried in soil. Ann. Appl. Biol. 25: 742-766.

GARRETT, S. D. 1940. Soil conditions and the take-all disease of wheat. V. Further experiments on the survival of *Ophiobolus graminis* in infected wheat stubble buried in the soil. Ann. Appl. Biol. 27: 199-204.

GARRETT, S. D. 1941. Soil conditions and the take-all disease of wheat. VI. The effect of plant nutrition upon disease resistance. Ann. Appl. Biol. 28: 14-18.

GARRETT, S. D. 1956. Biology of root-infecting fungi. Cambridge University Press, London and New York. 292 p.

GARRETT, S. D. 1959. Biology and ecology of root disease fungi. p. 309-316. *In* C. S. Holton et al. [ed.], Plant pathology, problems and progress 1908-1958, University of Wisconsin Press, Madison, Wisc.

GARRETT, S. D., and H. H. MANN. 1948. Soil conditions and the take-all disease of wheat. X. Control of the disease under continuous cultivation of a spring-sown cereal. Ann. Appl. Biol. 35: 435-442.

GRAHAM, V. E., and L. GREENBERG. 1939. The effect of salicylic aldehyde on the infection of wheat by *Pythium arrhenomanes* Drechsler, and the destruction of the aldehyde by *Actinomyces erythropolis* and *Penicillium* sp. Can. J. Res., Sec. C, 17: 52-56.

GREENWOOD, D. J. 1961. The effect of oxygen concentration on the decomposition of organic materials in soil. Plant Soil 14: 360-376.

GRIES, G. A. 1943. Juglone—the active agent in walnut toxicity. Northern Nut Grow. Assoc. Ann. Rep. 34: 52-55.

GRÜMMER, G. 1955. Die gegenseitige Beeinflussung höherer Pflanzen, Allelopathie. Gustav Fischer Verlag, Jena. 162 p.

GRÜMMER, G. 1961. The role of toxic substances in the interrelationships between higher plants. Soc. Exptl. Biol. Symp. 15: 219-228.

GUENZI, W. D., and T. M. McCALLA. 1962. Inhibition of germination and seedling development by crop residues. Soil Sci. Soc. Am. Proc. 26: 456-458.

HARRISON, T. B. 1958. Replanting peach trees. Am. Fruit Grower 78: 29.

HAWKINS, J. C. 1962. The effects of cultivation on aeration, drainage and other soil factors important in plant growth. J. Sci. Food Agr. 13: 386-391.

HILDEBRAND, A. A., and P. M. WEST. 1941. Strawberry root rot in relation to microbiological changes induced in root rot soil by the incorporation of certain cover crops. Can. J. Res., Sec. C, 19: 183-198.

KERR, A. 1956. Some interactions between plant roots and pathogenic soil fungi. Australian J. Biol. Sci. 9: 45-52.

KERR, A. 1961. A study of tomato root surface organisms antagonistic to *Verticillium albo-atrum*. Trans. Brit. Mycol. Soc. 44: 365-371.

KING, C. J., C. HOPE, and E. D. HEATON. 1934. Some microbiological activities affected in manurial control of cotton root rot. J. Agr. Res. 49: 1093-1107.

KOCH, L. W. 1955. The peach replant problem in Ontario. I. Symptomatology and distribution. Can. J. Botany 33: 450-460.

KRASIL'NIKOV, N. A. 1958. Soil micro-organisms and higher plants. Published by Acad. Sciences U.S.S.R. Moscow. (Transl. by Y. Halperin) (Engl. ed.) National Science Foundation, Washington, D.C. 1961. 474 p.

LEMON, E. R. 1962. Soil aeration and plant root relations. I. Theory. Agron. J. 54: 167-170.

LINGAPPA, B. T., and J. L. LOCKWOOD. 1962. Relationship of soil microbes to the widespread soil fungistasis. (Abstr.) Phytopathology 52: 739.

LOCHHEAD, A. G. 1959. Rhizosphere microorganisms in relation to root-disease fungi. p. 327-338. *In* C. S. Holton et al. [ed.], Plant pathology, problems and progress 1908-1958. University of Wisconsin Press, Madison, Wisc.

LOCHHEAD, A. G., and G. B. LANDERKIN. 1949. Aspects of antagonisms between microorganisms in soil. Plant Soil 1: 271-276.

LOEHWING, W. F. 1937. Root interactions of plants. Botan. Rev. 3: 195-239.

LUCAS, G. B. 1958. Diseases of tobacco. The Scarecrow Press, Inc., New York. 498 p.

LUDWIG, R. A. 1957. Toxin production of *Helminthosporium sativum* P. K. & B. and its significance in disease development. Can. J. Botany 35: 291-303.

LUDWIG, R. A. 1960. Toxins. vol. 2, p. 315-357. *In* J. G. Horsfall and A. E. Dimond [ed.], Plant pathology, an advanced treatise, Academic Press, New York and London.

LUDWIG, R. A., R. V. CLARK, J. B. JULIEN, and D. B. ROBINSON. 1956. Studies on the seedling disease of barley caused by *Helminthosporium sativum* P. K. & B. Can. J. Botany 34: 653-673.

LYLE, E. W., A. A. DUNLAP, H. O. HILL, and B. D. HARGROVE. 1948. Control of cotton root rot by sweet clover in rotation. Texas Agr. Expt. Sta. Bull. 699, 21 p.

MANN, H. H., and T. W. BARNES. 1947. The competition between barley and certain weeds under controlled conditions. II. Competition with *Holcus mollis*. Ann. Appl. Biol. 34: 252-266.

MANN, H. H., and T. W. BARNES. 1952. The competition between barley and certain weeds under controlled conditions. V. Competition with clover considered as a weed. Ann. Appl. Biol. 39: 111-119.

MARTIN, H. 1957. Chemical aspects of ecology in relation to agriculture. Canada Department of Agriculture, Publication 1015, Ottawa, Ontario. 96 p.

MARTIN, J. P. 1948. Effect of fumigation, fertilization, and various other soil treatments on growth of orange seedlings in old citrus soils. Soil Sci. 66: 273-288.

MARTIN, J. P. 1950. Effects of various leaching treatments on growth of orange seedlings in old citrus soil. Soil Sci. 69: 107-122.

MARTIN, J. P., D. G. ALDRICH, W. S. MURPHY, and G. R. BRADFORD. 1953. Effect of soil fumigation on growth and chemical composition of citrus plants. Soil Sci. 75: 137-151.

MARTIN, J. P., and L. D. BATCHELOR. 1952. The difficulties of replanting lands to the same species of orchard trees. Proc. Ann. Rio Grande Valley Hort. Inst., 6th, 1952, p. 1-10.

MARTIN, J. P., and J. O. ERVIN. 1958. Greenhouse studies on the influence of other crops and of organic materials on growth of orange seedlings in old citrus soil. Soil Sci. 85: 141-147.

MASSEY, A. B. 1925. Antagonism of the walnuts (*Juglans nigra* L. and *J. cinerea* L.) in certain plant associations. Phytopathology 15: 773-784.

McCALLA, T. M., and F. L. DULEY. 1950. Stubble mulch studies. III. Influence of soil microorganisms and crop residues on the germination, growth and direction of root growth of corn seedlings. Soil Sci. Soc. Am. Proc. (1949) 14: 196-199.

MENZIES, J. D. 1962. Effect of anaerobic fermentation in soil on survival of sclerotia of *Verticillium dahliae*. (Abstr.) Phytopathology 52: 743.

MENZIES, J. D. 1963. Survival of microbial plant pathogen in soil. Botan. Rev. 29: 79-122.

MEYERS, H. E., and K. L. ANDERSON. 1942. Bromegrass toxicity vs. nitrogen starvation. J. Am. Soc. Agron. 34: 770-773.

MILLAR, C. E. 1955. Soil fertility. John Wiley & Sons, Inc., New York; Chapman & Hall, London. 436 p.

MILLARD, W. A. 1923. Common scab of potatoes. Ann. Appl. Biol. 10: 70-88.

MILLER, C. E., L. M. TURK, and H. D. FOTH. 1958. Fundamentals of soil science. John Wiley & Sons, Inc., New York. 526 p.

MITCHELL, R., and M. ALEXANDER. 1961a. The mycolytic phenomenon and biological control of Fusarium in soil. Nature (London) 190: 109-110.

MITCHELL, R., and M. ALEXANDER. 1961b. Chitin and the biological control of *Fusarium* diseases. Plant Disease Reptr. 45: 487-490.

MITCHELL, R. B., D. R. HOOTON, and F. E. CLARK. 1941. Soil bacteriological studies on the control of *Phymatotrichum* root rot of cotton. J. Agr. Res. 63: 535-547.

MOORE, W. D. 1949. Flooding as a means of destroying the sclerotia of *Sclerotinia sclerotiorum*. Phytopathology 39: 920-927.

MOUNTAIN, W. B., and H. R. BOYCE. 1958. The peach replant problem in Ontario. VI. The relation of *Pratylenchus penetrans* to the growth of young peach trees. Can. J. Botany 36: 135-151.

MOUNTAIN, W. B., and Z. A. PATRICK. 1959. The peach replant problem in Ontario. VII. The pathogenicity of *Pratylenchus penetrans* (Cobb, 1917) Filip. & Stek. 1941. Can. J. Botany 37: 459-470.

NASH, SHIRLEY M., and W. C. SNYDER. 1962. Quantitative estimations by plate counts of propagules of the bean root rot *Fusarium* in field soils. Phytopathology 52: 567-572.

NIELSEN, K. F., T. F. CUDDY, and W. B. WOODS. 1960. The influence of the extracts of some crops and soil residues on germination and growth. Can. J. Plant Sci. 40: 188-197.

NORMAN, A. G. 1943. Soil organic matter. I. Problems in the chemistry of soil organic matter. Soil Sci. Soc. Am. Proc. (1942) 7: 7-15.

OSWALD, J. W., and O. A. LORENZ. 1956. Soybeans as a green manure crop for the prevention of potato scab. (Abstr.) Phytopathology 46: 22.

PAMMEL, L. H. 1890. Cotton root rot. Texas Agr. Expt. Sta. Bull. 7, 30 p.

PAPAVIZAS, G. C., and C. B. DAVEY. 1962. Activity of Rhizoctonia in soil as affected by carbon dioxide. Phytopathology 52: 759-766.

PARR, J. F., and H. W. REUSZER. 1962. Organic matter decomposition as influenced by oxygen level and flow rate of gasses in the constant relation method. Soil Sci. Soc. Am. Proc. 26: 552-556.

PATRICK, Z. A. 1955. The peach replant problem in Ontario. II. Toxic substances from microbial decomposition products of peach root residues. Can. J. Botany 33: 461-486.

PATRICK, Z. A., and L. W. KOCH. 1958. Inhibition of respiration, germination and growth by substances arising during the decomposition of certain plant residues in the soil. Can. J. Botany 36: 621-647.

PATRICK, Z. A., and L. W. KOCH. 1963. The adverse influence of phytotoxic substances from decomposing plant residues on resistance of tobacco to black root rot. Can. J. Botany 41: 447-458.

PATRICK, Z. A., T. A. TOUSSOUN, and W. C. SNYDER. 1963. Phytotoxic substances in arable soils associated with decomposition of plant residues. Phytopathology 53: 152-161.

PROEBSTING, E. L., and A. E. GILMORE. 1941. The relation of peach root toxicity to the re-establishing of peach orchards. Proc. Am. Soc. Hort. Sci. 38: 21-26. 1941.

RANDS, R. D., and E. DOPP. 1938. The influence of certain harmful soil constituents on severity of Pythium root rot of sugar cane. J. Agr. Res. 56: 53-68.

RIPLEY, R. O. 1941. Influence of crops upon those which follow. Sci. Agr. 21: 522-583.

RUSSELL, SIR E. 1957. The world of the soil. Collins, London. 237 p.

SANFORD, G. B. 1926. Some factors affecting the pathogenicity of *Actinomyces scabies*. Phytopathology 16: 525-547.

SANFORD, G. B. 1959. Root disease fungi as affected by other soil organisms. p. 367-376. *In* C. S. Holton et al. [ed.], Plant pathology, problems and progress 1908-1958. University of Wisconsin Press, Madison, Wisc.

SCHANDER, H. 1956. Die Bodenmüdigkeit bei Obstgehölzen. Bayrischer Landwirtschaftsverlag, Bonn-München-Wien. 66 p.

SCHREIBER, L. R., and R. J. GREEN, JR. 1962. Comparative survival of mycelium, conidia and microsclerotia of *Verticillium albo-atrum* in mineral soil. Phytopathology 52: 288-289.

SEQUEIRA, L. 1962. Influence of organic amendments on survival of *Fusarium oxysporum* f. *cubense* in the soil. Phytopathology 52: 976-982.

SIMMONDS, P. M. 1941. Root rots of cereals. Botan. Rev. 7: 308-332.

SIMMONDS, P. M. 1953. Root rots of cereals. II. Botan. Rev. 19: 131-146.

SKINNER, J. J. 1918. Soil aldehydes. A scientific study of a new class of soil constituents unfavorable to crops, their occurrence, properties and elimination in practical agriculture. J. Franklin Inst. 186: 165-186, 289-316, 449-480, 557-584, 723-741.

SNYDER, W. C. 1960. Antagonism as a plant disease control principle. p. 127-136. *In* Biological and chemical control of plant and animal pests. American Association for the Advancement of Science, Washington, D. C.

SNYDER, W. C., M. N. SCHROTH, and T. CHRISTOU. 1959. Effect of plant residues on root rot of bean. Phytopathology 49: 755-756.

STOVER, R. H. 1962. Fusarial wilt (Panama disease) of bananas and other *Musa* species. Commonwealth Mycol. Inst. (Kew, England) Phytopathol. Paper No. 4, 117 p.

TEPPER, J. G. O. 1893. "Take-all," and its remedies. Agr. Gaz. N. S. Wales 3: 69-72.

TOUSSOUN, T. A., SHIRLEY M. NASH, and W. C. SNYDER. 1960. Effect of nitrogen sources and glucose on the pathogenesis of *Fusarium solani* f. *phaseoli*. Phytopathology 50: 137-140.

TOUSSOUN, T. A., and Z. A. PATRICK. 1963. Effect of phytotoxic substances from decomposing plant residues on root rot of bean. Phytopathology 53: 265-270.

TOUSSOUN, T. A., Z. A. PATRICK, and W. C. SNYDER. 1963. Influence of crop residue decomposition products on the germination of *Fusarium solani* f. *phaseoli* chlamydospores in soil. Nature (London) 197: 1314-1316.

TRIBE, H. T. 1957. On the parasitism of *Sclerotinia trifoliorum* by *Coniothyrium minitans*. Trans. Brit. Mycol. Soc. 40: 489-499.

UPSHALL, W. H., and G. N. RUHNKE. 1935. Growth of fruit tree stocks as influenced by a previous crop of peach trees. Sci. Agr. 16: 16-20.

WAKSMAN, S. A. 1952. Soil microbiology. John Wiley & Sons, New York. 356 p.

WARCUP, J. H. 1955. On the origin of colonies of fungi developing on soil dilution plates. Trans. Brit. Mycol. Soc. 38: 298-301.

WARCUP, J. H. 1957. Studies on the occurrence and activity of fungi in a wheat field soil. Trans. Brit. Mycol. Soc. 40: 237-262.

WARD, G. M., and A. B. DURKEE. 1956. The peach replant problem in Ontario. III. Amygdalin content in peach root tissues. Can. J. Botany 34: 419-422.

WEINHOLD, A. R., J. W. OSWALD, T. BOWMAN, J. BISHOP, and D. WRIGHT. 1964. Influence of green manures and crop rotation on common scab of potato. Am. Potato J. 41: 265-273.

WEINKE, K. E. 1962. The influence of nitrogen on the root disease of bean caused by *Fusarium solani* f. *phaseoli*. (Abstr.) Phytopathology 52: 757.

WELBANK, P. J. 1960. Toxin production from *Agropyron repens*. Brit. Ecol. Soc. Symp. (1959) 1: 158-164.

WELBANK, P. J. 1961. A study of the nitrogen and water factors in competition with *Agropyron repens*. Ann. Botany (London) [N.S.] 25: 116-137.

WELBANK, P. J. 1962. The effects of competition with *Agropyron repens* of nitrogen- and water-supply on the nitrogen content of *Impatiens parviflora*. Ann. Botany (London) [N. S.] 26: 361-373.

WENSLEY, R. N. 1956. The peach replant problem in Ontario. IV. Fungi associated with replant failure and their importance in fumigated and nonfumigated soils. Can. J. Botany 34: 967-981.

WILHELM, S. 1959. Parasitism and pathogenesis of root disease fungi. p. 356-366. *In* C. S. Holton et al. [ed.], Plant pathology, problems and progress 1908-1958, University Wisconsin Press, Madison, Wisc.

WINTER, A. G. 1961. New physiological and biological aspects in the interrelationships between higher plants. Symp. Soc. Exptl. Biol. 15: 229-244.

WINTER, A. G., H. PEUSS, and F. SCHÖNBECK. 1960. The influence of biotic factors on the development of soil fungi. p. 76-83. *In* D. Parkinson and J. S. Waid [ed.], Ecology of soil fungi, Liverpool University Press, Liverpool.

WOOD, R. K. S., and M. TVEIT. 1955. Control of plant diseases by use of antagonistic organisms. Botan. Rev. 21: 441-492.

WOODS, F. W. 1960. Biological antagonisms due to phytotoxic root exudates. Botan. Rev. 26: 546-569.

WRIGHT, J. M. 1956. The production of antibiotics in soil. III. Production of gliotoxin in wheatstraw buried in soil. Ann. Appl. Biol. 44: 461-466.

YARWOOD, C. E. 1959. Predisposition. vol. 1, p. 521-562. *In* J. G. Horsfall and A. E. Dimond [ed.], Plant pathology, an advanced treatise, Academic Press, New York and London.

ZENTMYER, G. A., and A. O. PAULUS. 1957. *Phytophthora* avocado root rot. California Agr. Expt. Sta. Circ. 465, 15 p.

► DISCUSSION OF Z. A. PATRICK AND T. A. TOUSSOUN PAPER

R. J. Cook:

We have made a detailed study of the effects of mature barley straw on the steps of pathogenesis of *Fusarium solani* f. *phaseoli* on beans. Chlamydospore germination, growth through the rhizosphere, buildup of thalli, and penetration of the hypocotyl were all studied around the host in live, infested soil, both with and without 2% mature barley straw. When beans were planted 10 days after adding straw to the soil, chlamydospore germination in the vicinity of the host was reduced by approximately one half. Those that did germinate exhibited reduced growth in the vicinity of the host with only a few fungus germlings forming thalli on the hypocotyl. When straw was not present, fungus growth and thallus formation were abundant. All thalli forming on the hypocotyl penetrated regardless of whether or not straw was present; thus, the influence of barley straw in *Fusarium* root rot of bean appears to be due to influences in the prepenetration stages of pathogenesis.

L. W. Boyle:

We compared peanuts grown where residues of cotton, soybeans, corn, and a green rye cover had been buried below a depth of 5 in by tillage. The roots and pods where the cotton residue had been buried were very darkly discolored. No specific microorganisms were evident on or in the pod tissue. The dark pods appeared to be "chemically scorched." Less discoloration was found on pods grown following soybeans, and still less following corn. No discoloration was found on pods following the green rye cover. Greater reductions in yield were correlated with greater degrees of discoloration. No contact between organic matter and pods indicates these phytotoxic principles disperse in soil.

H. Burström:

Have you succeeded in identifying any of these toxic compounds, and do you know whether decomposition is necessary for them to appear? I ask because even fresh plant material contains many compounds—some 100 have been listed—which are phytotoxic and particularly kill sensitive root tips. The more specific ones of these are unsaturated lactones.

Z. A. Patrick:

We have not attempted to identify the toxic compounds. We suspect that many of them are intermediate breakdown products of lignin, cellulose, and other plant constituents. Many appear to be phenolic in nature. It is also true that many plant species contain specific phytotoxins in their tissues.

C. B. Davey:

By varying the C:N ratio of an amendment, by an unnatural but culturally practical method, Papavizas and I found that within a C:N ratio range of about 40 to 100, the competitive saprophytic activity of *Rhizoctonia* was substantially suppressed for a period of several weeks. At C:N ratios above and particularly below this range, the activity of the *Rhizoctonia* was either unaffected (above) or considerably enhanced (below the indicated C:N ratio range).

D. W. Burke:

Phytotoxin production during organic-matter decomposition in the soil appears to be a very important factor in the problem of developing reproducible measures for the biological control of bean *Fusarium* root-rot.

Field application of certain organic meals in or near the seed furrow control the disease in warm, well-aerated soil. The same treatment, however, may be detrimental to plant growth in cold or heavily irrigated soil.

Materials of comparatively narrow C:N ratio, such as alfalfa and bean-straw meal, produce phytotoxicity more often than wide C:N materials, like barley and wheat straws. Nevertheless, the more nitrogenous materials give better disease control than carbonaceous materials, if they are composted or applied to the soil a month before bean seeds are planted. Such preconditioning of organic materials largely removes their phytotoxic effects.

Many different soil fungi grown on autoclaved organic materials largely remove phytotoxic tendencies of the materials. Two *Fusidium* isolates grown on barley straw produced a gibberellinlike effect on bean plants, when the compost was placed in the seed furrow at a rate of 50 lb per acre.

K. H. Garren:

We have found that deep and irreversible burial of covercrop and other residue is essential to control *Sclerotium rolfsii* Sacc. on peanuts (*Arachis hypogaea* L.). We are grateful to Doctors Patrick and Toussoun for giving us additional ammunition for use against "organic gardeners," who are upset over what we are doing to their beloved organic material. I feel, however, that additional stress should be put on the time of exposure to phytotoxins from decomposing crop residues. For example, where we do not bury crop residues, it is about 6 weeks before appreciable *S. rolfsii* infection shows up. Is this sufficient time to be sure that decomposition toxins are not "triggering" some or all of the *S. rolfsii* infection?

Z. A. Patrick:

This could be possible. We have found with *Thielaviopsis basicola* and *Fusarium solani* f. *phaseoli*, for

example, that substances obtained in the relatively early stages of decomposition of crop residues increase disease severity while those obtained during the later stages of decomposition have no effect on the disease.

H. Katznelson:

Have you been able to associate the production of phytotoxic substances by different crop residues with specific types of bacteria, such as *Clostridia*, facultative bacilli, or other organisms? In work on strawberry root rot in the early 1940's there was a relation between the decomposition of clover and strawberry and specific bacterial groups, and this was related to the manifestation of root rot, whereas soybean favored the development of healthy roots and its breakdown was associated with the development of other bacterial groups.

Z. A. Patrick:

We have not carried out very many isolations of microorganisms from the decomposing plant residues. We have been considering doing this as it is a very important part of the problem. We suspect that there may be specific organisms associated with some of these residues.

H. Katznelson:

Further to the comments of Doctors Burke and Davey regarding C:N ratios in the control of root diseases, we found that a substance such as dried blood, of low C:N ratio, could control root rot of strawberry. On the other hand, glucose could also do this, suggesting that different chemical mechanisms of control may have been operative. The decomposition of dried blood results in the rapid liberation of ammonia and an increase in pH, both of which might have reduced the disease; glucose breakdown could be to acidic products which may be effective. Acetic acid, for example, also reduced the incidence of this root rot.

Z. A. Patrick:

This is true, and as we have tried to point out, decomposition of similar crop residues, or organic amendments, can give rise to beneficial effects at one time and detrimental ones at another. These contrasting effects appear to depend on conditions of decomposition and probably other soil factors.

L. F. Johnson:

Would you comment on whether or not the effect produced by residues on certain fungi in soil is caused by the same toxic principle(s) that affects plants?

Z. A. Patrick:

In some cases these may be similar compounds because in some of our studies we tested some of the phytotoxic extracts on *Thielaviopsis basicola*, for example, and found that they were fungistatic and the growth of the fungus was inhibited in culture. We have not tested all our extracts on soil fungi but of those that were tested, some stimulated the growth of fungi, others inhibited their growth, and some had no effects.

D. F. Weber:

The phytotoxic activity of organic-matter breakdown is tempered by soil *mineral* types and previous residue history. Have you noted differences in this activity due to the above?

In an experiment using virgin sandy loam very low

in organic matter, and the same soil type previously cropped and heavily manured for several years, quite large amendments of wheat straw and alfalfa hay showed marked phytotoxicity towards alfalfa seedlings in the virgin soil, but none in the cropped soil.

Z. A. Patrick:

We have not dealt with this problem very exhaustively, but in the tests that we carried out it was observed that the phytotoxic effect was more severe in sandy soil which had poor buffering ability.

W. B. Bollen:

Lower soil temperature resulting from sawdust mulches favors incidence of red stele disease of strawberry in wet soil where the fungus pathogen is present. Development of the fungus under field conditions is not as great when the sawdust is incorporated with the soil.

Certain bark materials mixed with infected soil appear effective in reducing the red stele. Ground whole Douglas fir bark (0.18%N), untreated, had little or no effect; however, ammoniated bark (4.3%N) lowered the incidence to about 50%, while hot-water-extracted bark almost completely suppressed the disease. Ammoniated, hot-water-extracted bark was less influential, and in this respect was comparable to the ammoniated plain bark. The main factors involved in these suppressions have not been determined. Bark phenolic acids may play a role.

G. W. F. Sewell:

Would you comment on the relation between the phytotoxic principles and their fungistatic activity in root rot of tobacco?

Z. A. Patrick:

From our studies, we believe that the main effect of the toxins is on the host rather than on the fungus. The host tissues appear to be predisposed so that black root rot (*Thielaviopsis basicola*) of tobacco is much more severe in plants treated with the toxins.

J. P. Martin:

The enhancement of biological-control processes by covercropping could be considered to occur in two steps. Growth of the new crop may favor the development of antagonists in the rhizosphere. In addition, antagonistic species may greatly increase in numbers after the covercrop has been turned into the soil. In greenhouse pot-culture (3-gal crock) studies with citrus at Riverside, it was noted that growth of certain crops in old citrus soil was much more effective in reducing root injury and improving subsequent growth of citrus plants than was applying the crop (top) residues to the soil and incubating for several months prior to replanting citrus.

K. C. Lu:

Please comment on the relation between C:N ratio and soil-toxin theory. It is a known fact that the wider the C:N ratio, the more soil nitrogen will be tied up. Unless sufficient nitrogen is added with wide C:N residues, the plants would show signs of nitrogen deficiency. The question whether the decomposed residue products are toxic to agricultural plants is a complex one. Our experiments with sunflower in the greenhouse and ponderosa-pine seedlings in the field where 100 tons per acre of organic amendments were incorporated with sufficient nitrogen fertilizer to narrow the C:N ratio have shown good results in yields and in minimizing disease incidence.

Z. A. Patrick:

In experiments conducted in Berkeley, California, on the control of bean root rot by means of organic residues, it was shown that materials having a high C:N ratio reduced the severity of the disease. This control was obtained through the tying up of the soil nitrogen by organisms decomposing the organic residue. The pathogen under such circumstances was deprived of this nutrient and its attack on the plant was thereby weakened. Addition of nitrogen fertilizer to the roots of such plants obviated nitrogen deficiency of the plants without increasing disease incidence, since the pathogen normally attacks the hypocotyl. These same residues, however, decomposing under cold, wet, or anaerobic conditions, may yield toxic products. These products, as we have shown, may increase the severity of bean root rot. It is then evident, therefore, that organic materials of high C:N ratio may control the disease or may aggravate it. These different effects are determined in great measure, we feel, by the current ecological, environmental factors of the soil under which decomposition of organic material takes place.

Effect of Mineral Nutrients on Soil Microorganisms and Plant Disease

T. S. SADASIVAN—*Botany Laboratory, University of Madras, Madras 5, India.*

The complex problem of mineral nutrition of higher plants can no longer be considered in isolation from the teeming millions of microorganisms of the soil. This interaction between the microbes and higher plants poses three problems: competition for available minerals, mobilization of unavailable complexes, and immobilization.

Instances of microbiologically induced mineral deficiencies in higher plants are not wanting, as for example the grey-speck disease of oats (Gerretsen, 1937; Leach, Bulman, and Kroeker, 1954). Microbial competition for nutrients can be particularly serious in soils containing chronically low amounts of an element. This is understandable since the absorbing surface of microbial cells is many times that of the root (Leeper, 1952). That microbes successfully compete with higher plants for available soil phosphorus when the ratios of phosphorus:carbon in soil organic matter fall below a minimum has been shown by Kaila (1949). Millikan (1942) reported that zinc deficiency was more severe in soils ploughed from cereal stubble than after a period of fallow; this supports the earlier observation of Ark (1937) that reinoculation of sterilized soil with unsterile soil brought about deficiency symptoms in fruit trees afflicted with little-leaf disease.

Of the microorganisms that play an important role in conditioning mineral uptake by plants may be mentioned the classical example of ectotrophic mycorrhizae, where the entry of PO_4 ions is accelerated by the fungal associate (Harley and Brierley, 1955; Morrison, 1962a), while the uptake of SO_4 ions remains unaffected (Morrison, 1962b). Microorganisms converting nonavailable Fe, S, K, etc., are well known (see Waksman, 1952). In this category also fall the well-known processes of soil nitrification and denitrification brought about by soil microorganisms.

Since the discovery of the rhizosphere (Hiltner, 1904), the whole subject has received a new orientation, and the existence of a two-way traffic of metabolites from and into the rhizosphere is now recognized (Lundegårdh, 1945; Sadasivan, 1960).

The advent of our knowledge that antibiotics and toxins are formed in the rhizosphere and in soils, in situ, intensified the quest for information on changes in the microecology with many inorganic and organic soil amendments with a view to reducing the effects of soil-borne pathogens. To these has to be added the use of the experimental technique of foliar sprays of inorganic and organic substances, which have shown profound effects on the rhizosphere (Ramachandra-Reddy, 1960; Venkata Ram, 1960; Lakshmi-Kumari, 1961).

Much of the evidence presented here is the outcome of small-scale controlled laboratory trials. It is to be hoped that eventually some general principles will emerge from these studies that will be capable of extension to the broad question of biological control in the field.

THE MICROFLORA.—*Soil populations.*—Changes in soil microflora following organic and inorganic amendments are known (Waksman, 1922). Zachariah (1949) has examined a number of soils given N, P, and K amendments at certain concentrations and indicated that normally dormant genera of fungi were stimulated without affecting the common soil inhabitants. She found that KCl, $Ca_3(PO_4)_2$, KNO_3, $(NH_4)_2SO_4$ and wood ash exerted a beneficial effect on fungal populations quantitatively. In a similar study on the survival of *Fusarium vasinfectum,* the cotton-wilt pathogen, on Cholodny slides buried in amended garden and wilt-infested soils, Thankam (1949) noticed that the application of both $(NH_4)_2SO_4$ and $NaNO_3$ to the soil increased the survival period of the fungus at all levels of nitrogen tried. The bacterial numbers in the soils amended with inorganic fertilizers decreased considerably with increase in survival of *F. vasinfectum* on Cholodny slides. The adverse influence of some of the inorganic fertilizers on the development of bacteria in soil has been reported by Waksman (1922), who observed in field trials that $(NH_4)_2SO_4$ stimulated the development of fungi with a definite decrease in numbers of bacteria, but that the application of $NaNO_3$ had the opposite effect.

The partial disappearance of pathogenic soil fusaria, their inability to sporulate well, and their consequent inability to colonize organic matter in trace-element-amended soils has been extensively studied in this laboratory. Sarojini (1950) studied disease development by *Fusarium udum* in *Cajanus cajan* (pigeon pea) and its colonization and survival in *F. udum*-infested soil amended with B, Mn, and Zn. Trace-element-treated series on the whole decreased the percentage of pre-emergence wilt as compared with the control. Boron at 20 ppm and Mn and Zn at 40 and 80 ppm reduced losses due to pre-emergence wilt and improved the vigour of host plants. Combinations of all three elements even at 20 ppm were detrimental to seedling emergence and growth of the host plant. Presoaking the seeds in solutions of these elements, however, improved germination, suggesting that this might be a feasible way to use such combinations for disease control.

The colonization of buried cotton stubble by fusaria in trace-element treatments was very much lower than in the controls, which showed 100% colonization throughout the course of the experiment. As has been the experience elsewhere (Sadasivan, 1939) with *Fusarium culmorum*, the wheat-foot-rot organism, fusaria were the dominant colonizers on buried cotton stubble in *Fusarium*-infested soils here. With increase in level of trace element, there was a fall in percentage colonization by fusaria. In B and Mn soil amendments, in the first few weeks' incubation, *Mucor, Macrophomina,* and *Cunninghamella* appeared in large numbers on the stubble. Subsequently, fusaria, aspergilli, and penicillia became dominant colonizers, although in the early period fusaria showed poor colonization. Zinc proved different in that colonization of fusaria began to fall from the second month onwards, the effect being marked at 40- and 80-ppm levels (Sarojini, 1950). These observations made with reference to Zn treatments on *Fusarium* colonization are comparable to the results reported by Millikan (1938, 1942) in Australia. Data on survival of *F. udum* in infected host stubble in garden soil in the presence of trace elements at 20-, 40-, and 80-ppm levels showed that these elements, especially Zn, tended to hasten the disappearance of the fungus. Efficacy of Mn amendment in controlling pigeon-pea wilt, presumably by reducing the survival of *F. udum* as evidenced by poor recovery of the fungus from the host roots and consequent low infection rates, has since been confirmed by Subramanian (1963).

Sulochana (1952*a*) included Al, Co, Li, Mo, and Ni in addition to B, Mn, and Zn and studied their effect on the saprophytic behaviour of *Fusarium vasinfectum* and other fusaria in wilt-infested cottonfield soils. The results indicated that all the eight element amendments markedly reduced the colonization by fusaria and further restricted its survival in organic matter over long periods. Colonization of buried cotton stems by fusaria was fairly high at the 20-ppm level of Mn, Mo, Ni, and Zn, while the other four elements appreciably retarded their colonization for several weeks after the treatments. At and above 100-ppm levels of Zn, Co, Al, and B, complete suppression of fusaria was recorded after 10 to 12 weeks' incubation. Survival of *F. vasinfectum* in artificially inoculated stubble continued to be 100% up to 12 months in unamended controls and in Co-, Ni-, and Mo-amended series. Survival was relatively good in Al, B, and Mn treatments. Among all elements tried, Zn alone was effective in hastening the disappearance of the pathogen. Sulochana (1952*b*) further showed that those trace elements (Al, Li, Mn, and Zn) bringing about loss of viability of the pathogen, favoured increased activities of actinomycetes, bacteria, and fungi in the amended soils, while other trace elements (B, Ni, Co, and Mo) exerted direct toxic effects on fusaria.

Further work by Varadarajan (1953) on trace-element effects at different levels of pH on the microflora of wilt-infested soils revealed some of the complexities of these interrelations. Besides the expected general increase in bacterial numbers with increasing pH from 4.0 to 6.0, a stimulation was also noted from the trace elements. Generally, the trace elements stimulated bacterial numbers but suppressed fungal populations. The order of trace elements in bacterial stimulation was Zn > B > Mn, whereas the order of fungus inhibition was Mn > Zn > B.

Rhizosphere populations.—Similar studies on the rhizosphere microflora of cotton plants (Varadarajan, 1953) also showed the same stimulation of bacterial numbers by trace elements, in the order Mn > Zn > B. Fungus populations responded less consistently, usually tending to increase in the rhizosphere following trace-element treatment but later decreasing below the control. Although the effects of trace elements on soil populations are not yet sufficiently understood to permit generalizations, it seems clear that these nutrients are important factors in microbial ecology. More complete elucidation of their role would seem to hold promise of their use in root-disease control through their effects on microbial populations.

PATHOGENS.—*Effects of mineral nutrition on pathogens.*—One of the difficult aspects in the control of soil-borne fungi has been the survival and colonization of most of these organisms on dead plant material. Some interesting results that have emerged from a study of colonization and survival have been presented earlier. Even with 1 week's incubation, a 100% colonization of fusaria on buried cotton stubble in wilt-infested soils was noticed. In all trace-element amendments, the most important result was a pronounced decrease in colonization by fusaria as compared with control soils with increasing concentration and incubation period. Percentage colonization decreased at the end of 2 weeks in all treatments. The lowest percentage colonization on stubble by fusaria after 12 weeks' incubation was noticed in amendments of 40 ppm Mn and 20 ppm Fe + 10 ppm Mn. Colonization of other fungi was also reduced by Fe and Mn amendments, individually and in combination, though not in the same sequence or to the same extent as fusaria (Varadarajan, 1953).

Soil amendments of $CaHPO_4$ at the 1.0% level not only retarded microbial decomposition of vegetative mycelium of *Fusarium vasinfectum* on Cholodny slides but also prolonged its survival by promoting chlamydospore and conidia formation (Subramanian, 1946). Inorganic amendments such as KCl, $(NH_4)_2SO_4$, $Ca_3(PO_4)_2$, and KNO_3 in the range of 0.01 to 5.0% to soil did not reduce the percentage colonization by fusaria on buried cotton-root bits; but *Macrophomina phaseoli*, among others, was partially eliminated (Zachariah, 1949).

Physiological effects.—Trace elements increased sporulation by *Fusarium vasinfectum, F. moniliforme,* and *F. udum* at lower concentrations (0.05 to 0.25 ppm) but at higher concentrations their effect was inhibitory

(Yogeswari, 1950). In pure culture, trace elements generally inhibited sporulation of *F. vasinfectum*. Of these, Li and Mo showed maximum inhibition of micro- and macroconidia production (Sulochana, 1952c). Germination studies using the Cholodny-slide technique revealed that trace elements in concentrations of 50 to 400 ppm also inhibited germination of spores of *F. vasinfectum* in the order Zn > Mo > Li > Al > Ni > B > Co > Mn (Table 1). These results emphasize that the trace-element concentration in the soil and rhizosphere regions is a critical factor in attaining suitable "inoculum potential" by root-infecting fungi.

The influence of nitrogen on sclerotia production and sporulation by five species of *Curvularia* isolated from ricefield soil and the rhizosphere of rice seedlings was studied in vitro. The results indicated that $NaNO_3$ and $(NH_4)_2HPO_4$ supported sporulation of most of the species of *Curvularia* grown on bacterial cellulose substrate. Potassium nitrate followed by $NaNO_3$ promoted sclerotia production in isolates of *C. pallescens;* ammoniacal sources were not favourable. The isolates of *C. lunata* produced only a few sclerotia on KNO_3 and none on $NaNO_3$. Among ammonium salts tried, only NH_4NO_3 slightly favoured sclerotia production in all these species (Ramachandra-Reddy, 1960).

After the discovery that organisms produce toxins and antibiotics in soils and in the rhizosphere, many interesting examples of the effects of trace elements have been adduced. Subramanian (1956a) investigated the effects of trace elements on the antibiotic activity of fusaric acid, which Kalyanasundaram (1955, 1958) has shown to be produced by *Fusarium* in both sterile and natural soil. Subramanian found that Mn, Cu, Co, and Ni reduced the antibiotic activity of fusaric acid against the test bacterium, Ni being the most effective, while Fe, Zn, B, and Al were ineffective. Gäumann (1951) reported that toxicity of lycomarasmin, a toxin produced by *F. lycopersici*, increased almost tenfold when applied together with Fe. This was later confirmed by other workers (Waggoner and Dimond, 1953; Scheffer and Walker, 1953).

It has been reported from our laboratory that Fe increases the toxicity of dialysed culture filtrates of *Fusarium vasinfectum* to cut shoots of cotton (Lak-

shminarayanan, 1955). Studies in vitro on the production of pectolytic enzymes by *F. vasinfectum* have shown that a deficiency of Fe induced very low production of PME (pectin methyl esterase). Iron at a concentration of less than 1 ppm seems essential for the production of PME. Fe, however, does not seem to have any effect on PG (polygalacturonase) production by *F. vasinfectum* (Subramanian, 1956a).

Omission of Mn from the culture medium resulted in a strikingly high PME as well as PG production. Progressive increase in the level of Mn in the culture solution caused an inhibition of production of both PME and PG, but the effects were more marked on PME. At 0.2 ppm the value for PME fell to nearly 40% of that without Mn. Iron and Mn thus have opposite effects on PME production, at least in the lower concentrations, and these results may explain the beneficial effects of Fe + Mn amendments (see Fig. 3) reported by Varadarajan (1953). It appears that Fe, which is essential for both the well-being of the plant and the production of pectolytic enzymes by the pathogen, should be applied not alone but along with Mn, which nullifies the effect of Fe on the production of enzymes by the pathogen without prejudice to the host.

The essentiality of Zn for the production of PME in cultures was evident, while PG was unaffected by Zn deficiency. An optimum concentration of Zn was indicated to be necessary for the maximal production of fusaric acid (Kalyanasundaram and Saraswathi-Devi, 1955). The optimum concentration of Zn for PME production is much higher (2.0 ppm) than for fusaric acid production (0.24 ppm). A further increase in concentration of Zn, however, inhibited PME production. Addition of Cu at an optimum level of 0.10 ppm resulted in very high PME production, while the optimum level for PG production was slightly higher (0.15 ppm). A further increase in Cu caused a reduction in both PME and PG. At 0.4 ppm Mo promoted peak PME and PG production by the fungus, although Mo did not appear to be essential for growth and enzyme production by the organism.

Comparing the behaviour of the different trace elements, it may be summarized that Fe, Zn, Cu, and Mo caused increased PME production by *Fusarium vasin-*

TABLE 1. Effect of trace-element amendments on germination of *Fusarium vasinfectum* in wilt-infested soil, and on sporulation in vitro

Trace-element amendments	Cholodny slide technique, % conidia germination, at various trace-element concentrations				In vitro culture: sporulation in millions, at 2 trace-element concentrations	
	50 ppm	100 ppm	200 ppm	400 ppm	50 ppm	100 ppm
Al	34	30	12	7	4.2	2.7
B	46	35	12	10	6.6	5.8
Co	57	42	39	18	4.9	4.2
Li	28	27	13	6	2.5	0.003
Mn	74	57	26	11	11.2	8.6
Mo	27	20	5	4	2.8	1.9
Ni	22	25	20	8	7.3	4.1
Zn	24	21	6	5	6.0	4.1
Control	66				12.1	

fectum and Mn had a definite inhibitory action. While Cu and Mo augmented PG production, Zn and Mn were inhibitory, and Fe had apparently no significant role in the synthesis of PG (Subramanian, 1956a).

The effects of certain inorganic nitrogen salts on the cellulolytic activities of soil fungi was studied with bacterial cellulose membranes. A good many of the fungi investigated possessed considerable cellulolytic activity, and this varied according to the nitrogen source. With $NaNO_3$, *Periconia* sp. exhibited very poor cellulolytic activity, whereas other fungi were quite active. In general, ammoniacal sources of nitrogen, especially NH_4NO_3 and $(NH_4)_2HPO_4$, seemed to favour cellulose decomposition by *Periconia* sp., *Penicillium* sp., and *Trichoderma* sp., while *Aspergillus nidulans* gave almost an identical response with any nitrogen source; and ammoniacal sources, except $(NH_4)_2HPO_4$, reduced cellulolytic activity of *Humicola grisea* and *Chaetomium globosum*. In *Chaetomium bostryochodes* all ammonium sources reduced the activity; *Curvularia pallescens* decomposed cellulose better with nitrates than with ammoniacal sources. Ammonium chloride appeared to reduce cellulolytic activity of *Phoma* sp. and *Memnoniella echinata* as compared with other nitrogen sources (Ramachandra-Reddy, 1960).

It may be mentioned here that Mn and Mo stimulated dehydrogenation of glucose, sucrose, and mannitol by rhizosphere bacteria in vitro, while Zn and B were not consistently stimulatory and Cu inhibited it in a majority of cases. The effect of the particular trace element also depended on the species of microorganism and was more pronounced on growing cells than on resting cells (Bershova, 1960).

The above findings suggest that the efficacy of soil amendments with trace elements is bound to be higher on active rhizosphere microflora than on microorganisms of uncropped soil.

HOSTS.—*Changes in susceptibility.*—The influence of mineral nutrition on the sensitivity of tomato plants to the toxin fusaric acid has been studied (Zähner, 1955). The technique used was to grow a wilt-susceptible variety of tomato (Tuckswood) under different nitrogen, phosphorus, and potassium levels and to treat cut shoots of these with fusaric acid by dipping the cut stem. The results showed that plants with normal nutrition were highly susceptible to the wilt toxin, whereas under- and overnourished ones were less sensitive. Generally, variation in N:K and N:P resulted in differences in sensitivity, but variation in P:K did not. Therefore, N nutrition appeared to be of great significance in physiologically altering the sensitivity of tomato plants to toxins. This finding of the importance of nitrogen among the major elements in conditioning tissues to toxin damage is in accord with the results presented by many investigators on intact plants (Garrett, 1956, p. 225). Studying the factors affecting the invasion of tomato roots by *Verticillium albo-atrum*, Selman and Buckley (1959) concluded that the effect of low N in reducing the incidence of infection was unlikely to be directly upon the inoculum potential of the fungus but was probably dependent upon its

effect on host metabolism. But Toussoun, Nash, and Snyder (1960) reported that in the case of *Fusarium solani* f. *phaseoli* on bean, nitrogen favours early penetration of the host, subsequent development of internal mycelia, and pathogenesis, organic sources of N being more effective than inorganic sources.

Soil amendments with N, P, and K (0.25%) have given some interesting results with *Fusarium* wilt of cotton in this laboratory. A mixture of NPK only slightly altered the wilt index as compared with the untreated control; single-element treatments brought about more obvious results: N amendment increased while P and K markedly reduced the wilt index (Fig. 1). An analysis of the microflora revealed significant

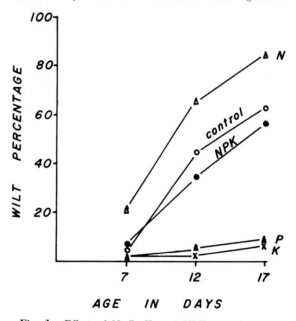

Fig. 1. Effect of N, P, K, and NPK amendments on fusarium wilt of cotton.

changes in the rhizosphere. The total numbers of rhizosphere fungi and bacteria were highest in N-amended series, whereas those of actinomycetes were highest with P and K treatments. More interesting, however, were the results obtained regarding the numbers of microorganisms antagonistic to the pathogen *Fusarium vasinfectum* (Fig. 2); the percentage of antagonistic microorganisms was high with P and K treatments and low with N treatment (T. A. R. Subbulakshmi, unpublished). Fusaria-infested black cotton soil amended with Fe and Mn singly and in combination showed the highest wilt percentage in susceptible cotton with Mn followed by Fe amendment. Adding Fe+Mn, however, lowered the wilt index as compared with individual amendments (Fig. 3). Although the initial symptom of vein clearing consequent upon initiation of the wilt syndrome by the pathogen was apparent in all treatments, after 2 weeks all the plants grown in Fe+Mn-amended series recovered completely with none of the initial symptoms. The combination of 40 ppm Fe and 80 ppm Mn was superior to individual elements. Percentage of wilt was highest at pH 8.3 and lowest at

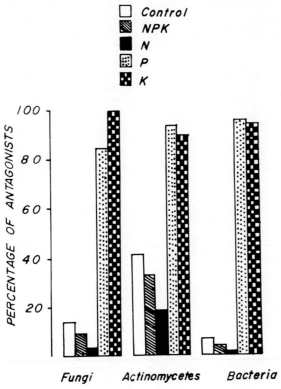

Fig. 2. Effect of N, P, K, and NPK amendments on the antagonistic microorganisms in the rhizosphere of susceptible cotton.

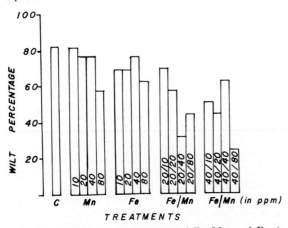

Fig. 3. Effect on wilt of cotton of Fe, Mn, and Fe + Mn amendments to *Fusarium*-infested soil.

pH 6.0 in every amended series. Incidentally, germination percentage of cotton seeds was the lowest at pH 8.3 (the pH of the natural wilt-infested soil) owing to pre-emergence failure, while maximum germination took place at pH 6.0. The results of this experiment indicate, therefore, that the cotton-wilt pathogen, *F. vasinfectum*, is amenable to control in pot-culture experiments by Fe+Mn soil amendments at pH 6.0 (Varadarajan, 1953).

Changes in inorganic constituents.—Impairment of semipermeability of plasma membranes by toxin action

has been emphasized by many workers in wilt diseases. This was evidenced by an increase of 300-fold in the cuticular excretions of K ions, in addition to increase in Na and Ca ions, amino acids, and peptides by tomato plants wilted by toxin action (Linskens, 1955). An increased electrical conductivity of plant sap due perhaps to accumulation of ions was recorded in *Fusarium*-infected cotton plants (Gnanam, 1956). A considerable decrease of cations such as Mg, Ca, and K with a slight increase of Mn has been reported in obviously wilting plants (Sadasivan and Saraswathi-Devi, 1957). But the disease escapes (plants showing no symptoms) registered a marked increase in Mg and Mn and a decrease of Ca and K. These findings indicate an ionic imbalance brought about by the presence of heavy inoculum of the pathogen in soil, whether or not the syndrome is apparent. A high Mg content of the tissue appears to reduce toxaemia. It is needless to emphasize the key role played by Mg ions in the various enzyme reactions of carbohydrate metabolism and of the respiratory-chain phosphorylations. Of particular interest here are the findings of Kalyanasundaram (1952, 1955), who recorded a reduction in ascorbic acid and an increase in reducing sugars in *Fusarium*-infected cotton plants. That fusaric acid, a vivotoxin reported in this disease, also uncouples oxidative phosphorylation by tomato and cauliflower mitochondria was reported by Sanwal and Waygood (1961), and perhaps this takes place by the removal of Mg ions. Conclusions about the effects of this primary loss in selectivity of host cells with the onset of wilting cannot be drawn until a thorough study of the sites of accumulation and depletion of the various ions in cellular fractions are worked out.

In view of the important role played by Fe in increasing the potency of toxins produced by *Fusarium vasinfectum* and its essentiality for both production and activity of pectolytic enzymes, Subramanian (1956a) studied the distribution of Fe in susceptible and resistant cotton (susceptible strain: *Gossypium arboreum*, diploid, $2n = 26$; resistant strain: *G. hirsutum*, amphidiploid, $2n = 52$). He found that the total Fe content in the roots of the resistant varieties was much higher than in the roots of susceptible varieties. He further observed that during pathogenesis Fe appears to move down towards the roots in the susceptible cotton. Reasons for this movement are, however, not clear. Nevertheless, what seems to matter for infection is the high available Fe in the roots for utilization by the pathogen; and this possibly is the situation in the susceptible root, which has less total Fe than the resistant but much of it in the available form. This is evidenced by the effects of chelating agents such as 8-quinolinol and EDTA that reduced available trace metals, especially Fe, in the susceptible host and thereby conferred protection from infection (Subramanian, 1956b). Indeed, with Mn or Fe+Mn amendments, the available Fe in the roots of the susceptible plants diminished to levels on a par with or even less than in the resistant variety; in fact, inoculation of these plants did not alter Fe levels. Wilt incidence was also lowered (Malini, 1961). In explaining the role of Fe in altering the potency of fusaric acid, the first evidence for preferential chelation in vivo of Fe with fusaric acid in susceptible cotton (Fig. 4), was recorded by Malini (1961). These facts at least partly explain the earlier observation that Mn or Fe+Mn amendment to soils brings about a recovery of the wilt syndrome of cotton (Varadarajan, 1953). There seems little doubt that Fe and Fe+Mn metabolism and wilt syndrome need greater attention.

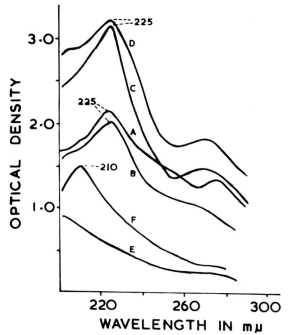

Fig. 4. Absorption spectra of Fe-fusaric acid complex from cotton plants fed with fusaric acid: A, 200 μg of fusaric acid; B, 400 μg of fusaric acid, and E, control—after 24 hours; C, 200 μg of fusaric acid; D, 400 μg of fusaric acid, and F, control—after 48 hours.

Gäumann and Naef-Roth (1956) considered that occurrence of excessive transpiration consequent on lycomarasmin poisoning in tomato cuttings was mainly because of its "vehicle effect" causing a "local iron plethora" in the leaves, which resulted in Fe injuries. Our findings on Fe distribution in cotton under pathogenesis do not indicate a local iron plethora in the leaves, instead showed accumulation in the roots. It should be mentioned, however, that Gäumann and Naef-Roth used tomato cuttings with lycomarasmin as the toxin, whereas normal rooted cotton plants were used by us, with fusaric acid produced in situ by the pathogen.

That fungi in the rhizosphere suppressed uptake of inorganic ions in preference to uptake of glucose has been shown recently in tomato by using C[14]-labeled glucose or C[14]-labeled bicarbonate (Subba-Rao, Bidwell, and Bailey, 1961). Summing up all this evidence, it appears that Fe does seem to influence wilt syndrome but its complicity with sugars and other organic substances in the rhizosphere has to be further explored.

Changes in organic constituents.—Earlier work in our laboratory had indicated the efficacy of trace-ele-

ment amendments in controlling fusarioses of cotton (Sulochana, 1952d; Varadarajan, 1953; Kalyanasundaram, 1954; Satyanarayana, 1955), of pigeon pea (Sarojini, 1950), and of rice (Shanta, 1953). Kalyanasundaram (1954) observed marked alterations in the carbohydrate metabolism of a susceptible variety of cotton (K2) grown in soil amended with Zn. These plants showed higher ascorbic-acid and lower reducing-sugar contents, a situation analogous to that in resistant varieties. Satyanarayana (1955), working on similar lines, found a marked reduction in the NPN (non-protein nitrogen) fraction in K2 plants consequent upon Zn application to the soil in which they were grown; also the depletion of NPN in inoculated plants was much less than in the controls. It was explained that the effect of Zn was twofold in that it not only reduced the NPN content, which if high, accentuated susceptibility, but also prevented depletion of NPN on infection. Zinc treatment also brought about a marked reduction in the α-amino acids, both qualitatively and quantitatively (Subramanian, 1956a).

A high content of pectin in roots was shown by Lakshminarayanan (1956) to be characteristic of a susceptible cotton variety. When these plants were grown in soil amended with either 50 or 100 ppm of Zn, there was a considerable reduction in pectin in the roots. In addition, the marked fall in pectin levels recorded in untreated plants inoculated with *Fusarium vasinfectum* was also prevented in the treated ones, and this was perhaps due to the in-vivo inhibition of PME enzyme. In the normal healthy plants the PME activity was retarded by Zn at all concentrations. In the inoculated series, however, while the higher concentrations of Zn inhibited PME activity, the lower levels of Zn significantly increased it (Fig. 5). The striking differences in the effects of Zn at lower concentrations on PME of healthy and inoculated plants indicated the existence of two enzymes, namely the one produced by the host and the other by the pathogen, showing different sensitivity to Zn (Subramanian, 1956a).

Foliar sprays and changes in microflora.—The demonstration that inorganic elements applied to soil may modify both the rhizosphere microflora and the behaviour of pathogens in the soil raises the question of whether such changes can also be induced by foliar application. There have been relatively few studies on this point. Ramachandra-Reddy (1960) investigated the effect of foliar sprays of trace elements on rice. When rice seedlings were sprayed either with trace-element salts or their chelates, the changes recorded in the pattern of the rhizosphere microfloras were similar. The Mn chelate increased the fungal numbers a little over twice that observed in unsprayed controls, and Fe chelate had no appreciable effect on the fungi of the rhizosphere. The chelates of Zn and Cu, on the other hand, caused a reduction in fungus flora. Qualitatively, Fe chelate stimulated penicillia in the rhizosphere, though only to a small extent, whereas Mn chelate tended to suppress these. Zinc and Cu chelates brought no appreciable change in the proportion of penicillia to

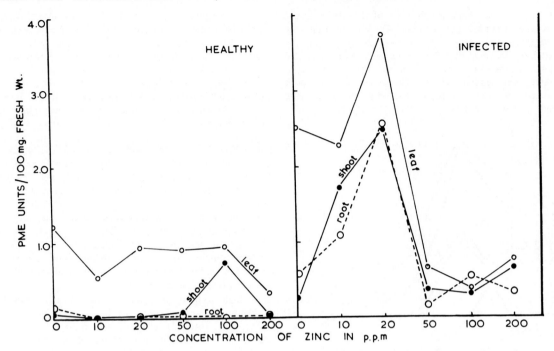

Fig. 5. In vivo PME (pectin methyl esterase) activity of tissue homogenates of healthy and infected susceptible cotton grown in Zn-amended soil.

aspergilli in the rhizosphere. In general, it may be stated that aspergilli predominated in the rhizosphere of rice plants. Correspondingly, the rhizosphere bacterial flora was stimulated by Mn chelate and even more by Zn chelate, while Fe and Cu chelates suppressed its numbers. Actinomycetes were boosted in plants sprayed with Zn chelate to a lesser extent than those sprayed with Mn chelate; little change was noticed with Cu and Fe chelates (Ramachandra-Reddy, 1960).

Some interesting work on a perennial crop plant was reported by Venkata Ram (1960): spraying tea (*Camellia sinensis*) with Na_2HPO_4 or KCl results in a significant increase in fungal numbers in the rhizosphere but with $MgSO_4$ in a reduction. A point of further interest emerging from this study was that more genera and species of fungi appeared in the rhizosphere as a result of foliar application of these fertilizers than in unsprayed controls.

Foliar sprays of 0.2% H_3PO_4 on *Dolichos lablab*, both healthy and infected with dolichos-enation-mosaic virus (DEMV), although slightly phytotoxic, produced significant changes in the rhizosphere microfloras (Lakshmi-Kumari, 1961). Preinoculation sprays increased bacteria, predominantly ammonifying and denitrifying groups, in the rhizosphere of DEMV-inoculated plants initially, but this effect wore off. A remarkable increase in actinomycetes was also observed after this treatment. Fungi which were suppressed in unsprayed DEMV-infected plants in the beginning were preferentially stimulated in the rhizosphere of both healthy and virus-infected plants by H_3PO_4 sprays later on. This effect, however, was not lasting and when the fungal and bacterial numbers went down there was

enormous increase in the numbers of actinomycetes. Another point of interest is that the percentage of bacteria requiring complex nutritional factors was low in the rhizosphere of sprayed control plants, and very high in that of unsprayed infected plants, but bacteria requiring only yeast extract were predominantly high in the sprayed infected plants. These qualitative changes in the rhizosphere microflora brought about by foliar application of minerals and other substances, open up possibilities for judicious manipulation leading to preferential suppression of specific pathogenic forms in soils.

DISCUSSION.—Whilst it is true that we have data on qualitative and quantitative changes in the rhizosphere microfloras of different crop plants in varying soil conditions, there is paucity of evidence as to how far these changes in the microflora aid or retard the progress of soil-borne pathogens in their destructive phase. For instance, major and trace elements are needed by saprophytic and parasitic soil microbes and also by roots of the growing plant; what proportion of these is used by any of the partners in the complex association is yet to be determined with a reasonable degree of accuracy. Further, what role these metals play in the production of antibiotics in the rhizosphere remains undetermined. The situation is more complex if we are to consider root exudates like organic acids, amino acids, and other products which freely diffuse in soil adjacent to roots and chelate with free metals available in the soil, since it is now well known that when $C^{14}O_2$ is supplied to tops of plants, labeled compounds exuded by roots migrate to regions well away from the root system (Subba-Rao, Bidwell, and Bailey, 1962). Therefore, this dynamic aspect of the utilization of limited amounts of organic substances in the rhizosphere by microorganisms and plant roots should engage our attention. In addition, we have not fully exploited the technique of foliar application of metals and their repercussions in the rhizosphere; further experiments in this field would be very rewarding. The role of inorganic amendments in promoting or inhibiting the production and germination of spores and resting bodies of soil microorganisms must be clearly understood. Similarly, an understanding of the alteration of host metabolism after inorganic supplement to the soil and the possible changes in the nature and quantity of root exudation is of paramount importance, since we have evidence to show that root exudates stimulated chlamydospore germination (Schroth and Snyder, 1961), and some amino acids blocked chlamydospore formation—e.g. arginine in *Thielaviopsis basicola*—while sulphur-containing amino acids stimulated it (Stover, 1956).

There are at least four leading questions that emanate from studies on the utilization of free ions in the rhizosphere by the pathogen (whose numbers seem to be severely delimited by microbial antagonism) in competition with plant roots. First, how is the pattern of selective absorption of ions altered in the presence of toxins formed in the rhizosphere, especially those ions like Zn and Fe known to be needed for plant well-being, enzyme and toxin formation, and toxin potentiation? Second, how do trace elements function in the rhizosphere and in vivo in conditioning substrates on which the fungus largely depends, on entry, for the establishment and development of its enzyme systems? Third, how far can mineral-nutrition schedules be so adjusted as to overcome the heavy foliar loss of ions by exudation, particularly of K and the general ionic imbalance consequent upon toxaemia in the cotton wilt? Fourth, can the tissue loss of K be replenished by foliar spray of the element? Obviously we have no evidence on the sequence of events: whether Zn, for instance, merely aids toxin elaboration in the rhizosphere or whether it simultaneously controls in-vivo enzyme development. Indeed, evidence is presented here indicating a striking difference in the sensitivity of PME to Zn in the healthy and infected cotton plants. In the Zn-amended series we are confronted with a Zn-sensitive host PME and a Zn-stimulated fungal PME. Similarly, evidence has been presented here on the dual role of available Fe in vivo in initiating *Fusarium* wilt in cotton and in controlling the potency of fusaric acid. In fact, it would be of more than academic interest if we were to employ in future studies of this problem fungal mutants that have only the toxin-forming ability and those that have only the capacity to produce the enzymes, as then the exact roles of metals and metallic chelates in the rhizosphere and in vivo could be more fruitfully assessed. There are many other soil-borne diseases that do not seem to involve toxins but are conditioned solely by factors that aid entry of the pathogens into root tissues. In these cases, manipulation of biotic factors in the rhizosphere capable of effectively prolonging or causing dormancy of the pathogens would be a worth-while mode of approach for control; even in this direction minerals could play an important role.

Evidence has been presented on the selective influence of major and trace elements as soil amendments or foliar sprays on the microfloras of the rhizosphere. It would be futile to deny the profundity of these changes in the rhizosphere; on the contrary, efforts should be made to understand the changes in host metabolism in this context. Indeed, plants with different ploidys seem to have different root-exudate patterns, which determine their rhizosphere microflora (Sadasivan, 1960). For instance, an analysis of root exudates of diploid (susceptible) and amphidiploid (resistant) strains of cotton grown in cottonfield soils from a wilt-free zone and a wilt-infested zone showed that diploid strains exuded greater amounts of amino acids than the amphidiploid strains. The exudates of amino acids in plants in the wilt-infested soils were generally higher than in the soils of the wilt-free area (Sulochana, 1962a). A somewhat similar study probing into the occurrence of B vitamins in the exudates of these diploid and amphidiploid strains of cotton grown in the two soils indicated that apart from the presence or absence of several components in the diploid or amphidiploid cottons, the amphidiploid strains showed comparatively lower amounts of these vitamins, with a few exceptions (Sulochana, 1962b). Pursuing this work further, it was shown that in general the influence of cotton roots on amino-acid-requiring bacteria was greater than on vitamin-requiring bacteria, and the rhizosphere effects of diploid strains were greater than those of amphidiploid strains. The effects were influenced by the initial proportion of these bacterial groups in the two soils. Notwithstanding all this, the most significant result was that differences in the rhizosphere effects between diploid and amphidiploid plants were correlatable with the amino-acid and vitamin exudations by roots of these strains but not with reference to soil types (Sulochana, 1962c). Intensive study of crop plants with different ploidys with regard to their rhizosphere microbial complex and root-exudate pattern in soils amended with many major and trace elements would yield additional data and help to clarify the triple interaction of externally supplied nutrients, exudates, and the microbial complex.

Instances of metals that selectively depress microbial numbers in the rhizosphere, particularly of the pathogens, and also those that interfere in some way with the ascending phase of toxaemia and bring about an observable reversal of disease syndrome have been presented above. Much scope, therefore, lies in the study of effects of minerals on disease development, which includes four major interactions: (1) the influence of metals on the normal microflora that forms the bulwark of antagonisms to pathogenic forms in the soils and in the rhizosphere; (2) the formation of toxins by pathogens in the rhizosphere and the inevitable implication of metals; (3) the pattern of the rhizosphere exudates and formation of metallochelates; and (4) the in-vivo changes brought about by metals in substrates that aid pathogenesis. Admittedly, the problem is full of potentialities.

To sum up, we have no doubt made satisfactory progress towards establishing essentiality of trace elements for microorganisms for growth and toxin or antibiotic production. Nevertheless, we have not yet succeeded in correlating this knowledge with the practical aspects of control of disease by effecting changes in the microbial complex, and perhaps by reducing the toxin-producing ability of pathogenic forms in the rhizosphere.

ACKNOWLEDGMENTS.—I am deeply indebted to my colleagues, Drs. C. B. Sulochana and D. Subramanian for reading through the manuscript and Mr. N. Sethunathan for preparing the illustrations.

LITERATURE CITED

ARK, P. A. 1937. Little-leaf or rosette of fruit trees. VII. Soil microflora and little-leaf or rosette disease. Proc. Am. Soc. Hort. Sci. 34: 216-221.

BERSHOVA, O. I. 1960. Vplyv mikroelementiv na dehidraznu aktyvńisl ryzosfernykh bakteryi. (In Ukranian with Russian summary.) Mikrobiol. Zhur. Akad. Nauk, Ukr. RSR. 22: 3-9.

BHUVANESWARI, K. 1958. Studies on the rhizosphere microfloras of crop plants. Ph.D. thesis, Univ. Madras.

GARRETT, S. D. 1956. Biology of root-infecting fungi. Cambridge Univ. Press, London and New York. 292 p.

GÄUMANN, E. 1951. Some problems of pathological wilting in plants. Adv. Enzymol. 11: 401-437.

GÄUMANN, E., and ST. NAEF-ROTH. 1956. Über die chelierende Wirkung einiger Welketoxine. IV. Die Verschiebungen der Toxizität durch steigende Absättigung mit vershiedenen Schwermetallionen. Phytopathol. Z. 25: 418-444.

GERRETSEN, F. C. 1937. Manganese deficiency of oats and its relation to soil bacteria. Ann. Bot. (London) [N.S.] 1: 207-230.

GNANAM, P. 1956. Conductivity studies in cotton plants infected by *Fusarium vasinfectum* Atk. Proc. Indian Acad. Sci., Sec. B, 44: 125-129.

HARLEY, J. L., and J. K. BRIERLEY. 1955. The uptake of phosphate by excised mycorrhizal roots of beech. VII. Active transport of ^{32}P from fungus to host during uptake of phosphate from solution. New Phytologist 54: 296-301.

HILTNER, L. 1904. Über neuere Erfahrungen und Probleme auf dem Gebiet der Bodenbakteriologie und unter besonderer Berücksichtigung der Gründungen und Brache. Arb. Deut. Landwirtsch.-Ges. Östereich 98: 59-78.

KAILA, A. 1949. Biological absorption of phosphorus. Soil Sci. 68: 279-289.

KALYANASUNDARAM, R. 1952. Ascorbic acid and *Fusarium* wilted plants. Proc. Indian Acad. Sci., Sec. B, 36: 102-104.

KALYANASUNDARAM, R. 1954. Soil conditions and root diseases. XII. The role of zinc and manganese in altering host metabolism. J. Indian Botan. Soc. 33: 197-202.

KALYANASUNDARAM, R. 1955. Antibiotic production by *Fusarium vasinfectum* Atk. in soil. Current Sci. (India) 24: 310-311.

KALYANASUNDARAM, R. 1958. Production of fusaric acid by *Fusarium lycopersici* Sacc. in the rhizosphere of tomato plants. Phytopathol. Z. 32: 25-34.

KALYANASUNDARAM, R., and L. SARASWATHI-DEVI. 1955. Zinc in the metabolism of *Fusarium vasinfectum* Atk. Nature (London) 175: 945.

LAKSHMINARAYANAN, K. 1955. Studies on fungal enzymes with special reference to the *Fusarium* wilt of cotton. Ph.D. thesis, Univ. Madras.

LAKSHMINARAYANAN, K. 1956. Physiology of host-parasite relationship in the *Fusarium* wilt of cotton. I. Pectin metabolism. Proc. Indian Acad. Sci., Sec. B, 44: 317-324.

LAKSHMI-KUMARI, M. 1961. Rhizosphere microfloras and host-parasite relationships. Ph.D. thesis, Univ. Madras.

LEACH, W., R. BULMAN, and J. KROEKER. 1954. Studies in plant mineral nutrition. I. An investigation into the

cause of grey speck disease of oats. Can. J. Botany 32: 358-368.

LEEPER, G. W. 1952. Factors affecting availability of inorganic nutrients in soils with special reference to micronutrient metals. Ann. Rev. Plant Physiol. 3: 1-16.

LINSKENS, H. F. 1955. Der Einfluss der toxigenen Welke auf die Blattausscheidungen der Tomatenpflanze. Phytopathol. Z. 23: 89-106.

LUNDEGÅRDH, H. 1945. Absorption, transport and exudation of inorganic ions by the roots. Arkiv. Botan. 32A: 1-139.

MALINI, S. 1961. Heavy metals and host-parasite relationships in plant wilts. Ph.D. thesis, Univ. Madras.

MILLIKAN, C. R. 1938. A preliminary note on the relation of zinc to disease in cereals. J. Dept. Agr. (Victoria) 36: 409-416.

MILLIKAN, C. R. 1942. Studies on soil conditions in relation to root-rot of cereals. Proc. Roy. Soc. (Victoria) [N.S.] 54: 145-195.

MORRISON, T. M. 1962a. Absorption of phosphorus from soils by mycorrhizal plants. New Phytologist 61: 10-20.

MORRISON, T. M. 1962b. Uptake of sulphur by mycorrhizal plants. New Phytologist 61: 21-27.

RAMACHANDRA-REDDY, T. K. 1960. Studies on soil fungi. Ph.D. thesis, Univ. Madras.

SADASIVAN, T. S. 1939. Succession of fungi decomposing wheat straw in different soils with special reference to *Fusarium culmorum*. Ann. Appl. Biol. 26: 497-508.

SADASIVAN, T. S. 1960. The problem of rhizosphere microfloras. Proc. Natl. Inst. Sci. India, Part B, 26: 71-79.

SADASIVAN, T. S., and L. SARASWATHI-DEVI. 1957. Vivotoxins and uptake of ions by plants. Current Sci. (India) 26: 74-75.

SANWAL, B. D., and E. R. WAYGOOD. 1961. The effect of fusaric acid on the oxidative phosphorylation of plant mitochondria. Experientia 17: 174.

SAROJINI, T. S. 1950. Soil conditions and root diseases. I. Micronutrient element and disease development by *Fusarium udum* on red gram (*Cajanus cajan* (Linn.) Millsp.). J. Madras Univ. 19 B: 1-32.

SATYANARAYANA, G. 1955. Soil conditions and wilt of cotton with special reference to host physiology. Ph.D. thesis, Univ. Madras.

SCHEFFER, R. P., and J. C. WALKER. 1953. The physiology of Fusarium wilt of tomato. Phytopathology 43: 116-125.

SCHROTH, M. N., and W. C. SNYDER. 1961. Effect of host exudates on chlamydospore germination of the bean root rot fungus, *Fusarium solani* f. *phaseoli*. Phytopathology 51: 389-393.

SELMAN, I. W., and W. R. BUCKLEY. 1959. Factors affecting the invasion of tomato roots by *Verticillium alboatrum*. Trans. Brit. Mycol. Soc. 42: 227-234.

SHANTA, P. 1953. Trace element nutrition of soil fungi with special reference to *Fusarium moniliforme*. M.Sc. thesis, Univ. Madras.

STOVER, R. H. 1956. Effect of nutrition on growth and chlamydospore formation in brown and gray cultures of *Thielaviopsis basicola*. Can. J. Botany 34: 459-472.

SUBBA-RAO, N. S., R. G. S. BIDWELL, and D. L. BAILEY. 1961. The effect of rhizoplane fungi on the uptake and metabolism of nutrients by tomato plants. Can. J. Botany 39: 1759-1764.

SUBBA-RAO, N. S., R. G. S. BIDWELL, and D. L. BAILEY. 1962. Studies of rhizosphere activity by the use of isotopically labeled carbon. Can. J. Botany 40: 203-212.

SUBRAMANIAN, C. V. 1946. Some factors affecting the growth and survival of *Fusarium vasinfectum* Atk., the cotton wilt pathogen in the soil, with special reference to microbiological antagonism. J. Indian Botan. Soc. 25: 89-101.

SUBRAMANIAN, D. 1956a. Studies on the control of fungal wilts of plants. Ph.D. thesis, Univ. Madras.

SUBRAMANIAN, D. 1956b. Role of trace element chelation in the *Fusarium* wilt of cotton. Proc. Indian Acad. Sci., Sec. B, 43: 302-307.

SUBRAMANIAN, S. 1963. *Fusarium* wilt of pigeon pea. III.

Manganese nutrition and disease resistance. Proc. Indian Acad. Sci., Sec. B, 57: 259-274.

Sulochana, C. B. 1952a. Soil conditions and root diseases. III. With special reference to colonization and survival of soil fusaria in soils treated with micro-elements. Proc. Indian Acad. Sci., Sec. B, 35: 209-213.

Sulochana, C. B. 1952b. Soil conditions and root diseases. IV. The effect of micro-elements on the occurrence of bacteria, actinomycetes and fungi in soils. Proc. Indian Acad. Sci., Sec. B, 36: 19-33.

Sulochana, C. B. 1952c. Soil conditions and root diseases. VII. Response of cotton plants to micro-element amendments and its relation to disease development. Proc. Indian Acad. Sci., Sec. B, 36: 234-242.

Sulochana, C. B. 1952d. Soil conditions and root diseases. VI. Germination of conidia of *Fusarium vasinfectum* in micro-element amended soils. Proc. Indian Acad. Sci., Sec. B, 36: 229-233.

Sulochana, C. B. 1962a. Amino acids in root exudates of cotton. Plant Soil 16: 312-326.

Sulochana, C. B. 1962b. B-vitamins in root exudates of cotton. Plant Soil 16: 327-334.

Sulochana, C. B. 1962c. Cotton roots and vitamin-requiring and amino acid-requiring bacteria. Plant Soil 16: 335-346.

Thankam, C. 1949. Antagonism between soil fungi and other microorganisms in the soil with special reference to *Fusarium* species. Ph.D. thesis, Univ. Madras.

Toussoun, T. A., S. M. Nash, and W. C. Snyder. 1960.

The effect of nitrogen sources and glucose on the pathogenesis of *Fusarium solani* f. *phaseoli*. Phytopathology 50: 137-140.

Varadarajan, P. D. 1953. Soil conditions and wilt of plants with special reference to trace element nutrition. Ph.D. thesis, Univ. Madras.

Venkata Ram, C. S. 1960. Foliar application of nutrients and rhizosphere microflora of *Camellia sinensis*. Nature (London) 187: 621-622.

Waggoner, P. E., and A. E. Dimond. 1953. Role of chelation in causing and inhibiting the toxicity of lycomarasmine. Phytopathology 43: 281-284.

Waksman, S. A. 1922. Microbiological analysis of soil as an index of soil fertility. III. Influence of fertilization upon numbers of microorganisms in the soil. Soil Sci. 14: 321-346.

Waksman, S. A. 1952. Soil microbiology. John Wiley & Sons, New York. 356 p.

Yogeswari, L. 1950. Trace element nutrition of fungi with special reference to *Fusarium* spp. Ph.D. thesis, Univ. Madras.

Zachariah, A. T. 1949. Micro-ecology of soils of cultivated fields of South India with special reference to the occurrence and physiology of fusaria. Ph.D. thesis, Univ. Madras.

Zähner, H. 1955. Über den Einfluss der Ernährung auf die Toxinempfindlichkeit von Tomatenpflanzen. Phytopathol. Z. 23: 49-88.

► DISCUSSION OF T. S. SADASIVAN PAPER

N. T. Flentje:

Organisms can be pathogenic without entry to a host. I feel we will find increasing examples of this as we understand the situation further.

There are good reasons why we might expect more than one organism to be essentially linked in causing a particular disease. We have been far too preoccupied with the idea of solely one organism causing a disease. If we keep an open mind we may find some very important interactions.

S. M. Nash:

Zinc may act as a cofactor of carbonic anhydrase which might play a part in incorporation of carbonyl groups in compounds elaborated by fusaria. Was this enzyme system looked for?

T. S. Sadasivan:

I agree that zinc can act as cofactor of carbonic anhydrase in fusaria metabolism in vitro. We shall look for this enzyme system.

W. C. Snyder:

This is in line with some of the observations we are making that the nutrition of the fungus is very important in relation to its pathogenesis. When we use weight as a measure of an optimum nutrition, it may be accurate for the vegetative growth, but not for sporulation, sexual fruiting, or pathogenesis. We have to have some appropriate measure, and this may not always be mycelial weight or rapidity of growth.

A. Kerr:

You have shown that both major and minor elements may have a marked influence on the incidence of disease and on the number of antagonists on the root surface. In India, do you have soils in which cotton wilt does not readily develop, in contrast to cotton-wilt-infested soils? Can you explain these differences in terms of chemicals in soil?

T. S. Sadasivan:

Yes, indeed. In India, particularly in Madras State, we have two major black cotton soils, and one has a long wilt history, whereas the other has not. One of the interesting factors which we feel may influence wilt production in the former soil is the presence of near-optimum quantities of zinc favoring toxin formation (shown by in-vitro tests). In the latter soil, zinc occurs in large quantities and may well explain the limiting of toxin production by the pathogen, which is present in both soils tested. All other physical conditions of the soil appear to be more or less similar. We have not yet analyzed fully the amounts of macroelements in these soils. This could be interesting.

D. J. D. Nicholas:

Zinc is not only essential for carbonic anhydrase, but it is also required for other enzymes, e.g. glutamic and alcohol dehydrogenases, in microorganisms.

You mention that iron is transported from the plant tops to the roots in plants that are less susceptible to fusarium wilt. Is this a specific effect for iron, or do other metals behave in the same way? Was this established with the use of tracer iron?

In view of the importance of cobalt on vitamin B_{12} for the growth of some of the rhizosphere microorganisms, what effect does this element have on the infection of plants by pathogens?

T. S. Sadasivan:

While following carbonic anhydrase, we have not thus far taken up the study of glutamic and alcohol dehydrogenases. We shall do this soon.

So far we have established only the transport of iron from plant tops to the roots in the fusarium-wilt problem. We have not yet screened for other metals under similar situations. We have not used tracer iron for this purpose, but propose doing so now.

We have not gone into the question of the role of cobalt in pathogenesis but have confined our attention hitherto only to its effect on the quantitative microfloras of soils with and without a wilt history.

D. Pramer:

Fusaric acid is of particular interest since it is both an antibiotic and a phytotoxin. Will you please describe for us the conditions required to obtain fusaric-acid production in the rhizosphere of cotton, and how you have established that the material is indeed fusaric acid?

T. S. Sadasivan:

We have estimated the fusaric acid produced in the rhizosphere by bioassay techniques using a strain of *Bacillus subtilis* sensitive to fusaric acid. This works well and is quite sensitive. A chromatography cum bioassay technique can also be employed. Copper-fusaric-acid complex has a specific *rf* value on a chromatogram.

The Role of Chemicals in the Biological Control of Soil-borne Plant Pathogens

R. A. LUDWIG—*Plant Research Institute, Research Branch, Canada Department of Agriculture, Ottawa.*

▶

Soil disinfestants and the microbial relations in soil and rhizosphere have been the subjects of a number of recent reviews (Baker, 1959*b*; Kreutzer, 1961; Newhall, 1955). No useful purpose would be served here by another such account. It is proposed to present a somewhat speculative treatment assessing the present state of our knowledge and suggesting profitable lines of approach to pest control in the future.

The traditional approaches to pest control are chemical, genetic, and biological. A plateau of activity has been reached in modern synthetic fungicides. Although we may achieve a breakthrough and discover materials with the specificity and high activity of modern insecticides, it is by no means certain that such a development would represent a practical advance. The fungi are at least as adaptable as insects and, with high specificity, the same resistant lines that plague the entomologists can be anticipated. The genetic approach is the ideal one, but the quest for immune varieties is likely to be never ending. In terms of soil-borne plant pathogens, partial host resistance simply raises the level of tolerance. Biological control is, for purposes of this paper, defined as the suppression of a pest in the presence of its host, through the manipulation of its ecological environment. Included under this head would be the various cultural practices designed to reduce the level of a pest in the soil. A period of fallow, for example, allows the ecological agencies in the soil time to equilibrate.

There is a growing realization that none of the traditional methods of control can alone provide the final answer to pest control. This is especially true in soil-borne plant pathogens. The hope for success lies in an "integrated program" which makes intelligent use of each of the traditional approaches, in other words, an integration of chemical and biological methods taking advantage of any help that can be derived from host resistance.

A NOTE ON ENTOMOLOGICAL EXPERIENCES.—A concise account of the integrated-controls concept applied in an entomological sense, has been published by Stern et al. (1959) from the University of California at Riverside. The general philosophy is illustrated in Fig. 1.

The picture is one of pest populations whose densities oscillate about a mean in waves of varying frequency and amplitude. It is only when the peaks rise above a critical level that economic losses can be anticipated and chemical treatments accordingly become necessary. Situations vary from those of potential pests whose densities never cross the critical threshold to perennial pests whose densities, in the absence of control measures, would always be above the threshold. They also vary from simple situations, as is the case with the two-component system of the greenhouse white fly and its specific parasite (Burnett, 1948) to the complex situation in an apple orchard, where general predacious feeding is involved (Pickett, 1949; Pickett and Patterson, 1953). It is not only a question of when to apply chemicals, but also of what chemical to apply and how much of it. The switch from harsh lime-sulphurs to mild sulphurs for apple-scab control induced a buildup of two previously incipient insect pests, the oyster-shell scale and the European red mite, in Nova Scotia apple orchards (Patterson, 1949; Pickett and Patterson, 1953). In both cases, the new treatment was relatively harmless to the pest, but deleterious to its predators. DDT applied for codling-moth control had a similar effect as far as the European red mite was concerned. This effect could be partly overcome by reduction of dosage to the minimal level.

The effect of chemical treatment in the cases cited above has been to shift the mean density level upward. This change is often a gradual one occurring over a period of years and thus the relation between the actual effect and its cause may be obscured. The orchard work in Nova Scotia has shown that the readjustment of the equilibrium to a relatively noninjurious density level may also take time. Further, it may be necessary to absorb losses during the adjustment period in order to reach the desired goal. Many reported entomological failures in the establishment of an integrated control program could be attributable to lack of persistence and vision on the part of researchers.

The entomological studies have dealt largely with mobile pest and parasite or predator systems. The chances of two antagonistic individuals coming together depends on the size of the world in which they find themselves and their relative mobility. Stationary antagonists can only interact if they happen to develop in association. Further, an omnivorous predator has a better chance of survival than a specific parasite in that it can adjust in population density to that of its most

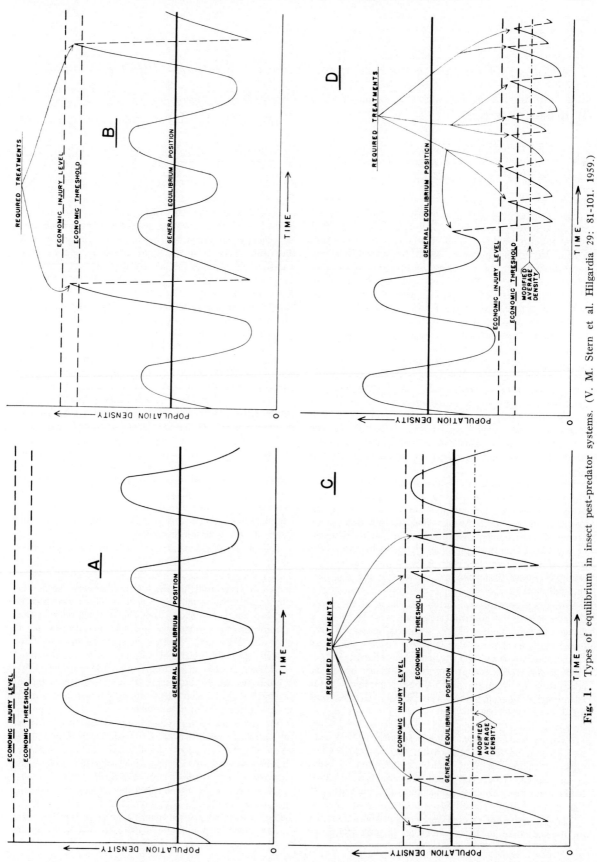

Fig. 1. Types of equilibrium in insect pest-predator systems. (V. M. Stern et al. Hilgardia 29: 81-101. 1959.)

abundant food supply and may be present in numbers during the period when its favourite lunch, a phytophagous pest, is at a low level.

Most insect pests spend their lives in relatively exposed positions and are therefore easy to control. Returning to orchard pests, it is interesting to note that the maggot, which spends a great deal of its life in seclusion within the apple, has not thus far been amenable to control through an "integrated approach."

Successful integrated control programs in entomology have depended on some knowledge of the effect of a pesticide on the general fauna in the area involved, and on the ability of entomologists to estimate the population status of the component systems at any given time, and hence to judge the timing of chemical treatments. Even with a visible population, experimentation is difficult because of the nature of the problem and the time, extending often into years, that may be involved. Faddists, whether they be for or against chemicals, can as a result see support for their philosophies.

The equilibrium situation diagrammed in Fig. 1 is that prevailing in the presence of a crop. Here an abundant and concentrated supply of food material for the pest insect is provided. It is then a new equilibrium that is actually involved and not the one that would have existed in an undisturbed environment. A seasonal continuity is maintained in long-lived crops such as apple and citrus. In comparison with annuals and short-lived perennials, this offers certain advantages for the establishment of a stable pest–predator balance. The interseason break with annuals often means a general shifting of balance.

PHYTOPATHOLOGICAL EXPERIENCES IN BIOLOGICAL CONTROL.—Plant pathologists interested in soil-borne pathogens were quick to seize on the idea of exploiting "microbial antagonisms" for plant-disease control. Continuing microbial interactions in the soil and the possibilities of biological control were soon demonstrated, as were the difficulties that had to be surmounted before a practical program could be implemented. Enthusiasm understandably waned but recently has undergone a revival. An outstanding appraisal of the situation was presented at the Golden Jubilee Meetings of the American Phytopathological Society (Baker, 1959b). Certainly the opportunities to achieve biological control of soil-borne plant pathogens are greater than they are for their aerial cousins (Krstic, 1956).

Experiments aimed at maintaining the population density below the economic threshold through the introduction of antagonistic microorganisms into soil have been generally unsuccessful (Baker, 1959b). There have, however, been a number of references in the Russian literature (for example, Kublanovskaya, 1957; Mishustin and Naumova, 1956) suggesting that both bacteria and actinomycetes added to soil in various organic substrates may reduce the incidence of disease. It has also been claimed that similar results can be achieved by dipping seeds in bacterial and actinomycete suspensions (for example, Mazunina, 1958). There are, of course, numerous references to the successful control of disease in experiments where an antagonist has been

added to sterilized soil along with a pathogen. Under greenhouse conditions the reinfestation of steam-sterilized soil with an antagonist represents a practical control measure (Baker, 1957).

The amelioration of disease can be accomplished through the addition of organic amendments to soil. The suppression of *Actinomyces scabies* by green manures is an example. Here the development of saprophytic actinomycetes, especially *Actinomyces praecox,* has been suggested as the cause. The treatment does not always work and may indeed increase the incidence of potato scab under some circumstances (Baker, 1959b). Partial heat sterilization or sterilization and subsequent recontamination with unsterilized soil results in an upsurge in saprophytic microbial activity and suppression of a variety of pathogens. In this connection, Baker's experiments, developing the use of steam-air mixtures, provide a practical basis for taking advantage of this observation under certain circumstances (Baker, 1957, 1959a, 1962a,b). Sterilized soil can, however, become reinfested and more disease result than would normally have been the case.

Chemicals have worked both favourably and unfavourably in the establishment of a biological-control system. The most striking practical success lies in our use of the so-called protectant seed fungicides. Seeds, especially large ones like peas, provide an ideal baiting mechanism (Durbin, 1961) for soil-borne plant pathogens. The use of hemp seed as a bait for the isolation of soil-borne *Pythium* species is well known. When seeds are added to soil, and selectively colonized by plant pathogens, there is an immediate rise in inoculum potential and an increase in the incidence of disease. Baker (1957) emphasizes the role of chemical treatments in preventing seed colonization, although such treatments are not generally looked upon as part of a biological-control system. Bliss (1951) showed that the relatively poor fungicide, carbon disulphide, used as a soil fumigant, controlled *Armillaria mellea.* He noted that the *Armillaria,* although not killed by the gas in pure culture, became overrun by *Trichoderma viride* under natural conditions and postulated selective toxicity. Although this may not be the correct explanation, the end result is the same. Richardson (1954) showed that the beneficial effects of soil treatment with thiram persisted long after the chemical itself degraded. Here again the effects may operate in reverse and a given disease increase as a result of treatment, or a new disease appear.

Regardless of how they are accomplished, these disturbances in soil balance are of relatively short duration. In general, the chemicals have been selected for their acute fungicidal activity rather than for long-term effects on microbial equilibria. Repetitive and costly treatments are required.

POPULATION DENSITY AND INOCULUM POTENTIAL.— Soil-borne plant pathogens exhibit the same sort of equilibria as insects, although the causes of fluctuation may be different. The population density of a fungus is not, for example, regulated by the same rhythmic life-history pattern as that of an insect. Further, Garrett's

(1955a) two groups of soil-borne pathogens, namely soil-inhabiting and root-inhabiting parasites, must be thought of in relation to the equilibrium. The common species of *Pythium, Fusarium,* and *Rhizoctonia,* associated with seedling diseases in a variety of horticultural crops, are examples of the soil-inhabiting class. They are able to compete successfully in the soil and maintain an expanding saprophytic phase. They are not in consequence usually eliminated by the prolonged absence of a susceptible host. *Ophiobolus graminis* and *Helminthosporium sativum,* associated with cereals and grasses, are definitely root fungi. These root-inhabiting parasites survive only on dead host debris and can be eliminated from soil by the prolonged absence of a susceptible host. Length of life depends on a variety of factors, such as the formation of resting spores or sclerotia as well as the size of the bit of debris they colonize and its resistance to decay. All these factors influence population density.

The parameter of interest is the inoculum potential, which depends in part on the density, or amount, of a pathogen present in the root environment and in part on what Garrett (1955a) terms mycelial momentum—really a combination of mass and energy. Energy implies development and this in turn suggests food supply and the absence of inhibitors. Population densities can be the same in two situations and yet diseases occur in one but not the other. In one series of experiments, for example, it has been reported that the quantities of *Actinomyces scabies* in soil were the same whether soybean meal or green clover was used as an amendment (Roualt and Atkinson, 1950). The former promoted a major reduction in potato scab while the latter effected no control whatever.

As mentioned earlier, the search for soil fungicides has been aimed at finding substances that will knock out high levels of the pathogen. The objective has been to eliminate the organism from the soil when its inoculum potential is well above the economic threshold. The hazards of this sort of approach have been emphasized by Garrett (1955b). To quote, "At other times, this difficulty over inadequate inoculum potential, in inoculation experiments, was too successfully surmounted. By the use of too high a dosage of inoculum, especially in association with environmental conditions (such as that of freshly sterilized soil) usually conducive to infestation, it was possible to produce an artificial centrum or even a new disease. With such experimental artifacts from the glass house to complicate a problem already sufficiently difficult, it was not surprising that early investigators sometimes incriminated a harmless fungus, or were left to scratch their heads over the difficulty of reproducing field symptoms of a disease in pot experiments." The relation of inoculum potential to growth is well illustrated by reference to Richardson's (1957) graphs on the isolation of *Corynebacterium sepedonicum* that are presented as Fig. 2. It will be noted that the lag period increased from 1 day to 6½ days as the number of bacteria decreased from 10^{10} to 1. Thus, as the potential drops, not only are there less organisms to control but there is more time for forces of control to operate. The lag period may be shortened

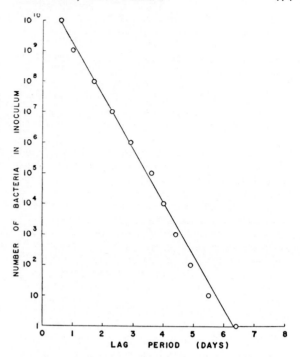

Fig. 2. The lag period in relation to inoculum concentration in cultures of *Corynebacterium sepedonicum.* (L. T. Richardson. Can. J. Botany 35: 647-656. 1957.)

or extended by nutritional influences. *Helminthosporium sativum* begins rapid growth in liquid culture when it is provided with an organic nitrogen source such as casamino acid, but there is a lag period of up to 5 days when it is provided with nitrogen in the form of ammonium sulfate. The total growth at the end of a 2-week period is, however, the same. Similarly, small amounts of a foreign chemical may exert a fungistatic effect and prolong the lag period even though it does not affect ultimate growth.

The growth of *Helminthosporium sativum* is self-inhibited since it produces a fungistatic toxin (Ludwig, 1957). If spores are sown in liquid cultures containing 2,000 to 4,000 ppm of the crude toxin they will lie quiescent for periods of up to 2 weeks and then begin to develop. During this period the toxin will have been degraded to a level permitting growth. Spores of *Trichoderma viride* behave in a like manner, but those of *Monilinia fructicola* are permanently inhibited by concentrations of 5 to 10 ppm. This not only illustrates the profound effect of a chemical on the lag phase, but also suggests how *H. sativum* persists in debris as a primary colonizer and indicates one of the mechanisms that serve to make *T. viride* an active and aggressive antagonist. There are few references in the literature to the effect of fungicides on the lag phase in the growth of an organism. Vincent (1947) studied the fungistatic properties of the esters of 4-hydroxybenzoic acid and related compounds using an agar method. He states, "All controls are satisfactorily linear after the colony has reached 10 mm diameter as are the curves for *A*[*spergillus*] *niger* and *P*[*enicillium*] *roquefortii* growing in the presence of the inhibitor. There is, however, a lag period between the time of inoculation and the attainment of 10 mm diameter." He goes on to base his results on the linear phase, stating in the discussion, "The nature and length of the lag phase might itself be important but it is simpler and more accurate to restrict comparisons to growth rate in the linear phase." The latter statement speaks for itself in relation to the search for and testing of soil fungicides. The materials required may indeed not even be fungicides in the traditional sense.

Not only will a fungus parasite be easier to inhibit when its population density is low but less chemical will be required. The dosage-response curve shifts to the right with increasing population density although shape is unaffected (Dimond et al., 1941).

Experimentation cannot be divorced from considerations of soil type. The importance of obtaining more basic information on the chemical and physical properties of soils in relation to the use of pesticides has been stressed by Kreutzer (1961). With certain organisms it is possible to demonstrate a direct relation between inoculum potential and disease incidence. Such a relation for *Helminthosporium sativum* is illustrated in Fig. 3. Fig. 4 compares the behavior of this fungus in sand and greenhouse compost. At high inoculum potentials there is little difference in the disease incidence, but this is certainly not the case over the critical range (Ludwig et al., 1956).

It is a common procedure for plant pathologists to test a dosage series of a fungicide against a fixed population of the test organism. In the examination of soil chemicals it is as important, and perhaps more important, to test against a range of inoculum potentials. The development of the mathematics of systems in which the dosages of the two components, pest and pesticide, are varied, might lead to rewarding conclusions.

THE QUEST FOR NEW CHEMICALS.—The quest for soil fungicides has been directed toward the search for compounds of high activity. Materials are generally chosen that will either disappear or inactivate rapidly because continued high activity leads to phytotoxicity. Since the general aim has been sterilization, compounds have been selected with properties that promote uniform and rapid dispersal in the soil. As a general rule, current soil fungicides work rapidly but do not provide protection lasting through the season and certainly not from year to year.

One approach to the search for new fungicides, an attack on the lag phase, has already been suggested. Fig. 5 suggests another. Depicted here are a series of dosage-response curves for a homologous series of N-n alkyl ethylenethioureas (Ross and Ludwig, 1957). It will be noted that the curves are parallel and that fungicidal activity increases up to the octyl derivative. The nonyl derivative has a flat curve resulting from limited water solubility. Although the phytotoxicity at the protoplast level is the same as the fungitoxicity, this does not hold true when the material is applied around the roots of growing plants. Here the maximum toxicity occurs with the amyl derivative. Although this example has not been chosen from a group of commercial fungicides, it illustrates a potentially useful type of compound (the nonyl derivative) that would be discarded by our standard screening programs. The properties reducing fungicidal activity also reduce phytotoxicity and, depending on the nature of the material, may increase persistence in the soil. Reduced fungicidal activity leaves room for a selective effect on the soil flora. Thiram is about five times more active against many plant pathogens than it is against *Trichoderma viride* and many other soil fungi. It is certainly much more active against fungi than against bacteria and actinomycetes. Although factors relating to stability

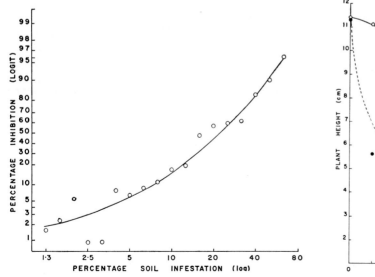
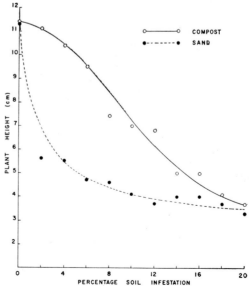

Figs. 3 and 4. Inoculum potential in relation to disease induction in barley seedlings by *Helminthosporium sativum*. (R. A. Ludwig et al. Can. J. Botany 34: 653-673. 1956.) **Fig. 3** (left). Inoculum potential versus disease induction. **Fig. 4** (right). A comparison of inoculum potential required for disease induction in two soil types.

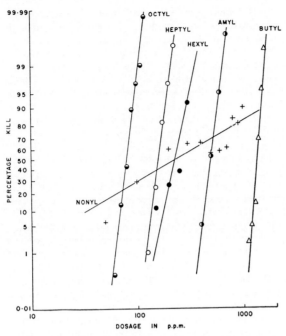

Fig. 5. Dosage-response curves for a homologous series of N-n alkylethylenethioureas. (R. G. Ross and R. A. Ludwig. Can. J. Botany 35: 65-95. 1957.)

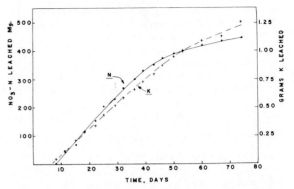

Fig. 6. Slow nutrient-release from coated fertilizers. (O. R. Lunt, A. M. Kofranek, and J. J. Oertli. California Agr. 15 (12): 2-3. 1961.)

do not render the series a promising one, it is interesting to note in passing that a sharp break in fungicidal activity occurs between tetra propyl and tetrabutyl-thiramdisulphide (Ludwig and Thorn, 1957). Nobody has examined the latter in a way that would bring to light its long-term effects as a fungicide. A study of structural modifications of well-known toxiphores along the above lines could be very rewarding. The answers might even be found if laboratory notebooks were reexamined.

Yet another approach to the problem is suggested by current research in the fertilizer field. Professor O. R. Lunt and colleagues in the Department of Irrigation and Soil Science at the University of California, Los Angeles, among others, have been working on the development of slow-release fertilizers (Lunt, Kofranek, and Oertli, 1961). Plastic-coated granules can be prepared which liberate mineral elements slowly over a long period of time, as illustrated in Fig. 6. Because of the slow release, exceedingly high starting concentrations can be used without fear of either plant damage or premature loss of the material itself. Coated fungicides and fungistats might be prepared in the same way. Fungicides applied as a part of the annual fertilizer treatment could be practical.

At the beginning of this paper, reference was made to the experiences of entomologists. Two points should be re-emphasized. First, it might not be possible to achieve the desired result quickly; the experiments may be lengthy ones calling for a great deal of persistence on the part of the researcher. Second, crop losses may be sustained in the process of establishing a desirable balance. The fungicides envisioned here might not give control under conditions exceptionally favourable to the

disease. The question of probabilities thus becomes involved. Diseases on the belowground parts of plants undoubtedly cause an annual unrecognized drain on yields. Control at this level could be very worthwhile even if an occasional loss were sustained.

LITERATURE CITED

BAKER, K. F. [ed.] 1957. The U.C. system for producing healthy container-grown plants. California Agr. Expt. Sta. Manual 23, 332 p.

BAKER, K. F. 1959*a*. Control of root-rot diseases. Recent Advan. Botany (Canada) (9th Intern. Botan. Congr., Montreal, University of Toronto Press) 1: 486-490.

BAKER, K. F. 1959*b*. Symposium on soil microbiology and root-disease fungi. p. 309-379. *In* C. S. Holton et al. [ed.], Plant pathology, problems and progress 1908-1958, University of Wisconsin Press, Madison, Wisc.

BAKER, K. F. 1962*a*. Principles of heat treatment of soil and planting material. J. Australian Inst. Agr. Sci. 28: 118-126.

BAKER, K. F. 1962*b*. Thermotherapy of planting material. Phytopathology 52: 1244-1255.

BLISS, D. E. 1951. The destruction of *Armillaria mellea* in citrus soils. Phytopathology 41: 665-683.

BURNETT, T. 1948. Model temperature for the greenhouse whitefly, *Trialeurodes vaporariorum*, and its parasite, *Encarsia formosa*. Ecology 29: 181-189.

DIMOND, A. E., J. G. HORSFALL, J. W. HEUBERGER, and E. M. STODDARD. 1941. Role of the dosage-response curve in the evaluation of fungicides Connecticut Agr. Expt. Sta. (New Haven) Bull. 451, pp. 635-667.

DURBIN, R. D. 1961. Techniques for the observation and isolation of soil microorganisms. Botan. Rev. 27: 522-560.

GARRETT, S. D. 1955*a*. Biology of root-infecting fungi. Cambridge University Press, London and New York. 292 p.

GARRETT, S. D. 1955*b*. A century of root-disease investigations. Ann. Appl. Biol. 42: 211-219.

KREUTZER, W. A. 1961. Soil fungicides. pp. 466-472. *In* Recent advances in botany (Canada) (9th Intern. Botan. Congr., Montreal) University of Toronto Press, Toronto.

KRSTIC, M. 1956. Prospects of application of biological control in forest pathology. Botan. Rev. 22: 38-44.

KUBLANOVSKAYA, G. M. 1957. [Actinomycetes against cotton wilt.] Tr. Tashkent. Sel'skokhoz. Inst. 1957: 21-26. *Seen in* Rev. Appl. Mycol. 38: 5. 1959.

LUDWIG, R. A. 1957. Toxin productions by *Helminthosporium sativum* P. K. & B. and its significance in disease development. Can. J. Botany 35: 291-303.

LUDWIG, R. A., R. V. CLARK, J. B. JULLIEN, and D. B. ROBINSON. 1956. Studies on the seedling disease of barley caused by *Helminthosporium sativum* P. K. & B. Can. J. Botany 34: 653-673.

LUDWIG, R. A., and G. D. THORN. 1957. Chemistry and

mode of action of dithiocarbamate fungicides. Advan. Pest Control Res. 3: 219-252.

LUNT, O. R., A. M. KOFRANEK, and J. J. OERTLI. 1961. Coated fertilizers. California Agr. 15(12): 2-3.

MAZUNINA, V. N. 1958. [The activity of actinomycetes antagonistic to the causal agent of bacteriosis of cabbage.] Tr. Inst. Mikrobiol. i Virusol. Akad. Nauk Kaz. SSR 2: 80-87. *Seen in* Rev. Appl. Mycol. 38: 43. 1959.

MISHUSTIN, E. N., and A. N. NAUMOVA. 1956. [Application of bacterial fertilizers when sowing vegetables in turf humus cubes.] Mikrobiologiya 25(1): 41-48. *Seen in* Rev. Appl. Mycol. 38: 233. 1959.

NEWHALL, A. G. 1955. Disinfestation of soil by heat, flooding and fumigation. Botan. Rev. 21: 189-250.

PICKETT, A. D. 1949. A critique on insect chemical control methods. Can. Entomologist 81: 67-76.

PICKETT, A. D., and N. A. PATTERSON. 1953. The influence of spray programs on the fauna of apple orchards in Nova Scotia. IV. A review. Can. Entomologist 85: 472-478.

RICHARDSON, L. T. 1954. The persistence of thiram in

soil and its relationship to the microbiological balance and damping-off control. Can. J. Botany 32: 335-346.

RICHARDSON, L. T. 1957. Quantitative determinations of viability of potato ring rot bacteria following storage, heat and gas treatments. Can. J. Botany 35: 647-656.

ROSS, R. G., and R. A. LUDWIG. 1957. A comparative study of fungitivity on phytotoxicity in an homologous series of N-n-alkylethylenethioureas. Can. J. Botany 35: 65-95.

ROUALT, J. W., and R. S. ATKINSON. 1950. The effect of incorporation of certain crops on the microbial balance of potato scab infested soils. Can. J. Res., Sec. C, 28: 140-152.

STERN, V. M., R. F. SMITH, R. VAN DEN BUSCH, and K. S. HOGEN. 1959. The integration of chemical and biological control of the spotted alfalfa aphid. *In* E. G. Linsley [ed.], The integrated control concept, Hilgardia 29: 81-101.

VINCENT, J. M. 1947. The esters of 4-hydroxybenzoic acid and related compounds, Part I. Methods for the study of their fungistatic properties. J. Soc. Chem. Ind. (London) 66: 149-155.

► DISCUSSION OF R. A. LUDWIG PAPER

L. T. Richardson:

Some work currently under way at Riverside in co-operation with Dr. D. E. Munnecke is pertinent to Dr. Ludwig's remarks and the previous discussions of inoculum potential.

We have attempted to correlate inoculum density in soil with chemical dosage required for effective control of seedling diseases. A series of dosages of chemicals in dry form are first intimately mixed with nonsterile soil. Then a series of concentrations of *Pythium* or *Rhizoctonia* inoculum [grown on vermiculite moistened with inorganic nutrient (E. H. Varney, Plant Disease Reptr. 45: 393, 1961)] is mixed with each batch of treated soil.

From emergence counts of peas planted in each soil mixture, the percentage control of pre-emergence damping-off is calculated. When percentage control (probit scale) is plotted against chemical dosage (log scale), a series of parallel curves are derived. In these data a linear relation exists between the log of the inoculum density and the log of the chemical control required for 50% disease control. This provides a basis for comparing effectiveness of different chemicals.

C. A. I. Goring:

It seems to me that it is difficult to distinguish clearly between chemical and biological control of plant pathogens. How much difference is there between deliberately killing the pathogens with chemicals, inducing the plant to defend itself by treating it with chemicals, and manipulating the population in the soil by organic practices or the genetic stock of the host so that they control the pathogen with their own particular chemical weapons?

It does not disturb me particularly to kill, in addition to the pathogens, some of the so-called beneficial organisms, so long as the pathogens that escape colonize less successfully than before treatment during the productive life of the crop. What does concern me is the necessity for using such crude and indiscriminate chemical weapons to do the job, when we know that with diligent search we can find far more effective and specific chemical weapons for the control of specific pathogens.

It seems to me that the continuing genetic selection of resistant hosts is our first line of defense. Failing this, we try to devise agronomic practices that solve or mitigate the problem. Should this fail, we try to select highly specific chemical weapons that directly control specific pathogens, or indirectly persuade the host to defend itself more successfully. The last line of defense is the nonspecific chemical club that destroys pathogens and harmless and beneficial organisms indiscriminately. We seem to have been most successful at the two ends of the scale. We are now wrestling vigorously with the vast middle ground. I would like to stress the need for a more positive and practical approach to this middle ground, such as was used by R. A. Fox and many others. We do not have inexhaustible amounts of time to solve our soil-pathogen problems and so we cannot afford to neglect the delicate, the crude, indeed, any of the practical weapons we have at our command.

D. A. Chant:

Entomologists generally recognize three sorts of biological control: environmental manipulation to increase effectiveness of native species of biological-control agents; mass rearing and release of large numbers of natural enemies in restricted environments, in a sense using them as one would a pesticide; and the introduction of natural enemies to environments where they do not normally occur. Dr. Ludwig and plant pathologists emphasize the first, and study this with much precision. Entomologists emphasize the last two and, in general, have taken an empirical approach. In Canada most entomologists define biological control in a very conservative classical way, as the direct or indirect control of a pest achieved by means of predators, parasites, or diseases. I think this definition, plus the obvious fact that insects are vastly easier to work with than soil microorganisms, has led us to emphasize the third method of biological control. Dr. Ludwig suggested that attempts at biological control of the codling moth had failed because it lives within the apple for most of its life, protected from natural enemies. It does indeed live that way and may be partially protected, but I think the critical point here is that the codling moth is what we call a direct pest, one that attacks and destroys the actual agricultural product that we wish to use; in this case, the apple. Indirect pests, such as aphids and leaf-eating insects, may reduce the vigor of a tree, and may in fact slightly reduce cropping indirectly.

I've been rather disappointed the last few days here not to hear much, if any, mention of two of what we consider the most significant advances that have been made in biological control in entomology and wildlife management. These are, firstly, the concept of density dependency, the idea that to be successful, an agent of biological control must increase in effectiveness out of proportion to an increase in the density of the pest it is controlling. If this doesn't occur, one finds it very hard to see how control could be achieved.

The second has to do with mathematical models. I've been vastly impressed with the incredibly complicated sophisticated techniques that have been reported here the last few days. One thing that worries me is how this wealth of complex, precise, quantitative information can be brought together in any practical way to achieve biological control of specific diseases in specific circumstances. Our approach to this problem, and I think this is almost unique with entomology and wildlife management, is the development of mathematical models to handle this wealth of complex information, to make it

meaningful and to help us make decisions regarding the strategy and tactics we are to employ in specific situations against specific pathogens. One gentleman yesterday said that if as many as 10 or 12 factors were involved it would be impossible to handle them. I think he will be interested to know that, using refinements of higher mathematics and electronic computers, we have several people in Canada who are building mathematical models, and thereby handling as many as 52 factors that may affect the population processes and the population dynamics of insect pests and their natural enemies. Such an approach might well be of considerable value and importance to soil microbiologists.

K. H. Garren:

In 1961 PCNB significantly increased pod rot of peanuts over the control, while the chemical known as Dexon (T.M.) significantly reduced the pod rot. In 1962, in another field, the situation was almost completely reversed: wherever PCNB was used pod rot was significantly reduced, while where Dexon was used, pod rot was increased (but not significantly). Undoubtedly, the pathogen was different in 1961 and 1962. But did PCNB destroy antagonists of the 1961 pathogen in 1961, and Dexon destroy antagonists of the pathogen in 1962?

►

The Effect of Altered Physical Condition of Soil on Biological Control

G. W. F. SEWELL—*East Malling Research Station, East Malling, England.*

►

BIOLOGICAL CONTROL: A DEFINITION.—Five years after Millard (1921) reported the control of potato scab by green manuring, Sanford (1926) suggested a control mechanism involving antibiotic effects and enhanced competition for nutrients resulting from increased populations of the saprophytic microflora. Evidence giving some support to this hypothesis was subsequently provided by experiments in which saprophytic organisms were coinoculated with the pathogen into sterilised soil (Millard and Taylor, 1927; Sanford and Broadfoot, 1931). Weindling (1932) demonstrated the parasitism of *Rhizoctonia* by *Trichoderma viride* and, together with Emerson, isolated the antifungal antibiotic gliotoxin (Weindling and Emerson, 1936). Thus the concept of microbial antagonism was born to soil biology. To pathologists, intent on the control of root-disease fungi, the terms biological control, microbial antagonism, and antibiosis tended to merge into synonymity: revelation of some of the complexities and indirect natures of the interrelations between saprophytes, parasites, hosts, and environment subsequently gave rise to considerable terminological confusion and awesome literary agility.

In more recent years the various aspects and mechanisms of microbial antagonism have largely been reassorted and these have been elegantly discussed by Park (1960), who also appealed against the tendency to restrict the usage of the term antibiotic to complex chemical substances with highly specific activity.

For biological control a refreshing broadness of concept has been accepted by Snyder (1960), who wrote that "biological control relies largely upon an interruption of host-parasite relationships through biological means. Biological control may be accomplished by imparting resistance to the host, usually through plant breeding or by modifying the culture of the crop so as to avoid or reduce infection. Modification of crop culture by utilising the action of other organisms against the pathogen invokes antagonism."

The term biological control possesses sufficient semantic range to encompass all interactions within the biological system set in motion by manipulation of the environment or host and resulting in control of pathogens or diseases, and it would be wasteful to use it otherwise, particularly when satisfactory terms are available to describe the specific types of interaction within the system; in our present state of knowledge, however, it is very rarely if ever possible to ascribe the control to a single mechanism alone. For these reasons it seems more profitable and practical that "biological control" should be permitted broad coverage, and the following definition is therefore proposed: *Biological control is the induced or natural, direct or indirect limitation of a harmful organism, or its effects, by another organism or group of organisms.*

The mechanisms of biological control are microbial antagonism and host resistance or tolerance. Antagonism may involve antibiosis, implicating antibiotics (ranging from simple metabolites, such as carbon dioxide, with a broad spectrum of inhibitory activity, to highly complex chemical substances of more specific activity); competition for food or space; parasitism; and predation. Host resistance and tolerance involve the limitation of the pathogenic organism or the mitigation of its harmful effects: often this action appears to be direct, but resistance may also operate indirectly by host-stimulation of organisms which antagonise the pathogen (Timonin, 1941). Host resistance is not an absolute quality. Its expression may be influenced by variations of the environment: certain soils possess factors of a biological or nonbiological nature which markedly lower host resistance relative to other areas, and the host is then said to be "predisposed to disease." Where these predisposing factors may be natural characteristics of an area, it is considered that their elimination, with consequent increased host resistance, invokes biological control.

The mechanisms of biological control may be induced or intensified by plant breeding, by the use of certain partially selective toxic or inhibitory chemicals, or by a variety of cultural practices including organic and inorganic soil amendment, crop rotation, fallowing, or direct and indirect modification of the physical environment. It is these last practices with which this paper is concerned. The mechanisms of biological control involved are antagonism and induced host resistance; among the methods by which they are utilised are variations of soil temperature, aeration, and moisture, ranging from drought to flood.

BIOLOGICAL CONTROL AND THE PHYSICAL ENVIRONMENT: APPRECIATION AND APPLICATION.—*Soil temperature.*—Almost forty years ago, L. R. Jones (1924) made his plea to pathologists to pay more attention to the effects of the physical environment on plant disease. Even at this time much had been achieved by Jones' group at Wisconsin, and their work was reported in a classic monograph by Jones, Johnson, and Dickson (1926). Although fully appreciative of the influences of soil moisture, aeration, reaction, and fertility, the studies of the Wisconsin group were directed primarily towards the effects of soil temperature.

Investigations of cabbage yellows (Tisdale, 1923), tomato wilt (Clayton, 1923) and flax wilt (L. R. Jones and Tisdale, 1922) revealed that these vascular *Fusarium* diseases were all favoured by high temperatures and, further, that temperature optima were similar for disease development and growth of the causal organism in culture. Some other, nonvascular, pathogens were shown to have markedly lower temperature optima for disease development than for growth in culture. These included: *Rhizoctonia solani*, causing stem canker of potato (Richards, 1923), *Thielaviopsis basicola* causing tobacco root rot (Johnson and Hartman, 1919), and *Gibberella saubinetii* causing corn seedling blight (Dickson, 1923). The optimum temperature for disease development, however, may vary for one pathogen on different hosts. For example, the last-named pathogen, *Gibberella saubinetii*, was found to cause most severe disease of another host (seedling blight of wheat) at high temperature similar to that for optimum growth in culture (Dickson, Eckerson, and Link, 1923); thus it affected different hosts over widely divergent temperature ranges—8°-16°C for corn, and 16°-28° for wheat. In each instance the host was affected at temperatures uncongenial for its growth. Jones, Johnson, and Dickson (1926) suggested that similar relations might exist for the *Helminthosporium* diseases of wheat (high temperature) and rice (low temperature), demonstrated respectively by McKinney (1923) and Ocfemia (1924). *Helminthosporium* disease of wheat provided an interesting example of a disease which was most severe at temperatures above the optima for growth both of the host and of the pathogen in culture.

The relations between temperature and disease development were generally attributed to effects on host predisposition or resistance such as the arrest of development from a susceptible immature phase to a resistant mature phase (e.g. onion smut, Walker and Jones, 1921), or to the ability of the host to develop specific resistance mechanisms under certain environmental conditions. In studies of *Gibberella* seedling blight of corn, Dickson and Holbert (1926) demonstrated that a resistance mechanism, genetically inherited in resistant cultivars, also operated in normally susceptible cultivars under certain environmental conditions. The demonstration by Goss (1923) that hydrogen-ion concentration influenced the temperature optimum for potato *Fusarium* cultures suggested that the so-called "optimum" for any factor should not be interpreted as a narrowly fixed point but should be expected to interact with other environmental factors.

L. R. Jones, Johnson, and Dickson (1926) scarcely considered the possibility of environmental variations affecting host-parasite relations indirectly through the influence of the soil microflora. McKinney and Davis (1925), working with take-all of wheat, reported: "The temperature optima shifted from time to time, regardless of the moisture content of the soil. This indicates that some other factors which were not so well controlled as soil temperature and soil moisture may have a decided influence on the occurrence of the disease. . . ." It was the work of Henry (1932) on this same disease which finally revealed the possible great significance of the microflora in affecting disease-temperature relations.

Henry demonstrated that a markedly different relation existed between disease expression and temperature in nonsterile soil from that in sterilised soil: whereas in nonsterile soil, infection ratings decreased with increase in temperature, no similar decrease was found in sterilised soil (Table 1). Henry's interpretation of

TABLE 1. Effect of temperature on the reaction of Marquis wheat seedlings to *Ophiobolus graminis* in sterilised and nonsterilised soils*

| Soil | Mean infection ratings (%) | | | |
	At 13°C	At 18°C	At 23°C	At 27°C
Sterilised soil	72	90	95	90
Nonsterilised soil	69	72	51	19

* Based on data from A. W. Henry. Can. J. Res. 7: 198-203. 1932.

these results was that in nonsterile soil the inhibition of *Ophiobolus graminis* by the saprophytic microflora increased with rise of temperature and resulted in disease control. The work is open to some criticism in that controls were inadequate and the soil sterilisation process so exceedingly vigourous that the sterilised soil undoubtedly differed from the unsterilised in many respects other than its microbial content. Nevertheless Henry's interpretation, eschewing the possibilities of coincident effects on host predisposition, was perhaps largely responsible for the transition from what Garrett (1956) has called the "environmental phase of root disease investigations" to the phase of "microbial ecology."

Shortly after Henry's publication, Garrett (1934a) also indicated the probable importance of microbial activity in soil on the relation between temperature and disease severity. Garrett's conclusions were based on comparisons of inoculation experiments in which nutrient-rich or nutrient-poor inocula were used. In these experiments, disease incidence decreased with rising temperature when nutrient-rich inocula were used, but the decrease was less marked with nutrient-poor inocula (spore suspensions). Garrett attributed this effect to stimulation of the soil microflora by the nutrient-rich inoculum. Garrett's studies of take-all disease of wheat showed that the temperature optimum for disease development in sterile soil gave rise to a high level of microbial antagonism in nonsterile soil and resulted in good disease control.

Relations between microbial activity, organic content, and disease control were also revealed by Garrett (1934b) and Ludwig and Henry (1943).

The markedly different disease-temperature relations for pea wilt (*Fusarium oxysporum* f. *pisi*, race 1) in sand and in soil led Schroeder and Walker (1942) to suggest that microbial antagonism to the pathogen in soil increases at higher temperatures and results in decreased disease incidence. These temperature effects on the pea-*Fusarium* relations are of particular interest in three respects. First, the disease behaviour pattern in sand varied, with temperature, from one typical of vascular wilt pathogens (in which disturbance of the host cortex is slight) to one in which there was severe cortical necrosis. Second, the effects of nutrient concentration on disease development differed at different temperatures. And third, the disease is unusual, for vascular-wilt fusaria (Jones, Johnson, and Dickson, 1926; Schroeder and Walker, 1942), in showing dissimilar temperature optima for disease development in soil and pathogen growth in culture.

The generally similar temperature optima for disease development and culture growth among vascular-wilt fusaria occurs also in the relatively low- and high-temperature wilt diseases of tomato caused by *Verticillium albo-atrum* and *V. dahliae* respectively (Isaac, 1949; Edgington and Walker, 1957); the latter organism may induce considerable symptom expression at a temperature somewhat above the optimum for growth in culture (Edgington and Walker, 1957). Field experience at East Malling Research Station with hop wilt, caused by *V. albo-atrum*, suggests that low soil temperature early in the growing season contributes towards the subsequent wilt behaviour of certain cultivars of intermediate tolerance, and it is possible that the development of defence mechanisms (Talboys, 1958) may be affected by temperature, as has been demonstrated in banana cultivars. Thus, Beckman, Halmos, and Mace (1962) demonstrated that the physical barriers obstructing the dispersal of *Fusarium* in the xylem of the cultivar Gros Michel was partly effective at 21°C, absent at 27°, and fully effective at 34°. Temporary occlusions of vessels by gels and permanent occlusions by tyloses at different temperatures related closely to disease expression.

Evidence for the development of mechanical barriers limiting host colonisation by root-infecting fungi is rather more plentiful than evidence for biochemical resistance, and one might suspect that this may reflect little more than the relative numbers of histologists and biochemists studying such phenomena. Polyphenolic metabolites, for example, appear to be of widespread importance as host factors in resistance, particularly in reference to air-borne diseases (Kirkham, 1959). Recently, Akazawa and Uritani (1961), in studies of black rot of sweet-potato roots, have suggested that increased resistance to *Ceratocystis fimbriata* at high temperatures is related to enhanced polyphenol oxidase activity in infected tissue.

The sum of information at present available relating effects of temperature to biological control of soil-borne diseases is at least sufficient to indicate the dynamic systems which may be implicated and interrelated. No one reaction is likely to be solely determinative, and considerations of single processes in isolation may lead to unjustified and erroneous conclusions.

Of all environmental soil factors, temperature is the least amenable to manipulation in the field. For this reason the most important practical value of knowledge of disease-temperature relations probably lies in contributing towards an understanding of geographical disease distribution, and in assessing the probable behaviour of diseases if introduced into new areas in relation to quarantine procedures.

Reports of more immediate practical application are few. Within limited areas a knowledge of the relative frequency of local temperature conditions associated with disease incidence may determine the choice of variety or crop. With annual crops, disease-favouring temperature conditions can be avoided by careful selection of planting dates, and relating planting dates to the known warming characteristics of the soil. In most instances, however, such knowledge is gained only by the hard-earned experience of the grower himself. The importance of careful selection of planting date is well illustrated by reference to the investigations of Dickson (1923) on seedling blight of wheat (caused by *Gibberella saubinetii*): wheat planted in March and April, when soil temperature was low, gave a disease-free crop, whereas plantings in May, germinating in warmer soils, suffered 30-40% mortality.

Disease control associated with soil-temperature reduction by shading is discussed by Hansford (1940) and Vasudeva (1941). Hansford describes experiments in which groundnuts (peanuts) or beans interplanted in cotton reduced wilt incidence (*Verticillium dahliae*) and suggested that the result was due to the shading effect of the intercrop plants. The observations of Vasudeva, on another disease of cotton, indicate that factors other than temperature may also influence disease incidence in mixed cropping. Thus, interplanting *Phaseolus aconitifolius* with cotton lowered soil temperature and reduced the incidence of root rot (caused by *Rhizoctonia* spp.), but disease reduction also occurred when *Panicum colonum*, which did not affect soil temperature, was intercropped with cotton. Soil-temperature reduction was claimed to be a factor determining control of chile wilt (caused by *Fusarium annuum*) by ridge-furrow cultivation (Garcia, 1933). In this method soil was successively ploughed up around plants as they grew, and the roots were consequently less subject to the high surface soil temperatures that favour this disease. Disease incidence over three years averaged 8.6% under ridge-furrow culture, as compared with 19.9% and 58.2% respectively in two native methods of culture in which root systems developed extensively in the surface soil layers.

Soil water.—Soil moisture content, aeration, and temperature are intimately interrelated. The warming of soil by radiation is in general inversely proportional to the water content, as Dr. Raney points out in his paper in this symposium; and moist soils retain heat longer than dry soils. These interactions may be influenced by soil texture and structure, and it must also be remembered that plant water requirements may be many times greater at higher temperatures. To a large extent moisture competes directly with air for soil space and consequently there is often a close reciprocal relation between these factors. Further, the effects of temperature and moisture on plant and microbial respiration and gaseous diffusion may appreciably alter the composition of the soil atmosphere. Thus, although moisture content is one property of the physical environment most readily amenable to manipulation in the field, the interpretation of its effects on diseases and pathogens requires considerable caution. It is seldom possible to attribute any disease response to this factor alone.

The effect of interactions of temperature and moisture were demonstrated by McKinney (1923) in studies of *Helminthosporium* disease of wheat. Whereas the temperature optimum for this disease remained constant over a range of soil moisture contents, changes of temperature resulted in marked shifts of soil-moisture optima. At higher temperatures, disease development was favoured by high soil moisture, and at low temperatures disease was favoured by low soil moisture content. McKinney commented that soil temperature thus appeared to be more influential than moisture. Even so it remains possible that disease development in the field may be considerably influenced by a combined effect of soil type and moisture content on the warming properties of the soil, and some of the conflicting evidence for the effect of environment on this disease may be closely associated with such interactions.

Garrett (1938) has listed a number of diseases favoured by high or low soil moisture content. Of those favoured by high moisture content it is not surprising to find that more than half are diseases caused by members of the Phycomycetes and Plasmodiophorales, largely dependent on water for the liberation and dispersal of free-swimming spores. With these diseases there is often a close positive relation between the level of infection and the quantity of soil water. The effects of high moisture content on the remaining diseases are considered mainly to result from predisposing effects on the host, either facilitating infection or, as in the case of *Fusarium* vascular-wilt diseases, resulting in increased symptom expression. Garrett's list of diseases favored by low soil moisture content are caused mostly by *Actinomyces* spp. and cereal smut fungi, which benefit directly from increased aeration and, in the latter instance, also from predisposition of the host to infection.

Thus, in general the effects described by Garrett fall into three categories: in one the pathogen is directly affected, and in the other two the host is affected either by being predisposed to infection, or by being more sensitive to infection so that symptom expression is increased. In the last two categories, in which the host is affected by the environment, biological control could justifiably be claimed in some instances when amelioration of the moisture conditions favouring disease results in reduction of disease. Biological control may here be invoked by enhancement of the natural capacity of the host to inhibit, limit, or tolerate the pathogen.

Even in those instances where soil moisture is known directly to affect the pathogen, host responses to moisture content may significantly affect the final result, and at certain moisture levels may be determinative.

Thus, the main effect of soil moisture on incidence of crown rot of apple could readily be attributed to a direct effect on the production, liberation, and dispersal of the zoospores of the causal organism, *Phytophthora cactorum*. Yet Welsh (1942) concluded that the influence of soil moisture was exerted particularly in the subsoil rather than in the more superficial soil, which is the locus of crown rot attack. Apparently, in this disease, soil water may affect predisposition to infection as well as providing a suitable medium for the reproduction and activity of the pathogen itself. A further example of complicating effects in an apparently straightforward reaction is provided by the studies of Rands and Dopp (1938) on *Pythium arrhenomanes* root rot of sugarcane. Their researches into possible predisposing effects of certain substances occurring in waterlogged soil revealed that salicylic aldehyde, while having no detectable effect on the host or pathogen separately, so predisposed roots to infection that plant weight reduction was two to seven times greater than that caused by the pathogen alone.

Evidence relating to the action of soil organisms in predisposing plants to disease is sparse, but recent work of particular interest concerns the effect of nematode infection on certain fungal diseases. Studies of verticillium wilt of eggplant (McKeen and Mountain, 1960) and fusarium wilt of cotton (Perry, 1963) indicate that nematode infections may have considerable physiological effects on the host that result in lowered resistance or tolerance to these fungal diseases. Nematodes have also been implicated with several other fungal diseases, and it is possible that they may subsequently prove to be of widespread significance as agents predisposing plants to fungal diseases. Restriction of nematode mobility by altered soil moisture levels could be one of a multiplicity of factors affecting disease incidence.

Direct experimental evidence relating to the effects of moisture content on the biological control of diseases by microbial antagonism is lacking. Garrett's general conclusion concerning soil-moisture effects on the importance of microbial antagonism in host-parasite relations of cereal foot-rot fungi was that "other conditions being suitable, biological antagonism increases with soil moisture content over the range 30 to 80% saturation" (Garrett, 1934a). The evidence supporting this statement, however, is not wholly convincing. For the present it can only be surmised that moisture content is very likely to influence host-parasite relations through the medium of microbial antagonism by deduction from our knowledge that this environmental factor affects soil respiration levels and microbial activity (E. Griffiths and Birch, 1961; Katznelson, 1960; Warcup, 1957).

Consideration, so far, has mainly been given to factors affecting the host-parasite relation or diseased condition. Factors limiting the pathogen directly, that is, in the nonparasitic phase, may be utilised in control under the host crop but, for the most part, they are aimed at eliminating or reducing the level of the pathogen between plantings of susceptible crops. Environmental conditions acting directly against the pathogen are not necessarily similar to those reducing disease severity. Thus, for example, Stover (1953) has demonstrated that six species and forms of *Fusarium* reproduced most abundantly and survived for the longest periods in soils of low moisture content, whereas most of the fusarioses they cause are favoured by high soil moisture levels. In the period between susceptible host crops most root-infecting fungi are able to withstand, often in dormancy, the effects of such changes in the physical environment as occur naturally. Indeed, they would rarely be troublesome were they sensitive to such vicissitudes. Certain control treatments (e.g. organic manuring) stimulate the pathogen into activity and so render it more vulnerable to the antagonism of the saprophyte microflora, which is also stimulated by the treatment. The moisture level of soils treated in this way is clearly important in determining the efficacy of the measure; thus irrigation is recommended immediately following organic manuring in the control of *Phymatotrichum omnivorum* (King, 1937). The use of such relatively slight variations of moisture content as a sole factor in control, however, is of little value, and it becomes necessary in the application of this factor to resort to the extreme conditions of drought and flood. Drought conditions would be limited in application to a few naturally hot and arid areas, and the effect of withholding water supply would be most likely to affect organisms directly by desiccation (McLennan, 1928; Saksena, 1955; Warcup, 1957) or associated temperature increases above the thermal tolerance level of the protoplast (review: Newhall, 1955). Soil saturation or flood fallowing has somewhat more widespread possibilities of application, although obviously water supply, topographical and pedological features, and land availability may be primary limiting factors. Again, the effect of soil saturation may directly restrict oxygen supply to the pathogen, but it is also possible that accumulation of carbon dioxide resulting from microbial respiration may be of considerable, or even greater, significance. The evidence at present available suggests that microbial activity may be directly or indirectly responsible for the destruction of certain pathogens in flooded soil: the efficiency of the antagonistic mechanism may be influenced by other factors including oxygen availability. The practical application of soil flooding in the control of widely differing types of fungal pathogens, and the diversity of the mechanisms which may be involved, are illustrated below by reference to recent studies of *Sclerotinia sclerotiorum*, *Phytophthora parasitica* var. *nicotianae*, and *Fusarium oxysporum* f. *cubense*.

Sclerotinia sclerotiorum causes serious diseases of celery and other crops in the Everglades of Florida. Pink rot of celery may affect any part of the plant but is most conspicuous and damaging at soil level. Control by deep ploughing has not proved satisfactory because of the practical difficulties of obtaining complete inversion of soil (Brooks, 1942). Brooks (1939) noted that sclerotia lost viability within 60 days in saturated muck soil, and that large irregular sclerotia, with the rind sharply folded or cracked, were the first to be affected. These facts suggested that complete flooding for up

to 8 weeks would give good control and this was supported by field observations in which 10% infection was recorded in inadequately flooded areas and less than 1% in areas flooded for 6-8 weeks. Moore (1949) and Stoddard (1949) subsequently demonstrated that sclerotia could be destroyed in soils flooded with static water for 5 weeks. The procedure, however, proved to be uneconomical in practice, and Stoner and Moore (1953) therefore investigated the possibility of including lowland rice culture, which requires circulating flood water, in a 3- or 4-year rotation. Their results revealed that circulating water brought about a considerably more rapid decomposition of sclerotia than occurred under static flooding, for sclerotial decomposition was virtually complete after 20 days. Stoner and Moore concluded that microbial action was an important factor in sclerotial destruction, rather than the direct effect of anaerobic conditions, because of the greatly increased effectiveness of circulating (and aerated) water, and they observed more rapid destruction of sclerotia when the rind was abraded.

An interesting example of destruction by flooding is reported from Java, where tobacco and wet rice culture are frequently used in 2-year rotation. Van Schreven (1948) found that *Phytophthora parasitica* var. *nicotianae* (the cause of tobacco black shank) was eradicated from infested soil after submergence in paddies for 3-4 months. No information is given relating to the method of destruction. In view of the relatively high tolerance level of this genus to partially anaerobic conditions, one might suspect that microbial antagonism may be implicated.

Flooding of banana land to eradicate *Fusarium oxysporum* f. *cubense* was first undertaken in 1939. Subsequent investigations by R. H. Stover and his colleagues, published over the last decade, have made valuable contributions to the meagre information available on the effects and after-effects of flood fallowing. Soils were flooded with 2-5 ft of water for up to 6 months. The flood lakes were considered to be well circulated and oxygenated by wind and a constantly inflowing water supply to replenish losses from evaporation and seepage. The greatest reduction of indigenous soil fungi and the greatest increase in bacterial numbers occurred in the surface mud in the first 35 days of flooding, and at least 85% of the indigenous fusaria were destroyed in the first 40 days. After 120 days most of the indigenous fungus flora was eradicated: however, a small fungus population was found at all times on the surface of the submerged soil, and this was considered to be derived from a "migratory" flora carried by inflowing water. This migratory flora occasionally included *F. oxysporum* f. *cubense* among other fusaria (Stover, Thornton and Dunlap, 1952, 1953). Stover (1959) reported that *F. oxysporum* f. *cubense*, while surviving in the surface soil and trash and freely suspended in water, could be very greatly reduced by ploughing to 8-10 in (thus redistributing the pathogen throughout this depth of soil) between flooding periods. The success of this approach, as illustrated in the report, suggests that a very small proportion of the surviving pathogen population may in fact be derived from the migratory flora.

Mainly on the basis of evidence from laboratory experiments, Stover has considered "that gaseous relationships of a chemical nature rather than a biological nature and the physiological state of the fungus are more important factors in determining survival than is the direct action of micro-organisms. The latter may be important indirectly in the utilisation or production of oxygen and other compounds" (Stover, 1954). And that "Fusarium survival in submerged soils is determined by oxygen available to the surface oxidised soil layer" (Stover, 1955).

Much of the evidence on which these conclusions are based is open to the alternative interpretation that carbon dioxide accumulation, rather than oxygen depletion, may be a factor determining survival. Stover and Freiburg (1958) demonstrated that increased carbon dioxide content of natural soil could result in stimulated multiplication of the pathogen. Newcombe (1960) substantiated this finding but pointed out that although the fungus could tolerate, and be stimulated by, relatively brief exposures to high carbon dioxide concentration, its long-term survival in such conditions was prejudiced. Newcombe studied the survival of *Fusarium oxysporum* f. *cubense* in nonsterile soil, under various environmental conditions, by the direct-observation technique of Legge (1952) and a soil-baiting isolation method. Over a period of 84 days the activity of *Fusarium* was little affected in moist soil, but in soils submerged under static water, aerated water, and oil-covered water, activity was similarly and greatly attenuated. This reduced activity was found, by reinoculation of these soils, not to be due to a gradual accumulation of toxic substances, and the result suggested that it was not specifically due to limitation of oxygen. The behaviour of the fungus on agar and in moist soil was then tested under atmospheres of air, nitrogen, air minus oxygen, and carbon dioxide: in soil, over 42 days, air and nitrogen had little effect, but attenuation was slight under air minus oxygen, and marked under carbon dioxide. None of the gases appeared to affect growth on agar (cf. Hollis, 1948). In another experiment with submerged soil, attenuation was considerably greater under carbon dioxide than under nitrogen (representing an oxygen-deficient atmosphere).

Direct observation revealed that conidia placed in sterile water and soil under atmospheres of air, air minus oxygen, and nitrogen, germinated over a period and formed chlamydospores, which after 37 days were the main fungal structures remaining. In soil under an atmosphere of carbon dioxide and in flooded soil a markedly different behaviour was noted, for conidia were mostly ungerminated after 37 days and very few chlamydospores were present. Newcombe concluded from these studies that the main factor in the elimination of the fungus by flood fallowing is a high carbon dioxide content in the submerged soil, inhibiting chlamydospore formation and thus leading to a depletion of viable conidia by their gradual germination and destruction in the absence of a colonisable substrate. Newcombe remarks that carbon dioxide production by anaerobic organisms in flooded soil must be considerable. Thus it appears that the mechanism of action of flood fallowing in eradicating *Fusarium oxysporum* f. *cubense* (and other fungi?) may be attributable, in part, to an intensification of the effects of one of the simplest and most widespread antibiotics.

Soil atmosphere.—Qualitative and quantitative aspects of soil aeration are intimately related to moisture and organic content, texture, compaction, and even reaction (Garrett, 1936, 1937). Some of these interrelations have been noted in discussions of soil moisture content. Aeration of soil affects host and pathogen through oxygen content, carbon dioxide content, and other volatile substances resulting mainly from anaerobic respiration such as hydrogen sulphide, methane, ammonia, hydrogen, and aldehydes. The balance of concentration of these substances is determined largely by the respiratory mechanisms of the soil-living organisms together with those physical properties of the soil that affect gaseous diffusion, solution, and absorption. The response of both plant and pathogen to the composition of the soil atmosphere may be modified by such factors as temperature and nutrient availability.

Although all filamentous fungi are strong aerobes and, from this point of view, might be expected to be most active in soils of light texture, Garrett (1944) points out that disease incidence is not necessarily greater in such soils—for they also tend to be nutrient-poor and acid in reaction, and consequently may not favour disease development. Garrett illustrated this by reference to *Ophiobolus graminis* and *Phymatotrichum omnivorum*, which have similar modes of spread in soil, yet take-all disease is favoured by any condition (such as light texture) making for improved aeration, whereas cotton root rot is more prevalent on heavy soils in which the alkaline reaction or high water-holding capacity may favour the disease.

While it is important to distinguish between the soil conditions favouring disease incidence and those favouring fungal activity and survival, the distinction is often necessarily a very broad one in which several major factors such as texture, reaction, and organic content are naturally linked. Soil moisture, particularly, is so intimately associated with aeration that the relative effects of the factors are rarely distinguished, or are in practice indistinguishable. Almost invariably poor aeration results from an excess of free soil moisture and the problem is considered one of water relations. Less frequently aeration may be affected by soil compaction, restricting gaseous interchange, and this type of impedance will be discussed. Primarily, however, it is proposed to indicate the importance of carbon dioxide in ecological aspects of soil biology and the possible role of this gas in biological control.

The carbon dioxide content of the air is 0.03%, in soil atmosphere it is commonly about 0.5% in temperate zones, and may rise to between 3.5 and 9.2% shortly after rain, even in soils of light texture (Burgess and Fenton, 1953). Carbon dioxide content is generally higher in poorly drained, fine-textured soils than in well-drained, open soils, and usually increases with soil depth (Boynton and Compton, 1944).

Fungi in general are very much more sensitive to the concentration of carbon dioxide than to that of oxygen. At low concentrations, increases of carbon dioxide content may actually stimulate growth (Durrell, 1924; Newcombe, 1960; Stover and Freiberg, 1958); as concentration increases, growth or specific growth phenomena, such as chlamydospore formation or sporulation, may be inhibited, but the effect in itself is not lethal (Hawker, 1950). Sensitivity to carbon-dioxide concentration varies with species and individuals and with environmental conditions such as temperature and nutrition (Brown, 1922), tolerance being lowest when other conditions are limiting. Carbon dioxide may be of considerable and general importance in determining the vertical distribution of soil fungi, for it has been demonstrated that certain fungi occurring in subsurface soils were more tolerant to high concentrations of carbon dioxide than were others restricted to the more superficial levels (Bisby, Timonin, and James, 1935; Burges and Fenton, 1953; Durbin, 1955).

Evidence of the limiting effects of reduced aeration and carbon-dioxide accumulation on growth of root-infecting fungi in soil is provided from investigations of *Rhizoctonia solani, Ophiobolus graminis,* and *Sclerotium rolfsii.* The mycelial growth of *R. solani* is most extensive through nonsterile soils of neutral reaction. Blair (1943) found growth to be reduced, and the soil-reaction optimum for growth to be shifted to more alkaline values, when soils were amended with organic matter. Blair considered that growth reduction resulted partly from the fungistatic action of respiratory carbon dioxide produced by the stimulated microbial population. This conclusion was supported by mitigation of the fungistatic effect when carbon dioxide was removed by absorption in solutions of strong alkali. Other experiments demonstrated that growth of *R. solani* was promoted by forced aeration of soil.

Earlier, Garrett (1936) related increased incidence of take-all in alkaline soils to the increased growth rate of *Ophiobolus graminis* along roots in these soils. Garrett suggested that alkaline soils acted as acceptors of carbon dioxide, whereas in soils of heavy texture and acid reaction this gas accumulated and limited the epiphytic growth of the pathogen. Forced aeration of acid soils stimulated increased growth rates to levels comparable with those in alkaline soils.

Such limitations of mycelial activity in the presence of host plants or colonisable substrates is clearly disadvantageous to the pathogen. In the absence of food sources, or when the pathogen is not suitably situated positionally to bring about host infection, then restriction of activity is likely to be advantageous. Such an advantage may be conferred on *Sclerotium rolfsii,* for the germination of the sclerotia of this fungus is affected by depth of burial, and only in the surface, detritus-rich layers is host colonisation successful. (This relation will be discussed in detail below). Abeygunawardena and Wood (1957) considered that germination was inhibited by carbon-dioxide accumulation, and

demonstrated that this inhibition could be reduced, in both surface-borne and buried sclerotia, by aeration.

Plant responses to poor aeration and high concentration of carbon dioxide vary from extreme sensitivity, in which case they may be killed, to a high level of tolerance, as in willow and rice. Cereals are intermediate in reaction. In general, however, plants are sensitive to poor aeration, and its use for disease control under the growing crop is limited by this fact. More often the grower has to concern himself with cultivation and hoeing, particularly after irrigation and rain, to check the harmful effects that might directly ensue from the accumulation of carbon dioxide. In the relatively few instances where poor aeration can be tolerated and the practice is of benefit, it is achieved by "puddling" (as in paddy rice cultivation), mechanical compaction followed by wetting, or by direct irrigation (Russell, 1950).

The probable controlling action of carbon dioxide on pathogens between crops, as in flood fallowing against *Fusarium,* has been noted, and it should be borne in mind that the antibiotic effects of carbon dioxide produced by soil organisms may play a significant role in control by green manuring. Physical manipulation of the soil has resulted in control—apparently through the agency of the soil atmosphere—of flag smut and take-all diseases of cereals. Studies in Egypt of the effects of depth of sowing and soil moisture on flag smut (caused by *Urocystis tritici*) of wheat enabled Jones and Seif el-Nasr (1940) to develop a control measure of striking efficiency. This soil- and seed-borne disease was found to increase in severity with increased depth of planting and decreased soil moisture. The results of these experiments, together with observations of local planting methods, suggested that sowing on the soil surface directly after flooding would give maximum disease control. This "mud-sowing" method was found to control flag smut so efficiently that it offered an alternative to seed disinfection or the use of resistant varieties. No studies were made of the effects of oxygen or carbon dioxide on this disease, but it is known to be favoured by aerobic conditions. Jones and Seif el-Nasr considered that the benefits of wet-soil sowing could be attributed to reduced aeration, and that surface sowing shortened the susceptible stage by rapid emergence of the seedling.

R. L. Griffiths (1933) reported of take-all disease of wheat that "More effective control will be obtained by correct methods of cultivation than by any other means. It is certain that the compactness of the seed-bed is a very important factor. Take-all does practically all its damage on loose seed beds. . . . The chief compacting agent is rain and all the farmer's cultivation work should assist the rain in this respect." Griffiths considered that these conditions favoured the wheat plant rather than limited the pathogen, but Garrett (1937) subsequently showed that the treatment was more likely to be associated with the inhibitory action of accumulated carbon dioxide in compacted soil on the growth of *Ophiobolus* hyphae along the wheat seedling roots.

The carbon dioxide content of the soil atmosphere is

perhaps one of the most important single factors determining the distribution in depth, survival, and behaviour of soil organisms and is an effective end-point common to many and diverse cultural practices.

Tillage, deep ploughing, and inversion of soil.—In the period between susceptible crops, root-infecting fungi may survive in a low state of vegetative activity, or in dormancy in the form of simple or complex resting structures. Such structures range from single-celled spores to multicellular sclerotia with differentiated tissues. Sclerotia-producing soil-borne fungi are among the most obstinate opponents that the pathologist has to face; consequently they have been the subjects of extensive investigations, particularly with respect to the effects of cultivation treatments on survival. For this reason studies of sclerotia-producing fungi have been selected for reference, but it should be borne in mind that the principles involved in their control apply equally to many other, perhaps less obdurate, soil-borne pathogens.

Pathogenic fungi in dormancy are not easily destroyed by variations of the natural environment. Their eradication or reduction is usually achieved, therefore, by cultivation practices that tend to overcome or prevent dormancy. Concomitant with such practices, the general level of microbial activity in the soil is stimulated and attenuation of the pathogen may result from antagonism and depletion of food reserves. Most effective among these measures are soil amendments such as green manuring, and the planting of "decoy" crops which, though immune to the pathogen, induce the germination of its resting structures. These particular treatments, however, are dealt with elsewhere and the present discussion is confined to somewhat similar, though less spectacular effects which may be promoted by soil tillage and deep ploughing, and also finally to the development and use of soil-inversion techniques resulting in deep burial of the pathogen.

Tillage of soil causes soil-aggregate disruption, the exposure of organic matter that was previously inaccessible, the release of accumulated carbon dioxide and an increased availability of oxygen. Consequent upon these effects is a marked increase in microbial activity which may further be stimulated by the drying or rewetting which frequently follows tillage (E. Griffiths and Birch, 1961; Rovira and Greacen, 1957; Russell, 1950; Warcup, 1957).

By soil disturbance some fungal structures may be exposed to inimical physical conditions, such as desiccation and radiation, and be killed. Sclerotia generally are very resistant to desiccation, although those of *Phymatotrichum omnivorum* provide a notable exception (King, Loomis, and Hope, 1931). Also sclerotia are probably resistant to intense light by virtue of their pigmentation (Hawker, 1957; Nicot, 1960). An interesting case of disruption of a biological-control mechanism was suggested by Simmonds, Sallans, and Ledingham (1950), who considered that exposure to ultraviolet light might kill the bacterial flora on and around spores of *Helminthosporium sativum* and so permit spore germination without antibiotic interference.

Within the disrupted soil layers, activity of the microflora may be enhanced and, if moisture conditions are suitable, the germination of resting structures stimulated. The reduction of carbon dioxide in the soil atmosphere—the gaseous background of soil antagonism—may be one important factor associated with this response. Thus, Abeygunawardena and Wood (1957) found that while germination of *Sclerotium rolfsii* sclerotia increased with increase of moisture content up to 75%, germination decreased with increasing depth of burial. These investigators induced germination of buried sclerotia by aeration and considered that this effect was attributable to decreased carbon dioxide content rather than oxygen availability. Within one year of burial at various depths in soil the sclerotia of *Sclerotinia trifoliorum* from depths of less than 2 in showed 70-90% germination to produce apothecia. No apothecia developed from sclerotia buried below this depth.

Dillon Weston, Loveless, and Taylor (1946) considered that *Sclerotinia trifolium* sclerotia buried below 2 inches failed to germinate, but they apparently did not recover and examine these sclerotia. Nevertheless the fact that this fungus survives for 7-8 years in the absence of host crops strongly suggests that the rate of germination is at least very low at deep soil levels. The evidence of Brooks (1942) indicates that *Sclerotinia sclerotiorium* behaves in a similar manner.

In the case of *Phymatotrichum omnivorum*, the effect of aeration on sclerotial germination is indicated by marked differences in survival in coarse- and fine-textured soils attributed to differences in spontaneous-germination rates (King and Eaton, 1934; Taubenhaus and Ezekiel, 1936). Such "spontaneous" germination, that is, in the absence of a host (Rogers, 1937, 1942), is considered by Garrett (1956) to be a serious defect in the functional efficiency of sclerotia, but even so it may serve as a mechanism compensating in some degree other shortcomings of an aerated environment. For such an environment will tend to be a coarse-textured, well-drained soil, and the effective stimulation range of host root excretions may be considerably less than that in a fine, less well-drained soil. This relation between soil moisture content and the stimulation effects of host roots is suggested by the increased germination of *Sclerotium cepivorum* sclerotia, in the vicinity of onion roots, as water content of soil increases up to 90% (Coley-Smith and Hickman, 1957; Coley-Smith, 1960). Unfortunately the manner of recording used by these investigators did not permit information to be gathered concerning the effect of moisture content on the distance between stimulated sclerotia and the root (Coley-Smith, personal communication). Further evidence of stimulated vegetative activity after tillage is provided by Garrett's (1959) observation that soil cultivation encouraged *Armillaria mellea* to produce fresh crops of rhizomorphs.

The effect of tillage in stimulating fungi to break dormancy and resume vegetative activity may result in the attenuation of pathogenic forms in the absence of hosts simply by starvation. In some instances the effect might appear to be primarily physical; thus in the case of *Sclerotinia,* when sclerotial germination is induced at soil levels too deep to permit apothecial formation on the soil surface, or, as in the case of *Armillaria,* when the effect of a series of cultivations may be both to stimulate rhizomorph production and to sever existing rhizomorphs from their food bases. Such physical effects, however, are not in themselves necessarily lethal. Admittedly, severance from a food base, and the act and consequences of germination, in the absence of a host, may reduce energy resources below those necessary for later host infection. But, at the same time, the fact that energy resources are so reduced, may reflect the inability of the pathogen to compete saprophytically for further food reserves when these are present. This point is illustrated by experiments with *Sclerotium rolfsii* which, while its sclerotia can initiate host infection under sterile conditions, does not infect groundnuts in nonsterile soil in the absence of supplementary, soil-borne food sources (Boyle, 1956). Boyle demonstrated that incidence of infection decreased as the length of time increased between soil amendment with fresh organic materials and host planting. This effect appears to be attributable to the low competitive saprophytic ability (sensu Garrett, 1956) of *Sclerotium,* as well as the rate of utilisation of the nutrient reserves. A further factor likely to be of importance is the decreased resistance of pathogens to microbial antagonisms after sclerotial germination and the consequent rupturing of the protective rind: this is indicated by experiments in which the sclerotia of *Sclerotinia sclerotiorum* were observed to lose viability most rapidly when the rind was cracked or abraded, referred to earlier (Brooks, 1939; Stoner and Moore, 1953).

These effects, of course, will mainly be limited to those soil levels actually disrupted by tillage. Since the distribution of many root-infecting fungi frequently coincides at least with the distribution of host roots, a large proportion of the pathogen population may survive in deep levels not affected by tillage treatment. Furthermore, even within the tilled soil layers, only a proportion of the population may be affected because of the incompleteness of mechanical disruption, and because of the inherent variability of pathogen response to the changed environmental conditions. The factors inhibiting germination of resting structures (generally covered by the phrase "soil fungistasis") may be considered important protective mechanisms, preventing wastage of contained nutrient reserves until the time when new sources (i.e. a host plant) are available and may directly stimulate germination. Clearly, for any individual organism, the balance between inhibitory and stimulatory factors must be delicate. Between individuals of a population the qualitative and quantitative effects of these factors are likely to vary—for "variability is itself a means of survival" (Hawker, 1957).

Differing somewhat from root-infecting fungi, some sclerotial species producing apothecia may largely be restricted to the surface soils, for ascospore infection commonly occurs in aboveground tissues and it is mainly in aerial tissues that sclerotia are subsequently formed. For control in these instances resort has been made to burial of the sclerotia by deep ploughing with the object of preventing apothecial emergence, rather than stimulating sclerotial germination. This measure has given some degree of control, but deep burial of all sclerotia has not been found possible, and also each subsequent cultivation has brought some buried sclerotia back to the surface (Dillon Weston, Loveless, and Taylor, 1946; Brooks, 1942). This approach, however, has yielded quite good control, at least in first plantings, of blind seed disease of perennial ryegrass, caused by *Phialea temulenta,* in which the seed is the only part of the plant to be infected: thus where the source of infection is contained only in the planting material, apothecial emergence was prevented by planting seed at least ½ in deep with complete soil coverage (Hardison, 1948).

A very high level of control of groundnut blight, caused by *Sclerotium rolfsii,* has resulted from a combination of ploughing and field sanitation. The theory behind the approach to this problem is based on the relation existing between the physical soil environment and the availability of organic food sources in the soil which must supplement those of the sclerotium before successful host infection can be achieved (Boyle, 1956). Both sclerotial germination rate and saprophytic colonising ability are determined by soil aeration, and the practices recommended by Boyle, in Georgia, are directed first at burying all organic residues in soil to a "depth where growth of the pathogen is checked by ecological factors" and, second, at preventing accumulation of organic debris on the soil surface during the crop season. Similar measures have been applied to control this disease in Tanganyika (Clinton, 1957). Clinton reported that ploughing to a depth of 8 in gave complete control, which indicates that sclerotia were mainly confined to this level and that only a very narrow horizon might exist in which sclerotia were not adversely affected by some factor or factors.

Tillage and deep ploughing have both been used with some degree of success for control of the cotton-root-rot pathogen, *Phymatotrichum omnivorum* (Rea, 1933, 1939; Streets, 1937). Streets found deep fall ploughing and subsoiling, followed by pulling and burning of cotton roots successful at first, but a reduced level of root rot began to appear later in the following season. He considered that these infections originated from deeply buried sclerotia. The success of cultivation treatments in reducing soil infectivity appears to depend on the one hand, on limiting colonisation of the dying roots of the preceding crop and the subsequent formation of sclerotia, and on the other hand, in stimulating existing sclerotia to germinate. The efficiency of the treatment in the first case is probably dependent on the degree of root system dissociation and laceration, which increases the rates both of root tissue death and subsequent colonisation of the tissues by saprophytic microorganisms. In the second case the effect is probably associated with improved aeration. In both cases the pathogen ultimately is rendered more vulnerable to microbial antagonism. Stimulation of the soil micropopulation by cultivations aimed specifically at reducing the level of survival of *Phymatotrichum* was

TABLE 2. Effects of normal bedding and deep rotary tillage on soil micropopulation, incidence of cotton root rot, and occurrence of sclerotia of *Phymatotrichum** †

Soil treatment, Oct. 3, 1939	Total micropopulation, millions per gram of air-dry soil				Plants killed, %		Sclerotial occurence Aug. 1940	
	Mid-Oct. 1939	Nov. 1939	May 1940	Jun. 1940	Aug. 1940	Oct. 1940	0-12"	Below 12"
Normal bedding	159	10	18	12	90	94	+	+
Deep rotary tillage	335	26	19	12	36	69	−	+

* From R. B. Mitchell, D. R. Hooton, and F. E. Clark. J. Agr. Res. 63: 535-547. 1941.

† 80-85% mortality occurred in the cotton crop preceding the treatments.

demonstrated by Mitchell, Hooton, and Clark (1941), who used deep rotary tillage to achieve efficient soil disruption and aeration. Comparisons of the effects of normal bedding and the rotary tillage of land which, before treatment, carried a severely infected cotton crop with 80-85% mortality, are summarised in Table 2. These investigators recommend that land should be cultivated as early as possible after the cotton crop to check further colonisation and sclerotial production by *Phymatotrichum*.

A particularly interesting approach to control by cultivation is Green's soil-inversion technique to combat *Verticillium* wilt of mint in the muck soils of Indiana, Michigan, and Wisconsin. Green (1957) discovered that this microsclerotia-producing species of *Verticillium* was largely confined to the upper 18 in of soils; below this level it was absent or of very infrequent occurrence. This distribution is similar to that demonstrated by Wilhelm (1940) in the mineral soils of California, and presumably reflects the distribution and density of occurrence of host plant roots and debris to which, by analogy with a dark-mycelial *Verticillium* (Sewell, 1959), this pathogen may be restricted. The muck soils are lightweight, often deep, and free from obstruction, and therefore are well suited to the soil-inversion technique developed by Green (1958). For this purpose a frame-mounted 36-in moldboard plough was modified by adding a 16-in jointer plough to the frame immediately ahead of the large moldboard. The small plough dropped the upper 12-14 in of topsoil into the furrow before the remainder of the subsoil was turned by the 36-in plough. A field experiment in which two plots, one conventionally ploughed and one deep-ploughed, were adjacent and subsequently cultivated as one unit, showed that deep-ploughing resulted in a marked reduction of wilt incidence over 3 years. These results are summarised in Table 3.

Green pointed out that most disease increase in the

TABLE 3. Incidence of mint wilt (per cent infection) following conventional ploughing and inversion of infested muck soil by deep ploughing*

Type of ploughing	Row mint, 1956	Row mint, 1957	Meadow mint, 1958
Conventional (6-8 in)	57.2	72.6	85.0
Deep (28-30 in)	4.0	8.6	10.2

* From R. J. Green. Phytopathology 48: 575-577. 1958.

deep-ploughed plot was due to encroachment from adjacent areas as a result of not cultivating the deep-ploughed area separately. The fact that the disease spread among plants growing in the deep-ploughed, and inverted soil suggested to Green that the initial absence of the pathogen at deep levels was due to physical rather than biological phenomena. No evidence is available of the fate of the buried fungal inoculum; one might suspect that this pathogen could survive for a considerable period under such conditions. The value of the control method over a long term must depend on the balance between the ability of the buried inoculum to survive, and the rate of spread of the disease in new mint plantings on the inverted soil. Deeply buried inocula may be rendered largely uninfective by reduced aeration, or by the effect of lower soil temperatures on the pathogen or host roots. But even so, in view of the unlikelihood of burying all infective material, and the ideal conditions for spread of this pathogen, provided by the discing operations used in mint cultivation, one might guess that this balance will be fine and may require to be weighted by a fallow period following soil inversion. The value of the control measure over the short term is demonstrated well enough by Green's estimation that more than 10,000 acres had been deep-ploughed by 1958. With a disease as devastating as mint wilt, any reprieve that can be given must be of immense value both to the specialist grower and to the investigators concerned with the development of alternative control measures.

BIOLOGICAL CONTROL AND CHANGING PHYSICAL CONDITIONS: THE DYNAMIC SYSTEM.—The effect of altered physical conditions of soil on the biological control of pathogens and diseases has been discussed under four subheadings. Within each section, many aspects have been omitted. One, undoubtedly playing a part in many of the over-all interactions already discussed, requires special mention and exemplifies particularly the dynamic nature of the soil biological system. This is the effect of the physical environment on the quality and quantity of root exudation, which in turn may affect the pathogen directly and host-parasite relations indirectly through the agency of the microbial population. These interacting effects are represented diagrammatically in Fig. 1. From the few studies that have been made it is apparent that soil moisture, soil temperature, and light intensity markedly influence the qualitative and quantitative composition of plant root exu-

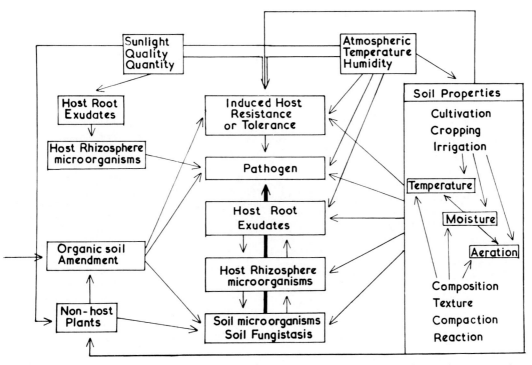

Fig. 1. Some interacting factors that may be influenced by the effect of the physical environment on host-plant root exudation.

dates (Katznelson, Rouatt, and Payne, 1955; Rovira, 1959). The reactions numbered 2 to 6 (Fig. 2) have been investigated and discussed by Buxton (1960) with reference to *Fusarium* wilt of pea, and other investigations relevant to these reactions are described by Buxton (1957a,b), Flentje (1959), Kerr and Flentje (1957), Rovira (1956), and Rovira and Harris (1961). Evidence that antagonistic reactions are enhanced under conditions of high nutrient availability, as in the rhizosphere, is abundant (reviews: Brian, 1957; Wood and Tveit, 1955). The role of the rhizosphere population in influencing the level of host resistance (Fig. 2, reaction 7) is a speculation based on the evidence that this population may influence host metabolism by affecting the availability of calcium, phosphate, iron, and manganese (Esterman and McLaren, 1961; Gerretsen, 1948; Starkey, 1955; Subba-Rao, Bidwell, and Bailey, 1961; Timonin, 1948) and perhaps also amino acids, vitamins, and other complex organic substances (Krasil'nikov, 1959).

Under natural conditions it is likely that reactions such as these will be masked or attributed to other factors, most particularly perhaps in consideration of temperature and moisture effects. In the case of light intensity affecting disease incidence, the reaction might not be so heavily obscured, and it is interesting to record Colhoun's tentative explanation of the effect of light on the relation between spore load (of *Plasmodiophora brassicae*) and club-root disease index: "The possibility may perhaps exist that light intensity may influence root diffusates which in turn may have an effect on spore germination and infection" (Colhoun, 1961).

Throughout all discussions an attempt has been made to draw attention to the interactions between the major variants of the physical environment and also, to a lesser extent, to the complexity of interaction set in motion by the variation of one or more environmental factors. In discussing and investigating problems of soil biology it is necessary, in some way or other, to separate effects and interactions into convenient, manageable units; the method of classification is most often determined by the particular specialisation or interests of the investigator. The object of this brief section is to emphasize that all interrelations are in fact part of a complete dynamic system: under field conditions each factor or group of factors is constantly varying under the influence of others. The relative importance of the several interrelations represented in Fig. 1 is unlikely ever to be fully appreciated, even under constant environmental conditions, and yet this cluster of interactions forms only a small part of the whole dynamic system—albeit, admittedly, a part which, from the pathologists' viewpoint, might be considered the centrepiece. In Fig. 2 an attempt has been made to integrate the system as far as it is known at the present time. This diagram is designed to illustrate the complexity of the system rather than its simplicity, and to indicate the dangers of oversimplified interpretation of phenomena relating to the effects of changing physical conditions on soil-borne diseases and their control.

Biological Control and the Physical Environment: Status and Prospects.—"From the times of Theophrastus (300 B.C.) and Pliny (70 A.D.) to approximately the year 1800 the prevailing agricultural

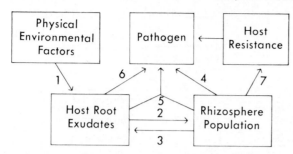

Fig. 2. Some interacting factors affecting soil-borne pathogens.

literature was filled with references to unfavourable soil and air conditions as precursors to plant diseases" (Chupp, 1946). Long before the mycological, causal researches of the 19th Century, the grower, forced to live from his land, had learned by the bitter experience of trial and error the use of many methods of biological control. The ecological researches of the twentieth century are still struggling to explain their effect. Undoubtedly the greatest advances in biological control (and indeed in all approaches to disease control) have been made in plant breeding and the development of disease-resistant varieties; concomitant with this has developed an ever-increasing understanding of the genetics of resistance and pathogenic variability. These advances, unfortunately, have not been paralleled by increased knowledge of the nature of resistance, and Walker (1959) had just cause to plead—in words similar to those of L. R. Jones 35 years earlier—for more assistance from biochemists and physiologists in elucidating these problems. The level of disease resistance of many cultivars is affected by environment, and manipulation of the physical condition of the soil may help to extend the geographical and pedological range of usefulness of these varieties. But without knowledge of the nature of resistance, ad-hoc research makes slow progress.

The control of diseases by soil cultivation and amendment is frequently attributed to the action of microbial antagonism by extrapolation of knowledge acquired from in-vitro experiments. While this may be justifiable in certain instances, extrapolation of such knowledge sometimes fails completely to explain phenomena in natural soil. Much evidence for the suppression of plant diseases by microbial antagonism is based on comparisons of disease development in natural, inoculated soil with that in sand culture or in similar soil which is treated in one of the following ways: amended with organic or inorganic materials; sterilised prior to inoculation with the pathogen; sterilised, recontaminated with nonsterile soil prior to or coincident with pathogen inoculation. Here again the assumption may not always be justified that the host plant is not affected by these differing media simply because no differences are detected in control series by measurements of plant height and weight. The use of test plants with two root systems might be of value in resolving this point. The circumstantial evidence for the role of microbial antagonism in disease control is considerable, but there

remains ample room for truly definitive work in this field, as there is also for studies of direct effects of soil organisms on the metabolism and resistance of plants.

Recent research has led to improvements and innovations in the approach to biological control by alteration of the physical environment. Even so these measures often form only part of a more extensive programme, which may include crop rotations and organic soil amendments. Generally the biological approach to control of a disease by soil management has developed, and been modified, over a long period and derives from palmier days when other methods were not available and land was not at its present premium. Today other methods are available to combat new disease situations and resort is often first made to resistant or tolerant cultivars, or chemical sterilants. Soil temperature, moisture content, and aeration are variable only to a degree which is usually well within the tolerance limits of the pathogen, and manipulation of the physical environment can often be considered only a first-aid measure. Broad soil-management programmes, however, still have a role to play, for no one method of disease control is universally possible or acceptable. The measure chosen at any time is determined by a variety of factors such as the type of crop, whether annual or perennial, and the availability of genetic material for breeding purposes; the nature and situation of the land on which it grows, including soil type and depth and topography; the prevailing climate; the history and nature of the disease and variability of the pathogen; the economics of the crop.

Tomorrow of course the situation may be different. With the advance of plant-breeding techniques and the development of cheaper, more manageable chemical sterilants with greater penetration, and perhaps more selective action, the part played by soil management in disease control may decline and fulfill Walker's prognostication that "There is little basis to hope that, in the future, soil management and fertilisation will solve any large percentage of the problems of plant disease control" (Walker, 1946). On the other hand, the wider and successful application of chemical sterilants may depend on their integration into established soil-management programmes. Particularly the techniques developed for altering the physical soil environment may become of increasing importance in facilitating the application of chemical sterilants, increasing their effectiveness, and controlling or guiding subsequent biological events.

LITERATURE CITED

ABEYGUNAWARDENA, D. V. W., and R. K. S. WOOD. 1957. Factors affecting the germination of sclerotia and mycelial growth of *Sclerotium rolfsii* Sacc. Trans. Brit. Mycol. Soc. 40: 221-231.

AKAZAWA, T., and I. URITANI. 1961. Influence of environmental temperatures on metabolic alterations related to disease resistance in sweet potato roots infected by black rot. Phytopathology 51: 668-674.

BECKMAN, C. H., S. HALMOS, and M. E. MACE. 1962. The interaction of host, pathogen and soil temperature in relation to susceptibility to Fusarium wilt of bananas. Phytopathology 52: 134-140.

BISBY, G. R., M. I. TIMONIN, and N. JAMES. 1935. Fungi isolated from soil profiles in Manitoba. Can. J. Res., Sec. C, 13: 47-66.

BLAIR, I. D. 1943. Behaviour of the fungus *Rhizoctonia solani* Kuhn in the soil. Ann. Appl. Biol. 30: 118-127.

BOYLE, L. W. 1956. Fundamental concepts in the development of control measures for southern blight and root rot of peanuts. Plant Dis. Reptr. 40: 661-665.

BOYNTON, D., and O. C. COMPTON. 1944. Normal seasonal changes of oxygen and carbon dioxide percentages in gas from the larger pores of three orchard subsoils. Soil Sci. 57: 107-117.

BRIAN, P. W. 1957. The ecological significance of antibiotic production. *In* Microbial ecology, Symp. Soc. Gen. Microbiol. 7: 168-188.

BROOKS, A. N. 1939. Pink rot of celery caused by *Sclerotinia sclerotiorum* (Lib.) Massee. Florida Agr. Expt. Sta. Ann. Rept. 1938-39: 127-128.

BROOKS, A. N. 1942. Control of celery pink rot. Florida Agr. Expt. Sta. (Gainesville) Press Bull. 567, 4 p.

BROWN, W. 1922. On the germination and growth of fungi at various temperatures and in various concentrations of oxygen and of carbon dioxide. Ann. Botany (London) 36: 257-283.

BURGES, A., and E. FENTON. 1953. The effect of carbon dioxide on the growth of certain soil fungi. Trans. Brit. Mycol. Soc. 36: 104-108.

BUXTON, E. W. 1957a. Some effects of pea root exudates on physiological races of *Fusarium oxysporum* Fr. f. *pisi* (Linf.) Snyder and Hansen. Trans. Brit. Mycol. Soc. 40: 145-154.

BUXTON, E. W. 1957b. Differential rhizosphere effects of three pea cultivars on physiologic races of *Fusarium oxysporum* f. *pisi*. Trans. Brit. Mycol. Soc. 40: 305-316.

BUXTON, E. W. 1960. Effects of pea root exudate on the antagonism of some rhizosphere micro-organisms towards *Fusarium oxysporum* f. *pisi*. J. Gen. Microbiol. 22: 678-689.

CHUPP, C. 1946. Soil temperature, moisture, aeration, and pH as factors in disease incidence. Soil Sci. 61: 31-36.

CLAYTON, E. E. 1923. The relation of temperature to the Fusarium wilt of the tomato. Am. J. Botany 10: 71-88.

CLINTON, P. K. S. 1957. A note on a wilt of groundnuts due to *Sclerotium rolfsii* Sacc. in Tanganyika. E. African Agr. J. 22: 137-141.

COLEY-SMITH, J. R. 1960. Studies on the biology of *Sclerotium cepivorum* Berk. IV. Germination of sclerotia. Ann. Appl. Biol. 48: 8-18.

COLEY-SMITH, J. R., and C. J. HICKMAN. 1957. Stimulation of sclerotium germination in *Sclerotium cepivorum* Berk. Nature (London) 180: 445.

COLHOUN, J. 1961. Spore load, light intensity and plant nutrition as factors influencing the incidence of club root of Brassicae. Trans. Brit. Mycol. Soc. 44: 593-600.

DICKSON, J. G. 1923. Influence of soil temperature and moisture on the development of the seedling blight of wheat and corn caused by *Gibberella saubinetii*. J. Agr. Res. 23: 837-870.

DICKSON, J. G., S. H. ECKERSON, and K. P. LINK. 1923. The nature of resistance to seedling blight of cereals. Proc. Natl. Acad. Sci. (U.S.) 9: 434-439.

DICKSON, J. G., and J. R. HOLBERT. 1926. The influence of temperature upon the metabolism and expression of disease resistance in selfed lines of corn. J. Am. Soc. Agron. 18: 314-322.

DILLON WESTON, W. A. R., A. R. LOVELESS, and R. E. TAYLOR. 1946. Clover rot. J. Agr. Sci. 36: 18-28.

DURBIN, R. D. 1955. The effect of carbon dioxide on the vertical distribution of various strains of *Rhizoctonia solani*. (Abstr.) Phytopathology 45: 693.

DURRELL, L. W. 1924. Stimulation of spore germination by carbon dioxide. Science 60: 499.

EDGINGTON, L. V., and J. C. WALKER. 1957. Influence of soil and air temperature on Verticillium wilt of tomato. Phytopathology 47: 594-598.

ESTERMAN, E. F., and A. D. McLAREN. 1961. Contribution of rhizoplane organisms to the total capacity of plants to utilise organic nutrients. Plant Soil 15: 243-260.

FLENTJE, N. T. 1959. The physiology of penetration and infection. p. 76-87. *In* C. S. Holton et al. [ed.], Plant pathology, problems and progress 1908-1958, University of Wisconsin Press, Madison, Wisc.

GARCIA, F. 1933. Reduction of chile wilt by cultural methods. New Mexico Agr. Expt. Sta. Bull. 216, 15 p.

GARRETT, S. D. 1934a. Factors affecting the pathogenicity of cereal foot-rot fungi. Biol. Rev. Cambridge Phil. Soc. 9: 351-361.

GARRETT, S. D. 1934b. Factors affecting the severity of take-all. I. The importance of soil micro-organisms. J. Dept. Agr. S. Australia 37: 664-674.

GARRETT, S. D. 1936. Soil conditions and take-all disease of wheat. Ann. Appl. Biol. 23: 667-699.

GARRETT, S. D. 1937. Soil conditions and the take-all disease of wheat. II. The relation between soil reaction and soil aeration. Ann. Appl. Biol. 24: 747-751.

GARRETT, S. D. 1938. Soil conditions and the root-infecting fungi. Biol. Rev. 13: 159-185.

GARRETT, S. D. 1944. Root disease fungi. Chronica Botanica Co., Waltham, Mass. 177 p.

GARRETT, S. D. 1956. Biology of root-infecting fungi. Cambridge University Press, London and New York. 292 p.

GARRETT, S. D. 1959. Armillaria root disease in orchards. Agriculture (London) 66: 331-335.

GERRETSEN, F. C. 1948. The influence of micro-organisms on phosphate intake by the plant. Plant Soil 1: 51-81.

GOSS, R. W. 1923. Relation of environment and other factors to potato wilt caused by *Fusarium oxysporum*. Nebraska Agr. Expt. Sta. Res. Bull. 23, 84 p.

GREEN, R. J. 1957. The vertical distribution of *Verticillium albo-atrum* in muck soils and its control (Abstr). Phytopathology 47: 522.

GREEN, R. J. 1958. Deep ploughing for controlling Verticillium wilt of mint in muck soils. Phytopathology 48: 575-577.

GRIFFITHS, E., and H. F. BIRCH. 1961. Microbiological changes in freshly moistened soil. Nature (London) 189: 424.

GRIFFITHS, R. L. 1933. Take-all, incidence and control on the lighter soils of the Mallee. J. Dept. Agr. S. Australia 36: 774-778.

HANSFORD, C. G. 1940. Vascular diseases of cotton in Uganda. E. African Agr. J. 5: 279-282.

HARDISON, J. R. 1948. Field control of blind seed disease of perennial ryegrass in Oregon. Phytopathology 38: 404-419.

HAWKER, L. 1950. Physiology of fungi. University of London Press Ltd., London. 360 p.

HAWKER, L. 1957. Ecological factors and the survival of fungi. *In* Microbial ecology, Symp. Soc. Gen. Microbiol. 7: 238-258.

HENRY, A. W. 1932. Influence of soil temperature and soil sterilisation on the reaction of wheat seedlings to *Ophiobolus graminis* Sacc. Can. J. Res. 7: 198-203.

HOLLIS, J. P. 1948. Oxygen and carbon dioxide relations of *Fusarium oxysporum* Schlecht. and *Fusarium eumartii* Carp. Phytopathology 38: 761-775.

ISAAC, I. 1949. A comparative study of pathogenic isolates of Verticillium. Trans. Brit. Mycol. Soc. 32: 137-157.

JOHNSON, J., and R. E. HARTMAN. 1919. Influence of soil environment on the root rot of tobacco. J. Agr. Res. 17: 41-86.

JONES, L. R. 1924. The relation of environment to disease in plants. Am. J. Botany 11: 601-609.

JONES, G. H., and A. EL-G. SEIF EL-NASR. 1940. Control of smut diseases in Egypt with special reference to sowing depth and soil moisture. Egypt Minist. Agr. Bull. 224, 46 p.

JONES, L. R., J. JOHNSON, and J. G. DICKSON. 1926. Wisconsin studies upon the relation of soil temperature to plant disease. Wisconsin Agr. Expt. Sta. Res. Bull. 71, 144 p.

JONES, L. R., and W. B. TISDALE. 1922. The influence

of soil temperature upon the development of flax wilt. Phytopathology 12: 409-413.

KATZNELSON, H. 1960. Observations on the rhizosphere effect. p. 192-201. *In* D. Parkinson and J. S. Waid [ed.], The ecology of soil fungi. Liverpool University Press, Liverpool.

KATZNELSON, H., J. W. ROUATT, and T. M. B. PAYNE. 1955. The liberation of amino-acids and reducing compounds by plant roots. Plant Soil 7: 35-48.

KERR, A., and N. T. FLENTJE. 1957. Host infection in *Pellicularia filamentosa* controlled by chemical stimuli. Nature (London) 179: 204-205.

KING, C. J. 1937. A method for the control of cotton root rot in the irrigated Southwest. U.S. Dept. Agr. Cir. 425, 9 p.

KING, C. J., and E. D. EATON. 1934. Influence of soil moisture on longevity of cotton root-rot sclerotia. J. Agr. Res. 49: 793-798.

KING, C. J., H. F. LOOMIS, and C. HOPE. 1931. Studies on sclerotia and mycelial strands of the cotton root rot fungus. J. Agr. Res. 42: 827-840.

KIRKHAM, D. S. 1959. Host factors in the physiology of disease. p. 110-118. *In* C. S. Holton et al. [ed.], Plant pathology, problems and progress 1908-1958, University of Wisconsin Press, Madison, Wisc.

KRASIL'NIKOV, N. A. 1959. Influence of certain bacteria on the accumulation of vitamins and amino-acids in plant tissues. Proc. Intern. Botan. Congr. 9th (Montreal) vol. II, p. 206.

LEGGE, B. J. 1952. Use of glass fibre material in soil mycology. Nature (London) 169: 759.

LUDWIG, R. A., and A. W. HENRY. 1943. Studies on the microbiology of recontaminated sterilised soil in relation to its infestation with *Ophiobolus graminis*. Can. J. Res., Sec. C, 21: 343-350.

McKEEN, C. D., and W. B. MOUNTAIN. 1960. Synergism between *Pratylenchus penetrans* (Cobb) and *Verticillium albo-atrum* R. and B. in eggplant wilt. Can. J. Botany 38: 789-794.

McKINNEY, H. H. 1923. Influence of soil temperature and moisture on infection of wheat seedlings by *Helminthosporium sativum*. J. Agr. Res. 36: 195-217.

McKINNEY, H. H., and R. J. DAVIS. 1925. Influence of soil temperature and moisture on infection of wheat plants by *Ophiobolus graminis*. J. Agr. Res. 31: 827-840.

McLENNAN, E. 1928. The growth of fungi in soil. Ann. Appl. Biol. 15: 95-109.

MILLARD, W. A. 1921. Rept. Univ. Leeds and Yorks. Coun. Agr. Ed., 118, p. 8-20. (Quoted from Garrett, 1956.)

MILLARD, W. A., and C. B. TAYLOR. 1927. Antagonism of micro-organisms as the controlling factor in the inhibition of scab by green manuring. Ann. Appl. Biol. 14: 202-215.

MITCHELL, R. B., D. R. HOOTON, and F. E. CLARK. 1941. Soil bacteriological studies on the control of Phymatotrichum root rot of cotton. J. Agr. Res. 63: 535-547.

MOORE, W. D. 1949. Flooding as a means of destroying the sclerotia of *Sclerotinia sclerotiorum*. Phytopathology 39: 920-927.

NEWCOMBE, M. 1960. Some effects of water and anaerobic conditions on *Fusarium oxysporum* in soil. Trans. Brit. Mycol. Soc. 43: 51-59.

NEWHALL, A. G. 1955. Disinfestation of soil by heat, flooding, and fumigation. Botan. Rev. 21: 189-250.

NICOT, J. 1960. Some characteristics of the microflora in desert sands. p. 94-97. *In* D. Parkinson and J. S. Waid [ed.], The ecology of soil fungi. Liverpool University Press, Liverpool.

OCFEMIA, G. O. 1924. The relation of soil temperature to germination of certain Philippine upland and lowland varieties of rice and infection by the Helminthosporium disease. Am. J. Botany 11: 437-460.

PARK, D. 1960. Antagonism—the background to soil fungi. p. 148-159. *In* D. Parkinson and J. S. Waid [ed.], The ecology of soil fungi, Liverpool University Press, Liverpool.

PERRY, D. A. 1963. Interaction of root knot and Fusarium wilt of cotton. Empire Cotton Growing Rev. 40: 41-47.

RANDS, R. D., and E. DOPP. 1938. Influence of certain harmful soil constituents on severity of Pythium root rot of sugar cane. J. Agr. Res. 56: 53-58.

REA, H. E. 1933. The effect of tillage on eradication of cotton root rot. J. Am. Soc. Agron. 25: 764-771.

REA, H. E. 1939. The control of cotton root rot in the Blackland region of Texas. Texas Agr. Expt. Sta. Bull. 573, 36 p.

RICHARDS, B. L. 1923. Further studies on the pathogenicity of *Corticium vagum* on the potato as affected by soil temperature. J. Agr. Res. 23: 761-770.

ROGERS, C. H. 1937. The effect of three- and four-year rotations on cotton root rot in the central Texas Blacklands. J. Am. Soc. Agron. 29: 668-680.

ROGERS, C. H. 1942. Cotton root rot studies with special reference to sclerotia, cover crops, rotations, tillage, seeding rates, soil fungicides and effects on seed quality. Texas Agr. Expt. Sta. Bull. 614, 45 p.

ROVIRA, A. D. 1956. Root excretions in relation to the rhizosphere effect. III. The effect of root exudate on the numbers and activity of micro-organisms in soil. Plant Soil 7: 209-217.

ROVIRA, A. D. 1959. Root excretions in relation to the rhizosphere effect. IV. Influence of plant species, age of plant, light, temperature, and calcium nutrition on exudation. Plant Soil 11: 53-64.

ROVIRA, A. D., and E. L. GREACEN. 1957. The effect of aggregate disruption on the activity of micro-organisms in the soil. Australian J. Agr. Res. 8: 659-673.

ROVIRA, A. D., and J. R. HARRIS. 1961. Root excretions in relation to the rhizosphere effect. V. The exudation of B-group vitamins. Plant Soil 14: 199-214.

RUSSELL, SIR E. J. 1950. Soil conditions and plant growth. 8th ed. Rev. by E. W. Russell. Longmans, Green, London. 635 p.

SAKSENA, S. B. 1955. Ecological factors governing the distribution of soil microfungi in some forest soils of Sagar. J. Indian Botan. Soc. 34: 262-298.

SANFORD, G. B. 1926. Some factors affecting the pathogenicity of *Actinomyces scabies*. Phytopathology 16: 525-547.

SANFORD, G. B., and W. C. BROADFOOT. 1931. Studies of the effects of other soil-inhabiting micro-organisms on the virulence of *Ophiobolus graminis*. Sci. Agr. 11: 512-528.

SCHREVEN, D. A. VAN. 1948. [Investigations on certain pests and diseases of Vorstenlanden tobacco.] Tijdschr. Plantenziekten 54: 149-174.

SCHROEDER, W. T., and J. C. WALKER. 1942. Influence of controlled environment and nutrition on the resistance of garden pea to Fusarium wilt. J. Agr. Res. 65: 221-248.

SEWELL, G. W. F. 1959. Direct observation of *Verticillium albo-atrum* in soil. Trans. Brit. Mycol. Soc. 42: 312-321.

SIMMONDS, P. M., B. J. SALLANS, and R. J. LEDINGHAM. 1950. The occurrence of *Helminthosporium sativum* in relation to primary infections in common root rot of wheat. Sci. Agr. 30: 407-417.

SNYDER, W. C. 1960. Antagonism as a plant disease control principle. p. 127-136. *In* Biological and chemical control of plant and animal pests. American Association for the Advancement of Science, Washington, D. C.

STARKEY, R. L. 1955. Micro-organisms and plant life. p. 179-195. *In* S. A. Waksman [ed.], Perspective and horizon in microbiology, Rutgers University Press, Brunswick, N. J.

STODDARD, D. L. 1949. Sclerotiniose disease of vegetables. Florida Agr. Expt. Sta. Ann. Rept. 1948-49: 209.

STONER, W. N., and W. D. MOORE. 1953. Lowland rice farming a possible cultural control for *Sclerotinia sclerotiorum* in the Everglades. Plant Disease Reptr. 37: 181-186.

STOVER, R. H. 1953. Effect of soil moisture on *Fusarium* species. Can. J. Botany 31: 693-697.

STOVER, R. H. 1954. Flood fallowing for the eradication

of *Fusarium oxysporum* f. *cubense*. II. Some factors involved in fungus survival. Soil Sci. 77: 401-414.

STOVER, R. H. 1955. III. Effect of oxygen on fungus survival. Soil Sci. 80: 397-412.

STOVER, R. H. 1959. Growth and survival of root disease fungi in soil. p. 339-355. *In* C. S. Holton et al. [ed.], Plant pathology, problems and progress 1908-1958, University of Wisconsin Press, Madison, Wisc.

STOVER, R. H., and S. R. FREIBERG. 1958. Effect of carbon dioxide on multiplication of *Fusarium* in soil. Nature (London) 181: 788-789.

STOVER, R. H., N. C. THORNTON, and V. C. DUNLAP. 1952. Changes in the soil flora of banana lands flood fallowed for the eradication of *Fusarium oxysporum* f. *cubense*. (Abstr.) Phytopathology 42: 476.

STOVER, R. H., N. C. THORNTON, and V. C. DUNLAP. 1953. Flood fallowing for the eradication of *Fusarium oxysporum* f. *cubense*. I. The effect of flooding on the fungus flora of clay loam soils in the Ulna Valley of Honduras. Soil Sci. 76: 225-238.

STREETS, R. B. 1937. Phymatotrichum (cotton or Texas) root rot in Arizona. Arizona Agr. Expt. Sta. Tech. Bull. 71, p. 299-410.

SUBBA-RAO, N. S., R. G. S. BIDWELL, and D. L. BAILEY. 1961. The effects of rhizoplane fungi on the uptake and metabolism of nutrients by tomato plants. Can. J. Botany 39: 1760-1764.

TALBOYS, P. W. 1958. Association of tylosis and hyperplasia of the xylem with vascular invasion of the hop by *Verticillium albo-atrum*. Trans. Brit. Mycol. Soc. 41: 249-260.

TAUBENHAUS, J. J., and W. N. EZEKIEL. 1936. Longevity of sclerotia of *Phymatotrichum omnivorum* in moist soil in the laboratory. Am. J. Botany 23: 10-12.

TIMONIN, M. I. 1941. The interactions of higher plants and soil microorganisms. III. Effects of by-products of plant growth on activity of fungi and actinomycetes. Soil Sci. 52: 395-413.

TIMONIN, M. I. 1947. Microflora of the rhizosphere in relation to the manganese deficiency disease of oats. Soil Sci. Soc. Am. Proc. (1946) 11: 284-292.

TISDALE, W. B. 1923. Influence of soil temperature and soil moisture upon the Fusarium disease in cabbage seedlings. J. Agr. Res. 24: 55-86.

VASUDEVA, R. S. 1941. Studies on the root-rot disease of cotton in the Punjab. XI. Effect of mixed cropping on the incidence of the disease. Indian J. Agr. Sci. 11: 879-891.

WALKER, J. C. 1946. Soil management and plant nutrition in relation to disease development. Soil Sci. 61: 47-54.

WALKER, J. C. 1959. Progress and problems in controlling diseases by host resistance. p. 32-41. *In* C. S. Holton et al. [ed.], Plant pathology, problems and progress 1908-1958, University of Wisconsin Press, Madison, Wisc.

WALKER, J. C., and L. R. JONES. 1921. Relation of soil temperature and other factors to onion smut infection. J. Agr. Res. 22: 235-262.

WARCUP, J. H. 1957. Studies on the occurrence and activity of fungi in a wheat field. Trans. Brit. Mycol. Soc. 40: 237-260.

WEINDLING, R. 1932. *Trichoderma lignorum* as a parasite of other soil fungi. Phytopathology 22: 837-845.

WEINDLING, R., and O. H. EMERSON. 1936. The isolation of a toxic substance from the culture filtrate of Trichoderma. Phytopathology 26: 1068-1070.

WELSH, M. 1942. Studies of crown rot of apple trees. Can. J. Res., Sec. C-D, 20: 457-490.

WILHELM, S. 1940. Vertical distribution of *Verticillium albo-atrum* in soils. Phytopathology 40: 368-376.

WOOD, R. K. S., and M. TVEIT. 1955. Control of plant diseases by antagonistic organisms. Botan. Rev. 21: 441-492.

▶ DISCUSSION OF G. W. F. SEWELL PAPER

A. Kerr:

Most plant pathologists dealing with soil describe soil moisture in terms of percentage of moisture-holding capacity. This gives no information on the availability of water or on any other aspect of soil water. It only indicates whether or not oxygen is likely to be limiting. I hope plant pathologists will define the soil water regime more precisely.

S. D. Garrett:

I wish to comment briefly on Dr. Kerr's statement on the effect of soil moisture content. Dr. D. M. Griffin (Biol. Rev. 38: 141-166, 1963) discusses this difficult problem of soil moisture content as it affects soil fungi, both the theoretical aspects of soil moisture and the practical question of techniques for its investigation. In particular, he has strongly emphasized the point made by Dr. Kerr—that a statement neither of percentage moisture content nor even of percentage moisture-holding capacity gives other investigators the full information that they may later require about the moisture regime existing during the course of any particular experiment.

G. W. F. Sewell:

I fully agree with the comments made by Doctors Kerr and Garrett concerning the need for more exact methods of analysis and specification of soil moisture conditions. But with regard to the interdependent gaseous effects on a pathogen, I feel that it would be more correct to say that moisture-holding capacity indicates whether the *aeration* condition (rather than oxygen availability) is likely to be limiting. There is a frequently unjustified tendency to use "oxygen availability" synonymously with aeration; in fact, where more detailed investigations of gaseous phenomena have been undertaken, they more often indicate that carbon dioxide accumulation is the limiting factor rather than oxygen availability.

J. L. Harley:

I should like to draw attention to a method of observation of mycelial spread of pathogens on the root system of host plants growing in unstructured soil (R. K. Robinson and R. L. Lucas, New Phytologist 62: 50-52, 1963). These observers used P^{32}-labeled *Ophiobolus* mycelium to observe its spread in soils with the minimum of manipulation. The further development of this method may well supply a solution to the problems of experimentation outlined by Dr. Sewell.

J. Louvet:

In our experiments in atmospheres artificially increased in CO_2 to 23%, the growth in vitro and the parasitic activity in the soil of *Sclerotinia minor* are greatly decreased when the concentration of CO_2 increases, while for *Fusarium oxysporum* f. *melonis* there is practically no decrease.

Carbon dioxide is thus an important ecological factor for these two fungi. *Sclerotinia minor* attacks plants only at the level of the collar, while *Fusarium oxysporum* penetrates generally into the roots, even when they are deeply established.

G. W. F. Sewell:

The work of Durbin (Am. J. Botany 46: 22-25, 1959) with *Rhizoctonia solani* similarly indicates the importance of carbon dioxide in determining parasitic activity at different soil depths, but in this instance strains of a single species were differentially affected.

K. H. Garren:

Eight years' research on *Sclerotium rolfsii* Sacc. and peanuts (groundnuts) has convinced me that: (1) *S. rolfsii* is strictly a soil-surface organism. It is not active at depths greater than ½ in. It is not a root-attacking organism. (2) Peanuts are attacked by *S. rolfsii* at the soil surface, and the damage is to peanut stems which have been brought from their aerial habitat to a soil-surface habitat by cultivation which covers them with soil. (3) Even under these conditions the stem is infected only when a bit of organic matter "triggers" *S. rolfsii* into activity and acts as a bridge to the peanut stem. *S. rolfsii* does not grow on organic matter buried below 2 in. Therefore, deep burial of organic matter partially prevents *S. rolfsii* infection on peanuts by a merely physical removal of the triggering and bridging bits of organic matter. It is not a matter of getting *S. rolfsii* to grow where it will do no damage, i.e. on buried organic matter.

H. Katznelson:

I cannot help but feel that the indirect changes induced in the number of microorganisms in the rhizosphere by altered temperatures must have some effect on the susceptibility or resistance of a host to a pathogen. Although we have not included pathogens in our experimental system, when bacterial counts on wheat change from 266×10^6 at 55°-60°F to 1166×10^6 at 85°-90°, and counts in the rhizosphere of soybean change from 186×10^6 at 55°-60° to $3{,}571 \times 10^6$ at 85°-90°, it seems to me that temperature is a very important parameter. Certain groups of bacteria show even greater changes; for soybean, as an example, numbers of ammonifiers increased from 2.5×10^6 to 950×10^6 per g of rhizosphere soil. Marked changes in the root-fungus population also occur in response to these temperature differences. Even if numbers per se may not be that important, the differences imply decided changes in exudation patterns, which also suggest changes in host metabolism. Surely this must affect infection patterns.

G. W. F. Sewell:

I agree that direct and indirect effects of temperature on host metabolism, root exudation, and microbial antagonism at the root surface are very likely to influence infection patterns. Your own work strongly supports this view, but, nevertheless, conclusive direct experimental evidence is not available.

A. D. Rovira:

Some members of this audience may be interested in results obtained by Dr. Bowen and myself on the growth of plants in sterilized soil. We found that heat sterilization of Urrbrae red brown earth at 212°F or above produced marked phytotoxicities causing root stunting very similar to those found by Patrick and Toussoun with decomposing plant residues. These heat-produced, toxic factors are probably organic in nature and can be detoxicated by many bacteria and fungi in soil. Inoculation of heat-sterilized soil with a soil suspension at time of planting resulted in healthy plants.

We have found that soil sterilized by gamma irradiation (2.5×10^6 rads) showed no evidence of phytotoxicity and provides a useful tool in the study of the effects of microorganisms on the growth of plants in soil.

The Reinfestation of Treated Soil[1]

WILLIAM A. KREUTZER—*Department of Botany and Plant Pathology, Colorado State University, Fort Collins.*

For as long as man has existed on the planet, he has attempted to curb or destroy life forms that threatened his existence. He learned very soon that these forms were of two kinds: the things that used him as food, and the things that competed with him for food.

Eventually he discovered that he had microenemies as well as macroenemies. Not only did carnivores attack him, but so did insects, protozoans, bacteria, and viruses. Not only did his own species and other mammals compete with him for food, but so did insects, fungi, bacteria, and viruses.

Contrary to popular belief, the purpose of man's endeavor is not merely to destroy his competitors for food and living space. His projected program is far more grandiose than this. He is attempting to reshape his own ecosystem. This means the predetermination of the coexistence of all life forms and near-life forms that exist on this planet. This is a most ambitious program, indeed. One is reminded of the words of H. G. Wells' Time Traveler, ". . . The air was free from gnats, the earth from weeds or fungi; everywhere were fruits and sweet and delightful flowers; brilliant butterflies flew hither and thither. The ideal of preventive medicine had been attained. Diseases had been stamped out."

This of course is science fiction. Science fiction within recent years, however, has shown the disconcerting tendency to become science fact. In any event, we are apparently busy tackling a few of the complexities involved in the attainment of Wells' utopia.

One of these complexities has to do with the study and regulation of the microorganisms that inhabit the soil. Here, we are concerned not only with those organisms responsible for the essential breakdown of organic materials and the recycling of vital plant nutrients, but those causing plant and animal diseases as well.

THE BIOLOGICAL IMPACT OF SOIL DISINFESTATION.—Soil is a complex ecosystem in a state of dynamic equilibrium, bounded by physicochemical parameters. The relative stability of this system depends upon the relative stabilities of its biological composition and its regulating parameters.

Sometimes dominant plant pathogens assume roles of major importance in this ecosystem. When this occurs, we attempt to suppress them. We have done this by sanitation, altered cultural practices, crop rotation, destruction of weed carriers, and plant breeding. Finally, where it was economically feasible, we have inhibited or destroyed soil pathogens by physical or chemical means.

The disinfestation of soil by heat or chemicals, when it works, is a spectacular way of controlling soil-borne phytopathogens. Unfortunately, spectacular ways of doing things frequently have serious drawbacks. Such treatments generally are not selective enough to affect only the pathogens at which they are aimed. Instead, large segments of the soil biophase are frequently eliminated. There is altogether too much powder and too much buckshot in the blast. All organisms susceptible to the treatment, friend and foe alike, are destroyed or inhibited. This leaves unnatural semisterile soil zones (Kreutzer, 1960; Baker, 1961).

To paraphrase an old saw, "Nature abhors a 'biological' vacuum." The stage, therefore, is set for the creation of new ecosystems. Organisms reinvade the treated soil zone, to establish themselves on and in the newly created soil substrates (Garrett, 1956). Wave after wave of biotic successions follows in which type after type of substrate is utilized, as the ecosystem drifts toward a climax equilibrium.

We have good evidence of the alteration of soil ecosystems by heat or chemical treatments. This evidence is both direct and indirect.

Direct evidence involves the actual observation or isolation of organisms reinvading treated soils. Rapid buildup of *Trichoderma viride* has been noted in soils treated with chemicals (Smith, 1939; Warcup, 1951, Evans, 1955). Abnormal increases in species of *Penicillium* and *Aspergillus* also have been reported (Katznelson and Richardson, 1943; Evans, 1955). We have observed that *Monilia sitophila* and *Rhizopus nigricans* commonly overrun soils treated with chloropicrin or steam. Finally, the "fire-fungus" *Pyronema* is known to be a common surface invader of treated soils.

Indirect evidence of ecosystem alteration has been obtained from reactions in the ensuing crop, as well as from critical changes noted in the types and quantities of soil nutrients.

Buildup of ammonia in treated soils with a corresponding decrease in nitrate is a commonly observed phenomenon. Most soil treatments apparently inhibit the special nitrifying organisms without a corresponding

[1] Published with the approval of the Director of the Colorado Experiment Station as Scientific Journal Series Paper No. 878.

effect on the greater numbers and kinds of ammonifying microorganisms (Tam and Clark, 1943; Aldrich and Martin, 1952; Davies and Owen, 1954). Increases in the quantities of minor elements (e.g. copper and manganese) after soil treatment have also been reported. This has resulted in the apparent correction of deficiencies, or brought about phytotoxic effects (Ark, 1937; Dalton and Hurwitz, 1948).

The most spectacular indirect evidence of soil-ecosystem alteration by treatment is based on plant response, and for the most part is phytopathological in nature. Here three distinct phenomena are involved.

The first of these has been described as "disease trading" (Kreutzer, 1960). This is a situation in which a dominant pathogen is controlled by soil treatment, and a minor pathogen is elevated to major importance, thus becoming the new dominant pathogen (Haasis, 1952; Gibson, 1953, Wilhelm, 1957, Gibson, Ledger, and Boehm, 1961).

The second phenomenon has been called the "boomerang" effect (Kreutzer, 1960). This involves the disappearance of the dominant pathogen after treatment, which is soon followed by its reappearance in even greater quantities (Gibson, 1956; Garrett, 1956; Baker, 1961).

The third and final kind of indirect evidence is found in increases or decreases in plant vigor after soil treatment, in the apparent absence of plant pathogens. Sometimes this response occurs only in juvenile stages. Sometimes the effect persists for the entire life of the plant. Plant "stimulation" was noted by Sabaté and others in the latter part of the nineteenth century after treatments of soil with carbon disulfide for *Phylloxera* control (French, 1893). Unexplained increased plant vigor after soil treatments with CS_2 was recorded by Loew (1909). In later years it was shown that many of these responses were due to control of now wellknown pathogenic nematodes and fungi. Nevertheless, unexplained responses following soil treatment with various chemicals continue to be observed (Kreutzer and Montagne, 1950; Martin et al., 1953; Koch, 1955). The explanation for such stimulatory effects probably lies either in control of unknown plant inhibitors, or in the initiation of beneficial ecosystem shifts in the plant rhizosphere favoring plant sustainers (Kreutzer, 1960).

The numerous fragmentary observations recorded in the literature, then, although many times of debatable interpretation, indicate the bare outlines of a broad and significant pattern. Underlying this pattern is the reinvasion of treated soils by soil microorganisms and the consequent creation of new soil ecosystems.

In this paper we will examine the evidence for reinvasion of soil by microorganisms after soil treatment. Further we will attempt to analyze factors governing reinvasion, and to set forth the principles suggested by this analysis.

Much which follows is necessarily theoretical in nature. In my opinion, however, the justification in this approach lies in the emphasis on broad concepts directed toward a better understanding of the principles of the biological control of soil-borne plant pathogens.

FACTORS AFFECTING THE REINFESTATION OF TREATED SOILS.—Many factors affect the reinfestation of treated soil. In general, however, *the degree of reinfestation apparently is directly proportional to the degree of alteration of the original ecosystem by the treatment.* This means that the degree of change in the qualitative and quantitative composition of the soil biophase, as well as the degrees of change in the physical and chemical constitution of the soil, will not only determine the quantity and quality of reinfestation, but its velocity as well.

Alteration of the physicochemical constitution of the soil by physical or chemical treatments appears to be a minor effect. Barring a few exceptions, changes in structure, aggregation, and minor-element content of soils following drastic treatment are slight to negligible (Martin and Aldrich, 1952; Aldrich and Martin, 1952; Cornfield, 1955).

A few cases of increased metal-ion and polyuronide content or increased nitrogen mineralization after soil treatment have been oberved (Dalton and Hurwitz, 1948; Martin et al., 1953; Stotzky, Martin, and Mortensen, 1956). It is doubtful, however, if such minor changes significantly affect reinvasion.

As Russell and Hutchinson (1909) suspected after their early work with carbon disulfide, the important effect of soil treatment is on the living portion of the soil. The change in soil as a result of soil treatment, then, comes not so much from alteration of the physicochemical parameters of the ecosystem, as from a stringent reduction in the microbial population.

The writer believes, therefore, that the principal factors determining the final degree of alteration in treated soil, which in turn determines the type and degree of reinfestation in this soil, are as follows:

1. The nature and quantity of both biological and chemical residues remaining in the critical soil zone after treatment;
2. The nature and quantity of available substrates, or specific energy sources, remaining in or introduced into the treated soil zone, and finally;
3. The degree of competitive saprophytism of potential soil reinvaders (sensu Garrett, 1956).

The reinfestation of treated soil first of all depends upon the kinds and quantities of living organisms surviving the treatment. Second it depends upon the chemical residues in the soil after treatment. Biological and chemical residues in the regions bordering the treated zone and contiguous to the nontreated outer soil are possibly of secondary importance.

The quality and quantity of biological residue left in the treated soil zone are dependent upon two things: (1) the type and severity of treatment applied, and (2) the kinds and numbers of organisms in the treated soil zone which are genetically or physiologically resistant, or escape the effects of treatment.

The effect of type and severity of treatment on biological residues.—There are two commonly employed ways of disinfesting soil: by use of heat (steam) and of chemicals. Disinfestation here is used not in an absolute sense, but rather in the restricted sense of killing or preventing the growth of many to few soil organisms.

The degree of disinfestation of soil by heat or chemicals in general is governed in both cases by the same basic principle. This is a concentration × time effect. For heat, disinfestation or biological control (B) is equal to temperature (T) at critical biological sites × time of exposure (dt); or:

$$B = Tdt$$

In like fashion, the degree of disinfestation for any one chemical is equal to the concentration or dosage of chemical (c) at critical biological sites × time of exposure (dt); or:

$$B = cdt$$

According to Hemwall (1962), a more exact expression of chemical disinfestation of soil would be:

$$B = \int_0^i cdt$$

where disinfestation or biological control (B) is equal to the summation or integral of the various concentrations present during the treatment (c) × the increment of time of exposure in every case (dt).

The actual temperature or chemical dosage applied, however, is not the same as that acting on critical biological sites. The treatments in all cases interact with the soil and many of its constituents (Kreutzer, 1960). In the case of chemical toxicants, dosages at critical biological sites may be markedly reduced because of bonding reactions with soil colloids and water films. These effects vary in degree according to the soil composition and the nature of the chemicals employed (Kreutzer, 1960). The situation is something like shooting at a target, obscured and protected by sheets of metal between the marksman and the target.

Based on the foregoing consideration, we can now modify Hemwall's equation, by introducing the broad effect of the soil factor (K) for any chemical:

$$B = K \int_0^i cdt$$

As long as we are considering mathematical models to express soil disinfestation, it would be appropriate to mention an equation introduced by Bald and Jefferson (1956), designed to express the cumulative action of a fumigant on a soil-borne pathogenic population. The percentage of disease in the host plants is used as a measure of disinfestation. Bald and Jefferson's basic expression is as follows:

$$Y\lambda = Y d (1 - Kd) \frac{\lambda}{d}$$

where: d = Initial dosage of toxicant
Y = Numbers of pathogenic organisms left alive after fumigation
λ = Dosage of toxicant greater than d

Kd = Fraction of the remaining pathogenic organisms killed with each additional increment (d_1) of fumigant applied.

All of the foregoing mathematics constitutes an obvious oversimplification of a most complex problem. Such an approach does indicate, however, that an attempt is being made to put the entire problem of biological residue as affected by chemical treatment on a rational basis.

From the standpoint of the over-all effect on the spectrum of organisms in the soil biophase, chemical treatments can be considered to be of two general types: eradicant treatments and protectant treatments (Kendrick and Zentmyer, 1957).

Eradicant chemicals kill organisms. These toxicants generally do not persist long in soils. They may be effective against either a wide or a narrow range of soil organisms. In other words, they can be general or specific in their action. Most soil fumigants are eradicants. General eradicants may be represented by such chemicals as chloropicrin, formaldehyde, propylene oxide, methyl isothiocyanate, allyl bromide, allyl alcohol, chlorobromopropene, acrolein, and acrolein diacetate. Examples of specific eradicants are dichloropropene, dibromochloropropane, ethylene dibromide, and carbon disulfide.

Protectant chemicals act primarily as biostats. They may kill, but their usual function is to inhibit. They may persist in soils for a few days to several weeks (i.e. seed and seed-zone treatments). As in the case of the eradicants, protectants may be general or specific in their effects. Examples of broad-spectrum or general protectant chemicals are the organic mercurials, the dithiocarbamates, captan, and dichlone. Specific or narrow-spectrum protectants are represented by such materials as pentachloronitrobenzene, trimethyl phosphorothioate, and dimethylaminobenzenediazo sodium sulfonate (Kreutzer, 1963).

At this point something must be said regarding the relation of dosage and exposure to degree of lethal effect (biostatic vs. biocidal action).

Some chemicals intrinsically are less toxic than others. *The intrinsic toxicity of a chemical, however, should be defined against the background of degree of exposure as delimited by practicality and acceptable side-reaction effects* (Kreutzer, 1963). Increased degrees of exposure can turn biostats into biocides; reduced exposures can transform biocides into biostats. In this connection one is reminded of the comment of the Texas rancher anent the problem of brush control in the Southwest: "Sure you can even kill mesquite if you dump enough whiskey on it, but who wants to waste that much whiskey on a bush!"

The degree of specificity combined with the degree of killing or inhibiting power of a soil toxicant, then, determines the degree of removal of microorganisms from the soil ecosystem. Highly specific soil toxicants have the least effect on the soil biophase; hence shift in the ecosystem due to reinvasion is at a minimum. General toxicants, on the other hand, by possessing broad killing or inhibiting powers, cause maximum disruption in the soil biophase, and hence trigger sweeping changes in the soil ecosystem.

The reinvasion potential in a soil after treatment is directly proportional to the degree and "depth" of kill. The more specific the chemical, the lower the reinvasion potential. Finally, eradicant-type chemicals should produce greater reinvasion potentials than protectant-type chemicals.

Before leaving the subject of the effect of treatment on biological residues, some comments should be made regarding the effects of steam. By varying temperature × exposure time, general to specific killing effects in soil can be obtained with steam heat (Baker and Roistacher, 1957). Further, by the use of "aerated" steam, final temperatures can be lowered in a controlled manner below 212°F (Bunt, 1955; Baker and Roistacher, 1957). Thus selectivity can be obtained by the use of heat. Baker has postulated that by use of such a procedure it should be possible to "strip off" layer after layer of the biophase population. This technique holds promise as a fine research tool to study the effect of removal of groups of related organisms on subsequent reinvasion.

Normally, maximum steam disinfestation should create the greatest "biological vacuum" of all treatments, since it is probably more effective as a killer of organisms than the most potent of our chemical eradicants (Kreutzer, 1960).

The effect of the natures of soil organisms on biological residues.—The portion of the soil biophase surviving a given treatment is determined not only by the type and severity of the treatment applied, but also by the natures of the organisms subjected to the treatment.

By "natures" is meant those all-inclusive properties possessed by organisms that affect their response to treatment. Such properties are: (1) the genetic-morphological factors per se that differentiate taxonomic groups; (2) physiological responses to environment within groups; and (3) ecological growth habits that cut across taxonomic lines.

Soil organisms by taxonomic groups vary widely in their resistance to chemical toxicants. Further, the significance of this resistance is difficult to evaluate because of marked differences in specificity of chemicals used in toxicity studies. All soil toxicants have some degree of "built-in" bias. They were developed because they were either good nematocides or fungicides (Kreutzer, 1963).

With these points in mind, let us consider some broad comparisons involving responses of bacteria, actinomycetes and fungi to soil toxicants.

Many soil bacteria are fairly resistant to the action of soil disinfestants. Methyl bromide, chloropicrin, and dichloropropene-dichloropropane mixture at standard fungicidal dosages have been reported to have no effect or to be stimulatory to the bacterial "alley-cat" population (Klemmer, 1957). Similar results have been obtained with the milder protectant-type fungicides, thiram and captan (Cram and Vaartaja, 1957; Domsch, 1959). Bacterial plant pathogens also have been found to be resistant to soil toxicants. Winfree, Cox, and Harrison (1958) were unable to control soft-rotting species of *Erwinia* and *Pseudomonas* with standard dosages of chloropicrin.

Nitrifying bacteria appear to be sensitive to almost any soil toxicant. Chemicals bringing about an accumulation of ammonia, with a concomitant inhibition of nitrification are: carbon disulfide, ethylene dibromide, chloropicrin, methyl bromide and allyl alcohol (Du Buisson, 1917; Tam and Clark, 1943; Kincaid and Volk, 1949; Overman and Burgis, 1956; Winfree and Cox, 1958). In fact, even the milder dithiocarbamates can adversely affect nitrification (Jaques, Robinson, and Chase, 1959).

Apparently there are some marked differences in sensitivity to toxicants between groups of specialized bacteria. Wensley (1953) noted that ammonifiers and denitrifiers were considerably more resistant to methyl bromide than nitrifiers or cellulose decomposers.

Actinomycetes, in general, appear to be more resistant to soil toxicants than either fungi or bacteria. Martin (1953) controlled *Sclerotium rolfsii* with soil treatments of dichloropropene-dichloropropane mixture which failed to control *Streptomyces ipomoea*. Domsch (1959) found that soil treatments with the methylisothiocyanate generator, sodium N-methyl dithiocarbamate, actually stimulated actinomycetes. Wensley (1953) reported that actinomycetes were more tolerant to methyl bromide treatment than either the fungi or the several groups of specialized bacteria studied.

Within the fungi, pythiaceous genera seem to be the most susceptible across-the-board to the fumigant-type toxicants. *Pythium* and *Phytophthora* spp. are the most sensitive fungi to such eradicants as formaldehyde, dichloropropene, and methyl isothiocyanate (Zentmeyer and Klotz, 1949; Warcup, 1952; Zentmyer, 1955).

Fungal genera intermediate in susceptibility to soil fumigants are *Rhizoctonia*, *Myrothecium*, *Phoma*, *Cladosporium*, *Thielaviopsis* and *Paecilomyces* (Zentmyer and Kendrick, 1949; Mollison, 1953; Munnecke, Domsch, and Eckert, 1962). *Fusarium* seems to be more resistant to the mild eradicants dichloropropene, ethylene dibromide, and carbon disulfide than to general eradicants such as chloropicrin or allyl bromide (Young, 1940; Christie, 1947).

Verticillium is somewhat resistant even to general killers such as methyl bromide and chloropicrin (Jacks and Smith, 1952; Munnecke and Lindgren, 1954). Most resistant of all the fungi to eradicant toxicants are species of *Penicillium* and *Aspergillus* and *Trichoderma viride* (Warcup, 1952; Mollison, 1953; Evans, 1955; Overman and Burgis, 1956; Saksena, 1960).

We can conclude that soil treatment with eradicant-type chemicals is likely to leave a residue of organisms consisting principally of heterotrophic bacteria, actinomycetes, and such fungi as *Aspergillus*, *Penicillium*, and *Trichoderma viride*.

The resistance of a microbial species to soil treatment is affected by induced physiological and morphological responses to environmental factors. Lowered metabolism as well as the formation of resistant structures (e.g. sclerotia, chlamydospores) influence resistance or susceptibility of an organism to treatment. The effect of unfavorable environmental conditions such as excessively high or low soil temperatures, low soil moisture contents, and lowered nutrient or energy-source levels, will lower the metabolism of a soil organism. This shift in physiology can bring about the formation of resistant structures such as chlamydospores, microsclerotia, and sclerotia.

Sclerotium-forming fungi are more resistant to soil toxicants such as chloropicrin than nonsclerotial fungi (Stark, 1948). Munnecke and Lindgren (1954) reported that methyl bromide controlled nonmicrosclerotial fungi but not the microsclerotium-forming *Verticillium albo-atrum*. Tarr (1956) concluded that the sclerotia of *Macrophomina phaseoli* were resistant to chloropicrin soil fumigation. We have observed that the hyphae of *Sclerotinia sclerotiorum* and *Sclerotium rolfsii* are more susceptible to chloropicrin and chlorbromopropene than are their sclerotia.

Lowered metabolism appears to enhance resistance to soil treatment. Fungi seem to be more resistant to treatment in dry soil than in moist soil (Newhall and Lear, 1948; Kreutzer, 1960). In studies in which the toxicities of ethylene oxide and chloropicrin were assessed against *Alternaria solani*, *Fusarium oxysporum* f. *lycopersici*, and *Bacillus subtilis*, Sampson and Ludwig (1956) noted that kill increased with increase in humidity. Davey and Leach (1941) reported that chloropicrin had no effect on the dry sclerotia of *Sclerotium rolfsii*. If, however, the sclerotia were soaked in water prior to treatment, 100% kill was obtained. I have made parallel studies with similar results, using the sclerotia of *Sclerotinia sclerotiorum*. I have also found that 100 times more chlorobromopropene was required to kill microsclerotia of *Verticillium albo-atrum* and chlamydospores of *F. solani* f. *phaseoli* in a dry soil (10% of the moisture equivalent) than in a moist soil (70% of the moisture equivalent).

It follows, then, that disinfestation will be enhanced by treating a soil in which the biophase is in a "high" metabolic state. Enhanced disinfestation in turn will increase the reinvasion potential.

Biological residues can arise from organic shielding. By "organic shielding" is meant the protection to organisms from toxicants because of embedment in living or dead organic material. This is an ecological growth habit crossing taxonomic lines.

Soil organisms may be relatively free in the soil or loosely associated with dead organic material. Or they may be deeply embedded in living or decayed plant tissue. This entire concept was brilliantly elucidated by Garrett (1956), who divided soil organisms into "soil inhabitants" and "root inhabitants." Soil inhabitants were considered to be those organisms capable of growing in the soil, being loosely associated with organic debris. Root inhabitants were considered to be those organisms normally found embedded in living or moribund root tissues, and not capable of independent growth in the soil.

Other factors being equal, the greater the degree of organic embedment, the greater the chance of an organism's escaping the toxic effects of a soil treatment.

There are considerable data available to support these contentions. A few years ago, I conducted tests with acrolein diacetate applied as an aqueous surface drench for the control of *Rhizoctonia* attack of cotton seedlings. The fungus was introduced into soil growing in and on whole oat kernels and from agar mats. The chemical was effective at 10 ppm in soils infested with free hyphae. It was ineffective even at a concentration of 200 ppm in soils infested with whole-kernel inoculum.

Living tissue is even more difficult to penetrate. Numerous studies have been conducted on the penetration of living galls infected with root-knot nematode (*Meloidogyne* spp.). Although some chemicals such as dichloropropene, ethylene dibromide, methyl bromide, and chlorobromopropene will penetrate galls with difficulty, other good nematocides will not. For example, chloropicrin and dichlorophenyl diethyl phosphorothioate will not penetrate undecayed nematode galls (Stark and Lear, 1947; Christie and Perry, 1958).

Other data of a similar nature are those of Matuo and Sakurai (1959), who found that although chloropicrin killed the naked hyphae of *Rosellinia necatrix* in the soil, it was not effective if the fungus was embedded in mulberry roots.

The fact that certain chemicals are better penetrants than others has little to do with the present analysis. The important thing is that organic shielding apparently affords protection against any chemical and thus enhances the possibility of escape. Shielded organisms, then, have a better chance of being present in the biological residue after treatment.

Chemical residues in the soil after treatment.—Almost any material introduced into soil for any purpose will leave some kind of residue. This is true whether the substance is inorganic or organic in nature.

Residues in soil may consist of the introduced material as well as any of its products of degradation. The quality and quantity of a residue will depend upon *the nature and amount of the substance originally introduced into the soil, and the interactions of this material with the components of the soil.*

Those chemicals introduced into soils that are not soon lost by volatilization or leaching undergo varying degree of bonding reactions with soil or soil constituents. Coulombic and van der Waal's forces are involved as well as hydrogen and covalent bonding. "Sorption" of biotoxicants in soils can, in my opinion, loosely involve any or all of these phenomena. These interactions are first of all dependent upon the intrinsic nature of the toxicant, such as the presence of polar groups affecting water solubility, and the presence of reactive moieties such as alpha-halo carbonyl groups or unsaturated linkages (Kreutzer, 1960). Second, they are dependent upon the physicochemical constitution of the soil, such as quantity and type of organic material (specifically, labile —SH and —NH_2 groupings), the type and quantity of clay content, and soil moisture content (Hanneson, 1945; Jurinak, 1957).

Even more important than the interactions with the physicochemical constituents of soil are the interactions of the introduced chemical with the soil biophase. This is the delayed interaction between the toxicant or any of its breakdown products and the biological residue.

We have good reason to believe that soil organisms will degrade any and all organic substances introduced into soil. Over half a century ago, Rahn (1906) showed that *Penicillium glaucum* could utilize paraffin as a source of energy, and Störmer (1908) reported the discovery of a bacillus that degraded toluene and xylene. Much of the pertinent literature on this subject has been reviewed by Thornton and Meiklejohn (1957). A few more observations on this general subject are worth mentioning, however. Henderson and Farmer (1955) reported the breakdown of complex aldehydes by soil fungi. Ladd (1956) isolated a *Corynebacterium* from soil capable of oxidizing both saturated and unsaturated long-chain hydrocarbons. Gundersen and Jensen (1956) demonstrated that a soil bacterium, *Corynebacterium simplex*, can utilize and degrade a number of substituted nitrophenols and nitrocresols. Finally, Jensen (1959) observed that allyl alcohol could be degraded in soil by two species of *Pseudomonas* and by *Nocardia corallina*.

Chemical toxicants vary widely in degree of resistance to biological degradation in soil. The instability of antibiotics in soil is well known. Streptomycin, streptothricin, clavacin, griseofulvin, and chloromycetin are biologically degraded in soil in a matter of hours to a few days (Siminoff and Gottlieb, 1951; Gottlieb, 1952; Wright and Grove, 1957). At the other extreme are the soil insecticides of the halogenated-hydrocarbon type. Insecticidal residues of aldrin, dieldrin, heptachlor, benzene hexachloride, DDT, and Chlordane have been known to persist in soil for the amazing period of 7 to 10 years (Hetrick, 1957). This was probably in dry soil. Still, 10 years is a long time.

In general, conditions favoring microbiological activity in soil also favor the degree and speed of chemical breakdown by soil organisms. Schuldt, Burchfield, and Bluestone (1957) reported that the nematocide 3,4-dichlorotetrahydrothiophene-1,1-dioxide persisted in dry soil three times as long as in moist soil. Further, these investigators found that this chemical was most stable in the acid range (pH 5.0) and least stable in the alkaline range (pH 8.3).

Finally, biological degradation of an introduced toxicant is enhanced in organic soils. This is probably because of the greater numbers and kinds of organisms present in organic soils which increase the possibility of survival and growth of resistant and toxicant-degrading types after treatment. Both thiram and captan can persist in soil or sand for weeks. They are both degraded in a matter of days, however, in soils high in organic matter (Richardson, 1954; Kennedy and Brinkerhoff, 1959; Burchfield, 1960).

Residues of toxicants in soils, after treatment of these soils, appear to be an important factor in reinfestation of soil by microorganisms. Jaques, Robinson, and Chase (1959) found that ferbam, ziram, zineb, and maneb, when incorporated into soil, caused a delay in nitrification for 150 days. Another dithiocarbamate, thiram, retains its fungicidal effectiveness for from 1 week to as long as 14 months (Hildebrand, McKeen,

and Koch, 1949; Richardson, 1954) after its introduction into soil. Kennedy and Brinkerhoff (1959) also noted that two other soil fungicides, captan and pentachloronitrobenzene, retained fungitoxic activity for from 4 to 6 weeks.

Phytotoxic effect in crops planted in soils treated with soil fumigants is a commonly observed phenomenon (Williamson, 1953). Because of the delayed nature of such phytotoxic responses, there can be little doubt that they are due to chemical residues in soils.

There is evidence to show that introduced toxicants can exert a selective action in the buildup of certain soil organisms. Jensen's (1959) report on the stimulation of *Trichoderma viride* and *Azotobacter* by allyl alcohol, as well as Wright and Grove's (1957) observations showing that a species of *Pseudomonas* increased at a steady rate with the decomposition of griseofulvin, are examples of supporting data. Such selective effects may be due not only to the toxicant per se, but to sorbed complexes of the chemical or its products of degradation to the organo-mineral gels of soil aggregates. This could result in poisoned substrates, useful only to highly selective enzyme systems.

All chemicals, then, that are incorporated into natural soils undergo a series of interactions with the components of soil. Following the impact of the toxicant on the soil biophase, two phenomena occur simultaneously. First, the toxicant undergoes various degrees of direct loss from soil. Second, the chemical interacts with the physicochemical components of the soil. Finally, a delayed interaction occurs involving degradation of the chemical as an energy-liberating substrate by the resistant residues of living organisms in the soil.

More work needs to be done on chemical residues and their possible role in poisoning existing substrates or acting in themselves as highly selective substrates.

The substrate in treated and "normal" soils.—"The substrate-fungus relationship is the key to the distribution of fungi within the soil" (Garrett, 1955). The greatest over-all factor in the reinfestation of treated soil is the presence of suitable substrates in the soil, coupled with the competitive saprophytic ability of a soil organism to utilize these substrates.

Vigorous competitive growth of a soil organism depends upon the availability of essential substrates. Competitive saprophytism can be defined primarily in terms of substrate.

Soil organisms, however, vary in their competitive ability to utilize a given substrate. *Rhizoctonia solani,* for example, is a good "sugar"-fungus competitor, but even though it can utilize cellulose (Garrett, 1962), it cannot be put in the same class with *Chaetomium* or *Cytophaga* as a degrader of cellulose.

Although the presence of suitable substrates and the ability of a soil organism to successfully compete for these substrates are inseparably linked as a single phenomenon, for the sake of clarity each of these phases will be taken up separately.

From the standpoint of a medium for the growth of organisms, a soil may be thought of as a porous siliceous framework, containing water, mineral salts, and air. Scattered throughout this framework are the sources of energy and raw materials necessary for the synthesis of heterotrophic life. These sources are the substrates. They may be living or dead plant or animal tissues. They may be simple or complex, inorganic or organic chemicals.

In "normal" or nontreated soils, in which higher plants are growing, there are three distinct substrate zones. First, there is the outer zone, representing the bulk of the soil external to living roots and beyond the direct influence of their excretions. This is the region of discrete islands of decaying organic matter and greatest saprophytic competition. All utilizable substrates are occupied and the environment is distinctly hostile to newcomers. This is the zone of lowest available energy in which organisms are rapidly drifting toward a state of quiescence.

Second, there is the rhizosphere zone, closely associated with the living roots. This is the soil region of greatest activity. Specialized heterotrophic organisms develop in rhizosphere zones, living on such substrates as root exudates, root-cap detritus, and secretions of neighboring specialized heterotrophs (Lochhead, 1959).

Third, and finally, is the root environment proper, involving the rhizoplane or root surface and the epidermal and cortical regions of the root. Here root-infecting organisms and closely related "scavengers" subsist on and in living or moribund root tissues.

When soil is treated with an eradicant treatment, such as chloropicrin or steam, a marked change takes place with regard to substrates. Living roots and their heterotrophic denizens are killed. Rhizosphere organisms are destroyed. Fungi, bacteria, and actinomycetes within the treated soil zone are eliminated or markedly reduced in numbers and types. The three distinct substrate zones characteristic of normal soil now no longer exist. Instead, there is only one zone in which dead and unoccupied substrates predominate. New high-energy substrates have been formed, primarily from the killing of living cells and tissues. The stage is now set for the reinfestation of the soil by heterotrophic organisms favored by the newly created substrates.

The energetics of substrate utilization.—Before discussing the successions in treated soils, we should first consider certain fundamental aspects of the situation. These aspects have to do with the energetics of soil organism—soil-substrate interactions.

The release of energy from a substrate in soil by an organism is basically an enzyme-substrate reaction. The velocity of any enzyme-substrate reaction follows the law of mass action. Essentially, this law dictates that the velocity of a reaction is proportional to the concentration of the reacting substances. Assuming a simple unimolecular reaction, this relation can be expressed as:

$$V = \frac{dx}{dt} = k(a-x);$$

where: a = the initial concentration,
         x = the change in concentration in time (t),

k = the unimolecular velocity constant, and
$$\frac{dx}{dt} = \text{the reaction velocity.}$$

The substrate-enzyme reaction can be further characterized by the equation:

$$\frac{-da}{dt} = kqa;$$

where: $\dfrac{da}{dt}$ = the velocity of growth of a soil-borne fungus,

a = the concentration of substrate acted upon in time (t), and

q = the quantity or mass of enzyme (fungus) under the edaphic conditions represented by k.

Simple but high-energy-yielding substrates are first attacked by correspondingly simple enzyme systems. As simple substrates are exhausted, the more complex substrates are left behind. These, in turn, are attacked by more complex enzyme systems. The situation becomes less and less "profitable" as exergonic reactions drift toward endergonic reactions.

Specific populations of soil organisms fall off because of diminishing requisite substrates, after which new populations arise with a resultant diminution of their requisite substrates (Fig. 1).

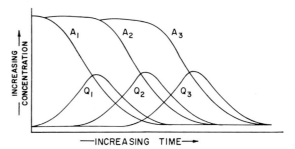

Fig. 1. Theoretical system of curves depicting degradation of specific soil substrates (A_1, A_2, A_3) by corresponding specific fungus-enzyme systems (Q_1, Q_2, Q_3) in time.

As Garrett (1946) has so succinctly put it, "Competition among soil microorganisms is for organic substrates which are finite and exhaustible; the end point of the succession on individual substrates is thus zero."

Further, if no "free" energy sources are added to the soil, there will be a slow "running down" in available energy for the growth of heterotrophs in the soil. This loss of free or available energy suggests a system following the second law of thermodynamics. Here we might apply Lotka's (1956) interpretation of the second law as it applies to a biological system: "That the system evolves toward a state in which certain functions (thermodynamic potentials) of the variables are at a minimum." For such an isolated system this is in the direction of increasing entropy.

We can conclude this section by agreeing with Brian (1957) that microbial life in the soil is governed by Malthusian principles, with ". . . periods of quiescence when all suitable organic matter has been used up, alternating with periods of rapid multiplication when food again becomes available in the form of plant or animal debris."

Heterotrophic soil organisms are like the improvident grasshopper of the old fable and more recent Walt Disney fame; they alternate between periods of over-abundance and periods of famine.

The role of substrate specificity.—There is evidence to show that the types of specific substrates present in the soil after treatment will markedly affect the kinds and numbers of organisms which will be established in these soils. This concept strongly suggests that given enough knowledge of the effect of the substrate, control of soil reinfestation is possible.

In 1954, Martin and Aldrich concluded from their fumigation studies in citrus soil that "the kinds of fungi becoming dominant depended on the nature of the organic residue added."

Changing the nature of the soil microfloral balance by the addition of various amendments has been recognized for years as a promising biological approach in the amelioration of the effects of soil-borne pathogens. Control of *Streptomyces scabies* by plowing under green manure (Millard and Taylor, 1927) and reduction of damage from attack by *Phymatotrichum omnivorum* by manure amendments (King, Hope, and Eaton, 1934) are two classic examples of this approach.

In each of these particular cases, it was simply a matter of adding a substrate specifically favoring the development of obligate soil saprophytes antagonistic to plant pathogens.

A good deal of research has been conducted recently on the importance of substrate specificity in the differential development of soil organisms.

Tyner (1961) compared the effects of peat and straw amendments in soil on subsequent fungal colonization. He found that *Trichoderma viride* dominated in the peat-amended but not in the straw-amended soils. Maier (1961) noted that straw amendments to bean-field soils favored saprophytic colonizers such as *Chaetomium* sp. over the root-rot pathogen, *Fusarium solani* f. *phaseoli.*

Exotic types of substrates have also been studied. Lingappa and Lockwood (1962) noted that chitin in soil suspensions selectively favored actinomycetes and suppressed most bacteria and fungi.

Mitchell and Alexander (1961) reported that *Bacillus cereus, B. megaterium,* and species of *Pseudomonas* could utilize chitin in soil as a sole carbon source. Further, these organisms, which were effective antagonists to both *Fusarium oxysporum* f. *cubense* and *F. solani* f. *phaseoli,* reduced disease from the latter plant pathogen after the addition of chitin amendments to soil.

Even special "trapping" techniques useful in obtaining hard-to-isolate organisms from soil illustrate the importance of substrate specificity. Methods such as Yarwood's (1946) raw-carrot substrate for *Thielaviopsis basicola,* Lowy's (1961) use of boiled hempseed to trap aquatic phycomycetes from soil, and Nadakavukaren and Horner's (1959) ethyl alcohol medium to

isolate *Verticillium albo-atrum* from soil all illustrate the importance of selective substrate action.

It must not be forgotten that even living roots and their excretions act as selective soil substrates. Ninhydrin-positive substances excreted by bean roots appear to act as substrates favoring germination and growth of chlamydospores of *Fusarium solani* f. *phaseoli* in soil (Schroth and Snyder, 1961; Pearson and Parkinson, 1961). Kerr (1956) shielded susceptible roots in soil from *Rhizoctonia solani* by means of cellophane bags, but found that the fungus aggregated on the cellophane at the point nearest the roots. Herzog (1961) found that *R. solani* was stimulated least by the rhizospheres of nonsusceptible graminaceous plants and most by susceptible leguminous and solanaceous host rhizospheres. Zentmyer (1961) reported selective chemotactic response of zoospores of *Phytophthora cinnamomi* to avocado seedling roots.

Even nonpathogenic fungi are affected by root exudates. Witness Jackson's (1957) observation that conidia of *Gliocladium roseum* and *Paecilomyces marquandi* were stimulated to germinate in soil only when in contact with pea roots.

The C:N ratio in soil substrates may affect the growth of fungi in soil. Papavizas and Davey (1961) noted that the saprophytic activity of *Rhizoctonia solani* in soil is enhanced by high nitrogen and low carbon. Lindsey (1962) showed that the bean-root-rot pathogen, *Fusarium solani* f. *phaseoli,* could not colonize soil competitively against *Fusarium roseum* unless inorganic nitrogen was added to the soil. Apparently the pathogen was not able to utilize effectively the organic nitrogen substrates in the soil under this competitive pressure.

It should be apparent, then, that the presence or absence of selective substrates is an extremely important factor in the reinfestation of treated soil. Much worth-while research remains to be done on this critical subject.

Competitive saprophytism.—Under any given set of conditions in a treated soil, with a fixed substrate level as to type and quantity, reinvasion will be determined by the degree of competitive saprophytism of the biological residue.

In 1956, Garrett defined competitive saprophytism "as the summation of physiological characteristics that make for success in competitive colonization of dead organic substrates."

According to Garrett, this definition includes: (1) high growth rate and germinability of spores, (2) good enzyme producing "equipment," (3) production of antibiotic toxins, and (4) tolerance of antibiotics produced by other organisms.

Ordinarily, the degree of competitive saprophytism for any given organism is ascertained by the vigor of its growth on dead plant tissue or artificial media (Garrett, 1956; Domsch, 1960).

There are some broad generalizations along both taxonomic and ecological lines that can be made. Fungi, as a rule, are better competitive saprophytes in soil than bacteria or actinomycetes. Actinomycetes grow slowly but make up for their lack of vigorous growth by their "staying power" (Hawker, 1957). In general, phycomycetes and imperfect fungi are vigorous reinvaders. This is because they are "sugar fungi."

In soils treated with steam or powerful fungicidal eradicants, initial colonization was by fast-growing phycomycetes such as *Mortierella* and *Pythium* (Warcup, 1951; Evans, 1955), as well as imperfect fungi such as *Trichoderma viride* (Warcup, 1951; Evans, 1955; Martin, Baines, and Ervin, 1957; Saksena, 1960). Wensley (1953) observed rapid reinvasion of methyl-bromide-treated soil by species of *Aspergillus*.

According to Hawker (1957), *Mucor, Sordaria, Chaetomium,* and *Pythium* grow rapidly through soil, whereas *Aspergillus* and *Penicillium* grow more slowly but compensate by abundant spore formation. Since isolation techniques favor the appearance of spore formers in soil plantings, some questions could be raised on the relative importance of *Pencillium* and *Aspergillus* as initial soil reinvaders (Warcup, 1957).

Evans (1955), using soil-recolonization tubes, noted that *Trichoderma viride* was the dominant invader of carbon disulfide and formaldehyde-treated soil only if the soil was loosely packed. If moisture was not limiting and the soil was tightly packed, fast-growing Phycomycetes, especially *Pythium,* were the initial recolonizers. Evans' observations may have a significant bearing on Wilhelm's (1957) report that strawberry decline caused by root attack by *Pythium ultimum* followed soil fumigation with chloropicrin that gave successful control of *Verticillium albo-atrum*.

Although *Pythium* appears to be a good initial invader of treated soil, it seems to lack "staying power." In fact, Barton (1961) noted that *Pythium mamillatum* was unable to colonize substrates already occupied by competitive fungi, presumably due to the accumulation of staling products.

Competitive saprophytic ability is easier to assess from the standpoint of ecological growth habit. This can be done almost by definition. Obligate soil saprophytes should be better competitors than nonobligate saprophytes. In turn, nonobligate saprophytes should have greater saprophytic ability than nonobligate parasites. Garrett (1956) has quite correctly pointed out that his soil inhabitants are by definition better saprophytic competitors than his "root inhabitants."

Finally, organisms alien to a soil should not be able to compete successfully with native soil organisms. Based on some relatively recent studies, this appears to be true. Voronkevich (1960) recently reported that species of *Erwinia* were unable to survive in soil from which they were not readily isolated. Park (1955) infested normal soils with both native and alien species. The aliens were recoverable only for a few days, whereas the natives were able to survive longer than 6 months.

Much more work is needed on the subject of competitive saprophytism. Improvement in isolation techniques is essential. Present methods do not distinguish between dormant and actively growing organisms in soils. Efforts must be made to overcome the present technique bias which favors spore formers. Finally, studies on competitive saprophytism should be made only in the presence of controlled substrates.

THE BIOLOGICAL SUCCESSION AFTER SOIL TREATMENT. —Let us now consider the over-all problem of microorganismal successions in treated soil, as well as possible control approaches.

To attempt a synthesis of the basic principles involved, the writer will assume a hypothetical situation following soil treatment with steam or a powerful eradicant fungicide. It is recognized that experimental evidence for much of the following is lacking. However, the isolated fragmentary pieces of the present jigsaw puzzle seem to fit the following postulated pattern.

Stage 1.—The soil is treated with a potent general fungicide, such as chloropicrin. This creates a treated zone perhaps 12 in or more in diameter, surrounded by untreated parent soil containing the complete complement of natural soil microorganisms available for reinfestation. We can assume, further, that the volatile biocide killed most of the organisms in the central 6-in-diameter portion of the treated zone, thus creating here a biological vacuum.

From this central zone of kill, overlapping spheres of lessening lethal intensity exist, being occupied by organisms possessing various degrees of resistance to the treatment. These islands of resistant organisms constitute the biological residues.

The treated zones now consist of regions of newly created high potential energy, as contrasted with the untreated soil in which potential energy sources are low.

With the dissipation of the toxic chemical, the treated zone is invaded first by fast-growing fungi. Concurrently, actinomycetes and miscellaneous bacteria develop slowly within the treated zone, arising from resistant biological residues.

Fungi favored in this initial invasion would be the vigorously competitive sugar- and amino-acid-utilizing kinds, especially those tolerant to any sorbed residues of biotoxicant. Assuming the presence of sufficient soil moisture, fast-growing Phycomycetes such as *Mortierella, Mucor, Rhizopus,* and *Pythium* will move rapidly into the treated zone to occupy simple-sugar substrates. The invading imperfect forms will be represented predominantly by species of *Trichoderma, Penicillium* and *Aspergillus*.

This is the period of Phycomycetes-Imperfecti dominance against a mutual background of actinomycetes and bacteria.

Let us assume that in the final phases of stage 1, a seed is planted.

Stage 2.—The second period is one of rapid transition. The sugar–amino-acid organisms are well on their way toward exhausting their immediately available sources of energy. A new energy-source zone, however, is now being created by the developing seedling. Small amounts of simple sugars and amino acids are beginning to leak from the regions of elongation and differentiation of the developing rootlets. Favored fungi, bacteria, and actinomycetes grow into this newly created region, thus forming the rhizosphere, which differs in organismal composition both qualitatively and quantitatively from the surrounding soil zone.

In the nonrhizosphere or outer soil region, slower-growing microorganisms make their appearance, which are capable of "cracking" the less readily decomposable substrates. These are the degraders of complex carbohydrates.

Fungi Imperfecti still dominate, being represented by species of *Alternaria, Myrothecium, Aspergillus,* and *Penicillium.* Ascomycetes such as *Sordaria* and *Chaetomium* make their appearance. Specialized actinomycetes as *Micromonospora;* myxobacterial and bacterial forms such as *Cytophaga, Sporocytophaga,* and *Cellvibrio* are present. The first Basidiomycetes develop, as the cellulose-degrading species of *Merulius, Stereum, Corticium, Marasmius,* and *Fomes* begin to take over the picked-over substrate "bones."

This is the period of Imperfecti-Ascomycetes dominance, against a background of actinomycetes, bacteria, and early Basidiomycetes.

Stage 3.—In the third period, the total potential energy source of the treated soil zone has appreciably diminished. With the exception of the rhizospheres of the developing seedling roots (don't forget the seed that was planted), all simple energy sources have been exhausted. The only energy sources left in nonrhizosphere zones are lignin and other extremely complex materials of biological origin.

Species of *Fomes, Psalliota, Coprinus, Hydnum* and *Polyporus* take over. This is the "mop-up" crew. A few bacteria commonly designated as autochthonous forms partake of this sad fare. Most of the other zymogenic forms have "packed up and gone home."

Most of the simple-sugar organisms and cellulose degraders are now limited to the rhizospheres of the rootlets of our seedling plant. A new pattern is forming in these restricted feeder-root zones. These confined regions create new sources of energy for sugar fungi. Further increases in energy sources occur when root pathogens such as *Thielaviopsis, Phytophthora,* or *Rhizoctonia* manage to penetrate root tissues. When this happens, intense temporary activity flares up in these microzones.

In nonrhizosphere regions, which still constitute the great bulk of the treated soil, this is the period of basidiomycete dominance.

Stage 4.—The fourth and final period could be considered ecologically to be the climax state. Most of the potential energy sources originally available have been depleted. Organisms in the predominant nonrhizosphere zones are either growing very slowly, attacking and parasitizing one another or becoming quiescent. It is the period of predators and famine.

The treated soil has now become ecologically indistinct from the surrounding nontreated soil. The only regions of available free energy left are in the rhizospheres of roots of our young plant, in sloughed root cells and in areas of decaying rootlets.

CONTROLLING REINFESTATION IN TREATED SOIL.—The ultimate objective of soil treatment with chemicals or heat is to kill or inhibit all organisms unfavorable for the growth and development of higher plants. This objective should be attained on a selective basis; that is, all organisms favorable to higher plants should be left in the biological residue. The goal then is to destroy plant inhibitors without harming plant sustainers (Kreutzer, 1960). Further, the treatment should create a minimum of new substrate. This keeps the potential energy available for reinfestation at a minimum.

Most of our present soil treatments are not selective. Even the range of organisms affected by the few so-called selective treatments is unknown. This will probably be the case for a long time to come.

It can be properly asked at this point, what can we do within our present state of knowledge to control reinfestation or at least direct it into the best possible channels? Let us briefly examine the possibilities open to us.

In a normal "climax" soil the activity of heterotrophic soil organisms is at a minimum. This is because available substrate levels are low, which means correspondingly low potential-energy levels for the growth of soil organisms.

When this soil is treated with a biocide or heat, the biophase shrinks and available substrates, or available sources of energy, increase. This creates a biological-vacuum effect. Organisms from either the resistant residue or from the untreated outside zone then invade to occupy newly created substrates.

These invading microorganisms constitute a normal biotic force tending to push the unbalanced state back toward the normal climax state (Fig. 2). Any treatment

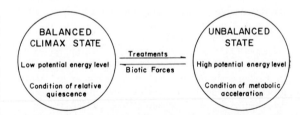

Fig. 2. Diagrammatic representation of the broad principles involved in the reinfestation of treated soil.

which increases substrate levels will create this unbalanced state. Even amendments to a limited degree should have such an effect.

Let us now consider tentative solutions in the light of the foregoing concept.

1. If possible, use selective chemicals or aerated steam designed to kill or restrict pathogens, and leave the great bulk of soil microorganisms undisturbed.

2. Add substrates favoring obligate saprophytes before or immediately after treatment. *Never add substrates favoring pathogens.* Where seeds of a host crop are planted immediately after treatment, living substrates which literally "bait" the pathogen are being introduced. The use of a nonhost crop immediately after treatment adds sub-

strates which do not favor the pathogen (Kommedahl and Brock, 1954; Menon and Williams, 1957).

3. Take advantage of the biotic force tending to drive treated soils back toward the climax state. "Seed" treated soils with favorable organisms only in the presence of available specific substrates for these plant sustainers. Organisms cannot be established against a substrate gradient.

Finally, to aid us in successfully managing reinfestation, research must throw more light on two important things. First, we must learn the identity of the majority of our friends and foes. We must be able to distinguish between plant sustainers and plant inhibitors. Second, we must discover the substrate preferences of these organisms, and learn more about the conditions in nature which favor or restrict their growth and development.

We have made a good beginning but there is much more to be done.

ACKNOWLEDGMENTS.—I wish to acknowledge helpful discussions with Dr. Paul Porter of the Shell Development Company. I also wish to thank Mr. Charles Maurer for assistance in the preparation of figures.

LITERATURE CITED

ALDRICH, D. G., and J. P. MARTIN. 1952. Effect of fumigation on some chemical properties of soils. Soil Sci. 73: 149-159.

ARK, P. A. 1937. Little-leaf or rosette of fruit trees. VII. Soil microflora and little-leaf or rosette disease. Proc. Am. Soc. Hort. Sci. 34: 216-221.

BAKER, K. F. 1961. Control of root-rot disease. p. 486-490. *In* Recent advances in botany (Canada) (9th Intern. Botan. Congr., Montreal). vol. 1. University of Toronto Press, Toronto.

BAKER, K. F., and C. N. ROISTACHER. 1957. Heat treatment of soil. p. 123-196. *In* K. F. Baker [ed.], The U. C. system for producing healthy container-grown plants, California Agr. Expt. Sta. Manual 23.

BALD, J. G., and R. N. JEFFERSON. 1956. Interpretation of results from a soil fumigation trial. Plant Disease Reptr. 40: 840-846.

BARTON, R. 1961. Saprophytic activity of *Pythium mamillatum* in soils. II. Factors restricting *P. mamillatum* to pioneer colonization of substrates. Trans. Brit. Mycol. Soc. 44: 105-118.

BRIAN, P. W. 1957. The ecological significance of antibiotic production. *In* Microbial ecology, Symp. Soc. Gen. Microbiol. 7: 168-188.

BUNT, A. C. 1955. Steam-air mixture. John Innes Hort. Inst. Ann. Rept. 45: 28.

BURCHFIELD, H. P. 1960. Performance of fungicides on plants and in soil—physical, chemical, and biological considerations. vol. 3, p. 477-520. *In* J. G. Horsfall and A. E. Dimond [ed.], Plant pathology, an advanced treatise, Academic Press, New York.

CHRISTIE, J. R. 1947. Preliminary tests to determine the nematocidal and fungicidal properties of certain chemical compounds when used as soil fumigants. Proc. Helminthol. Soc. Wash., D. C. 14: 23-28.

CHRISTIE, J. R., and V. G. PERRY. 1958. A low-phytotoxic nematocide of the organic phosphate group. Plant Disease Reptr. 42: 74-75.

CORNFIELD, A. H. 1955. The measurement of soil structure and factors affecting it: A review. J. Sci. Food Agr. 6: 356-360.

CRAM, W. H., and O. VAARTAJA. 1957. Rate and timing of fungicidal soil treatments. Phytopathology 47: 169-173.

DALTON, F. H., and C. HURWITZ. 1948. Effect of volatile disinfectants on survival of microflora in soil. Soil Sci. 66: 233-238.

DAVEY, A. E., and L. D. LEACH. 1941. Experiments with fungicides for use against *Sclerotium rolfsii* in soils. Hilgardia 13: 523-547.

DAVIES, J. N., and O. OWEN. 1954. Soil sterilization. III. Effect of cultivation on ammonia and nitrate production in a glasshouse soil steam-sterilized *in situ*. J. Sci. Food Agr. 5: 146-153.

DOMSCH, K. H. 1959. Die Wirkung von Bodenfungiziden. III. Quantitativ Veränderung der Bodenflora. Z. Pflanzenkrankh. 66: 17-26.

DOMSCH, K. H. 1960. Das Pilzspektrum einer Bodenprobe. II. Nachweis physiologischer Merkmale. Arch. Mikrobiol. 35: 229-247.

DU BUISSON, J. P. 1917. The extraction and saturation of soils with volatile antiseptics. Soil Sci. 3: 353-391.

EVANS, E. 1955. Survival and recolonization by fungi in soil treated with formalin or carbon disulphide. Trans. Brit. Mycol. Soc. 38: 335-346.

FRENCH, C. 1893. A handbook of the destructive insects of Victoria, 1st ed., Part II. Robert S. Brain, Government Printer, Melbourne, Australia. 222 p.

GARRETT, S. D. 1946. Soil as a medium for transfer and multiplication of disease organisms. Soil Sci. 61: 3-8.

GARRETT, S. D. 1955. Microbiol ecology of the soil. Trans. Brit. Mycol. Soc. 38: 1-9.

GARRETT, S. D. 1956. Biology of root-infecting fungi. Cambridge University Press, London and New York. 292 p.

GARRETT, S. D. 1962. Decomposition of cellulose in soil by *Rhizoctonia solani* Kühn. Trans. Brit. Mycol. Soc. 45: 115-120.

GIBSON, I. A. S. 1953. Crown rot, a seedling disease of groundnuts caused by *Aspergillus niger*. II. An anomalous effect of organo-mercurial seed dressings. Trans. Brit. Mycol. Soc. 36: 324-334.

GIBSON, I. A. S. 1956. An anomalous effect of soil treatment with ethyl mercury phosphate on the incidence of damping-off in pine seedlings. Phytopathology 46: 181-182.

GIBSON, I. A. S., M. LEDGER, and E. BOEHM. 1961. An anomalous effect of pentachloronitrobenzene on the incidence of damping-off caused by a *Pythium* sp. Phytopathology 51: 531-533.

GOTTLIEB, D. 1952. The disappearance of antibiotics from soil. (Abstr.). Phytopathology 42: 9.

GUNDERSEN, K., and H. L. JENSEN. 1956. Soil bacterium decomposing organic nitro compounds. Acta Agr. Scand. 6: 100-114.

HAASIS, F. A. 1952. Soil fumigation with chlorobromopropene for control of *Sclerotium rolfsii* in Dutch iris. Plant Disease Reptr. 36: 475-478.

HANNESON, H. A. 1945. Movement of carbon disulfide vapor in soils as affected by soil type, moisture content and compaction. Hilgardia 16: 503-510.

HAWKER, LILLIAN E. 1957. Ecological factors and the survival of fungi. *In* Microbiol ecology, Symp. Soc. Gen. Microbiol. 7: 238-258.

HEMWALL, J. B. 1962. Theoretical consideration of soil fumigation. Phytopathology 52: 1108-1115.

HENDERSON, MOIRA E. K., and V. C. FARMER. 1955. Utilization by soil fungi of p-hydroxybenzaldehyde, ferulic acid, syringaldehyde and vanillin. J. Gen. Microbiol. 12: 37-46.

HERZOG, W. 1961. Das Überdauern und der Saprophytismus des Wurzeltöters *Rhizoctonia solani* K. im Boden. Phytopathol. Z. 40: 379-415.

HETRICK, L. A. 1957. Ten years of testing organic insecticides as soil poisons against the eastern subterranean termite. J. Econ. Entomol. 50: 316-317.

HILDEBRAND, A. A., W. E. McKEEN, and L. W. KOCH. 1949. Row treatment of soil with tetramethylthiuram disulfide for control of blackroot of sugar-beet seedlings. I. Greenhouse tests. Can. J. Res., Sec. C, 27: 23-43.

JACKS, H., and H. C. SMITH. 1952. Soil disinfestation.

XII. Effect of fumigants on growth of soil fungi in culture. New Zealand J. Sci. Technol., Sec. A, 33: 69-73.

JACKSON, R. M. 1957. Fungistasis as a factor in the rhizosphere phenomenon. Nature (London) 180: 96-97.

JAQUES, R. P., J. B. ROBINSON, and F. E. CHASE. 1959. Effects of thiourea, ethyl urethane and some dithiocarbamate fungicides on nitrification in Fox sandy loam. Can. J. Soil Sci. 39: 235-243.

JENSEN, H. L. 1959. Allyl alcohol as a nutrient for microorganisms. Nature (London) 183: 903.

JURINAK, J. J. 1957. Adsorption of 1,2-dibromo-3-chloropropane vapor by soils. J. Agr. Food Chem. 5: 598-600.

KATZNELSON, H., and L. T. RICHARDSON. 1943. The microflora of the rhizosphere of tomato plants in relation to soil sterilization. Can. J. Res., Sec. C, 21: 249-255.

KENDRICK, J. B., JR., and G. A. ZENTMYER. 1957. Recent advances in control of soil fungi. vol. 1, p. 219-275. In R. L. Metcalf [ed.], Advances in pest control research, Interscience Publishers, New York.

KENNEDY, B. W., and L. A. BRINKERHOFF. 1959. Comparison of four soil fungicides in the greenhouse for the control of seedling diseases of cotton. Plant Disease Reptr. 43: 90-97.

KERR, A. 1956. Some interactions between plant roots and pathogenic soil fungi. Australian J. Biol. Sci. 9: 45-52.

KINCAID, R. R., and G. M. VOLK. 1949. Soil fumigation for cigar-wrapper tobacco in Florida. (Abst.) Phytopathology 39: 11.

KING, C. J., C. HOPE, and E. D. EATON. 1934. Some microbiological activities affected in manurial control of cotton root rot. J. Agr. Res. 49: 1093-1107.

KLEMMER, H. W. 1957. Response of bacterial, fungal, and nematode populations of Hawaiian soils to fumigation and liming. Soc. Am. Bacteriol. Proc. 57: 12.

KOCH, L. W. 1955. The peach replant problem in Ontario. I. Symptomatology and distribution. Can. J. Botany 33: 450-460.

KOMMEDAHL, T., and T. D. BROCK. 1954. Studies on the relationship of soil mycoflora to disease incidence. Phytopathology 44: 57-61.

KREUTZER, W. A. 1960. Soil treatment. vol. 3, p. 431-476. In J. G. Horsfall and A. E. Dimond [ed.], Plant pathology, an advanced treatise. Academic Press, Inc., New York.

KREUTZER, W. A. 1963. Selective toxicity of chemicals to soil microorganisms. Ann. Rev. Phytopathol. 1: 101-126.

KREUTZER, W. A., and J. T. W. MONTAGNE. 1950. Chlorobromopropene, a potential fungicidal soil fumigant. (Abstr.). Phytopathology 40: 16.

LADD, J. N. 1956. The oxidation of hydrocarbons by soil bacteria. I. Morphological and biochemical properties of a soil diphtheroid utilizing hydrocarbons. Australian J. Biol. Sci. 9: 92-104.

LINDSEY, D. 1962. Competition between soil fungi. M.S. Thesis. Colorado State University.

LINGAPPA, Y., and J. L. LOCKWOOD. 1962. Chitin media for selective isolation and culture of actinomycetes. Phytopathology 52: 317-323.

LOCHHEAD, A. G. 1959. Rhizosphere microorganisms in relation to root-disease fungi. p. 327-338. In C. S. Holton, et al. [ed.], Plant pathology, problems and progress 1908-1958. Univ. Wisconsin Press, Madison, Wisc.

LOEW, O. 1909. Soil disinfection in agriculture. Puerto Rico Agr. Expt. Sta. Circ. 11: 3-12.

LOTKA, A. J. 1956. Elements of mathematical biology. Dover Publications, Inc., New York. 465 p.

LOWY, B. 1961. A method for obtaining soil-free aquatic phycomycetes. Mycologia 50: 142-144.

MAIER, C. R. 1961. Selective effects of barley residue on fungi of the pinto bean root-rot complex. Plant Disease Reptr. 45: 808-811.

MARTIN, W. J. 1953. Circular spot, a disease of sweet potato roots. Phytopathology 43: 432-433.

MARTIN, J. P., and D. G. ALDRICH. 1952. Effect of fumigation on aggregation. Soil Sci. Soc. Am. Proc. 16: 201-203.

MARTIN, J. P., and D. G. ALDRICH. 1954. Effect of

various exchangeable cation ratios on kinds of fungi developing during decomposition of organic residues in soil. Soil Sci. Soc. Am. Proc. 18: 160-164.

MARTIN, J. P., D. G. ALDRICH, W. S. MURPHY, and G. R. BRADFORD. 1953. Effect of soil fumigation on growth and chemical composition of citrus plants. Soil Sci. 75: 137-151.

MARTIN, J. P., R. C. BAINES, and J. O. ERVIN. 1957. Influence of soil fumigation for citrus replants on the fungus population of the soil. Soil Sci. Soc. Am. Proc. 21: 163-166.

MATUO, T., and Y. SAKURAI. 1959. On the fungicidal effect of chloropicrin and other few drugs upon *Rosellinia necatrix* and *Corticium centrifugum* in soil. J. Sericult. Sci. Japan 28: 395-401.

MENON, S. K., and L. E. WILLIAMS. 1957. Effect of crop, crop residues, temperature and moisture on soil fungi. Phytopathology 47: 559-564.

MILLARD, W. A., and C. B. TAYLOR. 1927. Antagonism of micro-organisms as the controlling factor in the inhibition of scab by green manuring. Ann. Appl. Biol. 14: 202-216.

MITCHELL, R., and M. ALEXANDER. 1961. The mycolytic phenomenon and biological control of *Fusarium* in soil. Nature (London) 190: 109-110.

MOLLISON, JANET E. 1953. Effect of partial sterilization and acidification of soil on the fungal population. Trans. Brit. Mycol. Soc. 36: 215-228.

MUNNECKE, D. E., K. H. DOMSCH, and J. W. ECKERT. 1962. Fungicidal activity of air passed through columns of soil treated with fungicides. Phytopathology 52: 1298-1306.

MUNNECKE, D. E., and D. L. LINDGREN. 1954. Chemical measurements of methyl bromide concentration in relation to kill of fungi and nematodes in nursery soil. Phytopathology 44: 605-606.

NADAKAVUKAREN, M. J., and C. E. HORNER. 1959. An alcohol agar medium selective for determining *Verticillium* microsclerotia in soil. Phytopathology 49: 527-528.

NEWHALL, A. G., and B. LEAR. 1948. Soil fumigation for fungus control with methyl bromide. Phytopathology 38: 38-43.

OVERMAN, AMEGDA J., and D. S. BURGIS. 1956. Allyl alcohol as a soil fungicide. Phytopathology 46: 532-535.

PAPAVIZAS, G. C., and C. B. DAVEY. 1961. Saprophytic behavior of Rhizoctonia in soil. Phytopathology 51: 693-699.

PARK, D. 1955. Experimental studies on the ecology of fungi in soil. Trans. Brit. Mycol. Soc. 38: 130-142.

PEARSON, R., and D. PARKINSON. 1961. The sites of excretion of ninhydrin-positive substances by broad bean seedlings. Plant Soil 13: 391-396.

RAHN, O. 1906. Ein paraffin zersetzender Schimmelpilz. Zentrbl. Bakteriol. Parasitenk., Abt. II, 16: 382-384.

RICHARDSON, L. T. 1954. The persistence of thiram in soil and its relationship to the microbiological balance and damping-off control. Can. J. Botany 32: 335-346.

RUSSELL, E. J., and H. B. HUTCHINSON. 1909. The effect of partial sterilization of soil on the production of plant food. J. Agr. Sci. 3: 111-144.

SAKSENA, S. B. 1960. Effect of carbon disulphide fumigation on *Trichoderma viride* and other soil fungi. Trans. Brit. Mycol. Soc. 43: 111-116.

SAMPSON, R. E., and R. A. LUDWIG. 1956. Laboratory studies on the evaluation and activity of antifungal fumigants. Can. J. Botany 34: 37-43.

SCHROTH, M. N., and W. C. SNYDER. 1961. Effect of host exudates on chlamydospore germination of the bean root-rot fungus, *Fusarium solani* f. *phaseoli*. Phytopathology 51: 389-393.

SCHULDT, P. H., H. P. BURCHFIELD, and H. BLUESTONE. 1957. Stability and movement studies on the new experimental nematocide 3,4-dichlorotetrahydrothiophene-1, 1-dioxide in soil. (Abstr.) Phytopathology 47: 534.

SIMINOFF, P., and D. GOTTLIEB. 1951. The production and role of antibiotics in the soil. I. The fate of streptomycin. Phytopathology 41: 420-429.

SMITH, N. R. 1939. The partial sterilization of soil by chloropicrin. Soil Sci. Soc. Am. Proc. (1938) 3: 188.

STARK, F. L., JR. 1948. Investigations of chloropicrin as a soil fumigant. New York Agr. Expt. Sta. (Geneva, N. Y.) Mem. 278, 61 p.

STARK, F. L., JR., and B. LEAR. 1947. Miscellaneous greenhouse tests with various soil fumigants for the control of fungi and nematodes. Phytopathology 37: 698-711.

STÖRMER, K. 1908. Ueber die Wirkung des Schwefelkohlenstoffs und ähnlicher Stoffe auf den Boden. Zentrbl. Bakteriol. Parasitenk., Abt. II, 20: 282-286.

STOTZKY, G., W. P. MARTIN, J. L. MORTENSEN. 1956. Certain effects of crop residues and fumigant applications on the decomposition of an Ohio muck soil. Soil Sci. Soc. Am. Proc. 20: 392-396.

TAM, R. K., and H. E. CLARK. 1943. Effect of chloropicrin and other soil disinfectants on the nitrogen nutrition of the pineapple plant. Soil Sci. 56: 245-261.

TARR, S. A. J. 1956. Stem canker (*Macrophomina phaseoli*) of cotton seedlings in the Sudan Gezira. Nature (London) 178: 935.

THORNTON, H. G., and JANE MEIKLEJOHN. 1957. Soil microbiology. Ann. Rev. Microbiol. 11: 123-148.

TYNER, L. E. 1961. Colonization of organic matter in the soil by fungi. Phytopathology 51: 625-634.

VORONKEVICH, I. V. 1960. [On the survival in the soil of bacteria of the genus *Erwinia*—Causal agents of soft rots in plants.] Bull. Soc. Nat. Moscow, Ser. Biol. 65: 95-105. *Abstr. in* Rev. Appl. Mycol. 40: 201. 1961.

WARCUP, J. H. 1951. Effect of partial sterilization by steam or formalin on the fungus flora of an old forest nursery soil. Trans. Brit. Mycol. Soc. 34: 519-532.

WARCUP, J. H. 1952. Effect of partial sterilization by steam or formalin on damping-off of Sitka spruce. Trans. Brit. Mycol. Soc. 35: 248-262.

WARCUP, J. H. 1957. Studies on the occurrence and activity of fungi in a wheat-field soil. Trans. Brit. Mycol. Soc. 40: 237-262.

WENSLEY, R. N. 1953. Microbiological studies of the action of some selected soil fumigants. Can. J. Botany 31: 277-308.

WILHELM, S. 1957. Chloropicrin gives promising control of Verticillium wilt in strawberry. (Abstr.) Phytopathology 47: 37.

WILLIAMSON, C. E. 1953. Methyl bromide injury to some ornamental plants. (Abstr.). Phytopathology 43: 489.

WINFREE, J. P., and R. S. COX. 1958. Comparative effects of fumigation with chloropicrin and methyl bromide on mineralization of nitrogen in Everglades peat. Plant Disease Reptr. 42: 807-810.

WINFREE, J. P., R. S. COX, and D. S. HARRISON. 1958. Influence of bacterial soft rot, depth to water table, source of nitrogen, and soil fumigation on production of lettuce in the Everglades. Phytopathology 48: 311-316.

WRIGHT, JOYCE M., and J. F. GROVE. 1957. The production of antibiotics in soil. V. Breakdown of griseofulvin in soil. Ann. Appl. Biol. 45: 36-43.

YARWOOD, C. E. 1946. Isolation of *Thielaviopsis basicola* from soil by means of carrot disks. Mycologia 38: 346-348.

YOUNG, P. A. 1940. Soil fumigation with chloropicrin and carbon bisulphide to control tomato root knot and wilt. Phytopathology 30: 860-865.

ZENTMYER, G. A. 1955. A laboratory method for testing soil fungicides, with *Phytophthora cinnamomi* as test organism. Phytopathology 45: 398-404.

ZENTMYER, G. A. 1961. Chemotaxis of zoospores for root exudates. Science 133: 1595-1596.

ZENTMYER, G. A., and J. B. KENDRICK, JR. 1949. Fungicidal action of volatile soil fumigants. (Abstr.) Phytopathology 39: 864.

ZENTMYER, G. A., and L. J. KLOTZ. 1949. Soil fumigants for the control of Phytophthora root rots. (Abstr.) Phytopathology 39: 26-27.

► DISCUSSION OF W. A. KREUTZER PAPER

S. Wilhelm:

I would like to comment on the idea that spores when dormant are more resistant to chemical fumigants. Microsclerotia of *Verticillium albo-atrum* are many times more resistant to the lethal action of chloropicrin when dry than when moist. In atmospheres of about 5 to 95% relative humidity, chloropicrin is rather ineffective against microsclerotia, but in saturated atmospheres it is very effective (unpublished data).

Now a comment on the idea that selective fumigants are the ideal ones. Frequently we set out to search for a control for a certain soil pathogen, only to find that many different soil pathogens may influence the success of the crop. A specific fumigant may not take care of this problem at all. It may even augment the problem.

W. A. Kreutzer:

I believe Dr. Wilhelm is thinking of his work in strawberries for the control of *Verticillium albo-atrum* by soil fumigation, where although *Verticillium* was controlled, *Pythium* became a major root pathogen. "Disease trading" following soil treatment is not a surprising phenomenon. It is certainly the result of disruption of the microfloral balance. I still think that the more general the chemical in its effects, the greater the disturbing effect on the microbial balance. The use of specific chemicals will force us to learn which pathogens are major and which are minor.

G. H. Hepting:

Is it acceptable to use the term "soil pasteurization" for K. F. Baker's 140°F aerated-steam treatment of soil?

W. A. Kreutzer:

Even though this is within the correct temperature range as defined for pasteurization, I feel the use of this word has an unfavorable connotation. [K. F. Baker agrees with this.] We may wish to use other temperature ranges other than those in the "pasteurization range" to obtain Baker's selective effects. Perhaps something like "selective disinfestation" could be used.

C. A. I. Goring:

Dr. Wilhelm questioned the value of chemicals specific for particular pathogens because so many disease situations are caused by a complex of microorganisms. But the relative contributions of the various organisms of the pathogenic complex to reduction in yield are frequently not known and may never be known without the development of specific toxicants that can selectively control the individual pathogens. Such specific toxicants can be of great value even though they only partially solve the problem.

C. E. Horner:

Dr. Kreutzer, you emphasized reinvasion of soil treated with chemicals, suggesting that soil possessed a "reinvasion potential." Should we not consider "reinvasion potential" a capacity of organisms in treated soil and consider the chemical effect as bringing about a "susceptibility potential" to reinvasion?

W. A. Kreutzer:

This is an interesting point that I considered at some length prior to this meeting. I have suggested that certain soil treatments, or even soil treated by such chemicals, possessed a "reinvasion potential." A "susceptibility potential" to reinvasion seems to be but another way of expressing the same idea. Irrespective of how we eventually express this concept, I think it needs to be "spelled out."

W. D. Thomas:

Weak fungicides are often active against predacious fungi. Many of the stronger fungicides show specificity when used in more dilute forms. Perhaps, instead of trying to find more specific fungicides, we should learn how to use those which we have. This can be done by modified rates of application with better timing.

A. S. Sussman:

I would like to react to your generalization that organisms with lowered rates of metabolism are more resistant to chemical and physical treatments. Dr. Domsch's data disclose that the spores of several species are more sensitive to fungicides than are vegetative stages. In this case I assume lowered metabolism in the spores. However, in the case of actidione, which also is more effective on spores, it is clear these cells respire less actively than vegetative cells. Therefore, I would like to know about the data upon which your generalization was based.

W. A. Kreutzer:

The data of Leach and Davey and others show that moist sclerotia of *Sclerotium rolfsii* are more susceptible to chemical poisoning than are dry sclerotia. Further, in numerous tests I have noted that dried chlamydospores of *Fusarium solani* and microsclerotia of *Verticillium albo-atrum* are many times more resistant to the action of general biocides such as chlorobromopropene or chloropicrin, than are such structures in a moist atmosphere. This is mentioned in my paper. All this appears to support the classical concept.

I have also discussed the variation in susceptibility of vegetative structures and various types of spores. I question whether one can safely equate degree of metabolism with structure.

Proof or disproof of such a generalization as mine, in my opinion, should be obtained in tests involving only one type of vegetative or resting structure.

K. F. Baker:

Aerated-steam treatment, mentioned several times in this symposium, is a method for steaming soil at any desired temperature. At 140°F for 30 min (a steam:air ratio of 1:6.5 by weight, or 1:4 by volume), the plant pathogens and a portion of the saprophytic soil flora are killed, without inducing soil phytotoxicity. Dormant ascospores of soil saprophytes, and perhaps spore-forming bacteria, may be stimulated to germinate, increasing the active number of these antagonistic fungi in the soil. The antagonists remaining after treatment, adapted to the soil and site, increase to fill the available ecological niches. Contaminant pathogens arriving on such soil are, therefore, faced with such competition and antagonism that their parasitic activity is greatly restricted (K. F. Baker, J. Australian Inst. Agr. Sci. 28: 118-126. 1962). Similarly, treatment of soil for varying temperatures and times provides an exceedingly useful method for selective destruction of soil microorganisms in the analysis of interactions of soil microorganisms.

In practice, air flow is provided by a large-volume and low-velocity blower. Steam is injected into this air stream in the quantity necessary to provide the desired temperature; it may be manually or automatically controlled. Lowering of steam temperature below 212°F is due to dilution and an increase of the space between the BTU-carrying water molecules.

The method has proved very useful in commercial nursery operations, and as an experimental tool for selective study of soil microflora and fauna.

R. H. Ludwig:

The discovery of fungicides with the specificity and high activity of modern insecticides may not represent an advance. Fungi are at least as adaptable as insects and, with high specificity, the occurrence of their soil pesticide-resistant strains that plague the entomologists can be anticipated. There is also the possibility of breeding new plant pathogens or strains thereof.

Analysis of Biological Balance in Natural Soil

STEPHEN WILHELM—*Department of Plant Pathology, University of California, Berkeley.*

The task of analyzing the concept of biological balance in natural soil, which I accepted without hesitation months previous to the conference, turned out to be more difficult than was expected. Nearly all of the speakers touched upon the idea of balance in one way or another. Dr. Boswell in his opening remarks referred to the microbiological balance beneath our feet, Dr. Garrett to changes in balance, others to balanced parasites, balance between soil microflora and mushroom mycelium, finely balanced equilibria, upsets in balance, ionic balance, fungicidal balance, and finally, balanced climax state. Heraclitus of Ephesus seemed to have expressed the difficulty embodied in the concept of balance in his remark of some 2500 years ago, which translated is something like "upon those who step into the same river, different and ever different waters flow down." Nature to Heraclitus seemed to have the quality of continuous change, and yet this change was bounded by the banks of the river which determined the course and provided a measure of permanence. This idea of permanence in a broad sense is balance. We observe that long association between organisms in the "same" environment effects a kind of permanence or balance among them which in its simplest concept might be called an equilibrium between "needs" of the organisms and their "numbers." The soil is much like the river. To paraphrase Heraclitus, upon those who investigate the same soil, different and ever different horizons come to view. Soil, as the river, is ever changing, and this change is also bounded by banks, which we will elucidate within certain broadly applicable biological principles. These principles are essentially biological laws that limit.

The word "balance" has come to us as part of a language, and thus we tend to assume that it must accord with a class of certain naturally occurring phenomena. In the final analysis, it may be difficult to know always whether the supposed phenomena are tangible as facts or whether they are mostly conceptual, and the biologist must frequently select among many facts to identify a concept or a result he wishes to favor. Ehrlich and Holm (1962), Stanford University biologists, recently pointed out obvious incongruities in meanings and low information contents of many time-honored terms used in the language of population biology. Terms such as competition, niche, community, climax, species, were all exposed. No doubt "balance" should have been included. The omission however, may suggest that the term is clearly meaningful in biology; or perhaps Ehrlich and Holm simply intuitively avoided the difficulty. The problems of analysis clearly are numerous.

First, the information content of the phrase "balance in nature" is dubious unless certain reference points are set up which allow us to say, "in balance with respect to" this or that. This has its parallel in chemistry, where the principle of equilibrium is clarified only if the reactions are defined. Likewise, the concept of saturation is meaningful only within a framework of precisely stated conditions of temperature and pressure. Second, there is a lot said about "natural"—natural soil, natural foods, natural processes, and so on; and vastly different interpretations derive from this word. Natural to some means nature that man hasn't occupied, but my Weltanschauung is that all of nature, that is, the creation about us, is for man, so I take "natural soil" to mean the soil supporting mankind and "balance" to include, but not specifically to be, the impact of its cultivation on the resident microorganisms, including those that cause diseases. This makes the concept of balance in nature essentially anthropocentric, but I shall proceed in this vein, even at the risk of being considered teleological.

FACTORS THAT LIMIT PRODUCE BALANCE.—In the broad sense, balance among soil organisms implies some limitation on the biotic potential of all organisms of the microbial community so that no single organism or species is in a position to increase at its maximum potential rate, nor can it completely interfere with the independence of the other organisms. Upsets in nature do occur, in which one organism increases vastly out of proportion to others, threatening frequently the extinction of certain species. These are the epidemics. They correspond to disorder, or to any system to which energy is applied or made available, without sufficient limitations for restraining the effects. A steam engine, to illustrate the idea, moves because energy from expanding steam is turned into useful work by the orderly movement of the piston within the cylinder. The direction of movement of the piston is limited by the rigidity and shape of the cylinder. The piston does not create order among the randomly moving steam molecules; it merely selects among the complete disorder within the cylinder those molecules moving in a certain direction, and those only give up their energies to drive the engine. Without, however, the limitation imposed by the cylinder wall, selection for "useful" steam molecules would be impossible and disorder or chaos the only result. Limitation in the biological sense also acts to prevent disorder or chaos, the epidemics; at the same time it allows for a measure of directed "usefulness" to be accomplished, such as some successful agriculture in the presence of soil-borne pathogens. Also, it invites exploitation by man in the area of biological control of soil-borne pathogens. The problem of biological control resolves itself essentially into (1) understanding of the factors that limit, and (2) applying the information to solve problems. In this discussion of balance, the phenomena of direct predation, where for instance a nematode or mite may eat a fungus or bacterial colony, and host-parasite relations, where one microorganism parasitizes another, are not included. These subjects have been covered in the discussions of Kevan, and Boosalis and Mankau, and the principle of density dependency as derived by Nicholson (1933) from parasite-host and predator-prey interactions among certain insects and other animals probably has a general application to soil-borne organisms as well. Incidentally, Nicholson's classical treatise on balance, to which Dr. Kenneth F. Baker called my attention, should be better known by plant pathologists.

Balance has also been used to refer to an estimation of the differences in value between the increase of one or a group of organisms and the decrease of another, where this increase and decrease are always observed in conjunction with one another. This is also a form of limitation. Thus, the early work of Millard and Taylor (1927) on the control of potato scab demonstrated a competitive antagonism between the parasitic actinomycete *Streptomyces scabies*, and a saprophyte, *S. praecox*. High populations of *S. praecox* in the previously sterilized soil suppressed the growth of *S. scabies*, often to the point of controlling the disease, and vice versa, high populations of *S. scabies* apparently exerted an inhibitory effect upon *S. praecox*. Population densities could perhaps have been achieved where the limiting effects of these two interacting species would cancel one another and their numbers would stabilize about a narrow mean. This is essentially the idea of stationary balance. In natural soils always many more than two organisms or two groups of organisms interact, and the greater the number of interacting factors, the more stationary the balance achieved when food supply or any other factor in the environment becomes unfavorable. Throughout the conference it was stressed that organisms concerned in soil processes do not occur in pure culture, but usually bring about their reactions in associations, one organism often rapidly utilizing the products of another. Waksman (1945) earlier also emphasized this point.

The bacterial balance index described by Hildebrand and West (1941) in connection with studies on the etiology of the black-root-rot disease of strawberry also illustrated the idea that factors which limit microbial growth bring about balance. In the rhizosphere of diseased strawberries, Gram-negative bacteria nutritionally deficient for primarily thiamin and biotin (group 3) predominated as determined numerically, and in the rhizosphere of healthy plants Gram-negative bacteria requiring unidentified substances present in yeast or soil extract or both predominated (groups 5, 7, 9). By assigning a negative value to the percentage occurrence of types comprising group 3, considered to be unfavorable to the strawberry, and a positive value to the percentage occurrence of the normal or favorable types (groups 5, 7, 9) the bacterial-balance index was calculated. The closer the value approached 0, the greater the tendency for the two fluctuating groups of organisms to achieve stationary balance, i.e. equalization in rates of multiplication or of survival. Balance at other values expressed numerical relations of the two interacting groups of organisms stabilized about rather steady densities. This idea embodied important prediction value as to the occurrence and severity of the root-rot disease and illustrated as well that balance among soil microorganisms is effected by limitation of the potential impact of one species or group on the community of microorganisms by the residents of the community itself. Though the effects measured in the above example were in relation to fluctuations in numbers of two contrasting groups of soil-borne bacteria, they suggest that the total numbers of all residents of the soil environment are regulated similarly, and that factors which limit multiplication ultimately effect rather stationary densities in populations.

BIOLOGICAL COMPLEXITY ASSURES BALANCE.—(In the multitude of counsellors purposes are established. Proverbs 15:22.)

Usually laws that affect societies and crowds are not derivable directly from laws of physics and chemistry. The organizational level of even the cell, not to mention the multicellular individual for instance, or populations, manifests properties not derivable from mechanics. The idea of balance, however, has much in common, whether the microbial level or the sociological or political level, is considered. Power, for instance, or a substrate, held by one individual tempts upsets, but held by many, insures balance. The laws that effect balance are laws that limit, whether power or competition for a substrate is involved, though the idea of limiting is probably implied in all law. There are two general laws in biology that limit, one the Mendelian laws of inheritance which interpret the precise mechanism characteristic of sexually reproducing organisms for the distribution of genic material among offspring, and by and large set the limits for distinguishing species. The other is the thermodynamic principle that every successive colonization of a substratum by nongreen organisms results in a decrease in the total available or free energy of the system. Life processes among the saprophytic organisms involve the release of energy from chemical bonds or its transference from a higher to a lower state. Rarely, or probably never, does a single species in the soil release all of the free energy available in a substrate. The general experience of the microbiologist is that only some of the numerous chemical compounds present in natural substrates such as plant-tissue debris are utilized by any one species. The primary colonizer of a substrate, cellulose fiber for instance, may release substances to the advantage of a different species, one for instance, that cannot split the glucoside linkage of cellulose, but can utilize glucose, and in return, the primary colonizer may benefit from the supply of a highly complex factor such as a vitamin. The degradation reactions in soil are brought about by associations of organisms, and always, accomplishments of microorganisms in associations are greater than summations of the actions of individual components, or as Waksman and Hutchings (1937) stated, the total soil population will bring about processes which are very distinct from those resulting from the activities of single forms in pure culture. Waksman and Hutchings in studies on the decomposition of plant remains showed, for instance, that the presence of one organism may modify considerably the food preference of another. Thus in pure culture, *Trichoderma*, which is a vigorous cellulose decomposer, did not attack the cellulose of alfalfa, but decomposed the proteins in preference and also somewhat the hemicelluloses; yet in combination with noncellulose-decomposing organisms such as *Rhizopus, Cunninghamella,* and *Pseudomonas fluorescens, Trichoderma* readily attacked cellulose. This was interpreted as an effect of competition between *Trichoderma* and the associated organisms for protein, with the result that *Trichoderma*, which could utilize cellulose, was forced to do so by those which could not. Thus, this association of organisms, whatever the true nature, effected a greater change in substrate degradation than was possible by the organisms acting individually. Natural soil populations of unknown complexity brought about a still greater change in the extent of decomposition.

Instances of favorable effects of associations and strict symbioses among resident soil organisms are common and explain why organisms extremely fastidious in their nutritional requirements are numerous in the soil and thrive, though obviously not independently very fit. Thus, Lochhead and Thexton (1947) showed that essentially the same but only not as many heterotrophic types of bacteria, some with complex nutritional deficiencies occurred in the soil as in the rhizosphere, and L. F. Hewitt (1953) has pointed out that on the ordinary basis of natural selection and survival of the fittest, organisms fastidious in nutrient requirements should be overgrown and eliminated from nature. In the evolution sense, there is always pictured the mixture of competing mutants in the struggle for survival. Those mutants (still citing Hewitt) which produce the most offspring and are least fastidious in their nutrient requirements would surely overgrow the less well adapted or less prolific mutants and in time would predominate. Thus, if the Darwin idea were applicable to relations among soil microorganisms, there should have been a gradual evolution among soil microorganisms toward robust, hearty types, omnivorous in enzyme synthesis, the products of countless generations of natural selection. Any deficiency-type mutants now appearing should be less able to survive than the robust parent strains and thus should be eliminated. This is, however, not the present situation, and instead of the relatively few robust, hearty organisms that we would expect to dominate the soils if natural selection in the Darwin sense were operative, we have in soils a great diversity of types, and delicate, nutritionally fastidious strains are of common occurrence (Lochhead and Burton, 1956). Papacostos and Gate (1928), considerably earlier, also pointed out the nonacceptability of the Darwin concept as applied to interactions of microorganisms in general, and suggested its complete abandonment.

Organic degradation processes in soil are determined by the mutual interactions of mixed populations of insured complexity because neither are robust types selected nor are deficient types eliminated. Natural selection may set the lower limit of vitality and thus maintain among the microorganisms of the soil minimum standards of healthfulness and vigor, but minimum standards are difficult to define because associative or cooperative effects obviate the handicaps of many deficiencies. Agriculture, especially monoculture, with the ever-present threat of soil-borne pathogens, would probably not be possible without the great complexity of types of organisms in the soil. The greater the complexity of types of organisms the greater the tendency towards stationary balance, which is another way of saying the less likely is it that any one organism, a pathogen for instance, is in a position to multiply unrestrained or out of balance with the others. Successful agriculture in the presence of plant pathogens depends upon the biological complexity of the soil. It is the primary bulwark against the ravages of the few soil-borne pathogens that would destroy our crops. Man by growing crops always simplifies the natural environment, as Baker (1962) pointed out, and thus invites upsets in balance. The growing of crops in large measure has been responsible for the abnormal variations in the numbers of certain microorganisms that have resulted in epidemics. The typical picture in agriculture, especially in California, has been that farms are becoming larger and more specialized along the lines of specific crops. Cotton, tomatoes, asparagus, melons, beans, strawberries, are grown over larger and larger areas and thus present the organisms that can take advantage of this food with great opportunities for increasing. Plant pathologists were early to point out the hazards of the simple ecological system that results when crops are grown over vast areas. Ward (1882), at the postmortem of the coffee industry in Ceylon, elucidated the principle that man in single-crop agriculture, by providing immense quantities of suitable food, unconsciously offers the conditions favorable for the increase of parasites. A few years later, Grimaldi (1897), writing on the serious Italian broomrape (*Orobanche crenata*) and *Sclerotium* diseases of *Vicia faba*, stated that the more a crop is extended and the more intensive its cultivation becomes, so much more do the parasitic illnesses increase. So in agriculture we wish to maintain the steady state called "balance in nature" which is affected competitively by the interactions of many factors of the environment—in the soil by interactions of the complex populations—but at the same time, we offer great quantities of foods to certain organisms and thus invite those upsets of the steady state that occur in pronounced disease outbreaks.

The ultimate stationary balance in a system of non-photosynthetic organisms committed in existence to reducing organic substrates would be evident by the production of the various resting bodies—chlamydospores, sclerotia, and other dormant spores, or by quiescence or dormancy of one form or another. This stationary state is of course not reached by the entire diverse population of organisms at one and the same time or level of free energy of the substrate; organisms differ with respect to conditions favoring formation of resting structures, and here also associations of organisms may act for mutual or bilateral benefit. Kaiser (1963), for instance, studying factors involved in the formation of microsclerotia by *Verticillium albo-atrum* Reinke and Berth., showed that the vitamin biotin is essential. Many isolates of *Verticillium* synthesize sufficient biotin for vegetative growth and for limited microsclerotial production, but full microsclerotial development is achieved in the presence of supplemental biotin. This may be supplied by the substrate, such as tomato stem tissue, or by associated organisms, such as any number of common laboratory contaminants.

STUDIES WITH VERTICILLIUM.—My own studies on the growth of *Verticillium albo-atrum* (the microsclerotial form) in natural soils illustrated the principle that the greater the biological complexity of the soil the more stationary the balance. Studies centered around the ability of *Verticillium* to grow in soils dif-

fering in biological complexity as a result of differential fumigation treatments (Figs. 1 and 2). Results have been published thus far only in abstract (Wilhelm, 1955).

Growth of *Verticillium* was measured in terms of the ability of the fungus to colonize tomato trap pieces placed in three concentric circles, 1, 2, and 3 cm, respectively, from a point seeded with washed conidia of the fungus. This point was marked by a sterilized glass needle. Two days after seeding, the glass marker was removed and a sterilized piece of tomato stem tissue put into its place. The soils under experiment were maintained in a shaded place out of doors during winter and early spring months in Berkeley that were comparatively cool. Air temperatures fluctuated commonly from 35° to 75°F, the range favorable for the growth of *Verticillium*. At 1- to 2-week intervals for 8 weeks the tomato trap pieces placed in concentric rings around the point seeded with conidia, were examined for the presence of microsclerotia characteristic of the fungus, and soil between the trap pieces was assayed for *Verticillium* by a tomato-infection technique. Roots of 5 tomato seedlings were dipped into a suspension made of the test soil. The percentage infected as determined by laboratory culture indicated the presence and relative density of the fungus (Fig. 2).

In three different natural soils used for this experiment, *Verticillium* made no evident growth as determined by colonization of the tomato stem pieces and by assaying the soil between the traps. After the third week *Verticillium* could not be detected even at the

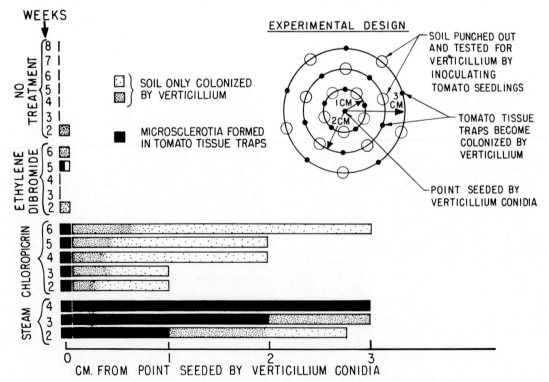

Fig. 1. Independent saprophytic growth of *Verticillium albo-atrum* in fumigated and nonfumigated soils during outdoor winter conditions in Berkeley. No apparent independent saprophytic growth was made in natural soil, nor was the fungus recovered at the point of seeding after 3 weeks. For details see text.

Fig. 2. The tomato seedling test used for detection and quantitative estimation for *Verticillium albo-atrum* from soil samples taken from between the tomato trap pieces in Fig. 1. The number of infected tomato plants per 6-in pot of soil ranges from 0 to 5 as determined by symptom expression and laboratory culture. Indices for pots A, B, C, were 1, 3, 5, respectively. Stippling in Fig. 1, is light, medium, and heavy corresponding to the indices.

point of seeding. It was detected at the second week, not in the tomato stem tissue, but by assaying the soil.

If the soils were steamed to sterilize them, and *Verticillium* added, growth was luxurious, and *Verticillium* colonized the trap pieces readily as evidenced by the production of microsclerotia. All competition was of course removed by the treatment, so biological complexity was reduced to 0. Growth of *Verticillium* was essentially unlimited. This type of experience has been reported by many investigators. An anonymous investigator (1933), for instance, showed that *Helminthosporium avenae* produced no growth whatsoever in nonsterilized soil, but grew luxuriantly in sterilized soil. He interpreted the results to mean that *Helminthosporium* was unable to compete with the normal saprophytic flora of the soil.

If the soils in the *Verticillium* study were first fumigated with chloropicrin (0.5 ml per gal, equivalent to at least 480 lb per acre) and then after airing, seeded with *Verticillium*, limited growth occurred. By the end of 6 weeks, soil 3 cm from the point of seeding was colonized as determined by assaying the soil. In no instance, except at the point of seeding, however, were the tomato trap pieces colonized. Chloropicrin at the rate used was lethal to numerous but not to all of the soil-borne organisms, and although detailed studies were not made on the identity of the survivors, there is no question that chloropicrin effected a reduction in complexity of the biology of the soil. Growth of *Verticillium* was limited but not to the same extent that it was in the untreated natural soil. Here antagonistic effects were apparent, because the main colonizers of the tomato stem tissues as determined by fruiting bodies developing, were *Chaetomium* and *Melanospora* spp., *Trichoderma*, and *Stachybotrys*. In a *Trichoderma-Verticillium* system set up as a separate study, there were no indications of antagonism. *Verticillium* readily invaded tomato stem tissues colonized previously by *Trichoderma* and *Trichoderma* invaded tissues colonized by *Verticillium*, but in a *Chaetomium-Verticillium* system, *Verticillium* did not invade tissues previously

colonized by *Chaetomium*. Here competition was manifest as antagonism.

Organisms alter the chemical and physical nature of their environments, and whereas this on the one hand may favor certain dependent organisms, on the other, it may determine what other species may occur in the same environment. Though the increase of one organism in a substrate causes it generally to become progressively less suitable for itself, the environment probably first becomes unsuited to many other kinds of organisms. Parmeter and Hood (1961) for instance, showed that filtrates of many fungi may serve as bases for media selective in isolating the kind of fungus producing the filtrate. In other words, fungus filtrates were often more antagonistic to other organisms than to the kind of fungus producing the filtrates. Competition manifest as antagonism is certainly an important aspect of balance, and this subject has been covered thoroughly in previous papers by Clark and Jackson.

If soils first fumigated with ethylene dibromide (0.25 ml per gal, equivalent approximately to 20 gal per acre) and then aired, were inoculated with *Verticillium*, extremely limited growth occurred. After 5-6 weeks *Verticillium* could be detected only at the point of seeding, and in no instance had it grown through the soil even to the first ring of tomato trap pieces only 1 cm away. Ethylene dibromide, which is primarily a nematocide, destroys the soil biology less than does a material such as chloropicrin, and competition or resistance to establishment of *Verticillium* was more intense. This simple experiment illustrated not only the principle that the more complex the biology of the soil is in terms both of numbers and kinds of organisms the more stationary the balance, but also that to upset an existing biological balance in a natural soil suitable for agriculture, rather drastic measures are required.

ADAPTABILITY OF SOIL MICROORGANISMS.—Biological complexity of the soil assures associative, competitive, and antagonistic relations which limit population explosions and thus bring about balance. The more numerous the kinds of organisms, and the greater their numbers, or perhaps the shorter their generation time, the more stationary the balance. The more stationary the balance, the smaller the effect on the community of adding or subtracting one or a few kinds. Physiological or genetic diversity of microorganisms, even of nutritionally deficient types, allows them to range over many environments with varying degrees of success. Soils the world over, at least throughout the temperate zone, though infinitely complex as biological systems, often vastly different according to physical classification schemes, and providing a complexity of substrates, nonetheless are inhabited by many of the same kinds of organisms. It is impossible to say that this or that precisely described niche in the soil is the precise habitat of this or that precisely adapted organism. I realize that some microbiologists may disagree with this. It has become fashionable as Ehrlich and Holm (1962) stated, to regard modern evolutionary theory as not just the best but the "only" possible explanation for observed patterns in nature. Fisher (1930), for instance, in his book

The Genetical Theory of Natural Selection stresses the hand-to-glove idea of adaptation of organisms to their environments. An organism, he states "is regarded as adapted to a particular situation, or to the totality of situations which constitutes its environment, only in so far as we can imagine an assemblage of slightly different situations, or environments, to which the animal would on the whole be less well adapted; and equally, only in so far as we can imagine an assemblage of slightly different organic forms, which would be less well adapted to that environment." Stanier (1953) has stated that hundreds or even thousands of microenvironments lie concealed from the gross ecological eye in any gram of soil. Precise adjustment of the properties of organisms to those of their environments, particularly in the sense of Fisher (1930), does not exist (Mac-Lagan, 1932; Nicholson, 1933), nor does any one set of conditions, nor any one single niche provide the optimum for all of the physiological processes of any one soil microorganism. There may be exceptions to this among highly specialized obligate endoparasites, such as *Olpidium* spp., but even this is doubtful. Among soil-borne microorganisms a few examples may suffice to illustrate the fact that soil-borne organisms range over many environments, inhabiting them with varying degrees of success, and without precise adaptation to any one. *Macrophomina phaseoli* (Maubl.) Ashby is a rather omnivorous root parasite, pathogenic to many plants under rather high soil temperatures (75°-90°F), and we have associated this organism typically with this rather specialized environment. Using a sand-culture technique (Wilhelm, 1956), it was possible to demonstrate this fungus readily and frequently in the roots of various weeds growing in the cool soil environment of coastal California, where the fungus is not pathogenic. Who is to say that *Macrophomina* is adapted to the environment of either a warm or a cool soil? It ranges over both. Nor can anyone predict that a certain habitat will develop a certain type of species to the exclusion of others. A great diversity of microorganisms lives together in the soil environment which cannot be so very diverse, and occupy habitats more on the basis of chance or proximity, than of adaptation. The diverse physiological ensemble of the individual species, even of nutritionally deficient types, allows them to increase or flourish with varying success over a wide range of environments, not so much because of adaptation to environment, as to increase in spite of environment.

Similarly, *Verticillium albo-atrum* occurs widespread throughout California soils and elsewhere, persisting in types ranging from desert sands to clay loams and peats. The pH range of these soils is fully as great as 4.0 to 8.5 (Wilhelm, 1950).

The life of the legume-nodule bacteria as shown in the work of Nutman (1959) also illustrates the range of diverse microhabitats parasitic microorganisms may occupy. Little is known about habitats the nodule bacteria occupies during saprogenesis in the soil, but increase in this phase is not improbable. The rhizosphere and rhizoplane, particularly but not exclusively of host legume species, provide a habitat favorable for increase. Host legume root hairs provide another habitat, and probably specific sites on the root-hair surface such as pores, another. Subsequent to infection, the infection thread, the cortical cell, the nodule tissue, including the intercellular spaces, and finally the disintegrated host tissue all are occupied by the bacteria. No one of the numerous microhabitats providing tenancy for the parasite during its life cycle provides either the optimum for or satisfies all of its physiological processes. The abundant physiological ensemble of the organism functioning as an integrated whole, where genic expression is modulated by gene interaction itself and by the physical, chemical, and biological environment, precludes in general narrow optima for phenotypic expression of any characteristic. If, as Baker (1940) discussed in his abundant teaching materials, a system could be established in which any single factor were operative, and all others held constant, a fairly steep curve, resembling a normal frequency distribution, might result. Under natural conditions, however, factors never act singly, and curves representing microbial growth or other measurable activity generally are broad at the apex with rather short "tails" (the German helmet type). Peterson (1937) derived these same curves from considerations where many factors interact to bring about a result. Though his subject was the law of diminishing returns in economics, the principles developed have immediate application to biological systems.

Biological complexity of soils in terms of numbers and kinds of organisms has its roots in the genetical complexity of the individual species, which allows many to range over environments differing markedly from one another. The genetical code does set limits, but not those corresponding to requirements of a specific niche. Interactions of the many genic factors making up the life code of a soil-borne organism endows it with a "buffering capacity" allowing for increase or survival often in spite of the unfavorable environment. For instance, about as soon as Georgopoulos (1962) showed the genetic nature of "acquired" tolerance of *Fusarium solani* f. *cucurbitae* Snyd. and Hans. to tetra- and penta-chloronitrobenzenes, genes at three different loci were shown to be equally and independently operative in effecting tolerance. (The third gene was discovered since publication of this work.) Why three genes when one could do it? There is a lot of truth in the suggestion that microorganisms are "over-endowed" with genetic material, and thus possess greater potential for adaptation and variability than can be accounted for on the basis of mutation and natural selection for advantage. Much of the work on screening of chemicals for fungicidal activity and on the so-called adaptive enzymes would bear this out. Genetic complexity assures the biological complexity which assures the interactions upon which balance in natural soils depends. Upon this in turn, depends agriculture as long as root pathogens may be part of the soil microflora.

SOIL ENRICHMENT AND MICROBIAL BALANCE.—Thus far we have considered balance largely in the stationary sense. The normally highly buffered capacity of the soil, as Baker (1962) put it—which is another way of expressing biological complexity oscillating numerically about a rather stationary mean—generally obviates ready disease control through biological means. A rather drastic initial shock more detrimental to the pathogen or pathogens present than to saprophytes, must first be applied to the soil environment. It is the task of biological control to manipulate soil environment and nutrition in such a way that the organisms which comprise the new balance are such as to prevent inroads by pathogens.

Add a source of energy to the soil, grow a crop in it, add an amendment or any source of food, even fumigate the soil, which kills large masses of organisms, and a great deal of microbial activity follows, and balance may shift in one direction or another (you may follow this only in terms of what you are measuring) until ultimately a new balance is established. Thus, Hildebrand and West (1941) showed that covercrops, Katznelson and Richardson (1948) that various organic amendments could markedly effect the severity of the black root rot of strawberry. In the Hildebrand and West experiments, rotations with soybeans for instance, caused a marked increase in the Gram-negative heterotrophic bacteria of groups 5, 7, and 9, and a corresponding decrease in those composing group 3. This shift in balance coincided with or effected control of the disease. Amendments such as bloodmeal and acetic acid also greatly reduced the incidence of the disease, apart from directly affecting the bacterial-balance index. Oat straw greatly increased the severity of the disease.

Shifts in microbial balance that result from growing crops, from crop residues, rotations, amendments, soil fumigation, are of great importance to us as plant pathologists, working pretty largely now with only a limited understanding of all that goes on. They correspond to the enrichment techniques developed first by Beijerinck for the isolation of specific microorganisms from soil (Stockhausen, 1907) and indicate strong possibilities that effective mechanisms for biological control of plant root diseases beyond that accomplished in the normal course of events, are well within our grasp. A few successes in this area are worth citing.

The root-rot disease of cotton caused by *Phymatotrichum omnivorum,* adapted to desert soils—low in moisture, low in nutrients, and in balance in its natural habitat with the rather meager or sporadic biological activity possible under dry conditions—is controlled by pronounced changes in the soil environment which upset this balance. Streets (1938 and personal communication) has recommended the following procedures for Arizona cotton growers. In November, the cotton crop residue together with 200 lb per acre of a commercial fertilizer supplying nitrogen and phosphorus are disked into the soil and the winter-growing Papago pea planted. This pea grows 3 to 4 ft in height. It, together with 200 lb per acre of ammonium sulfate, is plowed into the soil in April, to provide an abundant organic substrate for active saprophytic colonization during the period of adequate soil moisture. Cotton is planted early in May. *Phymatotrichum* may not always be eliminated by this procedure but it is effectively controlled.

Similarly, Snyder, Schroth, and Christou (1959) have shown that bean root rot caused by *Fusarium solani* (Mart.) Appl. & Wr. f. *phaseoli* (Burk.) Snyd. & Hans. can be controlled by applying mature dry barley straw or some other amendments rich in cellulose to infested soil. Low soluble-nitrogen levels resulting from microorganism populations attacking the straw prevent *Fusarium* chlamydospore germination, and thus control infection. The actual propagule density of *Fusarium* in the soil is essentially unaffected by the amendment. With a legume crop, low soluble-nitrogen levels are not limiting, but nonlegumes may suffer from deficiencies brought on by microorganisms stimulated to grow by large amounts of carbohydrate-type materials added to soil. This is why the growing of sorghum and sorghum-root residue have been notoriously injurious to other crops (Conrad, 1938).

The control of *Pratylenchus* populations in soil and around roots of other plants by cultivation of *Tagetes* spp. (*T. patula* and *T. erecta*) (Oostenbrink and S'Jacob, 1957) and control of rootknot nematode by *Crotalaria spectabilis* (McBeth and Taylor, 1944) represent direct action by growing plants, but the effects on microbial populations may be great, causing marked shifts in balance because food supplies in the form of nematode-induced gall tissue or injured roots no longer are available to injurious saprophytes which multiply in the rhizosphere of injured roots.

Where a specific chemical or a material is used to control a soil-borne pathogen, sufficient mixture must be applied to eliminate as much of the total pathogen population as possible, because the simplified biological balance resulting after fumigation may allow for growth of any inoculum not killed or of any introduced subsequent to the treatment. Yet excess of chemicals must be avoided, because the greater the dosage of chemical the fewer the number and kinds of organisms that survive to achieve the new balance. Essentially, the greater the dosage of fumigant, the greater the reinvasion hazard (Wilhelm, 1963). Thus, in the control of a soil-borne pathogen by chemicals, biological aspects are extremely important. The mode of action of carbon disulfide on *Armillaria mellea* for instance, is still uncertain because of shifts in populations of bacteria and of *Trichoderma* (Bliss, 1951; Lawyer, 1954) which attend fumigation.

BALANCE IN THE RHIZOSPHERE.—In the rhizosphere and at root surfaces, organic substrates are more continuously available than in the soil proper, and numbers of organisms in the rhizosphere exceed those in the soil often manyfold. Though the density of any one organism is independent of the absolute quantity of organic substrate—density being a function of the interactions of the organisms themselves—greater supplies of foods offer a greater variety of organisms opportunities for growth. Chlamydospores, for instance, of *Fusarium solani* f. *phaseoli* in nature germinate in the rhizosphere of bean and other plants (Schroth and Snyder, 1961), whereas germination in the soil proper is not known to occur. Specific root secretions of course, may stimulate germination of certain resting structures or seeds or organisms which in soil lie quiescent for years. Thus, balance in the rhizosphere would appear to be less stable than in the soil proper because energy sources for microorganisms are not only more abundant, but are often of a specific nature.

SUMMARY.—At one time it was thought that knowledge of the life cycle of a plant parasite was sufficient to ensure its speedy control, the objective sought in the cycle being the weakest link in the chain of biological events. Pathologists have now realized that a greater breadth of outlook is required which embraces the entire dynamics of microbial ecology, and that a knowledge of life cycles is but prerequisite to a proper understanding of the soil-borne fungus pathogen in relation to its surroundings. Surroundings of an organism in the soil are biologically complex, and the interactions of the organisms themselves produce balance. Interactions touched upon in this paper were limited to associative, competitive, and antagonistic effects, though predator-prey and parasite-host interactions are certainly part of the total picture. Microbial interactions in the soil act to limit the biotic impact of any one species or group of similar species upon the total community of organisms and thus establish rather steady numerical densities. Pathogens are often part of the community of microorganisms and to paraphrase Garrett (1955) it is no longer possible to doubt that the normal microflora of the soil exerts a natural biological control of most, if not all, soil-borne plant diseases.

The life of a soil-borne organism in nature is an expression of the reaction of the organism to the environment within its broad genetic framework. The rich genetic endowment of microorganisms allows for range over diverse environments, different factors in the environment such as temperature, kind of substrate, associated organisms, proximity to plant roots, calling forth different responses on the part of microorganisms. There are no precise niches to which microorganisms are precisely adapted, and no one environment supplies the ideal conditions for all of the physiological processes of organisms. Organisms even extremely fastidious in nutritional requirements are numerous in the soil and rhizosphere. Their existence depends upon complex compounds essential for growth supplied by associated organisms. During countless generations, selection for robust autotrophic organisms has not eliminated these "unfit" and "deficient" ones. This fact insures the biological complexity of the soil, which is the primary bulwark against inroads by root-destroying pathogens which threaten agriculture. With monoculture assuming ever greater importance in the agriculture of today, the trend may be toward a less diverse soil biology, which allows for specific explosive population increases of pathogens and their associates.

Organisms such as *Verticillium albo-atrum* unable to make independent saprophytic growth in natural soil or to colonize organic substrates competitively with vigorous saprophytes, may grow if the soil biology is first simplified by a drastic shock such as by steaming or fumigating with chloropicrin. Organisms first to invade a treated soil or an organic substrate often selec-tively determine the kinds of organisms which invade in succession.

Shifts in balance inevitably follow soil enrichment. Crop residues, root secretions, amendments, soil fumigation, are all forms of soil enrichment. Manipulation of balance after enrichment to eliminate and exclude pathogens is the primary problem of biological control of soil-borne root pathogens.

LITERATURE CITED

ANONYMOUS. 1933. Helminthosporium disease of oats. West of Scotland Agricultural College Res. Bull. 3, 74 p.

BAKER, K. F. 1940. Interrelationships of various plant disease-inducing agents. (Mimeo.)

BAKER, K. F. 1962. Principles of heat treatment of soil and planting material. J. Australian Inst. Agr. Sci. 28 (2): 118-126.

BLISS, D. E. 1951. The destruction of *Armillaria mellea* in citrus soils. Phytopathology 41: 665-683.

CONRAD, J. P. 1938. Distribution of sugars, root enclosed, in the soil following corn and sorghums and their effects on the succeeding wheat crop. J. Am. Soc. Agron. 30: 475-483.

EHRLICH, P. R., and R. W. HOLM. 1962. Patterns and populations. Basic problems of population biology transcend artificial disciplinary boundaries. Science 137: 652-657.

FISHER, R. A. 1930. The genetical theory of natural selection. The Clarendon Press, Oxford. 272 p.

GARRETT, S. D. 1955. A century of root-disease investigation. Ann. Appl. Biol. 42: 211-219.

GEORGOPOULOS, S. G. 1962. Genetic control of tolerance to tetra- and penta-chloronitrobenzene in *Hypomyces solani* f. *cucurbitae*. Nature (London) 196: 359-360.

GRIMALDI, C. 1897. I nemici delle Fave: Orobanche e mal dello Sclerozio. Libreria Internazionale, Alberto Reber gia Carlo Clausen, Palermo.

HEWITT, L. F. 1953. Influence of bacteriophage on bacterial variation and evolution. *In* Adaptation in microorganisms. Symp. Soc. Gen. Microbiol. 3: 273-293.

HILDEBRAND, A. A., and P. M. WEST. 1941. Strawberry root rot in relation to microbiological changes induced in root rot soil by the incorporation of certain cover crops. Can. J. Res., Sec. C, 19: 183-198.

KAISER, W. J., JR. 1963. Influence of nutrition and environment on the growth and sporulation of the plant pathogen, *Verticillium albo-atrum*. Ph.D. Thesis. U. C. Berkeley. 124 p.

KATZNELSON, H., and L. T. RICHARDSON. 1948. Rhizosphere studies and associated microbiological phenomena in relation to strawberry root rot. Sci. Agr. 28: 293-308.

LAWYER, L. O. 1954. Effects of partial sterilization of soil on microorganism populations. *In* Second Annual Pacific Coast Research Conference on control of soil fungi, Proceedings, Berkeley, California. (Processed.)

LOCHHEAD, A. G., and R. H. THEXTON. 1947. Qualitative studies of soil microorganisms VII. The 'rhizosphere effect' in relation to the amino acid nutrition of bacteria. Can. J. Res., Sec. C, 25: 20-26.

LOCHHEAD, A. G., and M. D. BURTON. 1956. Soil as a habitat of vitamin-requiring bacteria. Nature (London) 178: 144-145.

MacLAGAN, D. S. 1932. An ecological study of the "Lucerne flea" (*Smynthurus viridis* Linn.) I. Bull. Entomol. Res. 23: 101-149.

McBETH, C. W., and A. L. TAYLOR. 1944. Immune and resistant cover crops valuable in root-knot-infested peach orchards. Proc. Am. Soc. Hort. Sci. 45: 158-166.

MILLARD, W. A., and C. B. TAYLOR. 1927. Antagonism of micro-organisms as the controlling factor in the inhibition of scab by green manuring. Ann. Appl. Biol. 14: 202-216.

NICHOLSON, A. J. 1933. The balance of animal populations. J. Animal Ecol. 2: 132-178.

NUTMAN, P. S. 1959. Some observations on root-hair infection by nodule bacteria. J. Exptl. Biol. 10: 250-263.

OOSTENBRINK, K. K., and J. J. S'JACOB. 1957. Tagetes als Feindpflanzen von *Pratylenchus*-arten. Nematologica II, Suppl. (1957): 424-433.

PAPACOSTOS, G., and J. GATÉ. 1928. Les associations microbiennes, leurs applications thérapeutiques. Gaston Dous Paris. 438 p.

PARMETER, J. R., JR., and J. R. HOOD. 1961. The use of Fusarium culture filtrate media in the isolation of fusaria from soil. Phytopathology 51: 164-168.

PETERSON, G. M. 1937. Diminishing returns and planned economy. The Ronald Press Co., New York. 254 p.

SCHROTH, M. N., and W. C. SNYDER. 1961. Effect of host exudates on chlamydospore germination of the bean root rot fungus, *Fusarium solani* f. *phaseoli*. Phytopathology 51: 389-393.

SNYDER, W. C., M. N. SCHROTH, and T. CHRISTOU. 1959. Effect of plant residues on root rot of bean. Phytopathology 49: 755-756.

STANIER, R. Y. 1953. Adaptation, evolutionary and physiological or Darwinism among the microorganisms. *In* Adaptation in microorganisms, Symp. Soc. Gen. Microbiol. 3: 1-20.

STOCKHAUSEN, F. 1907. Ökologie, "Anhäufungen" nach Beijerinck. Institut für Gärungsgewerbe, Berlin. 278 p.

STREETS, R. B. 1938. Control of Phymatotrichum (cotton or Texas) root rot in Arizona. Arizona Agr. Ext. Circ. 103, 80 p.

WAKSMAN, S. A. 1945. Microbial antagonisms and antibiotic substances. The Commonwealth Fund, N. Y. 350 p.

WAKSMAN, SELMA A., and I. J. HUTCHINGS. 1937. Associative and antagonistic effects of microorganisms III. Associative and antagonistic relationships in the decomposition of plant residues. Soil Sci. 43: 77-92.

WARD, H. M. 1882. Researches on the life history of *Hemileia vastatrix* the fungus of the coffee-leaf disease. J. Linn. Soc. 19(121): 299-335.

WILHELM, S. 1950. Verticillium wilt in acid soils. Phytopathology 40: 776-777.

WILHELM, S. 1955. Some factors affecting substrate colonization and growth of the Verticillium wilt fungus in soil. (Abstr.) Phytopathology 45: 696.

WILHELM, S. 1956. A sand-culture technique for the isolation of fungi associated with roots. Phytopathology 46: 293-295.

WILHELM, S. 1963. The principles and practice of chemical fumigation of field soil. Oregon Hort. Soc. Ann. Rept. 54: 143-148.

► DISCUSSION OF STEPHEN WILHELM PAPER

H. Katznelson:

I wonder if a selecting system does necessarily simplify the biological complexity of the soil as you suggest. Changes in proportions of organisms may indeed occur but do these changes indicate simplification? In extreme cases this may be true but I question if it is generally true. For example, if we compare the proportions of certain groups of organisms in rhizosphere soil with those in root-free soil, we find a decrease in *Arthrobacter* in the rhizosphere, an increase in *Pseudomonas,* changes in *Bacillus, Micrococcus,* and *Agrobacterium,* but rarely is a group completely eliminated; therefore, selection has not necessarily changed the complexity. In fact, a selective system could even become more complex by drawing to it organisms which are normally dispersed.

S. Wilhelm:

What I had in mind was that a plant root or crop provides foods which certain organisms use. Organisms, often specific, increase in this enriched environment. Those actually parasitic, on invading the living substrate, comprise a simple biological community. The changes they induce in the substrate pave the way for secondary invaders which may comprise a more complex biological community, but still far simpler than that of the soil proper, at least in the early stages.

Outside of the root in the rhizosphere I picture microbial responses due to secretions, etc., as energizing first specific kinds of organisms, which often in the soil proper cannot grow successfully because interactions there are too complex, or foods too limiting. Some of this response in the rhizosphere may reflect activity triggered by specific chemical secretions. We know, for instance, that a fungus such as *Verticillium albo-atrum* may grow as a saprophyte in sterilized, or in certain fumigated soils, where biological complexity has been reduced over that of the natural soil, and also that it will grow in the rhizosphere (perhaps only rhizoplane) of hosts and nonhosts, or at least may be

far more readily isolated from this region than from the soil proper, which suggests that biological complexity is simpler in the rhizosphere. *Fusarium solani* f. *phaseoli* also, apparently, grows scarcely at all in the soil, but may grow in the rhizosphere of even nonhosts, suggesting a simpler biotic community. The generalization under question is not actually in my text, but was presented in an early outline of my subject. I found insufficient information to support it, but also no basis for rejecting it.

N. T. Flentje:

We have isolated a particular strain of *Rhizoctonia* from one soil type over a very wide area. The *Rhizoctonia* isolates are always identical in culture, yet when we study them in the laboratory we can obtain many variants either through basidiospores or single cells from the vegetative hyphae. These mechanisms for variation seem to occur in soil, but the variants apparently fail to survive. Will you comment on this apparent screening-out by the soil of these variants?

I would add the further comment that in view of the heterocaryon condition of field isolates of *Rhizoctonia* and other pathogenic fungi, our future studies on survival of these fungi in soil should be based on single-spore isolates. Such isolates, being homocaryon, may yield much more information on factors influencing survival than will studies with complex heterocaryons. These studies should be followed up by studies on synthesized heterocaryons.

S. Wilhelm:

If these variants obtained in the laboratory are introduced into the natural soil with suitable host material and they fail to become established, perhaps antagonisms are at work. If the variants are never encountered in the soil, though the genetic potential is present in the types encountered, perhaps basidiospores fail to form or fail after formation. Perhaps there is a parallel here with the conidial and mycelial cultural types of dual fungi such as *Verticillium albo-atrum*. In the laboratory, typically after radial vegetative growth on the agar slant slows down or ceases, the white mycelial type appears. While this type may be grown indefinitely as a distinct variant individual, is pathogenic, and is stable in culture, essentially never do we isolate it from nature. Growth of a fungus in the soil may be too sporadic, or not over a continuously long enough time, to allow the mutant nuclei, if that is what they are, to appear in the colony, or if they do appear, to become sufficiently abundant in the colony for us to detect them. If staling products act to invoke some of the variants, as the late Dr. H. N. Hansen believed in the case of dual fungi, perhaps these do not accumulate in the soil. The observation you cited is of great interest and the explanation would have far reaching fundamental significance.

M. Alexander:

I think, Dr. Wilhelm, you have thrown down a challenge to those of us who are interested in microbial ecology, in saying that deficient organisms are found in the soil. I don't believe it. I think that one would have a difficult time isolating from soil *Lactobacillus, Escherichia coli, Streptococcus,* or *Ruminococcus.* There are very many organisms, bacteria, actinomycetes, and fungi, which we cannot isolate from the soil. I do not think that the organisms which we find are really deficient. They may not be rapidly growing organisms, they may not be organisms of simple nutrition, but the soil ecosystem is such that it will favor those organisms at a specific time. Microorganisms of any deficient group will not grow in soil if they are not adapted to that particular ecosystem.

S. Wilhelm:

This is a matter of the meaning of the word deficient, and you certainly have to consider them heterotrophic for certain complex nutrients because they are dependent upon associations with other organisms if they are going to grow.

P. A. Ark:

What is a real meaning of interaction in soil microflora and what determines it? Will you elaborate on it?

S. Wilhelm:

Interaction typically has the meaning of mutual or reciprocal influence. The organisms, their activities, and potentialities as modulated by the environment, substrates, etc., determine it. Organisms alter the physical and chemical nature of a substrate they invade. The altered substrate may be favorable to certain organisms but unfavorable to others. In my own work, tomato stem tissue colonized by *Trichoderma* was readily invaded and also colonized by *Verticillium albo-atrum,* but when colonized by *Chaetomium* was not invaded by *Verticillium.* The actions of the organisms of a community themselves, as influenced by substrate and environment, determine the interactions, and the interactions of a community of organisms are not simply the sum of the interactions between the individual members.

Summary and Synthesis of Papers on Interactions Between the Soil, Microorganisms, and the Plant

A. W. DIMOCK—*Department of Plant Pathology, Cornell University, Ithaca, New York.*

To summarize adequately the excellent papers presented during the Friday sessions is at best a difficult task, perhaps a bit beyond my competence. I feel particularly hesitant since this summary cannot be argued or corrected in the presence of the Symposium participants. I shall try, however, to bring forward selected ideas which were of particular interest to me or which seemed to suggest profitable lines of inquiry.

The paper by Patrick and Toussoun, so ably presented by Dr. Patrick, focused attention on the fact that a sword has two edges, that crop residues which may indeed support and increase elements of the microflora antagonistic to plant pathogens, may under certain circumstances prove inimical to the health of the host plants, either by direct toxic action or by establishing conditions favorable for host invasion by parasites. The dramatic injury of the taproot of lettuce seedlings, whilst the lateral roots of the same seedlings showed no such evident injury, raised the question whether the apical tissues of the taproot are peculiarly susceptible to the "toxins" or whether the explanation is simply a reflection of time lapse, the laterals developing after dissipation of toxins. The latter view is suggested by the fact that "toxin" level is reduced in time, the former by the demonstrated fact that different plant tissues (root vs. stem) do differ in sensitivity to soil toxins.

Reference to the relation of anaerobiosis to "toxin" production brought out attention to the possible role of oxygen deficiency in root-disease phenomena. Might an anaerobic condition not only result in increased toxin production, but at the same time increase susceptibility of root tissue to the action of such toxins or even to invasion by "low-grade" pathogens? Be this as it may, the deleterious effects of toxic residues often may be avoided by improvement of drainage, good tillage, and field composting prior to planting.

Our attention was turned by Dr. Sadasivan to the role of nutrient elements, particularly the trace elements, in the development of soil microorganisms. Such elements as iron, manganese, and zinc, for example, may have important effects on production of pectolytic enzymes by wilt fusaria, and thus affect pathogenicity. These same elements likewise may directly influence the balance of the soil biophase and thus affect the disease potential. Of particular interest was evidence of dramatic effects on rhizosphere populations consequent upon foliage applications of mineral nutrients. Manganese, molybdenum, zinc, and boron all stimulated microflora, but the relative stimulation of specific components, e.g., actinomycetes, bacteria, and fungi, differed with the element. Might we find in this approach important functions of trace elements in plant development? Is it necessarily a simple matter of supplying an element essential to host metabolism? Or does the indirect effect, altered metabolism—increased root excretion—rhizosphere population increase or shift, deserve more prominent billing?

We were reminded by Dr. Ludwig that we have not yet reached the point at which we can depend solely on biological control of soil-borne pathogens, that an integrated approach, combining chemical control, biological control, and genetical control, remains our most certain defense. Although introduction of antagonists into soil has not proved generally satisfactory, certain chemical treatments, by virtue of selective action, have seemed to permit increase of antagonists and control of pathogens. But examples of the reverse, that is, increased activity of pathogens following treatment with selective fungicides, might also be cited.

Dr. Sewell's comments pointed up the fact that although much is known concerning effects of major physical factors on plant growth, the possible role of the soil microflora in explaining these effects has too often been ignored. We have learned, thanks to the Wisconsin soil-temperature tanks and their descendants, that some diseases flourish at high temperatures, some at low, yet in only few instances has the effect of temperature on the total soil microflora been considered.

In Dr. Sewell's discussions of soil moisture and soil tillage, the effect of these practices on O_2:CO_2 relations, and of these relations on the host and the soil microflora was again brought before us. It was suggested that CO_2 excess might best explain the reduction in the banana wilt *Fusarium* and in *Sclerotinia sclerotiorum* following flood fallowing, but a possible effect of oxygen depletion was not fully discussed.

Although soil treatment is usually aimed at suppression of a specific pest, Dr. Kreutzer pointed out that improvement in growth may depend not only on elimination of the pathogen but also upon many other consequences of alteration of the soil biology. The results may in some cases be actually an exacerbation of the disease for which control was intended, or a "trading" of that disease for another—that is, elimination of the intended pathogen while making possible reinfestation by another, possibly more serious, disease agent. Obviously the most effective treatment is one which, while effective against the intended pathogen, has minimal effect against other components of the soil biophase. The use of controlled-temperature aerated steam or of selective fungicides should offer promise in this direction.

The proposition that the more complex the soil biological system, the more stable the balance, was elaborated by Dr. Wilhelm. The ready reinfestation of "sterilized" soil, as discussed by Dr. Kreutzer, is an extreme example of the instability of a simple biological system. Upsets of the balance are brought about by most agricultural practices. Mineral nutrition, as we have seen, may cause complex shifts in the soil microflora. Tillage and changes in drainage affect the physical condition of the soil and, in turn, its biological balance. Excretions of a single root may well affect the biological balance in a localized area. Perhaps, as we learn more about the habits of our underground friends and foes, we may be able to shift the balance in the direction we desire and achieve effective biological control of important soil-borne plant pathogens.

► CONCLUDING COMMENTS BY PARTICIPANTS

G. H. Hepting:

In terminating this fascinating meeting, I cannot resist a couple of conclusions. Few here seem willing to admit that their pathogen, whether a fungus, virus, or bacterium, can grow happily through the soil, but has to encyst or form propagules and hibernate until fortune presents it with a host. Thus we must conclude that the old terra firma is a very uncongenial habitat for our pathogens unless they are asleep.

At this symposium we have learned a dizzying amount on the subject of soil microbiology, but not too much about biological control of pathogens. This is what we expected, however, since this meeting has been largely a matter of setting the stage for this new field. Progress in biology is slow, since one position often must be firmly established before the next can be intelligently tackled. Thus a crash-program approach, often successful in other fields, is unlikely to work in the field of soil microbiology, or any biological science for that matter.

N. A. Burges:

May I refer to the comment that higher-plant ecologists know more about competition than we do? At the Jubilee Meeting of the British Ecological Society, one of the speakers commented that higher-plant ecologists should look to the microbiologists, who really knew about competition and understood its mechanism. "The grass is always greener over the fence."

May I suggest we look to our entomological colleagues to help us in the handling of complex population problems? I believe we have much to learn from them.

Throughout the discussions we have, not unnaturally, kept referring to how little we know. This is very proper for our humility, but should not blind us to the successes already achieved.

R. R. Baker:

Although narrow definitions have faults, there is some value in standardizing terminology used in a discipline. This symposium has demonstrated wide divergence in opinion as to the use and meaning of many terms, some of which have been in common use for many years. I suggest that the Steering Committee of the next Symposium might consider this problem. Certainly if new terms are initiated in scientific papers or textbooks, they should be related to current terminology and, if possible, adequately defined according to standard experimental procedure.

J. L. Harley:

I would like to suggest that in any future meetings we might include a little more emphasis on fungal and microbial variation. It is perhaps a point that comes out of the present meeting, that we could do with expert advice on this subject.

S. D. Garrett:

I think this is an appropriate time for expressions of appreciation less formal than the resolutions passed. I think I can do this best by recalling what I heard Sir George Stapledon say in an address given in England many years ago. He said, "I am a scientist and my stock-in-trade is one in ideas." Our chief job as scientists is to produce and exchange ideas. This past week has given us an invaluable opportunity to exchange ideas, and I for one have enjoyed it tremendously.

E. J. Anderson:

The next symposium should include mathematicians to assist in setting some of the limits within which we should work in order to get data which can be integrated. We should look forward to a third symposium 10 years from now, and hope that this meeting will be held in Honolulu.

L. W. Boyle:

This meeting has been organized to allow development of perspectives; many of our crowded, modern meetings have squeezed this out. I am reminded of a remark once made by Robert Frost, "Confusion is the lack in the sense of shape or form. That is why at institutions for the treatment of confused people they put a pile of straws in front of them and teach them how to form little baskets." We have had quite a pile of straws laid before us to take home and weave into baskets.

J. Altman:

Many of us who participated by listening to the presentations have felt a need or desire for informal discussions on various aspects of the Symposium. Many of the techniques for study of particular problems were omitted, and perhaps informal discussion periods following the day's presentations would help to "clear the air" on some of the questions that arose in the minds of participants during the formal talks.

H. Katznelson:

First, I must add my compliments to those already expressed to the committee in charge of the arrangements for probably the best organized meeting I have attended. From the point of view of a soil and rhizosphere microbiologist concerned with interactions, ecology, and plant growth, I feel that the following areas need greater emphasis; these conclusions were supported by the statements of the many speakers at this meeting.

A. The chemical composition of root exudates should be studied by trained chemists. With apologies to the many who have done good work on root exudates, we now need the specialized skills of the organic and biochemist to identify the more specific substances liberated by roots, such as hatching factors, zoospore attractants, substances that overcome fungistasis or "attract" nematodes or mycorrhizal fungi. A knowledge of such substances will assist significantly in devising studies on biological control.

B. We need much more work on factors concerned with the establishment of desirable organisms, such as antagonists of plant pathogens in the root zone, as well as those concerned with the control and manipulation of the rhizosphere micropopulation. As this population is one of the major lines of defense of a root, anything that can be done to alter it to our advantage will constitute a major contribution to biological control. Some evidence that this can be done is available; we need much more!

C. Greater emphasis is needed on the role of soil and rhizosphere populations in supplying or competing with plants for minerals and nitrogen. The use of isotopes must be expanded in this kind of work. Since the nutrition of a plant affects its susceptibility to disease, the role and manipulation of the root population may be critical.

N. T. Flentje:

There is a wealth of talent in a number of minds on the whole range of problems discussed here. These scientists are, however, widely scattered over the earth and it seems necessary to go to 3 or 4 countries to see the 4 or 5 people who are most skilled in some given field. I wonder whether there's any way over the next 10 years that 4 or 5 such people may be able to spend 12 months together working in one laboratory. I think in many ways the modest cost of this would be offset by the advantages of getting those people together.

W. C. Schnathorst:

There appears to be a real need for pathologists to propose principles and laws. Many fundamentals in plant pathology are taken for granted and do not appear as formal principles. Philosophical experience shows that generalizations or laws established by induction, even when universally accepted as true, should be regarded only as probabilities. In other words, laws should not be regarded as immutable, as many workers tend to do. If this viewpoint were more generally held, I feel that more principles would be proposed and this would tend to accelerate the growth of the science.

In some of the formal papers and discussions in the conference, as well as in most of the literature dealing with mechanisms of action in biological systems, one

mechanism is usually proposed to account for a phenomenon. I believe that workers dealing with mechanisms should keep in mind that a phenomenon may have several causes or may result from the consecutive or simultaneous action of several mechanisms. I feel that we as investigators should look for *possible* mechanisms and should not consider that any *one* mechanism explains the situation. There appears to be no finality in science, and this attitude may help prevent perpetuation of dogma that tends to hamper the growth of science.

T. C. Vanterpool:

For the next meeting, some workers on soil microclimatology should be invited to help understand the microenvironment of the soil.

S. M. Alcorn:

Throughout the course of the Symposium the terms rhizosphere and rhizoplane have been used—frequently, seemingly, interchangeably. This is confusing, particularly when one speaker would relate his rhizosphere or rhizoplane effect to secondary or feeder roots, while another speaker would be referring to the effect on older primary roots.

W. C. Snyder:

As this symposium draws to a close I feel a deep satisfaction in the deliberations and their outcome. Certainly we have had among us this week many of the most qualified and highly motivated research people in the area of biological control of soil-borne plant pathogens in the world. Unfortunately some others who should have been here were unable to attend.

We have accomplished much and made excellent progress towards our objectives. This amply justifies the 5 years spent in organization of the symposium, and makes up for the disappointments and frequent discouragements along the way. I am glad the Symposium has come to a successful conclusion.

Most of all I wish to acknowledge the loyal, enthusiastic, and sustained efforts of my colleagues in the NAS-NRC Committee on Biological Control. Certainly without their support and effectiveness, along with that of the Committee on Local Arrangements, this symposium could not have been possible.

There have been several reviews of the symposium prior to the publication of these proceedings: N. T. Flentje (Nature 199: 327-329, 1963), H. Katznelson (World Rev. Pest Control 2 (2): 16-24, 1963), and W. C. Snyder (Science 141: 835-837, 1963). Nevertheless a few of the lasting attainments of the occasion deserve special comment.

The response and attention of over 300 participants have been exceptional for a meeting of this size and duration.

Many examples of proved, established instances of biological control of root diseases in various parts of the world have been brought to light. Among these have been discussed potato scab, take-all, and *Cercosporella* eyespot of wheat, *Sclerotium* stem rot of peanut, fomes white-root disease of rubber, *Phymatotrichum* root rot of cotton, and *Fusarium* root rot of bean.

It has been most encouraging to observe that a meeting organized broadly across many disciplines, as was this one, can be mutually stimulating to participants, and highly productive in ideas. This is particularly satisfying today, when most meetings are organized in depth in one discipline. Often, in examining the minutia of the cell, sight is lost of the organism itself.

Finally, and not of least importance, meeting face to face with colleagues from many parts of the world in an intensive week of professional activity has established a warm regard for the compatriots in a common endeavor. This can bring only lasting benefit to the profession and to the individual.

It is now quite clear that the biological control of root disease fungi is less a matter of direct attack on the pathogen by its own particular parasite than it is an indirect effect of biological elements of the soil operating through competition or antibiosis.

Ours is an extremely complex field, but it holds excitement and challenge for the scientist. I am optimistic about the future of biological control as a means of reducing or preventing losses from root diseases, and believe that the exchange of knowledge here will insure even greater progress at our next meeting in 1968 in Great Britain. I look forward to seeing all of you again at that time when we may evaluate together the advance of the ensuing 5 years.

► REPORT OF THE COMMITTEE ON FUTURE CONFERENCES

N. T. Flentje:

A representative group of participants of this symposium met on the evening of April 9, 1963, to consider the desirability and feasibility of future conferences on the biological control of root pathogens. Those attending were N. T. Flentje (chairman), K. F. Baker, R. R. Baker, N. A. Burges, F. E. Clark, S. D. Garrett, J. L. Harley, H. Katznelson, J. D. Menzies, P. S. Nutman, Z. A. Patrick, A. D. Rovira, T. S. Sadasivan, W. C. Snyder, R. D. Tinline, J. C. Walker, and G. A. Zentmyer.

There was complete agreement that this symposium met an important need by (1) bringing together the active workers in this field, and (2) moving across previous lines of division and including plant anatomists, plant physiologists, soil physicists, chemists, nematologists, and zoologists, together with the plant pathologists and soil microbiologists. The present Symposium has taken approximately 5 years to arrange since the first definite steps were made.

The control of soil-borne pathogens is obviously of tremendous importance in relation to the world's food supply. A working conference or symposium along similar lines to this first symposium should be planned for approximately 5 years from now, again drawing on all disciplines. We should look to the possibility of holding the next conference in Britain. Attendance, as in this instance, should be by invitation, to obtain the people who are actively working in these fields.

A Steering Committee of five people from Britain with an additional 10 or 12 people to act as an Advisory Council should be set up to begin the necessary planning.

RESOLUTIONS

Whereas, investigation of the behavior of soil-borne pathogens is an extremely difficult field which, because of the wide range of interactions involved, requires the close cooperation of plant anatomists, plant physiologists, soil physicists, soil chemists, biochemists, and geneticists, with soil microbiologists and plant pathologists, and it is only when such workers come together that problems can be properly defined and effective investigations planned,

Resolved, that the participants of this symposium have derived tremendous benefit from these meetings, both in exchange of ideas and information and in the stimulus for future work, and wish to express their indebtedness to the Agricultural Board of the National Academy of Sciences—National Research Council, to the National Science Foundation, the National Institutes of Health, and the Agricultural Research Service of the United States Department of Agriculture for making the Symposium possible.

Whereas, diseases caused by soil-borne pathogens continue to cause serious reductions in the world food supply,

Resolved, that the participants of this symposium recommend that a second symposium along similar lines should be held, possibly in Britain, in approximately 5 years. For this purpose, a Steering Committee of five people (S. D. Garrett, N. A. Burges, J. L. Harley, P. S. Nutman, and P. W. Brian) should be appointed together with 10 or 12 other people from different countries to serve as an Advisory Council.

Resolved, that the participants of this symposium express their admiration of the work of W. C. Snyder and K. F. Baker and the NAS-NRC Agricultural Board Committee on Biological Control of Soil-borne Plant Pathogens, and of the Local Arrangements Committee, for the outstanding efficiency and the warm and generous hospitality of the Symposium; they also thank the other organizations who contributed to the success of the Symposium, and in particular Tri-Cal Inc. for the social hour on Monday evening.

These resolutions were unanimously passed by the participants of the Symposium.

[EDITORS NOTE: At the Tenth International Botanical Congress in Edinburgh in August 1964 the plant pathologists proposed that a first International Phytopathological Congress be held in England during the summer of 1967. It was suggested there that this Congress be timed to coincide with the next Symposium on Biological Control. The Committee on the proposed Congress agreed that this Symposium as originally planned would constitute an important and distinct part of the program.]

◄

Participants

◄

Participants

Alcorn, Stanley M.
Department of Plant Pathology
University of Arizona
Tucson, Arizona

Alexander, J. V.
Department of Plant Pathology
University of California
Berkeley 4, California
Now: Department of Biology
      California State College at Long Beach
      Long Beach, California

Alexander, M.
Department of Agronomy
Cornell University
Ithaca, New York

Allen, M. W.
Department of Nematology
University of California
Davis, California

Allison, C. C.
Department of Botany and Plant Pathology
1735 Neil Ave.
Ohio State University
Columbus 10, Ohio

Altman, Jack
Department of Plant Pathology and Botany
Colorado State University
Fort Collins, Colorado

Altstatt, George E.
Bureau of Plant Pathology
California Department of Agriculture
1220 "N" Street
Sacramento 14, California

Anderson, E. J.
Pest Control Section
Pineapple Research Institute of Hawaii
P. O. Box 3166
Honolulu 2, Hawaii

Apt, Walter
United States Department of Agriculture
Utah State University
Logan, Utah

Ark, P. A.
Department of Plant Pathology
University of California
Berkeley 4, California

Ashworth, L. J., Jr.
Department of Plant Sciences
Texas A & M
College Station, Texas

Atkinson, T. G.
Canada Department of Agriculture
Research Station
Lethbridge, Alberta, Canada

Baines, R. C.
Department of Plant Nematology
University of California
Riverside, California

Baker, K. F.
Department of Plant Pathology
University of California
Berkeley 4, California

Baker, R. G.
Dow Chemical Company
10 Pacific Coast Highway
Seal Beach, California

Baker, R. R.
Department of Botany and Plant Pathology
Colorado State University
Fort Collins, Colorado

Bald, J. G.
Department of Plant Pathology
University of California
Los Angeles 24, California

Bankuti, M. (Mrs.)
California Chemical Company
Ortho at Lucas Way
Richmond, California

Barbe, Douglas
Department of Plant Pathology
University of California
Davis, California

Bardin, Roy
Office of the Agricultural Commissioner
120 Wilgart Way
Salinas, California

Barrett, J. T.
Department of Plant Pathology
University of California
Berkeley 4, California

Bartnicki-Garcia, Salomon
Department of Plant Pathology
University of California
Riverside, California

Bateman, D. F.
Department of Plant Pathology
Cornell University
Ithaca, New York

Bay, Ernest C.
Department of Biological Control
University of California
Riverside, California

Bega, R. V.
Pacific Southwest Forest and Range Experiment Station
United States Department of Agriculture
P. O. Box 245
Berkeley 4, California

Belli, Giuseppe
Instituto di Patologia Vegetale
Universita di Milano
Via Celoria 2
Milano, Italy

Berry, Stanley Z.
Campbell Soup Company
P. O. Box 356
Davis, California

Bird, L. S.
Department of Plant Sciences
Texas A & M
College Station, Texas

Bollen, W. B.
Department of Microbiology
Oregon State University
Corvallis, Oregon

Boosalis, Michael G.
Department of Plant Pathology
University of Nebraska
Lincoln 3, Nebraska

Boswell, Victor R.
Crops Research Division
Plant Industry Station
United States Department of Agriculture
Beltsville, Maryland

Bourret, James A.
Department of Plant Pathology
University of California
Berkeley 4, California

Bowman, Tully
Department of Plant Pathology
University of California
Berkeley 4, California
Boyle, Lytton W.
University of Georgia Agricultural Experiment Station
Experiment, Georgia

Brodie, William B.
United States Department of Agriculture
Texas Agricultural Substation No. 8
R. F. D. No. 3
Lubbock, Texas

Bruehl, G. W.
Department of Plant Pathology
Washington State University
Pullman, Washington

Buddenhagen, I. W.
Division of Tropical Research
United Fruit Company
La Lima, Honduras

Burges, Alan
Department of Botany
University of Liverpool
Liverpool, England

Burke, D. W.
United States Department of Agriculture
Crops Research Division
Irrigation Experiment Station
Prosser, Washington

Burström, Hans
Department of Plant Physiology
University of Lund
Lund, Sweden

Butler, E. E.
Department of Plant Pathology
University of California
Davis, California

Cadman, C. H.
Scottish Horticultural Research Institute
Mylnefield, Invergowrie, Dundee,
Scotland

Caldis, P. D.
California Packing Corporation
215 Fremont Street
San Francisco 19, California

Cameron, H. Ronald
Department of Botany and Plant Pathology
Oregon State University
Corvallis, Oregon

Campbell, R. N.
Department of Plant Pathology
University of California
Davis, California

Carlyle, R. E.
Soil Survey and Fertility Branch
Food and Agriculture Organization of United Nations
Vialedelle Terme di Caracalla
Rome, Italy

Chant, D. A.
Canada Department of Agriculture
Box 506
St. Catharines, Ontario, Canada
Now: Department of Biological Control
        University of California
        Riverside, California

Chapman, H. D.
Department of Soils and Plant Nutrition
University of California
Riverside, California

Chapman, Richard A.
Department of Plant Pathology
University of Kentucky
Lexington, Kentucky

Clark, F. E.
United States Department of Agriculture
Nitrogen Laboratory
P. O. Box 758
Fort Collins, Colorado

Cochrane, Vincent W.
Shankin Laboratory
Wesleyan University
Middletown, Connecticut

Converse, R. H.
United States Department of Agriculture
Crops Research Division
Plant Industry Station
Beltsville, Maryland

Cook, R. James
Department of Plant Pathology
University of California
Berkeley 4, California
Now: Department of Plant Pathology
        Waite Agricultural Research Institute
        Adelaide, South Australia

Crafts, A. S.
Department of Botany
University of California
Davis, California

Craig, James M.
Department of Biological Sciences
San Jose State College
San Jose 14, California

Cruickshank, I. A. M.
Division of Plant Industry
Commonwealth Scientific & Industrial Research Organization
Canberra, A. C. T., Australia

Curl, E. A.
Department of Botany and Plant Pathology
Auburn University
Auburn, Alabama

Davey, C. B.
Department of Soil Science
North Carolina State College
Raleigh, North Carolina

Davis, L. H. (Mrs.)
Department of Botany
University of California
Los Angeles 24, California

DeVay, J. E.
Department of Plant Pathology
University of California
Davis, California

Dimitman, J. E.
Biological Sciences
California State Polytechnic College
Kellogg-Voorhis Campus
Pomona, California

Dimock, A. W.
Department of Plant Pathology
Cornell University
Ithaca, New York

Dimond, A. E.
Department of Plant Pathology and Botany
Connecticut Agricultural Experiment Station
New Haven 4, Connecticut

Dobbs, C. G.
Department of Botany
University College of North Wales
Bangor, Caerns, United Kingdom

Domsch, K. H.
Institut für Getreide-Ölfrucht- und
Futterpflanzenkrankheiten
Biologische Bundesanstalt für
Land- und Forstwirtschaft
Schlosskoppelweg 8,
Kiel-Kitzeberg, Germany

Driver, Charles
Southlands Exepriment Forest
International Paper Company
Bainbridge, Georgia

Durbin, R. D.
Department of Plant Pathology
University of Wisconsin
Madison 6, Wisconsin

Durrell, L. W.
Department of Botany and Plant Pathology
Colorado State University
Fort Collins, Colorado

Earhart, Robert W.
Chemagro Corporation
Hawthorne Road
P. O. Box 4913
Kansas City 20, Missouri

Easton, Gene
Washington State University
Irrigation Experiment Station
Prosser, Washington

Eger, Gerlind (Miss)
Max Planck Institut für Kulturpflanzenzuchtung
Waldredder 4,
Hamburg-Volksdorf, Germany

Emden, J. H. van
Instituut voor Plantenziektenkundig Onderzoek
Binnenhaven 4a
Wageningen, Netherlands

Emmons, C. W.
National Institutes of Health
United States Public Health Service
Bethesda 14, Maryland

Endo, R. M.
Department of Plant Pathology
University of California
Riverside, California

English, W. Harley
Department of Plant Pathology
University of California
Davis, California

Erwin, D. C.
Department of Plant Pathology
University of California
Riverside, California

Feder, William A.
United States Department of Agriculture
Crops Research Division
2120 Camden Road
Orlando, Florida

Feichtmeir, E. F.
Shell Development Company
P. O. Box 3011
Modesto, California

Ferguson, John
Soil and Plant Laboratory
P. O. Box 689
Orange, California
Now: P.O. Box 488
       Bryanston
       Johannesburg, South Africa

Finstein, F. S.
Kearney Foundation
University of California
Berkeley, California

Flentje, N. T.
Department of Plant Pathology
Waite Agricultural Research Institute
Adelaide, South Australia

Forsyth, W. G. C.
Division of Tropical Research
Tela Railroad Company
La Lima, Honduras

Fox, R. A.
Pathological Division
Rubber Research Institute of Malaya
P. O. Box 150
Kuala Lumpur, Malaya

Freiberg, S. R.
Central Research Laboratories
United Fruit Company
Norwood, Massachusetts

Fulkerson, John F.
United States Department of Agriculture
Cooperative State Experiment Station Service
Washington 25, D. C.

Fuller, W. H.
Strawberry Institute of California
Rt. 2, Box 458
Morgan Hill, California
Now: Department of Plant Pathology
       University of California
       Berkeley 4, California

Fulton, Neil D.
Department of Plant Pathology
University of Arkansas
Fayetteville, Arkansas

Gabrielson, R. L.
Western Washington Experiment Station
Puyallup, Washington

Galindo, Jorge
Oficina de Estudios Especiales, S. A. G.
The Rockefeller Foundation
Londres #40. 2/o. Piso
Mexico 6, D. F., Mexico

Garber, R. H.
United States Department of Agriculture
United States Cotton Field Station
Shafter, California

Gardner, M. W.
Department of Plant Pathology
University of California
Berkeley 4, California

Garnsey, Stephen
Department of Plant Pathology
University of California
Davis, California

Garrard, E. H.
Department of Microbiology
Ontario Agricultural College
Guelph, Ontario, Canada

Garren, K. H.
United States Department of Agriculture
Tidewater Research Station
Holland, Virginia

Garrett, S. D.
Department of Botany
University of Cambridge
Downing Street
Cambridge, England

Garraway, M. O.
Charlotte Valley
Dominica, West Indies
Now: Department of Plant Pathology
       University of California
       Berkeley 4, California

Geraghty, Cecil J.
Tillo Products Company
615 Scott Avenue
Redwood City, California

Gerdemann, J. W.
Department of Plant Pathology
University of Illinois
Urbana, Illinois

Gerwitz, David L.
Monsanto Chemical Company
800 North Lindbergh Boulevard
St. Louis 66, Missouri

Ghafoor, Abdul
Department of Plant Protection
Block No. 52, Pakistan Secretariat
Karachi, Pakistan

Gill, C. C.
Department of Plant Pathology
University of California
Berkeley 4, California
Now: Canada Department of Agriculture
       Research Station
       P.O. Box 6200
       Winnipeg 1, Manitoba, Canada

Gilmer, R.
California Packing Corporation
850 Thornton Street
San Leandro, California

Glynne, Mary D. (Miss)
Department of Plant Pathology
Rothamsted Experimental Station
Harpenden, Herts., England

Gold, A. H.
Department of Plant Pathology
University of California
Berkeley 4, California

Goos, Roger D.
National Institutes of Health
Bethesda 14, Maryland

Goring, Cleve A. I.
Dow Chemical Company
10 Pacific Coast Highway
Seal Beach, California

Gould, C. J.
Western Washington Experiment Station
Washington State University
Puyallup, Washington

Greathead, Arthur
Farm Advisor
118 Wilgart Way
Salinas, California

Green, R. J.
Department of Botany and Plant Pathology
Purdue University
Lafayette, Indiana

Gries, G. A.
Department of Plant Pathology
University of Arizona
Tucson, Arizona

Grogan, R. G.
Department of Plant Pathology
University of California
Davis, California

Grossenbacher, K. A.
Department of Soils and Plant Nutrition
University of California
Berkeley 4, California

Hagedorn, D. J.
Department of Plant Pathology
University of Wisconsin
Madison 6, Wisconsin

Haglund, W
Northwestern Experiment Station
Washington State University
Mt. Vernon, Washington

Halisky, P. M.
Department of Plant Pathology
University of California
Davis, California

Hall, D. H.
Department of Plant Pathology
University of California
Davis, California

Hansberry, Roy
Shell Development Company
P. O. Box 3011
Modesto, California

Hanson, E. W.
Department of Plant Pathology
University of Wisconsin
Madison 6, Wisconsin

Harley, J. L.
Department of Agriculture
University of Oxford
Oxford, England

Harrison, Monty D.
Department of Botany and Plant Pathology
Colorado State University
Fort Collins, Colorado

Hartzfeld, E. G.
Olin Mathieson Chemical Corporation
13923 Heartside Place
Dallas 34, Texas

Hendrix, F. F., Jr.
United States Department of Agriculture
Southeastern Forest Experiment Station
P. O. Building
Asheville, North Carolina

Hepting, G. H.
United States Department of Agriculture
Southeastern Forest Experiment Station
P. O. Box 2570
Asheville, North Carolina

Hewitt, W. B.
Department of Plant Pathology
University of California
Davis, California

Hickman, C. J.
Department of Botany
University of Western Ontario
London, Ontario, Canada

Hildebrand, Donald C.
Department of Plant Pathology
University of California
Berkeley 4, California

Hirst, J. M.
Department of Plant Pathology
Rothamsted Experimental Station
Harpenden, Herts., England

Horner, C. E.
Department of Botany and Plant Pathology
Oregon State University
Corvallis, Oregon

Horsfall, J. G.
Connecticut Agricultural Experiment Station
P. O. Box 1106
New Haven 4, Connecticut

Houston, Byron R.
Department of Plant Pathology
University of California
Davis, California

Isenhour, L. L.
Rohm & Haas Co., Inc.
2150 Franklin Street
Oakland, California

Ishizawa, S.
The National Institute of Agricultural Sciences
No. 1, 2-Chome, Nishigahara
Kita-Ku, Tokyo, Japan

Jackson, R. M.
Taita Experimental Station
Private Bag
Lower Hutt, New Zealand
Now: Department of Soil Microbiology
     Rothamsted Experimental Station
     Harpenden, Herts., England

Johnson, Harold A., Jr.
Strawberry Institute of California
Rt. 2, Box 458
Morgan Hill, California

Johnson, L. F.
Department of Plant Pathology
University of Tennessee
Knoxville, Tennessee

Johnson, S. P.
Life Sciences Department, S.&I.D.
North American Aviation
3500 Torrance Boulevard
Torrance, California

Jordan, W. B.
Olin Mathieson Chemical Company
2041 Pioneer Court
San Mateo, California

Kado, Clarence I.
Department of Plant Pathology
University of California
Berkeley 4, California
Now: Department of Molecular Biology
     University of California
     Berkeley 4, California

Kaiser, W. J.
Department of Plant Pathology
University of California
Berkeley 4, California
Now: Division of Tropical Research
     Tela Railroad Company
     La Lima, Honduras

Katznelson, H.
Microbiology Research Institute
Canada Department of Agriculture
Ottawa, Ontario, Canada

Kaufman, D. D.
United States Department of Agriculture
Crops Protection Research Branch
Plant Industry Station
Beltsville, Maryland

Kelman, Arthur
Department of Plant Pathology
University of North Carolina
Raleigh, North Carolina

Kenaga, Clare B.
Research Laboratory
Morton Chemical Company
Woodstock, Illinois

Kendrick, J. B., Jr.
Department of Plant Pathology
University of California
Riverside, California

Kerr, A.
Department of Plant Pathology
Waite Agricultural Research Institute
Adelaide, South Australia
Now: The Tea Research Institute
  St. Coombs
  Talawakelle, Ceylon

Kevan, D. K. McE.
Department of Entomology
Macdonald College
McGill University
Ste. Anne de Bellevue
Quebec, Canada

Khadr, Abdel-Ghaffor S.
Ain Shams University
Faculty of Agriculture
Kobba Palace
Cairo, Egypt
Now: Department of Plant Pathology
  University of California
  Berkeley, California

Kilpatrick, R. A.
Department of Botany
University of New Hampshire
Durham, New Hampshire

Kimble, K. A.
Department of Plant Pathology
University of California
Davis, California

Kirkpatrick, J. D.
Department of Horticulture
University of California
Riverside, California

Klemmer, Erida Reichert
Pineapple Research Institute
P. O. Box 3166
Honolulu 2, Hawaii
Now: Biomedical Research Center
  University of Hawaii
  Honolulu, Hawaii

Klemmer, H. W.
Pineapple Research Institute
P. O. Box 3166
Honolulu 2, Hawaii
Now: Biomedical Research Center
  University of Hawaii
  Honolulu, Hawaii

Klisiewicz, J. M.
United States Department of Agriculture
Department of Plant Pathology
University of California
Davis, California

Knutson, K. W.
Branch Experiment Station
University of Idaho
Aberdeen, Idaho

Koepsell, Paul
Department of Plant Pathology
University of California
Davis, California

Koike, Hideo
Experiment Station
Hawaiian Sugar Planters Association
Honolulu 14, Hawaii

Kommedahl, Thor
Department of Plant Pathology and Botany
University of Minnesota
St. Paul 1, Minnesota

Kreitlow, K. W.
United States Department of Agriculture
Crops Research Division
Plant Industry Station
Beltsville, Maryland

Kreutzer, W. A.
Department of Botany and Plant Pathology
Colorado State University
Fort Collins, Colorado
Formerly: Shell Development Company
   Modesto, California

Lai, Ming-tan
Laboratory of Plant Pathology
College of Agriculture
National Taiwan University
Taipei, Taiwan, China
Now: Department of Plant Pathology
  University of California
  Berkeley, California

Latham, Archie J.
Spencer Chemical Company
Research Center
9009 West 67th Street
Merriam, Kansas

Lawyer, Adele (Mrs. L. O.)
California Packing Corporation
850 Thornton Street
San Leandro, California

Lawyer, L. O.
California Packing Corporation
850 Thornton Street
San Leandro, California

Leach, L. D.
Department of Plant Pathology
University of California
Davis, California

Lear, Bert
Department of Nematology
University of California
Davis, California

Lembright, H. W.
Dow Chemical Company
350 Sansome Street
San Francisco 4, California

Lindsey, Donald
Department of Botany and Plant Pathology
Colorado State University
Fort Collins, Colorado

Lockwood, J. L.
Department of Botany and Plant Pathology
Michigan State University
East Lansing, Michigan

Lorbeer, James W.
Department of Plant Pathology
Cornell University
Ithaca, New York

Louvet, Jean
Centre National des Recherches Agronomiques
Station Centrale de Pathologie Vegetale
Etoile de Choisy
Versailles, France

Lownsbery, B. F.
Department of Nematology
University of California
Davis, California

Lu, K. C.
United States Department of Agriculture
Forestry Sciences Laboratory
3200 Jefferson Way
Corvallis, Oregon

Ludwig, R. A.
Plant Research Institute
Canadian Department of Agriculture
Ottawa, Ontario, Canada

Lukezic, Felix
Department of Plant Pathology
University of California
Davis, California

McBeth, C. W.
Shell Development Company
P. O. Box 3011
Modesto, California

McCain, A. H.
Department of Plant Pathology
University of California
Berkeley 4, California

McIntosh, D. L.
Plant Pathology Section
Research Station
Canada Department of Agriculture
Summerland, B. C., Canada

McLaren, A. D.
Department of Soils and Plant Nutrition
University of California
Berkeley 4, California

McMinn, R. G.
Forest Entomology and Pathology Laboratory
Canada Department of Forestry
409 Federal Building
Victoria, B. C., Canada

Mace, M. E.
United Fruit Company
Central Laboratories
Norwood, Massachusetts

MacLeod, G. F.
Union Carbide Company
4852 North Van Ness Avenue
Fresno 4, California

MacSwan, Iain
Department of Plant Pathology
Oregon State University
Corvallis, Oregon

MacWithey, H. S.
Department of Botany and Bacteriology
Montana State College
Bozeman, Montana

Mai, W. F.
Department of Plant Pathology
Cornell University
Ithaca, New York

Maier, C. R.
Department of Botany and Entomology
New Mexico State University
University Park, New Mexico

Maino, Anne (Miss)
Department of Plant Pathology
University of California
Berkeley 4, California

Mankau, Reinhold
Department of Nematology
University of California
Riverside, California

Martin, J. P.
Department of Soils and Plant Nutrition
University of California
Riverside, California

Martinson, C. A.
Department of Botany and Plant Pathology
Oregon State University
Corvallis, Oregon
Now: Department of Plant Pathology
        Cornell University
        Ithaca, New York

Mather, Stanley M.
Bureau of Nursery Service
California Department of Agriculture
1220 "N" Street
Sacramento, California

Mathre, Donald
Department of Plant Pathology
University of California
Davis, California

Maxwell, K. E.
Moyer Chemical Company
P. O. Box 945
San Jose, California

Menzies, J. D.
United States Department of Agriculture
Plant Industry Station
Beltsville, Maryland
Formerly: United States Department of Agriculture
          Irrigation Experiment Station
          Prosser, Washington

Meyer, R. W.
Department of Plant Pathology
University of California
Berkeley 4, California

Millar, Roy L.
Department of Plant Pathology
Cornell University
Ithaca, New York

Miller, L. I.
Tidewater Research Station
Virginia Agricultural Experiment Station
Holland, Virginia

Miller, P. R.
Department of Plant Pathology
University of California
Berkeley 4, California

Mitchell, J. E.
Department of Plant Pathology
University of Wisconsin
Madison 6, Wisconsin

Monroe, Carl M.
Shell Development Company
P. O. Box 3011
Modesto, California

Mountain, W. B.
Research Station
Canada Department of Agriculture
Harrow, Ontario, Canada
Now: Research Station
        Canada Department of Agriculture
        St. Catherines, Ontario

Muñoz, Raul C.
Department of Plant Pathology
University of California
Berkeley 4, California

Nash, Shirley M. (Miss)
Department of Plant Pathology
University of California
Berkeley 4, California

Nelson, Earl E.
United States Department of Agriculture—Forest Service
P. O. Box 3141
Portland, Oregon

Nelson, P. E.
Ornamentals Research Laboratory
Cornell University
Farmingdale, Long Island, New York

Nicholas, D. J. D.
Research Station
University of Bristol
Long Ashton, Bristol, England
Now: Department of Biochemistry and Soil Science
       Waite Agricultural Research Institute
       Adelaide, South Australia

Nichols, Courtland
Campbell Soup Company
375 Memorial Avenue
Camden 1, New Jersey

Nielsen, L. W.
Department of Plant Pathology
North Carolina State College
Raleigh, North Carolina

Norman, A. G.
Department of Botany
University of Michigan
Ann Arbor, Michigan

Noveroske, Robert L.
Dow Chemical Company
10 Pacific Coast Highway
Seal Beach, California

Nutman, P. S.
Department of Soil Microbiology
Rothamsted Experimental Station
Harpenden, Herts., England

Offord, H. R.
United States Forest Service
Pacific Southwest Forest and Range Experiment Station
P. O. Box 245
Berkeley, California

Ogawa, Joseph M.
Department of Plant Pathology
University of California
Davis, California

Olsen, Carl M.
Department of Plant Pathology
University of California
Berkeley 4, California

Olson, Conrad J.
Yoder Brothers Inc.
Box 230
Barberton, Ohio

Oshima, Nagayoshi
Department of Botany and Plant Pathology

Colorado State University
Fort Collins, Colorado

Oswald, John W.
Department of Plant Pathology
University of California
Berkeley 4, California
Now: President's Office
       University of Kentucky
       Lexington, Kentucky

Papavizas, G. C.
United States Department of Agriculture
Plant Industry Station
Beltsville, Maryland

Park, David
Department of Botany
University of Manchester
Manchester, England
Now: Botany Department
       The Queen's University
       Belfast, N. Ireland

Parkinson, D.
Department of Botany
University of Liverpool
Liverpool, England
Now: Department of Biology
       University of Waterloo
       Waterloo, Ontario, Canada

Parmeter, J. R., Jr.
Department of Plant Pathology
University of California
Berkeley 4, California

Patrick, Z. A.
Research Station
Canada Department of Agriculture
Harrow, Ontario, Canada

Paulus, A. O.
Department of Plant Pathology
University of California
Riverside, California

Pentland, Gertrude D. (Miss)
Department of Biology and Botany
University of British Columbia
Vancouver 8, B. C., Canada

Peterson, G. H.
Department of Botany and Plant Pathology
Purdue University
Lafayette, Indiana

Phillips, Douglas J.
Department of Botany and Plant Pathology
Colorado State University
Fort Collins, Colorado

Poinar, Eva (Mrs.)
Department of Plant Pathology
University of California
Los Angeles 24, California

Poinar, George O., Jr.
Department of Biological Control
University of California
Riverside, California

Powelson, R. L.
Department of Botany and Plant Pathology
Oregon State University
Corvallis, Oregon

Pramer, D.
Department of Microbiology
College of Agriculture
Rutgers University
New Brunswick, New Jersey

Presley, J. T.
United States Department of Agriculture
Plant Industry Station
Beltsville, Maryland

Rader, W. E.
Shell Development Company
P. O. Box 3011
Modesto, California

Radewald, John D.
Department of Nematology
University of California
Riverside, California

Raney, W. A.
United States Department of Agriculture
Plant Industry Station
Beltsville, Maryland

Reichle, R. E.
Department of Plant Pathology
University of California
Berkeley 4, California
Now: Department of Botany
     University of California
     Berkeley 4, California

Reiling, Theodore
Green Giant Company
Dayton, Washington

Reuszer, H. W.
Department of Agronomy
Purdue University
Lafayette, Indiana

Richards, B. N.
School of Forestry
Yale University
New Haven, Connecticut

Richardson, L. T.
Research Institute
Canada Department of Agriculture
London, Ontario, Canada

Rodriguez, Antonio E.
Institute Nacional Investigaciones Agricolas
Mexico City, Mexico

Roth, L. F.
Department of Botany and Plant Pathology
Oregon State University
Corvallis, Oregon

Rovira, A. D.
Division of Soils
Commonwealth Scientific and Industrial Research Organization
Adelaide, South Australia

Sadasivan, T. S.
Botany Laboratory
University of Madras
Madras 5, India

Sagen, J. E.
Department of Plant Pathology
University of California
Berkeley 4, California

Scharpf, R. F.
Pacific Southwest Forest and Range Experiment Station
P. O. Box 245
Berkeley 4, California

Schisler, L. C.
Butler County Mushroom Farm, Inc.
West Winfield, Pennsylvania

Schmitthenner, A. F.
Department of Botany and Plant Pathology
Ohio Agricultural Experiment Station
Wooster, Ohio

Schnathorst, W. C.
United States Department of Agriculture
Agriculture Research Service
Department of Plant Pathology
University of California
Davis, California

Schroth, M. N.
Department of Plant Pathology
University of California
Berkeley 4, California

Scott, F. M. (Miss)
Department of Botany and Plant Biochemistry
University of California
Los Angeles, California

Semeniuk, George
Department of Plant Pathology
South Dakota State College
Brookings, South Dakota

Sewell, G. W. F.
East Malling Research Station
East Malling
Maidstone, Kent, England

Sharp, Paul F.
National Academy of Sciences—National Research Council
2101 Constitution Avenue
Washington, D. C.

Shepherd, R. J.
Department of Plant Pathology
University of California
Davis, California

Sher, S. A.
Department of Nematology
University of California
Riverside, California

Sinden, Stephen
Department of Plant Pathology
University of California
Davis, California

Skiles, R. L.
Rohm and Haas Company
P. O. Box 219
Bristol, Pennsylvania

Skotland, C. B.
Irrigation Experiment Station
Washington State University
Prosser, Washington

Smith, R. S., Jr.
Pacific Southwest Forest and Range Experiment Station
P. O. Box 245
Berkeley 4, California

Smith, Samuel
Department of Plant Pathology
University of California
Berkeley 4, California

Snyder, W. C.
Department of Plant Pathology
University of California
Berkeley 4, California

Stambaugh, William J.
School of Forestry
Duke University
Durham, North Carolina

Starr, M. P.
Department of Bacteriology
University of California
Davis, California

Stille, Bernd
Institut für Pflanzenkrankheiten
Universität Bonn
Nussallee 9
Bonn, Germany

Stolp, H.
Biologische Bundesanstalt Institut für Bakteriologie
Berlin, Dahlem
Germany

Stotzky, Guenther
Kitchawan Research Laboratory
Brooklyn Botanical Garden
RFD 1, Route 134
Ossining, New York

Stout, Gilbert L.
Bureau of Plant Pathology
California Department of Agriculture
1220 "N" Street
Sacramento 14, California

Strobel, Gary
Department of Plant Pathology
University of California
Davis, California

Sussman, A. S.
Department of Botany
University of Michigan
Ann Arbor, Michigan

Tammen, J.
Department of Botany and Plant Pathology
Pennsylvania State University
University Park, Pennsylvania

Taylor, J. Bruce
Department of Plant Pathology
Waite Agricultural Research Institute
Adelaide, South Australia
Now: Plant Diseases Division
     Department of Scientific and Industrial Research
     Private Bag
     Auckland, New Zealand

Taylor, Robert Hunter
Department of Agriculture
Plant Research Laboratory
Swan Street
Burnley, Victoria, Australia

Teakle, David
Department of Agriculture and Stock
Nambour, Queensland, Australia

Tharp, W. Hardy
National Cotton Council of America
P. O. Box 9905
Memphis 12, Tennessee

Thomas, Harold E.
Strawberry Institute of California
Rt. 2, Box 458
Morgan Hill, California

Thomas, W. D., Jr.
California Chemical Corporation
Lucas and Ortho Way
Richmond, California

Thomason, I. J.
Department of Nematology
University of California
Riverside, California

Thornton, N. C.
United Fruit Company
30 St. James Avenue
Boston 16, Massachusetts

Timonin, M. I.
Forest Biology Laboratory
Canada Department of Forestry
University Sub Post Office
Saskatoon, Saskatchewan, Canada

Tinline, R. D.
Research Station
Canada Department of Agriculture
Saskatoon, Saskatchewan, Canada

Toussoun, T. A.
Department of Plant Pathology
University of California
Berkeley 4, California

Trujillo, E. E.
Kauai Branch Station
University of Hawaii
Kapaa, Kauai, Hawaii

Tsao, P. H.
Department of Plant Pathology
University of California
Riverside, California

Ulrich, Jane
Department of Soils and Plant Nutrition
University of California
Berkeley 4, California

Van Gundy, Seymour
Department of Nematology
University of California
Riverside, California

Vanterpool, T. C.
Department of Botany
University of Saskatchewan
Saskatoon, Saskatchewan, Canada

Vaughan, E. K.
Department of Botany and Plant Pathology
Oregon State University
Corvallis, Oregon

Vertrees, G. L.
Department of Plant Pathology
University of California
Berkeley 4, California
Now: Department of Botany
     University of Indiana
     Bloomington, Indiana

Virgin, W. J.
California Packing Corporation
850 Thornton Road
San Leandro, California

von Ramm, Clas
Morton Chemical Company
1 First Avenue
Los Altos, California

Wagener, W. W.
Pacific Southwest Forest and Range Experiment Station
P. O. Box 245
Berkeley 4, California

Walker, J. C.
Department of Plant Pathology
University of Wisconsin
Madison 6, Wisconsin

Wallis, G. W.
Forest Entomology and Pathology Laboratory
409 Federal Building
Victoria, B. C., Canada

Warcup, J. H.
Department of Plant Pathology
Waite Agricultural Research Institute
Adelaide, South Australia

Watanabe, Tsuneo
Department of Agriculture
University of Tokyo
Mukogaoka, Bunkyo-ku
Tokyo, Japan
Now: Department of Plant Pathology
      University of California
      Berkeley, California

Waterhouse, Grace M. (Miss)
Commonwealth Mycological Institute
Ferry Lane
Kew, Surrey, England

Watson, R. D.
Department of Plant Pathology
University of Idaho
Moscow, Idaho

Weber, D. F.
United States Department of Agriculture
Irrigation Experiment Station
Prosser, Washington

Wehunt, E. J.
Division of Tropical Research
Tela Railroad Company
La Lima, Honduras

Weinhold, A. R.
Department of Plant Pathology

University of California
Berkeley 4, California

Weinke, K. E.
The Upjohn Company
1611 Bodega Court
Walnut Creek, California

Whaley, Julian
Department of Plant Pathology
University of Arizona
Tucson, Arizona

Whitney, H. S.
Canada Department of Forestry
Forest Entomology and Pathology Branch
P. O. Box 35
Sillery, Quebec, Canada

Wilcox, L. V., Jr.
Department of Biology
Lycoming College
Williamsport, Pennsylvania

Wilhelm, S.
Department of Plant Pathology
University of California
Berkeley 4, California

Williams, L. E.
Department of Botany and Plant Pathology
Ohio Agricultural Experiment Station
Wooster, Ohio

Wilson, Coyt
Alabama Agricultural Experiment Station
Auburn, Alabama

Yarwood, C. E.
Department of Plant Pathology
University of California
Berkeley 4, California

Young, R. A.
Department of Botany and Plant Pathology
Oregon State University
Corvallis, Oregon

Zak, Bratislav
United States Department of Agriculture
Forest Sciences Laboratory
3200 Jefferson Way
Corvallis, Oregon

Zentmyer, G. A.
Department of Plant Pathology
University of California
Riverside, California

Index[1]

---

[1] Repetition of the same page number indicates that there are two (or more) references to the topic on that page. Cross references for the main topic are given at the end of the entry, following subtopics.